KV-512-265

The Catalogue of Printed Music in the British Library to 1980

The Catalogue
of Printed Music
in the British Library
to 1980

34

LAE - LEHAN

1984

K·G·Saur

London · München · New York · Paris

Managing editor
Laureen Baillie B.A., Dip. Lib.

Editor
Robert Balchin M.A.

Assistant editor
Michael D. Chapman B.Mus., A.R.C.M.

Editorial assistants
Helen Dwyer B.A.
Robert L. Greenhill G.R.N.C.M.
Elizabeth Robinson M.Mus., B.A., A.R.C.M.
Maurice Rogers B.Mus., A.K.C.
Garance Worters A.L.A., L.T.C.L., Cert. Ed.

HERTFORDSHIRE
COUNTY LIBRARY

2311906

British Library Cataloguing in Publication Data

British Library
   The catalogue of printed music
   in the British Library to 1980
   Vol 34: Lae – Lehan
   1. British Library. Department of Printed
   Books — Catalogs
   I. Title   II. Baillie, Laureen

ISBN 0-86291- 331-4
ISBN 0-86291-300-4 Set of 62 vols

Copyright © 1984 British Library

Computerised typesetting by Satz-Rechen-Zentrum, Hartmann & Heenemann,
Lützowstrasse 105—106, 1000 Berlin 30.

Printed and bound in the Federal Republic of Germany

GUIDE TO THE ARRANGEMENT OF ENTRIES

1. Entry points

In principle each work in the Catalogue has one main entry, which is made under the name of the person or body with the primary intellectual responsibility for the work. In practice the main entry for a work may appear: under the name of the composer, if it appears in the publication; under the name of a compiler, e.g. of a songbook; under the name of a corporate author, e.g. a society; or under a heading derived from the title, if anonymous. The Catalogue also contains cross references of various kinds. These are explained in greater detail below.

2. Choice of main heading

Composers

If the composer or compiler is known, an entry will be found under his or her name. Most publications involving two composers are entered under the joint heading. A publication consisting of contributions by three or more authors will generally be entered: under the first named, with cross references from the other names; under the name of the editor or compiler, if there is one; or under a word derived from the title according to the rules for anonymous works.

Pseudonymous works

Works in which the composer is identified by initials or by a pseudonym are entered under those forms. Works in which the composer is identified by a descriptive *word* are entered under that word, but if a descriptive *phrase* is used the work is entered according to the rules for anonymous works. Thus, *Six Songs, by a Lady* is entered under LADY; but *Six Songs, by an Irish Lady* is entered under SONGS.

Anonymous works

Anonymous works are generally entered under the first word of the title* with the following exceptions:

> *Single songs.* Because the titles of anonymous songs often vary, while the words generally remain constant, anonymous single songs have their main entry under the first word of the text. A cross reference is made from the first word of the title.
>
> *Preferential headings.* Certain commonly occurring words (mainly denoting musical forms) are used as preferential headings. If such a word occurs in the title proper of an anonymous work, the work is entered under that word, not under the first word of the title. But if two or more preferential terms occur in the title proper, then the work is treated like other anonyma, and entered under the first word of the title. Thus, *A collection of French songs* is entered under SONGS; but *A collection of French songs and duets* is entered under COLLECTION ("songs" and "duets" are both preferential terms). Examples of preferential headings are: Airs, Anthems, Chansons, Concertos, Country Dances, Dances, Duets, Glees, Instructions, Madrigals, Marches, Masses, Minuets, Motets, Quadrilles, Sonatas, Songs, Tutors, Waltzes. Four preferential headings are treated somewhat differently: Hymns, Psalms, Chants [Anglican], Christmas Carols.

Here and throughout, this means the first word of the title other than the article.

These contain in addition cross references to collections of relevant material entered elsewhere in the Catalogue; they are arranged in chronological order, while HYMNS and PSALMS are also subdivided according to the language of the text.

An anonymous edition of a work whose composer is known is treated as an anonymous work. A cross reference is made from the name of the composer to the appropriate anonymous heading where the main entry will be found.

Editions of collective manuscripts without compiler are entered under the library where the manuscript is deposited, e.g. editions of the Fitzwilliam Virginal Book are entered under CAMBRIDGE. – University of Cambridge. – *Fitzwilliam Museum*.

Periodicals

Periodicals published by societies or other corporate authors are entered under the heading for the society; others are entered under the heading PERIODICAL PUBLICATIONS, followed by the name of the town where publication took place. In both cases a cross reference is made from the first word of the title of the periodical.

3.   Cross references

Cross references are made from various alternative entry points. The more important of these are:

from the names of editors, arrangers, etc. Note that cross references are not made from the names of the authors of the words of vocal works;

from the first word of the title of a vocal work, provided that the title is distinctive, e.g. *Songs of Travel* (song cycle) and not merely conventional, e.g. *Six Songs* Op.45. Note that cross references are not made for any titles of instrumental works, or vocal anthologies, e.g. *Songs for Hikers*;

from the first word of the name of a corporate body to the place where the body is entered, e.g. SOCIETY. Society for Promoting Christian Knowledge. *See* ENGLAND. – *Church of England*;

from one composition to other compositions based on it, e.g. from Donizetti to Liszt for his "Réminiscences de Lucia di Lammermoor".

4.   Arrangement of headings

Headings are arranged in alphabetical order, in accordance with the following list:

B.	Single initial representing a personal name.
B., M.K.	Two or more initials, ditto. The last initial in the book is normally taken to represent the family name and appears first in the Catalogue.
BBC	Other combinations of initials, or initials and words, and acronyms.
ROSE	Common noun, e.g. a flower or tool.
ROSE	Place names.
ROSE	Author.
ROSE AMELIA, *Queen*	Compounds in two or more words, irrespective of meaning. (Not compound surnames.)
ROSE AND COMPANY	
ROSE (J.)	Surnames.
ROSE (John)	
ROSE (John Daniel)	

ROSEBUD   Compounds, read as one word.
ROSE-JONES (J.)
ROSE Y HER-
    NÁNDEZ (C.)

5. Arrangement of entries within each heading

Under the names of composers entries are generally arranged as follows:

Thematic catalogues.

Collected editions of the composer's works, arranged in chronological order by date of publication. In the case of some large headings these may be further subdivided.

Composite works, e.g. BORODIN (A.P.) [*Composite Works.*] Kismet. . . Based on themes of A. Borodin.

General alphabetical sequence of single works and of collections of works which, if published separately, would all file in the same place, e.g. collections of quartets, sonatas, symphonies, etc. Note that this does not apply to collections of, e.g., overtures, since the individual overtures if published separately would be filed in the alphabetical place appropriate to their title.

Doubtful and supposititious works.

Appendix of cross references.

These sub-divisions may or may not be marked by printed sub-headings, depending on the extent of the composer's entries.

Within the general alphabetical sequence certain filing principles are tacitly observed even though they apparently contradict the alphabetical order:

certain types of composition are grouped together regardless of the title of any specific edition, e.g. Concerto, Concert, Konzert, Klavierkonzert, Violinkonzert, etc., are all grouped together under "C" for "Concerto".

certain adjectives which may vary from edition to edition are usually ignored, e.g. grand, famous, favourite, celebrated, admired, brilliant.

numbers which have an enumerative function only are ignored, e.g. *Three Songs* is filed under *Songs*. But numbers which are an integral part of the title are used as alphabetical filing elements, e.g. *Three fishers went sailing* will be under *Three*.

Within the general alphabetical sequence all editions of a work or parts of a work are grouped together under the title of the first edition, or the composer's own title (in the original language). They are arranged on the general principles that complete versions come before selections, original versions before adaptations, and scores before sets of parts. In addition to these general principles, special arrangements are used for major vocal works (operas, oratorios, etc.) and for major instrumental works (quartets, sonatas, symphonies, etc.). These are in outline as follows:

Vocal works
Complete work
    Scores
    Parts
    Vocal scores
    Instrumental arrangements
Selections
    Vocal

Instrumental

Individual items
  Overture
  Arias and other individual excerpts, e.g. marches, arranged alphabetically
    Original version
    Adaptations
    Cross references to works based on the excerpt, e.g. sets of variations
Appendix of cross references to works based on more than one part of the opera, e.g. "Fantasia on themes from. . ."
Note that the language of editions of vocal works is not a filing factor.

Instrumental works

Complete collections (of sonatas, etc.)

Incomplete and miscellaneous collections

Selections

Single works (usually in numerical order)
  Complete work
  Selections
  Individual movements (alphabetically by tempo designation, not in numerical order)
  Cross references, e.g. to a set of variations on a theme from the work

In the case of a particularly large group of entries these sub-divisions may be further subdivided, e.g. the miscellaneous instrumental selections from an opera may be subdivided into: orchestral, military band, chamber ensemble, piano, piano duet, other instruments. After all sub-divisions have been made, the arrangement within each is chronological.

6. Content of individual entries

Because the Catalogue has grown over a period of many years, the items of information in any individual entry and their form of presentation have changed in various ways. Some of the more important of these are:

Works in series. Where a whole series is placed at one shelfmark, the modern practice is to catalogue the individual works, giving the title of the series in an italic footnote. The older practice was to give the title of the series at the end of the entry, preceded by the word *See*, e.g. CAUSTON (Thomas) Evening Service for unequal voices in four parts. 1912. *See* SHORE (S.R.) The Cathedral Series. No. 4. [1912, *etc.*] Such entries are in effect main entries, and should not be confused with cross references.

Imprint and pagination. The name of the publisher is given only in entries made after 1889, the pagination (or number of parts) only in those made after 1946.

Dating. The date given in each entry is the date of issue of the particular copy being catalogued, so far as can be ascertained. The following conventions are used:

1852	Date of publication printed in the work.
[1852]	Firm date supplied from other source of information, whether internal or external.
[WM 1802]	Date appears in the watermark.
[1852?]	Probable date – actual date may be the year before or after.
[c. 1845] or [c. 1850]	Date approximate or conjectural. In older catalogue entries the form [1845?] or [1850?] was used.

LAECHELN

— Das Lächeln. [Part-song.] *See* BUECHTGER (F.) In der Traumstadt IV.

LAECHERLICHE

— Der lächerliche Prinz Jodelet. [Opera.] *See* KEISER (R.)

LAEGEL (JOHANN GOTTLIEB)

— Ach, was ist der Menschheit Loos. Kantate für 4 Singstimmen mit Begleitung des Orchesters. Partitur. *Gera,* [1830?] fol. **G. 603.**

— Er der Herr von Gottes Thron ... Kantate für eine concertirende Sopranstimme mit Begleitung des Chors und Orchesters ... Partitur. *Gera,* [1830?] fol. **H. 1187. f. (11.)**

LAENDLER

— XII Ländler samt Coda. Für das Forte-Piano. *Bey Joseph Sig.: Reitmayr: Straubing,* [1800.] *obl.* fol. *The music is lithographed throughout.* **Hirsch III. 354.**

LAENDLICH

— Ländlich Sittlich. Humoristisches Lied. *See* SUPPÉ (F. von)

LAENDLICHE

— Ländliche Brautwerbung. Humoreske. *See* GRIESBECK (J.)

— Ländliche Revolte. Humoristische Scene. *See* DORN (A.)

LAENDLICHES

— Ländliches Wiegenlied. [Song.] *See* WILKINSON (G. J.)

LAENGER

— Länger als Mond und Sterne. Serenade. *See* BARTH (R.) Sechs Lieder. Op. 6. No. 2.

LAENGIN (FOLKMAR)

— Meister der Gambe. Originalstücke aus drei Jahrhunderten für Viola da gamba und Cembalo (Klavier). Auswahl, Einrichtung und Generalbass-Aussetzung von F. Längin. [Score and part.] 2 pt. *Henry Litolff's Verlag; C. F. Peters: Frankfurt, etc.,* [1964.] 4°. **g. 511. k. (1.)**

— Meister der Gambe ... (Ausgabe für Violoncello und Klavier/Cembalo.) Auswahl, Einrichtung und Generalbass-Aussetzung von F. Längin. [Score and part.] 2 pt. *Henry Litolff's Verlag; C. F. Peters: Frankfurt, etc.,* [1964.] 4°. **g. 511. k. (1.*)**

— *See* BUXTEHUDE (D.) Sonata D-dur für Viola da Gamba oder Violoncello und Basso continuo ... Herausgegeben von F. Längin. Ausgabe für Viola da Gamba und Cembalo, *etc.* [1956.] 4°. **h. 1761. (9.)**

— *See* BUXTEHUDE (D.) Sonata D-dur ... für Viola da Gamba oder Violoncello und Basso continuo (Cembalo, Klavier). Herausgegeben von F. Längin ... Ausgabe für Violoncello und Cembalo, *etc.* [1956.] 4°. **g. 510. n. (12.)**

— *See* ROSENMUELLER (J.) [Kern-Sprüche. No. 9.] Lieber Herre Gott. Adventskantate ... Herausgegeben von F. Längin. [1964.] 8°. **F. 1195. hh. (5.)**

— *See* TELEMANN (G. P.) [Der getreue Musikmeister.] Sonate G-dur für Viola da gamba (Viola) und Basso continuo ... Herausgegeben von ... F. Längin, *etc.* [1966.] 4°. **g. 401. i. (3.)**

LAENGIN (FOLKMAR)

— *See* WEILAND (J. J.) Amor Jesu. Kantate für Tenor ... Violine, Viola da gamba ... und Basso continuo ... Herausgegeben von F. Längin. [1966.] 8°. **F. 1195. hh. (9.)**

— *See* WOELFL (J.) [Grand duo. Op. 31.] Sonate d-moll für Violoncello und Klavier ... Herausgegeben von F. Längin. [1953.] 4°. **g. 512. b. (3.)**

LAER (CHARLES E. VAN)

— Again as Evening's Shadow falls. Vesper Hymn [song], words by S. Longfellow. 2 no. [High and low.] *E. Schuberth & Co.: New York, London,* (1907.) fol. **G. 517. v. (27.)**

— As it began to dawn. *See infra:* Two Sacred Songs, *etc.* [No. 1.]

— Be Thou, O God. Hymn-Anthem. *O. Ditson Co.:* [*Boston, etc.,*] 1901. 8°. **F. 231. o. (56.)**

— Berceuse. [P. F.] *O. Ditson Co.: Boston,* 1900. fol. **h. 3282. w. (20.)**

— The Chase. [P. F.] *O. Ditson Co.: Boston,* 1900. fol. **h. 3282. w. (19.)**

— The City of God. Hymn-Anthem. Words by Johnson. *G. Schirmer: New York,* 1899. 8°. **F. 1173. (65.)**

— Come unto Me. *See infra:* Two Sacred Songs, *etc.* [No. 2.]

— Forget-me-not. (Vergissmeinnicht.) *See infra:* Leichte Stücke ... Op. 25. No. 5.

— In the Boat. [P. F.] *O. Ditson Co.: Boston,* 1900. fol. **h. 3282. w. (18.)**

— Jubilate Deo. *G. Schirmer: New York,* 1897. 8°. **F. 1173. (3.)**

— Lead, kindly Light. Hymn-Anthem for Quartette and Soprano Solo with Organ accompaniment. [Words by J. H. Newman.] *G. Schirmer: New York,* (1909.) 8°. **F. 281. m. (26.)**

— Leichte Stücke (Easy Pieces) für Pianoforte ... Op. 25. No. 1. The Mill. (Die Mühle.) No. 2. Polka-Mazurka. No. 3. Cradle Song. (Wiegenlied.) No. 4. Playfulness. (Spielerei.) No. 5. Forget-me-not. (Vergissmeinnicht.) No. 6. Menuetto. no. 4–6. *Edward Schuberth & Co.: New York, London,* [1903.] fol. *Imperfect; wanting no.* 1–3. **h. 4120. ll. (19.)**

— Lift your glad Voices. Easter Anthem. *G. Schirmer: New York,* 1900. 8°. *G. Schirmer's Octavo Church Music, No.* 1020. **F. 231. o. (57.)**

— Menuetto. *See supra:* Leichte Stücke ... Op. 25. No. 6.

— O Love divine. Hymn-Anthem. Words by J. G. Whittier. *G. Schirmer: New York,* 1899. 8°. **F. 1173. (66.)**

— Playfulness. (Spielerei.) *See supra:* Leichte Stücke ... Op. 25. No. 4.

— Four Responses. *G. Schirmer: New York,* 1900. 8°. *G. Schirmer's Octavo Church Music, No.* 1003. **F. 231. o. (58.)**

— Two Sacred Songs with Piano accompaniment. [No. 1.] As it began to dawn—Alto or Mezzo-Soprano— ... [No. 2.] Come unto Me—Baritone, *etc.* 2 no. *G. Schirmer: New York,* (1909.) fol. **G. 517. v. (28.)**

— Serenade. [P. F.] *O. Ditson Co.: Boston,* 1900. fol. **h. 3282. w. (21.)**

— Te Deum. Quartet with Soli for Soprano, Alto and Tenor. *G. Schirmer: New York,* 1900. 8°. *G. Schirmer's Octavo Church Music, No.* 1006. **F. 1170. z. (19.)**

LÆRŪM (INGA)

— Tre Norske Legender for Pianoforte. *C. Jefferys: London,* [1891.] fol.   **h. 1489. r. (56.)**

LAESTERSCHULE

— Die Lästerschule. Komische Oper. *See* KLENAU (P. A. von)

LAETAMINI

— Laetamini in Domino. Mottetto. *See* NANINO (G. M.)

LAETARE

— Laetare. Kantate. *See* MOHLER (P.)

LAETATUS

— Laetatus sum. [Motet.] *See* CAVALLI (P. F.) [Musiche sacre.]

— Laetatus sum. Concerto. *See* GORCZYCKI (G. G.)

— Lætatus sum. [Motet.] *See* MEWS (Douglas)

— Laetatus sum. [Cantata.] *See* PORPORA (N. A.)

LAETENTUR

— Laetentur caeli. Motet. *See* ANDREWS (Carroll T.)

— Laetentur coeli. Motet. *See* BYRD (W.) [Liber primus Sacrarum Cantionum.]

— Laetentur coeli. [Motet.] *See* GIORGI (G.)

— Lætentur Cœli. Christmas Hymn. *See* HAMMA (B.)

— Laetentur caeli. Motet. *See* MACGRATH (Joseph J.)

— Laetentur coeli. Motet. *See* MARSH (William J.)

— Laetentur caeli. Motet. *See* ROFF (Joseph)

— Lætentur cœli. Motet. *See* TAYLOR (W. R.)

LAEUTEN

— Läuten kaum die Maienglocken. [Song.] *See* BISCHOFF (K. J.) Vier Lieder ... Op. 45. No. 2.

LAFAGE (JUSTE ADRIEN LENOIR DE)

— *See* PALESTRINA (G. Pierluigi da) Cinq Messes ... édition revue et corrigée ... par A. de Lafage. [1855?] 8°.   **R. M. 8. k. 3.**

— *See* PALESTRINA (G. Pierluigi da) Vingt Motets ... édition revue et corrigée ... par A. de Lafage. [1855?] 8°.   **R. M. 8. k. 4.**

LA FAGE (PERCY)

— Summer Roses. Caprice. [P. F.] pp. 5. *K. Dehnhoff: New York,* [1906.] fol.   **h. 4120. ll. (20.)**

LAFARGE (GUY)

— La Seine. Pour harmonie & fanfare ... Poème de Flavien Monod & Guy Lafarge ... Arrangement pour harmonie et fanfare de Désiré Dondeyne. [Compressed score and parts.] 128 pt. *Éditions & productions théâtrales Chappell: Paris,* [1973.] 8° & obl. 8°.
With several copies of various parts.   **e. 503. v. (1.)**

LA FARGE (HALL)

— Ada, my sweet Potater! ⟨Cole and Europe.⟩ and The Big red Shawl. ⟨Johnson.⟩ Medley two step. Arr. by H. La Farge. [Orchestral parts.] 12 pt. *Jos. W. Stern & Co.:* [*New York,* 1908.] 8°.   **f. 800. (754.)**

— B. I. double L: Bill. ⟨Lloyd.⟩ and I want to be loved like a leading lady. ⟨Wade.⟩ Medley two step. Arr. by H. La Farge [Orchestral parts.] 12 pt. *Jos. W. Stern & Co.:* [*New York,* 1908.] 8°.   **f. 800. (755.)**

— By the old oaken Bucket, Louise ⟨Davis⟩ and ... "Lady Lady" ... ⟨Leighton & Hillbury⟩. Medley waltz. Arr. by H. La Farge. ⟨Solo B♭ cornet [and wind band parts].⟩ 32 pt. *Jos. W. Stern & Co.:* [*New York,* 1908.] 8°.
Various parts are in duplicate.   **f. 800. (756.)**

— Call around for me. ⟨Williams.⟩ and La-la! Oo-la-la-la! ⟨Murphy.⟩ Medley waltz. Arr. by H. La Farge. [Orchestral parts.] 12 pt. *Jos. W. Stern & Co.: New York,* [1909.] 8°.   **f. 800. (757.)**

— Call around for me ⟨Williams⟩ and La-la! Oo-la-la-la! ⟨Murphy⟩. Medley waltz. Arr. by H. La Farge. ⟨Solo B♭ cornet (conductor) [and wind band parts].⟩ 30 pt. *Jos. W. Stern & Co.:* [*New York,* 1909.] 8°.
Various parts are in duplicate.   **f. 800. (758.)**

— Everyone's in Love with someone ⟨Petrie⟩ and Georgie took me walking in the Park ⟨Meher & Tate⟩. Barn dance-schottische. Arr. by H. La Farge. [Orchestral parts.] 12 pt. *Jos. W. Stern & Co.:* [*New York,* 1908.] 8°.   **f. 800. (759.)**

— The Gibson bathing Girl ⟨Solman⟩ and "Say, Sis, give me a Kiss!" ⟨Clark.⟩ Medley march. Arr. by H. La Farge. ⟨Solo B♭ cornet (conductor) [and wind band parts].⟩ 32 pt. *Jos. W. Stern & Co.:* [*New York,* 1908.] 8°.
Various parts are in duplicate.   **f. 800. (760.)**

— Hammock Love Song and The Prince of Borneo. Medley march. [Selected from "The Beauty Spot" by Henry L. R. de Koven.] Arr. by H. La Farge. ⟨Solo B♭ cornet (conductor) [and wind band parts].⟩ 32 pt. *Jos. W. Stern & Co.:* [*New York,* 1909.] 8°.
Various parts are in duplicate. The orchestral version is entered unter KOVEN (H.L.R. de).   **f. 800. (761.)**

— I am longing for someone to love me ⟨Tate⟩, and The Recipe for Love ⟨Wenrich⟩. Medley two step. Arr. by H. La Farge. [Orchestral parts.] 12 pt. *Jos. W. Stern & Co.:* [*New York,* 1908.] 8°.   **f. 800. (762.)**

— I am longing for someone to love me and The Recipe for Love. Medley march-two-step. Arr. by H. L. La Farge. ⟨Solo B♭ cornet [and wind band parts].⟩ 32 pt. *Jos. W. Stern & Co.:* [*New York,* 1909.] 8°.
Various parts are in duplicate.   **f. 800. (763.)**

— I wish I had my old Girl back again ⟨Wallace⟩ and Under the Maples with Molly-O ⟨Henry⟩. Medley two-step. Arr. by H. La Farge. [Orchestral parts.] 12 pt. *Jos. W. Stern & Co.: New York,* [1909.] 8°.   **f. 800. (764.)**

— I wish I had my old Girl back again ⟨Solman⟩ and Under the Maples with Molly-O ⟨Henry⟩. Medley march-two step. Arr. by H. La Farge. ⟨Solo B♭ cornet (conductor) [and wind band parts].⟩ 30 pt. *Jos. W. Stern & Co.:* [*New York,* 1909.] 8°.
Various parts are in duplicate.   **f. 800. (765.)**

— If I had a thousand Lives to live, and Was it you? ⟨Solman.⟩ Medley waltz. Arr. by H. La Farge. [Orchestral parts.] 12 pt. *Jos. W. Stern & Co.:* [*New York,* 1908.] 8°.   **f. 800. (766.)**

— If I had a thousand Lives to live, and Was it you? ⟨Solman.⟩ Medley waltz. Arr. by H. La Farge. ⟨Solo B♭ cornet (conductor) [and wind band parts].⟩ 32 pt. *Jos. W. Stern & Co.:* [*New York,* 1909.] 8°.
Various parts are in duplicate.   **f. 800. (767.)**

LA FARGE (HALL)

— ... "Jennie" ... ⟨Montgomery.⟩ and ... "Land of Cotton" ... ⟨Leonard.⟩ Medley-two-step. Arr. by H. La Farge. [Orchestral parts.] 12 pt. *Jos. W. Stern & Co.:* [*New York*, 1908.] 8°.
f. 800. (768.)

— ... "Jennie" ... ⟨Montgomery⟩ and ... "Land of Cotton" ... ⟨Leonard⟩. Medley march. Arr. by H. La Farge. ⟨Solo B♭ cornet (conductor) [and wind band parts].⟩ 32 pt. *Jos. W. Stern & Co.:* [*New York*, 1908.] 8°.
Various parts are in duplicate.
f. 800. (769.)

— On the Road to Monterey ⟨Cole⟩ and I've lost my Teddy Bear ⟨Cole & Johnson⟩. Medley two step. Arr. by H. La Farge. [Orchestral parts.] 12 pt. *Jos. W. Stern & Co.:* [*New York*, 1908.] 8°.
f. 800. (770.)

— Stern's glittering "Glow-worm" Medley ... Arr. by H. La Farge. [Orchestral parts.] 12 pt. *Jos. W. Stern & Co.:* [*New York*, 1909.] 4°.
g. 1800. (186.)

— Stern's glittering "Glow-worm" Medley ... Arr. by H. La Farge. ⟨Solo or 1st B♭ cornet (conductor) [and wind band parts].⟩ 30 pt. *Jos. W. Stern & Co.: New York*, [1909.] 8°.
f. 800. (771.)

— Sugar Babe ⟨Johnson⟩, and How would you like to try a Honeymoon with me ⟨Wade⟩. Medley two step. Arr. by H. La Farge. [Orchestral parts.] 12 pt. *Jos. W. Stern & Co.:* [*New York*, 1908.] 8°.
f. 800. (772.)

— Your Picture says Remember 'though your Letter says Forget ⟨Henry⟩ and Up in my Balloon ⟨Wenrich⟩. Medley waltz. Arr. by H. La Farge. [Orchestral parts.] 12 pt. *Jos. W. Stern & Co.:* [*New York*, 1908.] 8°.
f. 800. (773.)

— *See* COLE (Bob) and JOHNSON (R.) I've lost my Teddy Bear ... Arr. [for wind band] by H. La Farge. [1909.] 8°.
f. 800. (291.)

— *See* HOWARD (George F.) First Infancy. March & two step ... Arr. [for wind band] by H. La Farge. [1909.] 8°.
f. 800. (660.)

— *See* KOVEN (Henry L. R. de) [The Beauty Spot.] Hammock Love Song and The Prince of Borneo. Medley two step ... Arr. [for orchestra] by H. La Farge. [1909.] 8°. **f. 800. (727.)**

LAFARGUE (GUSTAVE)

— Suzanne au Bain, opérette en un acte. Paroles et musique de G. Lafargue. [Vocal score.] *Paris*, [1872.] 8°. **F. 509.**

— [Suzanne au Bain.] *See* STRAUSS (J.) *the Younger*. Grande valse de Suzanne, *etc.* [1872.] fol. **h. 3193. b. (1.)**

LAFAYETTE, *pseud.*

— Saadi. Valse orientale. — Sur le [*sic*] Mélodie de V. Lyon. [P. F.] *F. Harris Co.: London*, (1909.) fol. **h. 3286. uu. (33.)**

LA FEILLÉE (FRANÇOIS DE)

— Méthode nouvelle pour apprendre parfaitement les regles du plain-chant et de la psalmodie, avec des messes et autres ouvrages en plain-chant figure et musical, à l'usage des paroisses et des communautés religieuses. pp. 384. *Chez Jean Faulcon: Poitiers*, 1748. 8°. **A. 1232. q. (1.)**

— Nouvelle Méthode pour apprendre facilement les Règles du Plain-Chant et de la Psalmodie. Avec des Messes & autres Ouvrages en Plain-chant figuré & musical ... à voix seule & en partie ... Nouvelle Édition, revue, corrigée, & augmentée par un Ecclésiastique, *etc. Chez J. F. Faulcon & F. Barbier: Poitiers*, 1782. 12°. **B. 813. a.**

LA FEILLÉE (FRANÇOIS DE)

— Méthode nouvelle pour apprendre parfaitement les règles du plain-chant et de la psalmodie, avec des messes et autres ouvrages en plain-chant figuré et musical, à voix seule et en partie. pp. 548. *Chez Amable Leroy: Lyon*, 1804. 12°.
B. 813.

— Méthode de Plain-Chant ... Nouvelle edition, revue, corrigée, et augmentée, par un ecclésiastique, *etc. F. Chambeau: Avignon*, 1824. 12°. **B. 813. b.**

— Le Nouveau La Feillée ou méthode de plain-chant et de psalmodie, suivie d'un traité de plain-chant figuré, d'une dissertation sur la manière de chanter avec goût, et d'un choix de morceaux de plain-chant et de plain-chant figuré par M. Dollé ainé, *etc.* pp. 580. *Chez Franç.-Aimé Barbier: Poitiers*, 1825. 12°. **B. 1170. gg.**

— [Méthode nouvelle ... du plain-chant.] Supplément à la méthode. pp. 48. *Chez Jean-Thomas Herissant: Poitiers*, 1751. 8°. **A. 1232. q. (2.)**

— [Méthode nouvelle ... du plain-chant — Te Sancte rursus.] *See* SAMPSON (G.) There is a blessed Home. Set to the tune, Annue Christe, from La Feillée, *etc.* 1940. 8°. [*Novello's Octavo Anthems. No.* 1244.] **E. 618. a.**

LA FERTÉ (CHARLES DE)

— Premier livre de sonates pour le violon et la basse ... Gravé par Roussel. pp. 38. *Chez l'auteur: Paris*, 1707. fol.
h. 2785. tt.

LA FEUILLADE (N.)

— The Prize Jig galop. [P. F.] *London*, [1862.] fol.
h. 1460. u. (23.)

LAFFAGE (ANTONIN)

— Musique arabe. Recueillie, annotée et transcrite pour piano ... Traductions arabisantes de N. Luciant. 12 fasc. *Antonin Laffage: Tunis; Paris* [printed, c. 1900.] fol. **h. 1095. a.**

— La Musique arabe ... Ses instruments et ses chants. ⟨El mouzika elarabia. Alatouha oa rinaïatouha.⟩ ... 1er fascicule ⟨2e & 3e fascicules⟩. 2 no. *L'Imprimerie Rapide: Tunis; Röder: Leipzig*, [c. 1905.] 1907. fol.
The cover of fasc. 2, 3 bears the words: "A la recherche de la musique arabe. Mission en Tripolitaine (1906)".
h. 1095. b. (2.)

LAFFAN (BERTHA JANE) *Mrs*

— A Cycle of Songs. *Ascherberg, Hopwood & Crew: London*, [1907.] fol. **H. 1794. uu. (51.)**

— We sing: "The King". Song, words and music by Mrs. De Courcy Laffan. *Ascherberg, Hopwood & Crew: London*, [1907.] fol. **H. 1794. uu. (52.)**

LAFFAN (*Mrs* ROBERT STUART DE COURCY)

— *See* LAFFAN (Bertha Jane) *Mrs*.

LAFFERTY (J. WESLEY)

— Dat Coon has got me guessin'. [Song.] Words by Herbert M. Saumenig and Arthur L. Robb. pp. 2–5. *M. Witmark & Sons:* [*New York*, 1901.] fol. **H. 3985. g. (4.)**

— "My Alabama Home." [Song.] Words by Herbert M. Saumenig and Arthur L. Robb. pp. 5. *M. Witmark & Sons: New York, Chicago*, [1900.] fol. **H. 3985. g. (5.)**

— Some Day I hope mah Honey you'll be mine. [Song.] Words by Arthur L. Robb. pp. 3–5. *M. Witmark & Sons:* [*New York*, 1902.] fol. **H. 3985. g. (6.)**

LAFFILLÉ (CHARLES)

— La Renaissance des Lis. Chant Gallique ... paroles et
musique par C. Laffillé. *Chez Mme. Benoist: Paris,* [1814.]
fol. **H. 346. (8.)**

— Le Siège de Paris, suivi de l'Entrée des troupes alliées, et le
Retour de Madame la Duchesse d'Angoulème en France ...
Arrangée pour le forte-piano par W. Paz ... The Seige [*sic*] of
Paris, *etc.* pp. 15. *Printed by N. Corri: Edinburgh,* [c. 1815.]
fol. **h. 60. p. (6.)**

— Le Souvenir des ménestrels, contenant une collection de
romances inédites. Le tout recueilli et publié par un amateur
⟨C. Laffillé⟩. année 2. *Chez l'éditeur: Paris,* 1815. 16°.
Hirsch III. 880.

LAFFORD (LINDSAY)

— Alleluia! The Lord is risen indeed. An Easter invitatory.
(S.A.T.B.) pp. 4. *J. Fischer & Bro.: Glen Rock, N.J.,* [1966.]
8°. **E. 335. uu. (6.)**

— Three Fancies. For two trumpets and organ, *etc.* [Score and
part.] 2 pt. *J. Fischer & Bro.: Glen Rock, N.J.,* [1967.] 4°.
The parts for two trumpets are printed in score.
g. 1378. w. (3.)

— He shall come down like Rain. (S.A.T.B.) Ps. 72. pp. 7.
J. Fischer: Glen Rock, N.J., [1968.] 8°. **F. 1106. b. (4.)**

— The Liturgy of the Lord's Supper ... ⟨Service music.⟩ Choir
and congregation with organ accompaniment. pp. 18.
J. Fischer & Bro.: Glen Rock, N.J., [1970.] 8°.
F. 1158. t. (11.)

LAFITTE (A.)

— Six Chœurs arrangés en mélodies, avec accompagnement de
Piano. 6 no. *Paris,* [1868.] fol. **H. 1774. e. (6.)**

— [Another issue of no. 4.] Six chants, *etc. Paris,* [1868.] fol.
Issued as music supplement to "La Musique populaire,"
année 6. no. 1. **P. P. 1948. s/2. (115.)**

— Ave Maria à 2 voix égales. [1861.] *See* NIEDERMEYER (L.) La
Maîtrise, *etc.* 4ᵉ Année. No. 17. [1857–61.] 8°. **F. 623.**

— Chanson Bachique, tirée du "Capitaine Fracasse". [Begins:
"De Bacchus".] Poésie de T. Gautier. *Paris,* [1864.] fol.
H. 1774. e. (5.)

— Les Chants d'autrefois. Choeur à trois voix égales [begins:
"De ces vieux chants"]. *Paris,* [1866.] 8°. **E. 600. a. (27.)**

— La Polka, choeur à trois voix égales. *Paris,* [1867.] 8°.
E. 600. a. (26.)

— La Vocation, choeur à 3 voix égales [begins: "Suivez votre
vocation"]. *Paris,* [1867.] 8°. **E. 600. a. (28.)**

— La Vocation. Chœur à 3 voix égales. *Paris,* [1883.] 8°.
E. 308. n. (26.)

LAFITTE (EDOUARD)

— 3 Melodious Pieces for Pianoforte. 1. Idylle. 2. Pastorale.
3. Romance. *A. Hammond & Co.: London,* [1913.] 4°.
The Academic Edition, No. 491. **g. 1130. y. (2.)**

— Idylle, pour Piano. *A. Hammond & Co.: London,* [1911.] fol.
g. 606. n. (28.)

— Pastorale, pour Piano. *A. Hammond & Co.: London,* [1911.]
fol. **g. 606. n. (29.)**

— Romance, pour Piano. *A. Hammond & Co.: London,* [1911.]
fol. **g. 606. n. (30.)**

LAFITTE (EMILE)

— Les Midinettes. Marche pour Piano. *A. Bosc: Paris,* [1903.]
fol. **g. 605. ll. (12.)**

LAFITTE (JACQUES)

— Baisers de Jeunesse. Valse. [P. F.] *L. Bathlot: Paris,* [1886.]
fol. **h. 3281. k. (49.)**

LA FLEUR

— La Fleur. Ballad. *See* MOULDS (John)

LAFLEUR (ALPHONSE)

— Les Menus Plaisirs quadrille. [P.F.] *London,* [1874.] 8°.
No. 219 *of the "Alliance Musicale. Album Bijou".* **f. 406.**

LAFLEUR (E.)

— Quadrilles on Nursery Rhymes. [Orchestral parts.] *J. R.*
Lafleur & Son: London, [1887.] 8°.
Part of the "Alliance Musicale". **f. 400. kk. (14.)**

— Quadrilles on Nursery Rhymes. [P. F.] *J. R. Lafleur & Son:*
London, [1887.] 8°.
Part of the "Alliance Musicale. Album Bijou".
f. 406. a. (11.)

LAFLEUR (J.)

— Adieu au Tyrol, idylle pour Piano. *London,* [1862.] fol.
h. 1462. q. (24.)

— Console Toi. Romance sans paroles pour Piano. *Londres,*
[1861.] fol. **h. 1462. q. (19.)**

— Dis Moi! Romance sans paroles pour Piano. *Londres,*
[1861.] fol. **h. 1462. q. (20.)**

— Feuille d'Album pour Piano. *Londres,* [1873.] fol.
h. 1487. o. (18.)

— Je t'écoute, romance sans paroles pour Piano. *Londres,*
[1860.] fol. **h. 1462. q. (18.)**

— Je t'écoute, romance sans paroles. [P. F.] *London,* [1871.] fol.
h. 1485. s. (3.)

— Je t'écoute. Romance sans paroles. [P. F.] *London,* [1871.] fol.
A new edition. **h. 1485. s. (4.)**

— Je t'écoute. Romance sans paroles pour Piano. *London,*
[1874.] fol. **h. 1482. y. (4.)**

— Je t'écoute, romance sans paroles pour Piano. (Duet.)
Londres, [1861.] fol. **h. 1462. q. (21.)**

— Malaïska. Mazurk hongroise pour Piano. *Londres,* [1862.]
fol. **h. 1462. q. (22.)**

— Regrettez-Moi, mélodie pour Piano. *Londres,* [1862.] fol.
h. 1462. q. (23.)

LAFLEUR (J. R.) **AND SON**

— Lafleur's Album of famous Rhythm Songs, *etc.* (Lafleur's ...
2nd Song & Dance Album.) 2 no. *J. R. Lafleur & Son:*
London, [1938, 40.] 4°. **F. 1835.**

— The Lafleur Motion Picture Edition by R. Howgill. [P. F.
conductor and orchestral parts.] *J. R. Lafleur & Son:*
London, 1927, *etc.* 8°. **g. 1447. a.**

— The Lafleur Motion Picture Edition. Piano Solo Album
No. 1(–3). R. Howgill. *J. R. Lafleur & Son: London,*
[1927–29.] 4°. **g. 1447.**

— Lafleur's ... 2nd Song & Dance Album. *See supra:* Lafleur's
Album of famous Rhythm Songs, *etc.*

LA FLEUR (James L.)

— Finger and Wrist Studies of Scales, Intervals and Chords, preparatory to the Study of Harmony, Grades I to V, *etc.* [P. F.]   *C. W. Homeyer & Co.: Boston, Mass.,* 1912. 4°.

g. 337. bb. (4.)

LAFON (Auguste)

— Il faut faire un heureux. Romance à trois voix [begins: "Interessante Adèle"]. *Paris,* [1830?] fol.   **G. 551. (18.)**

LA FOND (Jean François)

— A New System of Music, both Theorical and Practical, and yet not Mathematical, *etc.* (Vol. I.) (The Truth of the Twelve Notes; and one of their great Uses ... illustrated in two ... Preludes ... And two other ... Advantages ... examplify'd in Corelli's VI. Sonata, IV. Work, fitted for those Purposes.) 2 pt. *Printed for the Author: London,* 1725. 8° & 4°. *No more published.*   **785. f. 39. & 797. dd. 23.**

—[Another copy.]   **1042. k. 9.**

LAFOND (Philippe)

— *See* Lafont (Charles P.)

LAFONT (Auguste)

— *See* Verdi (F. G. F.) [La Traviata.] Souvenir de Traviata for the Piano Forte, arranged from Verdi's opera by A. Lafont. [1857.] fol.   **h. 725. f. (21.)**

LAFONT (C. M.)

— Le Messager d'Amour, barcarolle pour le Piano. *London,* [1870.] fol.   **h. 1485. s. (5.)**

LAFONT (Charles Philippe)

— Andante et Boleros pour le Violon, avec accompagnement de Piano. *Paris,* [1820?] fol.   **h. 1608. (10.)**

— Boleros pour le Violon avec accompagnement de Quatuor et Flûte ad libitum. *Vienne,* [1805?] fol.   **h. 1613. b. (4.)**

— C'est une larme. Romance ... Accomp^t de guitare ou lyre par Phills [or rather, Phillis] pere. *Chez Pierre Gaveaux: Paris,* [c. 1815.] 8°.   **E. 1717. o. (50.)**

— C'est une Larme. Romance ... Paroles du Chevalier de Messence. *Paris,* [1830?] fol.   **G. 554. (41.)**

— C'est une larme. Romance. *Londres,* [1830?] fol.   **H. 2835. (20.)**

— C'est une larme. [P. F.] *See* Cramer (A.) La Gerbe mélodique. No. 3. [1872.] fol.   **h. 1487. d. (18.)**

— [C'est une larme.] *See* Croisez (A.) C'est une larme. Romance variée pour Piano. [1879.] fol.   **h. 1259. b. (7.)**

— [C'est une larme.] [For editions and arrangements of the variations on "C'est une larme" composed jointly by H. Herz and C. P. Lafont:] *See* Herz (H.) and Lafont (C. P.) [Duo et variations concertants. Op. 18.]

— Troisième Concerto à Violon principal accompagné de 2 Violons, Alto, Basse, 2 Flûtes, 2 Hautbois, 2 Clarinettes, 2 Cors et 2 Bassons. *Offenbach sur le Mein,* [1805?] fol.   **h. 1729. b. (2.)**

— Sixième Concerto avec accompagnement d'Orchestre. *Offenbach s. M.,* [1820?] fol.   **h. 1729. b. (3.)**

— Le Départ du jeune Marin. Romance dramatique [begins: "Je ne puis"] de Mr. J. de la Boutrage. *Paris,* [1840?] fol.   **G. 543. (57.)**

LAFONT (Charles Philippe)

— Fantaisie et variations pour Violon principal avec accompagnement de quatuor. Op. 4.   *Paris,* [1815?] fol.   **h. 1613. b. (5.)**

— Grand Fantasia & Variations, on favorite airs in the opera of Masaniello [by D. F. E. Auber], for the violin, with an accompaniment for the piano forte. [Score and part.] 2 pt. *R. Cocks & Cº: London,* [1836.] fol.   **g. 619. e. (3.)**

— L'Illusion. Romance avec accompagnement de piano ou harpe, paroles du Chevalier de Messence, *etc.* pp. 3.   *Chez Simon Gaveaux: Paris,* [c. 1815.] fol.   **G. 561. d. (9.)**

— [Le Marin.] *See* Liszt (F.) [*Collected Works.—e.*] Grand duo concertant ... ⟨Based on the romance "Le Marin" by P. Lafont.⟩ Epithalam, *etc.* [1971.] 4°.   **g. 547. x. (2.)**

— [Le Marin.] *See* Liszt (F.) Grand duo pour piano et violon sur la romance de Lafont, le Marin. [1854.] fol.   **h. 1611. (3.)**

— Minuit, fantaisie sur [Auber's opera] "Le Domino Noir" ... arrangée pour la Concertina par G. Regondi. *London,* [1871.] fol.   **h. 2455. a. (12.)**

— La Pauvre Aveugle. Romance, paroles de Mr. J. Commerson. *Chez Pacini: Paris,* [1825?] fol.   **G. 561. a. (19.)**

— Le Plus Amoureux et la Plus Jolie. Romance [begins: "Personne n'aime"]. *Paris,* [1820?] fol.   **G. 547. (32.)**

— Les Souhaits. Romance, paroles de M^r le Comte la Garde de Messence ... Avec accompagnement de lyre ou guitare par Meissonnier. *Chez Meissonnier: Paris,* [c. 1820.] 8°. [*Journal de lyre ou guitar. année* 6. *livr.* 6.]   **E. 1717. e. (1.)**

— Le Souvenir. Romance, paroles de M^r le Comte la Garde de Messence ... Avec accompagnement de lyre ou guitare par Meissonnier. *Chez Meissonnier: Paris,* [c. 1820.] 8°. [*Journal de lyre ou guitar. année* 6. *livr.* 6.]   **E. 1717. e. (1.)**

— [Sur l'eau qui te balance.] *See* Méreaux (J. A. Le F. de) Sur l'eau qui te balance ... variée pour le piano ... Oe. 30. [1831?] fol.   **h. 721. t. (15.)**

— *See* Czerny (C.) and Lafont (C. P.) Variations Concertantes ... sur un Air militaire, *etc.* [1834?] fol.   **h. 514. i. (17.)**

— *See* Herz (H.) Introduction et variations brillantes, pour le piano forte, sur le [*sic*] chansonette favorite de l'Enfant du régiment ... Op. 24. [An arrangement of the work composed for violin and P. F. by H. Herz and. C. P. Lafont.] [1844.] fol.   **h. 465. (19.)**

— *See* Herz (H.) Récréations Musicales ... Arrangés pour le Violon avec Acct. de Piano par C. P. Lafont ... Suite 2. [1835?] fol.   **h. 1078. b. (7.)**

— *See* Herz (H.) Récréations musicales ... [Op. 71.] Arrangées pour le violon avec acc^t de piano par C. P. Lafont ... 3e suite. [1835?] fol.   **g. 1563. a. (1.)**

— *See* Herz (H.) [Variations brillantes. Op. 42.] Rossini's March, in Mosè in Egitto, with ... variations for the piano forte, *etc.* [An arrangement of the work composed for violin and P. F. by H. Herz and C. P. Lafont.] [1845?] fol.   **g. 1563. (6.)**

— *See* Herz (H.) [Variations brillantes. Op. 42.] Brilliant Variations on Rossini's March in Mosè in Egitto, for the piano forte, *etc.* [An arrangement of the work composed for violin and P. F. by H. Herz and C. P. Lafont.] [1857.] fol.   **h. 469. (1.)**

— *See* Herz (H.) and Lafont (C. P.) Duo & variations concertans pour piano et violon sur la romance "C'est une larme," *etc.* [c. 1825.] fol.   **h. 1608. (11.)**

— *See* Herz (H.) and Lafont (C. P.) Trois grands duos concertante pour piano & violon, *etc.* [1830.] fol.   **h. 1729. m. (2.)**

LAFONT (Charles Philippe)

— *See* Herz (H.) and Lafont (C. P.) Trois duos concertans pour le piano et violon sur des thèmes favoris. Op. 75. [1834.] fol.
h. 461. (12.)

— *See* Herz (H.) and Lafont (C. P.) Dernier grand duo concertant pour piano et violon sur une cavatine de la Niobe. [1840.] fol.
h. 463. (16.)

— *See* Herz (H.) and Lafont (C. P.) Fantaisie & variations pour piano et viol^{elle} sur des thèmes russes ... Op. 19, *etc.* [1834.] fol.
g. 514. d. (13.)

— *See* Herz (H.) and Lafont (C. P.) Variations concertantes pour piano et violon sur la chansonette favorite de l'Enfant du régiment, *etc.* [c. 1835.] fol.
h. 1568. c. (11.)

— *See* Herz (H.) and Lafont (C. P.) [Variations brillantes. Op. 42.] Brilliant variations for the Piano forte and violin on Rossini's march in Mose in Egitto. [1827.] fol.
h. 462. (8.)

— *See* Herz (H.) and Lafont (C. P.) Variations brillantes pour Piano et Violon, sur la Marche ... de Moïse ... Op. 42. [1830?] fol.
h. 1078. b. (15.)

— *See* Herz (H.) and Tulou (J. L.) Duo et variations, concertans, pour piano et flûte, sur la romance. C'est une larme ... Op. 18. [An arrangement of the work composed for violin and P. F. by H. Herz and C. P. Lafont.] [1828.] fol.
h. 462. (1.)

— *See* Kalkbrenner (F. W. M.) and Lafont (C. P.) Duo & Variations pour Piano & Violon sur ... Robert le Diable, *etc.* [1832?] fol.
h. 1568. c. (9.)

— *See* Moscheles (I.) and Lafont (C. P.) Grand Pot-Pourri concertant, *etc.* [1820?] fol.
g. 505. a. (4.)

— *See* Moscheles (I.) and Lafont (C. P.) Grand pot-pourri concertant pour pianoforte et violon ... Oeuvre 59. [c. 1830.] fol.
h. 1203. f. (5.)

— *See* Weber (C. M. F. E. von) [Grand duo concertant pour pianoforte et clarinette. Op. 48.] Grand duo concertant pour le piano et violon ... par C. M. von Weber, et Lafont [or rather, composed by Weber, the violin part arranged by Lafont], *etc.* [c. 1840.] fol.
h. 1336. y. (6.)

LAFONT (Charles Philippe) and **CZERNY** (Carl)

— Brilliant variations for violin and Piano Forte on a Spanish Romance. *London,* [1834.] fol.
h. 117. (2.)

— Concertante variations for the Violin and Piano Forte, on a military air. *London,* [1834.] fol.
h. 117. (3.)

— L'Espagnole. *See infra:* [Variations. Op. 305.]

— [Variations. Op. 305.] L'Espagnole. Romance variée pour violon et piano ... arrangée pour violon et harpe concertant par Parish Alvars. [Score and part.] 2 pt. *Chez Artaria & comp.: Vienne,* [c. 1860.] fol.
h. 176. a. (4.)

LAFONT (Charles Philippe) and **HERZ** (Henri)

— [For editions and arrangements of works composed jointly by C. P. Lafont and H. Herz:] *See* Herz (H.) and Lafont (C. P.)

LAFONT (Jacques)

— The Challenge, for BB♭ contrabass ... with pianoforte accompaniment. *Boosey & Co.: London and New York,* 1923. 4°.
g. 1110. (5.)

— The Conqueror. Tenor Trombone solo (with pianoforte accompaniment). *Boosey & Co.: London and New York,* 1924. 4°.
g. 1110. (22.)

— Fantasia. Bordogni's Works. Arranged by J. Lafont for E♭ Soprano ... with Pianoforte accompaniment. *Boosey & Co.: London and New York,* 1927. 4°.
g. 1110. (12.)

LAFONT (Jacques)

— Friendship. Duet for two B♭ cornets with pianoforte accompaniment. *Boosey & Co.: London, New York,* 1924. 4°.
g. 1105. a. (4.)

— Happy Memories. For bass trombone ... with pianoforte accompaniment. *Boosey & Co.: London and New York,* 1923. 4°.
g. 1110. (23.)

— The Invincible. E♭ Bombardon Solo with Pianoforte accompaniment. *Boosey & Co.: London and New York,* 1927. 4°.
g. 1110. (13.)

— Loving Hearts. Duet for two E♭ tenor horns with pianoforte accompaniment. *Boosey & Co.: London, New York,* 1924. 4°.
g. 1110. (6.)

— Triumphant. Solo for bass trombone with pianoforte accompaniment. *Boosey & Co.: London, New York,* 1924. 4°.
g. 1110. (24.)

— The Victor. For E♭ bombardon ... with pianoforte accompaniment. *Boosey & Co.: London and New York,* 1923. 4°.
g. 1110. (7.)

— *See* Bellini (V.) [Norma.] Ah! bello a me ritornó ... Arranged by J. Lafont for B♭ baritone, *etc.* 1923. 4°.
g. 1110. (1.)

— *See* Bellini (V.) [Norma.] Mira o Norma ... Arranged by J. Lafont for two B♭ cornets, *etc.* 1923. 4°. **g. 1105. a. (1.)**

— *See* Bellini (V.) [La Sonnambula.—Son geloso del ziffiro errante.] Yes, I'm jealous ... Arranged by J. Lafont for two E♭ tenor horns, *etc.* 1923. 4°. **g. 1110. (2.)**

— *See* Bellini (V.) [La Sonnambula.—Sovra il sen la man mi posa.] While this Heart its joy revealing ... Arranged by J. Lafont for E♭ soprano cornet, *etc.* 1923. 4°.
g. 1105. a. (2.)

— *See* Bellini (V.) [La Sonnambula.—Vi ravviso.] As I view these Scenes so charming ... Arranged by J. Lafont for B♭ euphonion, *etc.* 1923. 4°. **g. 1110. (3.)**

— *See* Bordogni (G. M.) [Douze Nouvelles Vocalises pour Contralto ou Mezzo-Soprano. No. 9.] Euphonion Solo. Arranged by J. Lafont. 1927. 4°. **g. 1110. (9.)**

— *See* Crescentini (G.) Baritone Solo. Arranged ... by J. Lafont. 1927. 4°. **g. 1110. (10.)**

— *See* Donizetti (D. G. M.) [Lucrezia Borgia.—Vieni, la mia vendetta.] Haste thee to glut a Vengeance ... Arranged by J. Lafont for euphonion, *etc.* 1923. 4°. **g. 1110. (4.)**

— *See* Mercadante (S.) [La Testa di Bronzo.] Cara valle solitaria, *etc.* (Arranged by J. Lafont.) 1927. 4°.
g. 1110. (15.)

— *See* Wallace (W. V.) The Bell Ringer, *etc.* (Arranged by J. Lafont.) 1927. 4°. **g. 1110. (17.)**

LAFONT (Philippe)
— *See* Lafont (Charles P.)

LAFONTAINE
— Lafontaine vengé. [Song.] *See* Vimeux (J.)

LA FONTAINE (DE)
— L'Absence. Romance, á Nirzé. [Written] Par M. Courcelles. [*Paris,* 1785?] 8°. **B. 362. a. (95.)**

— Le Conseil. Ariette, [written] par M. Courcelles, *etc.* [*Paris,* 1785?] 8°. **B. 362. c. (5.)**

LAFORCE (MARIE)

— Echoes of Lake Champlain. (Tercentenary.) Reverie. [P. F.]
pp. 7. *Plattsburgh: New York,* [1909.] fol.   **h. 4120. ll. (21.)**

LA FOREST (GUS.)

— *See* LEBOY (Grace) What's the Use of Moonlight? ... Song
with quartet chorus [for T.T.Bar.B.]. ⟨Arr. by G. La Forest.⟩
[1909.] fol.   **H. 3985. l. (35.)**

— *See* MORSE (Al. W.) and WILLIAMS (W. R.) What do I care ...
Song, *etc.* [Followed by arrangements for T.T.Bar.B. by G. La
Forest.] [1909.] fol.   **H. 3986. a. (1.)**

— *See* SILVER (Morris S.) and CONFARE (T. R.) Sunbeam, *etc.*
⟨March ballad.⟩ [Followed by an arrangement of the chorus
for T.T.Bar.B. by G. La Forest.] [1908.] fol.   **H. 3987. t. (32.)**

— *See* STUTZMAN (CHARLES) Sarah, won't you let me serenade
you, *etc.* [Song. Followed by an arrangement of the chorus
for T.T.Bar.B. by G. La Forest.] [1908.] fol.   **H. 3987. nn. (7.)**

— *See* THOMAS (W. A.) I want someone to be real nice to me,
etc. [Song. Followed by an arrangement of the chorus for
T.T.Bar.B. by G. La Forest.] [1908.] fol.   **H. 3987. ww. (42.)**

— *See* WILLIAMS (Will R.) In the Valley where the Daisies grow,
etc. ⟨Song.⟩ [Followed by an arrangement of the chorus for
T.T.Bar.B. by G. La Forest.] [1908.] fol.   **H. 3988. z. (39.)**

LAFORESTERIE (CHARLES)

— Simone. Opérette en un acte. Paroles de M.D. de Léris.
Partition Piano et Chant. *Paris,* [1858.] 8°.   **F. 804.**

LA FORGE (FRANK)

— Am See. *See* infra: Three Songs ... 1.

— An einen Boten. *See* infra: Three Songs ... 2.

— Before the Crucifix.—Dinanzi al crocifisso.— Sacred Song
with Piano accompaniment, words by Princess Gabriele
Wrede. (English version by R. Huntington, Italian version by
P. Rusca.) *G. Schirmer: New York,* (1912.) fol.   **H. 3597. (1.)**

— Two Children's Songs. [1.] A Heart mislaid. [2.] The
Dairy-maids. [Words by M. Conde.] 2 no. *H. Flammer: New
York City,* 1918. 4°.   **G. 383. dd. (36.)**

— Come unto these yellow Sands. *See* infra: Two Songs, *etc.*
[No. 1.]

— The Coyote. *See* infra: Four Songs, *etc.* [No. 1.]

— Erwartung. *See* infra: Three Poems ... 1.

— Flander's Requiem.—America's answer.—[Song.] Poem by
R. W. Lillard. *H. Flammer: New York,* 1919. 4°.   **G. 390. y. (18.)**

— Frühlingseinzug. *See* infra: Three Poems ... 2.

— Gavotte, for Pianoforte. *G. Schirmer: New York,* (1906.) fol.   **h. 3283. o. (43.)**

— Go, and sin no more. [Sacred song.] St. John 8: 3–11. pp. 7.
Galaxy Music Corporation: New York, 1946. 4°.   **G. 519. v. (25.)**

— I came with a Song. Song with Piano accompaniment, words
by E. Ruggles. *G. Schirmer: New York,* (1914.) fol.   **H. 3597. (14.)**

— I love but thee! Song for a medium voice with Piano
accompaniment. *G. Schirmer: New York,* (1906.) fol.   **G. 807. jj. (23.)**

— In der Abendstille. *See* infra: Three Poems ... 3.

LA FORGE (FRANK)

— In pride of May. Song with Piano accompaniment.
G. Schirmer: New York, (1914.) fol.   **H. 3597. (15.)**

— Like the Rosebud. Song for medium voice, with Piano
accompaniment, words by A. Bard. *G. Schirmer: New York,*
(1906.) fol.   **G. 807. jj. (24.)**

— Like the Rosebud.—Avec une Rose.— Song, *etc.* (French
version by M. T. E. Sandwith.) *G. Schirmer: New York,*
(1911.) fol.   **H. 3597. (2.)**

— Longing. *See* infra: 3 Songs ... No. 1.

— Love's Sympathy. *See* infra: 3 Songs ... No. 2.

— The Lovely Rose. Song with Piano accompaniment, words by
A. Bard. *G. Schirmer: New York,* (1914.) fol.   **H. 3597. (16.)**

— Men, come along. Marching Song ... (Words and music) by
F. La Forge. *G. Schirmer: New York,* 1943. 4°.   **G. 1275. zz. (18.)**

— Mexican Songs for voice and piano. Arranged and translated
by F. La Forge, *etc.* 10 no. *G. Ricordi & Co.: New York, etc.,*
1922–37. 4°.   **H. 3597. (21.)**

— My Love and I. Song with Piano accompaniment, words by
C. Hooper. *G. Schirmer: New York,* (1911.) fol.   **H. 3597. (3.)**

— Two Pieces for Piano. [No. 1.] Improvisation. [No. 2.] Gavotte
and Musette. 2 no. *G. Schirmer: New York,* (1912.) fol.   **h. 3284. f. (14.)**

— Plaint. Stesk. Four-part. S. A. T. B. (T. T. B. B.) (Three Part.
S. S. A.) Czech Folk-Song. Arranged by F. La Forge. 3 no.
M. Witmark & Sons: New York, 1939. 8°.   **F. 1771. g. (43.)**

— Three Poems by Princess Gabriele Wrede, for a high voice
with Piano accompaniment. 1. Erwartung.—Expectancy.—
2. Frühlingseinzug.—May's Coming.— 3. In der Abendstille.
—In Evening Stillness—, *etc.* 3 no. *G. Schirmer: New York,*
(1908.) fol.   **G. 805. mm. (9.)**

— Three Poems by Princess Gabriele Wrede, *etc.* [Low voice.]
3 no. *G. Schirmer: New York,* [1910.] fol.   **H. 3597. (4.)**

— Romance, for the Pianoforte. *G. Schirmer: New York,* (1911.)
fol.   **h. 3284. f. (15.)**

— Sanctuary. Chorus for mixed voices, *etc.* (Poem by S. T.
Shatford.) *H. Flammer: New York,* 1923. 8°.   **F. 585. ii. (46.)**

— Schlupfwinkel. "Ich flüchte mich."—Retreat.—Gedicht von
Prinzessin Gabriele Wrede, für eine Mittelstimme
componiert, *etc.* *G. Schirmer: New York,* (1906.) fol.   **G. 807. jj. (25.)**

— Schlupfwinkel ... für eine Solostimme mit Klavierbegleitung
... in B♭. *G. Schirmer: New York,* [1910.] fol.   **H. 3597. (5.)**

— Schlupfwinkel ... Retraite ... für eine Solostimme mit
Klavierbegleitung ... German and French words. (French
version by M. T. E. Sandwith.) *G. Schirmer: New York,*
(1911.) fol.   **H. 3597. (6.)**

— Der Schmetterling. *See* infra: Two Songs, *etc.* [No. 2.]

— Serenade. Song with Piano accompaniment, words by
R. Huntington. *G. Schirmer: New York,* (1911.) fol.   **H. 3597. (7.)**

— The Sheepherder. *See* infra: Three Songs ... 3.

— Two Songs for a high voice with Piano accompaniment,
poems by Princess Gabriele Wrede. [No. 1.] Verborgene
Wunden.—Hidden Wounds.— [No. 2.] Wiedererwachen.
—Reawakening—, *etc.* 2 no. *G. Schirmer: New York,* (1906.)
fol.   **G. 805. mm. (11.)**

LA FORGE (Frank)

— Two Songs with Piano accompaniment. [No. 1.] Come unto these yellow Sands. Words from Shakespeare's "Tempest" ... [No. 2.] Der Schmetterling.—The Butterfly.— Words by E. Robert, etc. 2 no. *G. Schirmer: New York*, (1907.) fol.
G. 805. mm. (10.)

— Four Songs with Piano accompaniment. [No. 1.] The Coyote. Poem by A. Chapman ... [No. 2.] Take, O take those Lips away. Shakespeare ... [No. 3.] To a Violet.—The Message.— Poem by E. Ruggles ... [No. 4.] To one afar. Poem by G. La Forge, etc. 4 no. *G. Schirmer: New York*, (1909.) fol.
H. 3597. (10.)

— Four Songs ... [No. 3.] To a Violet.—À une Violette—, *etc*. (French version by M. T. E. Sandwith.) *G. Schirmer: New York*, (1911.) fol.
H. 3597. (11.)

— Three Songs with Piano accompaniment ... 1. Am See.—By the Lake.— Poem by E. Robert ... (English version by H. G. Chapman.) 2. An einen Boten.—To a Messenger.— Poem from "Des Knaben Wunderhorn" ... (English version by H. G. Chapman.) 3. The Sheepherder. Poem by A. Chapman, *etc*. 3 no. *G. Schirmer: New York*, (1909.) fol.   **H. 3597. (8.)**

— Three Songs ... 2. An einen Boten ... À un Messager ... German and French words. (French version by S. Verbouwens.) *G. Schirmer: New York*, (1911.) fol.
H. 3597. (9.)

— 3 Songs with Pianoforte accompaniment. No. 1. Longing. Sehnsucht ... (E. Robert, English words by A. M. von Blomberg.) No. 2. Loves' Sympathy. Gleiches Leid ... (E. Robert, English version by F. Rogers.) No. 3. 'Twas long ago. Es war einmal, *etc*. (E. Robert.) 3 no. *A. P. Schmidt: Boston, etc*., 1915. fol.   **H. 3597. (17.)**

— Songs with piano accompaniment. [No. 1.] Supplication. (Poem by M. K. Breid.) [No. 2.] Sanctuary. (Poem by S. T. Shatford.) 2 no. *H. Flammer: New York City*, 1918. 4°.
G. 383. ff. (47.)

— Spuk.—Spooks.— Song with Piano accompaniment, words by E. Robert. *G. Schirmer: New York*, (1911.) fol.
H. 3597. (12.)

— Take, O take those Lips away. *See* supra: Four Songs, *etc*. [No. 2.]

— To a Violet. *See* supra: Four Songs, *etc*. [No. 3.]

— To one afar. *See* supra: Four Songs, *etc*. [No. 4.]

— 'Twas long ago. *See* supra: 3 Songs ... No. 3.

— Valse, carissima. Song, poem by K. Stieler, English version by F. Rogers. *G. Schirmer: New York*, (1912.) fol.
H. 3597. (18.)

— Valse de Concert, for Piano. *G. Schirmer: New York*, (1912.) fol.   **h. 3284. f. (16.)**

— Verborgene Wunden. *See* supra: Two Songs for a high voice, *etc*. [No. 1.]

— When your dear Hands. Song with Piano accompaniment, words by G. C. Eldred. *G. Schirmer: New York*, (1914.) fol.
H. 3597. (19.)

— Where the West begins. Song, *etc*. (Poem by A. Chapman.) *H. Flammer: New York*, 1920. 4°.   **H. 3597. (20.)**

— Where the West begins. Chorus for mixed voices ... Poem by A. Chapman. *H. Flammer: New York*, 1923. 8°.
F. 585. ii. (47.)

— "Wie lieb ich dich hab'."—"How much I love you."— Song, with Piano accompaniment, poem by F. Boegner, *etc*. *G. Schirmer: New York*, (1907.) fol.   **G. 805. mm. (12.)**

— Wiedererwachen. *See* supra: Two Songs for a high voice, *etc*. [No. 2.]

LA FORGE (Frank)

— Wozu?—Wherefore?— Song with Piano accompaniment, words by Princess Gabriele Wrede. (English version by R. Huntington.) *G. Schirmer: New York*, (1911.) fol.
H. 3597. (13.)

— Ye are the Light of the World. [Sacred song.] St. Matthew 5:14–16, 43–45, 48. pp. 7. *G. Schirmer: New York*, 1944. 4°.
G. 519. v. (26.)

— *See* BACH (J. S.) [Was mir behagt.—Schafe können sicher weiden.] Now the Sheep secure are grazing ... Arranged ... by F. La Forge. 1938. 4°.   **G. 136. i. (3.)**

— *See* BELLINI (V.) [I Puritani.—Qui la voce sua soave.] Here his Voice with tender Accents ... Concert arrangement by F. La Forge. 1938. 4°.   **G. 1275. tt. (4.)**

— *See* BISHOP (*Sir* H. R.) [The Slave.] Pretty Mocking Bird ... Transcribed by F. La Forge. 1927. 4°.   **G. 1275. z. (9.)**

— *See* BISHOP (*Sir* H. R.) [The Slave.] Pretty Mocking Bird ... Transcribed by F. La Forge. [1939.] 4°.   **G. 1275. vv. (12.)**

— *See* CHOPIN (F. F.) [12 Etudes. Op. 25. No. 2.] Torment. Tourment ... Chopin—[Transcribed by F.] La Forge. 1939. 4°.   **G. 1275. vv. (18.)**

— *See* DONIZETTI (D. G. M.) [Linda di Chamounix.—O luce di quest' anima.] O Radiance of my Being ... Concert arrangement by F. La Forge. 1939. 4°.   **G. 1275. vv. (19.)**

— *See* DONIZETTI (D. G. M.) [Lucia di Lammermoor.—Alfin son tua.] The Mad Scene. Ardon gl'incensi ... Edited by F. La Forge. 1940. 4°.   **G. 1275. ww. (17.)**

— *See* GLAZUNOV (A. K.) La Primavera d'or ... Transcription for Voice and Piano by F. La Forge. (1913.) fol.
G. 806. hh. (28.)

— *See* HAENDEL (G. F.) [Esther.] Hallelujah! Aria ... Concert arrangement by F. La Forge. 1938. 4°.   **G. 170. g. (30.)**

— *See* LISZT (F.) [Deux Arabesques. No. 1. Le Rossignol.] The Nightingale ... [Song.] Alabieff—La Forge ... Arranged from the Piano transcription by Liszt. 1939. 4°.   **G. 1275. vv. (27.)**

— *See* PESSARD (E. L. F.) [L'Adieu du Matin.] Farewell at Morn ... arranged [for S. A. T. B.] by F. La Forge. 1931. 8°.
F. 585. uu. (9.)

— *See* PESSARD (E. L. F.) [L'Adieu du Matin.] Farewell at Morn ... arranged [for T. T. B. B.] by F. La Forge. 1931. 8°.
F. 163. dd. (5.)

— *See* POLDINI (E.) [Marionnettes. No. 2. Poupée valsante.] Dancing Doll ... Poldini—La Forge. 1939. 4°.
G. 1275. vv. (34.)

— *See* REEVE (W.) and BISHOP (*Sir* H. R.) [Brother and Sister.] Echo Song ... by Sir H. R. Bishop. Arranged by F. La Forge. 1940. 4°.   **G. 1275. ww. (3.)**

— *See* ROSSINI (G. A.) [Il Barbiere di Seviglia.—Una voce poco fà] Ah! The Voice I lately heard ... Arrangement by F. La Forge. 1938. 4°.   **G. 1275. uu. (23.)**

— *See* ROSSINI (G. A.) [Ch'io mai vi possa lasciar d'amare.] The Promise: La Promessa ... Arrangement by F. La Forge. 1938. 4°.   **G. 1275. uu. (28.)**

— *See* ROSSINI (G. A.) [La Pastorella delle Alpi.] The Alpine Shepherdess ... Arrangement by F. La Forge. 1938. 4°.
G. 1275. uu. (24.)

— *See* ROSSINI (G. A.) [Soirées musicales. No. 8. La Danza.] Tarantella ... Arrangement by F. La Forge. 1938. 4°.
G. 1275. uu. (27.)

— *See* STRAUSS (J.) *the Younger*. [Geschichten aus dem Wiener Wald.] Storielle del Bosco Viennese ... Transcribed ... by F. La Forge, *etc*. (1912.) fol.   **G. 808. k. (45.)**

LA FORREST ( ) Mrs

— Dear father smile upon your child [song], etc. *New York*, 1844. fol.   **H. 1780. p. (27.)**

LA FORS ( )

— Indicateur des Touches. (The Gamut Indicator.) *Bruxelles*, 1879. *obl.* 16°.   **M.**

LAFORT (Jules)

— Watercresses. Song, words by M.E.T. *London*, [1879.] fol.   **H. 1785. c. (29.)**

— When the Mighty Ocean moans. Temperance Song for a Bass Voice, the words by A. J. Foxwell. [Tonic sol-fa and staff notation.] *J. Curwen & Sons: London*, [1884.] fol. *No. 68 of The Temperance Vocalist.*   **H. 3852.**

LAFOSSE (André)

— Méthode complète de trombone à coulisse en deux volumes. Nouvelle édition entièrement revue par l'auteur et considérablement augmentée d'exercices et d'études, *etc.* pp. xiv. vi. 280. *Alphonse Leduc: Paris*, 1948. fol.   **g. 1117. n.**

LAFRENIÈRE (Jean-Baptiste)

— À la Quebecquoise. Danse pour Piano, *etc. J. E. Belair:* [*Montreal*,] 1908. fol. *Album Musical du Passe-Temps.*   **h. 3283. o. (44.)**

— Marche nationale pour Piano. *Le Passe-Temps: Montreal*, [1904.] fol.   **h. 3282. ww. (27.)**

— Silly-Ass. Two step. [P. F.] [1907.] fol.   **h. 4120. ll. (22.)**

— Valse-Lanciers pour Piano. *J. E. Belair: Montreal*, 1904. fol.   **h. 3286. dd. (45.)**

— Valse Miroir. [P. F.] *Canadian Music Pub. Co.: Montreal*, [1907.] fol.   **h. 4120. ll. (23.)**

— Victo. Mazurka pour Piano. *Le Passe-Temps: Montreal*, 1904. fol.   **h. 3286. dd. (46.)**

— Yvette Valse. [P. F.] *E. Archambault: Montreal*, [1902.] fol.   **h. 3282. kk. (19.)**

LA FRESNAYE (Henry de)

— *See* BOCCHERINI (L.) [Quintets. Op. 13. No. 5. Minuet.] Célèbre Menuet ... transcrit ... par H. de la Fresnaye. [1877.] fol.   **h. 3272. a. (15.)**

LA FUENTE (James de)

— *See* BACH (J. S.) Concerto in D minor. [B. G. Jahrg. 17. No. 1.] Transcribed for violin and piano by J. de la Fuente, *etc.* [1954.] 4°.   **g. 699. m. (1.)**

LAFUENTE (M.)

— Le Bon Retour, caprice caractéristique pour le Piano. *London*, [1873.] fol.   **h. 1482. y. (6.)**

— La Brise du Sud, valse brillante pour le Piano. *London*, [1876.] fol.   **h. 1482. y. (16.)**

— Charmes de la Solitude, morceau pour le Piano. *London*, [1873.] fol.   **h. 1482. y. (9.)**

— L'Etoile Rouge, polka brillante pour le Piano. *London*, [1873.] fol.   **h. 1482. y. (5.)**

— Fantaisie sur deux airs Russes pour le Piano. *London*, [1874.] fol.   **h. 1482. y. (12.)**

LAFUENTE (M.)

— Fleur Marine, caprice de salon pour le Piano. *London*, [1874.] fol.   **h. 1482. y. (11.)**

— La Fontaine, (Morceau de salon) pour Piano. *London*, [1873.] fol.   **h. 1482. y. (7.)**

— Je suis prêt. Galop brillant pour Piano. *London*, [1875.] fol.   **h. 1482. y. (15.)**

— Je suis prêt! "I am ready!" Galop brillant pour Piano (à quatre mains). *London*, [1874.] fol.   **h. 1482. y. (10.)**

— Une Petite Illusion, nocturne pour le Piano. *London*, [1875.] fol.   **h. 1482. y. (14.)**

— Polonaise pour Piano. *London*, [1874.] fol.   **h. 1482. y. (13.)**

— Un Regard, caprice de salon pour le Piano. *London*, [1873.] fol.   **h. 1482. y. (8.)**

— Un Tour à la Campagne, morceau brillante pour Piano. *London*, [1876.] fol.   **h. 1482. y. (17.)**

LAG

— The Lag's Lament. Song. *See* ANDREWS (J. C. B.)

LAGACÉ ( ) Abbé

— Cantique national à Saint Joseph, premier patron du Canada, paroles d'un religieux de Ste-Croix. *Scolasticat Saint-Joseph: Montréal*, 1917. 4°.   **G. 519. g. (11.)**

LAGACHE ( )

— Ainsi qu'un papillon volage. *Ariette, etc.* [*Paris*,] 1777. *s. sh.* 8°. *Mercure de France, Sept.*, 1777.   **297. f. 16.**

LAGAN

— The Lagan. Song. *See* BADDELEY (*Mrs* F.)

LAGARD (A.)

— Belle Etoile. Rêverie, paroles de De **. *Paris*, [1878.] fol.   **H. 1781. i. (4.)**

— Bobinette. Polka. 1st Cornet [part]. *London*, [1874.] 8°. *Part of the "Alliance Musicale". Imperfect; wanting the other parts.*   **f. 402. f. (11.)**

— Les Deux Pigeons. Saynette (imitée de La Fontaine). Paroles de L. Quentin. Musique d'A. Lagard. *Paris*, [1863.] 8°.   **11739. g. 33.**

— Galoubet polka. [Orchestral parts.] *London*, [1873.] 8°. *Part of the "Alliance Musicale".*   **f. 400. c. (13.)**

— Galoubet polka. [P.F.] *London*, [1873.] 8°. *No. 153 of the "Alliance Musicale. Album Bijou".*   **f. 406.**

— Le Jour et la Nuit, Saynete [*sic*]. Paroles d'A. Deschamps. *Paris*, [1864.] 8°.   **11739. g. 40.**

— Méthode de cor d'harmonie. Illustrée de vignettes, *etc.* pp. 32. *Ikelmer frères: Paris*, [1878.] 8°.   **f. 181. (5.)**

— Méthode de cornet à pistons. Illustrée de vignettes, *etc.* pp. 100. *Alfred Ikelmer & cie: Paris*, [1876.] fol.   **h. 2233.**

— Méthode de sax-horn basse ou contrebasse à trois ou à quatre pistons (clé de fa). Illustrée de vignettes, *etc.* pp. 64. *Ikelmer frères: Paris*, [1878.] fol.   **h. 2261.**

— Méthode de trombone à trois & à quatre pistons (clé de fa). Illustrée de vignettes, *etc.* pp. 64. *Ikelmer frères: Paris*, [1878.] fol.   **h. 2289.**

LAGARD (A.)

— Mr. Benoiton quadrille. [P.F.] *London*, [1874.] 8°.
No. 231 *of the "Alliance Musicale. Album Bijou".*   **f. 406.**

— La Phocéenne polka. [P.F.] *London*, [1875.] 8°.
No. 95 *of the "Alliance Musicale. Album Bijou".*   **f. 406.**

LAGARDE (A.)

— Danish bridal Song. "Et Bonderbryllup [*sic*]". Transcription
alla marcia, *etc.* [P.F.] pp. 5. *John Shepherd: London,*
[c. 1860.] fol.   **h. 60. zz. (22.)**

LA GARDE (A. DE) *Count*

— Le Chant des Chasseurs, written and arranged to the
Hunters' Chorus in Der Freischütz [by C. M. F. E. von
Weber]. *London*, [1830?] fol.   **G. 797. (23.)**

— Douze Mélodies Françaises ... Paroles imitées de T. Moore.
Londres, [1823.] fol.   **H. 2832. l. (13.)**

LAGARDE (G. F. ALICE)

— Alice—Waltz. *See infra:* Cousin Randolphe's Favorites ...
Op. 10. no. 3.

— Alma—Polka. *See infra:* Cousin Randolphe's Favorites ...
Op. 10. no. 5.

— Cousin Randolphe's Favorites. Five compositions for the
piano. ⟨Opus 10.⟩ 1. Mario—Gavottina. 2. Melody.
3. Alice—Waltz. 4. Olga—Petite barcarolle. 5. Alma—Polka.
5 no. *J. Fischer & Bro.: New York*, [1903.] fol.
     h. 4120. ll. (24.)

— Mario—Gavottina. *See supra:* Cousin Randolphe's Favorites
... Op. 10. no. 1.

— Melody. *See supra:* Cousin Randolphe's Favorites ... Op. 10.
no. 2.

— Olga—Petite barcarolle. *See supra:* Cousin Randolphe's
Favorites ... Op. 10. no. 4.

LAGARDE (PAUL)

— L'Habit de Mylord. Opéra comique en un acte de MM.
T. Sauvage & De Léris. Partition Piano & Chant par Soumis.
Paris, [1860.] 8°.   **F. 805.**

LAGARDE (PIERRE DE)

— L'Adolescence. Cantatille, pour un dessus, avec
accompagnement de violon, basse, et clavecin ... tirée du
journal de musique. [Score.] pp. 21. *Chez l'auteur: Paris,*
1766. *obl.* 4°.   **C. 640. b. (6.)**

— Ægle, Ballet en un Acte ... Gravé par Labassée. [Score.]
pp. 70. *Chés l'auteur: Mme Boivin: Le Sᵣ Le Clerc: Paris,*
[1751.] fol.   **H. 537.**

— [Another copy.]   **G. 653. a. (2.)**

— Aeglé. Ballet en un acte ... Seconde et nouvelle édition avec
les changemens et augmentations tels qu'ils ont eté donné a
la derniere reprise ... Gravé par Le Sᵣ Hue. [Score.] pp. 65.
Chés l'auteur: Paris, [c. 1760.] fol.   **H. 537. a.**

— Ah! le beau temps. *Brunette, etc. Gravée par Labassée:*
[*Paris*, 1757.] *s. sh.* 8°.
Choix des Anciens Mercures, Tom. II., p. 168.   **297. h. 28.**

— Aimons, buvons. *Duo, etc.* [*Paris*, 1780?] 8°.
     B. 362. i. (41.)

— [Aimons, buvons.] Aimons, aimons. *Duo Parodié sur,*
Aimons, buvons, de Mr. de la Garde. [*Paris*, 1780?] 8°.
     B. 362. e. (44.)

LAGARDE (PIERRE DE)

— Le Bouquet. Cantatille, pour un dessus avec
accompagnement de violon, basse, et clavecin ... tirée du
Journal de musique. *Aux adresses ordinaires de musique;
chez l'auteur: Paris*, 1764. *obl.* 4°.
Imperfect; wanting all after p. 17, *the verso of which is blank.*
     C. 640. b. (4.)

— Diane. Cantatille, pour un dessus, avec accompagnement de
violon, basse, et clavecin ... tirée du Journal de musique.
[Score.] pp. 18. *Aux adresses ordinaires de musique; chez
l'auteur: Paris*, 1764. *obl.* 4°.   **C. 640. b. (7.)**

— Enée et Didon. Cantate Gravé par J. Renou. *Chez l'auteur:
Paris*, [1764.] *obl.* 4°.   **C. 640. (4.)**

— [Another copy.]   **Hirsch. III. 883.**

— Hé! quoi tout sommeille. *Chasse ... en Duo.* [*Paris*, 1780?]
8°.   **B. 362. e. (45.)**

— Journal de Musique ... Gravée par L. Hue. *Au Bureau du
Mercure: Paris*, 1758. *obl.* 4°.
The number for May only.   **C. 640. a. (1.)**

— Nouveaux airs à une et plusieurs voix ... Gravés par
J. Renou. livr. 1, 3. *Chez l'auteur: Paris*, [1760? 65?] *obl.* 4°.
Imperfect; wanting livr. 2.   **Hirsch III. 881.**

— Nouveaux Airs à une et Plusieurs Voix. 1ᵉʳ Livre 2ᵉ Edition
revue, *etc.* (Second Livre.) (Troisième Livre.) 3 livr. *Chez
l'Auteur: Paris*, [1765?] *obl.* 4°.   **C. 640. (2.)**

— Le Point du jour. Cantatille, pour un dessus, avec
accompagnement de violon, basse, et clavecin ... tirée du
journal de musique. [Score.] pp. 18. *Chez l'auteur: Paris,*
1766. *obl.* 4°.   **C. 640. b. (5.)**

— Premier (Second) Recueil d'Airs à Une, Deux et Trois Voix,
etc. Gravé par J. Renou. 2 pt. *Chez l'Auteur: Paris*, 1742(–3).
obl. 4°.   **C. 640. a. (2.)**

— I. (II.) Recueil de Brunettes avec accompagnement de
Guittare, de Clavecin ou de Harpe. (IIIᵉ Recueil ... Avec
accompagnement de Violon, Guitare, Clavecin ou Harpe.)
3 pt. *Chez l'Auteur: Paris*, 1764. *obl.* 4°.   **C. 640. (1.)**

— Quatrième(–Vᵢᵉ) Recueil de Duo, *etc.* 3 pt. *Chez l'Auteur:
Paris*, 1751 (1764). *obl.* 4°.   **C. 640. (3.)**

— La Rose. Cantatille, pour un dessus, avec accompagnement
de violon, basse, et clavecin ... tirée du Journal de musique.
pp. 19. *Aux adresses ordinaires de musique; chez l'auteur:
Paris*, 1764. *obl.* 4°.   **C. 640. b. (3.)**

— Le Songe. Cantatille, pour un dessus, avec accompagnement
de violon, basse, et clavecin ... tirée du Journal de musique.
[Score.] pp. 19. *Aux adresses ordinaires de musique; chez
l'auteur: Paris*, 1764. *obl.* 4°.   **C. 640. b. (1.)**

— Soyez toujours Songes charmans. *Ariette ... Avec
Accompagneᵐᵗ de Guithare par Mᵣ Guichard.* [*Paris*,] 1779.
8°.   **B. 362. g. (77.)**

— Tendre fruit des pleurs de l'aurore. *Ariette.* [*Paris*, 1770?] 8°.
     B. 362. e. (59.)

— [Another copy.]   **B. 362. b. (25.)**

— Tout dit qu'il faut aimer. *Chanson.* (Les paroles sont de M. de
B ... *etc.*) *Gravée par Mᵢₗₗₑ Leclair la fille:* [*Paris*,] 1756. *s. sh.*
8°.
Mercure de France, August, 1756.   **297. d. 2.**

— Venus retrouvée. Cantate. ⟨Gravée par Mᵢₗₗₑ Vendôme.⟩ pp. 19.
Chez l'auteur: Paris, [c. 1765.] *obl.* 4°.   **C. 640. b. (2.)**

LAGARDE MESSENCE (DE) *Count*

— Mes amis, c'est dans sa patrie ... Tyrolienne. *London,*
[1820?] fol.   **G. 809. b. (3.)**

LAGARDE MESSENCE (DE) *Count*

— Le Soupir. Romance ... Musique et accomp¹ de piano par
Crémont. pp. 3.   *Chez P. Gaveaux: Paris,* [c. 1815.] fol.
H. 3690. yy. (2.)

LAGARDÈRE (HENRI)

— "Je vous aime" valse. [P.F.]   *London,* [1873.] fol.
h. 1482. y. (18.)

LAGARDÈRE (J.)

— Aquila, suite de valses pour Piano.   *Paris,* [1869.] *obl.* fol.
e. 217. b. (24.)

LAGAS (R.)

— *See* SWEELINCK (J. P.) Opera omnia, Editio altera, *etc.* ⟨Vol. 2,
3 edidit R. Lagas.⟩ 1968, 57, *etc.* fol.   **H. 920. b.**

LA GAUDE (LOUIS DE)

— L'Étincélante quadrille pour Piano.   *London,* [1863.] fol.
h. 1485. s. (7.)

— Mignon fantaisie brillante pour Piano.   *London,* [1861.] fol.
h. 1485. s. (6.)

LÄGEL (JOHANN GOTTLIEB)

— *See* LAEGEL.

LAGER

— Lager Beer. [Solo and chorus.] *See* JOZÉ (T. R. G.) [Les
Amourettes.]

LAGER (HERBERT) and **DERSCHMIDT** (HERMANN)

— Österreichische Tänze ... Herausgegeben von Herbert Lager
und Hermann Derschmidt. 3., durchgesehene Auflage.
⟨Notenteil.⟩ 2 Tl. 4 pt.   *Österreichischer Bundesverlag: Wien,*
1978. 8° & *obl.* 8°.
Tl. 2 of the 2., durchgesehene Auflage is edited by Herbert
Lager alone.   **d. 64. r.**

LAGER (HERBERT) and **PETER** (ILKA)

— Perchentanz im Pinzgau ... Mit zwei Schwarz- und einer
Farbtafel. pp. 76.   *Hölder-Pichler-Tempsky A.G.: Wien,*
Leipzig, 1940. 8°.
Akademie der Wissenschaften in Wien. Phil.-hist. Klasse.
Sitzungsberichte. Bd. 218. Abh. 5.   **Ac. 810/6.**

LAGERTHA

— Musiken til Balletten Lagertha. [Ballet.] *See* SCHALL (C.)

LAGGARD

— Laggard Dawn. Chorus. *See* SMYTH (*Dame* E.) *D. B. E. Songs*
of Sunrise, etc. No. 1.

LAGGIÙ

— Laggiù lontan lontano. Sogno. *See* GIORZA (P.) Fogli sparsi.
No. 4.

LAGIER (   )

— Suzanna, polka. [Five and drum band parts.]   *London,* [1883.]
8°.   **f. 414. a. (44.)**

LAGKHNER (DANIEL)

— Flores Jessæi, Musicis modulis & ferè tribus paribus adaptati,
etc. Media.   *In officina typographica Pauli Kauffmanni:*
Noribergæ, 1606. 4°.   **C. 75.**

LAGNA FIETTA (HECTOR)

— *See* CENTENÁRIO. Centenário do choro. 20 choros para piano,
etc. [Mainly arranged by H. Lagna Fietta.] [1977.] 4°.
g. 1529. r. (1.)

— *See* RATTES VIEIRA FILHO (Luiz) O Menino de Braçanã.
Toada. Arranjo e harmonização de Hector Lagna Fietta, *etc.*
[P.F.] [1979.] fol.   **H. 2435. a. (5.)**

— *See* RATTES VIEIRA FILHO (Luiz) "Prelúdio prá ninar gente
grande" e grandes obras ... Piano. ⟨[Mainly arranged by]
H. Lagna Fietta.⟩ [1979.] fol.   **h. 1757. (3.)**

LAGNEAU (   )

— *See* DUPIERGE (F. T. A.) Daphnis et Chloe ... Arrangée pour
la guitare, par Lagneau. [c. 1815.] 8°.   **E. 1717. p. (31.)**

— *See* DUPIERGE (F. T. A.) Jamais, jamais ... Arrangé pour la
guitare par Lagneau. [c. 1815.] 8°.   **E. 1717. p. (32.)**

LAGO

— Il Lago. Duetto. *See* GABUSSI (V.)

— Il Lago delle Fate. Dramma fantastico. *See* DOMINICETI (C.)

— Il Lago di Como. Barcarola. *See* DENZA (L.)

— Il Lago di Garda. Barcarola. *See* BILETTA (G. E.)

LAGO (N.)

— As Evening closes. [For S.S.A. Words by] A. J. Foxwell. pp. 4.
J. Curwen & Sons: London; Leipzig [printed, 1895.] 8°.
[*Choruses for equal Voices. no.* 185.]   **E. 861.**

— The Shadows are flying. [For S.S.C. Words by] A. J. Foxwell.
pp. 4.   *J. Curwen & Sons: London; Leipzig* [printed, 1894.] 8°.
[*Choruses for equal Voices. no.* 184.]   **E. 861.**

LAGOANÈRE (DE)

— L'Abeille. Chansonnette [begins: "Gente ménagère"], de
A. Romagnesi.   *Paris,* [1835?] fol.   **G. 542. (39.)**

— Advienne que pourra. Chansonnette à deux voix, paroles de
Mʳ Paulin. pp. 3.   *Chez J. Meissonnier: Paris,* [c. 1830.] fol.
G. 559. a. (42.)

— [La Brigantine.] Scheiden. Barcarole für eine auch zwey
Stimmen, frei nach C. Delavigne von T. von Haupt. La
Brigantine. Barcarolle à 1 ou 2 voix, paroles de Mr. C.
Delavigne.   *Chez les Fils de B. Schott: Mayence,* [1830?] fol.
Auswahl von Arien und Duetten mit Clavier oder Guitarre
Begleitung. No. 263.   **H. 2134. a. (16.)**

— La Chapelle des Champs. Chansonnette à deux voix [begins:
"Par un beau jour"]. Paroles de Mr. A. Bétourné.   *Paris,*
[1835?] 8°.   **E. 1717. (18.)**

— La Chapelle des Champs. Chansonnette.   *Paris,* [1835?] fol.
G. 553. (51.)

— La Confidence. Chansonnette [begins: "J'ai seize ans"].
Paroles de Mr. Deleuze.   *Paris,* [1830?] fol.   **G. 553. (16.)**

— "Dolce sonno è calma amica," aria.   *London,* [1838.] fol.
H. 1675. (4.)

— Douce Erreur. Tyrolienne [begins: "Bois chéri"]. Paroles de
Mᵐᵉ. de la Besge.   *Paris,* [1835?] fol.   **G. 558. (19.)**

— La Feuille desséchée. [Song.] Paroles de Mʳ. Bourcier.   *Chez*
Ph: Petit: [*Paris,* c. 1830.] fol.   **G. 559. a. (26.)**

LAGOANÈRE (DE)

— Glisse, glisse, léger Bateau. Nocturne à deux voix. *Birchail & Co.: London,* [1829?] fol.   **H. 2262. b. (2.)**

— Grenade. Boléro [begins: "Salut, O toi, la ville"]. Paroles de Mr. le Bon de Maldigny. *Paris,* [1835?] fol.   **G. 540. (56.)**

— Grenade. Boléro. Paroles de Mr. le Bon de Maldigny. *Paris,* [1840?] fol.   **G. 554. (3.)**

— Les Guerillas. Bolero [begins: "Adieu, ma belle"]. Paroles de Mr. Crevel de Charlemagne. *Paris,* [1835?] fol.
G. 543. (73.)

— Hier et Aujourd'hui. Romance. *Paris,* [1830?] fol.
G. 552. (57.)

— Jeune beauté du haut parage. Boléro. Paroles de Mr. H. T. Poisson. *Paris,* [1835?] fol.   **G. 546. (15.)**

— La Jeune pastourelle. Nocturne à une ou deux voix avec accompagnement de piano, paroles de Madame Desbordes-Valmore. pp. 3. *Chez A. Farrenc: Paris,* [1830?] fol.
G. 559. a. (48.)

— Lucette. Chansonette [begins: "La fleur de son village"]. *Paris,* 1830. fol.   **G. 553. (34.)**

— Marche mexicaine. [Guitar solo.] *In:* AMON (J. A.) Schwarz auf Weiss. [1826.] 4°. [*Musikalischer Haus-Freund.* 1827, *after* p. 48.]   **Hirsch IV. 1124.**

— "La mestizia;" duettino per mezzo-soprano e tenore [begins: "Un' orrida affanno"], poesia del Conte Pepoli. *London,* [1838.] fol.   **H. 1675. (5.)**

— Ouvrez, ouvrez beau châtelain. Nocturne à 2 voix. [With P.F. or harp accompaniment.] pp. 3. *Chez Ph. Petit: Paris,* [c. 1830.] fol.   **G. 561. b. (14.)**

— Pietro. Ballad [begins: "Le flot grossit"] de C. Delavigne. *Paris,* [1835?] 8°.   **E. 1717. (17.)**

— Les Plus Beau Jours. Nocturne à deux voix [begins: "Déjà dans la plaine"]. Paroles de Mr. Crevel de Charlemagne. *Paris,* [1835?] fol.   **G. 540. (41.)**

— Plus de Bonheur. Romance [begins: "Gentille déesse"]. Paroles de Mr. Crevel de Charlemagne. *Paris,* [1835?] fol.
G. 540. (54.)

— La Rage des Parisiens. Petite Fantaisie sur la valse favorite du duc de Reichstadt, [by J. Strauss the Elder. Op. 31. No. 1,] composé par Lagoanère et Lemoine. *See* HAMMERS (J. E.) J. Clinton and Lemoine's Bagatelles for the Clarionet & Piano-Forte, *etc.* No. 4. [1845.] fol.   **h. 3212. (3.)**

— Ramène ton Bateau. Romance à deux voix. *Birchall & Co.: [London,* 1829?] fol.   **H. 2262. b. (3.)**

— Le Retour de Julien. [Song, begins: "Dans sa pauvre chaumière".] Paroles de A. Romagnesi. *Paris,* [1835?] fol.
G. 559. (30.)

— Scheiden. *See* supra: [La Brigantine.]

— "La Torre del mistero;" duettino da camera [begins: "Vedi là sulla Collina"], poesia del Signor Conte Pepoli. *London,* [1838.] fol.   **H. 1675. (6.)**

— Voguons toujours. Barcarolle à une ou deux voix. Paroles de M^r Ch: Durand. pp. 3. *Chez J. Meissonnier: [Paris,* c. 1830.] fol.   **G. 559. a. (37.)**

LAGOANÈRE (O. DE)

— La Double Étoile. Grande valse pour piano. *Paris,* [1884.] fol.   **h. 3285. b. (36.)**

— Il était une fois. Opérette en 3 actes, paroles de A. Jaime et D. Sémiane. Partition chant et piano. *Paris,* [1886.] 8°.
F. 1450.

LAGOANÈRE (O. DE)

— Jeunesse! [Song.] Poésie de A. Lénéka. [*Paris,*] 1903. 8°. *Supplement to "L'Illustration," No.* 3150.   **P. P. 4283. m. (3.)**

— Jeunesse.—Youth— ... English words by E. M. Lockwood, *etc. Schott & Co.: London, etc.,* (1911.) fol.
G. 807. yy. (18.)

— Yes! valse pour Piano. *Paris,* [1881.] fol.   **h. 3272. j. (4.)**

LAGRANGE (MADELINE)

— Feuille d'Amour. Gavotte. [P. F.] *Francis Bros. and Day: London,* [1885.] fol.   **h. 1484. s. (2.)**

LA GRASSA (PETER)

— Union Valse. [P. F.] *New York,* 1861. fol.   **h. 1459. p. (1.)**

LA GRAVELIÈRE (ALBERT DE)

— Je veux me marier. Chansonnette [begins: "Au village"]. Paroles de A. Gaston. *Paris,* [1875.] fol.   **H. 1777. e. (27.)**

— La Musique apprise par la copie des exemples, *etc.* 5 cah. *Paris,* [1887.] 4°.   **d. 250.**

— Polka des Mascottes ... pour le piano. *L. Bathlot: Paris,* [1886.] fol.   **h. 3281. k. (50.)**

— Qui va piano. Chansonnette [begins: "Mes cheveux sont tous blancs"]. Paroles de A. Gaston. *Paris,* [1875.] fol.
H. 1777. e. (28.)

LAGRÈZE (GASTON DE)

— Ave Verum pour Soprano ... avec accompagnement de Piano, Orgue ou Harmonium. *Paris,* [1877.] fol.
H. 1028. h. (23.)

— Phylloxera polka pour Piano. [Solo and duet.] 2 no. *Paris,* [1877.] fol.   **h. 1493. n. (6.)**

— Songe Mensonge. Nocturne pour le Piano. *Paris,* [1874.] fol.   **h. 1487. o. (19.)**

— Sous les Branches. Mélodie [begins: "Palpitante encore"]. Poésie de F. Coppée. *Paris,* [1877.] fol.   **H. 1781. i. (3.)**

LAGRIME

— Lagrime. Canzonet. *See* DERING (R.) [Canzonette a Quattro Voci.]

— Lagrime d'amante al sepolcro dell'amata. [Madrigal.] *See* MONTEVERDI (C.) [Il sesto libro di madrigali a cinque voci.—Sestina.]

— Le Lagrime d'Erminia. [Songs.] *See* MARINI (B.)

LA GROTTE (NICOLAS DE)

— Chansons de P. de Ronsard, Ph. Desportes, et autres. ⟨Superius.—Tenor.—Bassus.⟩ [Parts.] *Par Adrian le Roy & Robert Ballard: Paris,* 1569. obl. 8°. *Imperfect; wanting the contratenor part. Ff.* 1–4, 8 *of the bassus part are mutilated.*   **K. 11. e. 3. (1.)**

— [Chansons de P. de Ronsard, Ph. Desportes, et autres.] [*Par Adrian le Roy, & Robert Ballard: Paris,* 1572.] *obl.* 8°. *Imperfect; ff.* 21–24 *of the tenor part only.*   **K. 2. b. 4. (1.)**

— Chansons de P. de Ronsard, P. Desportes et autres, mises en musique par N. de La Grotte ... Paris, 1575. Nouvelle édition fac-simile augmentée d'une notice par A. de Rochambeau, *etc. Paris,* 1873. *obl.* 8°. *Only* 250 *copies printed.*   **A. 275.**

LA GROTTE (NICOLAS DE)

— [Chansons de P. de Ronsard, Ph. Desportes, et autres.] [Parts.] [*Par Adrian le Roy, & Robert Ballard: Paris,* 1580.] *obl.* 8°. *Imperfect; wanting the contratenor and bassus parts, and all before fol.* 9 *of the tenor and superius parts.*   **K. 2. b. 5. (3.)**

— Quand je te veux raconter. Paroles de Ronsard. [Part-song, edited by Kenneth Jay Levy.] *Éditions de l'Oiseau-lyre: Monaco,* [1953.] fol. *A reissue of pp.* 69–72 *of "Anthologie de la chanson parisienne au xvie siècle," edited by François Lesure. No.* 30 *of an edition of fifty-five copies.*   **H. 1860. n. (2.)**

LAGUÉRIVIÈRE (EDMOND DU PIN DE) *Viscount*

— *See* DU PIN DE LA GUERIVIÈRE.

LAGUERRE (ÉLISABETH CLAUDE JACQUET DE)

— *See* JACQUET DE LAGUERRE.

LAGUS (ERNST)

— Nyländska Folkvisor, ordnade och utgifna af E. Lagus. 2 Dl. *Nyländska Afdelningens Förlag: Helsingfors,* 1887–1900. 8°. *Hft.* 3, 5 *of "Nyland. Samlingar Utgifna af Nyländska Afdelningen" of the Finska Universitet.*   **Ac. 1095/2.**

LAGYE (ALEXANDRE)

— L'Ange Gardien. Chœur pour 2 voix de sopranos [begins: "Parfois la nuit, quand tout repose"], paroles de G. Lagye. *See* RÉPERTOIRE. Répertoire des Pensionnats ... Quinze Chœurs ... No. 1. 1886. fol.   **H. 2833. (2.)**

— L'Angelus. Chœur à 2 voix [begins: "Le soir vient rembrunir la terre"], paroles de G. Lagye. *See* RÉPERTOIRE. Répertoire des Pensionnats ... Quinze Chœurs ... No. 3. 1886. fol.   **H. 2833. (2.)**

— Croquemitaine. Chœur pour 2 voix de sopranos [begins: "Il est, m'a dit un jour"], paroles de G. Lagye. *See* RÉPERTOIRE. Répertoire des Pensionnats ... Quinze Chœurs ... No. 4. 1886. fol.   **H. 2833. (2.)**

— Grand père. Chœur pour 2 voix de sopranos, [begins: "Grand père! jouez donc!"] paroles de G. Lagye. *See* RÉPERTOIRE. Répertoire des Pensionnats ... Quinze Chœurs ... No. 5. 1886. fol.   **H. 2833. (2.)**

— Le Pierrot d'à Coté. Opéra comique en 1 acte. Partition Piano et Chant. *Bruxelles,* [1879.] 8°.   **F. 812.**

— Saint Nicolas. Chœur pour 2 voix de sopranos [begins: "Aux méchants cherchant chicane"], paroles de G. Lagye. *See* RÉPERTOIRE. Répertoire des Pensionnats ... Quinze Chœurs ... No. 6. 1886. fol.   **H. 2833. (2.)**

— Vielle Chanson [begins: "Quand l'oiseau chante"]. Paroles de H. Liesse. *Bruxelles,* [1879.] fol.   **H. 1781. i. (5.)**

— *See* LAUWERYNS (E.) Reporter-polka ... Orchestrée par A. Lagye. [1879.] 8°.   **e. 370. b. (10.)**

LAGYE (BENONI)

— Bagatelle. Polka. Op. 27. *See infra:* Deux Danses ... No. 1.

— Bataillon Scolaire. Marche militaire pour piano. Op. 30. *Bruxelles,* [1884.] fol.   **h. 3285. b. (38.)**

— Deux Danses pour piano. 2 no. *Hambourg,* [1884.] fol.   **h. 3285. b. (37.)**

— Le Rêve d'un Ange. Petite rêverie facile pour violon avec accompagnement de piano. Op. 18. *Bruxelles,* [1884.] fol.   **h. 1609. u. (10.)**

— Romance facile ... pour violon avec accompagnement de piano. Op. 20. *Bruxelles,* 1885. fol.   **h. 1609. u. (11.)**

LAGYE (BENONI)

— Les Tsiganes. Polka-Mazurka. Op. 28. *See supra:* Deux Danses ... No. 2.

LA HACHE (THEODOR VON)

— Birds of the Wildwood, polka brillante for the Pianoforte. *London,* [1862.] fol.   **h. 1460. u. (24.)**

— Come to me, love. Serenade, words by Mrs. P. L. Cox. *New Orleans,* [1864.] fol.   **H. 1780. f. (1.)**

— La célèbre Missa pro Pace. *New York,* 1867. 8°.   **E. 540. a. (1.)**

— Messe de S[te]. Thérèse à trois voix d'hommes ... avec accompagnement ... d'Orgue. Op. 421. *Mayence,* 1861. fol.   **H. 1187. f. (12.)**

— The celebrated Unison Mass in F. *Boston,* [*Mass.,* 1870?] fol.   **H. 1028. e. (1.)**

— Near the banks of that lone river. Ballad, written by G. P. Morris. *New Orleans,* 1854. fol.   **H. 1780. f. (2.)**

— True to the Call, polka march ... for the Piano. *New Orleans,* [1864.] fol.   **h. 1459. g. (1.)**

— Twelve o'clock waltz ... for the Pianoforte. *New Orleans,* [1864.] fol.   **h. 1459. g. (2.)**

LA HALLE (ADAM DE)

— *See* ADAM, *de la Halle.*

LAHANTE (   )

— *See* LANDRIN (   ) *Maître de Danse.* 1er Recueil d'Airs Figurée, *etc.* (4me Recueil de Menuet de Mr Lahante, *etc.*) [1785? *etc.*] 8°.   **c. 57. (3.)**

LÀ-HAUT

— Là-haut! Opéra-bouffe. *See* YVAIN (M.)

LA HAYE (   )

— *See* CHAMPEIN (S.) [Le Manteau.] Nos bons parens parlent sans cesse ... Accomp[t] de Guittare par M. La Haye. [1790?] 8°.   **B. 362. h. (6.)**

LA HAYE BLACKITH (HANSON DE)

— *See* BLACKITH.

LAHEE (HENRY)

— Ah! Woe is me. Madrigal for six voices, the words and music by H. Lahee. [1885.] *See* NOVELLO AND CO. Novello's Part-Song Book. Second Series. Vol. XVIII. No. 515. [1869, *etc.*] 8°.   **F. 280. b.**

— All ye Woods and Trees and Bow'rs. Ballet for five Voices, the words by Beaumont and Fletcher. *See* NOVELLO AND CO. Novello's Part-Song Book. Second Series. Vol. II. No. 83. [1869, *etc.*] 8°.   **F. 280. b.**

— All ye Woods and Trees and Bow'rs. Ballet, *etc.* [1905.] *See* NOVELLO AND CO. Novello's Tonic Sol-fa Series. No. 1458. [1876, *etc.*] 4°.   **B. 885.**

— Altdeutsches Lied ... of F. Mendelssohn Bartholdy, transcribed for the Pianoforte. *London,* [1866.] fol.   **h. 3097. (7.)**

— And they brought young children unto him. [Anthem.] *London,* [1871.] 8°. *No.* 30 *of "Plaistow Part-Music".*   **E. 627.**

LAHEE (Henry)

— And they brought young Children unto Him. [Anthem.] [1908.] *See* Church. The Church Choralist. No. 386. [1886, *etc.*] 8°.   **E. 1330.**

— Andante and Variations ... for the piano forte. pp. 9. *Leader & Cock: London,* [1853?] fol.
The titlepage bears an MS dedication to W. Sterndale Bennett in the composer's autograph.   **g. 354. b. (10.)**

— Auf Flügeln des Gesänges, transcription of Mendelssohn's ... melody for the Pianoforte. *London,* [1863.] fol.
                                                          h. 3097. (1.)

— Auf Flügeln des Gesänges, *etc. London,* [1866.] fol.
                                                          h. 3097. (2.)

— The Bells. Arranged for Female Voices with Pianoforte accompaniment by P. J. Mansfield. Op. 128. No. 1. [Words by] Edgar Allan Poe, *etc. Ascherberg, Hopwood & Crew: London,* 1937. 8°.
[*Ascherberg's Series of Part Songs. No. 28.*]   **F. 1659. a.**

— The Bells. Part-Song for Mixed Voices, S.C.T.B., unaccompanied, *etc. Ascherberg, Hopwood & Crew: London,* [1945.] 8°.
[*Ascherberg's Series of Part-Songs. No. 149.*]   **F. 1659. a.**

— The Blessing of the Children. A sacred cantata ... The words ... by G. Bennett. *London,* [1872.] 8°.   **E. 1594. a. (7.)**

— The Blessing of the Children ... Tonic Sol-Fa edition. *London,* [1872.] 8°.   **A. 887. (7.)**

— [The Blessing of the Children.] Sing, sing, sing. Children's Song, *etc.* [Tonic sol-fa and staff notation.] [1888?] *See* Choral. Choral Leaflets. No. 59. [1882, *etc.*] *s. sh.* 4°.
                                                              F. 569.

— The Building of the Ship, a cantata, the words selected from Longfellow's poem. *London,* [1869.] fol.   **H. 2616.**

— The Building of the Ship ... Tonic Sol-Fa edition, edited ... by J. Curwen. *London,* [1870.] 8°.   **B. 553.**

— Chant du pêcheur Napolitain pour le piano. *London,* [1854.] fol.   **h. 723. l. (14.)**

— Come away! the sunny hours. *See* Trios. Chamber Trios. No. 62. [1844, *etc.*] fol.   **H. 2260.**

— Cradle song, for the piano forte. *London,* [1854.] fol.
                                                          h. 723. l. (15.)

— Danse à l'Espagnole. [Violoncello and P. F.] *See infra:* Suite ... No. 4.

— Duo brillant pour deux Pianos sur des motifs du Stabat Mater de G. Rossini. *Mayence,* [1873.] fol.   **h. 1487. o. (20.)**

— The Fandango from Mozart's "Le Nozze di Figaro," arranged as a Pianoforte duet. *London,* [1866.] fol.
                                                          h. 3097. (9.)

— The Fandango ... arranged as a Pianoforte duet by H. Lahee. [1877.] fol. *See* Mozart (W. A.) [Le Nozze di Figaro.]
                                                          h. 321. f. (4.)

— Fantaisie sur Lohengrin de R. Wagner pour Piano. *Mayence,* [1876.] fol.   **h. 1487. o. (21.)**

— Gavotte. [Violoncello and P. F.] *See infra:* Suite ... No. 6.

— Go when the morning shineth. [Part-song.] Words by the Earl of Carlisle. *London,* [1872.] 8°.
No. 4 of "Plaistow Part Music".   **E. 627.**

— Go, when the Morning shineth. [Four-part song.] Words by the Earl of Carlisle. [1885.] *See* Choral. The Choral Handbook. No. 29. [1885, *etc.*] 8°.   **E. 862.**

LAHEE (Henry)

— [Grant, we beseech Thee.] A Short Anthem for Ascension-tide. The Collect for the Day. 1870. *See* Periodical Publications.— *London.* The Musical Times, *etc.* No. 326. 1844, *etc.* 8°.   **P. P. 1945. aa.**

— Hark, how the Birds on ev'ry bloomy Spray. Madrigal for six Voices, the words by Pope. *See* Novello and Co. Novello's Part-Song Book. Second Series. Vol II. No. 82. [1869, *etc.*] 8°.
                                                          F. 280. b.

— Hence, loathed Melancholy. A cheerful glee for five voices. The words ... by Milton. *London,* [1878.] 8°.
                                                          E. 308. e. (21.)

— Hence, loathed Melancholy. A cheerful Glee for five voices. The words ... by Milton. [1880.] *See* Novello and Co. Novello's Part-Song Book. Second Series. Vol. xv. No. 424. [1869, *etc.*] 8°.   **F. 280. b.**

— Hence, loathed Melancholy ... Glee [for S. S. A. T. B.]. The words from 'L'Allegro,' by Milton. [1879.] *See* Novello and Co. Novello's Tonic Sol-fa series. No. 99. [1876, *etc.*] 4°.
                                                          B. 885.

— Higher, higher will we climb. [Part-song.] The words by J. Montgomery. *London,* [1872.] 8°.
No. 12 of "Plaistow Part-Songs".   **E. 627.**

— Higher, higher will we climb. [Four-part song.] The Words by J. Montgomery. [1885.] *See* Choral. The Choral Handbook. No. 45. [1885, *etc.*] 8°.   **E. 862.**

— How oft upon the sunny past. Ballad, written by S. W. Partridge. *London,* [1848.] fol.   **H. 1706. (19.)**

— Hurrah for the Queen of England. [Part-song.] Words by B. Cornwall. *London,* [1871.] 8°.
No. 28 of "Plaistow Part-Music".   **E. 627.**

— Hurrah for the Queen of England. [Four-part song.] Words by B. Cornwall. [1885.] *See* Choral. The Choral Handbook. No. 30. [1885, *etc.*] 8°.   **E. 862.**

— I loved a Lass. [Four-part song.] Words by G. Wither. [1885.] *See* Choral. The Choral Handbook. No. 70. [1885, *etc.*] 8°.
                                                          E. 862.

— Ich dien. [Part-song.] Words by G. Bennett. [1889.] *See* Choral. The Choral Handbook. No. 171. [1885, *etc.*] 8°.
                                                          E. 862.

— Ich liebe dich, Beethoven's ... song, transcribed for the Pianoforte. *London,* [1866.] fol.   **h. 3097. (3.)**

— If ye love me, keep my commandments, sacred song. *London,* [1857.] fol.   **H. 1187. a. (12.)**

— Labour. [Part-song, begins: "Ho! ye who at the anvil toil".] Words by C. Orne. *London,* [1872.] 8°.
No. 6 of "Plaistow Part-Songs".   **E. 627.**

— Labour. [Four-part song.] Words by C. Orne. [1885.] *See* Choral. The Choral Handbook. No. 43. [1885, *etc.*] 8°.
                                                          E. 862.

— Love me little, love me long, *etc.* [Four-part song.] 1871. *See* Periodical Publications.— *London.* The Musical Times, *etc.* No. 335. 1844, *etc.* 8°.   **P. P. 1945. aa.**

— Mélodie. [Violoncello and P. F.] *See infra:* Suite ... No. 3.

— Menuet. [Violoncello and P. F.] *See infra:* Suite ... No. 2.

— The merry, merry lark, song [begins: "Oh! the merry, merry lark"], the poetry by C. Kingsley. *London,* [1857.] fol.
                                                          H. 1771. l. (5.)

— The Metrical Psalter ... (with appendix of hymns for festivals,) by William J. Irons ... The music, arranged and harmonized for four voices by H. Lahee. pp. 229. ii. 47. *J. Alfred Novello: London,* [1855.] 4°.   **C. 19. rr.**

LAHEE (Henry)

— The Mulberry tree; song, written by S. W. Partridge. *London*, [1845.] fol. **H. 1695. (9.)**

— Never say fail! [Part-song, begins: "Keep pushing".] *London*, [1872.] 8°. *No. 7 of "Plaistow Part-Songs".* **E. 627.**

— Never say Fail! [Four-part song.] [1885.] *See* CHORAL. The Choral Handbook. No. 44. [1885, *etc.*] 8°. **E. 862.**

— The New Year. [Part-song, begins: "Ring out, wild bells".] Words by Tennyson. *London*, [1871.] 8°. **E. 627.**

— The New Year. [Four-part song.] Words by Tennyson. [1885.] *See* CHORAL. The Choral Handbook. No. 47. [1885, *etc.*] 8°. **E. 862.**

— Non però d'ampi tesori. Arietta ... Music by B. Marcello. Arranged and edited by H. Lahee. *See* ECHI. Echi d'Italia. Raccolta prima, *etc.* No. 87. [1880? *etc.*] fol. **H. 2397.**

— Now on the first Day of the Week. Easter Anthem. 1877. *See* PERIODICAL PUBLICATIONS.— *London*. The Musical Times, *etc.* No. 409. 1844, *etc.* 8°. **P. P. 1945. aa.**

— Now on the first Day of the Week. (Easter Anthem.) [1884.] *See* NOVELLO AND CO. Novello's Tonic Sol-fa Series. No. 225. [1876, *etc.*] 4°. **B. 885.**

— Oh! di che lode. Aria ... Music by B. Marcello. Edited and arranged by H. Lahee. *See* ECHI. Echi d'Italia. Raccolta prima, *etc.* No. 88. [1880? *etc.*] fol. **H. 2397.**

— O Lord, rebuke me not. Short Anthem for Lent. [1890.] *See* NOVELLO AND CO. Novello's Short Anthems. No. 15. [1889, *etc.*] 8°. **F. 280. f.**

— Two piano forte studies. 2 no. *London*, [1854.] fol. **h. 1082. (3.)**

— Praise the Lord, O my Soul. Harvest Anthem. 1881. *See* PERIODICAL PUBLICATIONS.— *London*. The Musical Times, *etc.* No. 461. 1844, *etc.* 8°. **P. P. 1945. aa.**

— Praise the Lord, O my Soul. (Harvest Anthem.) [1884.] *See* NOVELLO AND CO. Novello's Tonic Sol-fa Series. No. 226. [1876, *etc.*] 4°. **B. 885.**

— Prière pendant l'orage. [Violoncello and P. F.] *See* infra: Suite ... No. 5.

— Ring out, wild Bells. Trio for Female Voices, the words written by Alfred, Lord Tennyson ... Full Score. *Novello, Ewer and Co.: London & New York*, 1893. fol. **H. 2368. a. (4.)**

— Ring out, wild Bells. Trio for female voices, the words written by Alfred, Lord Tennyson. 1893. *See* NOVELLO AND CO. Novello's Collection of Trios, *etc.* No. 286. [1879, *etc.*] 8°. **E. 1746.**

— Ring out, wild Bells. [1912.] *See* NOVELLO AND CO. Novello's Tonic Sol-fa Series. No. 1993. [1876, *etc.*] 4°. **B. 885.**

— Romance. [Violoncello and P. F.] *See* infra: Suite ... No. 1.

— Première romance variée pour le piano. *London*, [1854.] fol. **h. 723. l. (16.)**

— S'io fossi un'angelo, melody by G. Marras, transcribed for the Pianoforte. *London*, [1866.] fol. **h. 3097. (4.)**

— The Scale Book for Pianoforte Students. *London*, [1870.] fol. **h. 3097. (10.)**

— Shepherds, rise! and shake off Sleep. Glee for male voices, the words ... by Beaumont and Fletcher. [1893.] *See* ORPHEUS. The Orpheus, *etc.* New Series. No. 220. [1879, *etc.*] 8°. **E. 1748.**

LAHEE (Henry)

— Signor! dall'empia gente. Arietta ... Music by B. Marcello. Arranged and edited by H. Lahee. *See* ECHI. Echi d'Italia. Raccolta prima, *etc.* No. 89. [1880? *etc.*] fol. **H. 2397.**

— Sing, sing, sing. *See* supra: [The Blessing of the Children.]

— The Sleeping Beauty, a cantata for female voices. The poetry ... by A. Tennyson. *London*, [1878.] 8°. **F. 1238.**

— The Sleeping Beauty ... Translated into Tonic Sol-fa notation by W. G. Mc Naught. *London*, [1880.] 8° **B. 559. g. (7.)**

— Sonntagslied ... of F. Mendelssohn Bartholdy, transcribed for the Pianoforte. *London*, [1866.] fol. **h. 3097. (8.)**

— Spring, duet for soprano & contralto voices, the poetry from Longfellow. [Begins: "Gentle spring".] *London*, [1854.] fol. **H. 1758. (3.)**

— The Spring. A Four-Part Song, *etc.* 1869. *See* PERIODICAL PUBLICATIONS.— *London*. The Musical Times, *etc.* No. 319. 1844, *etc.* 8°. **P. P. 1945. aa.**

— Suite pour violoncelle ou violon et piano, *etc. Mayence*, [1885.] fol. **h. 1847. d. (17.)**

— [Another copy.] **h. 204. c. (34.)**

— Sweet Content. [Part-song, begins: "Art thou poor".] Poetry by T. Dekker. *London*, [1872.] 8°. *No. 2 of "Plaistow Part-Songs".* **E. 627.**

— Sweet Content. [Four-part song.] Poetry by T. Dekker. [1885.] *See* CHORAL. The Choral Handbook. No. 42. [1885, *etc.*] 8°. **E. 862.**

— The three fishers, song [begins: "Three fishers went sailing"], the poetry by C. Kingsley. *London*, [1857.] fol. **H. 1771. l. (6.)**

— The Thresher. [Part-song, begins: "Oh! his limbs are strong".] Words by G. Bennett. *London*, [1871.] 8°. *No. 27 of "Plaistow Part-Music".* **E. 627.**

— The Thresher. [Four-part song.] Words by G. Bennett. [1885.] *See* CHORAL. The Choral Handbook. No. 48. [1885, *etc.*] 8°. **E. 862.**

— Twilight Musings, nocturne for the Pianoforte. *London*, [1866.] fol. **h. 3097. (5.)**

— Tyrolienne pour le Piano. *London*, [1866.] fol. **h. 3097. (6.)**

— The Unfaithful Shepherdess. A Four Part Song, *etc.* 1885. *See* PERIODICAL PUBLICATIONS.— *London*. The Musical Times, *etc.* No. 507. 1844, *etc.* 8°. **P. P. 1945. aa.**

— The Unfaithful Shepherdess. A four-part Song. Poetry from The Golden Treasury. [1885.] *See* NOVELLO AND CO. Novello's Tonic Sol-fa Series. No. 314. [1876, *etc.*] 4°. **B. 885.**

— Waiting for the May. [Part-song.] *London*, [1872.] 8°. *No. 20 of "Plaistow Part-Music".* **E. 627.**

— Waiting for the May. [Four-part song.] 1885. *See* CHORAL. The Choral Handbook. No. 46. [1885, *etc.*] 8°. **E. 862.**

— When Twilight's parting Flush. [Four-part song.] Poetry by H. Smith. 1876. *See* PERIODICAL PUBLICATIONS.— *London*. The Musical Times, *etc.* No. 400.[a.] 1844, *etc.* 8°. **P. P. 1945. aa.**

— When Twilight's parting Flush, *etc.* [1905.] *See* NOVELLO AND CO. Novello's Tonic Sol-fa Series. No. 886[a]. [1876, *etc.*] 4°. **B. 885.**

— Ye countless warblers of the grove ... song of F. Gumbert, transcribed for the Pianoforte. *London*, [1881.] fol. **h. 3273. a. (57.)**

LAHEE (HENRY)

— See BISHOP (*Sir* H. R.) [Clari.] Home! sweet Home ...
Arranged by H. Lahee. [1915.] 8°.   **F. 590. a. (9.)**

— See DUSSEK (J. L.) [Sonatas. Op. 18.] First movement ...
Edited by H.Lahee. [1876.] fol.   **h. 751. c. (12.)**

— See HAYDN (Franz J.) [*Doubtful and Supposititious Works.*]
[Variations. Hob. XVII/12*.] Tema & Variations ... for the
piano forte. (Edited by H. Lahee.) [1880.] fol.
    h. 3035. b. (17.)

— See MARCELLO (B.) [Estro poetico-armonico.] Five Sacred
Duets ... from the Psalms ... Edited ... by H. Lahee. [1885.]
fol.   **G. 517. c. (22.)**

— See VIVALDI (A.) [Sonate a violino e basso. Op. 2. No. 2.] Giga
... Transcribed for the pianoforte by H. Lahee. [1876.] fol.
    h. 1495. e. (34.)

LA HELE (GEORGE DE)

— Collected Works. Edited by Laverne J. Wagner. [With
facsimiles.] 2 pt. *American Institute of Musicology:* [*Dallas,
Tex.?,*] 1972. fol.
[*Corpus mensurabilis musicae.* 56.]   **H. 3.**

LAHMER (REUEL)

— Lover's Lament. Kentucky Mountain Folk Melody.
Paraphrase by R. Lahmer. Arranged for a cappella Choir,
Mixed Voices S.A.T.B., including optional Piano part. *Mills
Music: New York,* 1941. 8°.   **F. 1771. h. (12.)**

— Never said a mumbalin Word. Negro Spiritual arranged by
R. Lahmer, a cappella choir, *etc. Mills Music: New York,*
1941. 8°.   **F. 1176. o. (16.)**

LAHMEYER (CARL)

— At Night. Song, written by T. Moore. *London,* [1881.] fol.
    H. 1787. j. (5.)

— Comin' thro' the Rye ... Song [begins: "Gin a body"].
London, [1876.] fol.   **H. 1778. x. (4.)**

— From Forest & Meadow ... for the Pianoforte. *London,*
[1876.] fol.   **h. 3275. j. (6.)**

— In the Springtime. Song [begins: "It was a lover"] written by
Shakespeare. *London,* [1881.] fol.   **H. 1787. j. (6.)**

— The Lord Mayor's state march. [P. F.] *London,* [1876.] fol.
    h. 1482. y. (19.)

— Peter the Shipwright. (Czar und Zimmermann [by G. A.
Lortzing].) Souvenir pour Piano. *London,* [1871.] fol.
    h. 1485. s. (8.)

— Romance sans paroles pour le Piano. *London,* [1872.] fol.
    h. 1485. s. (9.)

— See BACH (J. S.) [Also hat Gott die Welt geliebt.—Mein
gläubiges Herz.] Aria ... "My heart ever faithful,"
transcribed ... by C. Lahmeyer. [1880.] fol. **h. 3007. a. (11.)**

LAHONEN (AURA) and KOSKIMIES (AIRI)

— Leiki ja soita. pp. 102. *Werner Söderström: Porvoo, Helsinki,*
1954. 4°.   **12844. k. 3.**

LA HOUSSAYE (JEANNE DE)

— The Baden-Powell British Scouts' March, *etc.* Words and
music by J. de la Houssaye, *etc.* [P. F.] *Hawkes & Son:
London,* 1910. fol.   **h. 3283. jj. (26.)**

— Commonwealth March ... Piano Solo. *Star Music Publishing
Co.: London,* (1912.) fol.   **h. 3284. f. (17.)**

LAHOUSSAYE (PIERRE)

— Sei Sonate a Violino solo e Basso ... Opera prima. Gravé par
Fouchault. *Chez le Sr Sieber: Paris,* [1765?] fol.
    g. 422. a. (4.)

LAHOZ (FLORENCIO)

— Ayes en la Inquisiciòn. Melodia [begins: "Desde negras
prisiones"]. Poesia de Dn. I. L. Pinto. *See* ARIAS. Arias y
Canciones, *etc.* No. 12. [1871, *etc.*] fol.   **H. 2403.**

— Introducciòn y gran jota aragonesa con 5 cantos y 42
variaciones, *etc.* [P. F.] pp. 13. [*The author:*] *Madrid,* [c. 1850.]
fol.   **g. 1580. (7.)**

— See ARRIETA Y CORERA (P. J. E.) Marina ... Reducción por
F.Lahoz. [1865?] fol.   **H. 770. o.**

— See ARRIETA Y CORERA (P. J. E.) La Vuelta del Corsaro ...
Reducción por F. Lahoz. [1860?] fol.   **H. 770. e. (5.)**

— See BARBIERI (F. A.) El Secreto de una Dama ... Reducción
por F.Lahoz. [1870?] fol.   **H. 773.**

— See GAZTAMBIDE (J.) En la Astas del Toro ... Reducción por
F. Lahoz. [1860?] fol.   **H. 771. e. (3.)**

— See GAZTAMBIDE (J.) Una Vieja ... Reducción por F. Lahoz.
[1865?] fol.   **H. 771. e. (5.)**

— See INZENGA (J.) Si yo fuera Rey ... Reducción por F. Lahoz.
[1865?] 8°.   **E. 1069.**

— See OUDRID (C.) Nadie se muere ... Reducción por F. Lahoz.
[1860?] fol.   **H. 775. a. (2.)**

— See OUDRID (C.) El Ultimo Mono ... Reducción por
F. Lahoz. [1860?] fol.   **H. 775. a. (3.)**

LAHUSEN (CHRISTIAN)

— Geistliche Lieder. [Melodies only.] pp. 23. *Bärenreiter:
Kassel, etc.,* [1974.] 8°.   **A. 697. k.**

— [Heimkehr im Abend.] Um Mitternacht. ([Words by] Eduard
Mörike.) [S.A.T.B.] *Bärenreiter-Verlag: Kassel,* [1967.] *s. sh.*
8°.   **F. 1744. jj. (19.)**

— Die Hochzeit der Schäferin. Ballett zu einem Lustspiel von
Molière. Klavierauszug zu zwei Händen eingerichtet vom
Komponisten. pp. 35. *Breitkopf & Härtel: Leipzig,* [1920.] 4°.
    g. 230. t. (3.)

— Um Mitternacht. *See supra:* [Heimkehr im Abend.]

— Der Wald. Ein Tanzspiel. Klavierauszug zu zwei Händen
eingerichtet vom Komponisten. The Forest. A pantomime,
etc. pp. 94. *Breitkopf & Härtel: Leipzig,* [1920.] 4°.
    g. 230. t. (4.)

LA HYE (DE) *Madame*

— Le Corsaire Rouge. [Song, begins: "Bondis, O ma gazelle".]
(Paroles de Mr. de La Hye.) *Paris,* [1840?] fol.
    G. 542. (34.)

— Je l'ai tué. Romance dramatique. (Paroles de Mr. de la Hye.)
Paris, [1835?] fol.   **G. 542. (36.)**

LAI

— I Lai del Desolato. [Song.] *See* PALMERINI (R.)

— Le Lai du chasseur prisonnier. Ballade. *See* ROBERT MAZEL
(Hélène)

LAI (Francis)

— [Un Homme et une femme.] "A Man and a Woman" ...
Arranged by W. E. C. Godly. (Solo B♭ cornet conductor [and
brass band parts].) 24 pt. *Leeds Music: London*, [1969.] *obl.*
8°.
With several copies of various parts. **h. 3210. j. (346.)**

Love Story

— Love Story. (Organ. Arranged by Ethel Smith.) pp. xvi. 47.
Famous Music Corp.: New York, [1971.] 4°. **f. 337. d. (2.)**

— [A reissue.] Love Story. (Organ. Arranged by Ethel Smith.)
Famous Chappell: London, [1971.] 4°. **f. 337. d. (1.)**

— Love Story. [Film.] (Souvenir album. Piano/vocal edition.)
Famous Music Corp.: New York, [1971.] 4°. **g. 352. y. (19.)**

— Love Story. [Film.] (Souvenir music album. Edited and
arranged by John Brimhall and Larry Stanton.) [P.F.] pp. 42.
Famous Music Corp.: New York, [1971.] 4°. **g. 352. y. (18.)**

— Love Story. (Easy guitar solos and duets.) pp. xvi. 32.
Famous Music Corp.: New York, [1971.] 4°. **g. 660. rr. (5.)**

— Love Story. (Story-teller edition. Piano/organ/guitar/vocal.)
pp. xvi. 31. *Famous Music Corp.: New York*, [1971.] 4°.
f. 760. cc. (2.)

— Selections from Love Story ... Piano and organ duet.
Arranged by John Brimhall. [Score.] pp. 16. *Famous Music
Corp.: New York*, [1971.] 4°.
Two copies. **g. 352. y. (20.)**

— Selections from Love Story ... Two piano arrangement by
John Brimhall. pp. 16. *Famous Music Corp.: New York*,
[1971.] 4°.
Two copies. **g. 1122. ee. (4.)**

— Selections from Love Story ... Arranged for easy piano by
John Brimhall. pp. 7. *Famous Music Corp.: New York*, [1971.]
4°. **g. 352. y. (17.)**

— Theme from Love Story ... Arranged by Jay Arnold. (String
orchestra. Conductor—Piano conductor [and parts].) 34 pt.
Famous Music Corp.: New York, [1971.] 4°.
With several copies of various parts. **h. 3210. j. (497.)**

— Theme from Love Story ... Arranged by Jerry Coker. Stage
band. (Conductor's guide [and parts].) 18 pt. *Famous Music
Corp.: New York*, [1971.] 4°. **h. 3210. j. (465.)**

— Theme from Love Story ... Arranged for brass and reed
band by Allan Street. (Conductor [and parts].) 27 pt. *Famous
Chappell: London*, [1971.] 8°.
*Brass and Reed Band Journal. no. 249. With several copies of
various parts.* **h. 3210. j. (458.)**

— Theme from Love Story ... Arranged by John Edmondson.
(Conductor [and military band parts].) 49 pt. *Famous
Chappell: London*, [1971.] 4°.
*Part of "Funway Concert Band Series". With several copies of
various parts.* **f. 806. (12.)**

— Theme from "Love Story" ... Arranged by John Edmondson.
(Conductor [and military band parts].) 49 pt. *Famous Music
Corp.: New York*, [1971.] 4°. **h. 3210. j. (496.)**

— Theme from Love Story ... Arrangement by Peter Nero.
Transcribed by Earl Rose. [P.F.] pp. 5. *Famous Music
Corporation: New York*, [1974.] 4°. **f. 770. xx. (11.)**

— Love Story. (Where do I begin.) For interchangeable chorus.
SA. SSA. SAB. Arranged by Arnold Freed, *etc.* pp. 13.
Famous Music Corp.: New York, [1971.] 8°. **F. 1874. p. (2.)**

— Love Story. (Where do I begin.) (S.A.) Arranged by John
Edmondson, *etc.* pp. 8. *Famous Music Corp.: New York*,
[1971.] 8°. **F. 217. xx. (4.)**

LAI (Francis)

— Love Story. (Where do I begin.) Lyric by Carl Sigman.
Arranged by Lou Leaman. [For three voices.] pp. 8. *Famous
Music Corp.: New York*, [1971.] 8°. **F. 1874. p. (3.)**

— Theme ... Religious version ... Special lyric by Paul
Sandberg. pp. 4. *Famous Music Corp.: New York*, [1973.] 4°.
F. 1174. a. (6.)

— A Man and a Woman. *See* supra: [Un Homme et une
femme.]

— The Music's too sweet not to dance. *See* infra: [Oliver's
Story.]

— [Oliver's Story.] Love Theme from "Oliver's Story". (Piano
solo.) pp. 4. *Charles Hansen: New York*, [1978.] 4°.
g. 1425. g. (10.)

— [Oliver's Story.—Love Theme.] The Music's too sweet not to
dance ... For S.A.T.B. voices and piano, with optional
combo accompaniment. Arranged by Robert Sterling. Words
by John Korty. [With P.F. accompaniment only.] pp. 12.
Shawnee Press: Delaware Water Gap, Pa., [1979.] 8°.
Part of "Music from Films choral Series". **E. 1830. g. (8.)**

LAIANA (L.)

— Ka Hae hoonani; oia na mele a pau i pai pu ia me na leo
maloko o "Ke alaula," mai ka hoomaka ana a hiki i ka
makahiki 1871. Hoopukaia e ka papa euanelio Hawaii.
[Edited by L. Laiana.] pp. 36. 1874. *obl.* 8°. *See* Hae.
A. 1237. t.

— Hoku ao nani. He buke mele no na kula sabati, no na aha
haipule, no na anaina hoomana, no na aha hoike makahiki,
&c., &c. pp. 304. *L. Laiana: Waimea; New York*, [printed,
1881?] *obl.* 8°.
The imprint is taken from the cover. **A. 1236. r.**

— Ka Lei Alii. He buke mele no na kula sabati i
hoomakaukauia e L. Laiana. pp. 160. *Ka Papa Hawaii:
Honolulu*, 1884. *obl.* 8°. **A. 1236. s.**

LAID

— Laid on Thine Altar. Sacred Song. *See* Brooks (W. W.)

— Laid to rest. Song. *See* Flower (R.)

LAIDLAW (George B.)

— Octavia. Waltz. [P. F.] *Akerman & Attwood: London*, [1890.]
fol. **h. 3285. p. (47.)**

LAIDLAW (William)

— Drumlanrig Quadrilles ... Arranged by R. W. Manning, *etc.*
[P. F.] *W. & J. Kennedy: Hawick*, [1886.] fol. **h. 975. u. (18.)**

LAIGHTON (Ruth)

— First Steps in Shifting. Exercises and etudes ... for the violin.
A. P. Schmidt Co.: Boston, New York, 1919. 4°.
g. 498. z. (8.)

— Six Folk Tunes for Violin with Piano accompaniment. *A. P.
Schmidt Co.: Boston, New York*, 1929. 4°. **g. 822. e. (3.)**

— From long ago and far away. Three and thirty folk tunes
[arranged] for piano by R. Laighton. *A. P. Schmidt Co.:
Boston, New York*, 1920. 4°. **g. 1129. t. (8.)**

— Tunes and Technique. A beginner's book for the violin,
based on folk-songs. 2 pt. *A. P. Schmidt Co.: Boston, New
York*, 1918, 21. 4°. **g. 498. y. (3.)**

LAIGHTON (Ruth)

— *See* Gluck (C. W. von) [Armide.—On s'étonnerait moins.] Andante amabile. Transcribed (for Violin and Pianoforte) by R. Laighton. (1912.) fol.　　　　**h. 1612. y. (29.)**

LAILA

— Laila. Operetta. *See* Stratton (G. W.)

LAILĀH

— Lailah feleh. [Part-song.] *See* Fastalsky (　　　)

LAIMABLE (　　　)

— Le Départ quick march. [Reed band parts.]　*London,* [1879.] fol.
Part of the "Alliance Musicale".　　　　**f. 401. m. (11.)**

LAIN (E. F.)

— I've locked my heart. [Song, begins: "Oh! I'm a merry".] *London,* [1867.] fol.　　　　**H. 1772. r. (5.)**

LAINE (Denny)

— *See* MacCartney (Paul) and Laine (D.) Mull of Kintyre ... ⟨S.A.T.B.⟩ Words and music by McCartney-Laine. [1978.] 8°.
　　　　F. 1874. w. (9.)

LAINE (Jean de) *pseud.*

— A Winter's Eve. Graceful Dance for the pianoforte.　*Beal & Co.: London,* [1896.] fol.　　　　**h. 3282. f. (5.)**

LAINÉ (Paul)

— The Moon Fairy. Valse Intermezzo. For Piano.　*E. Ashdown: London, etc.,* 1912. fol.　　　　**g. 606. n. (31.)**

LAING (David)

— An Account of the Scottish Psalter of A.D.1566, containing the Psalms, Canticles and Hymns set to music in four parts, in the manuscripts of T. Wode, or Wood, *etc.* [With facsimiles.]　*Edinburgh,* 1871. 4°.　　　　**4999. e. 35.**

— *See* Stenhouse (W.) Illustrations of the Lyric Poetry and Music of Scotland ... with additional notes and illustrations [and an introduction by D. Laing]. 1853. 8°.　　**1077. k. 63.**

LAING (F.)

— A Cradle Hymn. Words by I. Watts.　*J. B. Cramer & Co.: London,* [1901.] *s. sh.* 8°.　　　　**I. 600. b. (47.)**

— Ivy Song. Words by F. D. Hemans.　*J. B. Cramer & Co.: London,* 1902. fol.　　　　**H. 1799. cc. (37.)**

— Two Songs. [No. 1.] The Garland. Words by M. Prior. [No. 2.] Song of Hesperus. Words by Ben Jonson.　*J. B. Cramer & Co.: London,* 1900. fol.　　　　**H. 1799. cc. (38.)**

LAING (P. M. T.)

— A short setting of the Benedictus qui venit and Agnus Dei in ... F.　*Novello, Ewer and Co.: London and New York,* [1893.] 8°.　　　　**F. 1170. i. (15.)**

— Two Three-fold Amens.　*Novello, Ewer and Co.: London and New York,* [1893.] *a card.*　　　　**I. 600. (104.)**

LAINI (F.)

— Si loin! So far ... Caprice impromptu pour Piano.　*Mackay Bros.: Johannesburg, etc.,* [1911.] fol.　　**h. 3284. f. (18.)**

LAIRD

— The Laird. [Part-song.] *See* Moodie (W.)

— The Laird and the Minstrel. Song. *See* Barnett (John)

— The Laird o' Cockpen. Scotch ballad.　*London,* [1855.] fol. *No.* 345 *of the "Musical Bouquet".*　　　　**H. 2345.**

— The Laird o' Cockpen. Quartet. *See* Bantock (*Sir* G.)

— The Laird o' Cockpen. Chorus. *See* Davidson (M.)

— The Laird o' Cockpen. Unison Song. *See* Jacobson (M.)

— The Laird of Cockpen. Song. *See* Parry (*Sir* C. H. H.) *Bart.*

— The Laird o' Cockpen. [Part-song.] *See* Roberton (*Sir* H. S.)

— The Laird o' Cockpen. Chorus. *See* Shaw (G. T.)

— The Laird o' Cockpen. Ballad for Chorus. *See* Stephen (D.)

— The Laird of Cockpen. Song. *See* West (William)

— The Laird o' Loch Dee. Song. *See* Munro (D. R.)

— The Laird of Lochan's Daughter. Song. *See* Evelyn.

— Laird Ronald's Fall. [Song.] *See* Reeve (W.) [The White Plume.]

— The Laird's Fling. Song. *See* Roeckel (J. L.)

LAIRD (　　　) *Mrs*

— Father Christmas. Song [begins: "Awake, awake"].　*London,* [1876.] fol.　　　　**H. 1778. x. (5.)**

LAIRD (Alice-Kerr)

— *See* Bruhier (Antoine) Missa carminum zu 4 Stimmen. Herausgegeben von A.-K. Laird und N. S. Josephson. [1977.] 8°. [*Das Chorwerk. Hft.* 127.]　　　　**E. 1317.**

LAIRD (William)

— A Hundred Years hence. Song, the words by Thomas Jordan (17th century). pp. 4.　*Boosey & Hawkes: London,* [1961.] 4°.
　　　　G. 1276. v. (8.)

— The Miner's Song. [Song.] ⟨From the revue "Battle together for Britain".⟩ Words & music by W. Laird.　*M.R.A.* [*Moral Re-Armament*]*: London,* [1945.] 4°.　　**G. 1271. b. (24.)**

— Minuet and Trio, *etc.* ⟨For piano.⟩ pp. 3.　*G. Ricordi & Co.: London,* [1961.] 4°.
Part of "Modern festival Pieces".　　　　**g. 1128. oo. (15.)**

— Pastorale and Dance, *etc.* ⟨For piano.⟩ pp. 3.　*G. Ricordi & Co.: London,* [1961.] 4°.
Part of "Modern festival Pieces".　　　　**g. 272. zz. (20.)**

— Prairie Song and Covered Waggon, *etc.* ⟨For piano.⟩ pp. 3. *G. Ricordi & Co.: London,* [1961.] 4°.
Part of "Modern festival Pieces".　　　　**g. 272. zz. (19.)**

LAIR DE BEAUVAIS (Alfred)

— Album, 1848, de A. Lair de Beauvais. Paroles de MM. E. Barateau, E. de Lonlay, A. Richomme et E. Allain. 12 no. *A. Meissonnier-Heugel: Paris,* 1848. fol.
With an inscription in the composer's autograph.
　　　　R. M. 13. d. 28.

— L'Heure des Rêveries. Mélodie [begins: "Ah! pour moi"]. Paroles de G. Desnoiresterres.　*Paris,* [1845?] fol.
　　　　H. 2831. f. (12.)

— La Lune de miel. Chansonette normande ... Paroles de M^r. Eugène de Lonlay. pp. 3.　*Chez les fils de B. Schott: Mayence,* [1858.] fol.
Lyre française. no. 578.　　　　**Hirsch M. 1301. (11.)**

LAIR DE BEAUVAIS (ALFRED)

— Ma Promise. [Song, begins: "De Francette".] Paroles d'E. Barateau. *Paris,* 1848. fol.   **H. 2825. (12.)**

LAIRDS

— Lairds and Ladies. Song. *See* JEWITT (J. M.)

LAIS

— Lais, now old. [Part-song.] *See* GIBBONS (O.) [First Set of Madrigals.]

LAISSE

— Laisse moi donc. Chansonnette. *See* DANIEL (A.) Recueil, *etc.* No. 3.

— Laisse moi gouter le plaisir. [Song.] *See* CAMPAN (   )

— Laisse moi prier. Romanza. *See* OTWAY (E. P. N.) *Lady.*

— Laisse-moi t'aimer. Romance. *See* COTTRAU (G.)

— Laisse moi t'aimer. [Song.] *See* GAËL (P.) 3 Poèsies, *etc.* No. 2.

— Laisse moi t'aimer. [Song.] *See* SAINT QUENTIN (G. de)

— Laisse tes Agneaux. Ariette. *See* ALBANESE (É. J. I. A.)

LAISSEZ

— Laissez chanter les oiseaux. Duettino. *See* TAGLIAFICO (D.)

— Laissez moi le pleurer, ma mère. Romance. *See* BRUGUIÈRE (E.)

— Laissez moi ma douleur. Romance. *See* BEAUPLAN (A. de) *pseud.*

— Laissez-moi valser avec eux. Chansonnette. *See* PANSERON (A. M.)

— Laissez vous adorer. Chansonnette. *See* BEAUPLAN (A. de) *pseud.*

— Laissez vous sous mes doigts ployer avec souplesse. *Ariette Nouvelle.* Avec Accompag.ᵗ de Guitare. *Chez M. Camand: Paris,* [1780?] 8°.   **B. 362. g. (30.)**

LAISSON

— *See* LAISSONS.

LAISSONS

— Laissons aux chansonniers du jour. *Le Vent de Bise.* [Song.] [*Paris,* 1780?] 8°.   **B. 362. e. (106.)**

— Laisson laisson à la gaîté. Vaudeville. *See* POÈTE. Le Poëte Supposé.

— Laissons, mon cœur. *See* REGNART (F.) [Poësies de P. de Ronsard.]

LAISTNER (MAX)

— Dead Mountain Flowers. Song ... by A. Tennyson. *Schott & Co.: London,* [1902.] fol.   **G. 807. z. (27.)**

— Etude sur la Valse en Ré bémol, Op. 64, No. 1, de F. Chopin, pour piano. *B. Schott's Söhne: Mayence,* [1891.] fol.   **h. 1489. r. (57.)**

— Festmarsch für Pianoforte zu 4 Händen. *B. Schott's Söhne: Mainz,* [1890.] fol.   **g. 545. d. (22.)**

LAISTNER (MAX)

— The Friar's Mere.—Geisterpredigt.— Ballad for Baritone Solo, Male Chorus and Orchestra, the poem by L. Laistner —The English translation by E. M. Lockwood ... Op. 11. *Novello and Co.: London,* 1909. 8°.   **F. 1268. (5.)**

— *See* BOHM (C.) [Lieder. Op. 326. No. 27. Still wie die Nacht.] Still as the Night ... For piano. [Arranged by] M. Laistner. 1913. fol.   **h. 3351. e. (12.)**

— *See* BRAHMS (J.) [Fünf Lieder. Op. 49. No. 4.] Wiegenlied ... [Arranged by] M. Laistner. [1940.] 4°.   **g. 609. l. (5.)**

— *See* BRAHMS (J.) [Volks-Kinderlieder. No. 4. Sandmännchen.] The Sandman ... Arranged for female voices by M. Laistner. (1912.) 8°.   **F. 328. o. (7.)**

— *See* BRAHMS (J.) [Volks-Kinderlieder. No. 4. Sandmännchen.] The Sandman ... Arranged for mixed voices by M. Laistner. [1912.] 8°.   **F. 321. z. (5.)**

— *See* DVOŘÁK (A.) [Symphonies. No. 9.] Largo ... [Arranged for P. F. by] M. Laistner. (1913.) fol.   **h. 2779. b. (4.)**

— *See* DVOŘÁK (A.) [Symphonies. No. 9.] A. Dvořák's ... Largo ... Piano Solo. [Arranged by] M. Laistner. 1913. fol.   **h. 2779. b. (8.)**

— *See* DVOŘÁK (A.) [Zigeunermelodien. Op. 55. No. 4.] Als die alte Mutter ... [Arranged by] M. Laistner. 1913. fol.   **h. 2779. b. (6.)**

— *See* ELGAR (*Sir* E. W.) *Bart.* Romance ... Édition pour Piano à 2 mains par M. Laistner. [1906.] fol.   **h. 3930. g. (4.)**

— *See* ELGAR (*Sir* E. W.) *Bart.* [Salut d'Amour.] Woo thou, sweet Music ... Vocal Adaptation by M. Laistner. [1900.] fol.   **G. 807. m. (2.)**

— *See* ELGAR (*Sir* E. W.) *Bart.* Sursum Corda ... Op. 11. No. 5 ... No. 8 ... (Transcr. par M. Laistner.) 1901. fol.   **h. 3930. c. (5.)**

— *See* FLAGNY (L. de) Pavane ... Orchestr. par M. Laistner. 1912. 8°.   **f. 760. j. (7.)**

— *See* LEMARE (E. H.) Intermezzo pour Piano. Op. 83. No. 2. Transcription par M. Laistner. (1911.) fol.   **h. 2710. b. (3.)**

— *See* MARTI (E.) Aragonaise ... Transcription ... par M. Laistner. [1903.] fol.   **g. 605. ll. (31.)**

— *See* MARTI (E.) Carmencita ... Transcription ... par M. Laistner. [1903.] fol.   **g. 605. ll. (33.)**

— *See* NEVIN (E. W.) [*Collections.*] Songs ... Transcribed for Pianoforte by M. Laistner. [1904.] fol.   **h. 3619. (27.)**

— *See* NEVIN (E. W.) A Dutch Lullaby, *etc.* (Arranged by M. Laistner.) [1902.] fol.   **H. 2663. (16.)**

— *See* NEVIN (E. W.) [A Dutch Lullaby.] Wynken, Blynken and Nod ... Arranged by M. Laistner. 1914. 4°.   **G. 805. xx. (9.)**

— *See* NEVIN (E. W.) 3 Piano Duets. Op. 6 ... Arranged ... by M. Laistner. [1902–04.] fol.   **h. 3619. (17.)**

— *See* NEVIN (E. W.) [Sketch Book. Op. 2. No. 13.] The Night has a Thousand Eyes. Arr. by M. Laistner. [1902.] fol.   **H. 2663. (17.)**

— *See* NUÑEZ (G. de J.) Cavatina ... Arrangée ... par M. Laistner. 1906. fol.   **g. 505. x. (6.)**

— *See* RUBINSTEIN (A. G.) Valse-Caprice in E flat, *etc.* (Arrangement by M. Laistner.) [1916.] fol.   **g. 606. ee. (13.)**

— *See* WIDOR (C. M.) Pièces choisies ... Transcrites ... par M. Laistner. [1903–08.] fol.   **h. 2751. a. (4.)**

— *See* WIDOR (C. M.) [Quatre Pièces en Trio. No. 4.] Sérénade. Arranged by M. Laistner. 1916. fol.   **g. 606. gg. (23.)**

LAISTNER (MAX)

— *See* WOLSTENHOLME (W.) [Die Frage. Die Antwort.] Question (Arr. by M. Laistner) and Answer. [1916.] fol.

g. 606. gg. (27.)

LAISVŲJŲ

— Laisvųjų daina. [Song.] *See* JAKUBĖNAS (V.)

LAITIÈRE

— La Laitière de Trianon. Opérette. *See* WECKERLIN (J. B. T.)

LAJARTE (THÉODORE EDOUARD DUFAURE DE)

— Airs à danser de Lulli à Méhul. Transcrits d'après les manuscrits originaux de la Bibliothèque de l'Opéra de Paris. [P. F.] *Paris*, [1877.] 8°.

f. 87.

— La Boîte à Musique. Opéra comique en un acte. Paroles de C. Nuitter et A. Beaumont. *Paris*, [1884.] 8°.

F. 806. c.

— [La Boîte à Musique.] Caquetage. *See* RÉCRÉATIONS. Récréations Musicales. Chœurs ... extraits d'opéras-comiques ... par ... T. de Lajarte, *etc.* [1888.] 4°.

C. 457.

— Cendrillon, opéra comique de Nicolo, souvenir pour le Piano. *Paris*, [1877.] fol.

h. 1493. n. (7.)

— Les deux Toinon. Opéra-comique en un acte. Paroles de E. Adenis. *Paris*, [1886.] 8°.

F. 806. d.

— [Les deux Toinon.] Les Moissonneuses. *See* RÉCRÉATIONS. Récréations Musicales. Chœurs ... Extraits d'opéras-comiques ... par ... T. de Lajarte, *etc.* [1888.] 4°.

C. 457.

— La Fille à Nicaise, Chanson [begins: "C'est la fille à Nicaise"], paroles de E. Leterrier & A. Vanloo. *Paris*, [1884.] fol.

H. 2836. h. (26.)

— Gavotte des Muscadins pour le piano. *Brandus et Cie.: Paris*, [1886.] fol.

h. 3281. k. (51.)

— Les Jumeaux de Bergame. Ballet-Pantomime en un acte de C. Nuitter & L. Mérante. *Paris*, [1886.] 8°.

f. 87. b.

— Six Marches performed by the band of the Garde Républicaine, arranged as duets for the Pianoforte. 6 no. *London*, [1871.] fol.

h. 1482. y. (20.)

— Méditation pour violon, piano, orgue-harmonium et harpe non obligée. *Brandus et Cie.: Paris*, [1887.] fol.

h. 2575. i. (7.)

— Monsieur de Floridor. Opéra comique en un acte. Paroles de MM. C. Nuitter et E. Tréfeu. Partition Chant et Piano. *Paris*, [1881.] 8°.

F. 806. a.

— Les Musiciens méridionaux au XVIIIᵉ siècle. Fragments reconstitués, instrumentés et réduits pour le piano par Théodore de Lajarte. pp. 72. *Paul Dupont: Paris*, [1890?] 4°.

F. 876. a. (2.)

— [Les Oiseaux en Cage.] Chœur des Paysannes. *See* RÉCRÉATIONS. Récréations Musicales. Chœurs ... extraits d'opéras-comiques ... par ... T. de Lajarte, *etc.* [1888.] 4°.

C. 457.

— Orientale, petite fantaisie pour Piano. *Paris*, [1863.] fol.

h. 1462. q. (25.)

— Le Portrait. Opéra Comique en deux actes par MM. Laurencin & J. Adenis. Partition piano & chant réduite par A. Bazille. *Paris*, [1883.] 4°.
Format Lemoine.

F. 806. e.

— [Le Portrait.] *See* CRAMER (W.) Le Portrait. Fleurs d'Opéra pour piano. [On T. de Lajarte's opera.] [1883.] fol.

h. 3281. d. (40.)

LAJARTE (THÉODORE EDOUARD DUFAURE DE)

Le Roi de Carreau

— Le Roi de Carreau. Opéra comique en 3 actes. Paroles de MM. E. Laterrier & A. Vanloo. Partition Chant & Piano arrangée par C. Geng. *Paris*, [1883.] 8°.

F. 806. b.

— Le Roi de Carreau ... Parties d'Orchestre. *Paris*, [1884.] fol.

h. 4040.

— Le Roi de Carreau ... Partition Piano seul arrangée par J. de Brayer. *Paris*, [1884.] 8°.

f. 87. a.

— Airs ... arrangés pour cornet seul par E. Guilbaut. *Paris*, [1884.] fol.

h. 2202. c. (14.)

— Airs du Roi de Carreau ... arrangés pour Flûte seule par G. Gariboldi. *Brandus & Cie.: Paris*, [1884.] fol.

h. 2140. l. (15.)

— Airs ... arrangés pour violon seul par A. Müller. *Paris*, [1884.] fol.

h. 1609. y. (14.)

— *See* ARBAN (J. J. B. L.) Parade-Polka pour piano sur des motifs du Roi de Carreau, *etc.* [1884.] fol.

h. 3285. (21.)

— *See* ARBAN (J. J. B. L.) Quadrille sur le Roi de Carreau, *etc.* [1883.] *obl.* fol.

e. 272. n. (2.)

— *See* BULL (G.) Fantaisie ... pour piano sur les motifs du Roi de Carreau, *etc.* [1884.] fol.

h. 3358. a. (11.)

— *See* CRAMER (H.) Bouquet de Mélodies ... du Roi de Carreau, *etc.* [1884.] fol.

h. 371. c. (17.)

— *See* GENG (C.) Benvenuta-valse ... sur des motifs du Roi de Carreau, *etc.* [1883.] *obl.* fol.

e. 272. n. (23.)

— *See* HABANS (C.) Polka Mazurka pour le Piano sur des motifs du Roi de Carreau, *etc.* [1884.] fol.

h. 3285. b. (12.)

— *See* HESS (J. C.) Le Roi de Carreau ... Transcription pour piano. [1884.] fol.

h. 3061. a. (3.)

— *See* MÉTRA (J. L. O.) Quadrille ... sur des motifs du Roi de Carreau, *etc.* [1884.] *obl.* fol.

f. 276. b. (3.)

— *See* RENAUD DE VILBAC (A. Z. C.) Duo facile pour piano à 4 mains sur Le Roi de Carreau, *etc.* [1884.] fol.

h. 1228. n. (28.)

— *See* STREABBOG (L.) *pseud.* Petite fantaisie pour piano sur Le Roi de Carreau, *etc.* [1884.] fol.

h. 3197. c. (32.)

— Salmigondis, quadrille brillant pour Piano. *Paris*, [1875.] *obl.* fol.

e. 272. f. (6.)

— Le Secret de l'Oncle Vincent. Opéra comique en un acte ... Paroles de H. Boisseaux. *Paris*, [1855.] 8°.

F. 806.

— Sous la Feuillé. Rondo facile pour Piano. *Paris*, [1863.] fol.

h. 1462. q. (26.)

— *See* CAMPRA (A.) L'Europe Galante ... réduite pour Piano et Chant par T. de Lajarte. [1880.] 8°.

F. 699. c.

— *See* LULLI (J. B.) Alceste. Tragédie ... réduite pour Piano et Chant par T. de Lajarte. [1882.] 8°.

F. 699. o.

— *See* LULLI (J. B.) Armide, tragédie ... réduite pour Piano et Chant par T. de Lajarte. [1878.] 8°.

F. 699. a.

— *See* LULLI (J. B.) Atys, tragédie lyrique ... Réduite pour Piano et Chant par T. de Lajarte. [1880.] 8°.

F. 699. h.

— *See* LULLI (J. B.) Bellerophon, tragédie lyrique ... réduite pour Piano et Chant par T. de Lajarte. [1880.] 8°.

F. 699. g.

— *See* LULLI (J. B.) Cadmus et Hermione. Tragédie lyrique ... reduite pour piano et chant par T. de Lajarte. [1881.] 8°.

F. 699. j.

LAJARTE (Théodore Edouard Dufaure de)

— *See* Lulli (J. B.) Isis. Tragédie lyrique ... réduite pour Piano et Chant par T. de Lajarte. [1882.] 8°. **F. 699. t.**

— *See* Lulli (J. B.) Persée. Tragédie lyrique ... réduite pour Piano et Chant par T. de Lajarte. [1883.] 8°. **F. 699. z.**

— *See* Lulli (J. B.) Phaéton. Tragédie lyrique ... réduite pour Piano et Chant par T. de Lajarte. [1883.] 8°. **F. 700. j.**

— *See* Lulli (J. B.) Proserpine. Tragédie lyrique ... réduite pour Piano et Chant par T. de Lajarte. [1883.] 8°. **F. 700. a.**

— *See* Lulli (J. B.) Psyché, tragédie lyrique ... réduite pour Piano et Chant par T. de Lajarte. [1878.] 8°. **F. 699. b.**

— *See* Lulli (J. B.) Thesée. Tragédie ... Reconstituée et réduite pour Piano et Chant par T. de Lajarte, *etc.* [1878.] 8°. **R. M. 9. d. 20.**

— *See* Rameau (J. P.) Castor & Pollux. Tragédie ... réduite pour Piano & Chant par T. de Lajarte. [1880.] 8°. **F. 699. d.**

— *See* Rameau (J. P.) Les Festes d'Hébé. Opéra-ballet ... réduite pour Piano et Chant par T. de Lajarte. [1880.] 8°. **F. 699. e.**

LAJARTHE DE SAINT AMAND (A.)

— Un Brigand de Fantaisie. Chansonnette [begins: "Vous tremblez"]. Paroles de F. Tourte. *Paris,* [1866.] fol. **H. 1774. e. (8.)**

— Ne pleure pas, enfant. Berceuse [begins: "Sur tes yeux bleus"]. Paroles de E. Humbert. *Paris,* [1866.] fol. **H. 1774. e. (7.)**

LAJOVIC (Anton)

— Album samospevov zu glas s klavirjem. pp. 138. *Ljubljana,* 1956. fol.
Slovenska akademija znanosti in umetnosti. Razred za umetnosti. Dela. Serija za glasbeno umetnost. Series B: Musica. 8. **H. 2175. e. (1.)**

— Caprice. ⟨Za orkester.⟩ [Score.] pp. 86. *Ljubljana,* 1955. fol.
Slovenska akademija znanosti in umetnosti. Razred za umetnosti. Dela. Serija za glasbeno umetnost. Series B: Musica. 4. **h. 1438. g. (4.)**

— Gozdna samota ⟨Troglasni ženski zbor s spremljavo orkestra⟩. Psalm 41. in 42 ⟨Za tenorski solo, mešani zbor in orkester⟩. Šest samospevov. Partiture. ⟨Delo je pripravil za tisk in mu napisal uvod Lucijan Marija Škerjanc.⟩ pp. 290. *Ljubljana,* 1974. fol.
Slovenska akademija znanosti in umetnosti. Razred za umetnosti. Dela. Serija za glasbeno umetnost. Series B: Musica. 33. **H. 2175. j.**

— Pesem jeseni. Simfonična lirska pesnitev. Partitura, *etc.* pp. 98. *Ljubljana,* 1956. fol.
Slovenska akademija znanosti in umetnosti. Razred za umetnosti. Dela. Serija za glasbeno umetnost. Series B: Musica. 12. **h. 1438. i. (2.)**

— Pesmi mladosti, *etc.* [Orchestral score.] pp. 178. *Ljubljana,* 1958. fol.
Slovenska akademija znanosti in umetnosti. Razred za umetnosti. Dela. Serija za glasbeno umetnost. Series B: Musica. 14. **h. 1438. g. (3.)**

— Tri pesmi za visoki glas s spremljevanjem klavirja. Trois mélodies pour chant et piano. 1. Somotni pevec v pomladni večer ... 2. Orientalski sonet ... 3. Begunka pri zibeli, *etc.* pp. 18. *Ljubljana,* 1952. fol.
Slovenska akademija znanosti in umetnosti. Razred za umetnost. Dela. Serija za glasbeno umetnost. Series B: Musica. 1. **H. 2175. b. (5.)**

LAJOVIC (Anton)

— Zbori. Zbral in uredil L. M. Škerjanc. pp. 75. *Ljubljana,* 1963. fol.
Slovenska akademija znanosti in umetnosti. Razred za umetnosti. Dela. Serija za glasbeno umetnost. Series B: Musica. 23. **H. 2175. e. (2.)**

LAJTHA (Ladislas)

— *See* Lajtha (László)

LAJTHA (László)

— Trois berceuses ... Three Lullabies. Pour piano ou chant et piano, *etc.* pp. 4. *Centre d'art national français: Toulouse,* [1970.] 4°. **G. 295. zz. (2.)**

— [Le Bosquet des quatre dieux.] Deuxième suite pour orchestre. MCML. ⟨Op. 38. Partition.⟩ pp. 128. *Chez Alphonse Leduc: Paris,* [1950.] 8°. **c. 156. ff. (4.)**

— Concert pour violoncelle et piano. 1. Thrène dramatique — 2. Ballade des torches. ⟨Op. 31.⟩ [Score and part.] 2 pt. *Éditions musicales Alphonse Leduc: Paris,* [1962.] fol. **h. 1851. aa. (9.)**

— Divertissement pour orchestre. [Op. 25.] ⟨Partition.⟩ pp. 73. *Alphonse Leduc: Paris,* [1938.] fol. **h. 1540. h. (4.)**

— Cinq études pour quatuor à cordes, *etc.* ⟨Op. 20.⟩ [Score.] pp. 27. *Alphonse Leduc: Paris,* [1936.] fol. **h. 2830. y. (1.)**

— Quatre hommages pour flûte, hautbois, clarinette en la et basson. ⟨Op. 42.⟩ [Score.] pp. 51. *Alphonse Leduc: Paris,* [1957.] *obl.* 4°. **e. 668. z.**

— Hortobagy. Pour orchestre. ⟨Op. 21.⟩ I. La Grande plaine hongroise. II. Galopade dans la Puszta. Partition, *etc.* pp. 82. *Alphonse Leduc: Paris,* [1965.] 8°. **c. 116. d. (3.)**

— In memoriam. Pièce symphonique pour orchestre. Partition d'orchestre. pp. 61. *Universal-Edition: Wien,* [1947.] 4°. **g. 727. nn. (1.)**

— Intermezzo pour saxophone alto et piano. [Score and part.] 2 pt. *Alphonse Leduc: Paris,* [1955.] fol. **h. 2784. x. (3.)**

— [Lysistrata. Op. 19.] Suite pour orchestre. I. Prélude et hymne. II. Marche burlesque. III. Valse lente. IV. Can-can. ⟨Partition.⟩ pp. 104. *Chez Alphonse Leduc: Paris,* [1935.] fol. **h. 4029. a.**

— [Lysistrata. Op. 19.] Ouverture pour orchestre. [Op. 19a.] Extrait du ballet Lysistrata. ⟨Partition.⟩ pp. 37. *Chez Alphonse Leduc: Paris,* [1939.] fol. **h. 141. qq. (1.)**

— Magnificat pour chœur de femmes et orgue. Op. 60. pp. 22. *Alphonse Leduc: Paris,* [1955.] fol. **H. 1186. h. (6.)**

— Missa pro choro mixto et organo. MCMLII. ⟨Op. 54.⟩ [Score.] pp. 30. *Alphonse Leduc: Paris,* [1952.] fol. **H. 1186. j. (8.)**

— Népzenei monográfiák ... Szerkeszti: Lajtha László.
1. Szépkenyerüszentmártoni gyűjtés. pp. 159. 1954.
2. Széki gyűjtés. pp. 363. 1954.
3. Kőrispataki gyűjtes. pp. 446. 1955.
4. Sopron megyei virrasztó énekek. pp. 623. 1956.
Zeneműkiadó Vállalat: Budapest, 1954, *etc.* 8°. **D. 476.**

— Ouverture pour orchestre. [Op. 19a.] *See supra:* [Lysistrata. Op. 19.]

— Prélude pour piano, *etc.* pp. 3. *Centre d'art national français: Toulouse,* [1970.] 4°. **g. 1138. ff. (5.)**

— 3ᵉ quatuor ... Op. 11. Partition, *etc.* pp. 64. *Universal Edition: Wien, Leipzig,* [1931.] 8°. **d. 85. f. (9.)**

— IV. quatuor à cordes. Op. 12. [Score.] pp. 42. *Rózsavölgyi & cᵈᵉ: Budapest et Leipzic,* [1932.] 4°. **g. 417. nn. (5.)**

LAJTHA (László)

— Septième quatuor pour 2 violons, alto et violoncelle ...
Op. 49. [Score.] pp. 20. *Alphonse Leduc: Paris*, [1951.] fol.
i. 170.

— Huitième quatuor à cordes. ⟨Op. 53.⟩ [Score.] pp. 37. *Alphonse
Leduc: Paris*, [1954.] 4°. **g. 417. xx. (2.)**

— Neuvième quatuor pour 2 violons, alto et violoncelle.
⟨Op. 57.⟩ [A facsimile of the composer's autograph. Score.]
pp. 32. *Alphonse Leduc: Paris*, [1954.] obl. 4°. **f. 390. j. (1.)**

— [Sérénade.] Dialogue de la "Sérénade" pour trio à cordes. *In:*
La Revue internationale de musique. tom. 1. no. 1. Cahier de
musique inédite. pp. 1, 2. 1938. 8°. **Hirsch 5762.**

— Sinfonietta pour orchestre à cordes. ⟨Op. 43. Partition.⟩ pp. 39.
Alphonse Leduc: Paris, [1948.] fol. **h. 1508. w. (9.)**

— Deuxième sinfonietta pour orchestre à cordes. ⟨Op. 62.⟩
[Score.] pp. 51. *Alphonse Leduc: Paris*, [1957.] fol.
h. 1567. p. (1.)

— Sonate en concert pour flûte et piano. ⟨Op. 64.⟩ [Score and
part.] 2 pt. *Éditions musicales Alphonse Leduc: Paris*, [1960.]
fol. **h. 4029. (3.)**

— Sonate en concert. Pour violon et piano. ⟨Op. 68.⟩ [Score and
part.] 2 pt. *Alphonse Leduc: Paris*, [1963.] 4°. **h. 4029. (4.)**

— Sonate pour violoncelle et piano, *etc.* ⟨Op. 17.⟩ [Score and
part.] 2 pt. *Alphonse Leduc: Paris*, [1933.] fol. **h. 4029. (1.)**

— Suite pour orchestre. *See* supra: [Lysistrata. Op. 19.]

— Deuxième suite pour orchestre. Op. 38. *See* supra: [Le
Bosquet des quatre dieux.]

— Troisième suite pour orchestre. ⟨Partition.⟩ pp. 160. *Alphonse
Leduc: Paris*, [1955.] 8°. **d. 134. u. (4.)**

— Symphonie pour orchestre. ⟨Op. 24. Partition.⟩ pp. 89.
Alphonse Leduc: Paris, [1939.] fol. **h. 1507. ww. (1.)**

— Symphonie ("Les soli") pour orchestre à cordes, harpe et
batterie. Op. 33. Partition d'orchestre. pp. 141. *Universal
Edition: Wien, etc.*, [1955.] 4°. **g. 727. pp. (3.)**

— Troisième symphonie pour orchestre, *etc.* ⟨Op. 45. Partition.⟩
Chez Alphonse Leduc: Paris, [1949.] 8°. **d. 135. o. (1.)**

— Cinquième symphonie. Pour orchestre. MCMLIV. ⟨Op. 55.⟩
[Score.] pp. 105. *Alphonse Leduc: Paris*, [1954.] 8°.
d. 134. bb. (2.)

— Sixième symphonie pour orchestre, *etc.* ⟨Op. 61.⟩ [Score.]
pp. 183. *Alphonse Leduc: Paris*, [1959.] 8°. **d. 95.**

— Septième symphonie pour orchestre, *etc.* [Score.] pp. 167.
Alphonse Leduc: Paris, [1960.] 8°. **d. 95. a.**

— Huitième symphonie pour orchestre. MCMLXII. ⟨Op. 55.
Partition de poche.⟩ pp. 176. *Chez Alphonse Leduc: Paris*,
[1962.] 8°. **c. 156. q. (1.)**

— Neuvième symphonie pour orchestre, *etc.* ⟨Op. 67.⟩ [Score.]
pp. 125. *Alphonse Leduc: Paris*, [1963.] 8°. **d. 135. o. (4.)**

— IIᵉᵐᵉ trio à cordes. Op. 18. [Score.] pp. 42. *Rózsavölgyi & cⁱᵉ:
Budapest, Leipzic*, [1933.] 4°. **g. 417. ll. (9.)**

— IIIᵉ trio à cordes. Soirs transylvains. Erdélyi esték. ⟨Op. 41.⟩
Quatre esquisses pour trio à cordes, *etc.* [With a portrait.
Score.] pp. 64. *Universal Edition: Wien*, [1953.] 8°.
Philharmonia. no. 383. **c. 160. b. (2.)**

— Deuxième trio pour flûte, violoncelle et harpe. ⟨Op. 47.⟩
[Score and parts.] 3 pt. *Alphonse Leduc: Paris*, [1950.] fol.
h. 4029. (2.)

LAJTHA (László)

— Vocalise-étude pour voix élevées. pp. 5. *Alphonse Leduc:
Paris*, [1931.] fol.
Répertoire moderne de vocalises-études. no. 127.
H. 1860. o. (16.)

— *See* GÖNYEY (S.) 111 táncdal. Lajtha L. és mások gyűjtéséből
összeállította Dr. Gönyey S. [c. 1950.] 8°. **A. 1162. i. (1.)**

— *See* PAULINI (B.) The Pearly Bouquet, *etc.* (Folk Songs ...
collected by L. Lajtha.) 1937. 8°. **E. 1571.**

LAKE

— The Lake. [Song.] *See* DUQUESNE (E.)

— The Lake. [Song.] *See* KETTENUS (A.) Der See.

— The Lake. Trio. *See* MOFFAT (A. E.)

— The Lake. Part-Song. *See* PEARSON (W. W.)

— The Lake. [Song.] *See* SALTER (M. T.) Eight Songs, *etc.* [No. 4.]

— A Lake and a Fairy Boat. [Song.] *See* COCHRANE (M.)

— A Lake and a Fairy Boat. Song. *See* DAVIDSON (M.)

— A Lake and a Fairy Boat. Two-Part Song. *See* DUNHILL
(T. F.)

— A Lake and a Fairy Boat. [Two-part song.] *See* EDMUNDS
(C. M.)

— A Lake and a Fairy Boat. Duet. *See* GREEN (M.)

— A Lake and a fairy boat. [Part-song.] *See* HARRISON (J. A. G.)

— A Lake and a Fairy Boat. [Song.] *See* HOLBROOK (J. C.) [Six
Romantic Songs. Op. 30. No. 1.]

— A Lake and a fairy Boat. [Song.] *See* HOMER (S.) Three Songs.
(Op. 19.) No. 1.

— A Lake and a Fairy Boat. [Song.] *See* HOWARTH (A.) Two
Songs. [No. 2.]

— A Lake and a Fairy Boat. Song. *See* HUTCHINSON (K. H.)

— A Lake and a Fairy Boat. [Song.] *See* JOHNS (L. E.)

— A Lake and a fairy Boat. Duet. *See* LEHMANN, afterwards
BEDFORD (L.)

— A Lake and a Fairy Boat. [Two-part song.] *See* LORIOT (M.)

— A Lake and a Fairy Boat. Two-part Song. *See* PHILLIPS
(M. F.)

— A Lake & a Fairy Boat. Song. *See* THOMAS (A. G.)

— A Lake and a Fairy Boat. [Part-song.] *See* TRINDER (W.)

— A Lake and a fairy Boat. [Song.] *See* WALLACE (William V.)

— Lake and Waterfall. Part-Song. *See* THORNE (E. H.)

— The Lake Isle of Innisfree. Chorus. *See* BANTOCK (*Sir* G.)

— The Lake Isle of Innisfree. [Song.] *See* FOOTE (A. W.)

— The Lake Isle of Innisfree. [Song.] *See* FORREST (O.)

— The Lake Isle of Innisfree. [Song.] *See* HERBERT (M.)

— The Lake Isle of Innisfree. Song. *See* LEHMANN, afterwards
BEDFORD (L.)

— The Lake Isle of Innisfree. [Song.] *See* LEY (Henry G.)

— The Lake Isle of Innisfree. Song. *See* MORRISON (A.)

— The Lake Isle of Innisfree. [Song.] *See* PALMER (J.) *of
Chicago.*

LAKE

— The Lake Isle of Innisfree. [Song.] *See* POSTON (E.)

— The Lake Isle of Innisfree. [Song.] *See* TAYLOR (G.)

— The Lake Isle of Innisfree. [Song.] *See* TENNANT (S.)

— The Lake of Beauty. Song. *See* BOUGHTON (R.)

— The Lake of Cashmere. [Song.] *See* EMANUEL (L.)

— Lake of Como. [Song.] *See* HODSON (G. A.)

— The Lake of Dreams. [Two-part song.] *See* MARSHALL (Charles) *Songwriter.*

— The Lake of Gazelles. Song. *See* BRENT (E.) *Mrs.*

— The Lake of Killarney. *See* BUTLER (T. H.) Lady Cathcart's Reel, and the Lake of Killarney, *etc.* [1805?] fol.
h. 280. (20.)

— The Lake of Killarney. Ballad. *See* CLIFTON (J. C.)

— The Lake of Love. Song. *See* MASCHERONI (A.)

— The Lake, of the dismal Swamp. [Song.] *See* BALL (S.)

— The Lake of the Dismal Swamp. Choral Ballad. *See* MATTHEWS (H. A.)

— The Lake of the dismal Swamp. Choral Ballad. *See* MILES (R. H.)

— The Lake of the Dismal Swamp. [Cantata.] *See* SHAPLEIGH (B.)

— Lake of the glen. Song. *See* BAKER (W. C.)

— The Lake Sheen. [Song.] *See* BURTON (F. R.) Songs of the Ojibways.

— Lake Song. Barcarolle. *See* STODDART (L.)

— Lake Werna's Water. [Part-song.] *See* BALLANTINE (Edward)

LAKE (ANNE BUCKLER)

— Three Songs. [No. 1.] The Hills o' Skye. (Words by W. McLennan.) [No. 2.] Sonnet. (Words by E. B. Browning.) [No. 3.] The Wild Bird's Song. (Words by F. Wood.) *J. B. Cramer & Co.: London,* 1902. fol. **H. 1799. cc. (39.)**

LAKE (ARTHUR)

— Andante in A flat, for the Organ. *Weekes & Co.: London,* 1902. fol. **h. 2732. k. (8.)**

— Magnificat & Nunc Dimittis in G. *Weekes & Co.: London,* [1889.] 4°. **F. 334. (22.)**

LAKE (ERNEST)

— *See* LAKE (George Ernest)

LAKE (F. E.)

— Coronation Ode; or, National Song (for three female voices), words by G. Board. *Novello and Co.: London,* [1902.] 8°. **F. 328. c. (23.)**

LAKE (GENEVIEVE)

— The Christmas Tree. Book of carols and other songs. 23 easy arrangements ... for piano, *etc.* pp. 40. *G. Schirmer: New York,* [1968.] *obl.* 4°. **e. 282. p. (4.)**

— You and who. 2 marches + 2 waltzes. Piano duets without octaves, *etc.* pp. 23. *G. Schirmer: New York,* [1969.] 4°. **g. 545. aa. (10.)**

LAKE (GEORGE)

— Daniel, an oratorio. The words selected from the Holy Scriptures, and from H. More's sacred drama. [Vocal score.] *London,* 1852. fol. **H. 1075.**

— Dream the dream that's sweetest. A four-part song, the words ... by A. T. *London,* [1862.] fol. **H. 1772. r. (8.)**

— One Glance from thee. Song, written by Annie. *London,* [1866.] fol. **H. 1772. r. (10.)**

— Summer is sweet. Song ... written by M. Collins. *London,* [1862.] fol. **H. 1772. r. (7.)**

— Summer is sweet. Song. ⟨In F.⟩ *London,* [1862.] fol. **H. 1772. r. (6.)**

— Sweet Love, those idle fears are vain. [Song, begins: "One evening".] Written by T. Loker. *London,* [1868.] fol. **H. 1772. r. (11.)**

— The Wormwood Star. Song [begins: "There's a star"] written by A. W. Hammond. *London,* [1863.] fol. **H. 1772. r. (9.)**

LAKE (GEORGE ERNEST)

— Blessed are the Pure in Heart. Anthem for three female voices. [1887.] *See* NOVELLO AND CO. Novello's Collection of Trios, *etc.* No. 195. [1879, *etc.*] 8°. **E. 1746.**

— Blessed are the Pure in Heart, *etc.* [1907.] *See* NOVELLO AND CO. Novello's Tonic Sol-fa Series. No. 1533. [1876, *etc.*] 4°. **B. 885.**

— Daily studies & complete pedal scales for the Organ. *London,* [1882.] *obl.* fol. **e. 174. n. (25.)**

— Ferial Confession. Story of the Cross. Choir prayers with antiphon. *See* PARISH. Parish Church Music, *etc.* No. 2. [1884.] 8°. **E. 605. j. (24.)**

— Magnificat & Nunc Dimittis in F. *Weekes & Co.: London,* [1884.] 4°. **F. 334. (4.)**

— My Love and Delight. Song, words by M. Gillington. 2 no. [In E flat and F.] *R. Cocks & Co.: London,* 1892. fol. **H. 1797. o. (24.)**

— O Lamb of God. Anthem for ferial seasons. 1884. *See* PERIODICAL PUBLICATIONS.— *London.* The Musical Times, *etc.* No. 493. 1844, *etc.* 8°. **P. P. 1945. aa.**

LAKE (GEORGE H.)

— Les Étoiles, a series of short pieces for concertina solo. No. 1, 2. *London,* [1855.] fol. **h. 262. (5.)**

— German air with variations, composed and arranged for the concertina, with an accompaniment (ad lib.) for the piano forte. *London,* [1854.] fol. **h. 2336. (14.)**

— The original Schottische. [P. F.] *London,* [1850?] fol. **h. 1480. r. (12.)**

— *See* ROSSINI (G. A.) [Stabat Mater.] Cujus animam, arranged for Concertina, with piano forte accompaniment by G. Lake. [1858.] fol. **h. 2337. (5.)**

LAKE (HAROLD CHARLES)

— Charm me asleep. Madrigal for five voices, words by Herrick. *Stainer & Bell: London,* 1919. 8°. *Choral Library, No.* 158. **F. 1137. d.**

— Come live with me. Madrigal for five voices. [Words by] C. Marlowe. *Stainer & Bell: London,* 1929. 8°. *Choral Library, No.* 251. **F. 1137. d.**

— Contemplation. For organ. pp. 7. *Oxford University Press: London,* [1949.] 4°. **g. 575. rr. (3.)**

LAKE (HAROLD CHARLES)

— Contentment. Impromptu for Pianoforte. *Laudy & Co.: London*, 1927. fol. **h. 3865. g. (20.)**

— A Devon Lane. [Words by] Douglas A. Chandler. [T.T.B.B. Staff and tonic sol-fa notation.] pp. 4. *Banks & Son: York*, [1963.] 8°.
York Series. no. 1545. **F. 163. ss. (17.)**

— The Early Spring Sun. Poem by J. Carlie ... For Mezzo-Soprano Solo, Chorus and Orchestra. [Vocal score.] *Stainer & Bell: London*, 1930. 8°. **F. 1267. e. (7.)**

— How amiable are Thy Tabernacles. Anthem, *etc. Boosey & Co.: London and New York*, 1931. 8°.
[*Boosey's Choral Miscellany. no.* 145.] **F. 160. e.**

— Lament for Flodden. [Four-part song, words by] J. Elliot. *Stainer & Bell: London*, 1929. 8°.
Stainer & Bell's Choral Library, No. 252. **F. 1137. d.**

— The Lost Love. Part-song for S.A.T.B., words by William Wordsworth. [Staff and tonic sol-fa notation.] pp. 4. *Elkin & Co.: London*, [1953.] 8°.
Elkin new choral Series. 2295. **F. 1744. l. (12.)**

— Love, unto thine own who camest. Anthem, words adapted by Robert Bridges. *Novello & Co.: London*, 1946. 8°.
[*Octavo Anthems. No.* 1265.] **E. 618. a.**

— Oh blessed Summer Night. [Words by] Douglas A. Chandler. [T.T.B.B. Staff and tonic sol-fa notation.] pp. 4. *Banks & Son: York*, [1963.] 8°.
York series. no. 1546. **F. 163. ss. (18.)**

— O gladsome Light, O Grace. Short anthem for unaccompanied voices. From the Yattendon Hymnal, *etc.* [Staff and tonic sol-fa notation.] pp. 8. *Banks & Son: York*, [1955.] 8°.
York Series. no. 1468. **E. 442. x. (31.)**

— O Lorde, the Maker of al Thing. Anthem for S.A.T.B. (unaccompanied), works by King Henry VIII. pp. 6. *Novello & Co.: London*, [1951.] 8°.
[*Musical Times. no.* 1297.] **P. P. 1945. aa.**

— The Old man can't keep his Wife at Home. Devonshire folk-song, words by S. Baring-Gould ... Arranged [for T.T.B.B.] by H. C. Lake. [Staff and tonic sol-fa notation.] pp. 11. *Elkin & Co.: London*, [1953.] 8°.
Elkin new choral Series. 2296. **F. 163. kk. (11.)**

— Three Pieces for Violin and Piano (for solo or class use). [Parts.] 2 pt. *Oxford University Press: London*, [1949.] 4°. **g. 505. vv. (7.)**

— The Rover. [Unison song, words by] John W. Doddridge. pp. 4. *Oxford University Press: London*, [1949.] 8°.
[*Oxford Choral Songs. no.* 1201.] **F. 1777. a.**

— Sweet, come again! Madrigal for five voices, words by Thomas Campian. pp. 7. *Novello & Co.: London*, [1947.] 8°.
[*Part-Song Book.* 1537.] **F. 280. b.**

— To Daffodils. Part-song for T.T.B.B. (unaccompanied), words by Robert Herrick. pp. 4. *Novello & Co.: London*, [1952.] 8°.
[*The Orpheus. no.* 668.] **E. 1748.**

LAKE (HENRY)

— The Parting, or "Oh Ellen do not say 'Farewell'," *etc.* [Song.] pp. 5. *Cramer, Addison & Beale: London*, [c. 1835.] fol. **H. 1980. u. (5.)**

— "Sleep my child," a song, the poetry by Thomas Blake. *London*, [1838.] fol. **H. 1675. (7.)**

— Sleep! my Child. [Song.] ... The poetry by Thomas Blake, *etc.* ⟨Second edition.⟩ pp. 5. *D'Almaine & Cº: London*, [c. 1840.] fol. **G. 809. yy. (13.)**

LAKE (IAN)

— Classics for the young Pianist. ⟨[Compiled and edited by] Ian Lake.⟩ pp. 32. *Chappell & Co.: London*, [1974.] 4°. **f. 65. ee. (6.)**

— Divertimento. For string trio ... ⟨Op. 45.⟩ 1. Fanfare. 2. Berceuse. 3. Tambourin. 4. Theme and variations. Score and parts, *etc.* 4 pt. *Chappell & Co.: London*, [1968.] 4°. **g. 1067. w. (2.)**

— Music for young Pianists. 3 bk. *Chappell & Co.: London*, [1966.] 4°. **g. 1128. ww. (5.)**

LAKE (J. W.)

— *See* CRIVELLI (D. F.) I wish I was married, edited by J. W. Lake. [1845.] fol. **H. 1696. (58.)**

LAKE (MAYHEW LESTER)

— Aloha-Oe. Reverie. [Hawaiian melody.] Transcribed for piano solo by M. L. Lake. *C. Fischer: New York, etc.*, 1917. fol. **h. 3284. mm. (33.)**

— American Symphonic Bandbook. (Score and Parts.) 2 ser. *American Book Co.: New York, etc.*, 1934, 37. 4°. **g. 1446.**

— Mammoth Orchestra Collection, Songs of the World. National and patriotic airs of all countries, folk songs, college songs and hymns. Compiled and arranged by M. L. Lake. [Orchestral parts.] *C. Fischer: New York, etc.*, [1916.] 8°. **e. 1346.**

— The Wizard Trombone Jazzer ... Treatise on practical glissandos, or smears, showing how and when they should be employed. *C. Fischer: New York, etc.*, 1919. 8°. **f. 760. j. (13.)**

— *See* BACH (J. S.) [*Collected Works.—h.*] Sixteen Chorales ... Compiled and arranged by M. Lake, *etc.* 1938. 4°. **g. 548. gg.**

— *See* BACH (J. S.) [*Collected Works.—h.*] Bach Chorales. For mixed ensembles. Strings, woodwind, brass ... Arranged by M. Lake. [1963.] 4°. **g. 699. jj.**

— *See* BERGER (H.) Hawaiian Waltz ... Arr. by M. L. Lake. 1917. fol. **h. 3284. v. (39*.)**

— *See* CHAIKOVSKY (P. I.) [Symphony. No. 5. Op. 64.] Andante cantabile ... Arranged by M. Lake, *etc.* 1935. 8°. **h. 3210. h. (532.)**

— *See* DANN (H.) [*Junior Songs.*] Orchestral arrangements of selected numbers from Junior Songs, *etc.* (Orch. by M. L. Lake.) 1925. 4° & 8°. **g. 940.**

— *See* MALOTTE (A. H.) The Lord's Prayer ... Arranged by M. Lake, *etc.* 1944. 8°. **h. 3210. h. (882.)**

— *See* WAGNER (W. R.) [Der Ring des Nibelungen.—Die Walküre.—Wotan's Abschied und Feuerzauber.] Wotan's Farewell and Magic Fire Music ... Arranged by M. L. Lake. 1937. 4°. **h. 3210. h. (666.)**

LAKE (NELLIE E.)

— *See* LAWRIE (Edith M.) and LAKE (N. E.) Manitoba Nelledi Waltzes. [1903.] fol. **h. 4120. mm. (32.)**

LAKE (TALBOT)

— The Old Abbey Chimes. Gavotte for the pianoforte. *S. J. Brewer & Co.: London*, [1883.] fol. **h. 1484. s. (3.)**

— Riverside Sketches for the Piano Forte. 12 no. *Brewer & Compy.: London*, [1882–3.] fol. **h. 1484. s. (4.)**

— Rose-Leaves. Four Sketches for the pianoforte. 4 no. *E. Ashdown: London, etc.*, 1892. fol. **g. 605. f. (1.)**

LAKE (TALBOT)

— Spring Blossoms. Four little Pieces for the Pianoforte. 4 no. *E. Ashdown: London*, [1891.] fol.   **g. 605. f. (2.)**

— Tubal Cain. Song, words by A. B. Millington. *S. J. Brewer & Co.: London*, [1884.] fol.   **H. 1788. u. (33.)**

LAKE (WALEY B.)

— Nydia. Waltz. [P. F.] *Weekes & Co.: London*, [1887.] fol.   **h. 975. u. (19.)**

LAKE (WILBUR F. S.)

— Six Christmas Carols. 1. Yule-tide Joys. 2. Song of the Shepherds. 3. Joyful Noel Time. 4. Virgin's Lullaby. 5. Story of the Wise Men. 6. Venite adoremus. Words by E. Manners. *M. M. Leidt: Buffalo*, (1903.) 8°.   **F. 1529. d. (15.)**

LAKELET

— The Lakelet. Song. *See* KRENKEL (G.)

LAKEMAN (J. ED.)

— Be sure and write to me. [Song.] ... Words and Music by J. E. Lakeman. *O. Ditson Company: Boston, etc.*, 1893. fol.   **H. 1798. u. (4.)**

— Bye, bye, Melinda Jane. Plantation song with chorus and dance. Words and music by J. E. Lakeman. pp. 5. *Oliver Ditson Co.: Boston, London*, [1893.] fol.   **H. 3980. oo. (27.)**

— Coon's March. ⟨Song.⟩ Words and music by J. E. Lakeman. pp. 5. *Oliver Ditson Co.: Boston, London*, [1893.] fol.   **H. 3980. oo. (28.)**

— The Coon's March. [P. F.] *O. Ditson Company: Boston, etc.*, 1893. fol.   **h. 1489. r. (58.)**

— The Dashing Grenadiers ... Marching song and chorus. ⟨Words and music by J. E. Lakeman.⟩ pp. 5. *Oliver Ditson Co.: Boston, etc.*, [1896.] fol.   **H. 3980. oo. (29.)**

— Dear Nellie. [Song.] ⟨Words and music by J. E. Lakeman.⟩ pp. 5. *Oliver Ditson Co.: Boston, etc.*, [1894.] fol.   **H. 3980. oo. (30.)**

— Don't you care. ⟨A fin de siècle song on various topics.⟩ Words and music by J. E. Lakeman. pp. 5. *Oliver Ditson Co.: Boston, London*, [1894.] fol.   **H. 3980. oo. (31.)**

— Handsome Maria Jane. [Song.] Words and music by J. E. Lakeman. pp. 5. *Oliver Ditson Co.: Boston, London*, [1894.] fol.   **H. 3980. oo. (32.)**

— Hannah Jackson. [Song.] Words & music by J. E. Lakeman. pp. 5. *Oliver Ditson Co.: Boston, London*, [1876.] fol.   **H. 3980. oo. (33.)**

— Hickory Bill. ⟨Song with chorus and dance.⟩ Words & music by J. E. Lakeman. pp. 5. *Oliver Ditson Co.: Boston, London*, [1893.] fol.   **H. 3980. oo. (34.)**

— Hickory Bill ... Schottisch. (Arranged by L. Knight.) [P. F.] *O. Ditson Company: Boston, etc.*, 1893. fol.   **h. 3285. p. (48.)**

— Hie—Spy. [Song.] ⟨Words and music by J. E. Lakeman.⟩ pp. 5. *Oliver Ditson Co.: Boston, etc.*, [1895.] fol.   **H. 3980. oo. (35.)**

— "I'm going to be a Soldier, Ma." ⟨Ballad.⟩ With chorus for mixed or male quartette. Words and music by J. E. Lakeman. pp. 5. *Oliver Ditson Co.: Boston, London*, [1892.] fol.   **H. 3980. oo. (36.)**

— Imogene. Ballad for Baritone ... words and music by J. E. Lakeman. *O. Ditson Company: Boston, etc.*, 1894. fol.   **H. 1798. u. (5.)**

LAKEMAN (J. ED.)

— The Kind of a Nig I am. ⟨Song, chorus and dance.⟩ Words and music by J. E. Lakeman. pp. 5. *Oliver Ditson Co.: Boston, London*, [1892.] fol.   **H. 3980. oo. (37.)**

— Mazie. Plantation song and chorus ... Words and music by J. E. Lakeman. pp. 5. *Oliver Ditson Co.: Boston, London*, [1895.] fol.   **H. 3980. oo. (38.)**

— My Darling Emeline. Song and dance. ⟨Words and music by J. E. Lakeman.⟩ pp. 5. *Oliver Ditson Co.: Boston, London*, [1895.] fol.   **H. 3980. oo. (39.)**

— My handsome Mary Ann ... [Song.] Words and music by J. E. Lakeman. pp. 5. *Oliver Ditson Co.: Boston, etc.*, [1895.] fol.   **H. 3980. oo. (40.)**

— Susie ... [Song.] Words and music by J. E. Lakeman. pp. 5. *Oliver Ditson Co.: Boston, etc.*, [1895.] fol.   **H. 3980. oo. (41.)**

— The Voyager. Baritone Song with chorus ... for male voices, words and music by J. E. Lakeman. *O. Ditson Company: Boston, etc.*, 1894. fol.   **H. 1798. u. (6.)**

— Waitin' for de Horn to blow. [Song.] Words and music by J. E. Lakeman. pp. 5. *Oliver Ditson Co.: Boston, London*, [1894.] fol.   **H. 3980. oo. (42.)**

— Whang-i-ty-bang. Song and chorus. Words and music by J. E. Lakeman. pp. 5. *Oliver Ditson Co.: Boston, etc.*, [1894.] fol.   **H. 3980. oo. (43.)**

LAKEN (ALAN)

— Christmas Time. [Songs.] Arranged by Alan Laken. ⟨Flute [and P. F.].⟩ [Score and part.] 2 pt. *Chappell & Company: [London,]* 1978. 4°.   **f. 241. j. (1.)**

— Flute Magic. [Songs and dances.] Arranged by Alan Laken. [Flute and P. F. Scores and parts.] 2 no. 4 pt. *Chappell & Company: London*, 1978,79. 4°.   **f. 241. l. (1.)**

LAKES

— The Lakes of Windermere. [Song.] *See* DIBDIN (C.) [Tom Wilkins.]

LAKMÉ

— Lakmé. Opéra. *See* DELIBES (L.)

LAKOPSKI (ANDRO.)

— Danse continental for Piano. *C. Wood: London*, [1901.] fol.   **h. 3282. w. (22.)**

LAKS (SIMON)

— Sonate pour violoncelle et piano. [Score and part.] 2 pt. *Henry Lemoine & cᵈᵉ: Paris, Bruxelles*, [1962.] fol.   **h. 1850. e. (1.)**

LAKSHMAN (LILAVATHI)

— The Call of the East. For the pianoforte. pp. 6. *Lilavathi Lakshman: Jubbulpore; made in England*, [1935.] 4°.   **g. 606. tt. (7.)**

— Humoreske. For the pianoforte. pp. 3. *Lilavathi Lakshman: Jubbulpore; made in England*, [1935.] 4°.   **g. 606. tt. (8.)**

— A Lament. For the pianoforte. pp. 3. *Lilavathi Lakshman: Jubbulpore; made in England*, [1935.] 4°.   **g. 606. tt. (9.)**

LAKSHMĪDĀS ĀDITRĀM VYĀS

— Indian Anthem, "British Taḳhto Tája". Hindi words and music by Lakshmidas Aditram Vyas. *Lakshmidas Aditram Vyas: Ahmedabad*, 1916. *obl.* 8°. **A. 868. o. (1.)**

LAL

— Lal Dinah Grayson. [Song.] *See* MARK (J.) Four North Country Songs ... I.

LALA

— Lala and La. [Part-song.] *See* KENNEDY (John B.)

— La-la! Oo-la-la-la! [Song.] *See* MURPHY (Al. C.)

LALAGE

— Lalage. Song. *See* STEPHENSON (T. W.)

— Lalage. Part-Song. *See* THANE (C.)

LALANDE (MICHEL RICHARD DE)

— Catalogue thématique. *In:* DUFOURCQ (N.) Notes et références pour servir à une histoire de M. R. Delalande, *etc.* pp. 285–356. 1957. 8°. **07903. b. 1/3.**

— Cantate Domino. Motet à 5 voix mixtes pour fin de cérémonie. pp. 4. *Éditions musicales de la Schola Cantorum et de la Procure générale de musique: Paris*, [1957.] 8°. **E. 1439. c. (6.)**

— Cantemus Domino. (Mottet à voix seule.) *In:* GILLES (Jean) Motets à une voix et basse continue, *etc.* pp. 77–84. 1975. 4°. [*Le Pupitre.* 55.] **G. 51.**

— Confitebimur tibi. *See* infra: Motets [Liv. 9].

— De profundis. *See* infra: Motets [Liv. 9].

— Deus in adjutorium. *See* infra: [Motets. Liv. 4.]

— L'Inconnu, premier ballet dansé par sa majesté, dans son palais des Tuilleries, au mois de fevrier 1720. [By M. R. de Lalande. Score.] pp. 56. 1720. 4°. *See* INCONNU. **K. 7. c. 25. (1.)**

— [L'Inconnu.] Forlane ... transcrite par J. B. Wekerlin. [P. F.] *Paris*, [1881.] fol. **h. 3272. j. (5.)**

— Les III Leçons da Ténèbres et la Miserere à voix seule ... Gravé par L. Hue. *Chez Madem^le Hue: Paris*, 1730. fol. **I. 170. a.**

— Lord, have Mercy upon us. *See* infra: [Motets. Liv. 6.—Te Deum laudamus.—Miserere nostri, Domine.]

— Motets de Feu M^r de La Lande ... Avec un discours sur la Vie et les Œuvres de l'Autheur, *etc.* Gravé par L. Hue. I^er(-IXe) (XIe-XVe) (XVIIe-XXe) Livre. 18 vol. *Chez le Sr Boivin: Paris*, 1729. fol. *Imperfect; wanting pp.* 13–16 *of liv.* 7. **I. 170.**

— [Motets. Liv. 3.] Regina cœli. Motet pour soli, chœurs et petit orchestre. Édition réalisé par S. Spycket. [Score.] pp. 23. *Éditions Durand & c^ie: Paris*, [1951.] 4°. *L'Atelier musical. no.* 2. **G. 1277. k. (7.)**

— [Motets. Liv. 4.] Deus in adjutorium. Psaume LXIX pour soli, chœurs à 5 voix, orchestre et orgue. Réalisation d'Alex. Cellier. ⟨Réduction pour chant & piano.⟩ pp. 37. *Éditions Salabert: Paris*, [1958.] fol. **H. 1186. o. (1.)**

— [Motets. Liv. 6.—Te Deum laudamus.—Miserere nostri, Domine.] Lord, have Mercy upon us ... For three-part chorus of mixed voices with organ or piano accompaniment ... Edited and arranged by Robert S. Hines. pp. 6. *G. Schirmer: New York*, [1966.] 8°. **E. 1439. f. (18.)**

LALANDE (MICHEL RICHARD DE)

— [Motets. Liv. 6.—Te Deum laudamus.—Salvum fac.] Save me, O God, by thy Name. ⟨Psalm 54: 1, 2, 7.⟩ For 2-part chorus of female voices with piano ... arranged by Robert S. Hines. pp. 4. *Roberton Publications: Wendover*, [1976.] 8°. *Part of "Treble Clef choral Series".* **E. 460. cc. (12.)**

— Motets [Liv. 9] ... Confitebimur tibi. Psaume LXXIV pour soli, chœur et orchestre. Réalisation d'Alex. Cellier. ⟨Réduction pour chant et piano.⟩ pp. 56. *Rouart Lerolle: Paris*, [1952.] fol. **H. 1186. j. (9.)**

— Motets [Liv. 9] ... De profundis. Psaume CXXX pour soli, chœurs et orchestre. Réalisation d'A. Cellier. ⟨Réduction pour piano et voix.⟩ pp. 50. *Rouart Lerolle: Paris*, [1944.] fol. **H. 1186. j. (10.)**

— Motets [Liv. 17] ... Quare fremuerunt. Psaume II pour soli, chœurs et orchestre. Réalisation d'Alex. Cellier. ⟨Réduction pour chant et piano.⟩ pp. 62. *Rouart Lerolle: Paris*, [1949.] fol. **H. 1186. j. (11.)**

— Noël françois sur les paroles: Or nous ditez, Marie. [P. F.] *In:* Berlinische musikalische Zeitung. p. 192. 1794. 4°. **Hirsch IV. 1133.**

— [Passacaille.] De Chambonnières, Destouches, Duphly, Lalande ... Pièces choisies, *etc.* [P. F.] 1912. *See* DIÉMER (L.) Les Clavecinistes français. 4e volume, *etc.* [1895?–1912.] 4°. **g. 152.**

— Quare fremuerunt. *See* supra: Motets [Liv. 17].

— Regina cœli. *See* supra: [Motets. Liv. 3.]

— Save me, O God, by thy Name. *See* supra: [Motets. Liv. 6.—Te Deum laudamus.—Salvum fac.]

— Sur le bonheur des justes, & sur le malheur des réprouvez. Cantique quatrième. ⟨Les paroles de Mr Racine.⟩ *In:* MOREAU (J. B.) Cantiques chantez devant le roi, *etc.* pp. 38–57. 1728. *obl.* 4°. [*AIRS.* Recueil d'airs spirituels, *etc.*] **K. 7. c. 8.**

— Symphonie des Noëls. Für Melodieinstrumente und Basso continuo. Nach der Handschrift in der Bibliothèque Nationale Paris herausgegeben von Rudolf Ewerhart, *etc.* [Scores and parts.] 3 Hft. 11 pt. *Moeck Verlag: Celle*, [1979.] 4°. **g. 1503. d. (1.)**

— Symphonie des soupers du Roy. Première suite, d'après le manuscrit de la bibliothèque du Conservatoire de Paris. Révision et réalisation de la basse chiffrée par Alexandre Cellier. [Score.] pp. 46. *Éditions du magasin musical Pierre Schneider: Paris*, [1955.] 4°. **g. 860. e. (2.)**

— *See* MOREAU (J. B.) Œuvres de Racine ... Musique ... des Cantiques Spirituels. [The hymn by M. R. de Lalande.] 1873. 8°. **E. 1654.**

LALANDE (MICHEL RICHARD DE) and DESTOUCHES (ANDRÉ CARDINAL)

— Les Élémens, troisième ballet dansé par le Roy, *etc.* [Words by P. C. Roy, music by A. C. Destouches and M. R. de Lalande.] 1725. *obl.* 4°. *See* ÉLÉMENS. **C. 398.**

— Les Éléments. Ballet du Roi en 4 entrées et 1 prologue. Paroles de Roy ... Reconstitué et réduit pour Piano et Chant par V. d'Indy. *Paris*, [1883.] 8°. *One of the "Chefs-d'-œuvre de l'opéra français".* **F. 700. f.**

LA LANDELLE (GUILLAUME JOSEPH GABRIEL DE)

— Le Gaillard d'avant. Chansons maritimes [written and collected] par G. de la Landelle. [Words and melodies only.] *E. Dentu: Paris*, 1862. 12°. **A. 763.**

— Poëmes et Chants marins. [Melodies and words only.] *E. Dentu: Paris*, 1861. 12°. **11481. ccc. 19.**

LALANNE (J. M. DE)

— Air de Noce, rigaudon pour le Piano. *Paris,* [1881.] fol.
h. 3272. j. (6.)

— Ave Maria pour Tenor ou Soprano, Violon, Orgue, Piano ou Harpe. *Paris,* [1879.] fol. **H. 1028. h. (24.)**

— Sois heureuse. Mélodie [begins: "Dieu qui sourit"]. Paroles de V. Hugo. *Paris,* [1863.] fol. **H. 1781. i. (6.)**

LA LAURENCIE (JEAN DE)

— Petit recueil historique et populaire de la chanson royale en France. Préface et notes par J. de La Laurencie. Bois de Jean Chièze. [With the airs.] pp. 156. *Au Pigeonnier: Paris,* 1929. 8°. **Hirsch 1951.**

LA LAURENCIE (LIONEL DE)

— *See* MAIRY (A.) Chansons au Luth et Airs de Cour français du XVIᵉ siècle. Introduction de Lionel de la Laurencie, *etc.* 1934. 4°. [*Publications de la Société Française de Musicologie. Première Série. Tomes* III *et* IV.]
Hirsch IV. **1006.**

L'ALBERT ( )

— *See* ALBERT (L.)

LĀLJÎ

— Lāljî. Song. *See* HAMILTON (D.)

L'ALL**** ( )

— Je le tiens ce nid de fauvette. I. D'ylle de Mʳ Berquin. Musique de Mʳ L'all****. [*Paris,* 1780?] 8°. **B. 362. b. (13.)**

— [Another copy.] **B. 362. e. (111.)**

LALLA

— Lalla Rookh. Cantata. *See* CLAY (F.)

— Lalla Roukh. Opéra-comique. *See* DAVID (F. C.)

— Lalla Rookh. Operette. *See* HORN (C. E.)

— Lalla Rookh. Romanza. *See* MACDONALD (E. J.)

— Lalla Roukh. Lyrische Oper. *See* RUBINSTEIN (A.) Feramors.

— Lalla Rûkh. Festspiel. *See* SPONTINI (L. G. P.)

LALLA

— The Alpine Queen ... Song [begins: "Away to the mountain pass," written] by W. White. Music by Lalla. *London,* [1873.] fol. **H. 1778. x. (6.)**

— Little Toddlekins quadrilles, by Lalla. [P. F.] *London,* [1872.] fol. **h. 1485. s. (10.)**

LAL-LA-PA-LOO-ZER

— Lal-la-pa-loo-zer. [Song.] *See* LIND (W. M.)

LALLEMAN ( )

— Au matin dans les prés de Flore. Chanson. (Les Paroles et la Musique sont de M. Lalleman.) [*Paris,*] 1778. 8°. *Mercure de France, Dec.,* 1778. **297. f. 28.**

LALLEN

— Das Lallen. [Song.] *See* REISSIGER (C. G.) Sechs Gesänge ... 3. Werk. No. 6.

LALLIET (CASIMIR THÉOPHILE)

— Alizia. Mazurka de Salon pour piano. *Richault et Cie.: Paris,* [1886.] fol. **h. 3281. k. (52.)**

— Caprice-Valse pour Hautbois avec accompᵗ. de Piano. Op. 25. *Paris,* [1882.] fol. **h. 2665. (10.)**

— Echo des Bois, fantaisie originale pour Hautbois avec accompt. de Piano, *etc. Paris,* [1869.] fol. **h. 2152. (8.)**

— Fantaisie pour Hautbois avec accompagnement de Piano sur Le Comte Ory de Rossini. *Paris,* [1881.] fol.
h. 3212. e. (13.)

— Fantaisie sur Martha, de Flotow, composée pour le Hautbois avec acct. de Piano. *Paris,* [1876.] fol. **h. 2152. (11.)**

— Lucia di Lammermoor [by D. G. M. Donizetti]. Fantaisie pour Hautbois avec accompt. de Piano ... Op. 18. *E. Gerart et Cie.: Paris,* [1870.] fol. **h. 2152. (10.)**

— Prélude et variations sur le Carnaval de Venise pour le Hautbois avec accompagnement de Piano. *Paris,* [1877.] fol.
h. 3213. o. (6.)

— Souvenir de Berlin. Fantaisie brillante ... pour Hautbois avec accompt. de Piano, *etc. Paris,* [1869.] fol. **h. 2152. (9.)**

— Souvenir de Saint-Gratien. Fantaisie Caprice pour hautbois avec accompᵗ. de piano. Op. 26. *Paris,* [1884.] fol.
h. 2665. (11.)

— *See* HERMAN (J.) Fantaisie d'après T. Lalliet ... pour la Flûte, *etc.* [1868.] fol. **h. 2100. (3.)**

LALLIET (TH.)

— *See* LALLIET (Casimir T.)

LALLOUETTE (JEAN FRANÇOIS)

— Motets à I. II. et III. voix, avec la Basse-Continue ... Livre Premier. *Chez l'Auteur: Paris,* 1726. fol. **I. 514.**

— [Motets à 1, 2, et 3 voix. Liv. 1.] O mysterium ineffabile. [Unison voices and organ.] J. F. Lallouette. Edited by Simon Lindley. (Love divine. [Two-part chorus and organ.] Words: Charles Wesley. [Music by] W. A. Mozart. Originally 'Lasst uns mit geschzungnen [*sic*] Händen'. Arranged by Arthur Hutchings.) pp. 4. *The Royal School of Church Music: Croydon,* [1979.] 8°. **F. 1143. n. (9.)**

— O mysterium ineffabile. *See supra:* [Motets à 1, 2, et 3 voix. Liv. 1.]

LALLY (JIMMY)

— *See* DVOŘÁK (A.) [*Composite Works.*] [Summer Song.] No one told me ... Arranged by J. Lally. [1956.] 8°.
E. 1500. b. (23.)

— *See* GERSHWIN (George) [A Damsel in Distress.] A Foggy Day. Arranged for orchestra by J. Lally, *etc.* [1958.] 8°.
E. 1897. a. (1.)

— *See* GERSHWIN (George) [A Damsel in Distress.] Nice Work if you can get it ... Arranged for orchestra by J. Lally, *etc.* [1954.] 8°. **E. 1897. a. (2.)**

— *See* GERSHWIN (George) [George White's Scandals of 1922.] I'll build a Stairway to Paradise. Arranged for orchestra by J. Lally, *etc.* [1955.] 8°. **E. 1897. a. (3.)**

— *See* GERSHWIN (George) [George White's Scandals of 1924.] Somebody loves me. Arranged [for orchestra] by J. Lally, *etc.* [1950.] 8°. **E. 1897. a. (4.)**

— *See* GERSHWIN (George) [Girl Crazy.] Bidin' my Time ... Arrangement for orchestra by J. Lally, *etc.* [1962.] 8°.
E. 1897. a. (7.)

LALLY (JIMMY)

— *See* GERSHWIN (George) [Girl Crazy.] But not for me.
Arranged for orchestra by J. Lally, *etc.* [1959.] 8°.
E. 1897. a. (8.)

— *See* GERSHWIN (George) [Girl Crazy.] Embraceable you.
Arranged for orchestra by J. Lally, *etc.* [1950.] 8°.
E. 1897. a. (9.)

— *See* GERSHWIN (George) [Girl Crazy.] I got Rhythm.
Arranged for orchestra by J. Lally, *etc.* [1954.] 8°.
E. 1897. a. (6.)

— *See* GERSHWIN (George) [The Goldwyn Follies.] I was doing
all right. Arranged for orchestra by J. Lally, *etc.* [1959.] 8°.
E. 1897. b. (1.)

— *See* GERSHWIN (George) [The Goldwyn Follies.] Love is here
to stay. Arranged for orchestra by J. Lally, *etc.* [1958.] 8°.
E. 1897. b. (2.)

— *See* GERSHWIN (George) [The Goldwyn Follies.] Love walked
in. Arranged for orchestra by J. Lally, *etc.* [1953.] 8°.
E. 1897. b. (3.)

— *See* GERSHWIN (George) [Lady be good.] Fascinating Rhythm.
Arranged [for orchestra] by J. Lally, *etc.* [1950.] 8°.
E. 1897. b. (4.)

— *See* GERSHWIN (George) [Lady be good.] The Man I love.
Arranged [for orchestra] by J. Lally, *etc.* [1950.] 8°.
E. 1897. b. (5.)

— *See* GERSHWIN (George) [Lady be good.] Oh! Lady, be good.
Arranged for orchestra by J. Lally, *etc.* [1953.] 8°.
E. 1897. b. (6.)

— *See* GERSHWIN (George) [Oh, Kay!] Do-do-do. Orchestral
arrangement by J. Lally, *etc.* [1950.] 8°. **E. 1897. b. (7.)**

— *See* GERSHWIN (George) [Oh, Kay!] Someone to watch over
me. Arrangement for orchestra by J. Lally, *etc.* [1952.] 8°.
E. 1897. b. (8.)

— *See* GERSHWIN (George) Please do it again, *etc.* ⟨Arranged for
orchestra by J. Lally.⟩ [1960.] 8°. **h. 3210. j. (167.)**

— *See* GERSHWIN (George) [Shall we dance.] Let's call the whole
Thing off ... Arranged for orchestra by J. Lally, *etc.* [1954.]
8°. **E. 1897. c. (1.)**

— *See* GERSHWIN (George) [Shall we dance.] Shall we dance.
Arranged for orchestra by J. Lally, *etc.* [1956.] 8°.
E. 1897. c. (2.)

— *See* GERSHWIN (George) [Shall we dance.] They all laughed
... Arranged for orchestra by J. Lally, *etc.* [1959.] 8°.
E. 1897. c. (3.)

— *See* GERSHWIN (George) [Shall we dance.] They can't take
that away from me. Arranged for orchestra by J. Lally, *etc.*
[1956.] 8°. **E. 1897. c. (4.)**

— *See* GERSHWIN (George) [Show Girl.] Liza. (All the Clouds'll
roll away.) ... Arrangement for orchestra by J. Lally, *etc.*
[1951.] 8°. **E. 1897. c. (5.)**

— *See* GERSHWIN (George) [Smarty.] 'S wonderful ...
Arrangement for orchestra by J. Lally, *etc.* [1952.] 8°.
E. 1897. c. (6.)

— *See* GERSHWIN (George) [Strike up the Band.] Strike up the
Band ... Arrangement for orchestra by J. Lally, *etc.* [1952.]
8°. **E. 1897. c. (7.)**

— *See* GERSHWIN (George) [Tip-toes.] Looking for a Boy ...
Arranged for orchestra by J. Lally, *etc.* [1959.] 8°.
E. 1897. c. (8.)

— *See* GERSHWIN (George) [Tip-toes.] That certain Feeling ...
Arranged for orchestra by J. Lally, *etc.* [1955.] 8°.
E. 1897. c. (9.)

LALLY (JIMMY)

— *See* GRUBER (F. X.) [Stille Nacht, heilige Nacht.] Silent Night,
holy Night, *etc.* ⟨Arranged by J. Lally.⟩ [1949.] 12°.
B. 512. r. (5.)

— *See* HUGHES (Jimmy) and CORMACK (Charles) In
Baden-bei-Wien. Arranged for orchestra by J. Lally. [1960.]
4°. [*Chappell & Co.'s Orchestral Works.* no. 543.] **f. 424.**

— *See* MONKTON (Lionel) and CARYLL (I.) *pseud.* [A Runaway
Girl.—Soldiers in the Park.] Oh, listen to the Band! ...
Arranged by J. Lally. [P. F., clarinet, trumpet, saxophone,
guitar.] [1962.] 8°. **h. 3210. i. (799.)**

— *See* RODGERS (R.) [Carousel.] You'll never walk alone, *etc.*
⟨Arranged for orchestra by J. Lally.⟩ [1963.] 8°.
h. 3210. i. (871.)

— *See* SCHUBERT (F. P.) [*Collected Works.—h.*] [Das
Dreimäderlhaus.] Lilac Time. Waltz medley of melodies from
the musical play, *etc.* ⟨Arranged for orchestra by J. Lally.⟩
[1956.] 8°. **E. 1500. b. (22.)**

— *See* SULLIVAN (*Sir* Arthur S.) Gilbert and Sullivan Operas.
Waltz medley no. 1 ... Orchestration by J. Lally. [1961.] 8°.
h. 3210. i. (688.)

— *See* SULLIVAN (*Sir* Arthur S.) Gilbert & Sullivan Operas.
Waltz medley no. 2 ... Orchestration arranged by: J. Lally.
[1961.] 8°. **h. 3210. i. (689.)**

— *See* WOOD (Haydn) Roses of Picardy, *etc.* ⟨Arranged for
orchestra by J. Lally.⟩ [1967.] 8°. **h. 3210. j. (93.)**

LALO (ÉDOUARD VICTOR ANTOINE)

— Allegretto. *See infra*: [Divertissement. No. 1.]

— Allegro pour piano et violoncelle ... Op:16. [Score and part.]
2 pt. *J. Maho: Paris,* [c. 1875.] fol. **h. 3959. a. (1.)**

— Allegro appassionato pour orchestre ... Op. 27. Partition, *etc.*
J. Hamelle: Paris; Leipzig [printed, 1880?] 8°. **f. 211. b.**

— Allegro maestoso. Pour piano et violon ... Oeuv: 2. [Score
and part.] 2 pt. *Costallat & c^{ie}: Paris,* [c. 1910.] fol.
h. 3959. a. (2.)

— Au fond des halliers. Duo. Paroles de A. Theuriet.
Choudens: Paris, [1887.] fol. **H. 2836. v. (14.)**

— Aubade. *See infra*: [Le Roi d'Ys.—Vainement, ma bien
aimée.]

— Two Aubades for small Orchestra. *See infra*: [Divertissement.
No. 1, 3.]

— Chanson Villageoise ... Op. 14. No. 1. Édition revue par
R. Ortmans. [Violin and P. F.] *Laudy & Co.: London,* [1912.]
fol. **g. 505. ee. (30.)**

— Chants Russes. *See infra*: [Concerto Russe. Op. 29.]

— Concerto pour piano (et orchestre). Partition d'orchestre, *etc.*
G. Hartmann & Cie: Paris, [1889?] 8°. **f. 211. c.**

— Concerto pour piano ... Partie de piano avec réduction de
l'orchestre pour un 2e piano. [Score.] pp. 49. *G. Hartmann &
c^{ie}: Paris,* [1889?] fol. **h. 4015. y. (1.)**

— Concerto pour violon ... Op. 20. Partition d'orchestre.
Durand, Schœnwerk & Cie: Paris, [c. 1880.] 8°.
The titlepage bears a MS. dedication from the composer.
f. 211. d.

— Concerto pour violon ... avec accompagnement de piano ...
Op. 20. Avec accompagnement de piano par l'auteur. [Score
and part.] 2 pt. *Durand, Schœnewerk & c^{ie}: Paris,* [1874.] fol.
h. 1609. h. (4.)

— Concerto Russe pour le Violon avec accompagnement ... de
Piano. *Mayence,* [1880.] fol. **h. 1729. c. (4.)**

LALO (Édouard Victor Antoine)

— [Concerto Russe. Op. 29.] Chant Russe ... Bearb. von
L. Windsperger. [Parts.] *Schott & Co.: London,* [1924.] 4°.
[*Schott & Co.'s Domesticum Salon Orchestra. No.* 111.]

    g. 1053. a.

— [Concerto Russe. Op. 29.] Chants russes, *etc.* [Violin and P. F.]
See Kross (E.) Sammlung characteristischer Stellen aus
Violin-Concerten, *etc.* No. 3. [1890.] fol.   **h. 1732. (3.)**

— [Concerto Russe. Op. 29.] Chants Russes, Lento du Concerto
... Op. 29, transcrit pour violoncelle avec accomp. de piano
par l'auteur. *Mayence,* [1886.] fol.   **h. 1847. f. (29.)**

— [Concerto Russe. Op. 29.] Chants russes ... Violoncello part
revised by Herbert Withers. [Violoncello and P. F. Score and
part.] 2 pt. *Schott & Co.: London,* [1971.] 4°.
[*Schott Cello Series. no.* 23.]   **g. 112. m.**

— Concerto en ré pour violoncelle avec accompagnement
d'orchestre: Partition d'orchestre, *etc.* pp. 153. *Ed. Bote &
G. Bock: Berlin & Posen,* [1879.] 8°.   **f. 211. a.**

— Concerto en ré pour violoncelle avec accompagnement
d'orchestre ... Arrangement pour violoncelle et piano, *etc.*
[Score and part.] 2 pt. *Ed. Bote & G. Bock: Berlin,* [c. 1900.]
fol.   **h. 3959. b. (3.)**

— Concerto en ré pour violoncelle avec accompagnement
d'orchestre. Révision par L. Fournier. Transcription pour
violoncelle et piano. [Score and part.] 2 pt. *A. Durand & fils:
Paris,* [1923.] 4°.   **h. 4090. x. (1.)**

— Concerto in D for violoncello & piano. Revised & edited by
Arnold Trowell. *Augener: London,* 1924. 4°.

    g. 510. i. (32.)

— Concerto in D minor. For violoncello and piano. Edited by
Otto Deri. [Score and part.] 2 pt. *G. Schirmer: New York,*
[1970.] 4°.
Schirmer's Library of musical Classics. vol. 1870.

    g. 512. i. (8.)

— Divertissement pour orchestre ... Partition, *etc.* pp. 92.
Ed. Bote & G. Bock: Berlin, Posen, [c. 1880.] 8°.

    f. 641. r. (3.)

— Divertissement pour orchestre ... Réduction pour piano seul
par J. Massenet. pp. 23. *G. Hartmann: Paris,* [c. 1875.] fol.

    h. 3959. b. (1.)

— [Divertissement. No. 1, 3.] Aubade pour dix instruments ou
petit orchestre. N°. 1. Allegretto. ⟨N°. 2. Andantino.⟩ [Score.]
pp. 24. *Heugel et cⁱᵉ: Paris,* [1872?] 8°.   **f. 390. nn. (5.)**

— [Divertissement. No. 1, 3.] Two Aubades for Small Orchestra.
Full Score. *Hawkes & Son: London,* 1942. 4°.

    g. 727. o. (1.)

— [Divertissement. No. 1.] Allegretto ... Arranged for two
pianos by R. Sterndale Bennett. pp. 12. *Augener: London,*
[1951.] 4°.   **g. 1122. n. (5.)**

— L'Esclave. *See* infra: Trois Mélodies ... No. 2.

— Fantaisie-ballet pour violon & orchestre. Édition pour violon
et piano, *etc.* [Based on themes from "Namouna". Score and
part.] 2 pt. *J. Hamelle: Paris,* [c. 1900.] fol. **h. 3959. b. (2.)**

— Fantaisie norwégienne pour violon-solo et orchestre ...
Violon et piano. [Score and part.] 2 pt. *Ed. Bote & G. Bock:
Berlin & Posen,* [1879.] fol.   **h. 1609. m. (1.)**

— Fantaisie originale. Pour le violon [and P. F.] ... Oeuv: 1.
[Score and part.] 2 pt. *Costallat & cⁱᵉ: Paris,* [c. 1910.] fol.

    h. 3959. a. (3.)

— Fiesque. Grand opéra en trois actes imité de Schiller par
Ch. Beauquier. [Vocal score.] pp. 264. *Durand, Schoenewerk
& cⁱᵉ: Paris,* [c. 1875.] 8°.   **F. 798. d.**

LALO (Édouard Victor Antoine)

— Fiesque. Grand Opéra en trois actes, imité de Schiller par
C. Beauquier, *etc. Hartmann: Paris,* c. 1875. 8°.   **F. 798. c.**

— [Fiesque.] Ouverture de Fiesque ... Partition d'orchestre, *etc.*
pp. 25. *Durand, Schœnwerk & cⁱᵉ: Paris,* [c. 1875.] 8°.
*The titlepage bears a MS. dedication in the composer's
autograph.*   **f. 641. c.**

— Guitare. Pour violon et piano ... Op. 28. [Parts.] 2 pt.
J. Hamelle: Paris, [1885?] fol.   **h. 1613. h. (7.)**

— 2 impromptus pour le violon avec accompagnement de
piano. Opéra 4. ⟨N° 1. Espérance. N° 2. Insouciance.⟩ [Score.]
pp. 11. *Lemoine et fils: Paris, Bruxelles,* [c. 1890.] fol.

    h. 3959. a. (4.)

— In olden Spain. *See* infra: [Le Roi d'Ys.—Vainement, ma
bien aimée.

— Cinq Lieder à une voix avec accompagnement de piano.
N° 1. Prière de l'enfant à son reviel (Lamartine.) (Des Kindes
Morgengebet.) N° 2. A celle qui part. (Armand Silvestre.) (An
die Geschiedene.) N° 3. Tristesse. (Armand Silvestre.)
(Traurigkeit.) N° 4. Viens! (Lamartine.) (Komm!) N° 5. La
Chanson de l'alouette. (V. de Laprade.) (Das Lied der
Lerche.) Fr. & Ger. pp. 21. *Les fils de B. Schott: Mayence,*
[1880.] fol.   **H. 1786. e. (6.)**

— [Cinq Lieder. No. 1.] Prière de l'enfant à son réveil. (Des
Kindes Morgengebet.) Lamartine. Pour 4 voix de femmes
avec acc. de piano ... Deutscher text von Dʳ G. Fr. Reiss.
[Score and parts.] *Fr. & Ger.* 5 pt. *Schott & Co.: Londres;
printed in Germany,* [1880.] 8°.   **F. 217. m. (12.)**

— [Cinq Lieder. No. 1.] Prière de l'enfant à son réveil. Prayer of
the awakening Child ... ⟨Arr. par Francis Salabert.⟩ Piano-
conducteur [and 1° violini-conducteur, violoncello,
contrabasso parts], *etc. Editions Francis Salabert: Paris,*
[1928.] 8°.   **h. 3210. i. (148.)**

— Mélodies pour Chant et Piano. *J. Hamelle: Paris,* [1890?] 8°.

    F. 798. b.

— 6 mélodies avec accompagnement de piano, poésies de Victor
Hugo ... (Op. 17). pp. 23. *J. Maho: Paris,* [1856.] fol.

    H. 2004. c. (6.)

— Trois mélodies pour voix de contralto sur des poésies
d'Alfred de Musset. ⟨[1.] A une fleur. [2.] Chanson de
Barberine. [3.] La Zuecca.⟩ pp. 11. *G. Hartmann: Paris,*
[1870?] 8°.   **E. 270. dd. (3.)**

— Trois Mélodies pour piano et chant. No. 1. La Fenaison.
No. 2 et 3. L'Esclave (poésie de T. Gautier). Souvenir (poésie
de V. Hugo). 2 no. *G. Hartmann et Cie: Paris,* [1887.] fol.
Imperfect; wanting no. 1.   **H. 2836. v. (15.)**

— [Trois Mélodies. No. 2.] L'Esclave.—The Captive, *etc.*
[English version by J. D. W.] 1912. *See* Thurwanger (C.)
Thurwanger's Phonetically annotated Songs ... Series B.
No. 7. (1911, *etc.*) fol.   **H. 3858.**

— Namouna. Ballet en 2 actes et 3 tableaux de M. M. Ch.
Nuitter et Petipa ... Partition pour piano. pp. 122.
J. Hamelle: Paris; Leipsic [printed, c. 1885.] 8°.   **f. 211. f.**

— Namouna. Suite d'orchestre extraite du ballet en deux actes
... No. 1. Prélude. 2. Sérénade. 3. Thème varié. 4 a. Parades de
foire. b. Fête foraine ... Partition. *J. Hamelle: Paris,* [1885?]
fol.   **h. 3959.**

— Namouna. Valse de la cigarette. ⟨Pour orchestre. Partition.⟩
pp. 43. *J. Hamelle: Paris,* [c. 1910.] 8°.   **f. 641. r. (4.)**

— Namouna. Ballet en deux actes et trois tableaux de MM.
C. Nuitter et Petipa ... Valse lente. [P. F.] *[Paris,]* 1908. 8°.
Supplement to "L'Illustration," No. 3399.   **P. P. 4283. m. (3.)**

— [Namouna.] *See* supra: Fantaisie-ballet pour violon &
orchestre, *etc.* [Based on themes from "Namouna".] [c. 1900.]
fol.   **h. 3959. b. (2.)**

LALO (Édouard Victor Antoine)

— Pastorale et scherzo alla Pulcinella, piano et violon. ⟨Oeuvre 8.⟩ [Score and part.] 2 pt. *Costallat & c^{ie}: Paris,* [c. 1910.] fol.   **h. 3959. a. (5.)**

— Pastorale ... Op. 8. Édition revue par J. H. Henry. [Violin and P. F.] *Laudy & Co.: London,* [1912.] fol.   **g. 505. ee. (29.)**

— Prière de l'enfant à son réveil. *See* supra: [Cinq Lieder. No. 1.]

— Quartett. Es dur. Op. 19. [Strings. Parts.] 4 pt. *Breitkopf & Härtel: Leipzig, etc.,* [c. 1900, 1859?] fol.
The second violin part is of an earlier issue.   **h. 3959. c.**

— Rapsodie pour Orchestre. Partition. *Berlin & Posen,* [1880.] 8°.   **f. 245. e. (10.)**

Le Roi d'Ys

— Le Roi d'Ys. Opéra en trois actes. Poème de Edouard Blau. [Score.] pp. 428. [*Heugel et cie.: Paris,* c. 1900.] fol.
                                                                H. 1881. b.

— Le Roi d'Ys. Légende bretonne. Opéra en 3 actes & 5 tableaux. Poème de Édouard Blau ... Partition pour chant & piano. pp. 230. *G. Hartmann & c^{ie}: Paris,* [1888.] 8°.
                                                                F. 798. e.

— Le Roi d'Ys. Légende Bretonne. Opéra en 3 actes & 5 tableaux. Poème de E. Blau. Partition pour chant & piano. pp. 231. *G. Hartmann & Cie: Paris,* [1888.] 8°.   **F. 798.**

— [Another issue.] Le Roi d'Ys. Légende Bretonne. Opéra en 3 actes et 5 tableaux, poème de Édouard Blau ... Partition pour Chant & Piano. pp. 231. *G. Hartmann et Cie.: Paris,* [1888.] 8°.   **R. M. 9. d. 15.**

— Ouverture to the Bretonic legend Le Roi d'Ys ... Revised and with foreword by Maurice Cauchie, *etc.* [Score.] pp. iv. 66. *Ernst Eulenburg: London,* [1949.] 8°. [*Edition Eulenburg. no.* 1104.]   **b. 212.**

— Le Roi d'Ys. (The King of Ys.) Overture ... Arranged by Frank Wright. [Brass band.] ⟨Full score.⟩ pp. 39. *W. Paxton & Co.: London,* [1959.] obl. 8°.   **b. 285. (1.)**

— "Le Roi d'Ys". ⟨Overture⟩ ... Arranged for military band by Dan Godfrey. ⟨Conductor [and parts].⟩ 32 pt. *Chappell & Co: London,* [1964?] fol. [*Chappell's Army Journal. no.* 351.]   **h. 1562.**

— [Vainement, ma bien aimée.] In olden Spain. Aubade. [Song.] English words by Clarence Lucas. pp. 5. *Edwin Ashdown: London,* [1947.] 4°.   **F. 607. xx. (29.)**

— [Vainement, ma bien aimée.] Le Roi d'Ys. Aubade. [Aria.] French words by Edouard Blau, English words by Arthur Davenport. *Eng. & Fr.* pp. 5. *United Music Publishers: London,* [1951.] 4°.   **G. 1276. g. (19.)**

— [Vainement, ma bien aimée.] Aubade ... Words by Clarence Lucas. pp. 5. *Edwin Ashdown: London,* [1950.] 8°. [*Ashdown vocal Duets. no.* 246.]   **E. 1601.**

— *See* OUDSHOORN (Antoine) Souvenir du Roi d'Ys ... Trancription pour violoncelle avec accompag^t de piano par A. Oudshoorn. [c. 1890.] fol.   **h. 4090. s. (7.)**

— Romance-Sérénade pour Violon Solo et Orchestre. Partition. *Berlin & Posen,* [1880.] 8°.   **f. 245. e. (9.)**

— 6 romances populaires de P. J. de Béranger. N° 1. La pauvre femme. N° 2. Beaucoup d'amour. N° 3. Le suicide. N° 4. Si j'étais petit oiseau. N° 5. Les petits coups. N° 6. Le vieux vagabond. *Chez Mme Vve Launer: Paris,* [c. 1850.] fol.
                                                                H. 1881. a.

— Le Rouge-Gorge. Poésie d'A. Theuriet. *G. Hartmann & Cie.: Paris,* [1887.] fol.   **H. 2836. v. (16.)**

LALO (Édouard Victor Antoine)

— Scherzo pour Orchestre. Partition. *Paris,* [1885.] 8°.
                                                                e. 666. e. (8.)

— Sérénade ... Op. 14. No. 2. Édition revue par R. Ortmans. [Violin and P. F.] *Laudy & Co.: London,* [1912.] fol.
                                                                g. 505. ee. (31.)

— Sonate pour piano & violon ... Op: 12. [Score and part.] 2 pt. *Durand, Schœnewerk & c^{ie}: Paris,* [1874.] fol.   **h. 1728. d. (2.)**

— Sonate pour piano & violoncelle, *etc.* [Score and part.] 2 pt. *Heugel & c^{ie}: Paris,* [c. 1880.] fol.   **h. 3959. d. (2.)**

— Sonate pour piano et violoncelle. [Score and part.] 2 pt. [*G. Hartmann: Paris,* c. 1885.] fol.   **h. 3959. a. (7.)**
                                                         & h. 3959. d. (1.)

— Souvenir. *See* supra: Trois Mélodies ... No. 3.

— Symphonie en sol mineur ... Partition d'orchestre. *G. Hartmann: Paris,* [1887?] 8°.   **f. 211. e.**

— Symphonie en sol mineur. Réduction pour piano à quatre mains par X. Leroux. *G. Hartmann: Paris,* [1887.] fol.
                                                                h. 3290. h. (17.)

— Symphonie espagnole pour violon principal & orchestre ... Op. 21 ... Partition d'orchestre, *etc.* pp. 145. *Durand, Schœnewerk & cie: Paris,* [1876.] 8°.   **f. 211.**

— [A reissue.] Symphonie espagnole pour violon principal & orchestre ... Op. 21 ... Partition d'orchestre, *etc. Durand & Schœnewerk: Paris,* [1880?] 8°.   **Hirsch M. 209.**

— [Symphonie espagnole. Op. 21.] Romantic and modern Violin Concertos. (Brahms ... Lalo, *etc.*) Edited ... by A. E. Wier. [Score.] *Longmans, Green and Co.: New York,* 1940. 4°. [*Longmans Miniature Arrow Score Series. Vol.* 10.]   **g. 1075.**

— Symphonie espagnole, D minor, for Violin with Orchestra ... Op. 21, *etc.* [Score.] pp. 160. *Ernst Eulenburg: London,* [1950.] 8°. [*Edition Eulenburg. no.* 728.]   **b. 212.**

— Symphonie espagnole pour violon principal & orchestre ... Op: 21. Partition piano et violon. [Score and part.] 2 pt. *Durand, Schœnewerk & c^{ie}: Paris,* [1875.] fol.   **h. 1609. h. (5.)**

— Symphonie espagnole pour violon et orchestre ... Op. 21. Violon et piano, *etc.* ⟨Nouvelle édition.⟩ [Score.] pp. 49. *A. Durand & fils: Paris,* [1908.] fol.   **h. 1613. o. (8.)**

— Symphonie espagnole. For violin and piano. Edited by Leopold Lichtenberg. [Parts.] 2 pt. *Chappell & Co.: London,* [1950.] 4°.
Schirmer's Library of musical Classics. vol. 1236.
                                                                g. 500. w. (4.)

— Symphonie espagnol [sic]. Op. 21 ... Adapted and arranged for piano solo by Albert Marland. pp. 15. *Chappell & Co.: London,* [1948.] 8°.   **f. 133. oo. (3.)**

— Trio en ut mineur (op. 7) pour piano, violon et violoncelle. [Score and parts.] 3 pt. *Costallat & c^{ie}: Paris,* [c. 1910.] fol.
                                                                h. 3959. a. (8.)

— 2^e trio (si mineur) pour piano, violon et violoncelle. [Score and parts.] 3 pt. *J. Hamelle: Paris,* [1900?] fol.
                                                                h. 2784. q. (6.)

— 3e. Trio (en La mineur) pour Piano, Violon et Violoncelle. *Paris,* [1880.] fol.   **h. 2850. c. (11.)**

— *See* WEHLE (C.) and LALO (É. V. A.) Soirées parisiennes, *etc.* [c. 1860.] fol.   **h. 1612. qq. (5.)**

LALO (ÉDOUARD VICTOR ANTOINE) and COQUARD (ARTHUR)

— La Jacquerie. [Opera. Score.] pp. 367. [*Choudens fils: Paris*, 1894?] fol.
Without titlepage. **H. 1881.**

— La Jacquerie. Opéra en quatre actes de E. Blau et S. Arnaud ... Partition chant et piano. *Choudens Fils: Paris*, 1894. 8°.
F. 798. a.

— La Jacquerie ... Chant de "Jacques Bonhomme". [*Paris*,] 1895. 8°.
Supplement to "L'Illustration," No. 2717. **P. P. 4283. m. (3.)**

LALOUX (FERNAND)

— The Buckle. Unison Song, poem by Walter de la Mare, *etc.*
J. Curwen & Sons: London, 1930. 8°.
[*Choruses for equal voices. No.* 1789.] **E. 861.**

— Three Cameos. Piano duets ... I. Morning Song. II. Lazy
Afternoon. III. Revel. pp. 11. *Cecilian Press: London*, [1936.]
4°. **g. 606. tt. (10.)**

— Joseph, mild and noble. [Christmas carol.] Words by Shamus
O'Sheel. pp. 11. *Cecilian Press:* [*London*, 1940.] 8°.
F. 260. e. (5.)

— Lent Graduals and Tracts. With refrains for the congregation.
Arranged for choir in unison or harmony with organ ad lib
... [by] F. Laloux ... Timothy Baxter ... Laurence Bévenot.
pp. 14. *St. Martins Publications: Croydon*, [1970.] 8°.
[*Parish Choir Book. no.* 32.] **D. 835. bb.**

— Mass in E. In honour of Our Lady of Lourdes. pp. 28.
[*London?* 1931?] 4°. **G. 519. bb. (2.)**

— Mass in Honour of Saint Ignatius, *etc.* pp. 15. *Cary & Co.:*
London, [1953.] 8°.
Cary Edition. 898. **F. 1175. u. (9.)**

— Missa in gratiarum actione ... 8 part choir and organ, *etc.*
pp. 24. *St. Martins Publications: London*, [1961.] 4°.
F. 274. gg. (3.)

— Two national Songs. (S.A.T.B. unaccompanied.) Arranged by
F. Laloux. 1. The Robin's last Will. ⟨2. The Campbells are
comin'.⟩ pp. 20. *Boosey & Hawkes:* [*London*, 1971.] 8°.
F. 1874. b. (8.)

— Trois Pièces pour Grand Orgue. 1. Canzonetta. 2. Allegro.
3. Finale in G. 3 no. *Laudy & Co.: London*, 1924. fol.
h. 2732. n. (20.)

— Proper of the Mass for a Sovereign Pontiff. Set to psalm tone
3a and fauxbourdon by F. Laloux, *etc.* [S.A.T.B.] pp. 4.
St. Martins Publications: London, [1962.] 8°. **F. 274. jj. (2.)**

— Proper of the Mass for the Nativity of St. John the Baptist,
etc. [S.A.T.B.] pp. 4. *St. Martins Publications: London*, [1962.]
8°. **F. 274. jj. (3.)**

— This joyful Eastertide. [Carol.] Arranged for S.A.B. (or S.A.)
by F. Laloux. pp. 3. *St. Martins Publications: London*, [1965.]
8°. **B. 512. u. (12.)**

— Toccatina. For pianoforte. pp. 6. *Cecilian Press: London*,
[1938.] 4°. **g. 606. tt. (11.)**

— Trio in D, for Piano, Violin and Violoncello. [P. F. score and
parts.] *J. Curwen & Sons: London*, 1929. 4°. **g. 409. q. (5.)**

— *See* VIADANA (L.) [100 concerti ecclesiastici. Op. 12. Falsi
bordoni.—Terzo tuono.] Proper of the Mass ⟨4th Sunday in
Lent⟩ set to psalm tone 3a and fauxbourdon by Viadana
arranged by F. Laloux, *etc.* [1961.] 8°. **F. 1183. k. (2.)**

LALOUX (FERNAND) and TAMBLYN (WILLIAM)

— Graduals and Alleluias. Sundays after Pentecost. With
refrains for the congregation. Arranged for choir in unison or
harmony with organ ad lib. [by] F. Laloux [and] W. Tamblyn.
pp. 20. *St. Martins Publications: Croydon*, [1969.] 8°.
[*Parish Choir Book. no.* 62.] **D. 835. bb.**

LALOY (LOUIS)

— La Musique chinoise ... Étude critique, illustrée de douze
reproductions hors texte. ⟨Mélodies notées.⟩ pp. 126. *Henri
Laurens: Paris*, [1910.] 8°.
Part of "Les Musiciens célèbres". **7894. ss. 1/21.**

— [Another copy.] **Hirsch 1125.**

— *See* MUSORGSKY (M. P.) [*Collections, Vocal.*] Années de
jeunesse ... Revision ... et version française de L. Laloy.
[1923.] fol. **H. 3659. g.**

LALU

— Lalu, ma lubly Queen. Song. *See* MYDDLETON (William H.)

LALULABY

— Lalulaby. Christmas carol. *See* SABESTON (May)

LAM (BASIL)

— *See* DOWLAND (John) The Collected Lute Music of John
Dowland. Transcribed and edited by D. Poulton and B. Lam.
1974. fol. **g. 942. a.**

— *See* DOWLAND (John) The Collected Lute Music of John
Dowland. Transcribed and edited by D. Poulton and B. Lam.
1978. fol. **g. 942. b.**

— *See* HAENDEL (Georg F.) [9 Sonatas or Trios. H. G. Op. 2.
No. 1, 2, 4–7.] Trio Sonatas ... Edited by B. Lam. [1978.] 8°.
[*Edition Eulenburg. no.* 1364, 1365.] **b. 212.**

— *See* HAENDEL (Georg F.) [9 Sonatas or Trios. H. G. Op. 2.
No. 3, 8, 9.] Dresden Trio Sonatas ... Edited by B. Lam.
[1978.] 8°. [*Edition Eulenburg. no.* 1366.] **b. 212.**

LAMAL (PROSPER)

— *See* WULF (Charles de) Blue Mountain's [*sic*] ... Editor:
P. Lamal. [P. F.] [1879?] fol. **g. 1529. d. (17.)**

LA MANCHA (D.)

— Oh! my love he is a saileur boy ... Serio-comic song.
London, [1874.] fol.
No. 2382 *of the "Musical Bouquet".* **H. 2345.**

LA MANIERE (EXUPÈRE DE)

— Vᵐᵉ recueil d'airs variés pour la harpe, *etc.* pp. 18. *Chez
Cousineau père et fils: Paris*, [c. 1785.] fol. **h. 2605. y. (2.)**

— VI receuil [*sic*] d'airs variés pour la harpe, *etc.* pp. 27. *Chez
Cousineau père et fils: Paris*, [c. 1795.] fol. **h. 2605. z. (1.)**

— *See* PERIODICAL PUBLICATIONS.— *Paris.* Abonnement de harpe,
ou Recueil périodique, composé d'ouvertures, pots pourris ...
par les Sieurs Krumpholtz, La Maniere, *etc.* [1790.] fol.
h. 2605. dd.

L'AMANT (CHARLES)

— The Leetle Spanish Man. Humorous ballad [begins: "It was a
leetle Spanish man"] written by F. Desprez. *London*, [1880.]
fol. **H. 1783. o. (2.)**

LAMAR (C.)

— I adore thee. [Song.] Words by E. Oxenford. *M. Witmark & Sons: New York, etc.*, 1900. fol. **H. 1799. g. (61.)**

— My Sweetheart's Face. Song. *O. Ditson Company: Boston, etc.*, 1896. fol. **H. 1798. u. (7.)**

— Remember, oh, Beloved! Song, words by O. Meredith. *O. Ditson Company: Boston, etc.*, 1895. fol. **H. 1798. u. (8.)**

— Les Sauterelles. Polka. [P. F.] *Phillips & Page: London*, [1895.] fol. **h. 3286. g. (2.)**

— There must be something wrong about my Face. [Song.] Words by Fred Egerton. pp. 5. *M. Witmark & Sons: New York, Chicago*, [1900.] fol. **H. 3985. g. (7.)**

— Wondering Willie, *etc*. [Song.] pp. 5. *Jefferys: London*, [1898.] fol. **H. 3980. oo. (44.)**

LAMAR (LOUIS)

— Loving Hearts. Waltzes. [P. F.] *A. Hammond & Co.: London*, [1883.] fol. **h. 975. u. (20.)**

— Marche des Pages pour Piano. *London*, [1880.] fol. **h. 1494. p. (7.)**

LAMARA (FRANÇOIS) *pseud.* [i.e. CHARLES ARTHUR RAWLINGS.]

— Danse Bohémienne. *See* infra: [Six European Dances. No. 5.]

— Danse Espagnole. *See* infra: [Six European Dances. No. 1.]

Six European Dances

— [No. 1.] Danse Espagnole, *etc*. [P. F.] *C. Wood: London*, (1901.) fol. **h. 3283. p. (1.)**

— [No. 2.] Polish Dance, *etc*. [P. F.] *C. Wood: London*, (1901.) fol. **h. 3283. p. (2.)**

— [No. 3.] Valse Parisienne—Jour de Fête, *etc*. [P. F.] *C. Wood: London*, (1901.) fol. **h. 3283. p. (3.)**

— [No. 4.] La Fête Vénitienne ... for Pianoforte. *Leonard & Co.: London*, [1903.] fol. **h. 3283. p. (4.)**

— [No. 5.] Danse Bohémienne ... for Pianoforte. *Leonard & Co.: London*, [1903.] fol. **h. 3283. p. (5.)**

— [No. 6.] Russian Rustic Dance ... for Pianoforte. *Leonard & Co.: London*, [1903.] fol. **h. 3283. p. (6.)**

— La Fête Vénitienne. *See* supra: [Six European Dances. No. 4.]

— Polish Dance. *See* supra: [Six European Dances. No. 2.]

— Russian Rustic Dance. *See* supra: [Six European Dances. No. 6.]

— Valse Parisienne. *See* supra: [Six European Dances. No. 3.]

LAMARE (JACQUES MICHEL)

— Concerto de violoncelle avec accomp^t de piano. ⟨Premier concerto.⟩ De J. M. Lamare, et attribué à Auber ... La partie de piano ... arrangée par Mr Babaud [or rather, Rabaud]. [Parts.] 2 pt. *Richault et c^{ie}: Paris*, [1881.] fol. **h. 1849. k. (10.)**

— Deux concertos de violoncelle avec accomp^t de piano. ⟨Deuxième concerto.⟩ De J. M. Lamare et attribués à Auber ... La partie de violoncelle ... revue, et la partie de piano ... arrangée par Mr Rabaud. [Score and part.] 2 pt. *Richault et c^{ie}: Paris*, [c. 1900.] fol. *Imperfect; wanting no.* 1. **h. 1851. n. (4.)**

LAMARQUE (   )

— Burgundy pas redoublé. [Brass band parts.] *London*, [1877.] 8°. **f. 413. b. (28.)**

LAMARQUÉ (HENRI)

— Quatre Morceaux de Salon pour Piano. 1. Chant d'Amour. 2. Doux Souvenir. 3. Danse des Nymphes. 4. Menuet. *A. Hammond & Co.: London*, [1911.] 4°. The Academic Edition, No. 461. **g. 1130. t. (2.)**

— Aquilla. Pianoforte Solo. *W. H. Broome: London*, 1907. fol. **h. 3283. p. (7.)**

— Chant joyeux, for the Pianoforte. *Collard Moutrie: London*, 1910. fol. **h. 3283. jj. (27.)**

— A Child's Evening Hymn. Words by H. I. Brandon. *A. E. Parcell: Hull*, [1914.] *s. sh.* 8°. **C. 549. e. (20.)**

— Children of Jerusalem. [Hymn.] Words by H. I. Brandon. *A. E. Parcell: Hull*, [1914.] *s. sh.* 8°. **C. 549. e. (22.)**

— The Children's King. March Hymn, words by H. J. Brandon, *etc*. *A. E. Parcell: Hull*, [1914.] *s. sh.* 8°. **C. 549. e. (21.)**

— Country Life. Three Pieces. 1st (2nd) Set. [P. F.] (1912.) *See* DUNHILL (T. F.) and VOLK (W. A.) Recreative Pieces, *etc.* Series I. No. 5b, 5c. (1912, *etc.*) fol. **h. 2912. a.**

— Danse des Nymphes, pour Piano. *A. Hammond & Co.: London*, [1906.] fol. **g. 605. vv. (28.)**

— Danse des Spectres et des Fées, pour Piano. *M. Allan: Glasgow*, [1910.] fol. **h. 3283. jj. (28.)**

— Danse fantastique. [P. F.] *Orpheus Publishing Co.: London*, (1903.) fol. The Academy Collection of semi-classical works, no. 2. **h. 3283. y. (37.)**

— A Day at the Seaside. A set of 8 descriptive Pieces. [P. F.] *See* LITTLE. Little Pieces for little Pupils, *etc.* No. 5. [1910.] 4°. **g. 1130. t. (9.)**

— A Day in a Child's Life. Eight easy and descriptive Pieces for little hands, *etc*. [P. F.] *Ascherberg, Hopwood & Crew: London*, [1908.] fol. **h. 3283. p. (8.)**

— [A Day in a Child's Life. No. 6, 7.] Valsette and Fairy Tale. [P. F.] (1913.) *See* DUNHILL (T. F.) and VOLK (W. A.) Recreative Pieces, *etc.* Series II. No. 8a. (1912, *etc.*) fol. **h. 2912. a.**

— [A Day in a Child's Life. No. 8.] Good Night. [P. F.] (1913.) *See* DUNHILL (T. F.) and VOLK (W. A.) Recreative Pieces, *etc.* Series II. No. 11d. (1912, *etc.*) fol. **h. 2912. a.**

— Doux Souvenir, pour Piano. *A. Hammond & Co.: London*, [1902.] fol. **g. 605. ee. (27.)**

— Esquisse, pour Piano. *M. Allan: Glasgow*, [1910.] fol. **h. 3283. jj. (29.)**

— A Garland of Flowers. 10 easy Pieces for small hands. 1. Chrysanthemums. 2. Narcissus. 3. Poppies. 4. Buttercups & Daisies. 5. Hawthorn. 6. Roses. 7. Hollyhocks. 8. Forget-me-not. 9. Lilac. 10. Mignonette. [P. F.] *A. Hammond & Co.: London*, [1907.] 4°. The Academic Edition, No. 367. **g. 1130. r. (3.)**

— God's Gift. Sacred Song, words by K. M. Luck. *R. Maynard: London*, [1912.] fol. **H. 1187. rr. (1.)**

— Good Night. *See* supra: [A Day in a Child's Life. No. 8.]

— Just you. Song, words by E. Houlston. *Weekes & Co.: London*, 1917. fol. **H. 1846. x. (7.)**

— A Light upon the Shore. Sacred Song, words by ... H. Burton, *etc*. *R. Culley: London*, [1910.] fol. **H. 1187. rr. (2.)**

LAMARQUÉ (HENRI)

— Two Little Dances. [P. F.] (1912.) *See* DUNHILL (T. F.) and
VOLK (W. A.) Recreative Pieces, *etc.* Series I. No. 4c. (1912,
etc.) fol.   **h. 2912. a.**

— Love divine. Sacred song. Words by Katie M. Luck. pp. 4.
R. Maynard: London, [c. 1915.] fol.   **H. 1860. gg. (23.)**

— Love's golden Chain. Song for Mezzo-Soprano, words by
H. J. Brandon. *Richards & Co.: London*, (1912.) fol.
                                                 H. 1792. r. (5.)

— March on! ye deathless Heroes. Choral March, words by
H. J. Brandon, *etc. A. E. Parcell: Hull*, [1914.] 8°.
                                                 C. 549. e. (23.)

— Mélodie Lyrique, pour Piano. *Agate & Co.: London*, [1911.]
fol.   **h. 3284. f. (19.)**

— Menuetto, pour Piano. *A. Hammond & Co.: London*, [1906.]
fol.   **g. 605. vv. (29.)**

— Nuit d'Été. Souvenir pour Piano. *Lenoard & Co.: London*,
[1905.] fol.   **g. 605. ll. (13.)**

— O give Thanks. Anthem, *etc.* [1913.] *See* WOOD AND SONS.
Wood's Collection of Glees, *etc.* No. 287. [1896, *etc.*] 8°.
                                                       E. 1689.

— Once a Child. [Hymn.] Words by H. J. Brandon, *etc. A. E.
Parcell: Hull*, [1914.] *s. sh.* 8°.   **C. 549. e. (24.)**

— "Only To-day." [Sacred song.] Words by ... H. Burton.
R. Culley: London, [1908.] fol.   **H. 1187. ll. (1.)**

— The Pageant. A Morris Dance. [P. F.] *W. H. Broome:
London*, 1907. fol.   **h. 3283. p. (9.)**

— "Parting." Sacred Song for Mezzo-Soprano, words by ...
H. Burton. With Tonic Sol-fa. *Blackburn & Co.: Leeds*,
[1912.] fol.   **H. 1187. rr. (3.)**

— Pensée Lyrique, for the Pianoforte, *etc. Chase Music Co.:
London*, 1913. fol.   **h. 3284. f. (20.)**

— Pensée lyrique ... Arranged for the organ by F. W. Pacey.
Chase Music Co.: London, 1914. obl. fol.   **f. 314. gg. (16.)**

— Petite Valse, pour Piano. *A. Hammond & Co.: London*,
[1906.] fol.   **g. 605. vv. (30.)**

— Trois Petits Morceaux. (Three Little Sketches.) [P. F.]
Orpheus Music Publishing Co.: London, 1909. 4°.
The Guildhall Edition, No. 24.   **g. 1440.**

— Praise the Lord! ye Heav'ns adore Him. Anthem, *etc. Angus,
Ward & Co.: Leeds*, [1910.] 8°.
Premier Series, No. 1.   **F. 1176. f. (26.)**

— Romance—in F—pour Piano. *Leonard & Co.: London*,
[1905.] fol.   **g. 605. ll. (14.)**

— Sing out, my Soul. [Anthem.] Words by H. I. Brandon, *etc.
A. E. Parcell: Hull*, [1914.] 8°.   **C. 549. e. (25.)**

— Song without Words, for the Pianoforte with Violin, ad lib.
Whitehall Music Co.: London, (1912.) fol.   **h. 1612. aa. (12.)**

— Soul-Music. Sacred Song, words by ... H. Burton. *R. Culley:
London*, [1909.] fol.   **H. 1187. ll. (2.)**

— Springtime and Flowers. A Service of Recitations and
Melodies ... lyrics by G. E. Ward. *J. Broadbent & Son:
Leeds*, 1910. 8°.   **E. 496. l. (2.)**

— The Starry Pathway. [Sacred song.] Words by H. J. Brandon.
W. Paxton: London, [1912.] fol.   **H. 1187. xx. (8.)**

— Valsette, pour Piano. *M. Allan: Glasgow*, [1910.] fol.
                                                h. 3283. jj. (30.)

LAMARQUÉ (HENRI)

— The Way of Rest. Sacred Song, words by C. L. Rotherham.
R. Maynard: London, [1912.] fol.
H. Burton also appears as the author of the words.
                                                 H. 1187. rr. (4.)

— White Heather. Mazurka for the Pianoforte. *Agate & Co.:
London*, [1911.] fol.   **h. 3284. f. (21.)**

— *See* FRASER (D.) The River Song ... Pianoforte
accompaniment by H. Lamarqué. [1907.] fol.
                                                H. 1794. mm. (18.)

LA MARRE (DE)

— Les Chansons pour Danser et pour Boire. Du Sieur de La
Marre. *Robert Ballard: Paris*, 1650. 8°.   **A. 765.**

— [Another copy.] *In:* CHANSONS. [2.] Recueil de differens Livres
de Chansons, *etc.* Liv. V. 1699. 8°.   **A. 428.**

LAMARTER (ERIC DE)

— *See* DE LAMARTER.

LAMAS (JOSÉ ÁNGEL)

— Partituras para piano. [Sacred vocal works.] Edición
homenaje del Senado de la República a la memoria del
autor, a los doscientos años de su nacimiento. ⟨Popule meus.
Salve regina. O María.⟩ *Ediciones del Congreso de la
República: Caracas*, 1975. 4°.   **G. 980. n. (5.)**

— Tres lecciones para el oficio de difuntos. Partitura para voces
y orquesta. ⟨Revisión por Juan B. Plaza.⟩ pp. 77. *Instituto
interamericano de musicología: Montevideo*, 1943. 4°.
[*Archivo de música colonial venezolana. no. 2.*]   **H. 2596.**

— Misa en re. Partitura de coro y orquesta. pp. 220. *Ediciones
musicales de la Radio nacional Venezuela: Caracas*, [1959?]
fol.   **H. 2596. a.**

— Popule meus. Partitura para voces y orquesta. ⟨Revisión por
Juan B. Plaza.⟩ pp. 25. *Instituto interamericano de
musicología: Montevideo*, 1943. 4°.
[*Archivo de música colonial venezolana. no. 7.*]   **H. 2596.**

— Popule meus. *In:* MÚSICA. Música religiosa de cinco maestros
caraqueños 1771–1881, *etc.* pp. 25–33. 1967. fol.
                                                   H. 980. n. (6.)

— El Psalmo "Miserere" ... (Fragmento de una evocación.)
[Edited by] Vicente Emilio Sojo. [S.A.T.B. and orchestra.
Score.] pp. 92. *Ministerio de Educación:* [*Caracas?*, 1973.] fol.
[*Collección cuadernos de música. 2.*]   **G. 980. ff.**

— Salve regina. Partitura para voces y orquesta. ⟨Revisión por
Juan B. Plaza.⟩ pp. 35. *Instituto interamericano de
musicología: Montevideo*, 1943. 4°.
[*Archivo de música colonial venzolana. no. 5.*]   **H. 2596.**

LA MATA (MANUEL DE)

— Método completo de Harmonium. *Madrid*, [1859.] 8°.
                                                         f. 118.

— Método completo de Piano. *Madrid*, 1871. fol.   **h. 3749.**

LAMATER (EUGENE DE)

— *See* DE LAMATER.

LAMAZOU (PASCAL)

— Airs basques les plus populaires. *See* infra: [50 chants
pyrénéens.]

LAMAZOU (Pascal)

— 50 chants pyrénéens. 36 airs béarnais, 12 airs basques, 2 airs des Pyrénées orientales (avec traduction française) recueillis, chantés et publiés par P. Lamazou. Avec accompagnement de piano par M.M. D. F. E. Auber [and others], *etc.* [With a portrait.] pp. 101. *Chez Pascal Lamazou: Paris, Pau,* [1869.] fol. **H. 1248. x.**

— 50 chants pyrénéens, 34 airs béarnais, 14 airs basques, 2 airs des pyrénées-orientales. Recueillis, chantés et publiés par P. Lamazou. Avec accompagnement de piano par D. F. E. Auber [and others] ... Précédés d'une preface par Paul Lacome. Dessin de Gustave Doré, *etc.* (Troisième et nouvelle édition. Texte original et texte français.) pp. 101. *Cachau jⁿᵉ: Pau,* [c. 1880.] fol. **H. 1248. i. (2.)**

— [50 chants pyrénéens.] Airs basques les plus populaires. Texte originale et texte français. Extraits du recueil des chants pyrénéens de P. Lamazou. Avec accompagnement de piano par D. Allard, Ad. Barthe, Félicien David, Ch. Gounod [and others], *etc.* pp. 33. *Cachau jⁿᵉ: Pau,* [1880?] fol. **H. 1248. h. (1.)**

— 20 noëls français sur des airs béarnais et basques par M. Henri d'Andichon ... Recueillis, chantés et publiés par Pascal Lamazou. Avec accompagnement de piano par D. F. E. Auber ... Ch. Gounod [and others] ... Précédés d'une préface par Gustave Chouquet, *etc.* pp. 41. *Chez Pascal Lamazou: Paris, Pau,* 1873. fol.
The titlepage bears a MS. dedication to Gounod in the editor's autograph. **H. 1186. i. (14.)**

LAMB

— The Lamb. [Part-song.] *See* Binkerd (Gordon W.)

— The Lamb. [Part-song.] *See* Brian (H.)

— The Lamb. [Unison song.] *See* Brook (H.)

— The Lamb. Part Song. *See* Browne (P. A.)

— The Lamb. Unison song. *See* Bullock (*Sir* Ernest)

— The Lamb. [Part-song.] *See* Chorbajian (John)

— The Lamb. Song. *See* Collins (A.)

— The Lamb. Trio. *See* Davies (*Sir* H. W.) Four Songs of Innocence. Op. 4. No. 1.

— The Lamb. [Two-part song.] *See* Davis (Katherine K.)

— The Lamb. [Song.] *See* Densmore (J. H.) Three Songs ... 2.

— The Lamb. Two-Part Song. *See* Dunhill (T. F.)

— The Lamb. [Song.] *See* Furnivall (L. L.)

— The Lamb. [Part-song.] *See* Godfrey (H. G.)

— The Lamb. [Unison song.] *See* Henschel (*Sir* G.)

— The Lamb. [Two-part song.] *See* Hutchinson (C. V. H.) Five Songs of Innocence. No. 2.

— The Lamb. [Song.] *See* Jacob (Gordon P. S.) Three Songs of Innocence. No. 1.

— The Lamb. Unison song. *See* Javal (Guirne)

— The Lamb. Two-Part Song. *See* Jenkins (D. C.)

— The Lamb. Part-Song. *See* Jones (G. H.)

— The Lamb. [Unison song.] *See* Jones (William B.)

— The Lamb. [Part-song.] *See* Lyon (J.)

— The Lamb. [Unison song.] *See* Mills (Henry)

— The Lamb. Anthem. *See* Moore (Undine S.)

— The Lamb. Two-part Song. *See* Powell (L.)

— The Lamb. Song. *See* Raphael (M.)

LAMB

— The Lamb. [Part-song.] *See* Read (Gardner)

— The Lamb. [Unison song.] *See* Ritchie (John)

— The Lamb. Two-part Song. *See* Robinson (L.)

— The Lamb. Song. *See* Rodger (J.)

— The Lamb. [Part-song.] *See* Ross (Orvis)

— The Lamb. [Part-song.] *See* Schwadron (A. A.)

— The Lamb. Unison Song. *See* Sharman (C.)

— The Lamb. Unison song. *See* Shaw (Geoffrey T.)

— The Lamb. [Part-song.] *See* Silver (Frederick)

— The Lamb. Two-part song. *See* Tester (Archibald F.)

— The Lamb. Unison song. *See* Williams (Patrick)

— The Lamb. Part Song. *See* Wood (C.) *Mus. Doc.*

— The Lamb and the Dove. [Song.] *See* Gibbs (Cecil A.) Three Lyrics by Christina Rossetti ... 1.

— The Lamb and the Shepherd. Hymn. *See* Parcell (A. E.)

— The Lamb-Child. [Sacred song.] *See* Arba (E. d.)

— Lamb enthroned. [Song.] *See* Mozart (W. A.) [Masses. K. 317.—Agnus Dei.]

— De Lamb from Alabam'! [Song.] *See* Le Brunn (G.)

— Lam', Lam', Lam'. [Song.] *See* Jerome (Benjamin M.)

— The Lamb lay asleep. [Anthem.] *See* Marguerie (Lyndon)

— Lamb of God. Chorus. *See* Bach (J. S.) [Kyrie eleison. Christe, du Lamm Gottes. B.G. Jahrg. xli. p. 187.]

— Lamb of God. [Anthem.] *See* Barber (Samuel) [String Quartet. Op. 11.—Molto adagio.]

— The Lamb of God. Cantata. *See* Blose (J. M.)

— Lamb of God. [Sacred song.] *See* Frey (A.)

— The Lamb of God. Passion Service. *See* Gilchrist (W. W.)

— Lamb of God. [Motet.] *See* Hassler (H. L.) [Missae quaternis, v. vi. et viii. vocibus. No. 1.—Agnus Dei.]

— Lamb of God. Cantata. *See* Hector (C. W. G.)

— Lamb of God. [Motet.] *See* Monteverdi (C.) [Messa a quattro voci et salmi ... con le letanie della B.V.—Agnus dei.]

— Lamb of God. [Chorus.] *See* Monteverdi (C.) [Selva morale e spirituale.—Messa a 4 da cappella.—Agnus Dei.]

— Lamb of God. [Anthem.] *See* Mozart (W. A.) [Masses. K. 49.—Agnus Dei.]

— Lamb of God. Anthem. *See* Nevin (E. W.)

— Lamb of God. Introit. *See* Palestrina (G. P. da) [Missarum Liber Octavus. O admirabile commercium.—Agnus Dei.]

— Lamb of God. [Anthem.] *See* Powell (Robert J.)

— Lamb of God. Hymn. *See* Tilleard (James)

— Lamb of God. [Anthem.] *See* Verdi (F. G. F.) [Messa di requiem.—Agnus Dei.]

— Lamb of God. Cantata. *See* Williams (David H.)

— Lamb of God, I look to Thee. Anthem. *See* Bengson (Winifred J.)

— Lamb of God, I look to Thee. [Anthem.] *See* Lewis (John L.)

LAMB

— Lamb of God, whose bleeding Love. Hymn. *See* E., H.

— The Lamb shall lead them. Anthem. *See* SIMPER (C.)

— The Lamb that for us was slain. Chorus. *See* BACH (J.S.) [Ich hatte viel Bekümmerniss.—Das Lamm, das erwürget ist.]

— The Lamb that strayed from the Fold. [Song.] *See* CARLETON (Sidney)

— The Lamb that was slain. [Hymn.] *See* DENNIS (H.) School Anniversary Music ... Part II. No. 33.

— The Lamb that was slain for us. Chorus. *See* BACH (J.S.) [Ich hatte viel Bekümmerniss.—Das Lamm, das erwürget ist.]

LAMB ( ) *Miss*

— Music to be sung at the 150th anniversary of the Foundation School of Sir John Cass, Feb: 20th 1860. Arranged for the organ by Miss Lamb ... at the request of Mr White. pp. 4. [*London?* 1860.] fol.   **H. 1846. ww. (13.)**

LAMB (ARTHUR J.)

— I don't want to go in no Auto with you. [Song.] pp. 2–5. *Francis, Day & Hunter: London, New York,* [1906.] fol.   **H. 3985. g. (8.)**

— The Jasmine Speaks of you Jessie mine. [Song.] pp. 3–5. *Francis, Day & Hunter: London, New York,* [1906.] fol.   **H. 3985. g. (9.)**

— The Same Street leads to the green Fields. [Song.] Words & music by A. J. Lamb. pp. 5. *Willis Woodward & Co.: New York,* [1906.] fol.   **H. 3985. g. (10.)**

— Yes, Dear! [Song.] pp. 3–5. *Francis, Day & Hunter: London, New York,* [1906.] fol.   **H. 3985. g. (11.)**

— *See* THORNTON (James) *Songwriter* and LAMB (A. J.) He sent her a Piece of the Wedding Cake. [Song.] [1905.] fol.   **H. 3987. xx. (19.)**

LAMB (BESSIE)

— Dar's no Scandal in our Family. [Song.] Words & music by B. Lamb. pp. 5. *Philip Kussel: Cincinnati,* [1899.] fol.   **H. 3980. oo. (45.)**

LAMB (CAROLINE) *Lady*

— *See* HODSON (George A.) "Waters of Elle," [song,] words and melody from Glanarvon [or rather Glenarvon, novel by Lady C. Lamb] ... Arranged ... by G. A. Hodson. (New edition.) [WM1821.] fol.   **G. 425. pp. (17.)**

LAMB (CAROLINE FRANCES)

— *See* NIXON, afterwards LAMB.

LAMB (DENNIS)

— Four Hymns ... the words selected ... from Hymns Ancient and Modern. *Novello, Ewer & Co.: London & New York,* [1893.] 8°.   **C. 799. b. (12.)**

LAMB (EDWARD RECKITT)

— Not unto us. Sacred Song. *Novello, Ewer and Co.: London & New York,* [1894.] fol.   **G. 517. j. (17.)**

LAMB (F. GILBERT)

— The Breath of a Rose. [Song.] Words by A. Clare, *etc.* 1905. *See* PERIODICAL PUBLICATIONS.—*London.* The Vocalist. No. 44. The Vocalist Series. No. 132. 1902, *etc.* fol.   **P. P. 1947. fb.**

— E'en as a lovely Flower. *See infra*: [Two Songs. No. 1.]

— I heard the Voice of Jesus say. Sacred Song. [Words by] H. Bonar. *H. W. Gray:* [*New York,*] 1914. 4°.   **G. 519. c. (11.)**

— Love and the Rose. Song, words by Sir W. Scott. *Bunz & Co.: London,* 1907. fol.   **H. 1794. uu. (53.)**

— Primroses. Song, words by E. Cook. *Houghton & Co.: London,* 1901. fol.   **H. 1799. cc. (40.)**

— Primroses, *etc.* 1904. *See* PERIODICAL PUBLICATIONS.—*London.* The Vocalist. No. 29. The Vocalist Series. No. 92. 1902, *etc.* fol.   **P. P. 1947. fb.**

— Roses. *See infra*: [Two Songs. No. 2.]

— Two Songs. [No. 1.] E'en as a lovely Flower. Words by Heine. [No. 2.] Roses. Words by M. J. Farrah. *Houghton & Co.: London,* 1901. fol.   **H. 1799. vv. (17.)**

— [Two Songs. No. 1.] E'en as a lovely Flower, *etc.* 1904. *See* PERIODICAL PUBLICATIONS.—*London.* The Vocalist. No. 32. The Vocalist Series. No. 100. 1902, *etc.* fol.   **P. P. 1947. fb.**

— [Two Songs. No. 2.] Roses, *etc.* 1904. *See* PERIODICAL PUBLICATIONS.—*London.* The Vocalist. No. 26. The Vocalist Series. No. 85. 1902, *etc.* fol.   **P. P. 1947. fb.**

— There was a pretty Maid. Song, words by R. Burns. 2 no. [Low and high.] *Ascherberg, Hopwood & Crew: London,* 1912. fol.   **H. 1793. r. (41.)**

— The Winter is past. Song, words by R. Burns. *Leonard & Co.: London,* 1911. fol.   **G. 807. yy. (19.)**

LAMB (FLORENCE)

— Berceuse, for Violin & Piano. *Stainer & Bell: London,* (1909.) fol. *Stainer & Bell's Violin Library, No. 4.*   **h. 1612. v. (1.)**

LAMB (GORDON HOWARD)

— Hodie Christus natus est ... Four-part chorus of men's voices, a cappella. pp. 6. *G. Schirmer: New York, London,* [1971.] 8°. *Part of "Gordon H. Lamb Conductors choral Series".*   **F. 538. s. (6.)**

— Sit down, Lord. Spiritual (S.A.T.B.). Adapted and arranged by Gordon H. Lamb. pp. 7. *G. Schirmer: New York, London,* [1972.] 8°. *Part of "Gordon H. Lamb Conductors choral Series".*   **F. 538. s. (7.)**

LAMB (HARRY)

— *See* LAMB (Henry) *Songwriter.*

LAMB (HENRY) *Organist*

— Te Deum set to music in chant form. *London,* [1881.] 8°.   **E. 597. i. (15.)**

LAMB (HENRY) *Songwriter*

— Dainty Step. Caprice ... Arr. by Theo. Bendix. ([With] Bissextile Polka. G. H. Rowell.) [Orchestral parts.] 32 pt. *Oliver Ditson Co.: Boston,* [1893.] 8°.   **f. 800. (774.)**

LAMB (HENRY) *Songwriter*

— Eliza Jane McCue. Waltz song. Words by Wm. B. Glenroy.
pp. 5. *Spaulding & Kornder: Brooklyn*, [1893.] fol.
H. 3980. oo. (46.)

— My Mary Green ... Waltz. (Arranged for piano by
N. McDonald.) *O. Ditson Co.: Boston, etc.*, 1892. fol.
h. 3285. p. (49.)

— The Very best Girl I know. 〈Waltz song and chorus. Written
and composed by H. Lamb.〉 pp. 5. *Frank Harding: New
York*, [1892.] fol. **H. 3980. oo. (47.)**

— The Volunteer Organist. Descriptive song. Words by W. B.
Glenroy. 〈New edition with tonic solfa added.〉 pp. 4.
London Music Publishing Stores: London, [1902.] fol.
H. 3985. g. (12.)

— The Volunteer Organist. Descriptive song, *etc.* 〈With
additional verse by Andrew J. Orr.〉 pp. 5. *Orpheus Music
Publishing Co.: London*, [1904.] fol. **H. 3985. g. (13.)**

— The Volunteer Organist. Descriptive song. Words by W. B.
Glenroy. 〈With tonic sol-fa.〉 pp. 4. [c. 1905.] fol.
A pirated edition. **H. 1848. b. (6.)**

— *See* GLENROY (William B.) and LAMB (H.) Carrie. 1893. fol.
H. 1798. m. (60.)

— *See* GLENROY (William B.) and LAMB (H.) Just to be obliging.
Song. [1894.] fol. **H. 3980. y. (61.)**

— *See* GLENROY (William B.) and LAMB (H.) Sitting on the
Hillside. 1893. fol. **H. 1798. m. (61.)**

LAMB (HUBERT)

— Carol for Harvest-tide, words by T. H. Parker. *Novello, Ewer
and Co.: London & New York*, [1889.] 8°. **B. 579. d. (33.)**

— Two Kyries. *Hull*, [1884.] 8°. **C. 736. a. (4.)**

— The Voice of the People: Cantata, written by J. B. Cox.
Taylor & Rayward: Hull, [1887.] 8°. **E. 1594. h. (7.)**

— Whom seek ye? Easy Easter anthem, *etc. London*, [1883.] 8°.
E. 442. h. (4.)

LAMB (JESSE)

— "Child Jesu lay on Mary's Knee." Christmas Carol, words by
Mrs. De Courcy Laffan. *Weekes & Co.: London*, [1910.] 8°.
D. 619. hh. (7.)

LAMB (JOHN DAVID)

— Spring Festival. For elementary string orchestra with optional
piano. Score, *etc.* pp. 7. *Galaxy Music Corp.: New York;
Galliard: London; printed in England*, [1966.] 4°.
g. 934. f. (5.)

LAMB (JOSEF F.)

— *See* LAMB (Joseph F.)

LAMB (JOSEPH F.)

— Celestine Waltzes. [P. F.] *H. H. Sparks: Toronto*, (1905.) fol.
h. 3286. dd. (47.)

— Dear blue Eyes—true Eyes. 〈Song.〉 Words by Llyn Wood.
pp. 5. *Harry H. Sparks: Toronto*, [1908.] fol.
H. 3985. g. (14.)

— Florentine. Valse. [P. F.] pp. 5. *H. H. Sparks: [Toronto*, 1906.]
fol. **h. 4120. ll. (25.)**

— The Homestead where the Suwanee River flows. [Song.]
Words & music by J. F. Lamb. pp. 5. *Harry H. Sparks:
Toronto*, [1909.] fol. **H. 3985. g. (15.)**

— If Love is a Dream, let me never awake. Song. Words by
Llyn Wood. pp. 5. *Harry H. Sparks: Toronto*, [1908.] fol.
H. 3985. g. (16.)

LAMB (JOSEPH F.)

— The Liliputian's Bazaar. [P.F.] *Harry H. Sparks: Toronto*,
[1904.] fol. **h. 4120. ll. (26.)**

— The Lost Letter ... 〈Song.〉 Words by Margret Anger
Cawthorpe. pp. 5. *Harry H. Sparks: Toronto*, [1908.] fol.
H. 3985. g. (17.)

— Love in Absence. [Song.] Poem by M. A. O'Reilly. *G. Hurst
Music Co.: New York*, (1909.) fol. **G. 807. yy. (20.)**

— Love's ebb Tide. Ballad. Words by S. A. White. pp. 5.
Harry H. Sparks: Toronto, [1908.] fol. **H. 3985. g. (18.)**

— Three Leaves of Shamrock on the Watermelon Vine. [Song.]
Words by Harry Moore. pp. 5. *Harry H. Sparks: Toronto*,
[1908.] fol. **H. 3985. g. (19.)**

LAMB (LOUISA MARY CAROLINE) *Lady*

— Come when thou wilt. Song. *London*, [1876.] fol.
H. 1778. x. (9.)

— Love at Sea. Song [begins: "We are in love's land"]. The
words by A. C. Swinburne. *London*, [1876.] fol.
H. 1778. x. (11.)

— Il Rubino. Valse chantée [begins: "Gentil al par d'un
cherubino"] ... Paroles de F. Mottino. *London*, [1877.] fol.
H. 1778. x. (12.)

— Schiuda alle rose il calice. Romanza. *Bruxelles*, [1878.] fol.
H. 1781. i. (7.)

— Written on Sand. Song [begins: "I wrote upon the shining
sands"] ... The words by V. Fane. *London*, [1876.] fol.
H. 1778. x. (10.)

LAMB (PETER)

— Concertante Music. For double bass, wind and strings. 〈Piano
reduction.〉 [Score and part.] 2 pt. *Yorke Edition: London*,
[1974.] 4°. **g. 270. ll. (9.)**

— Pastoral. Trio for B♭ clarinets. [Score.] pp. 3. *Boosey &
Hawkes: [London*, 1967.] 4°. **g. 1104. ff. (15.)**

— Reflections for solo Flute. *In:* WASTALL (Peter) Contemporary
Music for Flute, *etc.* no. 3. [1977.] 4°. **g. 280. kk. (5.)**

— Sonatina for Flute and Piano. [Score and part.] 2 pt. *Boosey
& Hawkes: London, etc.*, [1974.] 4°. **g. 70. rr. (7.)**

LAMB (ROBERT)

— Seven symphonic Preludes. For narrator & orch., *etc.* [Score.
A facsimile of the composer's autograph.] *Robert Lamb:
Thornton Heath*, [1967.] fol.
Printed on one side of the leaf. **I. 525. x.**

LAMB (SYDNEY)

— Rex.—Onward, Christian Soldiers.—Eddell. [2 hymn tunes.]
S. Lamb: Sheffield, [1900.] 8°. **D. 619. o. (17.)**

— Sandwath. 'Saviour, while my Heart is tender' ... Ecclerigg.
[2 hymn tunes.] *S. Lamb: Sheffield*, [1900.] 8°.
D. 619. o. (16.)

— Four Vespers. *S. Lamb: Sheffield*, [1909.] *obl.* 8°.
I. 600. d. (83.)

LAMB (T. G.)

— Merry little Folks. A Short Operetta for Juniors ... Both
Notations. *J. Curwen & Sons: London*, 1901. 8°.
E. 890. c. (2.)

— Merry little Folks ... Tonic Sol-fa edition. *J. Curwen &
Sons: London*, [1904.] 8°. **D. 832. f. (4.)**

LAMB (T. G.)

— On my Coaster ... Action Song for children, written by
E. F. E. Lamb. *J. Curwen & Sons: London*, 1916. fol.
H. 1984. h. (5.)

LAMB (W. J.)

— A Christmas Welcome. Song [begins: "A greeting to old
Christmas"]. The poetry by J. Askham. *London*, [1874.] fol.
H. 1778. x. (13.)

— I sing a song. Serio-comic song, written by A. I. Randall.
London, [1871.] fol.
H. 1775. t. (9.)

— The Keel Row for the Pianoforte. *London*, [1871.] fol.
h. 1485. s. (11.)

— Ould Ireland quadrille for two performers on the Pianoforte.
London, [1874.] fol.
h. 1482. y. (21.)

LAMBALLE, MARIE THÉRÈSE LOUISE, *Princesse de*

— *See* MARY THERESA LOUISA [of Savoy Carignan], *Princesse de Lamballe.*

LAMBARDI (FRANCESCO)

— Canzonette a tre, et a quattro, et a cinque voci, con alcune
Arie per cantar solo nella parte del tenore ... Libro terzo.
⟨Canto.⟩ *Per Costantino Vitale: Napoli.* 1616. 4°.
Imperfect; wanting the other parts.
D. 230. c.

LAMBARDUS (HIERONYMUS)

— Antiphonarium Vespertinum Dierum Festorum Totius Anni
iuxta ritum Romani Breuiarij Pij v. reformati, nunc nuper
pulcherrimis contrapuntis exornatum atque auctum a
Reverendo D. Hieronymo Lambardo ... In tres partes
distributum ... Secunda Pars. *In Cænobio Sancti Spiritus
prope Venetias,* 1597. fol.
K. 9. b. 12.

— Vespertina Omnium Solemnitatum Totius anni Psalmodia
Ternis Vocibus decantanda. Cum duobus Canticis Beatæ
Marię Virginis ... Primus Chorus. Cum Basso ad Organum,
etc. Tenor. (Bassus.) (Bassus ad Organum.) 3 pt. *Ære
Bartholomei Magni. Stampa del Gardano: Venetia,* 1613. 4°.
D. 110.

LAMBE (JOHN)

— A new and complete Preceptor for the Royal Key'd Bugle,
etc. London, [1830?] *obl.* 4°.
b. 160. a. (3.)

— "Three Cheers for the Tyne," a favourite song ... The words
by W. G. Tate ... with an accompaniment for the piano forte.
J. King: North Shields, [c. 1850.] fol.
H. 1654. j. (11.)

LAMBE (JOHN F.)

— "All Girls are beautiful, but not one like you." ⟨Song.⟩
Written and composed by J. F. Lambe. [Staff and tonic sol-fa
notation. Voice part.] *Francis, Day & Hunter: London,*
[1906.] *s. sh.* fol.
H. 3985. g. (20.)

— "All Girls are beautiful, but not one like you," *etc.* ⟨Song.⟩
[With separate voice part.] 2 pt. *Francis, Day & Hunter:
London,* [1906.] fol.
H. 3985. g. (21.)

— Be advised by your Father. ⟨Song.⟩ Written & composed by
J. F. Lambe, *etc.* pp. 4. *Shapiro, von Tilzer Music Co.:
London,* [1906.] fol.
Popular 6ᵈ Edition. no. 60.
H. 3985. g. (22.)

— By the Banks o' Allan Water. (A Scottish komic song.)
Written and composed by J. F. Lambe. Arranged by J. Chas.
Moore. pp. 3. *Shapiro, von Tilzer Music Co.: London,* [1907.]
4°.
H. 3985. g. (23.)

LAMBE (JOHN F.)

— "I can't forget Auld Reekie," *etc.* ⟨Song.⟩ [Staff and tonic
sol-fa notation. Voice part.] *Francis, Day & Hunter: London,*
[1907.] *s. sh.* fol.
H. 3985. g. (24.)

— I can't forget Auld Reekie, *etc.* ⟨Song.⟩ [With separate voice
part.] 2 pt. *Francis, Day & Hunter: London,* [1907.] fol.
H. 3985. g. (25.)

— I wonder what we'd do without our Girls! ... ⟨Song.⟩ Written
and composed by J. F. Lambe. [Staff and tonic sol-fa
notation. Voice part.] *Francis, Day & Hunter: London,*
[1906.] *s. sh.* fol.
H. 3985. g. (26.)

— I wonder what we'd do without our Girls! *etc.* ⟨Song.⟩ [With
separate voice part.] 2 pt. *Francis, Day & Hunter: London,*
[1906.] fol.
H. 3985. g. (27.)

— "Keep on doing it, Sandy!" *etc.* ⟨Song.⟩ [Staff and tonic
sol-fa notation. Voice part.] *Francis, Day & Hunter: London,*
[1906.] *s. sh.* fol.
H. 3985. g. (28.)

— "Keep on doing it, Sandy!" ⟨Song.⟩ Written & composed by
J. F. Lambe, *etc.* [With separate voice part.] 2 pt. *Francis,
Day & Hunter: London,* [1906.] fol.
H. 3985. g. (29.)

— The King's a right good Fellow! ... ⟨Song.⟩ Written and
composed by J. F. Lambe, *etc.* [Staff and tonic sol-fa
notation. Voice part.] *Francis, Day & Hunter: London,*
[1902.] *s. sh.* fol.
H. 3985. g. (30.)

— The King's a right good Fellow! *etc.* ⟨Song. Arranged by
H. E. Pether.⟩ [With separate voice part.] 2 pt. *Francis, Day &
Hunter: London,* [1902.] fol.
H. 3985. g. (31.)

— Kissing in old Japan ... [Song.] Written & composed by J. F.
Lambe, *etc. Reader & Walsh: London,* [1908.] fol.
Reeder & Walsh's Sixpenny Musical Marvels. no. 87.
H. 3985. g. (32.)

— "Kitty Brady." ⟨Song.⟩ Written and composed by J. F. Lambe,
etc. [With separate voice part.] 2 pt. *Monte Carlo Publishing
Co.: London,* [1907.] fol.
M.C.P. Co. Sixpenny Successes. no. 68.
H. 3985. g. (33.)

— My Lily Love. ⟨Song.⟩ Written and composed by J. F. Lambe.
[With separate voice part.] 2 pt. *Monte Carlo Publishing Co.:
London,* [1906.] fol.
M.C.P. Co. Sixpenny Successes. no. 41.
H. 3985. g. (34.)

— My Mother's Face. ⟨Song.⟩ Written and composed by J. F.
Lambe, *etc.* [Staff and tonic sol-fa notation. Voice part.]
Francis, Day & Hunter: London, [1903.] *s. sh.* fol.
H. 3985. g. (35.)

— My Mother's Face, *etc.* ⟨Song.⟩ [With separate voice part.]
2 pt. *Francis, Day & Hunter: London,* [1903.] fol.
H. 3985. g. (36.)

— Oh! dear little Ireland ... ⟨Song.⟩ Written and composed by
J. F. Lambe, *etc.* [Staff and tonic sol-fa notation. Voice part.]
Francis, Day & Hunter: London, [1900.] *s. sh.* fol.
H. 3985. g. (37.)

— One little Cottage all our own. ⟨Song.⟩ Written and composed
by J. F. Lambe, *etc.* [Staff and tonic sol-fa notation. Voice
part.] *Francis, Day & Hunter: London,* [1904.] *s. sh.* fol.
H. 3985. g. (38.)

— One little Cottage all our own, *etc.* ⟨Song.⟩ [With separate
voice part.] 2 pt. *Francis, Day & Hunter: London,* [1904.] fol.
H. 3985. g. (39.)

— Queen of old Samara. ⟨Song.⟩ Written and composed by J. F.
Lambe. [With separate voice part.] 2 pt. *Monte Carlo
Publishing Co.: London,* [1906.] fol.
M.C.P. Co. Sixpenny Successes. no. 36.
H. 3985. g. (40.)

— Tillietudlum ... ⟨Song.⟩ Written and composed by J. F.
Lambe. [Staff and tonic sol-fa notation. Voice part.] *Francis,
Day & Hunter: London,* [1907.] *s. sh.* fol.
H. 3985. g. (41.)

LAMBE (John F.)

— Tillietudlum, etc. ⟨Song.⟩ [With separate voice part.] 2 pt. *Francis, Day & Hunter: London*, [1907.] fol.
H. 3985. g. (42.)

— "What's the Good of Fame?" ... ⟨Song.⟩ Written and composed by J. F. Lambe. [Staff and tonic sol-fa notation. Voice part.] *Francis, Day & Hunter: London*, [1906.] *s. sh.* fol.
H. 3985. g. (43.)

— What's the Good of Fame? etc. ⟨Song.⟩ [With separate voice part.] 2 pt. *Francis, Day & Hunter: London*, [1906.] fol.
H. 3985. g. (44.)

— "When the Berry's on the Holly." ⟨Song.⟩ Written and composed by J. F. Lambe. [Staff and tonic sol-fa notation. Voice part.] *Francis, Day & Hunter: London*, [1908.] *s. sh.* fol.
H. 3985. g. (45.)

— "When the Berry's on the Holly," etc. ⟨Song.⟩ [With separate voice part.] 2 pt. *Francis, Day & Hunter: London*, [1908.] fol.
H. 3985. g. (46.)

— "Widow Doolin." ⟨Song.⟩ Written and composed by J. F. Lambe. [With separate voice part.] 2 pt. *Monte Carlo Publishing Co.: London*, [1906.] fol.
M.C.P. Co. Sixpenny Successes. no. 22. **H. 3985. g. (47.)**

— "Won't you come again to Ehren on the Rhine?" ⟨Song.⟩ Written and composed by J. F. Lambe. [Staff and tonic sol-fa notation. Voice part.] *Francis, Day & Hunter: London*, [1907.] *s. sh.* fol. **H. 3985. g. (48.)**

— "Won't you come again to Ehren on the Rhine?" Song, etc. [With separate voice part.] 2 pt. *Francis, Day & Hunter: London*, [1907.] fol. **H. 3985. g. (49.)**

— "Yer an awfu' Tickler, Jock McRaw." ⟨Song.⟩ Written and composed by J. F. Lambe. *B. Feldman & Co.: London*, [1907.] 4°. **H. 3985. g. (50.)**

— *See* GODFREY (Fred) and LAMBE (J. F.) "A Grain of Help is worth a Peck of Pity" ... ⟨Song.⟩ Written and composed by F. Godfrey and J. F. Lambe. [1907.] *s. sh.* fol.
H. 3984. c. (35.)

— *See* GODFREY (Fred) and LAMBE (J. F.) "A Grain of Help is worth a Peck of Pity," etc. ⟨Song.⟩ [1907.] fol.
H. 3984. c. (36.)

— *See* HARRINGTON (John P.) Of course! [Song.] Written and composed by J. P. Harrington, J. F. Lambe and George Le Brunn, etc. [1899.] *s. sh.* fol. **H. 3980. dd. (4.)**

— *See* MELLOR (Tom) and LAMBE (J. F.) "Can't you hear me callin', Mister Primrose Brown" ... ⟨Song.⟩ Written and composed by T. Mellor & J. F. Lambe. [1906.] *s. sh.* fol.
H. 3985. rr. (39.)

— *See* MELLOR (Tom) and LAMBE (J. F.) "Can't you hear me callin', Mister Primrose Brown," etc. ⟨Song.⟩ [1906.] fol.
H. 3985. rr. (40.)

LAMBE (John F.) and HARRISON (E. Denham)

— It wasn't so nice as she thought. Written by J. F. Lambe, etc. [Song. Staff and tonic sol-fa notation. Voice part.] *Francis, Day & Hunter: London*, [1899.] *s. sh.* fol. **H. 3980. oo. (48.)**

LAMBE (John F.) and HIPPLE (J.)

— I've got a Girl to care for. ⟨Song.⟩ Written and composed by J. E. Lambe and J. Hipple, etc. [Staff and tonic sol-fa notation. Voice part.] *Francis, Day & Hunter: London*, [1902.] *s. sh.* fol. **H. 3985. g. (51.)**

— I've got a Girl to care for, etc. ⟨Song.⟩ [With separate voice part.] 2 pt. *Francis, Day & Hunter: London*, [1902.] fol.
H. 3985. g. (52.)

LAMBE (John F.) and MELLOR (Tom)

— "Can't you find a Sweetheart of your own?" ⟨Song.⟩ Written and composed by J. F. Lambe & T. Mellor. [Staff and tonic sol-fa notation. Voice part.] *Francis, Day & Hunter: London*, [1906.] *s. sh.* fol. **H. 3985. g. (53.)**

— "Can't you find a Sweetheart of your own?" etc. ⟨Song.⟩ [With separate voice part.] 2 pt. *Francis, Day & Hunter: London*, [1906.] fol. **H. 3985. g. (54.)**

— "Don't tell me funny Stories." ⟨Song.⟩ Written and composed by J. F. Lambe & T. Mellor, etc. [Staff and tonic sol-fa notation. Voice part.] *Francis, Day & Hunter: London*, [1905.] *s. sh.* fol. **H. 3985. g. (55.)**

— "Don't tell me funny Stories," etc. ⟨Song.⟩ [With separate voice part.] 2 pt. *Francis, Day & Hunter: London*, [1905.] fol.
H. 3985. g. (56.)

— "Don't you see I want you for my only?" ⟨Song.⟩ Written and composed by J. F. Lambe and T. Mellor. [Staff and tonic sol-fa notation. Voice part.] *Francis, Day & Hunter: London*, [1906.] *s. sh.* fol. **H. 3985. g. (57.)**

— "Don't you see I want you for my only?" etc. ⟨Song.⟩ [With separate voice part.] 2 pt. *Francis, Day & Hunter: London*, [1906.] fol.
H. 3985. g. (58.)

— "I'm longing for someone like you." ⟨Song.⟩ Written and composed by J. F. Lambe and T. Mellor. [Staff and tonic sol-fa notation. Voice part.] *Francis, Day & Hunter: London*, [1906.] *s. sh.* fol. **H. 3985. g. (59.)**

— "I'm longing for someone like you," etc. ⟨Song.⟩ [With separate voice part.] 2 pt. *Francis, Day & Hunter: London*, [1906.] fol.
H. 3985. g. (60.)

— They were thinking of Home, sweet Home. ⟨Song.⟩ Written and composed by J. E. Lambe & T. Mellor. [Staff and tonic sol-fa notation. Voice part.] *Francis, Day & Hunter: London*, [1906.] *s. sh.* fol. **H. 3985. g. (61.)**

— They were thinking of Home, sweet Home, etc. ⟨Song.⟩ [With separate voice part.] 2 pt. *Francis, Day & Hunter: London*, [1906.] fol.
H. 3985. g. (62.)

— We can't forget the old Love. ⟨Song.⟩ Written and composed by J. F. Lambe and T. Mellor, etc. [Staff and tonic sol-fa notation. Voice part.] *Francis, Day & Hunter: London*, [1904.] *s. sh.* fol. **H. 3985. g. (63.)**

— We can't forget the old Love, etc. ⟨Song.⟩ [With separate voice part.] 2 pt. *Francis, Day & Hunter: London*, [1904.] fol.
H. 3985. g. (64.)

LAMBE (John F.) and THURBAN (T. W.)

— Fair Lady sigh no more. ⟨Song.⟩ Written and composed by J. F. Lambe & T. W. Thurban. pp. 4. *Shapiro, von Tilzer Music Co.: London*, [1906.] 4°. **H. 3985. g. (65.)**

— The Gipsy's Wedding. ⟨Song.⟩ Written and composed by J. F. Lambe and T. W. Thurban. [Staff and tonic sol-fa notation. Voice part.] *Francis, Day & Hunter: London*, [1907.] *s. sh.* fol.
H. 3985. g. (66.)

— The Gipsy's Wedding, etc. ⟨Song.⟩ [With separate voice part.] 2 pt. *Francis, Day & Hunter: London*, [1907.] fol.
H. 3985. g. (67.)

— My beautiful Avon Rose. ⟨Song.⟩ Written and composed by J. F. Lambe and T. W. Thurban. [Staff and tonic sol-fa notation. Voice part.] *Francis, Day & Hunter: London*, [1907.] *s. sh.* fol. **H. 3985. g. (68.)**

— My beautiful Avon Rose, etc. ⟨Song.⟩ [With separate voice part.] 2 pt. *Francis, Day & Hunter: London*, [1907.] fol.
H. 3985. g. (69.)

LAMBE (John F.) and THURBAN (T. W.)

— "Pretty Maid of the Pyrenees." ⟨Song.⟩ Written and composed by J. F. Lambe and T. W. Thurban, *etc.* [Staff and tonic sol-fa notation. Voice part.] *Francis, Day & Hunter: London*, [1907.] *s. sh.* fol. **H. 3985. g. (70.)**

— "Pretty Maid of the Pyrenees," *etc.* ⟨Song.⟩ [With separate voice part.] 2 pt. *Francis, Day & Hunter: London*, [1907.] fol. **H. 3985. g. (71.)**

— "Won't you go with me to Gogo?" ⟨Song.⟩ Written and composed by J. F. Lambe and T. W. Thurban, *etc.* [Staff and tonic sol-fa notation. Voice part.] *Francis, Day & Hunter: London*, [1907.] *s. sh.* fol. **H. 3985. g. (72.)**

— "Won't you go with me to Gogo?" *etc.* ⟨Song.⟩ [With separate voice part.] 2 pt. *Francis, Day & Hunter: London*, [1907.] fol. **H. 3985. g. (73.)**

LAMBE (John F.) and WELLS (Gilbert)

— Down Quality Street. ⟨Song.⟩ Written and composed by J. F. Lambe and G. Wells, *etc.* [Staff and tonic sol-fa notation. Voice part.] *Francis, Day & Hunter: London*, [1903.] *s. sh.* fol. **H. 3985. g. (74.)**

— Down Quality Street, *etc.* ⟨Song.⟩ [With separate voice part.] 2 pt. *Francis, Day & Hunter: London*, [1903.] fol. **H. 3985. g. (75.)**

LAMBELERT (Vivien)

— *See* Lambelet.

LAMBELET (Napoleon)

— Anemones. Intermezzo for Piano. *Ascherberg, Hopwood & Crew: London*, 1910. fol. **h. 3283. jj. (31.)**

— Au bord de l'eau. Chanson. Paroles de S. Prudhomme. *Boosey & Co.: London & New York*, 1899. fol. **H. 3598. (1.)**

— [Au bord de l'eau.] Beside the Stream. Song ... English version by P. Pinkerton. *Boosey & Co.: London & New York*, 1899. fol. **H. 3598. (2.)**

— Autumn Rose. Waltz Song, written by A. R. Cleveland. *Hopwood & Crew: London*, 1905. fol. **H. 3598. (14.)**

— Beside the Stream. *See* supra: [Au bord de l'eau.]

— "Chic." [Song.] Words by A. R. Cleveland. *Hopwood & Crew: London*, 1906. fol. **H. 3598. (15.)**

— Come merry Folk all. [Song.] Words by A. Sturgess. *Hopwood & Crew: London*, 1905. fol. **H. 3598. (16.)**

— The Cretan Patrol. [P. F.] *Boosey & Co.: London and New York*, 1899. fol. **h. 3282. f. (6.)**

— Curly-Headed Kit. Song. The words by G. M. Slater. *Boosey & Co.: London & New York*, 1900. fol. **H. 3598. (3.)**

— The Domestic Brigade. Song. The words by G. M. Slater. *Boosey & Co.: London & New York*, 1900. fol. **H. 3598. (4.)**

— The Dream of the Roses. Song, the words by P. Hope. *Enoch & Sons: London*, 1901. fol. **H. 1799. cc. (41.)**

— Dream on. Song—with chorus ad lib.—Words by A. Chapman. *Chappell & Co.: London*, 1900. fol. **H. 3598. (5.)**

— Electra. Waltz, *etc.* [P. F.] *Ascherberg, Hopwood & Crew: London*, [1910.] fol. **h. 3286. uu. (34.)**

— [Another edition.] Electra. Valse, *etc.* [P. F.] *Ascherberg, Hopwood & Crew: London*, 1910. fol. **h. 3286. uu. (35.)**

LAMBELET (Napoleon)

— The English Mees! ⟨Song.⟩ Words by Adrian Ross. pp. 8. *Francis, Day & Hunter: London*, [1901.] fol. **H. 3985. g. (76.)**

— Fenella. Opera in One Act, libretto by A. R. Cleveland. Vocal Score. *Francis, Day & Hunter: London*, 1906. 4°. **F. 688. c. (3.)**

— Gavotte pour piano. *E. Ashdown: London*, [1898.] fol. **g. 605. p. (15.)**

— Grammatical Grievances. Song. Words by Herbert Harraday. pp. 5. *Chappell & Co.: London*, [1903.] fol. **H. 3985. g. (77.)**

— A Greek Nocturne. [Song.] The words by P. Pinkerton. *Boosey & Co.: London & New York*, 1899. fol. **H. 3598. (6.)**

— Greetings. Song and Chorus. Words by R. Carse. *Chappell & Co.: London*, 1900. fol. **H. 3598. (7.)**

— How to kiss. *See* infra: [The Topsy-Turvy Hotel.]

— I'm a Monarch with original Ideas. *See* infra: [The Yashmak.]

— In my Canoe.—A River Song.—Words by R. Carse. *Hopwood & Crew: London*, 1905. fol. **H. 3598. (17.)**

— Intermezzo-Patrol. [P. F.] *E. Ascherberg & Co.: London*, 1905. fol. **h. 3283. p. (10.)**

— The Last Waltz. [Song.] Words by A. Cleveland. *Francis, Day & Hunter: London*, (1912.) fol. **H. 1792. r. (6.)**

— [Another edition.] The Last Waltz, *etc. Francis, Day & Hunter: London*, 1912. fol. **H. 1792. r. (7.)**

— Lisette. Song. The words by P. Pinkerton. *Boosey & Co.: London & New York*, 1899. fol. **H. 3598. (8.)**

— Love's Eternity. *See* infra: [The Yashmak.]

— Marche Arabe, *etc.* [P. F.] *Ascherberg, Hopwood & Crew: London*, 1911. fol. **h. 3284. f. (22.)**

— Mary was a Housemaid. *See* infra: [Pot-Pourri.]

— Menuet pour piano. *E. Ashdown: London*, [1898.] fol. **g. 605. p. (16.)**

— Miss Chutney of Putney; or, The Pickle Girl. [Song.] Words by P. Hope. *Hopwood & Crew: London*, 1905. fol. **H. 3598. (18.)**

— Peep O! Song, words by A. R. Cleveland. *Francis, Day & Hunter: London, New York*, 1906. fol. *Two copies, one without a cover.* **H. 3598. (19.)**

Pot-Pourri

— Pot-Pourri. An 1899 Review, written by J. T. Tanner. Lyrics by W. H. Risque. *Boosey & Co.: London and New York*, 1899. 4°. **F. 1449. a. (1.)**

— Selection ... Selected and arranged [for military band] by J. Ord Hume. ⟨Conductor [and parts].⟩ 26 pt. *Boosey & Co.: London*, 1899. fol. [*Boosey's military Journal. ser.* 107. *no.* 3.] **h. 1549.**

— Selection ... Arranged for the pianoforte by C. Kiefert. *Boosey & Co.: London and New York*, 1899. fol. **h. 3282. f. (7.)**

— Doll-Gavotte, *etc.* [P. F.] *Boosey & Co.: London and New York*, 1899. fol. **h. 3282. f. (8.)**

— Graceful Waltz, *etc.* [P. F.] *Boosey & Co.: London*, 1899. fol. **h. 3286. g. (4.)**

— Mary was a Housemaid. Song. The words by W. H. Risque. *Boosey & Co.: London & New York*, 1899. fol. **H. 3598. (9.)**

LAMBELET (NAPOLEON)

— [Mary was a Housemaid.] Barn Dance, *etc.* [P. F.] *Boosey & Co.: London,* 1899. fol. **h. 3286. g. (3.)**

— Selling Papers. Song. The words by W. H. Risque. *Boosey & Co.: London & New York,* 1899. fol. **H. 3598. (10.)**

— *See* KIEFERT (C.) Pot Pourri. Lancers (Waltz) on Airs ... by N. Lambelet. 1899. fol. **h. 829. (26.)**

— *See* KIEFERT (C.) "Pot-pourri." ⟨Lancers.⟩ On airs from the musical revue "Potpourri" ... The music by N. Lambelet. [Military band.] 1900. fol. [*Boosey's supplemental military Journal. no.* 422.] **h. 1544.**

— Romance pour Piano. *Ascherberg, Hopwood & Crew: London,* 1911. fol. **h. 3284. f. (23.)**

— Sail on. [Song.] Words by R. Carse. *Hopwood & Crew: London,* 1905. fol. **H. 3598. (20.)**

— Sally was a shy Maid. ⟨Song.⟩ Written by Street Parker. [Staff and tonic sol-fa notation. Voice part.] *Francis, Day & Hunter: London,* [1902.] *s. sh.* fol. **H. 3985. g. (78.)**

— Sally was a shy Maid, *etc.* ⟨Song.⟩ [With separate voice part.] 2 pt. *Francis, Day & Hunter: London,* [1902.] fol. **H. 3985. g. (79.)**

— Selling Papers. *See supra*: [Pot-Pourri.]

— Sentinel March. [P. F.] *Francis, Day & Hunter: London,* 1903. fol. **h. 3282. ww. (28.)**

— Slave of her Eyes. Song. Written by L. C. Byng. *Metzler & Co.: London,* 1900. fol. **H. 3598. (11.)**

— The Sunshade Girl. [Song.] Words by A. R. Cleveland. *Hopwood & Crew: London,* 1906. fol. **H. 3598. (21.)**

— Tarentelle pour piano. *E. Ashdown: London,* [1898.] fol. **g. 605. p. (17.)**

— There's an End to all our Labours. Squire's Song in The Last Load, written by A. Sturgess. *Hopwood & Crew: London,* 1905. fol. **H. 3598. (22.)**

— 'Tis you I love for aye. Je veux toujours t'aimer. [Song.] Words by A. Cleveland, French words by J. Rodor, *etc.* 2 no. [High and medium.] *Ascherberg, Hopwood & Crew: London,* 1912. fol. **H. 1792. r. (8.)**

— [The Topsy-Turvy Hotel.] How to kiss. Song ... Words by R. Carse. *Chappell & Co.: London,* 1898. fol. **H. 3598. (12.)**

— Valentine. A Romantic Comedy Opera, written by A. Davenport and C. Wibrow, the lyrics by A. Davenport, *etc. Boosey & Co.: London,* 1918. 4°. **F. 690. bb. (1.)**

— [Valentine. 5 detached vocal no.] *Boosey & Co.: London, etc.,* 1918. fol. **H. 1846. x. (8.)**

— [Valentine.] Selection ... Piano solo. *Boosey & Co.: London, etc.,* 1918. fol. **h. 3284. nn. (1.)**

— [Valentine.] The Butterflies in the Garden of Roses. Ballet music from the ... Opera ... Pianoforte solo. *Boosey & Co.: London,* 1918. 4°. **g. 603. xx. (6.)**

— Vivienne. Valse. [P. F.] *Francis, Day & Hunter: London,* 1904. fol. **h. 3286. dd. (48.)**

— Vivienne. Valse. [P. F.] *Francis, Day & Hunter: London,* 1904. fol. *Another copy, with a different titlepage.* **h. 3286. dd. (49.)**

— Who goes there?—The Sentry.—Song, words by F. W. Leigh. *Francis, Day & Hunter: London, New York,* 1906. fol. *Two copies, one without a cover.* **H. 3598. (23.)**

LAMBELET (NAPOLEON)

— The Wonderful Island. Song. The words by A. Chapman. *Boosey & Co.: London & New York,* 1900. fol. **H. 3598. (13.)**

The Yashmak

— The Yashmak. A Musical Play, words by C. Raleigh and S. Hicks. Music by N. Lambelet. With additions. Vocal Score. *Francis, Day & Hunter: London,* 1897. 4°. **F. 1449.**

— The Yashmak ... Piano Score. *Francis, Day & Hunter: London,* [1897.] 4°. **f. 540. j. (4.)**

— I'm a Monarch with original Ideas. Song, *etc. E. Ascherberg & Co.: London,* 1897. fol. **H. 1798. u. (9.)**

— Love's Eternity. Duet, *etc. Francis, Day & Hunter: London,* 1897. fol. **H. 1798. u. (10.)**

— *See* ALLAN (E.) Selections from ... The Yashmak [by N. Lambelet], arranged for the pianoforte, *etc.* 1897. fol. **h. 3281. u. (21.)**

— *See* WILLIAMS (W.) The Yashmak. Lancers [on N. Lambelet's musical play]. 1897. fol. **h. 3806. a. (34.)**

— *See* RICE (E. E.) Hush, little Girl, don't cry. Song ... arranged by N. Lambelet, *etc.* 1897. fol. **H. 1798. ff. (1.)**

LAMBELET (VIVIEN)

— Ah, do not be so sweet. Song. ⟨Poem by Mary Webb.⟩ pp. 4. *J. & W. Chester: London,* 1946. 4°. **G. 1270. vv. (17.)**

— Faint Heart. Song, the words by G. Hadath. *Schott & Co.: London,* 1927. fol. **H. 1846. mm. (7.)**

— Idyll. Song, the words by P. Askew. *Boosey & Co.: London,* 1933. 4°. **G. 1275. ll. (1.)**

— In a green London Square. Song, words by P. Wing. *Boosey & Co.: London,* 1941. 4°. **G. 1275. xx. (17.)**

— King's Messenger. Song, words by L. Cranmer-Byng from the Odes of Confucius. *Elkin & Co.: London,* 1926. 4°. **G. 1270. r. (8.)**

— A Litany. Song, poem by F. E. Young. *Boosey & Co.: London,* 1933. 4°. **G. 1275. nn. (14.)**

— The Lovely House. [Song.] Words by J. Earle, *etc. G. Ricordi & Co.: London, etc.,* 1935. 4°. **G. 1270. jj. (34.)**

— Memory. [Song.] Words by T. B. Aldrich. Music by V. Lambelert [*sic*]. pp. 3. *J. B. Cramer & Co.: London,* 1946. 4°. **F. 607. ww. (30.)**

— Six Nursery Rhymes, *etc. W. Paxton & Co.: London,* 1926. 4°. **G. 1270. r. (9.)**

— Oh, for my true Love. Song. ⟨Poem, 1800.⟩ pp. 4. *J. & W. Chester: London,* 1946. 4°. **G. 1270. vv. (18.)**

— Ribbons. Song. (Words by P. Wing.) *G. Ricordi & Co.: London, etc.,* 1935. 4°. **G. 1270. ll. (35.)**

— Searching the World for Love. [Song.] Words and music by V. Lambelet. *G. Ricordi & Co.: London, etc.,* 1933. 4°. **G. 1275. nn. (15.)**

— Simple Things. Song. (Words by P. Wing.) *G. Ricordi & Co.: London,* 1938. 4°. **G. 1270. pp. (1.)**

— Spanish Intermezzo. To the Memory of a Toreador ... For string orchestra, piano & harmonium. [Harmonium and] String Parts. *Augener: London,* 1926. 4°. **h. 3210. h. (219.)**

— Spanish Intermezzo. To the Memory of a Toreador. For piano. *Augener: London,* 1926. 4°. **g. 1127. dd. (1.)**

— Straws in my Hair. [Song.] Words & music by V. Lambelet. *G. Ricordi & Co.: London, etc.,* 1934. 4°. **G. 1275. nn. (16.)**

LAMBELET (Vivien)

— Yesterday's Roses. Song, the words by H. Taylor. *Boosey & Co.: London*, 1933. 4°.   G. 1275. ll. (2.)

— You Fever, *etc.* [Song.] (Words and music by V. Lambelet.) *G. Ricordi & Co.: London, etc.*, 1934. 4°.   G. 1275. nn. (17.)

LAMBERG (Josef)

— Abends. *See* infra: Zwei Gesänge ... Op. 55. No. 1.

— Zwei Gesänge für vier Frauenstimmen a capella. Op. 55. No. 1. Abends, [begins: "Nun wird es Abend," words by] E. Peschkau. No. 2. Das Mädchen und der Schmetterling, [begins: "Lustwandelnd schritt ein Mädchen," words by] R. E. Wegener. *Offenbach a. Main*, [1866.] 8°.
                                        E. 308. q. (21.)

— Das Mädchen und der Schmetterling. *See* supra: Zwei Gesänge ... Op. 55. No. 2.

— Vladimir. Valse de Concert. [P. F.] *Chappell & Co.: London*, [1884.] fol.   h. 1484. s. (5.)

LAMBERT

— Lambert Simnel. Opéra comique. *See* Monpou (H.) and Adam (A. C.)

LAMBERT (   )

— Rondeau avec accompagnement de piano forte ... Paroles de M^r****. Œuvre 10, *etc.* pp. 9. *Chez Naderman: Paris*, [c. 1800.] fol.   H. 1653. zz. (17.)

LAMBERT (   ) *Mlle*

— Le Satyre et le Passant. Fable mise en vers par Mr de la Fontaine, *etc. Chés Camand:* [*Paris*, 1780?] 8°.
                                        B. 362. e. (99.)

LAMBERT (Agnes Helen)

— Aria for Violin and Piano. *Schott & Co.: London*, (1913.) fol.   g. 505. ee. (32.)

— Aubade. *See* infra: [Ten Songs from a Garden. No. 4.]

— The Bracelet. *See* infra: Songs ... No. 1.

— Dear little Maid. *See* infra: Songs ... No. 2.

— Faire Daffadills. Song, words by Herrick. *Weekes & Co.: London*, [1897.] fol.   H. 1798. u. (11.)

— Far have you come, my Lady from the Town. [Song.] Words by R. L. Stevenson. *Stainer & Bell: London*, (1911.) fol. *Stainer & Bell's Modern Songs, No. 39.*   H. 1792. r. (9.)

— The Flower Song. *See* infra: [Love and the Dryad.]

— Give a Man a Horse he can ride. Song, words by J. Thomson, *etc. Metzler & Co.: London*, 1908. fol.   H. 1794. uu. (54.)

— Good-Night and The Pedlar. Two Songs, the words by E. H. *Boosey & Co.: London and New York*, 1922. 4°.
                                        G. 1270. f. (8.)

— The Holiday Song. Song, the words & music by A. H. Lambert. *Boosey & Co.: London, etc.*, 1920. fol.
                                        H. 1846. x. (9.)

— The Holy Angels. A Mystery Play, in mime. Arranged ... by A. Hubbard and J. Russell. *Boosey & Co.: London, New York*, 1926. 4°.   G. 782. yy. (1.)

— [The Holy Angels.] The Amen, *etc. Boosey & Co.: London & New York*, 1927. 8°.
A card.   I. 600. f. (38.)

LAMBERT (Agnes Helen)

— [The Holy Angels.] To the Lord our God we sing. *Hymn.* From The Holy Angels, Mystery Play. Music and words by A. H. Lambert. *Boosey & Co.: London & New York*, 1924. 8°.
                                        E. 1498. t. (25.)

— I will give Thanks unto Thee, O Lord. Festival Anthem. *Weekes & Co.: London*, [1897.] 8°.   F. 231. f. (14.)

— Little Daisies close their Eyes. *See* infra: [Ten Songs from a Garden. No. 8.]

— [Love and the Dryad.] The Flower Song. From the Masque, Love and the Dryad. Words and music by A. H. Lambert, *etc. Boosey & Co.: London and New York*, 1914. fol.
                                        H. 1793. r. (43.)

— [Love and the Dryad.] My Ladye singing. Song ... the words by S. Manley. *Boosey & Co.: London and New York*, 1914. fol.   H. 1793. r. (44.)

— My Ladye singing. *See* supra: [Love and the Dryad.]

— My Thoughts are Swallows. Vocal Duet for soprano & contralto, or baritone, the words by L. Nightingale. *Boosey & Co.: London, etc.*, 1921. 4°.   G. 426. u. (20.)

— The Nightingale has a Lyre of Gold. Song, the words by W. E. Henley. *Boosey & Co.: London and New York*, 1906. fol.   H. 1794. k. (52.)

— O like a Queen's her happy Tread. Song, words by W. Watson, *etc. Metzler & Co.: London*, 1908. fol.
                                        H. 1794. uu. (55.)

— Rest, Holy Child. A Christmas Song, with Accompaniment for Pianoforte or Organ. The words by F. A. H. L. *Boosey & Co.: London & New York*, 1900. fol.   H. 1187. z. (11.)

— The Singer. Song, words by F. Arthur. 2 no. [In C and F.] *Ascherberg, Hopwood & Crew: London*, 1913. fol.
                                        H. 1793. r. (45.)

— Song of the Dawn. [Song.] The words by F. E. Weatherly. *Boosey & Co.: London and New York*, 1908. fol.
                                        H. 1794. uu. (56.)

— Songs ... No. 1. The Bracelet. (Words by Herrick.) No. 2. Dear little Maid. (Words by F. A. H. L.) 2 no. *Vincent Music Co.: London*, [1902.] fol.   H. 1799. cc. (42.)

— Ten Songs from a Garden, *etc. Boosey & Co.: London and New York*, 1909. 4°.   G. 383. v. (7.)

— [Ten Songs from a Garden. No. 1, 3.] Love made a Garden for my Soul, and May Day, *etc. Boosey & Co.: London and New York*, [1910.] fol.   H. 1792. r. (10.)

— [Ten Songs from a Garden. No. 4.] Aubade, *etc. Boosey & Co.: London and New York*, [1913.] fol.   H. 1793. r. (42.)

— [Ten Songs from a Garden. No. 8.] Little Daisies close their Eyes, *etc.* [Song.] *Boosey & Co.: London and New York*, [1911.] fol.   H. 1792. r. (11.)

— Symbols. Song, the words by E. Higginbotham, *etc. Boosey & Co.: London and New York*, 1906. fol.   G. 807. jj. (26.)

— The Throstle. Song, the words by Tennyson. *Boosey & Co.: London and New York*, 1907. fol.   H. 1794. uu. (57.)

— Thy Day is done. Song. Words by Lord Byron. *B. Hollis & Co.: London*, 1900. fol.   H. 1799. g. (62.)

— To April. Song, words by L. Nightingale. *Boosey & Co.: London and New York*, 1907. fol.   H. 1794. uu. (58.)

— The Whispering Waves were half asleep. Song, the words by Shelley, *etc. Boosey & Co.: London and New York*, 1907. fol.
                                        H. 1794. uu. (59.)

LAMBERT (AGNES HELEN)

— Who's coming with the Daffodils? [Song.] Words by
S. Manley. *Stainer & Bell: London,* [1911.] fol.
Stainer & Bell's Modern Songs, No. 40.   **H. 1792. r. (12.)**

LAMBERT (ALEXANDER)

— Alexander Lambert's Instructive Course of pieces for the
piano. Early (Intermediate) (Primary) Grade. 3 vol. *J. W.
Stern & Co.: New York,* 1917. 4°.   **g. 337. mm. (4.)**

— Piano Method for Beginners. A practical and simple course
of Piano Instruction. *G. Schirmer: New York,* (1907.) 4°.
                                              g. 761. c. (4.)

— *See* BACH (J. S.) [Das wohltemperirte Clavier. Tl. I.] Prelude
No. 1 ... edited ... by A. Lambert. 1917. fol.
                                              h. 3007. d. (14.)

— *See* BEETHOVEN (L. van) Für Elise ... Edited ... by
A. Lambert. 1917. fol.   **h. 400. n. (19.)**

— *See* HELLER (S.) [25 études mélodiques. Op. 45. No. 13.] Etude
in form of a Valse ... Edited ... by A. Lambert. 1917. fol.
                                              h. 3870. f. (20.)

— *See* MAYER (C.) [Jugendblüthen. Op. 121. No. 2.] Tarantella
... Edited ... by A. Lambert. 1917. fol.   **h. 3284. pp. (29.)**

LAMBERT (ALEXANDRE)

— Bourrée et Étude pour pianoforte. Op. 4. *Berlin,* [1884.] fol.
                                              h. 3280. k. (18.)

— Étude. [P. F.] *See supra:* Bourrée et Étude ... Op. 4. No. 2.

— Frühlingsblume. Polka für das Pianoforte. *Berlin,* [1884.] fol.
                                              h. 3285. b. (39.)

LAMBERT (ARTHUR)

— The Robin Hood March. [P.F.] pp. 8. *Henry Farmer:
Nottingham; Joseph Williams: London,* [1875?] fol.
                                              h. 62. o. (15.)

LAMBERT (ARTHUR J.)

— Benedicite, omnia opera, in easiest form of Chant Service.
Weekes & Co.: London, [1892.] 4°.   **E. 602. p. (15.)**

LAMBERT (ARTHUR W.)

— Little Maiden. Song, words by R. Lee. *Boosey, Patey & Co.:
London,* [1878.] fol.   **H. 1783. o. (3.)**

— Marion. Gavotte for the pianoforte. *Weekes & Co.: London,*
[1886.] fol.   **h. 1484. s. (6.)**

LAMBERT (C. T.)

— Parting. Pianoforte solo. *West & Co.: London,* 1915. fol.
                                             h. 3284. nn. (2.)

LAMBERT (CECILY)

— Aubade. 4 recorders, *etc.* [Score.] pp. 3. *Universal Edition:
London,* [1962.] 4°.
[*Dolmetsch Recorder Series. no.* 64.]   **g. 125.**

— Copeo. (Majorcan dance.) Arranged by C. Lambert. ⟨For
violin and piano.⟩ [Score and part.] 2 pt. *Schott & Co.:
London,* [1965.] 4°.
[*First Solo Pieces. no.* 29.]   **g. 832.**

— Dance Music from three Centuries ... Thirty-eight dance
pieces selected and edited by C. Lambert, *etc.* [P.F.] 2 bk.
J. Curwen & Sons: London, [1966.] 4°.   **g. 1126. nn. (4.)**

LAMBERT (CECILY)

— Dances from various Lands. Arranged for violin and piano
by C. Lambert, *etc.* [Score and part.] 2 pt. *Forsyth Bros.:
London,* [1966.] fol.   **g. 223. ss. (8.)**

— A Duet a Day. [P.F. duet.] pp. 11. *Forsyth Bros.: Manchester,
London,* [1968.] 4°.   **g. 545. dd. (1.)**

— English and American traditional and folk Songs. For
recorder and piano ... Arranged by C. Lambert. [Score.]
pp. 15. *Forsyth Bros.: London, Manchester,* [1966.] 4°.
                                              g. 109. g. (13.)

— For me to play. For descant recoder, *etc.* ⟨Arranged by
C. Lambert.⟩ pp. 16. *Forsyth Bros.: London, Manchester,*
[1967.] 4°.   **g. 109. g. (16.)**

— Going up to London. Suite for piano, *etc.* pp. 4. *J. Curwen &
Sons: London; G. Schirmer: New York,* [1962.] 4°.
                                              g. 272. yy. (3.)

— Greek Scenes. [P.F.] pp. 11. *Forsyth Bros.: London,
Manchester,* [1970.] 4°.   **g. 1129. jj. (12.)**

— London Scenes. For piano solo. pp. 8. *Schott & Co.:
London,* [1965.] 4°.   **g. 1126. o. (12.)**

— More Fancy. For treble recorder with fingering instruction,
solos and duets for descant and treble recorders. ⟨Arranged
by⟩ C. Lambert, *etc.* [Score.] pp. 20. *Forsyth Bros.: London,
Manchester,* [1970.] 4°.   **g. 109. ii. (6.)**

— Plain and fancy. For treble recorder. With fingering
instruction and duets for descant and treble recorders, *etc.*
⟨Arranged by C. Lambert.⟩ [Score.] pp. 20. *Forsyth Bros.:
London, Manchester,* [1968.] 4°.   **g. 109. k. (5.)**

— Pleasures and Pastimes. [P.F.] pp. 9. *Forsyth Bros.: London,*
[1965.] 4°.   **g. 1138. i. (8.)**

— Processional ... Piano solo. *Composers Press: New York;*
[*printed in Holland,* 1954.] 4°.   **g. 1128. v. (16.)**

— Set of five. ⟨Piano duets.⟩ pp. 27. *Forsyth Bros.: London,*
[1974.] 4°.   **h. 141. aa. (6.)**

— Set of Five. Piano duets. pp. 27. *Forsyth Bros.: London,*
[1974.] 4°.   **g. 606. kk. (10.)**

— Won't you sit down? Four four-part chorus of male voices
with piano accompaniment. Negro camp meeting song.
Arranged by C. Lambert. [Staff and tonic sol-fa notation.]
pp. 8. *Chappell & Co.: London,* [1960.] 8°. **E. 1850. g. (38.)**

— *See* BEETHOVEN (L. van) [Bagatelles. Op. 33. No. 6.] Bagatelle.
Arranged [for violin and piano] by C. Lambert. [1965.] 4°.
[*First Solo Pieces. no.* 23.]   **g. 832.**

— *See* BIZET (A. C. L.) [Jeux d'enfants. Op. 22. No. 2. La Toupie.]
The Spinning Top ... Arranged by C. Lambert. [Violin and
P.F.] [1965.] 4°. [*First Solo Pieces. no.* 25.]   **g. 832.**

— *See* BRAHMS (J.) [*Collected Works.*—c.] Folk Song and The
Hunter. ⟨Arranged for violin and piano by C. Lambert.⟩
[1964.] 4°. [*First Solo Pieces. no.* 5.]   **g. 832.**

— *See* CORELLI (A.) [Sonatas. Op. 5. No. 6.] Allegro ... Arranged
by C. Lambert. ⟨For violin and piano.⟩ [1965.] 4°. [*First Solo
Pieces. no.* 28.]   **g. 832.**

— *See* HAYDN (F. J.) [Trios. Hob. XV/25.] Rondo all'ongarese ...
Arranged by C. Lambert. ⟨For violin and piano.⟩ [1965.] 4°.
[*First Solo Pieces. no.* 30.]   **g. 832.**

— *See* KIRNBERGER (J. P.) [Recueil d'airs de danse. Partie I.
No. 20. Les Carillons.] Carillon. Arranged by C. Lambert.
[Violin and P.F.] [1964.] 4°. [*First Solo Pieces. no.* 13.]
                                              g. 832.

— *See* KREISLER (F.) Rondino (on a Theme by Beethoven) ...
Arranged ... by Cecily Lambert. 1945. 4°.   **h. 1694. c. (14.)**

LAMBERT (CECILY)

— *See* KREISLER (F.) Tambourin Chinois … Arranged … by C. Lambert. 1945. 4°.   **h. 1694. c. (18.)**

— *See* LYADOV (A. K.) [8 russische Volksweisen. Op. 58. No. 6, 4.] Berceuse. ⟨Dance of the Mosquito⟩ … Arranged by C. Lambert. [Violin and P.F.] [1965.] 4°. [*First Solo Pieces. no.* 18.]   **g. 832.**

— *See* LYADOV (A. K.) [8 russische Volksweisen. Op. 58. No. 6, 4.] Two Russian Folk Songs. Arranged for descant recorder and piano … by C. Lambert, *etc.* [1966.] *obl.* 8°.   **a. 40. u. (3.)**

— *See* MACDOWELL (Edward A.) [Woodland Sketches. Op. 51. No. 1.] To a wild Rose … E. MacDowell, *etc.* ⟨Watchman's Song. E. Grieg. Op. 12. No. 3.⟩ [Arranged for violin and piano by C. Lambert.⟩ [1964.] 4°. [*First Solo Pieces. no.* 1.]   **g. 832.**

— *See* MOZART (W. A.) Minuet and Trio in G. (K. 1.) Arranged by C. Lambert. [Violin and P.F.] [1964.] 4°. [*First Solo Pieces. no.* 10.]   **g. 832.**

— *See* RAKHMANINOV (S. V.) [Rapsodie sur un thème de Paganini. Op. 43.] Eighteenth Variation. Rapsodie on a Theme of Paganini … Piano solo, *etc.* ⟨Arranged by C. Lambert.⟩ [1953.] 4°.   **h. 3984. h. (13.)**

— *See* SCHUBERT (F. P.) [Original-Tänze. Op. 9. No. 4.] Waltz. Arranged by C. Lambert. [Violin and P.F.] [1964.] 4°. [*First Solo Pieces. no.* 8.]   **g. 832.**

LAMBERT (CECILY) and KNECHTEL (RIED)

— Adventures in Music. bk. 1. pp. 28. *Forsyth Bros.: London, Manchester,* [1967.] 8°.
No more published.   **e. 138. o. (1.)**

— Forsyth Descant Recorder Tutor. By Cecily Lambert & Ried Knechtel, *etc.* pp. 40. *Forsyth Bros.: London, Manchester,* [1974.] 8°.   **e. 184. c. (2.)**

— Forsyth Descant Recorder Tutor. pp. 40. *Forsyth Bros.: London, Manchester,* [1975.] 8°.   **e. 138. v. (2.)**

LAMBERT (CONSTANT)

— Aubade Héroïque for Small Orchestra, *etc.* (Full Score.) *Oxford University Press: London,* 1944. 4°.   **g. 727. n. (1.)**

— Concerto for Solo Pianoforte and nine Players … Full score. pp. 49. *Oxford University Press: London,* [1933.] fol.   **h. 1508. oo. (2.)**

— Concerto for solo Pianoforte and nine Players. Piano solo [with the accompaniment in short score]. pp. 47. *Oxford University Press: London,* [1933.] fol.   **h. 3958. a.**

— Dirge from Shakespeare's Cymbeline … for Tenor Solo, Baritone Solo, Male Voice Chorus and Strings. [Vocal score.] *Oxford University Press: London,* 1942. 8°.   **F. 163. gg. (54.)**

— Elegiac Blues, for Pianoforte. *J. & W. Chester: London,* 1928. fol.   **h. 3865. g. (36.)**

— Elegy. For Piano Solo. *Oxford University Press: London,* 1940. 4°.   **g. 1125. tt. (19.)**

— Horoscope. A Ballet in one act. Piano arrangement by the Composer. *Oxford University Press: London,* 1938. fol.   **h. 3958. (2.)**

— Horoscope. Orchestral Suite from the Ballet. Full Score. *Oxford University Press: London,* 1939. fol.   **h. 3958. (1.)**

— Horoscope. Orchestral suite from the ballet … Full score. pp. 118. *Oxford University Press: London,* [1961.] 8°.   **e. 669. (2.)**

LAMBERT (CONSTANT)

— The Long-departed Lover. [Song.] Poem by Li-Po, translated by Shigeyoshi Obata. *Oxford University Press: London,* 1930. 4°.   **G. 1275. ff. (27.)**

— Merchant Seamen. Suite for Orchestra … Reduced version. (Full Score.) *Boosey & Hawkes: London,* 1944. 4°.   **g. 727. o. (4.)**

— Music for Orchestra. Full Score. *Oxford University Press: London,* 1930. fol.   **h. 1509. mm. (2.)**

— Trois pièces nègres pour les touches blanches. Piano à 4 mains, *etc.* pp. 18. *Oxford University Press: London,* [1950.] 4°.   **g. 1123. d. (3.)**

— Four Poems by Li-Po. Translated by Shigeyoshi Obata … for Medium Voice and Pianoforte. (1. A summer day. 2. Nocturne. 3. With a man of leisure. 4. Lines.) *Oxford University Press: London,* 1927. 4°.   **G. 1270. x. (30.)**

— Three Poems by Li-Po. Translated by Shigeyoshi Obata … 1. The ruin of the Ku-Su palace. 2. The intruder. 3. On the city street. [Songs.] *J. & W. Chester: London,* 1928. 4°.   **G. 1270. x. (29.)**

— Pomona. A Ballet in one act. Theme by T. McGreevy. Choreography by La Nijinska … Pianoforte Duet arrangement by the Composer. Cover design by J. Banting. *Oxford University Press: London,* 1928. fol.   **g. 230. e. (5.)**

— [Pomona.] Siciliana … Piano Solo. *Oxford University Press: London,* 1930. 4°.   **g. 1125. bb. (24.)**

— The Rio Grande. The Poem by S. Sitwell. Full Score. *Oxford University Press: London, New York,* 1930. fol.   **H. 1850. (14.)**

— The Rio Grande … Miniature Score. *Oxford University Press: London,* [1942.] 8°.   **B. 990.**

— [A reissue.] The Rio Grande … Miniature score. *London,* [1974.] 8°.   **B. 418. o. (7.)**

— The Rio Grande … Vocal Score. *Oxford University Press: London,* 1929. fol.   **H. 1860. g. (20.)**

— The Rio Grande. Poem by Sacheverell Sitwell set for chorus, orchestra, and solo pianoforte … German version by Beryl de Zoete. ⟨Vocal score.⟩ pp. 26. *Oxford University Press: London,* [1929.] fol.
No. 6 of an edition of seventy-five copies, signed by the author and composer.   **K. 11. d. 5.**

— The Rio Grande. Poem by S. Sitwell, set for Chorus, Orchestra, and Solo Pianoforte … German version by B. de Zoete. [Vocal score with 2 P. F.] *Oxford University Press: London,* 1929. fol.
One of an edition of seventy-five copies.   **K. 10. a. 35.**

— The Rio Grande … Solo Piano. *Oxford University Press: London,* [1929.] fol.   **h. 3865. h. (9.)**

— Romeo and Juliet. Ballet in two tableaux … Choreography by Nijinska. Arrangement for Piano Solo by the Composer, *etc. Oxford University Press: London,* 1926. fol.   **g. 230. e. (4.)**

— Sonata for Pianoforte. *Oxford University Press: London,* 1930. fol.   **h. 3865. h. (16.)**

— [A reissue.] Sonata for Pianoforte. *London,* [1973.] 4°.   **g. 352. uu. (4.)**

— Summer's last Will and Testament. A Masque for Orchestra, Chorus, and Baritone Solo … Words taken from the Pleasant Comedy of that name written in 1593 by Thomas Nashe. (Vocal Score. As a Piano Duet. Arranger, Achibald Jacob.) *Oxford University Press: London,* 1937. fol.   **H. 3594.**

LAMBERT (CONSTANT)

— Summer's last Will and Testament. A masque ... The drawings by Michael Ayrton. [Vocal score arranged by Archibald Jacob.] pp. 78. *Oxford University Press: London*, 1946. fol.　　**I. 575.**

— Summer's last Will and Testament, *etc.* (Choruses only.) *Oxford University Press: London*, 1935. 8°.　**F. 1267. t. (6.)**

— [Tiresias.] *See* RAWSTHORNE (Alan) Improvisations on a Theme by Constant Lambert. ⟨Theme taken from the ballet "Tiresias".⟩ [1962.] 8°.　　**e. 640. (2.)**

— *See* BOYCE (W.) [An Ode performed in the Senate House at Cambridge.] Overture in D minor ... Transcribed ... by C. Lambert. 1939. 4°. [*Oxford Orchestral Series. No.* 123.]　　**g. 1263.**

— *See* BOYCE (W.) Pan and Syrinx ... Overture ... Transcribed and edited by C. Lambert. 1937. 4°. [*Oxford Orchestral Series. No.* 117.]　　**g. 1263.**

— *See* BOYCE (W.) The Power of Music ... Overture ... Transcribed and edited by C. Lambert. 1937. 4°. [*Oxford Orchestral Series. No.* 116.]　　**g. 1263.**

— *See* BOYCE (W.) Eight Symphonies ... [Op. 2.] Transcribed ... by C. Lambert, *etc.* 1928. 4°. [*Oxford Orchestral Series. No.* 62–69.]　　**g. 1263.**

— *See* BOYCE (W.) [8 Symphonies. Op. 2. No. 5.] Symphony v, *etc.* ⟨Transcribed and edited for strings and optional wind by C. Lambert.⟩ [1967.] 4°. [*Oxford orchestral Series. no.* 66.]　　**g. 1263.**

— *See* CHOPIN (F. F.) [*Collected Works.—f.*] Les Sylphides ... Edited by C. Lambert, *etc.* 1942. 4°.　**g. 553. n. (22.)**

— *See* HAENDEL (G. F.) [Organ Concertos. Op. 4. No. 2, 6.] Concerto in B flat for Pianoforte and Small Orchestra. Arranged ... by C. Lambert. Score. 1934. 4°.　**g. 74. z. (19.)**

— *See* HAENDEL (G. F.) [Organ Concertos. Op. 4. No. 2, 6.] Concerto in B flat for Pianoforte and Small Orchestra ... Arranged by C. Lambert. Solo Pianoforte. 1934. 8°.　　**g. 74. z. (20.)**

— *See* MEYERBEER (G.) Suite from the Ballet Les Patineurs, The Skaters ... Arranged by C. Lambert, *etc.* 1943. 4°.　　**h. 3210. h. (883.)**

— *See* PURCELL (Henry) [*Collected Works.—c.*] Comus. Suite from the ballet ... Arranged by C. Lambert. [1947.] 4°.　　**g. 25. c. (9.)**

— *See* WALTON (*Sir* William T.) Façade ... Pianoforte Duet arrangement by C. Lambert. 1927. fol.　**h. 4015. (7.)**

— *See* WALTON (*Sir* William T.) [Façade.] Swiss Jodelling song ... Arranged for pianoforte duet ⟨by C. Lambert⟩. [1968.] 4°.　　**h. 4005. e. (5.)**

— *See* WALTON (*Sir* William T.) [Façade.] Tango ... Arranged for pianoforte duet ⟨by C. Lambert⟩. [1968.] 4°.　　**h. 4005. e. (8.)**

— *See* WILLIAMS (R. V.) Concerto Academico ... Arrangement for Violin and Piano. (Piano arrangement by C. Lambert.) 1927. fol.　　**i. 115. b. (3.)**

— *See* WILLIAMS (R. V.) The Wasps ... Transcribed for piano duet by C. Lambert, *etc.* 1926. 4°.　**g. 1266. (3.)**

LAMBERT (E. AINSWORTH)

— The Choir Boy's Dream. [Song.] ... Words by H. H. Lemmel. With violin and organ obligato. *J. Flanner: Milwaukee, Wis.*, 1900. fol.　　**H. 1187. z. (12.)**

— Morning Glory.—Danse caracteristique. [P. F.] *J. Flanner: Milwaukee*, 1900. fol.　　**h. 3282. w. (23.)**

LAMBERT (E. AINSWORTH)

— [Another edition.] Morning Glory, *etc. J. Flanner: Milwaukee*, 1900. fol.　　**h. 3282. w. (24.)**

LAMBERT (E. FRANK)

— Frank Lambert Album. [Songs.] *Chappell & Co.: London, etc.*, [1909.] 4°. *Part of "The Portrait Series".*　　**G. 1121. (4.)**

— Album of short Songs. Volume I. (High.) (Volume II.) [Low and high.] 3 no. *Chappell & Co.: London, etc.*, [1913.] 4°.　　**G. 390. e. (6.)**

— Favourite Songs, *etc. G. Newnes: London*, [1913.] fol. *No. 57 of "The Music-Lovers' Library".*　　**H. 3928.**

— Across the Moor. Song, words by E. Alfieri. *Ransford & Son: London*, 1892. fol.　　**H. 1797. o. (25.)**

— L'Adieu du Soir. Entr'acte for Piano. *A. Hammond & Co.: London*, 1927. fol.　　**h. 3870. f. (26.)**

— Apart. Song, words by A. M. Lambert. *Ransford & Son: London*, 1892. fol.　　**H. 1797. o. (26.)**

— "Apples." A Child's Song, written by E. C. Taylor, *etc. Keith, Prowse & Co.: London*, 1908. fol.　　**H. 3605. b. (15.)**

— Aubade à la Fiancée. [Song.] *Chappell & Co.: London*, 1899. fol.　　**H. 3605. (12.)**

— A Barque at Midnight. [Song.] Words Anon. [Translated from the French of L. de Peyre.] 3 no. [In E flat, F and G.] *See* infra: Series of Short Songs. No. 3.

— Because my Heart-Wound. [Song.] Words by L. G. Ackroyd. 2 no. [In G minor and B flat minor.] *See* infra: Series of Short Songs. No. 7.

— Beyond. Song, the words by J. Gade. *Boosey & Co.: London and New York*, 1908. fol.　　**H. 3605. b. (16.)**

— Beyond the Veil. Song, the words by C. Dick. *Boosey & Co.: London & New York*, 1898. fol.　　**H. 3605. (13.)**

— Bid you good morrow. Song, words by H. Simpson. 3 no. [In D, E flat and F.] *Chappell & Co.: London, etc.*, 1906. fol.　　**H. 3605. b. (1.)**

— The Birth of Song. Song. The Words by L. Renton. *Boosey & Co.: London and New York*, 1896. fol.　　**H. 3605. (1.)**

— Bonjour Pierrot. Song, words by F. E. Weatherly. *Chappell & Co.: London*, 1897. fol.　　**H. 3605. (14.)**

— Bonnie wee Thing. Song, words by Burns. *Keith, Prowse & Co.: London*, 1920. fol.　　**H. 3605. c. (16.)**

— The Bud's on the Briar. Song, words by H. Boulton, *etc.* 2 no. [In D and F.] *Chappell & Co.: London, etc.*, 1907. fol.　　**H. 3605. b. (17.)**

— The Buried Rose. Song, words by W. E. Grogan. *Chappell & Co.: London and Melbourne*, 1906. fol.　　**H. 3605. b. (2.)**

— Calm be thy Sleep and Here let me lie. Two Songs. Written by E. Alfieri. *Reynolds & Co.: London*, [1897.] fol.　　**H. 3605. (8.)**

— Caressante. (Come to my Heart.) Valse chantée, paroles de M. Farkoa, English version by A. B. *Chappell & Co.: London*, 1903. fol.　　**H. 3605. (40.)**

— [Caressante.] Hab' mich lieb! ... Lied für eine Singstimme mit Begleitung des Pianoforte. (Deutscher Text von P. Grossmann, Französischer Text von M. Farkoa.) *Chappell & Co.: London und Melbourne*, (1906.) fol.　**H. 3605. b. (6.)**

— Caressante. Valse. [P. F.] *Chappell & Co.: London*, 1903. fol.　　**h. 3286. dd. (50.)**

LAMBERT (E. Frank)

— Caressante. Arranged for military band by W. J. Duthoit. ⟨Conductor [and parts].⟩ 32 pt. *In:* ELGAR (*Sir* Edward W.) *Bart.* Salut d'amour, *etc.* [1941.] fol. [*Chappell's Army Journal. no.* 679.]   **h. 1562.**

— Charmante. Valse. [P. F.] *J. Church Co.: London, etc.,* 1909. fol.   **h. 3286. uu. (36.)**

— Come close, Beloved. [Song.] Words by A. M. Lambert. 3 no. [In E flat, F and G.] *See* infra: Series of Short Songs. No. 10.

— Come, Love, in the Springtime. *See* infra: [Springtide.]

— Darkness and Dawn. Song, words by J. L. Best. 3 no. [In E flat, F and G.] *Chappell & Co.: London,* 1902. fol.   **H. 3605. (27.)**

— Dear Hands. Song, words by W. E. Henley. 3 no. [In F, G and B flat.] *Chappell & Co.: London and Melbourne,* 1906. fol.   **H. 3605. b. (3.)**

— Dear Yesterday. Song, words by L. L. Cooke. *Keith, Prowse & Co.: London,* 1918. 4°.   **G. 426. d. (46.)**

— Dearest. Song, the words by A. Clayton-East. *Enoch & Sons: London,* 1910. fol.   **H. 3605. c. (1.)**

— Dearest, when I am dead. Song, words by W. E. Henley. 3 no. [In E flat, F and A flat.] *See* infra: Series of Short Songs. No. 13.

— Deep in my Heart. Song, words by H. Simpson. 3 no. [In D flat, E flat and F.] *Chappell & Co.: London and Melbourne,* 1905. fol.   **H. 3605. b. (4.)**

— The Dewdrop and the Tear. Song, words by A. M. Lambert. 3 no. [In E flat, F and G.] *Chappell & Co.: London and Melbourne,* 1904. fol.   **H. 3605. (36.)**

— Dinkly Winkly. A Southern Melody. [Song.] Words by Mrs. A. S. Bradshaw, *etc. Greening's Music: London,* 1912. fol.   **H. 3605. c. (7.)**

— Don't be afraid to try. [Song.] Written by A. Hopwood, *etc. Chappell & Co.: London,* 1898. fol.   **H. 3605. (15.)**

— Evermore.—Ici-bas.—Song, English words by C. Fabri. —French words by S. Prudhomme.—2 no. [In C and E flat.] *Chappell & Co.: London and Melbourne,* 1904. fol.   **H. 3605. b. (5.)**

— A Fair Exchange, *etc.* [Song.] *Francis, Day & Hunter: London,* 1897. *s. sh.* fol.   **H. 3605. (2.)**

— Fair Land of Dreams. Song, words by A. Valdemar. 3 no. [In E flat, F and G.] *Chappell & Co.: London, etc.,* 1908. fol.   **H. 3605. b. (18.)**

— A Farewell. Song, words by C. Bingham. 3 no. [In A flat, B flat and C.] *Chappell & Co.: London,* 1901. fol.   **H. 3605. (28.)**

— Farewell, thou outbound Ship. Song, the lyric by M. Osborne. *Enoch & Sons: London,* 1923. 4°.   **H. 3605. c. (18.)**

— Father's Lullaby. Song. With Violin or Violoncello Obbligato ad lib. Words by H. Aïdé. *Chappell & Co.: London,* 1897. fol.   **H. 3605. (3.)**

— The Fighting Chance. Song, the lyric by C. D. Furber. (New edition.) *Enoch & Sons: London,* 1925. 4°.   **H. 3605. c. (24.)**

— Flow on thou crystal Nith. *See* infra: Two Songs ... No. 2.

— For my Heart's Rest. Song, with cello obbligato, words by H. Smith. *Wilford: London,* 1922. fol.   **H. 3605. c. (19.)**

— Forethought. [Song.] Words by J. Peabody. 2 no. [In F and G.] *See* infra: Series of Short Songs. No. 11.

LAMBERT (E. Frank)

— The Fountains mingle with the River. Song, words by P. B. Shelley. 3 no. [In E flat, F and G.] *Chappell & Co.: London,* 1902. fol.   **H. 3605. (29.)**

— The Garden of her Heart. Song, words by H. Simpson. 3 no. [In F, G and A.] *Chappell & Co.: London, etc.,* 1911. fol.   **h. 3605. c. (2.)**

— Give me that Rose. *See* infra: [Valse d'Automne.]

— God's Garden. Sacred song. (With [additional] organ, or harmonium accompaniment, ad lib.) Words by D. F. Gurney. pp. 5. *Chappell & Cⁱᵉ: London,* [1902.] fol.   **G. 503. s. (11.)**

— "Gogy-o-gay!" Song, words from "Cradle Songs," *etc. Francis, Day & Hunter: London,* 1909. fol. *Two copies, one without a cover.*   **H. 3605. b. (20.)**

— Hab' mich lieb! *See* supra: [Caressante.]

— Here let me lie. *See* supra: Calm be thy Sleep, *etc.*

— The Hour of Sleep. Song, words by W. Akerman. 3 no. [In C, E flat and G.] *Chappell & Co.: London,* 1902. fol.   **H. 3605. (37.)**

— How can I tell? Song. Written by G. Annibal. *J. Williams: London,* 1893. fol.   **H. 3605. (4.)**

— I gave my Heart to you. Song, words by M. Osborne. *Keith, Prowse & Co.: London,* 1917. fol.   **H. 3605. c. (13.)**

— I know a Glade of Daffodils. Song, words by R. B. Haymes. 2 no. [In E flat and F.] *Chappell & Co.: London, etc.,* 1908. fol.   **H. 3605. b. (21.)**

— I know a Wood. Song, words by E. C. Taylor. 3 no. [In E flat, F and G.] *Chappell & Co.: London, etc.,* 1908. fol.   **H. 3605. b. (22.)**

— I love you. Song, words by A. A. Procter. 2 no. [In D and F.] *Leonard & Co.: London,* [1901.] fol.   **H. 3605. (30.)**

— I love you. [In C.] *Leonard & Co.: London,* [1905.] fol.   **H. 3605. b. (7.)**

— I love you all. Song, the words by F. E. Weatherly. *Enoch & Sons: London,* 1900. fol.   **H. 3605. (18.)**

— I meant the Words I said. [Song.] Words by C. McDonell, *etc. Chappell & Co.: London,* 1898. fol.   **H. 3605. (17.)**

— I never knew I lov'd thee so. *See* infra: Two Songs ... No. 1.

— I pack my bag and go. Song, words by R. Horniman. *Chappell & Co.: London,* 1900. fol.   **H. 3605. (19.)**

— I think of thee. Ballad, *etc. Ascherberg, Hopwood & Crew: London,* 1911. fol.   **H. 3605. c. (3.)**

— If we should meet. Song, words by E. Alfieri. 2 no. [In C and E flat.] *E. Ashdown: London,* 1900. fol.   **H. 3605. (16.)**

— In June. Song, words by E. Teschemacher. 3 no. [In E flat, F and G.] *See* infra: Series of Short Songs. No. 17.

— In Memory of my Sweet. Song, words by M. Osborne. *Chappell & Co.: London, etc.,* 1920. fol.   **H. 3605. c. (17.)**

— In that Hour. Song, words by J. Gade. 3 no. [In G, A flat and B flat.] *Chappell & Co.: London, etc.,* 1907. fol.   **H. 3605. b. (23.)**

— A Lament. [Song.] Words by H. L. Rogers. 2 no. [In D flat and F.] *See* infra: Series of Short Songs. No. 9.

— The Land of my Heart's Desire. Song, words by E. Ponsonby. 2 no. [In D flat and F.] *Francis, Day & Hunter: London,* 1905. fol.   **H. 3605. b. (8.)**

LAMBERT (E. FRANK)

— Look down, dear Eyes. Song, words by W. E. Henley. 3 no. [In D flat, D and F.] *Chappell & Co.: London and Melbourne*, 1904. fol.　　　　**H. 3605. b. (9.)**

— Lotus Land. Song, words by C. Bingham. 2 no. [In B flat and D flat.] *Chappell & Co.: London*, 1901. fol.　**H. 3605. (31.)**

— Love in Absence, *etc.* [Song.] 2 no. [In F and G.] *See* infra: Series of Short Songs. No. 2.

— Love or forget? Song, words by P. Ferrell. *Lublin & Co.: London*, 1908. fol.　　　　**H. 3605. b. (24.)**

— Love that is gone. Song, *etc.* (In F & A flat.) 2 no. *See* infra: Series of Short Songs. No. 18.

— Love that lives. Song, words by E. Ponsonby. *Francis, Day & Hunter: London*, 1905. fol.　　**H. 3605. b. (10.)**

— Mabel. Graceful Dance. [P. F.] *Reynolds & Co.: London*, [1893.] fol.　　　　**g. 605. f. (3.)**

— Menuet d'Antan. [P. F.] *Chappell & Co.: London, etc.*, 1906. fol.　　　　**h. 3286. ll. (17.)**

— My Love is dead. Song, words by G. S. Aspinall. *E. Ashdown: London, etc.*, [1909.] fol.　**H. 3605. b. (25.)**

— The Night has a thousand Eyes. [Song.] Words by F. W. Bourdillon. 2 no. [In F and A flat.] *See* infra: Series of Short Songs. No. 4.

— Oh! breathe not his Name. Song, words by T. Moore. 3 no. [In C, E flat and G.] *Ascherberg, Hopwood & Crew: London*, 1910. fol.　　　　**H. 3605. c. (4.)**

— O Falmouth is a fine Town. Song, words by W. E. Henley. *Ransford & Son: London*, 1892. fol.　**H. 1797. o. (27.)**

— O heedless Flower. [Song.] Words by J. Gade. 2 no. [In F and A flat.] *See* infra: Series of Short Songs. No. 14.

— O let me weep. [Song.] 3 no. [In F, A flat and B flat.] *See* infra: Series of Short Songs. No. 12.

— O purest Pearl of Paradise. [Song.] Words by H. Boulton. *See* infra: Series of Short Songs. No. 6.

— O steer my Bark. Song, words by T. H. Bayley. (In D and F.) 2 no. *Ascherberg, Hopwood & Crew: London*, (1913.) fol.　　　　**H. 3605. c. (8.)**

— Of all Septembers. Song, words by F. G. Bowles. 3 no. [In C, D and E flat.] *Chappell & Co.: London, etc.*, 1907. fol.　　　　**H. 3605. b. (26.)**

— Old Heidelberg. Alt Heidelberg. [Song, words by] J. V. von Scheffel, the English words by Sir Lees Knowles. [*Simpkin, Marshall & Co.: London*, 1913.] 8°. *Pp.* 52 *and* 53 *of "A Day with Corps-Students in Germany," by Sir Lees Knowles.*　　　　**8358. i. 5.**

— One. Song, words by C. Bingham. 2 no. [In F and G.] *Chappell & Co.: London*, 1901. fol.　**H. 3605. (32.)**

— One Life, one Love. Song. Words by L. Cranmer-Byng. 2 no. [In D and F.] *Chappell & Co.: London*, 1901. fol.　　　　**H. 3605. (20.)**

— One more Clasp. [Song.] Words Anon. 2 no. [In D flat and F.] *See* infra: Series of Short Songs. No. 5.

— The Orchid and the Butterfly. Song, written by F. Richardson. *Reynolds & Co.: London*, [1901.] fol.　　　　**H. 3605. (33.)**

— The Passionate Shepherdess. Song, the words by P. England. *Boosey & Co.: London and New York*, 1908. fol.　　　　**H. 3605. b. (27.)**

LAMBERT (E. FRANK)

— Philip the Fusilier. Humorous Song … written … by Pat à Beckett. *Reynolds & Co.: London*, (1914.) fol.　　　　**H. 3605. c. (9.)**

— The Pipes of Destiny. Song, words by T. Heffernan. *C. Lennox & Co.: London*, 1921. fol.　**H. 3605. c. (20.)**

— Queen of all. Song, words by E. Ponsonby. *Francis, Day & Hunter: London*, 1905. fol.　　**H. 3605. b. (11.)**

— Qui sait?—Fallen Roses.—Song, English words by J. Gade. 2 no. [In F and A flat.] *Chappell & Co.: London and Melbourne*, 1905. fol.　　**H. 3605. b. (12.)**

— Rose Aylmer. Song, words by W. S. Landor. *Jameson & Co.: London*, 1921. fol.　　　**H. 3605. c. (21.)**

— The Secret. Song, words by M. Garford. 3 no. [In F, G and A flat.] *Chappell & Co.: London and Melbourne*, 1904. fol.　　　　**H. 3605. (38.)**

— See, Love, I bring thee Flowers.—Solatia Florum.—[Song.] Words by H. L. Rogers. 2 no. [In D flat and F.] *See* infra: Series of Short Songs. No. 8.

— Series of Short Songs. *Chappell & Co.: London*, 1899, *etc.* fol.　　　　**H. 3605. a.**

— She is far from the Land. Song. Words by T. Moore. 3 no. [In G, A flat and C.] *Chappell & Co.: London*, 1897. fol.　　　　**H. 3605. (5.)**

— She walks in Beauty. Song, words by Lord Byron. *Ransford & Son: London*, 1892. fol.　　**G. 807. h. (1.)**

— Two Short Songs.—a—Dear sad brown Eyes. Words by H. E. Warner.—b—O strike thy Harp. Words by L. Chandler. 2 no. [In A and D; C and F.] *Ascherberg, Hopwood & Crew: London*, 1911. fol.　　　　**H. 3605. c. (5.)**

— Silent Love. Song, the word by R. M. Milnes, *etc.* 2 no. [In C and E flat.] *Novello & Co.: London*, 1910. 4°.　　　　**G. 424. z. (10.)**

— Sleep, little one. Song, words by E. Alfieri. *Leonard & Co.: London*, [1899.] fol.　　**H. 3605. (21.)**

— Slumber, my Darling. Song. Words by A. Valdemar. *O. Ditson Company: Boston, etc.*, 1896. fol.　**H. 3605. (6.)**

— Sometimes, with deep regret, *etc. Boosey & Co.: London and New York*, 1922. 4°.　　　**H. 3605. c. (22.)**

— The Song of the Mill-Wheel. Words by E. Alfieri. *Chappell & Co.: London*, [1897.] fol.　**H. 3605. (7.)**

— Two Songs … [No. 1.] I never knew I lov'd thee so. [No. 2.] Flow on thou crystal Nith! (Words by J. S. Binnie.) *Reynolds & Co.: London*, [1896.] fol.　　**H. 3605. (9.)**

— Sourire d'Amour. Valse. [P. F.] *Chappell & Co.: London*, 1905. fol.　　　　**h. 3286. dd. (51.)**

— Speak but one Word. Song. Words by E. Teschemacher. *O. Ditson Company: Boston, etc.*, 1896. fol.　**H. 3605. (10.)**

— Speak but one Word. Song, words by E. Teschemacher. *Chappell & Co.: London*, [1900.] fol.　**H. 3605. (22.)**

— [Springtide.] Come, Love, in the Springtime. Song from the Musical Operette, Springtide. Words by A. Fitzgerald. *Chappell & Co.: London, etc.*, 1913. fol.　**H. 3605. c. (6.)**

— The Street sounds to the Soldier's Tread. [Song.] Words by A. E. Housman, *etc. Stainer & Bell: London*, (1914.) fol. *Stainer and Bell's Modern Songs, No.* 92.　**H. 3605. c. (10.)**

— Swallows over Sea. Song, words by H. O. Beeching. 3 no. [In E flat, F and A flat.] *Chappell & Co.: London*, 1902. fol.　　　　**H. 3605. (39.)**

LAMBERT (E. Frank)

— Sweet Afton. Song, words by R. Burns. 3 no. [In C, D and F.] *Chappell & Co.: London, etc.,* 1909. fol.   **H. 3605. b. (28.)**

— Sweet Zephyrs, breathe my gentle Love. Song, words by B. Fennell. 2 no. [In C and E flat.] *Chappell & Co.: London,* 1900. fol.   **H. 3605. (23.)**

— Tell her. Song, words by L. Cooke. *West & Co.: London,* 1919. fol.   **H. 3605. c. (14.)**

— There sits a Bird on yonder Tree. Song, words from Ingoldsby Legends. *E. Ascherberg & Co.: London,* 1901. fol.   **H. 3605. (34.)**

— There was a Star. Song, words by C. Fabri. 2 no. [In E flat and F.] *Chappell & Co.: London,* 1900. fol.   **H. 3605. (24.)**

— There was a Star, *etc.* [In G.] *Chappell & Co.: London,* 1900. fol.   **H. 3605. (26.)**

— Though thou art far. Song, written by E. Alfieri. *Chappell & Co.: London,* 1891. fol.   **H. 1797. o. (28.)**

— Though you leave me now in Sorrow. Song, *etc. Chappell & Co.: London, etc.,* 1913. fol.   **H. 3605. c. (11.)**

— Through coming Years. [Song.] Words by H. Simpson. *J. Church Co.: London, etc.,* 1909. fol.   **H. 3605. b. (29.)**

— 'Tis Night. [Song.] Words by A. B. S. 2 no. [In D flat and F.] *See* supra: Series of Short Songs. No. 1.

— To a Palace rich and rare. [Song.] Words by E. Ponsonby. *Francis, Day & Hunter: London,* 1905. fol. *Two copies, one without a cover.*   **H. 3605. b. (13.)**

— The Touch of Night. Song, words by F. E. Weatherly. 3 no. [In D, F and G.] *Chappell & Co.: London, etc.,* 1908. fol.   **H. 3605. b. (30.)**

— Two Questions. Song, words by G. H. Jessop. *E. Ascherberg & Co.: London,* 1901. fol.   **H. 3605. (35.)**

— Upward trusty Brothers. A Song of the air, words by H. Russell. *H. Darewski Music Publishing Co.: London,* 1918. fol.   **H. 3605. c. (15.)**

— Valse d'Automne. [P. F.] *Chappell & Co.: London, etc.,* 1905. fol.   **h. 3286. ll. (18.)**

— [Valse d'Automne.] Give me that Rose. Song, adapted to Valse d'Automne, words by C. H. Bovill. *Chappell & Co.: London, etc.,* 1907. fol.   **H. 3605. b. (19.)**

— Valse insouciante. [P. F.] *Francis, Day & Hunter: London, New York,* 1908. fol. *Two copies, one without a cover and wanting pp. 3 and 4.*   **h. 3286. ll. (19.)**

— Valse. "Insouciante." (Arr. by M. Retford. Conductor [and military band parts].) 33 pt. *In:* BERGER (R.) Valse lente. "Vertige," *etc.* 1909. fol. [*Boosey's military Journal. ser.* 126. *no.* 5.]   **h. 1549.**

— Were you alone. Song, the word by J. Gade. *Boosey & Co.: London and New York,* 1908. fol.   **H. 3605. b. (31.)**

— What a clever Man you are! Humorous song. Words by Claud Nugent. pp. 5. *Reynolds & Co.: London,* [1897.] fol.   **H. 3980. oo. (49.)**

— What all Men dream. Song. The Words by R. S. Hichens. *Boosey & Co.: London and New York,* 1896. fol.   **H. 3605. (11.)**

— When Love bends low. [Song.] Words by J. Gade. 3 no. [In E flat, F and G.] *See* supra: Series of Short Songs. No. 16.

— Who shall foretell? Song, words by L. Cooke. 3 no. [In E flat, F and A flat.] *J. B. Cramer & Co.: London,* 1912. fol.   **H. 3605. c. (12.)**

LAMBERT (E. Frank)

— "Why should I not my Love confess?" Duet, words by E. Ponsonby. *Francis, Day & Hunter: London,* 1905. fol. *Two copies, with different covers.*   **H. 3605. b. (14.)**

— Yesterdays. [Song.] Words by E. Teschemacher. 3 no. [In E flat, F and A flat.] *See* supra: Series of Short Songs. No. 15.

— Yesterdays. Vocal Duet, words by E. Teschemacher. *Chappell & Co.: London, etc.,* 1909. fol.   **H. 3605. b. (32.)**

— Your Love. Song, words by E. Alfieri. *Leonard & Co.: London,* [1899.] fol.   **H. 3605. (25.)**

— Youth's Rhapsody. Song, words by M. Osborne. *G. Ricordi & Co.: London, etc.,* 1921. fol.   **H. 3605. c. (23.)**

LAMBERT (Edward)

— Alone. Song, words by M. Alison. *H. Sharples & Sons: Blackpool,* 1917. fol.   **H. 1846. x. (10.)**

LAMBERT (Emily Bardsey)

— *See* FARMER, afterwards LAMBERT (E. B.)

LAMBERT (F.)

— Just twenty years ago [Song, begins: "I've wandered to the village"]. *Boston,* [*Mass.,* 1863.] fol.   **H. 1780. f. (3.)**

LAMBERT (F. A. H.)

— Oh lull me charming air. Part Song for mixed voices. Words, anon.,—reign of Charles I. *London,* [1884.] 4°.   **F. 585. p. (17.)**

— Six Songs. (1. Gold'ne Brücken ... Adapted from Geibel. 2. Frühling ... Uhland. 3. Es ziehen die brausenden Wellen ... Heine. 4. Das Blümchen Wunderhold ... Bürger. 5. Ungarisches Volkslied ... 6. The Lovely Lass of Inverness ... Burns.) *Weekes & Co.: London,* [1897.] 4°.   **F. 637. d. (4.)**

LAMBERT (F. J.)

— The Mate of the Albatross. Song, words and music by F. J. Lambert. *Nicholson & Co.: Sydney,* 1908. fol.   **H. 1794. uu. (60.)**

LAMBERT (Farran)

— Triumphal March. Pianoforte. *Weekes & Co.: London,* [1889.] fol.   **h. 1489. r. (59.)**

LAMBERT (Frank)

— *See* LAMBERT (E. F.)

LAMBERT (G. J.)

— Duett for two performers on the Pianoforte. *London,* [1815?] fol.   **g. 272. w. (13.)**

— Duett for two performers on the Piano Forte. *London,* [1818.] fol.   **h. 117. (4.)**

— A favorite French air, with introduction & variations. [P. F.] *London,* [1820?] fol.   **g. 272. e. (17.)**

— A favorite quadrille ... for the Pianoforte. *London,* [1820?] fol.   **g. 272. e. (16.)**

— Major Campbell's waltz, with variations. [P. F.] *York,* [1830?] fol.   **g. 272. e. (18.)**

LAMBERT (Georges Joseph Laurent)

— Céline, ou l'Amour vrai. Romance [begins: "De ma Céline"] ... Paroles de Millevoye. *Paris*, [1835?] fol.   **G. 544. (33.)**

— Le Flux de la Mer. Romance [begins: "Je revais à toi"] ... Paroles de E. Dupaty. *Paris*, [1835?] fol.   **G. 551. (36.)**

— Trois Romances avec accompagnement de Piano. *Paris*, [1810?] fol.   **G. 555. (19.)**

— La Violette ... [Song.] Accomp[t] de lyre ou guitarre par Lemoine. pp. 3. *Chez Mlles Erard: Paris*, [c. 1815.] 8°.
A slip bearing the imprint "Chez Benoit Pollet" has been pasted over the original imprint.   **E. 1717. p. (45.)**

LAMBERT (Gillis)

— Een rechte en gemakkelyke wegwyzer der contra danssen, Un veritable et facile guide des contre dances, Verrykt met de muzyk, *etc.* pp. 27. *Gedrukt by de wed: H: van Hulkenroy, en zoon Aäron van Hulkenroy: te Haarlem*, 1723. obl. 4°.   **K. 8. a. 16.**

LAMBERT (Grace)

— Animated Pictures. Overture ... for the Pianoforte. *A. Oliver & Co.: London*, (1912.) fol.   **h. 3284. f. (24.)**

— Brise des Nuits. Evening Breezes. Romance de Salon. [P. F.] *A. Oliver & Co.: London*, [1909.] fol.   **h. 3283. jj. (32.)**

— Butterfly Dance, for the Pianoforte, *etc. W. Lambert: London*, [1911.] fol.   **h. 3284. f. (25.)**

— Dreams of Love. Song, written & composed by G. Lambert. *W. Lambert: London*, [1913.] fol.   **H. 1793. r. (46.)**

— Evening Clouds. Nocturne for Piano. *W. Lambert: London*, [1912.] fol.   **g. 606. n. (32.)**

— Falling Stars. Piano Solo. *Regent Music Stores: London*, [1912.] fol.   **h. 3284. f. (26.)**

— The Flying Fox. March à la Chasse. [P. F.] *A. Oliver & Co.: London*, (1911.) fol.   **h. 3284. f. (27.)**

— Happy Childhood Singing Games. Dramatised. Words & dramatisation by E. M. Allard, *etc.* 2 bk. *Davidson Bros.: London*, [1914.] 4°.   **F. 636. ii. (8.)**

— I shall love the same for ever. Song, written & composed by G. Lambert, *etc. W. Lambert: London*, (1912.) fol.   **H. 1793. r. (47.)**

— The Infant Hymn Book. Pianoforte Arrangement by G. Lambert, *etc. Davidson Bros.: London*, [1915.] 8°.   **E. 602. ee. (14.)**

— Inspiration. Solo for Piano. *W. Lambert: London*, [1912.] fol.   **h. 3284. f. (28.)**

— The King's Territorial. Grand March for the Pianoforte. *A. Oliver & Co.: London*, [1913.] fol.   **h. 3284. f. (29.)**

— A Midnight Dream, for the piano. *W. Lambert: London*, [1915.] fol.   **h. 3284. nn. (3.)**

— Pedlar Songs, word by M. Ackley. *J. Saville & Co.: London*, [1924.] 4°.   **F. 607. hh. (9.)**

— Pixie Pipes. [Songs.] Words by M. F. Ackley. *J. Saville & Co.: London*, [1922.] 4°.   **F. 637. ww. (17.)**

— La Princesse dormante. The Sleeping Princess. Romance de Salon. [P. F.] *A. Oliver & Co.: London*, (1910.) fol.   **h. 3284. f. (30.)**

— The Silver Wedding. March. [P. F.] *W. Lambert: London*, [1911.] fol.   **h. 3284. f. (32.)**

— Soleil d'Or. Golden Sun. Barcarolle. [P. F.] *W. Paxton, for the Composer: London*, [1913.] fol.   **h. 3284. f. (31.)**

LAMBERT (Grace)

— Spring Flowers. Song, from the Waltz Spring Flowers. Vocal Score for Voice, Violin, or Mandoline, written and composed by G. Lambert. *W. Lambert: London*, [1912.] fol.   **H. 1792. r. (13.)**

— Sunset on the Lake. Caprice for Piano. *W. Lambert: London*, [1911.] fol.   **h. 3284. f. (33.)**

— Thinking my Love of you. Song, written and composed by G. Lambert, *etc. W. Lambert: London*, [1912.] fol.   **H. 1792. r. (14.)**

— Thistledown. Air de ballet. [P. F.] *W. Lambert: London*, [1914.] fol.   **h. 3284. nn. (4.)**

— Très joli, pour le piano. *W. Lambert: London*, [1915.] fol.   **h. 3284. nn. (5.)**

— Vesuvius. Fantasia for Piano. *W. Lambert: London*, [1911.] fol.   **h. 3284. f. (34.)**

— *See* KIDSON (F.) Old English Country-Dance Tunes ... pianoforte arrangements by G. Lambert, *etc.* [1915.] 4°.   **f. 133. cc. (3.)**

LAMBERT (Gustave)

— Forget me not valse. [Orchestral parts.] *See* CHAPPELL AND Co. Popular Quadrilles, *etc.* No. 26. [1862, *etc.*] 8°.   **e. 249.**

— The Forget me Not waltz. [P. F.] *London*, [1864.] fol.   **h. 1460. u. (25.)**

— Happy Moments valse. [Orchestral parts.] *See* CHAPPELL AND Co. Popular Quadrilles, *etc.* No. 25. [1862, *etc.*] 8°.   **e. 249.**

— Happy Moments valse. [P. F. with cornet accompaniment.] *London*, [1864.] fol.   **h. 1460. u. (26.)**

— Happy Moments. Valse. [P. F.] *See* RIMBAULT (E. F.) The Juvenile Ball Room, *etc.* No. 22. [1870–78.] fol.   **h. 486. c. (6.)**

— Rita valse. [P. F.] *London*, [1872.] fol.   **h. 1485. s. (12.)**

LAMBERT (Guy)

— *See* CHARPENTIER (M. A.) De profundis ... à 4 voix mixtes (et orgue) ... Transcrit et réalisé par G. Lambert, *etc.* [1952?] 8°.   **F. 1176. x. (6.)**

— *See* CHARPENTIER (M. A.) [Filius prodigus.] Gratias tibi Deus ... Transcription et réalisation par G. Lambert, *etc.* [1953.] 4°.   **G. 519. u. (14.)**

— *See* CHARPENTIER (M. A.) Messe "Pour le Samedy de Pasques" ... Transcription et réalisation G. Lambert, *etc.* [1958?] fol.   **H. 1186. m. (2.)**

— *See* CHARPENTIER (M. A.) [Médée.] Passecaille ... Transcrite et réalisée par G. Lambert. [1953.] 8°.   **f. 390. e. (1.)**

— *See* CHARPENTIER (M. A.) O crux ave ... Transcrit et réalisé par G. Lambert. [1957.] 8°.   **F. 1175. hh. (2.)**

— *See* CHARPENTIER (M. A.) Te Deum. (Transcrit et réalisé par G. Lambert.) Réduction pour chant et clavier. [1964.] 4°.   **G. 519. ll. (2.)**

— *See* CORRETTE (M.) Nouveau livre de noëls avec un carillon pour le clavecin ou l'orgue ... Choix méthodique réalisé, annoté, transcrit par G. Lambert. [c. 1960.] 4°.   **h. 2733. l. (12.)**

— *See* KOECHLIN (C.) Six chorals pour cérémonies funèbres ... Choisis et annotés par G. Lambert. [1954.] obl. 4°.   **e. 1093. aa. (7.)**

LAMBERT (Harry W.)

— Hush, my Baby. Lullaby with violin accomp^t ad lib., words
by E. Webb. *Beal & Co.: London*, [1896.] fol.
H. 1798. u. (12.)

LAMBERT (Henri)

— En Poste, valse pour Piano. *Paris*, [1869.] fol.
h. 1462. r. (1.)

LAMBERT (J.)

— Je t'aimerai toujours. [Song, begins: "Les fleurs ne sont pas".]
Paroles de Du Camp. *Paris*, [1864.] fol. **H. 1774. e. (9.)**

— Petits Enfants. [Song, begins: "Enfants, lorsque dans la
charmille".] Paroles de Du Camp. *Paris*, [1864.] fol.
H. 1774. e. (11.)

— Les Ténèbres du Cœur. Romance [begins: "Vous étiez la
douce lumière"]. Paroles de A. van Hasselt. *Paris*, [1864.] fol.
H. 1774. e. (10.)

LAMBERT (J. C.)

— "The Lancashire Witches" quadrilles for the pianoforte.
London, [1856.] fol. **h. 977. f. (21.)**

LAMBERT (Jack)

— *See* Leisy (James F.) Scrooge. A musical play ... Arranged
for s. a. b. voices and piano by J. Lambert ... Vocal score, *etc.*
[1980.] 4°. **F. 1208. (1.)**

LAMBERT (James)

— *See* Lambert (Jack)

LAMBERT (Jasper)

— Christmas Bells. [Hymn.] Words and music by J. Lambert.
Novello and Co.: London, [1925.] *s. sh.* 8°. **E. 1498. t. (26.)**

— Draw near, O Lord, and bless us. *Vesper.* Hymn. Words and
music by J. Lambert. *Novello and Co.: London*, 1926. *a card.*
I. 600. f. (28.)

— Once again the Story tell. Christmas Carol, words and music
by J. Lambert. *Novello & Co.: London*, [1914.] *s. sh.* 8°.
C. 549. e. (26.)

— We praise Thee, God the Father ... [Hymn.] Words and
music by J. Lambert. *Novello and Co.: London*, [1925.] *s. sh.*
8°. **E. 597. z. (18.)**

LAMBERT (John)

— Dream Carol ... Words from the Selden manuscript,
Bodleian Library, Oxford. *In:* Christmas Carols. A Garland
of Carols. pp. 13–17. 1975. 4°. **G. 950. j. (1.)**

— Missa brevis in C. For mixed voices. ⟨Edited for the Latin rite
by Kevin Mayhew.⟩ pp. 16. *L. J. Cary & Co.: London*, [1961.]
4°. **F. 274. gg. (1.)**

— Organ Mass. 1. Kyrie. 2. Sanctus. 3. Agnus Dei, *etc.* pp. 30.
International Music Co.: London, [1968.] *obl.* 4°.
e. 1096. z. (5.)

— A Song-Cycle on the Birth of Jesus ... For soprano and harp
(or piano). pp. 19. *J. & W. Chester: London*, [1956.] 4°.
G. 519. bb. (3.)

— Tota pulchra es Maria, *etc.* [Motet.] ⟨Two voices.⟩ pp. 7. *L. J.
Cary & Co.: London*, [1960.] 8°.
[*Praise and Prayer.* 5.] **E. 1439. h.**

LAMBERT (John)

— Veni creator spiritus. ⟨Cantata. For two tenors and organ.⟩
pp. 20. *International Music Co.: London*, [1968.] *obl.* 4°.
D. 835. h. (4.)

LAMBERT (*Sir* John)

— Antiphonarium Vesperale. Organ accompaniments to the
antiphons of the Roman Vesperal, *etc.* 5 pt. *Burns and
Lambert: London*, 1851. 8°. **E. 444.**

— Antiphonarium Vesperale. Organ Accompaniments to the
Antiphons of the Roman Vesperal. Proprium Sanctorum. I.
December—May. (II. June—November.) [By Sir J. Lambert.]
2 pt. [1865?] 8°. *See* Antiphonarium. **E. 444. a.**

— Dulcis Jesu Memoria, a mediaeval sequence or Hymn (in
Latin and English), from the Sarum Graduale, printed in
1528. The musical text reduced into modern notation and
time with an accompaniment for the Organ or Pianoforte ...
by J. Lambert. *Salisbury*, [1857.] fol. **H. 1187. a. (13.)**

— Hymnarium vesperale. Organ accompaniments for the whole
of the hymns of the Roman vesperal; with an appendix
containing the three festal sequences of the Roman gradual.
London, 1851. 8°. **C. 529.**

— Vesper Psalter. Organ Accompaniments; containing the eight
Psalm-tones with their festal and ferial mediations and
various endings ... With a preface of the true method of
harmonising and singing the ritual song. *James Burns:
London*, 1849. 8°. **D. 447.**

— Vesper Psalter. Organ Accompaniments; containing the eight
Psalm-tones, *etc. Burns and Lambert: London*, [1850?] 8°.
D. 447. a.

— *See* Formby (H.) and Lambert (*Sir* J.) Collection of Catholic
hymns (Catholic Sacred Songs) ... Edited by H. Formby and
J. Lambert. 1853. 8°. **D. 451.**

LAMBERT (Louis) *of Belesta*

— Chants et chansons populaires du Languedoc. Recueillis et
publiés avec la musique notée et la traduction française par
L. Lambert. 2 tom. *H. Welter: Paris, Leipzig*, 1906. 8°.
C. 431. k.

— Magalouno. [Song, begins: "L'aureto de la mar".] Poésie de
W. C. Bonaparte-Wyse. *Montpellier*, 1877. 8°.
F. 607. o. (7.)

— Magalouno, *etc. Montpellier*, 1878. 8°. **F. 607. o. (6.)**

— *See* Montel (A.) and Lambert (L.) *of Belesta.* Chants
populaires du Languedoc, *etc.* 1880. 8°. **11498. h. 10.**

LAMBERT (Louis) *Songwriter*

— When Johnny comes marching Home. Unison Chorus with
Descant. [Music by] Louis Lambert [or rather, J. Williams].
Arranged by D. Malin. *C. Fischer: New York, etc.*, 1939. 8°.
E. 1830. e. (27.)

— When Johnny comes marching Home. Words and music by
L. Lambert ... Arrangement for treble voices (S. S. A.) with
piano accompaniment and optional B♭ trumpet, timpani and
drums by Van A. Christy, *etc.* [Vocal score.] pp. 9. *Mills
Music: New York*, [1960.] 8°. **F. 217. s. (9.)**

LAMBERT (Lucien)

— Bresiliana, grande valse brilliante pour Piano. *Paris*, [1875.]
fol. **h. 1487. o. (23.)**

— Le Carnaval de Paris. Variations brillantes sur un chanson ...
de L. Abadie. [P. F.] *Paris*, [1861.] fol. **h. 1462. r. (2.)**

LAMBERT (LUCIEN)

— La Flamenca. Drame musical de H. Cain, Eug. et Ed. Adenis ... Chanson havanaise de la Flamenca, *etc.* [Begins: "Tu m'as quittée".] [*Paris,*] 1903. 8°.
Supplement to "L'Illustration," No. 3166.   **P. P. 4283. m. (3.)**

— Il pleut bergère. Transcription variée. [P. F.] *Paris,* [1882.] fol.   **h. 3276. g. (2.)**

— Polka Havanaise pour Piano. *Paris,* [1862.] fol.   **h. 1462. r. (3.)**

— La rose et le Bengali, inspiration pour le piano. Op. 4. *Paris,* [1854.] fol.   **h. 723. l. (17.)**

— Le Spahi. Poème lyrique en quatre actes, tiré du roman de P. Loti par L. Gallet et A. Alexandre ... Entr'acte—Acte II.—. [P. F.] [*Paris,*] 1897. 8°.
Supplement to "L'Illustration," No. 2853.   **P. P. 4283. m. (3.)**

— Voix Célestes, rêverie pour Piano. *Paris,* [1873.] fol.   **h. 1487. o. (22.)**

— Zamacueca, danse Chilienne de J. White, transcrite pour le Piano. *Paris,* [1882.]   **h. 3276. g. (3.)**

— *See* BEETHOVEN (L. van) [Sonatas. P. F. Selected Movements.] Nouveaux exercices journaliers extraits des Sonatas de Beethoven, classés et doigtés par L. Lambert. [1882.] fol.   **h. 400. i. (5.)**

— *See* BEETHOVEN (L. van) [Trios. Op. 11.] Adagio du Trio. Op. 11 ... pour Piano seul par L. Lambert. [1862.] fol.   **h. 400. c. (9.)**

— *See* BRUNEAU (L. C. B. A.) La Belle au bois dormant. Poème symphonique pour orchestre ... Réduction pour piano à quatre mains par L. Lambert. [1902?] fol.   **h. 3290. y. (6.)**

LAMBERT (MARGARET C.)

— Cupid and the Maid. Song, words and music by M. C. Lambert, *etc. J. B. Cramer & Co.: London,* 1910. fol.   **H. 1792. r. (15.)**

— Fairyland. A Play for Children, words and music by M. C. Lambert, *etc. Weekes & Co.: London,* 1914. 4°.   **G. 782. t. (3.)**

LAMBERT (MICHEL)

— Les Airs du Sieur Lambert. Grauez par Richer. *Chez Charles de Sercy: Paris,* [1660.] obl. 4°.   **K. 3. f. 14.**

— Airs a une, II. III. et IV. parties avec la basse-continue, *etc. Christophe Ballard: Paris,* 1689. fol.   **R. M. 13. f. 8.**

— Evening Song. Chanson ... Edited by D. Freer. *J. Williams: London,* 1925. 4°.
[*Classical and Standard Songs. Series* I. *No.* XVI.]   **G. 1173.**

— Ombre de mon Amant. Air. [*Paris,*] 1679. *s. sh.* obl. 4°.
Nouveau Mercure Galant, June, 1679, *p.* 31.   **P. P. 4482.**

— Que faites vous, Silvie. *Air.* ⟨Quelle: Airs de Monsieur Lambert, non imprimez. Bibl. du Conservatoire, Paris, Ms. Rés. 585.⟩ *In:* NOSKE (F.) Das ausserdeutsche Sololied 1500–1900. pp. 40–41. [1958.] 4°. [*Das Musikwerk. Hft.* 16.]   **G. 16.**

— *See* PARODIES. Parodies spirituelles ... sur des airs choisis de Messieurs Le Camus, Lambert, *etc.* 1717. *obl.* 4°.   **Hirsch** III. **977.**

LAMBERT (PH.)

— Les Regrets d'un Fils. Romance [begins: "Ah! j'ai perdu"], *etc. Paris,* [1825?] fol.   **G. 546. (54.)**

LAMBERT (SYDNEY)

— Le Camélia, mazurka de salon pour Piano. *Paris,* [1883.] fol.   **h. 3276. g. (5.)**

— Mazurka-Tyrolienne pour Piano. *Paris,* [1874.] fol.   **h. 1487. o. (24.)**

— Murmures du Soir, caprice pour Piano. *Paris,* [1876.] fol.   **h. 1487. o. (28.)**

— Six Pieces in the early Grades. *See* infra: [Premières leçons de piano.]

— [Premières leçons de piano.] Six Pieces in the early Grades. Edited by Paul Glass. For piano. pp. 11. *Associated Music Publishers: New York, London,* [1977.] 4°.   **g. 1529. s. (9.)**

— Romance de la Cruche Cassée, opéra comique d'E. Pessard, pour Piano. *Paris,* [1874.] fol.   **h. 1487. o. (26.)**

— Les Sylphes. Impromptu pour Piano. *Paris,* [1874.] fol.   **h. 1487. o. (25.)**

— Transports Joyeux, valse de salon pour Piano. *Paris,* [1875.] fol.   **h. 1487. o. (27.)**

— Valse-Caprice pour piano. Op. 23. *Paris,* [1885.] fol.   **h. 3280. k. (19.)**

— Vive la Polka! pour Piano. *Paris,* [1883.] fol.   **h. 3276. g. (4.)**

LAMBERT (VICTOR)

— Le Rêve. Berceuse pour violon ou violoncelle avec accompagnement de piano. *Paris,* [1884.] fol.   **h. 1608. l. (8.)**

— Rêverie andante pour Violon ou Violoncelle avec accomp. de Piano ou Orgue. *Paris,* [1879.] fol.   **h. 1609. m. (2.)**

— Souvenir du Tréport, fantaisie pour Violon avec accomp. de Piano. *Paris,* [1883.] fol.   **h. 1608. l. (7.)**

LAMBERT (W. S.)

— All hail to thee. (Ave Maria.) ... Tenor solo and chorus. *London,* [1884.] 8°.   **E. 605. m. (25.)**

— Dancing Waves. [P. F.] *H. W. Stansfield: London,* [1884.] fol.   **h. 975. u. (21.)**

— The Lark, song. [Begins: "Bird of the summer sky".] *London,* [1857.] fol.   **H. 1771. l. (7.)**

— Many happy returns of the season. Song [begins: "There's a pleasure"]. *London,* [1876.] fol.   **H. 1778. x. (14.)**

— Nature's festive Music. [Four-part song.] Words by G. Bennett. [1872.] *See* CRAMPTON (T.) The Part-Singer, *etc.* No. 97. [1868–98.] 8°.   **E. 628.**

— Over the Mountain Side. Serenade (A. T. T. B.), *etc. Weekes & Co.: London,* 1897. 8°.
No. 17 *of "Weekes & Co.'s Male Voice Part Songs".*   **F. 334. e.**

LAMBERT (WILLIS F. A.)

— Benedicite, omnia opera in chant form ... in ... F. *Houghton & Co.: London,* 1900. 8°.   **F. 1169. (13.)**

— Six Kyries. *Weekes & Co.: London,* [1886.] 8°.   **E. 605. r. (30.)**

— Kyries, Ancient and Modern, edited by W. F. A. Lambert. *Weekes & Co.: London,* [1887.] obl. 4°.   **A. 487. b. (2.)**

LAMBERTI (Giuseppe)

— Il Casino di campagna. Operetta in 1 atto. Libretto e musica del maestro Giuseppe Lamberti. [Vocal score.] pp. 73. *L. Stoppa: Milano,* [c. 1925.] 4°.   **F. 1373. d. (2.)**

LAMBETH

— The Lambeth Walk. Song. *See* ROGERS (E. W.)

LAMBETH (Henry A.)

— Auld Edinburgh Cries. Music by J. R. Perry ... Arranged by H. A. Lambeth. [1885.] *See* STRATHEARN. The Strathearn Collection of Part-Songs ... No. 4. [1885–91.] 8°.   **F. 205.**

— The Auld House. [Words] By Lady Nairne, arranged as a Part-Song by H. A. Lambeth. [1885.] *See* STRATHEARN. The Strathearn Collection of Part-Songs ... No. 1. [1885–91.] 8°.   **F. 205.**

— Begone, dull Care. Old English Tune ... arranged by H. A. Lambeth. [1887.] *See* STRATHEARN. The Strathearn Collection of Part-Songs ... No. 11. [1885–91.] 8°.   **F. 205.**

— The Bonnie Brier Bush. Arranged by H. A. Lambeth. [1891.] *See* STRATHEARN. The Strathearn Collection of Part-Songs ... No. 24. [1885–91.] 8°.   **F. 205.**

— Bonnie ran the Burnie. Arranged by H. A. Lambeth. [1887.] *See* STRATHEARN. The Strathearn Collection of Part-Songs ... No. 23. [1885–91.] 8°.   **F. 205.**

— Cam' ye by Athol. Music by Neil Gow Junr ... Arranged by H. A. Lambeth. [1885.] *See* STRATHEARN. The Strathearn Collection of Part-Songs ... No. 6. [1885–91.] 8°.   **F. 205.**

— Claribel. Song [begins: "Where Claribel low lieth"]. The poetry by A. Tennyson. ⟨In B flat minor.⟩ *London,* [1871.] fol.   **H. 1775. t. (10.)**

— Claribel. Song. ⟨In G minor.⟩ *London,* [1871.] fol.   **H. 1775. t. (11.)**

— Gala Water. Arranged by H. A. Lambeth. [1885.] *See* STRATHEARN. The Strathearn Collection of Part-Songs ... No. 5. [1885–91.] 8°.   **F. 205.**

— God is our Hope and Strength. A Full Anthem, *etc. See* PATERSON, SONS AND CO. Paterson's Part Music, *etc.* No. 22. [1890–1909.] 8°.   **F. 1686.**

— Gude Nicht and Joy be wi' ye a', words by Lady Nairne, arranged ... by H. A. Lambeth. [1891.] *See* STRATHEARN. The Strathearn Collection of Part-Songs ... No. 30. [1885–91.] 8°.   **F. 205.**

— The Jolly Miller. Old English Tune ... arranged by H. A. Lambeth. [1887.] *See* STRATHEARN. The Strathearn Collection of Part-Songs ... No. 10. [1885–91.] 8°.   **F. 205.**

— Joy of my earliest Days. Arranged by H. A. Lambeth. [1891.] *See* STRATHEARN. The Strathearn Collection of Part-Songs ... No. 25. [1885–91.] 8°.   **F. 205.**

— "Lesbia hath a beaming Eye." [Part-song.] Words by Moore. Arranged by H. A. Lambeth. *See* PATERSON, SONS AND CO. Paterson's Part Music, *etc.* No. 43. [1890–1909.] 8°.   **F. 1686.**

— March! march! Ettrick & Teviotdale. Part Song for mixed voices. Arranged by H. A. Lambeth. *See* PATERSON, SONS AND CO. Paterson's Part Music, *etc.* No. 40. [1890–1909.] 8°.   **F. 1686.**

— The March of the Cameron Men. Words and Music by M. M. Campbell. Arranged by H. A. Lambeth. 2 no. [Staff and tonic sol-fa notation.] [1885.] *See* STRATHEARN. The Strathearn Collection of Part-Songs ... No. 2. [1885–91.] 8°.   **F. 205.**

LAMBETH (Henry A.)

— My Nannie's Awa'. Words by Burns, arranged by H. A. Lambeth. [1891.] *See* STRATHEARN. The Strathearn Collection of Part-Songs ... No. 29. [1885–91.] 8°.   **F. 205.**

— Of a' the Airts the Win' can blaw, words by Burns, arranged as a part-song by H. A. Lambeth. [1891.] *See* STRATHEARN. The Strathearn Collection of Part-Songs ... No. 28. [1885–91.] 8°.   **F. 205.**

— The Old Folks at Home. Melody by W. Harrington [or rather, S. C. Foster]. Arranged ... by H. A. Lambeth. *See* PATERSON, SONS AND CO. Paterson's Part Music, *etc.* No. 41. [1890–1909.] 8°.   **F. 1686.**

— Romance for the piano forte. *London,* [1852.] fol.   **h. 723. l. (18.)**

— Roslin Castle. Arranged by H. A. Lambeth. [1887.] *See* STRATHEARN. The Strathearn Collection of Part-Songs ... No. 7. [1885–91.] 8°.   **F. 205.**

— The Rowan Tree. [Part-song.] Words by Lady Nairne. [1887.] *See* STRATHEARN. The Strathearn Collection of Part-Songs ... No. 22. [1885–91.] 8°.   **F. 205.**

— Savourneen Deelish. Words by G. Coleman, arranged by H. A. Lambeth. [1887.] *See* STRATHEARN. The Strathearn Collection of Part-Songs ... No. 9. [1885–91.] 8°.   **F. 205.**

— The Scottish Book of Praise, being selections from the Psalms ... and other parts of Scripture, with a collection of Hymns, Paraphrases and Anthems, *etc. London and Glasgow,* 1876. 8°.   **C. 721.**

— Scottish part songs ... arranged by H. A. Lambeth. The Balmoral edition. 12 no. *J. M. Wood: Glasgow,* [1885.] 8°.   **F. 321. c. (18.)**

— Scottish Part Songs ... The Balmoral edition. Tonic sol-fa notation. 12 no. *J. M. Wood & Co.: Glasgow,* [1885.] 4°.   **C. 738. c. (7.)**

— The Trump of War, from 'Lays of Strathearn,' by Lady Nairne. Arranged by H. A. Lambeth. [1891.] *See* STRATHEARN. The Strathearn Collection of Part-Songs ... No. 26. [1885–91.] 8°.   **F. 205.**

— Up in the Morning early. [Four-part song.] Arranged by H. A. Lambeth. *See* PATERSON, SONS AND CO. Paterson's Part Music, *etc.* No. 38. [1890–1909.] 8°.   **F. 1686.**

— The War-Song of the Men of Glamorgan. Words by Sir Walter Scott. Arranged by H. A. Lambeth. [1887.] *See* STRATHEARN. The Strathearn Collection of Part-Songs ... No. 8. [1885–91.] 8°.   **F. 205.**

— Will ye no come back again. [Words] By Lady Nairne, arranged as a part-song by H. A. Lambeth. [1885.] *See* STRATHEARN. The Strathearn Collection of Part-Songs ... No. 3. [1885–91.] 8°.   **F. 205.**

— Ye Banks and Braes. Words by Burns. [Melody by J. Miller.] Arranged [as a four-part song] by H. A. Lambeth. *See* PATERSON, SONS AND CO. Paterson's Part Music, *etc.* No. 36. [1890–1909.] 8°.   **F. 1686.**

— *See* RUSSELL (A.) O Mavis singing in the Wood ... Symphonies & Accompaniments by H. A. Lambeth. [1909.] fol.   **H. 1797. ee. (9.)**

LAMBILLOTTE (François)

— *See* LAMBILLOTTE (L.) Oeuvres posthumes des Pères L., F. & J. Lambillotte, *etc.* [1875, *etc.*] fol.   **H. 1030. b.**

— *See* LAMBILLOTTE (L.) Grand Saluts ... Oeuvres posthumes des trois Pères L., J. & F. Lambillotte. [1870.] fol.   **H. 1030. (2.)**

LAMBILLOTTE (FRANÇOIS)

— *See* LAMBILLOTTE (L.) Souvenirs de Fêtes de Collége. Oeuvres posthumes des trois Pères L., F. et J. Lambillotte, *etc.* [1870.] 8°.   **F. 606. (4.)**

LAMBILLOTTE (JOSEPH)

— *See* LAMBILLOTTE (L.) Oeuvres posthumes des Pères L., F. & J. Lambillotte, *etc.* [1875, *etc.*] fol.   **H. 1030. b.**

— *See* LAMBILLOTTE (L.) Grands Saluts ... Oeuvres posthumes des trois Pères L., J. & F. Lambillotte. [1870.] fol.
                                                                                   H. 1030. (2.)

— *See* LAMBILLOTTE (L.) Souvenirs de Fêtes de Collége. Oeuvres posthumes des trois Pères L., F. et J. Lambillotte, *etc.* [1870.] 8°.   **F. 606. (4.)**

LAMBILLOTTE (LOUIS)

— Oeuvres posthumes des Pères L., F. & J. Lambillotte ... revues et publiées par C. de la Croix. Edition originale. (Edition à trois voix égales.) *Paris*, [1875, *etc.*] fol.
                                                                                   H. 1030. b.

— Chant Grégorien restauré ... Accompagnements d'Orgue par C. Franck. 5 liv. *Paris*, 1857, 58. fol.   **H. 1030. a.**

— Chants communs des Messes d'après le Graduel Romain ... Contenant de plus une Messe à deux parties, *etc. Paris*, 1858. 8°.   **C. 635.**

— Choix de Cantiques sur des airs nouveaux pour toutes les fêtes de l'année ... à trois et quatre voix avec accompagnement d'Orgue ou de Piano. *Paris*, 1855. 8°.
                                                                                     E. 1424.

— Choix de Cantiques sur des airs nouveaux, pour toutes les fêtes de l'année ... à trois et quatre voix, avec accompagnement d'orgue ou de piano, *etc. V*. *Poussielgue et Fils: Paris*, 1865. 8°.   **E. 1424. a.**

— Grands Saluts pour les fêtes solennelles, avec accompagnement d'Orgue ... Corrigés ... par A. L. Dessane. Liv. 1–4. *Paris*, [1878.] fol.   **H. 1030. (1.)**

— Grands Saluts pour les principales fêtes de l'année, avec accompagnement d'Orgue ... Corrigées ... par C. de la Croix. Oeuvres posthumes des trois Pères L., J. & F. Lambillotte. Liv. 1–3. *Paris*, [1870.] fol.   **H. 1030. (2.)**

— Quatre Motets d'Eglise pour sociétés chorales. Œuvres posthumes ... avec accompt. d'Orgue ad libitum par C. de la Croix. *Paris*, [1875.] fol.   **H. 1028. f. (24.)**

— O Salutaris. Duo, *etc.* [*Cincinnati*, 1863.] fol.
                                                                                 H. 1780. f. (4.)

— Souvenirs de Fêtes de Collége. Oeuvres posthumes des trois pères L., F. et J. Lambillotte ... corrigés et réorchestrés par C. de la Croix. No. 1. *Paris*, [1870.] 8°.
Imperfect; wanting all the other no.   **F. 606. (4.)**

LAMBIRI (G.)

— Les Gouttes de Rosée quadrilles pour Piano. *Milan*, [1880.] fol.   **h. 3274. b. (7.)**

— Les Hirondelles. Polka ... pour piano. *Milan*, [1884.] fol.
                                                                                 h. 3285. b. (40.)

— Olga. Mazurka pour piano. *Milan*, [1884.] fol.
                                                                                 h. 3285. b. (41.)

LAMBKIN

— The Lambkin and the Maiden. [Song.] *See* ARNOLD (A. W.)

LAMBLEY (J.)

— The Barcarolles. A ballad [begins: "Oh! hark!"]. *London*, [1825?] fol.   **H. 2832. g. (27.)**

LAMBLY (NORMAN)

— The Canadian Overland March. [P. F.] *Whaley, Royce & Co.: Toronto*, 1899. fol.   **h. 3282. w. (25.)**

— A Father's Lullaby. Sacred Song, words & music by N. Lambly. *H. H. Sparks: Toronto*, (1907.) fol.
                                                                                 H. 1187. ll. (3.)

— To you is born a Saviour. Sacred Song, words & music by N. Lambly. *H. H. Sparks: Toronto*, (1906.) fol.
                                                                                 H. 1187. ll. (4.)

— Whom have I on Earth beside Thee. Sacred Song, words & music by N. Lambly. *H. H. Sparks: Toronto*, (1907.) fol.
                                                                                 H. 1187. ll. (5.)

LAMBO (KNUT)

— Oden. [Songs.] pp. 32. *Gedruckt bey J. G. Trausold: Hamburg*, 1754. 4°.   **Hirsch III. 884.**

LAMBOOIJ (TH. P. A.)

— *See* LEEUWARDEN.— *Fryske Akademy.— Musikologyske Wurkgroep.* Frysk Lieteboek ... Fersoarge troch de Musikologyske Wurkgroep fan de Fryske Akademy. ⟨Th. P. A. Lambooij, skriuwer.⟩ 1979. 4°.   **F. 1821. kk.**

LAMBORD (BENJAMIN)

— Clytie. [Song, French words by] A. Chénier, English version by S. A. Trench ... Op. 10. No. 2. *H. W. Gray Co.: [New York,]* 1914. 4°.   **G. 425. o. (8.)**

— Two Descriptive Pieces for the piano. Op. 13. I. Spring song. II. Little white lily. 2 no. *G. Schirmer: New York*, 1922. 4°.
                                                                                   g. 1127. g. (12.)

— God of Mercy, God of Grace. Hymn-Anthem. [Words by] H. F. Lyte. *O. Ditson Co.: [Boston]*, 1905. 8°.   **F. 281. (15.)**

— A Health to King Charles. [Song, words by] Sir W. Scott. *H. W. Gray Co.: [New York,]* 1914. 4°.   **G. 390. m. (11.)**

— Hey-ho Robin. Madrigal for mixed voices with Piano accompaniment, words by C. L. Betts. Op. 2. No. 2. *H. W. Gray Co.: New York*, 1914. 8°.
Modern Series, No. 57.   **F. 585. cc. (16.)**

— The King of Love my Shepherd is. *See infra*: Sacred Songs. [No. 2.]

— Two Love Songs from the German ... Op. 7. (No. 1.) Love's Yearning. "Lehn' deine Wang' an meine Wang'." H. Heine. (No. 2.) Love's Fulfillment. "Mir ist, nun ich dich habe." F. Rückert. 2 no. *C. Saerchinger: New York*, (1908.) fol.
                                                                                   G. 805. mm. (13.)

— Love's Fulfillment. *See supra*: Two Love Songs ... Op. 7. No. 2.

— Love's Yearning. *See supra*: Two Love Songs ... Op. 7. No. 1.

— Now from the Altar of our Hearts. Hymn-Anthem. [Words by] J. Mason. *O. Ditson Co.: [Boston,]* 1905. 8°.
                                                                                     F. 281. (16.)

— O gracious God in whom I live. *See infra*: Sacred Songs. [No. 1.]

— Rejoice in the Lord, O ye Righteous. Anthem, *etc. O. Ditson Co.: [Boston,]* 1904. 8°.   **F. 281. (17.)**

LAMBORD (Benjamin)

— Sacred Songs. [No. 1.] O gracious God in whom I live. [Words by] A. Steele. [No. 2.] The King of Love my Shepherd is. [Words by Sir H. W. Baker.] 2 no. *J. Church Co.: Cincinnati, etc.,* (1904.) fol.   **H. 1187. ff. (48.)**

— Saviour, Source of every Blessing. Two-part Anthem for women's voices, the poem by P. Robinson. *W. Maxwell Music Co.: New York City,* (1914.) 8°.   **F. 281. nn. (23.)**

— Suffer little Children. Anthem for mixed voices, *etc. H. W. Gray Co.: New York,* 1912. 8°. *Chuch Music Review, No.* 320.   **F. 281. ee. (55.)**

— To God our Strength sing loud and clear. Anthem—mixed voices—for festival occasions. Psalm lxxxi. 1–3; done into metre by J. Milton. *H. W. Gray Co.: New York,* 1908. 8°.   **F. 281. n. (19.)**

— Valse fantastique, for Pianoforte. (Op. 6.) *Wa-Wan Press: Newton Center, Mass.,* 1905. fol. *Part of the "Wa-Wan Series".*   **h. 3799. (7.)**

— Verses from Omar. Chorus for mixed voices, text from Omar Khayyám. Translated by E. Fitzgerald. Op. 11. No. 1. *H. W. Gray Co.: New York,* 1914. 4°.   **G. 426. w. (1.)**

LAMBORNE (Will Duncan)

— Lady Betty. Waltzes ... Arranged by R. B. Brewer. [P. F.] pp. 7. *Sam Fox Publishing Co.: Cleveland,* [1907.] fol.   **h. 4120. ll. (27.)**

LAMBOURN (   ) Mr

— The Lion and Fox. A cantata taken from Æsop's Fables. [c. 1770.] fol.   **H. 1601. c. (19.)**

LAMBRANZI (Gregorio)

Neue und Curieuse Theatrialische Tantz-Schul

— Neue und Curieuse Theatrialische Tantz-Schul. 2 Tl. L.P. *Verlegts Johan Jacob Wolrab: Nurnberg,* (1716.) fol. *Engraved by J. G. Puschner.*   **K. 8. g. 5.**

— Neue und curieuse theatrialische Tantz-Schul. Tl. 1. *In Kupfer gebracht und verlegt von Johann Georg Puschner: Nurnberg,* 1716. fol. *Imperfect; wanting Tl. 2.*   **K. 8. g. 19.**

— [Another copy.] *Part I. only. Cropped.*   **K. 8. g. 4.**

— Deliciæ theatrales. ⟨Nuoua e curiosa scuola de' balli theatrali ... Neue und curieuse theatralische Tantz-Schul ... Gezeichnet und in Kupffer gestochen von Johann Georg Puschner.⟩ 2 Tl. *Nürnberg,* 1716. fol.   **Hirsch I. 298.**

— New and curious School of Theatrical Dancing ... With all the original plates by J. G. Puschner. Translated from the German by D. de Moroda. Edited with a preface by C. W. Beaumont. *C. W. Beaumont: London,* 1928. 8°.   **Case 100. k. 15.**

— New and curious School of Theatrical Dancing ... With all the original plates by Johann Georg Puschner. Translated from the German by Derra de Moroda. Edited with a preface by Cyril W. Beaumont. 2 pt. *C. W. Beaumont: London,* 1928. 8°.   **Hirsch M. 210.**

— Curious Character Dances adapted ... [by] A. Hayworth and K. M. Powell-Tuck. Music arranged by K. M. Wollaston. (Music Supplement.) 2 pt. *E. J. Arnold & Son: Leeds, etc.,* [1944.] 8°.   **e. 77.**

LAMBS

— Lambs. Unison Song. *See* Gwynne (Una)

LAMBS

— The Lambs. Two-part song. *See* Parry (William H.)

— The Lambs in the Fields. Unison song. *See* Thiman (Eric H.)

— Lambs of Thy Fold, O Jesus. [Hymn.] *See* Dennis (H.) School Anniversary Music ... Part II. No. 42.

LAMBSTON (Maud Val Noel John Bert) pseud.

— Three little Songs. Words by O'-tis-a-Masher. *Vincent Music Co.: London,* [1902.] fol.   **H. 1799. cc. (43.)**

LAMBTON

— The Lambton Worm. [Cantata.] *See* Hutchinson (Godfrey)

LAMBURN (Emily)

— Nydia's Love Song [begins: "The wind and the beam"]. Words by Lord Lytton. *London,* [1872.] fol.   **H. 1775. t. (12.)**

LAMBURN (R. S.)

— The Prince Albert Victor March. [P. F.] *Weekes & Co.: London,* [1885.] fol.   **h. 1484. s. (7.)**

LAME

— The Lame Dog and the Stile. Song. *See* Stevens (George A.)

— Lame Lenny. [Song.] *See* Rowley (A.)

LAMENT

— The Lament. *See* I. I wish I were, *etc.* [1845.] fol.   **H. 1252. (19.)**

— A Lament. (In einem kühlen Grunde.) *See* German. German Volkslieder, *etc.* No. 4. [1864.] fol.   **H. 2827. a. (3.)**

— A Lament. [Song.] *See* Aïdé (H.)

— A Lament. [Song.] *See* Amohia, *pseud.*

— Lament. [Song.] *See* Barlow (H.)

— A Lament. Song. *See* Beningfield (E.)

— The Lament. [Song.] *See* Birt (E. H.)

— A Lament. Song. *See* Bowen (Y.)

— A Lament. [Part-song.] *See* Button (H. E.)

— A Lament. Part song. *See* Bye (Frederick)

— Lament. [Part-song.] *See* Castelnuovo-Tedesco (M.)

— A Lament. Song. *See* Clarke (R. B.)

— A Lament. Song. *See* Cooke (W.)

— A Lament. Part-song. *See* Davies (Ivor R.)

— Lament. Solo and Chorus. *See* Elgar (*Sir* E. W.) *Bart.* [Caractacus.]

— The Lament. Song. *See* Esipoff (S.) *pseud.*

— A Lament. Song. *See* Ettrick (H. H.)

— Lament. [Part-song.] *See* Farjeon (H.)

— A Lament. [Part-song.] *See* Fine (Irving G.) The Hour-Glass ... v.

— A Lament. Song. *See* Forrest (O.)

— A Lament. Song. *See* Godfrey (A. E.)

LAMENT

— A Lament. [Song.] *See* HAIGH (R.)

— A Lament. Song. *See* HARRISON (J. A. G.)

— Lament. Song. *See* HEALE (Hélène)

— A Lament. Song. *See* HOPEKIRK (H.)

— Lament. Part Song. *See* JENKINS (D. C.)

— A Lament. Part-Song. *See* JOZÉ (T. R. G.)

— A Lament. [Song.] *See* KEMP (V.)

— Lament. Song. *See* L., A.

— Lament. [Song.] *See* L., M.

— A Lament. [Song.] *See* LAMBERT (E. F.)

— A Lament. Part-Song. *See* LEGGE (R. H.)

— Lament. [Part-song.] *See* LEKBERG (S.)

— A Lament. [Part-song.] *See* LOOMIS (H. W.)

— Lament. [Song.] *See* LYTTELTON (Julian)

— The Lament. [Song.] *See* MATTIOLI (L.)

— Lament. [Song.] *See* NOVELLO (J.)

— A Lament. Part song. *See* O'BRIEN (V.)

— Lament. [Song.] *See* PALMER (C.) Two Songs, *etc.* [No. 1.]

— Lament. [Part-song.] *See* PITFIELD (Thomas B.)

— Lament. Part-Song. *See* POINTER (J.)

— A Lament. Part Song. *See* ROEDER (M.)

— A Lament. [Song.] *See* SCHAEFER (G. A. G.)

— A Lament. [Song.] *See* SHAW (M. F.)

— The Lament. Song. *See* SPARLING (H.)

— The Lament. [Song.] *See* TAPPERT (W.) [Es steht ein' Lind'.]

— Lament. Song. *See* TAYLOR (C.) [A Pageant of the Months.]

— A Lament. Song. *See* TAYLOR (Samuel C.)

— A Lament. Song. *See* TREVOR (D. W.)

— The Lament. Song. *See* VERRINDER (C. G.)

— The Lament. Song. *See* WEBBE (S.) *the Younger.*

— Lament. [Song.] *See* WEINER (L. S.) Three Melodies, *etc.* [No. 1.]

— A Lament. Part-Song. *See* WEST (J. E.)

— A Lament. [Song.] *See* WILLIAMS (J. G.) Four Songs ... 3.

— A Lament. Song. *See* WOOD (*Mrs* E.)

— Lament and Alleluia. Cantata. *See* MORGAN (Haydn M.)

— Lament and Hope. [Song.] *See* BECK (J.)

— Lament and Prayer. Song. *See* CARTER (F. A.)

— Lament for a Cameron Highlander. [Song.] *See* MACDONALD (F. D.)

— Lament for a Larchwood. Song. *See* COX (F.)

— Lament for a Sparrow. [Part-song.] *See* RAWSTHORNE (Alan)

— Lament for Adonis. [Part-song.] *See* GIANNINI (V.)

— Lament for Adonis. [Song.] *See* HEYMAN (K. R. W.)

LAMENT

— The Lament for Amanda. Canzonet. *See* GIARVIZZIO (C.)

— The Lament for Beowulf. [Cantata.] *See* HANSON (H.)

— Lament for Culloden. [Song.] *See* HUNTER (G. S.)

— Lament for Culloden. [Song.] *See* SPEDDING (J. D.)

— A Lament for Cupid. Two-part Song. *See* ROWLEY (A.)

— Lament for Earl Patrick Stewart. Song. *See* GREENWOOD (A. M.)

— Lament for Fidele. [Song.] *See* KEEL (Frederick)

— Lament for Flodden. [Part-song.] *See* LAKE (H. C.)

— Lament for Glencoe. [Song.] *See* C., M. M.

— Lament for Glencoe. Song. *See* RODDIE (W. S.)

— A Lament for Havelock. [Song.] *See* DANCE (W. H.)

— Lament for Maclean of Ardgour. [Part-song.] *See* STATHAM (H. D.)

— A Lament for Nurse Cavell. [Song.] *See* MACFARLANE (M.)

— Lament for Owen Roe-O'Neill. [Part-song.] *See* WHITING (A.) Two Folk-Songs, *etc.* [No. 1.]

— Lament for Prince Llewelyn. Part-Song. *See* JENKINS (D. C.)

— Lament for Robin Hood. [Song.] *See* GIBBS (Cecil A.)

— The Lament for Shuil Donald's Daughter. Song. *See* ARKWRIGHT (F. C.)

— A Lament for the Duke. *See* LOW. Low droops the mourning flag. [1852.] fol.   **H. 1253. (29.)**

— A Lament for the Summer. Duet. *See* HECHT (E.)

— A Lament for the Summer. [Song.] *See* MALLINSON (J. A.)

— A Lament for the Summer. [Part-song.] *See* MOORAT (J. S.) Six Part-Songs ... Op. 2. No. 5.

— A Lament for Wellington. [Song.] *See* RUSSELL (H.)

— Lament from Enceladus. Aria. *See* STATON (J. F.)

— Lament not. Song. *See* PHILP (E.)

— The Lament of a Kiss. [Song.] *See* LLEWELLYN (L.)

— The Lament of Deirdré. [Song.] *See* GILBERT (H. F. B.)

— The Lament of Fanny Brawne. [Two-part song.] *See* STORR (Emma)

— The Lament of Flora Mc.Donald. [Song.] *See* GOW (N.) *the Younger.*

— The Lament of Ian the Proud. [Song.] *See* GRIFFES (C. T.) Three Poems ... Op. 11. No. 1.

— Lament of Isis. [Song.] *See* BANTOCK (*Sir* G.) [Songs of the East. Vol. 3. Songs of Egypt.]

— A Lament of Israel. [Song.] *See* HERBERT (F.)

— The Lament of Kilcash. [Song.] *See* HANNAGAN (M.) and CLANDILLON (S.) ["Londubh an Chairn."]

— The Lament of Lise. Song. *See* PHILP (E.)

— Lament of Mary Queen of Scots. [Part-song.] *See* JOHNSTON (Peter F.)

— The Lament of Mary Queen of Scots. [Song.] *See* SMITH (T. S.)

— The Lament of Shah Jehan. Scena. *See* RONALD (*Sir* L.)

LAMENT

— Lament of the caged Larks. [Song.] *See* TINDAL, afterwards MADDISON (A.)

— The Lament of the Daughters of Sion. Song. *See* WEST (W.)

— Lament of the Frontier Guard. Chorus. *See* BANTOCK (*Sir* G.)

— The Lament of the Irish Emigrant. Ballad. *See* DEMPSTER (William R.)

— The Lament of the Pig. [Song.] *See* FENWICK (Frank B.)

— The Lament of the Rose. Song. *See* CROSSLEY (H.)

— The Lament of the Rose. [Song.] *See* FRANZ (R.) [Aus Osten. Op. 42. No. 5. Es hat die Rose sich beklagt.]

— The Lament of the Scotch Fisherman's Widow. Ballad. *See* MILLARD (V. P.)

— Lament of the Winds. [Song.] *See* WHYTE (E.) Twelve Songs, *etc.* [No. 1.]

— A Lament on the Death of the Princess Charlotte. *See* BRIGHT. The bright light of joy ... on the death of the Princess Charlotte. [1818.] fol.　　　**H. 835. (11.)**

— A Lament on the Wooden Walls of Old England. Song. *See* WAND (W. W.)

LAMENTACIÓN

— Lamentación. [Motet.] *See* COMES (J. B.)

LAMENTATIO

— Lamentatio damnatorum. [Cantata.] *See* CARISSIMI (G.)

LAMENTATION

— Lamentation. For Solo and Choir. *See* ANTALFFY (D. d') Divertimenti ... 3.

— Lamentation. [Song.] *See* CLARKE (R. C.) Two Little Songs. [No. 2.]

— Lamentation. [Song.] *See* LOVEL (P.)

— Lamentation. [Sacred cantata.] *See* NILES (John J.)

— Lamentation de la Vierge au pied de la croix. [Song.] *See* ROKSETH (Y.)

— The Lamentation of Don Roderick. Ballad. *See* ARKWRIGHT (Frances C.) [Set of six ancient Spanish Ballads. No. 2.]

— Lamentation of Marie Antoinette. [Song.] *See* STORACE (S.)

— The Lamentation of Old Father Thames. *See* BLEWITT (J.)

— The Lamentation of the Children of Zion. [Anthem.] *See* TOLLEMACHE (W. J.)

— Lamentation over Boston. *See* BILLINGS (William) [The Singing Master's Assistant.]

LAMENTATIONES

— [Lamentationum Jeremie prophete liber primus.] *Impressum ... per Octauianum Petrutiū, etc.: Venetijs,* 1506. *obl.* 4°. *Imperfect; wanting the first leaf, supplied in photostat facsimile, and containing the titlepage and list of contents. The composers named are Tinctoris, B. Ycart, Alexander Agricola, De orto, Jo. De quadris, and Fran. Vene.*　　**K. 1. d. 6*. (1.)**

— Lamentationum liber Secundus. Auctores Tronboncinus Gaspar. Erasmus. [*Impressum ... per Octauianum Petrutiū: Venetiis,* 1506.] *obl.* 4°. *Imperfect; wanting sig. G 3, supplied in photostat facsimile, and containing the conclusion of the music and the colophon.*　　**K. 1. d. 6*. (2.)**

LAMENTATIONES

— Lamentationes Jeremiae prophetae. [Cantata.] *See* CAVALIERI (E. del)

LAMENTATIONS

— [The Lamentations, for Holy Week. Soprano and contralto parts.] *Brazzini:* [*Florence,* c. 1810.] 4°.　　**C. 2.**

— Lamentations de Joad. Air dramatique. *See* REY (E.)

LAMENTED

— Lamented Maid, what cruel fate. Song. *See* HUDSON (R.)

LAMENTI

— Lamenti. Trittico teatrale. *See* ORFF (C.)

— I Lamenti d'Amore. Solocantate. *See* GLUCK (C. W. von)

LAMENTO

— Lamento. [Song.] *See* BOËLLMANN (L.)

— Il Lamento. Canzonetta. *See* BORDÈSE (L.)

— Il Lamento. Romanza. *See* CAMPANA (F.)

— Lamento. [Part-song.] *See* CHAGRIN (Francis)

— Lamento. Mélodie. *See* CIRILLI (G.)

— Lamento. [Song.] *See* FAURÉ (G. U.) [Chanson du Pêcheur.]

— Lamento. Kantate. *See* HARTMANN (K. A.)

— Lamento. Mélodie. *See* LENEPVEU (C.)

— Il Lamento. Romance. *See* LIVERANI (D.)

— Il Lamento. Melodie. *See* MECATTI (E.)

— Lamento. [Song.] *See* MONPOU (H.) Souvenirs de Naples. No. 2.

— Il Lamento. Romanza. *See* SCHUBERT (F. P.) [Winterreise. Op. 89. No. 23. Die Nebensonnen.]

— Lamento. [Song.] *See* TINEL (E.) Drie Liederen. No. 3.

— Lamento. [Song.] *See* VIARDOT-GARCIA (M. P.)

— Il Lamento. Arietta. *See* ZIMMERMANN (S. A.)

— Lamento amoroso. [Song.] *See* BEETHOVEN (L. van) [Vier Arietten und ein Duett. Op. 82. No. 2.]

— Lamento d'Amore. Melodia. *See* TOSTI (*Sir* F. P.)

— Lamento d'Arianna. Madrigal. *See* MONTEVERDI (C.) [Arianna.]

— Il Lamento d'Arianna. Madrigali. *See* PARI (C.)

— Lamento d'Arianna. [Song.] *See* PETRASSI (G.)

— Il Lamento dell' Orfano. Canzone. *See* CUNIO (A.) Inspirazioni Italiane. No. 1.

— Il Lamento della Ghisa. Canzonetta. *See* BOTTESINI (G.)

— Lamento della ninfa. [Madrigal.] *See* MONTEVERDI (C.) [Madrigali guerrieri et amorosi ... Libro ottavo.—Non havea Febo ancora.]

— Il Lamento della Prigionera. Canzone. *See* ROMANO (G.)

— Lamento di Clori. [Aria.] *See* PERI (Jacopo)

— Lamento di Federico. [Song.] *See* CILÉA (F.) L'Arlesiana.

LAMENTO

— Lamento di Iole. Aria. *See* HAENDEL (G. F.) [Hercules.—Peaceful rest.]

— Lamento di Jole. [Aria.] *See* PERI (Jacopo)

— Lamento di Maria Antonietta, Regina di Francia. Cantata. *See* ROSSELLI (A.)

— Il Lamento di Olimpia. [Madrigals.] *See* ROSSETTO (S.)

— Lamento per la morte di Bellini. [Song.] *See* DONIZETTI (D. G. M.)

LAMENTUM

— Lamentum matris Euryali. [Aria.] *See* MAZZOCCHI (Domenico) [Dialoghi e sonetti posti in musica.]

LAMI (   )

— *See* BALOCHI (L.) L'Amandier. Romance ... accompt. de lyre ou guitare par Lami. [1820?] 8°.　　**E. 1717. c. (48.)**

— *See* BERTON (H. M.) Duo de Ninon chez Mme. de Sévigné ... Accomp^t de lyre ou guitare par Mr Lami. [1810?] 8°.
　　Hirsch M. 660. (11.)

— *See* BERTON (H. M.) [Les Maris garçons.—Dieu des beaux arts.] Air des Maris garçons ... Arrangé pour lyre ou guitar par Lami, *etc.* [c. 1815.] 8°.　　**E. 1717. o. (8.)**

— *See* BERTON (H. M.) [Les Maris garçons.—Pour triompher.] Air ... Arrangé pour lyre guitare par Lami, *etc.* [c. 1810.] 8°.
　　E. 1717. p. (9.)

— *See* GAVEAUX (P.) [Avis aux femmes.—On a cherchez.] Romance ... Arrangée pour la guitare ou lyre, par Lami. [1805?] 8°.　　**E. 1717. g. (25.)**

— *See* GAVEAUX (P.) [Le Bouffe et le tailleur.—Plaignez, plaignez mes tourmens.] Romance ... Avec accomp^t de lyre ou guitare par Lami. [1805?] 8°.　　**E. 1717. g. (28.)**

— *See* MOZART (W. A.) [Le Nozze di Figaro.—Sull'aria.] Duo ... Accomp^t de lyre ou guitarre par Lami. [1810?] 8°.
　　Hirsch M. 660. (26.)

— *See* STERKEL (J. F. X.) Il Dolore ... Accomp^t de guitare ou lyre. Par Lami. [1810?] 8°.　　**Hirsch M. 660. (18.)**

— *See* STERKEL (J. F. X.) La Felicità ... Accompagnement de lyre ou guitare par Lami. [1810?] 8°.　**Hirsch M. 660. (17.)**

LAMIENTO

— Lu Lamiento. Canzone napolitana. *See* TU. Tu vide Nenna comme so arreddutto, *etc.* [1855?] fol.　　**H. 1652. m. (43.)**

LAMIRA

— Lamira and Virnus together have join'd. Song. *See* WALKER (T.)

LAMKAY (WILL)

— Take me, Honey. [Song.] Words by Phil. Myers. pp. 2–5. *F. A. Mills:* [*New York*, 1899.] fol.　　**H. 3985. h. (1.)**

LAMLEY (RICHARD)

— How do I love thee? [Song.] Sonnet from the Portuguese by E. B. Browning. With Cello obbligato. *C. Vincent: London*, [1899.] fol.　　**H. 1799. g. (63.)**

LAMM (PAVEL A.)

— *See* BORODIN (A. P.) Романсы и песни. Редакция П. А. Ламма. 1947. 4°.　　**G. 560. c. (3.)**

LAMM (PAVEL A.)

— *See* DARGOMUIZHSKY (A. S.) Русалка. Опера ... Редакция П. А. Ламма. 1949. 4°.　　**G. 1409. a.**

— *See* LYADOV (A. K.) Полное собрание сочинений для фортепиано ... Редакция ... П. А. Ламма ... Л. Н. Оборина. 1947. 4°.　　**h. 3581. d.**

— *See* MUSORGSKY (M. P.) Sämtliche Werke ... Herausgegeben von P. Lamm. 1931, *etc.* fol. & 4°.　　**H. 3659. c.**

— *See* MUSORGSKY (M. P.) Романсы и песни. [Edited by A. N. Dmitriev on the basis of the edition of P. A. Lamm.] 1960. 4°.　　**G. 1066. i.**

— *See* MUSORGSKY (M. P.) Boris Godunof ... Edited by P. Lamm, *etc.* 1928. 4°.　　**G. 1066. d.**

— *See* MUSORGSKY (M. P.) Boris Godunov ... Edited ... by P. Lamm, *etc.* [1968.] 4°.　　**H. 3659. h.**

— *See* MUSORGSKY (M. P.) Борис Годунов. Опера ... Составил и отредактировал ... П. Ламм, *etc.* 1974. 4°.　**G. 1066. n.**

— *See* MUSORGSKY (M. P.) Boris Godunov ... Edited by P. Lamm ... Chorus parts. [1968.] 4°.　　**G. 1273. f. (4.)**

— *See* MUSORGSKY (M. P.) [Картинки с выставки.] Pictures at an Exhibition. For the piano, *etc.* ⟨Original version, edited by P. Lamm.⟩ [1952.] 4°.　　**g. 272. vv. (5.)**

— *See* MUSORGSKY (M. P.) Хованщина ... Редакция П. Ламма. Инструментовка Д. Шостаковича, *etc.* 1963. 4°.
　　H. 3659. e.

— *See* MUSORGSKY (M. P.) Хованщина. Народная музыкальная драма ... Редакция П. Ламма, *etc.* 1976. 4°.　**G. 1066. o.**

— *See* MUSORGSKY (M. P.) Раёк, *etc.* ⟨Вторая редакция. Редакция П. Ламма.⟩ 1948. 4°.　　**G. 1066. g. (2.)**

— *See* MUSORGSKY (M. P.) Сорочинская ярмарка ... Составил и проработал по автографам композитора П. Ламм, *etc.* 1957. 4°.　　**G. 1066. f.**

— *See* MUSORGSKY (M. P.) Торжественный марш ... Для фортепиано в 4 руки, *etc.* ⟨Редакция и переложение П. Ламм.⟩ 1931. fol.　　**g. 1593. g. (6.)**

— *See* MUSORGSKY (M. P.) Женитьба ... Редакция П. А. Ламма. 1965. 4°.　　**G. 936. h. (1.)**

— *See* RAKHMANINOV (S. V.) Полное собрание сочинений для фортепиано ... Редакция проф. П. А. Ламма. 1948, *etc.* 4°.
　　h. 3984. k.

— *See* RAKHMANINOV (S. V.) Романсы. Полное собрание. ⟨Общая редакция П. Ламма.⟩ 1957. 4°.　　**G. 1433.**

— *See* RAKHMANINOV (S. V.) Фантазия ... ⟨Соч. 5.⟩ Редакция П. Ламма. 1960. 4°.　　**h. 3984. j. (4.)**

— *See* RAKHMANINOV (S. V.) Князь Ростислав ... Редакция П. Ламма, *etc.* 1947. 4°.　　**h. 3984. j. (1.)**

— *See* RAKHMANINOV (S. V.) 24 прелюдии для фортепиано. Редакция П. А. Ламма. 1966. 4°.　　**h. 3984. x. (1.)**

— *See* RAKHMANINOV (S. V.) Скерцо ... Редакция П. Ламма, *etc.* 1947. 4°.　　**h. 3984. j. (2.)**

— *See* RAKHMANINOV (S. V.) Юношеская симфония. Редакция П. Ламм. 1947. fol.　　**h. 3984. h. (8.)**

— *See* RAKHMANINOV (S. V.) Вариации на тему Корелли ... Редакция П. Ламма, *etc.* 1964. 4°.　　**g. 1593. i. (3.)**

— *See* TANEEV (S. I.) Сочинения для фортепиано. Редакция П. А. Ламма и В. Я. Шебалина. 1953. 4°.　　**h. 3641. a.**

— *See* TANEEV (S. I.) Адажио для малого симфонического оркестра ... Редакция П. Ламма. 1950. 4°.　**g. 727. jj. (3.)**

LAMM (Pavel A.)

— *See* Taneev (S. I.) Канцона для кларнета и струнного оркестра или квинтета ... Редакция П. Ламм и А. Семенова, *etc.* 1947. 4°.   **g. 1593. qq. (2.)**

— *See* Taneev (S. I.) Канцона ... Переложение для кларнета (или виолончели) и фортепьяно автора, *etc.* ⟨Редакция П. Ламма.⟩ 1962. 4°.   **g. 1590. kk. (4.)**

— *See* Taneev (S. I.) Konzert ... Для фортепьяно с оркестром ... Редакция П. Ламма, *etc.* 1957. 4°.   **h. 3641. b.**

— *See* Taneev (S. I.) Увертюра на русскую тему ... Редакция Павла Ламма, *etc.* 1948. 4°.   **g. 1265. l. (2.)**

— *See* Taneev (S. I.) Симфония № 1, e-moll, для большого оркестра. Редакция П. Ламма, *etc.* 1948. 4°.   **h. 3641. e.**

LAMMEL (Inge)

— *See* Degeyter (Pierre) L'International. Faksimile-Ausgabe des Autographs. ⟨Herausgegeben von I. Lammel und G. Stübe.⟩ [1976.] 4°.   **F. 1965. o.**

LAMMERMOOR

— Lammermoor. Song. *See* Scott (A. A.) *Lady John Scott.*

LAMMERS (Julius)

— Bilder aus dem Tonleben. 25 characteristische Klavierstücke ... Op. 39. *Leipzig*, [1885.] fol.   **h. 3280. k. (20.)**

— Neues Leben. Song [begins: "O leuchtende Erde"]. Gedicht von E. Scherenberg. Op. 16. *Bremen*, [1866.] fol.   **H. 2139. b. (22.)**

LAMMY

— The Lammy. [Song.] *See* Whar. Whar hae ye been a' Day, *etc.* [1790?] fol.   **H. 1652. u. (48.)**

— The Lammy. [Song.] *See* Gray (J.) *Songwriter.*

LAMO (George)

— Looking around. Polka, introducing a popular melody. [P. F.] *New York*, 1855. fol.   **h. 1459. p. (2.)**

LA MODE (   )

— Waterfall polka for Piano. *Cincinnati*, [1864.] fol.   **h. 1459. g. (3.)**

LAMOND (Frederic A.)

— Aus dem schottischen Hochlande. Concert-Ouverture für grosses Orchester ... Op. 4. Partitur, *etc.* pp. 39. *Steyl & Thomas: Frankfurt a/Main*, [1894.] fol.   **Hirsch M. 937.**

— Clavierstücke ... Op. 1. Erstes Heft. 1. Capriccio. 2. Romanza & Intermezzo. 3. Etude. 4. Intermezzo ... Zweites Heft. 5. Impromptu. 6. Capriccio. 7. Intermezzo. 8. Etude. 2 Hft. *Aug. Cranz: Hamburg*, [1889.] fol.   **h. 3865. m. (14.)**

— Symphonie, A dur, für grosses Orchester ... Op. 3. Partitur, *etc.* pp. 71. *Steyl & Thomas: Frankfurt a/Main*, [1893.] fol.   **h. 1508. bb. (6.)**

— Trio (H moll) für Pianoforte, Violine und Violoncello ... Op. 2. [Score and parts.] 3 pt. *Aug. Cranz: Hamburg*, [1889.] fol.   **h. 2850. y. (6.)**

— *See* Beethoven (L. van) Sonaten ... ([Edited by] F. Lamond.) [P. F.] [c. 1925.] 4°.   **g. 700. q.**

LAMONINARY (Jacques Philippe)

— Six sonates pour deux violons avec la basse ... Gravées par Mme Leclair. Oeuvre Ier. [Parts.] 3 pt. *Chez la Ve Boivin, etc.: Paris*, [1749?] fol.   **h. 2784. ss. (1.)**

— Six trios pour deux violons et la basse ... Gravés par Mme Leclair. Oeuvre IIme. [Parts.] 3 pt. *Chez l'auteur: Valencienne; Chez la Ve Boivin, etc.: Paris*, [c. 1750.] fol.   **h. 2784. ss. (2.)**

LA MONNOYE (Bernard de)

— Noei Borguignon ... Quatreime Édicion, *etc. Ché Abran Lyron de Modene: Ai Dioni*, 1720. 8°.
With a (separately-paginated) appendix of music. Published under the pseudonym "Gui Barôzai".   **11498. cc. 5.**

— Noei Borguignon ... Cinqueime Edicion, reveue, & augmentée de la Nôte de l'Ar de chécun dé Noei, &c. *An Bregogne*, 1738. 8°.   **1464. b. 2.**

— Les Noels Bourguignons ... avec une traduction littérale en regard du texte patois et précédés d'une notice sur la Monnoye et de l'histoire des Noels en Bourgogne par F. Fertiault. [Melodies and words only.] *Lavigne: Paris*, 1842. 12°.   **11498. c. 17.**

— 10 noëls bourguignons de Guy Barôzai composés en l'an 1700. Transcrits & harmonisés par A. Ravizé. pp. 53. *Durand & c^ie: Paris*, [1933.] fol.   **H. 346. q. (1.)**

— Noël Bourguignon. French Christmas Carol. SAB a cappella. Translation by Edmond W. Rickett ... Attributed to Bernard de la Monnoye (1641–1712). Arr. by Wallingford Riegger. pp. 3. *Harold Flammer: New York*, [1951.] 8°.   **F. 260. f. (6.)**

LAMONT (Alfred)

— *See* Alexandre (Emilie) She'd never done a Thing like that before, *etc.* [Song.] ⟨Arranged by A. Lamont.⟩ [1894.] fol.   **H. 3980. (19.)**

— *See* Alexandre (Emilie) What could the poor Girl do?, *etc.* [Song.] ⟨Arranged by A. Lamont.⟩ [1894.] fol.   **H. 3980. (20.)**

— *See* Bedford (Harry) Janey Delaney, *etc.* [Song.] ⟨Arranged by A. Lamont.⟩ [1895.] fol.   **H. 3980. c. (25.)**

— *See* Bedford (Harry) The Old Village Home in the East. Ballad, *etc.* ⟨Arranged by A. Lamont.⟩ [1895.] fol.   **H. 3980. c. (26.)**

— *See* Connor (T. W.) I'm one of the Jays, *etc.* [Song.] ⟨Arranged by A. Lamont.⟩ [1894.] fol.   **H. 3980. l. (32.)**

— *See* Costello (Thomas) Madame Duvan, *etc.* [Song.] ⟨Arranged by A. Lamont.⟩ [1891.] fol.   **H. 3980. m. (10.)**

— *See* Godwin (Will J.) He was only a Cabin Boy, *etc.* [Song.] ⟨Arranged by A. Lamont.⟩ [1894.] fol.   **H. 3980. z. (17.)**

— *See* Howard (Carl) I'll get my own back, *etc.* [Song.] ⟨Arranged by A. Lamont.⟩ [1894.] fol.   **H. 3980. ii. (13.)**

— *See* Murphy (Clarence W.) A Thing he had never done before, *etc.* [Song.] ⟨Arranged by A. Lamont.⟩ [1895.] fol.   **H. 3981. (44.)**

— *See* Powell (O.) I couldn't get in. [Song.] (Arranged by A. Lamont.) [1891.] fol.   **H. 3740. (6.)**

— *See* Richards (S. W.) She was fair, *etc.* [Song.] ⟨Arranged by A. Lamont.⟩ [1894.] fol.   **H. 3981. n. (37.)**

— *See* Robson (T. F.) The Duchess of Drury Lane, *etc.* ⟨Song. Arranged by A. Lamont.⟩ [1895.] fol.   **H. 3981. o. (23.)**

— *See* Rodney (C. M.) La-didily-idily, umti-umti-ay! *etc.* [Song.] ⟨Arranged by A. Lamont.⟩ [1894.] fol.   **H. 3981. o. (36.)**

LAMONT (ALFRED)

— *See* ROGERS (E. W.) "He'll get it where he's gone to now," *etc.* [Song.] ⟨Arranged by A. Lamont.⟩ [1891.] fol.
H. 3981. o. (63.)

— *See* ROGERS (E. W.) My Hat's a brown 'Un … [Song.] ⟨Arranged by A. Lamont.⟩ [1891.] fol. **H. 3981. p. (13.)**

— *See* ROGERS (E. W.) The Simple Pimple … [Song.] ⟨Arranged by A. Lamont.⟩ [1891.] fol. **H. 3981. p. (37.)**

— *See* RUDD (Austin) The Pretty little Maid said "Oui Monsieur," *etc.* ⟨Song. Arranged by A. Lamont.⟩ [1895.] fol.
H. 3981. r. (34.)

— *See* WINCOTT (Harry) Can't stop! can't stop!! can't stop!!! *etc.* ⟨Song. Arranged by A. Lamont.⟩ [1895.] fol.
H. 3981. tt. (24.)

— *See* YARNOLD (Frederick) Good old Uncle Brown, *etc.* ⟨Song. Arranged by A. Lamont.⟩ [1894.] fol. **H. 3981. vv. (8.)**

LAMONT (CHARLES)

— Courting in the moonlight. [Song, begins: "I have a most peculiar style".] Written by M. de Frece. *London*, [1880.] fol.
H. 1783. o. (4.)

LAMONT (LEOPOLD)

— *See* BRAHE (M. H.) The Piper from over the Way … Arranged by L. Lamont. 1937. 8°. **F. 217. h. (30.)**

— *See* OLIVER (H.) What's the Time. Blackbird … Arranged by L. Lamont. 1937. 8°. **F. 217. h. (48.)**

LAMONT (W. C.)

— Violet Galop. [Military band parts.] 25 pt. *In:* ZIEHRER (C. M.) Hand in Hand Quadrille, *etc.* [1869.] fol.
[*Boosé's supplemental military Journal. no.* 238.] **h. 1544.**

LAMONTAGNE (J. EUG.)

— Deneige. Valse. [P. F.] *La Cie D'Imprimerie Moderne: Montreal*, 1902. 4°. **g. 603. m. (14.)**

LA MONTAGNE (JOACHIM HARVARD DE)

— Aubépin … aubépine … Chœur à 4 voix mixtes. Poème de Jeannie Barrault. *Éditions Chappell: Paris*, [1972.] 4°.
F. 1874. q. (1.)

LA MONTAINE (JOHN)

— Birds' courting Song. American folk song, setting by J. La Montaine. pp. 6. *Cordon Press: New York*, [1954.] 4°.
G. 981. ff. (5.)

— Concerto for Piano and Orchestra. Opus 9. Two pianos. [Score.] pp. 68. *Galaxy Music Corp.: New York: Galliard: London; printed in England*, [1965.] 4°. **h. 4015. u. (4.)**

— Even Song. [Organ.] pp. 4. *H. W. Gray Co.: New York*, [1962.] 4°.
Saint Cecilia Series. no. 889. **g. 1378. d. (21.)**

— The Lord is my Shepherd. Sacred song for medium voice. ⟨Opus 36, No. 2. Psalm XXIII.⟩ pp. 5. *H. W. Gray Co.: New York*, [1968.] 4°. **G. 518. m. (2.)**

— Nativity Morn. Christmas carol for S. A. T. B. with optional chimes or hand bells. [Words by] John Milton. [Score.] pp. 8. *H. W. Gray Co.: New York*, [1957.] 8°. **F. 260. i. (42.)**

LA MONTAINE (JOHN)

— Novellis, novellis. A pageant opera. ⟨Op. 31. Libretto adapted by the composer from "The Coventry Corpus Christi Play of the Taylors and Shearmen" and the "Chester Corpus Christi Play of the Nativity".⟩ [Vocal score.] pp. vi. 73. *G. Schirmer: New York*, [1962.] 4°. **G. 1268. j. (4.)**

— Novellis, Novellis. A pageant opera. ⟨Op. 31. Chorus parts.⟩ pp. 17. *G. Schirmer: New York*, [1963.] 8°. **F. 1256. a. (6.)**

— Three Poems of Holly Beye. I. Definition of the Highest. II. Happiness. III. Song from the Bamboo Cycle. Medium voice and piano. pp. 12. *Cordon Press: New York*, [1954.] 4°.
G. 1276. m. (25.)

— Processional. [Organ.] pp. 7. *H. W. Gray Co.: New York*, [1964.] 4°.
Saint Cecilia Series. no. 912. **g. 1378. q. (5.)**

— Songs of the Nativity. For chorus of mixed voices unaccompanied … Opus 13 … I. Behold, a Virgin shall be with Child. St. Matthew 1:23. ⟨II. Now begin on Christmas Day. [Words by] Gerard Manley Hopkins. III. The Birds. Traditional Czech. IV. Lullaby. Traditional Czech. V. Alleluia.⟩ pp. 20. *H. W. Gray Co.:* [*New York*, 1954.] 8°.
F. 1176. y. (17.)

— Songs of the Nativity. A cycle of Christmas songs for medium voice, *etc.* ⟨Opus 13a.⟩ pp. 31. *H. W. Gray Co.: New York*, [1963.] 4°. **G. 950. (11.)**

— Stopping by Woods on a snowy Evening. For medium voice … Poem by Robert Frost. pp. 4. *Galaxy Music Corporation: New York*, [1963.] 4°. **G. 1276. z. (25.)**

— A Summer's Day. A sonnet for orchestra … Opus 32 … Score, *etc.* pp. ii. 13. *G. Schirmer: New York*, [1963.] 4°.
g. 1620. ii. (8.)

— Te Deum … Op. 35. [S. A. T. B., narrator, wind and percussion. Vocal score.] *In:* WORKMAN (William G.) and DIRKSEN (W.) The Gloria in excelsis Tower Dedication Book, *etc.* pp. 61–84. 1964. 8°. **F. 1158. aa.**

— Wonder Tidings. A cycle of Christmas carols for mixed voices with soprano, alto, tenor and baritone soli. pp. 72. *H. W. Gray Co.: New York*, [1966.] 8°. **F. 260. nn. (18.)**

LAMONTE (G. W.)

— Sweet Dreams are flitting softly o'er me. Song & chorus, words by Mrs. R. J. Healy. *Boston* [*Mass.*], 1864. fol.
H. 1780. f. (5.)

LAMONTE (H.)

— Elise waltz. [P. F. with cornet accompaniment.] *London*, [1872.] fol. **h. 1485. s. (13.)**

LA MORINIÈRE (C. S. HERVÉ DE)

— *See* HERVÉ DE LA MORINIÈRE.

LAMORNA

— Lamorna. Song. *See* GOFFRIÉ (L. J.)

LAMOT (LOUIS)

— Marche du Soir pour Piano. *London*, [1879.] fol.
h. 1494. p. (8.)

LAMOTE (JULIUS)

— Valse di Bravoura … pour le Pianoforte. Solo & duet. 2 no. *London*, [1877.] fol. **h. 1482. y. (22.)**

LAMOTHE (CARL)

— Happy Eliza quadrilles. [P. F.] *London*, [1881.] fol.

h. 3275. j. (7.)

LAMOTHE (GEORGES)

— Lamothe's Waltz Album, *etc.* [P. F.] *Boosey's: London and New York*, [1877.] 4°.
[*Boosey's Musical Cabinet. No.* 200.] **F. 160.**

— Georges Lamothe's ... Waltzes for violin (two violins) (flute) (cornet) (violoncello) and piano. 5 no. *R. Cocks & Co.: London*, [1893.] 4°.
No. 92, 93½, 94, 100 *and* 116 *of the* "*Philharmonic Edition*".

g. 1450.

— [Four Waltzes. Mandoline and P. F.] *See* TURNER (J. A.) Turner's Mandoline Journal, *etc.* No. 25. [1898, *etc.*] 4°.

f. 581.

— Adorée waltzes. [P. F.] *London*, [1881.] fol. **h. 3100. c. (37.)**

— L'Aérienne polka pour Piano. *Paris*, [1872.] fol.

h. 3100. (19.)

— Aida, opéra de G. Verdi, petit caprice. [P. F.] *Paris*, [1876.] fol. **h. 3100. (53.)**

— Aïda, opéra de Verdi, valse pour Piano. *Paris*, [1877.] fol.

h. 3100. d. (5.)

— Amour et Jeunesse valse. [P. F.] *London*, [1876.] fol.

h. 3100. a. (21.)

— Amour et Jeunesse. Valse. [Orchestral parts.] *See* HOPWOOD AND CREW. Hopwood & Crew's Orchestral Journal ... No. 53. [1860? *etc.*] 8°. **e. 1340.**

— Angelina, caprice espagnol pour Piano. *Paris*, [1873.] fol.

h. 977. l. (16.)

— Anthémis. Valse pour piano. *V*ᵉ. *E. Girod: Paris*, [1886.] fol.

h. 3100. f. (9.)

— Antiquités musicales. [P. F.] 3 no. *Paris*, [1878.] fol.

h. 3100. d. (9.)

— Les Archers d'Amagnac, morceau caractéristique pour le Piano. *London*, [1876.] fol. **h. 3100. a. (22.)**

— Baiser de Printemps. Valses. [Conductor's P. F. part.] *London*, [1877.] 8°. **e. 217. e. (24.)**

— Baiser de Printemps valses. [Orchestral parts.] [*London*, 1877.] 8°. **f. 410. b. (14.)**

— Barque Jolie, grande valse sur des motifs de V. Robillard, pour Piano. *Paris*, [1876.] fol. **h. 3100. (47.)**

— La Bataille de Fleurs. Souvenir de Nice. Valse pour Piano. *Paris*, [1883.] fol. **h. 3100. e. (20.)**

— La Bayadère, air de ballet pour Piano. *Paris*, [1879.] fol.

h. 3100. d. (13.)

— Bella valse pour Piano. *Paris*, [1872.] fol. **h. 3100. (18.)**

— Bella, valse brillante pour Piano. [Solo and duet.] 2 no. *Paris*, [1883.] fol. **h. 3100. e. (21.)**

— Les Bersagliers, caprice militaire pour Piano. *Paris*, [1876.] fol. **h. 3100. (48.)**

— Les Bersagliers (the Riflemen). Caprice militaire pour le Pianoforte. *London*, [1876.] fol. **h. 3100. a. (28.)**

— Billet Doux waltzes. [P. F.] *London*, [1876.] fol.

h. 3100. a. (34.)

— Blonde et brune. *See* infra: [Brune et Blonde.]

LAMOTHE (GEORGES)

— The Blue Alsatians waltz on S. Adams' ... song. [P. F. solo and duet.] 2 no. *London*, [1878.] fol. **h. 3100. c. (21.)**

— Bon Soir valse. [P. F.] *London*, [1877.] fol. **h. 3100. c. (6.)**

— Bouquet de Bal waltzes. [P. F.] *London*, [1876.] fol.

h. 3100. a. (40.)

— Bouquet de Noces. Valse pour piano. *E. Fromont: Paris*, 1887. fol. **h. 3100. f. (10.)**

— Bouquet de Noces. Valse pour le Piano. [*Paris*,] 1894. 8°. *Supplement to "L'Illustration", No.* 2687. **P. P. 4283. m. (3.)**

— Bouquet de Roses, polka-mazurka pour Piano. Op. 17. *Paris*, [1866.] fol. **h. 3100. (1.)**

— Brise des Nuits, valse pour le Piano. *Paris*, [1870.] fol.

h. 3100. (16.)

— Brise des Nuits valses. [P. F.] *London*, [1874.] fol.

h. 3100. c. (2.)

— Brise des Nuits valses. [P. F.] Duet. *London*, [1875.] fol.

h. 3100. a. (4.)

— [Brise des nuits.] Waltz—Brise des nuits ... Arranged [for military band] by Fred Godfrey. [Parts.] 25 pt. *S. A. Chappell: London*, [1876.] fol.
[*Army Journal. no.* 110.] **h. 1562.**

— Brune et Blonde, valse brillante. [P. F.] *Paris*, [1878.] fol.

h. 3100. d. (8.)

— [Brune et Blonde.] Blonde et brune. Valse. [Orchestral parts.] 15 pt. *Augener & Co.: London*, [1887.] 8°. **f. 800. (775.)**

— [Brune et Blonde.] Blonde et brune. Valse. ⟨For septet.⟩ [Parts.] 9 pt. *Augener & Co.: London*, [1887.] 8°. **f. 800. (776.)**

— Cachucha-Mazurk pour Piano. *Paris*, [1875.] fol.

h. 3100. (40.)

— Caresses, suite de valses pour le Piano. *Paris*, [1882.] fol.

h. 3100. e. (13.)

— Carillon valse. [P. F.] *London*, [1878.] fol. **h. 3100. c. (22.)**

— Les Castagnettes, valse Espagnole. [P. F.] *London*, [1878.] fol.

h. 3100. c. (16.)

— Cavalcade galop pour Piano. *Paris*, [1877.] fol.

h. 3100. d. (1.)

— Chaconne du bon vieux temps, pour le Piano. *London*, [1876.] fol. **h. 3100. a. (7.)**

— Chanson Arabe pour Piano. *Paris*, [1882.] fol.

h. 3100. e. (14.)

— Chanson du Vert-Galant. *See* infra: Deux transcriptions pour Piano. ⟨2.⟩

— Chant d'amour. Valse. ⟨For septet.⟩ [Parts.] 9 pt. *Augener & Co.: London*, [1887.] 8°. **f. 800. (777.)**

— Chant des Alpes, mazurka Tyrolienne pour Piano. *Paris*, [1880.] fol. **h. 3100. e. (1.)**

— Chant du Soir, nocturne pour Piano. *London*, [1876.] fol.

h. 3100. a. (16.)

— Chants d'Allemagne valse, orchestrated by St. Jacome. [Orchestral parts.] *London*, [1873.] 8°.
Part of the "Alliance Musicale". **f. 400. c. (14.)**

— Chants de l'Aube, suite de valses. [P. F.] *Paris*, [1876.] obl. fol. **e. 272. f. (14.)**

— Chants de l'Aube valses. [P. F.] *London*, [1876.] fol.

h. 3100. a. (32.)

LAMOTHE (GEORGES)

— Chants de l'Aube. Valses ... Arranged by F. J. H. Millars. [Orchestral parts.] [1876.] *See* CHAPPELL AND CO. Popular Quadrilles, *etc.* No. 90. [1862, *etc.*] 8°.　　　　**e. 249.**

— La Charmeuse valse. [P. F.]　*Paris,* [1875.] *obl.* fol.
　　　　　　　　　　　　　　　e. 272. f. (10.)

— Le Chemin des Violettes. Souvenir de Pau. Valse pour piano. *Paris,* [1883.] fol.　　　　**h. 3100. e. (30.)**

— Les Chevaliers du Guet, caprice militaire pour Piano.　*Paris,* [1881.] fol.　　　　　　**h. 3100. e. (9.)**

— Cheveux au Vent, suite des valses. [P. F.]　*London,* [1876.] fol.
　　　　　　　　　　　　　　　h. 3100. a. (15.)

— Ciel de Feu, suite de valses. [P. F.]　*Paris,* [1881.] fol.
　　　　　　　　　　　　　　　h. 3100. e. (3.)

— Ciel et Enfer. Valse brillante pour piano.　*J. Vasseur: Paris,* 1886. fol.　　　　　　　**h. 3100. f. (11.)**

— Cinq-Mars, valse brillante sur l'opéra de C. Gounod, pour Piano.　*Paris,* [1878.] *obl.* fol.　　**e. 272. h. (45.)**

— Le Cirque Américain, quadrille equestre pour Piano.　*Paris,* [1876.] *obl.* fol.　　　　　**e. 272. f. (11.)**

— Les Cloches de Paris waltzes. [P. F.]　*London,* [1876.] fol.
　　　　　　　　　　　　　　　h. 3100. a. (39.)

— Le Cloître, souvenir de la Grande Chartreuse, marche religieuse. [P. F.]　*Paris,* [1874.] fol.　**h. 3100. (29.)**

— [Le Cloître.] The Cloister, marche religieuse. [P. F.]　*London,* [1876.] fol.　　　　　　**h. 3100. a. (36.)**

— Les Clowns, polka brillante pour Piano.　*Paris,* [1869.] fol.
　　　　　　　　　　　　　　　h. 3100. (7.)

— Combien j'ai douce souvenance, mélodie de Chateaubriand. [P. F. fantasia.]　*Paris,* [1870.] fol.　**h. 3100. (14.)**

— Coquillette polka sur l'opérette Ondines au Champagne, de C. Lecocq. [P. F.]　*Paris,* [1876.] fol.　**h. 3100. (45.)**

— Corail polka pour Piano.　*Paris,* [1874.] fol.　**h. 3100. (23.)**

— La Corrida de los Torros ... Caprice. [P. F.]　*Paris,* [1881.] fol.　　　　　　　　　　**h. 3100. e. (7.)**

— Croquetaine, polka mazurka pour Piano. Op. 22.　*Paris,* [1866.] fol.　　　　　　　　**h. 3100. (3.)**

— Dame de Coeur, polka-mazurka. [P. F.] Op. 17.　*Paris,* [1866.] fol.　　　　　　　　　**h. 3100. (4.)**

— Danse Arabe pour Piano.　*Paris,* [1874.] fol.　**h. 3100. (31.)**

— Danse Arabe pour Piano.　*London,* [1876.] fol.
　　　　　　　　　　　　　　　h. 3100. a. (37.)

— La Danse des Roses, air de ballet pour le Piano.　*Paris,* [1875.] fol.　　　　　　　　**h. 3100. (36.)**

— La Danse des Roses, air de ballet pour le Piano.　*London,* [1876.] fol.　　　　　　　**h. 3100. a. (14.)**

— Danse des Savoyards. Danse caractéristique pour piano. (Op. 238.)　*Hopwood & Crew: London,* [1882.] fol.
　　　　　　　　　　　　　　　h. 3100. e. (32.)

— Danse des Savoyards. [Orchestral parts.] *See* HOPWOOD AND CREW. Hopwood & Crew's Orchestral Journal ... No. 100. [1860? *etc.*] 8°.　　　　　　　　**e. 1340.**

— De Paris à Vienne polka. [P. F.]　*Paris,* [1875.] fol.
　　　　　　　　　　　　　　　h. 3100. (35.)

— Les Délices (Souvenir Helvétique) valse pour le Piano. *Paris,* [1873.] fol.　　　　　　**h. 3100. (21.)**

LAMOTHE (GEORGES)

— Les Délices (Souvenir Helvetique) valse pour Piano. *London,* [1876.] fol.　　　　　**h. 3100. a. (17.)**

— Dernier Baiser, valse pour le Piano.　*Paris,* [1882.] fol.
　　　　　　　　　　　　　　　h. 3100. e. (11.)

— [Dernier Baiser.] The Last Kiss ... Waltz. [P. F.]　*C. Sheard: London,* [1893.] fol.
No. 6993–4 *of the Musical Bouquet.*　　**H. 2345.**

— Un Désir, suite de valses pour Piano.　*Paris,* [1876.] *obl.* fol.
　　　　　　　　　　　　　　　e. 272. f. (15.)

— Dormez ma Belle, berceuse pour Piano. Op. 32.　*Paris,* [1866.] fol.　　　　　　　　　**h. 3100. (2.)**

— Dreaming, valse on M. Welling's song. [P. F.]　*London,* [1882.] fol.　　　　　　　　**h. 3100. c. (43.)**

— Éclat de Rire, polka fantaisie pour le Piano.　*Paris,* [1875.] fol.　　　　　　　　　**h. 3100. (38.)**

— Eliane polka-mazurka pour Piano.　*Paris,* [1872.] fol.
　　　　　　　　　　　　　　　h. 977. l. (6.)

— En Forêt. Chasse, *etc.* [P. F.]　*J. Iochem: Paris,* [1887.] fol.
　　　　　　　　　　　　　　　h. 3100. f. (15.)

— En Marche, caprice militaire. [P. F.]　*London,* [1878.] fol.
　　　　　　　　　　　　　　　h. 3100. c. (18.)

— En Palanquin, marche Indienne. [P. F.]　*Paris,* [1879.] fol.
　　　　　　　　　　　　　　　h. 3100. d. (11.)

— En Palanquin. Marche Indienne. (Op. 206.) [P. F.]　*Metzler & Co.: London,* [1884.] fol.　　**h. 3100. e. (33.)**

— En récréation. Galop marche. 2ᵉ. edᵒⁿ.　*J. Iochem: Paris,* [1887.] fol.　　　　　　**h. 3100. f. (14.)**

— Enfantillages pour piano. Six danses graduées sur les cinq notes. 6 no.　*André: Paris,* [1887.] fol.　**h. 3100. f. (18.)**

— L'Éperon d'Or. Caprice hongrois pour piano. Op. 272. *Nuyens & Cie.: Paris,* [1886.] fol.　**h. 3100. f. (2.)**

— Esmeralda. Valse on A. G. Thomas's opera.　*Boosey & Co.: London,* [1884.] fol.　　　**h. 3100. e. (34.)**

— Estudiantina. Caprice espagnol sur le ... duo de P. Lacome. [P. F.]　*Hopwood & Crew: London,* [1887.] fol.
　　　　　　　　　　　　　　　h. 3100. e. (35.)

— Étendard-polka pour Piano.　*Paris,* [1876.] fol.
　　　　　　　　　　　　　　　h. 3100. (57.)

— L'Étoile du bal. Valse. [Orchestral parts.] 17 pt.　*Augener & Co.: London,* [1887.] 8°.　　**f. 800. (778.)**

— L'Étoile du bal. Valse. ⟨For septet.⟩ [Parts.] 9 pt.　*Augener & Co.: London,* [1887.] 8°.
Orchestra Music. no. 7065.　　　**f. 800. (779.)**

— Fédora, grande valse brillante. [P. F.]　*Paris,* [1883.] fol.
　　　　　　　　　　　　　　　h. 3100. e. (22.)

— La Fée de Nuit, valse brillante sur les motifs de C. Pourny pour Piano.　*Paris,* [1876.] fol.　**h. 3100. (46.)**

— La Fée de la Nuit (de Ch. Pourny) valse, orchestrée par E. Deransart. [Orchestral parts.]　*Paris,* [1881.] 8°.
　　　　　　　　　　　　　　　f. 245. d. (6.)

— La Fée des Bruyères valse. [P. F.]　*London,* [1879.] fol.
　　　　　　　　　　　　　　　h. 3100. c. (24.)

— Les Femmes de France. Valse pour piano.　*Vᵛᵉ. E. Girod: Paris,* 1886. fol.　　　　　**h. 3100. f. (12.)**

— La Fiancée, valse brillante pour Piano.　*Paris,* [1874.] fol.
　　　　　　　　　　　　　　　h. 3100. (30.)

LAMOTHE (Georges)

— La Fiancée waltzes. [P. F.] *London*, [1876.] fol.
    h. 3100. a. (38.)

— Flamberge au Vent, caprice militaire pour Piano. *Paris*, [1877.] fol.
    h. 3100. d. (2.)

— Flamberge au Vent, caprice militaire pour Piano. *London*, [1879.] fol.
    h. 3100. c. (25.)

— Fleurs des Champs, trois danses faciles pour Piano. Op. 49. *Paris*, [1869.] fol.
    h. 3100. (9.)

— The Flower of the Season, polka-mazurka ... for the Pianoforte. *London*, [1866.] fol.
    h. 3100. (15.)

— The Flower of the Season. Mazurka. [P. F. solo and duet.] *See* SMALLWOOD (W.) Home Treasures, *etc.* No. 60. [1872, *etc.*] fol.
    h. 1412. o.

— Fontainebleau valse fanfare pour Piano. *Paris*, [1874.] fol.
    h. 3100. (25.)

— Fontainebleau, valse fanfare pour Piano. *London*, [1876.] fol.
    h. 3100. a. (25.)

— France et Navarre, air ancien attribué à Henri IV. Transcrit pour Piano. *London*, [1879.] fol.
    h. 3100. c. (26.)

— François les Bas Bleus ... Fantaisie brillante pour piano. Op. 260. [On the opera of F. Bernicat and A. C. P. Messager.] *Paris*, [1884.] fol.
    h. 3100. e. (28.)

— Frascati valse. [P. F.] *Paris*, [1875.] fol.
    h. 3100. (33.)

— Frascati valse. ⟨Op: 169.⟩ [P. F.] pp. 9. *Evans & Cº: London*, [c. 1880.] fol.
    h. 60. zz. (23.)

— From foreign Parts. *See* infra: [My Darling's Album. No. 1–6.]

— Galop-Tonnerre pour Piano. *Paris*, [1882.] fol.
    h. 3100. e. (12.)

— [Galop-Tonnerre.] Tonnerre Galop. (Op. 250.) [P. F.] *Rivière & Hawkes: London*, [1887.] fol.
    h. 3100. e. (47.)

— Galop Tonnerre. Thunder Galop. Op. 250. Arranged by S. V. Balfour. [Orchestral parts.] *Rivière & Hawkes: London*, [1887.] 8°.
    e. 370. g. (1.)

— Gavotte de la Reine pour Piano. *Paris*, [1881.] fol.
    h. 3100. e. (8.)

— Gavotte de Vestris. *See* infra: Deux transcriptions pour Piano. ⟨1.⟩

— Gavotte Marion de Lorme, pour piano. Op. 274. *Nuyens & Cie.: Paris*, [1886.] fol.
    h. 3100. f. (4.)

— Gavotte Pompadour transcrite et variée pour Piano. *London*, [1873.] fol.
    h. 3100. c. (1.)

— Golden Love waltz on M. Welling's ... song. [P. F.] *London*, [1882.] fol.
    h. 3100. c. (39.)

— Golden Love. Valse. [Fife and drum band parts.] *London*, [1882.] 8°.
    f. 414. a. (45.)

— Good Company waltz on S. Adams' songs. [P. F.] *London*, [1880.] fol.
    h. 3100. c. (29.)

— Grain de Beauté. Valse brillante. [P. F.] *Vᵉ. E. Girod: Paris*, 1887. fol.
    h. 3100. f. (13.)

— Grenade valse pour Piano. *Paris*, [1874.] fol.
    h. 3100. (24.)

— Guillaume Tell. [Fantasia on G. A. Rossini's opera] pour orgue et piano. Op. 183. *Paris*, [1876.] fol. *No. 5 of Duos de Salon pour orgue et piano.*
    h. 2576. a. (11.)

— Hallali, valse-fanfare pour Piano. *Paris*, [1879.] fol.
    h. 3100. d. (14.)

LAMOTHE (Georges)

— Hallali, valse fanfare pour Piano. *London*, [1881.] fol.
    h. 3100. c. (30.)

— The Happy Little Couple, waltz ... for the Pianoforte. *London*, [1881.] fol.
    h. 3100. c. (35.)

— Happy Vision. Waltz. [P. F.] *E. Ascherberg & Co.: London*, [1888.] fol.
    h. 3100. e. (36.)

— Impériale, polka brillante. [P. F.] Op. 21. *Paris*, [1866.] fol.
    h. 3100. (5.)

— Je vous aime valse. [P. F.] *Paris*, [1875.] *obl.* fol.
    e. 272. f. (9.)

— Je vous aime, valse pour Piano. *London*, [1875.] fol.
    h. 3100. a. (1.)

— Je vous aime valse. [P. F.] *London*, [1878.] 8°. *No. 422 of the "Alliance Musicale. Album Bijou".*
    f. 406.

— Je vous aime valse. [Orchestral parts.] *London*, [1878.] 8°. *Part of the "Alliance Musicale".*
    f. 400. p. (18.)

— Jeunesse Dorée, valse pour Piano. *Paris*, [1883.] fol.
    h. 3100. e. (23.)

— Joyeux Carillon, valse-caprice pour Piano. *Paris*, [1881.] fol.
    h. 3100. e. (6.)

— Juliette valses. [P. F.] *London*, [1876.] fol.   **h. 3100. a. (24.)**

— Ko-Ki-Ko, polka Chinoise pour le Piano. *Paris*, [1870.] fol.
    h. 3100. (17.)

— Land of Dreams. *See* infra: [Le Pays des Songes.]

— Larmes d'Amour, suite de valses. [P. F.] *London*, [1876.] fol.
    h. 3100. a. (5.)

— The Last Kiss. *See* supra: [Dernier Baiser.]

— Lisbonne, boléro pour Piano. *Paris*, [1875.] fol.
    h. 3100. (41.)

— Lovely Flowers. *See* infra: [Songes Roses.]

— Lulu-Galop pour Piano. *Paris*, [1877.] fol.   **h. 3100. (58.)**

— Ma Mie. Gavotte. (Op. 236.) [P. F.] *Hopwood & Crew: London*, [1882.] fol.
    h. 3100. e. (38.)

— Ma Mie. Gavotte. [Orchestral parts.] *See* HOPWOOD AND CREW. Hopwood & Crew's Orchestral Journal ... No. 106. [1860? *etc.*]
    e. 1340.

— Mademoiselle Clairon, polka militaire pour Piano. *Paris*, [1880.] fol.
    h. 3100. e. (2.)

— Magdeleine. Valse. [P. F.] *F. Pitman: London*, [1887.] fol.
    h. 3100. e. (37.)

— La Malle des Indes, galop brillant pour Piano. *Paris*, [1874.] fol.
    h. 3100. (28.)

— La Malle des Indes. Galop brillant pour piano ... Op: 161. pp. 7. *Enoch père et fils: Paris; Enoch & Sons: London*, [printed, c. 1875.] fol.
    h. 3870. vv. (7.)

— [La Malle des indes.] Galop, *etc.* [Military band parts.] 23 pt. *In:* ROSSINI (G. A.) [Tancredi.—Tu che i miseri conforti. G major setting.] Arietta, *etc.* [1880.] fol. [*Boosé's military Journal. ser.* 62. *no.* 4.]
    h. 1549.

— Manon. Opéra-comique de J. Massenet. Valse pour piano. *Paris*, [1884.] *obl.* fol.   **e. 283. c. (8.)**

— The March Past, morceau militaire for the Pianoforte. *London*, [1876.] fol.
    h. 3100. a. (19.)

— The March Past pas redoublé. [Reed band parts.] [*London*, 1878.] 8°.
    f. 412. k. (9.)

LAMOTHE (GEORGES)

— Marche Chinoise pour Piano. *London*, [1878.] fol.
h. 3100. c. (13.)

— Marche des Pupazzi. Mirlitonade pour piano avec partie de Mirliton ad libitum. Op. 271. *Nuyens & Cie.: Paris*, [1886.] fol.
h. 3100. f. (1.)

— Marche des Souverains. [P. F.] *Paris*, [1877.] fol.
h. 3100. d. (3.)

— Marche funèbre et Dies Iræ pour Piano. *Paris*, [1878.] fol.
h. 3100. d. (7.)

— Marche Venitienne pour Piano. Op. 82. *Paris*, [1870.] fol.
h. 3100. (13.)

— Marche Vénitienne pour Piano. *London*, [1876.] fol.
h. 3100. a. (31.)

— La Marjolaine set of waltzes on Lecocq's ... opera. [P. F.] *London*, [1877.] fol.
h. 3100. c. (12.)

— La Marseillaise [by C. J. Rouget de Lisle]. Transcription militaire pour Piano. *Paris*, [1876.] fol.
h. 3100. (44.)

— La Marseillaise [by C. J. Rouget de Lisle]. Transcription militaire for the Pianoforte. *London*, [1878.] fol.
h. 3100. c. (14.)

— Masques & Dominos, sérénade pour Piano. *Paris*, [1875.] fol.
h. 3100. (43.)

— Mélancolie valse. [P. F.] *Paris*, [1876.] fol.
h. 3100. (56.)

— Le message des fleurs, valse ... Op. 172. [P. F.] *Paris*, [1876.] fol.
h. 3100. (50.)

— Le Message des Fleurs, valse. [P. F.] *London*, [1876.] fol.
h. 3100. a. (33.)

— Le Message des Fleurs. Valse. [P. F.] [1878.] *See* RIMBAULT (E. F.) The Juvenile Ball Room, *etc.* No. 20. [1870–78.] fol.
h. 486. c. (6.)

— Le Message des Fleurs. Valse. Arranged by F. J. H. Millars. [Orchestral parts.] [1876.] *See* CHAPPELL AND CO. Popular Quadrilles, *etc.* No. 89. [1862, *etc.*] 8°.
e. 249.

— Trois Morceaux. *See* infra: [My Darling's Album. no. 9, 10, 7.]

— Un Mot d'Amour valse. [P. F.] *London*, [1879.] fol.
No. 673–74 of C. Boosey's "Universal" music. **H. 2324.**

— Les Muses valses. [P. F.] *London*, [1877.] fol.
h. 3100. c. (9.)

— My Darling's Album. 12 Silhouettes for the pianoforte. 2 bk. *E. Ascherberg & Co.: London*, [1888.] fol. **h. 3100. e. (39.)**

— [My Darling's Album. no. 1–6.] From foreign Parts. 6 Pieces in Dance Rhythms. [P. F.] (1912.) *See* DUNHILL (T. F.) and VOLK (W. A.) Recreative Pieces, *etc.* Series 1. No. 3c. (1912, *etc.*) fol.
h. 2912. a.

— [My Darling's Album. no. 8, 12, 11.] Petite Suite. Rondino, Menuet & Gavotte. [P. F.] (1912.) *See* DUNHILL (T. F.) and VOLK (W. A.) Recreative Pieces, *etc.* Series 1. No. 3d. (1912, *etc.*) fol.
h. 2912. a.

— [My Darling's Album. no. 9, 10, 7.] Trois Morceaux. [P. F.] (1912.) *See* DUNHILL (T. F.) and VOLK (W. A.) Recreative Pieces, *etc.* Series 1. No. 3a. (1912, *etc.*) fol. **h. 2912. a.**

— Nadeshda. Waltz on A. G. Thomas' opera. *Boosey & Co.: London*, [1885.] fol.
h. 3100. e. (40.)

— The Night Patrol, morceaux caractéristique for the Pianoforte. *London*, [1876.] fol.
h. 3100. a. (20.)

— Nuit d'Orient, grande valse de salon pour Piano. *Paris*, [1875.] fol.
h. 3100. (34.)

LAMOTHE (GEORGES)

— Nuit d'Orient valse. [P. F.] *London*, [1877.] fol.
h. 3100. c. (5.)

— Nuit et Jour, grande valse pour Piano. *Paris*, [1874.] fol.
h. 3100. (22.)

— The Old Lock. Waltz on M. Wellings' ... song. [P. F.] *Enoch & Sons: London*, [1883.] fol. **h. 3100. e. (41.)**

— The Old Lock. Waltz, arr^d. by H. Millars. [Reed band parts.] *London*, [1885.] 8°.
Part of the "Alliance Musicale". **f. 401. aa. (2.)**

— Opéra-quadrille. [P. F.] *Paris*, [1875.] *obl.* fol. **e. 272. f. (7.)**

— Opéras de Verdi. Six grands duos pour Piano et Orgue. 6 no. *Paris*, [1880.] fol. **h. 2575. h. (6.)**

— Or et Azur valse. [P. F.] *Paris*, [1874.] fol. **h. 3100. (26.)**

— Or et Azur valse. [P. F.] *London*, [1876.] fol.
h. 3100. a. (12.)

— "Or et Azur." ⟨Valse.⟩ Lamothe.—Mazurka, "La Charmeuse". O. Heyer. [Op. 38. Military band parts.] 25 pt. *Boosey & Co.: London*, 1877. fol.
[Boosé's supplemental military Journal. no. 283.] **h. 1544.**

— Our last Waltz, on Molloy's ... song. [P. F.] *Boosey & Co.: London*, [1885.] fol. **h. 3100. e. (42.)**

— "Our last Waltz" ... (On Molloy's popular song.) Quadrille "London Life". C. Coote. (On popular tunes.) [Military band parts.] 26 pt. *Boosey & Co.: London*, 1885. fol.
[Boosey's military Journal. ser. 78. no. 3.] **h. 1549.**

— Page d'Amour, valse brillante pour Piano. *Paris*, [1882.] fol.
h. 3100. e. (15.)

— Page d'Amour. Valse. [P. F.] *Metzler & Co.: London*, [1885.] fol.
h. 3100. e. (43.)

— Paris polka pour le Piano. Op. 20. *Paris*, [1866.] fol.
h. 3100. (6.)

— Les Parisiennes, suite de valses. [P. F.] *Paris*, [1872.] *obl.* fol.
e. 217. b. (25.)

— Pastorale valse. [P. F.] *London*, [1878.] fol. **h. 3100. c. (20.)**

— Paul & Virginie, opéra de V. Massé, grand duo pour Orgue & Piano. *Paris*, [1877.] fol. **h. 2576. (8.)**

— Paul & Virginie, suite de valses sur l'opéra de V. Massé, pour Piano. *Paris*, [1877.] *obl.* fol. **e. 272. f. (16.)**

— Pavane Renaissance pour piano. Op. 278. *E. Lacombe: Paris*, [1886.] fol. **h. 3100. f. (5.)**

— [Le Pays des Songes.] Land of Dreams waltzes. [P. F.] *London*, [1876.] fol. **h. 3100. a. (35.)**

— Pendant la valse. Impromptu. Op. 301. No. 1. Pour orgue. No. 2. Pour piano. 2 no. *Lissarrague: Paris*, [1887.] fol.
h. 3100. f. (8.)

— Pervenches, polka-mazurka pour Piano. *Paris*, [1883.] fol.
h. 3100. e. (18.)

— La Petite Mariée, opéra bouffe de C. Lecocq, fantaisie brillante pour Piano. *Paris*, [1876.] fol. **h. 3100. (54.)**

— La Petite Muette, opéra comique ... de Serpette, fantaisie-transcription pour Piano. *Paris*, [1878.] fol.
h. 3100. d. (6.)

— Petite Suite. *See* supra: [My Darling's Album. no. 8, 12, 11.]

— Petits Enfants (Berceuse de Paladilhe) transcription mélodique. [P. F.] *London*, [1876.] fol. **h. 3100. a. (13.)**

— Phœbe valse pour le Piano. *Paris*, [1876.] fol.
h. 3100. (52.)

LAMOTHE (GEORGES)

— Pièces Mignonnes pour piano. 6 morceaux de genre. 6 no. *André: Paris*, [1887.] fol.　　　　　　　**h. 3100. f. (19.)**

— Pluie de Roses, valse pour Piano. *Paris*, [1881.] fol.
　　　　　　　h. 3100. e. (4.)

— Poésie. Rêverie Caprice. [P. F.] *Hopwood & Crew: London*, [1882.] fol.　　　　　　　**h. 3100. e. (44.)**

— Polka militaire. [P. F.] *London*, [1881.] fol.　　**h. 3100. c. (34.)**

— Pomme d'Amour waltzes. [P. F.] *London*, [1881.] fol.
　　　　　　　h. 3100. c. (38.)

— Le Premier Baiser valse pour le Piano. Op. 68. *Paris*, [1869.] fol.　　　　　　　**h. 3100. (11.)**

— Le Premier Baiser valse. [P. F.] *London*, [1874.] fol.
　　　　　　　h. 3100. c. (3.)

— "Le Premier Baiser" valse. [Op. 68.] Arr. [for military band] by Fred Godfrey. [Parts.] 25 pt. *S. A. Chappell: London*, [1875.] fol.
[*Army Journal. no.* 104.]　　　　　　　**h. 1562.**

— Princess Beatrice. Waltz. [P. F.] *Metzler & Co.: London*, [1885.] fol.　　　　　　　**h. 3100. e. (45.)**

— Princess Hélène of Waldeck Pyrmont, suite de valses. [P. F.] *London*, [1882.] fol.　　　　　　　**h. 3100. c. (41.)**

— Promenade champêtre, fantaisie pastorale pour Piano. *Paris*, [1875.] fol.　　　　　　　**h. 3100. (39.)**

— La Reine des Papillons valse. [P. F.] *London*, [1882.] fol.
　　　　　　　h. 3100. c. (42.)

— Le Retour des Hirondelles, valse pour Piano. *Paris*, [1883.] fol.　　　　　　　**h. 3100. e. (24.)**

— Rêve d'Amour valse. [P. F.] *London*, [1876.] fol.
　　　　　　　h. 3100. a. (23.)

— Rêve d'Amour. Waltz … simplified for the Piano by J. Rochard. [Solo and duet.] 2 no. [1881.] *See* ROCHARD (J.) Popular Melodies, *etc.* No. 43. [1878, *etc.*] fol.　**h. 3032. b.**

— Rêve de Jeunesse, valse. [P. F.] *London*, [1881.] fol.
　　　　　　　h. 3100. c. (32.)

— Rêve Doré valse pour Piano. *Paris*, [1873.] fol.
　　　　　　　h. 3100. (20.)

— Rêvé Doré valse. [P. F.] *London*, [1876.] fol.
　　　　　　　h. 3100. a. (11.)

— Le Reveil des Anges, prière pour Orgue ou Harmonium. *London*, [1876.] fol.　　　　　　　**h. 2575. e. (13.)**

— Le Reveil du Régiment, marche pour Piano. *London*, [1875.] fol.　　　　　　　**h. 3100. a. (3.)**

— Rêverie d'Automne pour Piano. *London*, [1879.] fol.
　　　　　　　h. 3100. c. (23.)

— Rêverie sur l'eau, barcarolle pour Piano. *Paris*, [1876.] fol.
　　　　　　　h. 3100. (51*.)

— Rêverie sur l'Eau, barcarolle pour le Pianoforte. *London*, [1876.] fol.　　　　　　　**h. 3100. a. (26.)**

— Rêves de Printemps, suite de valses. [P. F.] *Paris*, [1876.] *obl.* fol.　　　　　　　**e. 272. f. (12.)**

— Rêves de Printemps, suite de valses. [P. F.] *London*, [1876.] fol.　　　　　　　**h. 3100. a. (9.)**

— Rêves de Printemps. Suite de Valses. [P. F.] *R. Cocks & Co.: London*, [1895.] fol.　　　　　　　**h. 3285. p. (50.)**

— Reviendra-t-elle? Valse pour Piano. *Paris*, [1881.] fol.
　　　　　　　h. 3100. e. (5.)

LAMOTHE (GEORGES)

— Les Rives de l'Arno, rêverie italienne pour le Piano. *Paris*, [1875.] fol.　　　　　　　**h. 3100. (42.)**

— Royal-Defilé, caprice militaire pour Piano. *Paris*, [1882.] fol.
　　　　　　　h. 3100. e. (16.)

— Royale Gavotte pour le Piano. *London*, [1876.] fol.
　　　　　　　h. 3100. a. (8.)

— La Ruse d'Amour, valse. [P. F.] *London*, [1881.] fol.
　　　　　　　h. 3100. c. (31.)

— Les Saisons, 4 fantaisies études pour le Piano. 4 no. *Paris*, [1876.] fol.　　　　　　　**h. 3100. (55.)**

— Séduction. Valse brillante pour piano. *Paris*, [1884.] fol.
　　　　　　　h. 3100. e. (31.)

— Séville polka-mazurka pour Piano. *Paris*, [1869.] fol.
　　　　　　　h. 3100. (8.)

— Sigurd. Opéra de E. Reyer. Valse pour piano. *Paris*, [1884.] *obl.* fol.　　　　　　　**e. 283. c. (9.)**

— Sigurd. Valse sur l'opéra de E. Reyer. [P. F.] *Boosey & Co.: London*, [1884.] fol.　　　　　　　**h. 3100. e. (46.)**

— Une Soirée au Cirque, quadrille pour Piano. *London*, [1876.] fol.　　　　　　　**h. 3100. a. (29.)**

— Une Soirée au Skating Concerts, valse pour Piano. *Paris*, [1878.] *obl.* fol.　　　　　　　**e. 272. h. (46.)**

— Some Day, valse on M. Welling's … song. [P. F.] *London*, [1881.] fol.　　　　　　　**h. 3100. c. (33.)**

— Some Day valses, arranged by E. Binding. [Brass band parts.] *London*, [1882.] 8°.　　　　　　　**f. 413. f. (9.)**

— Songes Roses, suite de valses pour le Piano. *Paris*, [1875.] fol.　　　　　　　**h. 3100. (32.)**

— [Songes Roses.] Lovely Flowers set of waltzes. [P. F.] *London*, [1876.] fol.　　　　　　　**h. 3100. a. (6.)**

— [Songes Roses.] Lovely Flowers set of valses. [P. F.] *London*, [1876.] 8°.
No. 367 *of the "Alliance Musicale. Album Bijou".*　　**f. 406.**

— Sous la Feuillée, rêverie-nocturne pour Piano. *Paris*, [1879.] fol.　　　　　　　**h. 3100. d. (16.)**

— Sous le Balcon, boléro populaire, *etc.* [P. F.] *J. Iochem: Paris*, [1887.] fol.　　　　　　　**h. 3100. f. (17.)**

— Sous les Drapeaux, fanfare pour Piano. Op. 66. *Paris*, [1869.] fol.　　　　　　　**h. 3100. (10.)**

— Sous les Drapeaux, fanfare. [P. F.] *London*, [1876.] fol.
　　　　　　　h. 3100. a. (18.)

— Souvenir de Calais. Carillon. [P. F.] *J. Iochem: Paris*, [1887.] fol.　　　　　　　**h. 3100. f. (16.)**

— Souvenir de Hongrie … Caprice pour piano. Op. 279. *E. Lacombe: Paris*, [1886.] fol.　　　　　　　**h. 3100. f. (6.)**

— Souvenir du St. Bernard. Angelus for Harmonium, with Pianoforte accompaniment (ad lib.). *London*, [1876.] fol.
　　　　　　　h. 2575. e. (11.)

— Souvenir du Village pour Piano. *Paris*, [1879.] fol.
　　　　　　　h. 3100. d. (12.)

— Starter-galop pour Piano. *Paris*, [1883.] fol.
　　　　　　　h. 3100. e. (25.)

— Succès mélodiques. 18 caprices brillants sur les opéras de Verdi pour Piano. Op. 200. 18 no. *L. Escudier: Paris*, [1878.] fol.　　　　　　　**h. 3100. d. (10.)**

LAMOTHE (GEORGES)

— Succès Mélodiques, *etc.* no. 2–12. *L. Escudier: Paris,* [1878.]
fol.
Imperfect; wanting no. 1, 13–18.   **h. 3100. b.**

— Succès mélodiques. Caprices brillants sur les opéras célèbres
pour piano. no. 1, 3–5, 8, 10, 15. *Paris,* [1883.] fol.
Imperfect; wanting no. 2, 6, 7, 9, 11–14, 16–18.
h. 3100. e. (27.)

— Les Sultanes, suite de valses pour Piano. *Paris,* [1879.] *obl.*
fol.   **e. 272. j. (23.)**

— Sur la Falaise. Rêverie. Nocturne pour piano. Op. 273.
Nuyens & Cie.: Paris, [1886.] fol.   **h. 3100. f. (3.)**

— La Sympathique, grande valse de salon. [P. F.] *London,*
[1876.] fol.   **h. 3100. a. (30.)**

— Tambours et Clairons, polka militaire pour Piano. *Paris,*
[1883.] fol.   **h. 3100. e. (19.)**

— Tantum ergo. [Solo.] *See* LYRA. Lyra Sacra. No. 12. [1875.] 4°.
G. 990.

— Tête-à-Tête valse pour Piano. [Solo and duet.] 2 no. *London,*
[1877.] fol.   **h. 3100. c. (10.)**

— Tête-à-Tête valse. [P. F.] *London,* [1878.] 8°.
No. 457 of the "Alliance Musicale. Album Bijou".   **f. 406.**

— Tête-à-Tête valse. [Orchestral parts.] *London,* [1878.] 8°.
Part of the "Alliance Musicale".   **f. 400. p. (19.)**

— Tête folle. Valse brillante pour piano. *Paris,* [1884.] fol.
h. 3100. e. (29.)

— Thinking and Dreaming. Ballad [begins: "Under the cliff"].
Words by C. J. Rowe. *London,* [1882.] fol.
H. 1789. a. (33.)

— Tonnerre Galop. *See* supra: [Galop-Tonnerre.]

— Toujours et Encore valse. [P. F.] *London,* [1878.] fol.
h. 3100. c. (19.)

— [Toujours et encore.] Valse, *etc.* ⟨[Followed by] Quadrille—
"Lieder". H. Siewart.—The Lost Chord. A. Sullivan.⟩
[Military band parts.] 25 pt. *Boosey & Co.: London,* [1880.]
fol.
[Boose's military Journal. ser. 68. *no.* 3.]   **h. 1549.**

— Tout-de-Suite galop. [P. F.] *London,* [1877.] fol.
h. 3100. c. (11.)

— Tramway-galop pour Piano. *Paris,* [1876.] fol.
h. 3100. (49.)

— Tramway-Galop pour le Pianoforte. *London,* [1876.] fol.
h. 3100. a. (27.)

— Deux transcriptions pour Piano. ⟨1. Gavotte de Vestris. 2.
Chanson du Vert-Galant.⟩ 2 no. *Paris,* [1882.] fol.
h. 3100. e. (10.)

— Très-Belle, valse pour Piano. *London,* [1881.] fol.
h. 3100. o. (40.)

— Triomphe-Polka pour le Piano. Op. 67. *Paris,* [1869.] fol.
h. 3100. (12.)

— Tunis-Marche pour piano. Op. 280. *E. Lacombe: Paris,*
[1886.] fol.   **h. 3100. f. (7.)**

— Turquoise-polka. [P. F.] *Paris,* [1874.] fol.   **h. 3100. (27.)**

— Le Val des Fées, air de ballet. [P. F.] *London,* [1879.] fol.
h. 3100. c. (27.)

— Le Val des Roses waltzes. [P. F.] *London,* [1880.] fol.
h. 3100. c. (28.)

LAMOTHE (GEORGES)

— Valse des Amoureuses pour Piano. *Paris,* [1875.] fol.
h. 3100. (37.)

— Valse des Amoureuses pour Piano. *London,* [1875.] fol.
h. 3100. c. (4.)

— Valse des Horizons, suite de valses. [P. F.] *Paris,* [1876.] *obl.*
fol.   **e. 272. f. (13.)**

— Valse des Horizons. [P. F.] *London,* [1876.] fol.
h. 3100. a. (10.)

— Valse des Perles pour Piano. *Paris,* [1875.] *obl.* fol.
e. 272. f. (8.)

— Valse des Perles pour Piano. *London,* [1875.] fol.
h. 3100. a. (2.)

— Valse Royale. [P. F.] *London,* [1877.] fol.   **h. 3100. c. (7.)**

— Valse Royale. [P. F.] *London,* [1879.] fol.
No. 600 of C. Boosey's "Universal" music.   **H. 2324.**

— Varsovie, impromptu-mazurka pour Piano. *Paris,* [1879.] fol.
h. 3100. d. (15.)

— Victoria quadrille pour Piano. *Paris,* [1873.] fol.
h. 977. l. (22.)

— Viennoise-polka pour Piano. *Paris,* [1877.] fol.
h. 3100. d. (4.)

— Le Vieux Paris, ronde nocturne. [P. F.] *Paris,* [1876.] fol.
h. 3100. (51.)

— Vis-à-Vis quadrille. [P. F.] *London,* [1878.] fol.
h. 3100. c. (15.)

— Vivacité polka. [P. F.] *London,* [1881.] fol.   **h. 3100. c. (36.)**

— Les Volontaires, transcription militaire sur le célèbre pas
redoublé de O. Métra. [P. F.] *Paris,* [1883.] fol.
h. 3100. e. (26.)

— Voulez-vous? valse pour Piano. *Paris,* [1882.] fol.
h. 3100. e. (17.)

— Voulez-vous? Valse. [P. F.] *Boosey & Co.: London,* [1888.]
fol.   **h. 3100. e. (48.)**

— Yedda, suite de valses sur le ballet de O. Métra. [P. F.] *Paris,*
[1880.] *obl.* fol.   **e. 272. j. (24.)**

— Les Yeux Bleus valse. [P. F.] *London,* [1877.] fol.
h. 3100. c. (8.)

— Les Zephyrs valse. [P. F.] *London,* [1878.] fol.
h. 3100. c. (17.)

— Les Zéphyrs, suite de valses. [P. F.] *Paris,* [1879.] *obl.* fol.
e. 272. j. (22.)

— *See* KETTERER (E.) Valse des fleurs ... arrangée pour orgue et
piano [by] G. Lamothe. [1876.] fol.   **h. 2576. a. (10.)**

— *See* MASSENET (J. É. F.) Aragonaise. Arranged for piano by
G. Lamothe. [1894.] fol.   **h. 1489. u. (56.)**

— *See* MATINÉES. Matinées Classiques. Transcriptions ... pour
Piano [by G. Lamothe and others]. [1878.] fol.
h. 1481. p. (9.)

— *See* MENDELSSOHN-BARTHOLDY (J. L. F.) [Lieder ohne Worte.
Smaller Collections.] Transcriptions ... des plus célèbres
Romances sans paroles ... par G. Lamothe. [1879.] fol.
h. 575. n. (13.)

— *See* MOZART (W. A.) [Io ti lascio, o cara, addio. K. Anh. 245.]
Adieu ... Transcrit pour orgue ou harmonium par
G. Lamothe. [1876.] fol.   **h. 2575. e. (12.)**

LAMOTHE (Georges)

— *See* Seligmann (H. P.) La Berceuse de l'Enfantelet …
Transcription … par G. Lamothe. [1880.] fol.

h. 2575. h. (16.)

LAMOTTE

— Lamotte Houdar, comédie anecdotique en un acte et en
prose, mêlée de vaudevilles. Par les citoyens Piis et Auger …
avec la musique. *Chez le Libraire au Théâtre du Vaudeville:*
Paris, An VIII [1800]. 8°.

11738. l. 19. (6.)

LAMOTTE (Arthur)

— Merrie Old England, melodious fantasia on national airs.
[P. F.] *London*, [1873.] fol.

h. 1482. y. (23.)

— Le Retour à ma Patrie … Caprice joyeuse pour le Piano.
London, [1868.] fol.

h. 1485. s. (14.)

LAMOTTE (C. E. G.)

— Dorado. Valse. [P. F.] *S. Clark: London*, [1883.] fol.

h. 975. u. (22.)

LA MOTTE (Diether de)

— Alle sind unterwegs. *See* infra: Hörtheater. 5.

— Es wartet alles auf dich. Predigt über Psalm 104 für
fünfstimmigen gemischten Chor, fünf Instrumente und Orgel.
[Score.] pp. 104. *Bärenreiter: Kassel, etc.*, [1969.] 8°.

F. 1257. c. (3.)

— 10 Fantasien am Klavier. 1968. [A facsimile of the composer's
autograph.] pp. 34. *Bärenreiter: Kassel, etc.*, [1969.] fol.

h. 1568. kk. (3.)

— Drei Gesänge nach Gedichten von Andreas Gryphius für
Bariton und Orgel. pp. 19. *Bärenreiter: Kassel, etc.*, [1967.]
8°.

F. 1196. aa. (10.)

— Hinter dem Spiegel. *See* infra: Hörtheater. 3.

— Hörtheater. 1. Schwierigkeiten beim Telefonieren, für
Sprechstimmen und Melodieinstrumente (mindestens 5), *etc.*
⟨2. Klingende Gedanken, für einen Sprecher, Summchor und
Melodieinstrumente (mindestens 7). 3. Hinter dem Spiegel,
für Sing- und Sprechstimmen. 4. Der Minister spricht, für
Sing-und Sprechstimmen und Melodieinstrumente
(mindestens 7). 5. Alle sind unterwegs, für 18 Sprechstimmen
und Melodieinstrumente (mindestens 7). Partituren.⟩ 5 no.
Bärenreiter: Kassel, etc., 1977. 4° & obl. 4°. **F. 424. o.**

— Klingende Gedanken. *See* supra: Hörtheater. 2.

— Liebeserklärung für ein verkanntes Instrument. 6 Stücke für
Akkordeon. 1977. Spieltechnische Einrichtung und
Registrierung von Hugo Noth. pp. 16. *Bärenreiter: Kassel,*
etc., 1978. fol. **g. 657. t.**

— Der Minister spricht. *See* supra: Hörtheater. 4.

— Präludium für Orgel. pp. 12. *Bärenreiter: Kassel, etc.*, [1967.]
obl. fol. **e. 1096. w. (4.)**

— Psalmen-Motette für gemischten Chor a cappella. pp. 16.
Bärenreiter: Kassel, etc., [1964.] 8°.
Part of "Musica sacra nova". **E. 1439. r. (1.)**

— Schwierigkeiten beim Telefonieren. *See* supra: Hörtheater. 1.

— Ständchen für Don Quixote. Für Männerchor 1960.
Textfassung vom Komponisten nach der anonymen
Übertragung (1837) des "Don Quixote" von Miguel de
Cervantes … Partitur, *etc.* pp. 15. *B. Schott's Söhne: Mainz,*
[1961.] 8°. **F. 1256. h. (4.)**

LA MOTTE (Diether de)

— Wie eine Rose. Fünf Lieder für gemischten Chor a cappella
nach Gedichten von J. R. Jiménez. ⟨Übertragung von Hans
Leopold Davi.⟩ pp. 28. *Bärenreiter-Verlag: Kassel*, [1967.] 8°.

F. 1744. jj. (22.)

LAMOTTE (F.)

— Rondo pour le piano forte. pp. 6. *Chez Auguste le Duc et*
compagnie: Paris, [1808.] fol.
[*Journal de forte piano. année* 1. *no.* 9.] **h. 61. l.**

LA MOTTE (Franz)

— Six Airs Mis en Variations pour le Violon Avec
Accompagnement de Basse … et la Marche des Deux Avares
[by A. E. M. Grétry]. Avec six variations. *Aux Adresses*
Ordinaires de Musiques [sic]*: Paris; Chez M* Castaud: Lion,
[1770?] fol. **g. 166. (2.)**

— Six Airs with Variations for the Violin and a Bass. pp. 12.
Printed for W Forster: London*, [c. 1785.] fol.
Plate number 31. **g. 166. (3.)**

— Sonate pour le Violon avec Accompagnement de Basse …
Œuvre V, Gravé par Mme Lobry, *etc. Chez M* Henry: Paris,*
[1770?] fol.
With MS. notes by Alfred Moffat. **g. 166. (1.)**

— [Sonate. Op. 5.] A Solo for the Violin and a Bass for the
Harpsichord or Violoncello. *Printed for W. Forster: London,*
[1799?] fol. **h. 1608. (12.)**

— Sei sonate a violino e basso, tre composte da Franceso
Lamota et altre tre da altro autore. pp. 28. *Welcker: London,*
[1775?] fol. **Hirsch III. 355.**

LA MOTTE (I. H. R. de)

— *See* Mott (Isaac H. R.)

LAMOTTE (Nicolas Antony)

— Adelaide Valse. [P. F.] Op. 313. *London*, [1857.] fol.

h. 856. (28.)

— 2nd Air varié, for cornet [and P. F.]. *London*, [1881.] 8°.
Imperfect; wanting the cornet part. No. 615 *of the "Alliance*
Musicale, Album Bijou". **f. 406.**

— Andalousia. Mazurka. Op. 984. [Orchestral and P. F. parts.]
J. R. Lafleur & Son: London, [1887.] 8°.
Part of the "Alliance Musicale". **f. 400. mm. (1.)**

— Anges et Démons … polka fantastique. [Orchestral parts.]
London, [1877.] 8°. **f. 410. (15.)**

— Anges et Démons. Polka. [P. F.] *London*, [1881.] 8°.
No. 623 *of the "Alliance Musicale, Album Bijou".* **f. 406.**

— Angot polka … arrangée sur les principaux motifs de l'opéra
comique de C. Lecocq. *Paris*, [1873.] fol. **h. 1487. o. (29.)**

— "La ballade du ménestrel," 17e redowa pour le piano forte.
Op. 182. *London*, [1855.] fol. **h. 856. (11.)**

— La Ballade du Ménestrel, redowa. [P. F.] *Paris*, [1855.] fol.

h. 3213. c. (13.)

— "La bannière étoilée de l'Union," Varsoviana … pour Piano.
Op. 298. *London*, [1858.] fol. **h. 856. (23.)**

— Beadsman Cornet polka. [Orchestral parts.] *London*, [1878.]
8°. **f. 410. b. (15.)**

— La Belle Bordelaise, grande polka de concert, avec solo et
variations de Piston. [Octet band parts.] *London*, [1877.] 8°.

f. 411. b. (8.)

LAMOTTE (NICOLAS ANTONY)

— La Belle Bordelaise, grande polka de concert with solo and variations for Cornet-à-Pistons. *London*, [1877.] fol.
h. 2284. a. (8.)

— La Belle Californienne, schottisch brillante. [Orchestral parts.] *London*, [1878.] 8°.
Part of the "Alliance Musicale".
f. 400. p. (20.)

— Belle Enchanteresse, polka mazurka élégante. [Orchestral parts.] *Paris*, [1881.] 8°.
f. 245. d. (7.)

— Belle Enchanteresse! Polka-Mazurka pour Piano. Op. 856. *Paris*, [1883.] 8°.
No. 721 of the "Alliance Musicale, Album Bijou".
f. 406.

— La belle Orientale, quadrille. [P. F.] *London*, [1856.] fol.
h. 856. (30.)

— Blushing Rose schottische, arranged by Hare. [Fife and drum band parts.] *London*, [1880.] 8°.
Part of the "Alliance Musicale".
f. 403. d. (46.)

— Bon vivant, quadrille. [P. F.] *London*, [1854.] fol.
. h. 975. e. (20.)

— Bordeaux-polka pour Piano. *Paris*, [1881.] fol.
h. 3272. j. (7.)

— Les Bords de la Sèvres quadrille. [P. F.] *London*, [1877.] 8°.
No. 425 of the "Alliance Musicale. Album Bijou".
f. 406.

— "Le Brésilien" quadrilles sur des Motifs Brésiliens Nationaux pour le piano-forte. Op. 139. *London*, [1854.] fol.
h. 975. e. (17.)

— Californian schottische. [P. F.] *London*, [1878.] 8°.
No. 486 of the "Alliance Musicale. Album Bijou".
f. 406.

— Les canotiers du Rhone et de la Saône, 155ᵐᵉ Quadrille (avec Ronde et Choeurs) pour Piano. Op. 279. *London*, [1858.] fol.
h. 856. (20.)

— Castles in the Air, quadrille. [Orchestral parts.] *London*, [1881.] 8°.
Part of the "Alliance Musicale".
f. 400. y. (18.)

— Castles in the air. Quadrille. [P. F.] *London*, [1881.] 8°.
No. 669 of the "Alliance Musicale, Album Bijou".
f. 406.

— La Chasse Quadrille. *See* BOOSEY AND CO. Boosey's Orchestral Journal, *etc.* No. 53. [1860, *etc.*] 8°.
e. 69.

— La chasse quadrille. [P. F.] *London*, [1856.] fol.
h. 856. (1.)

— Quadrille—"Le Château à Toto". [On melodies from Offenbach's opera. Military band parts.] 25 pt. *In:* BRUNETTE ( ) [La Galathée.] Galatea Waltz. [1871.] fol. [*Boosé's military Journal. ser. 45. no. 4.*]
h. 1549.

— "Colette" quadrilles sur l'opéra de Cadaux pour le piano-forte. Op. 138. *London*, [1854.] fol.
h. 975. e. (16.)

— Les Colombes valses. [Orchestral parts.] *London*, [1876.] 8°.
Part of the "Alliance Musicale".
f. 400. k. (5.)

— Les Colombes (the Doves) set of valses. [Orchestral parts.] *London*, [1877.] 8°.
Part of the "Dance Music Orchestral Journal".
f. 415. d. (1.)

— Les Colombes set of valses. [Brass band parts.] *London*, [1877.] 8°.
f. 413. b. (29.)

— [Les Colombes.] The Doves valses. [P. F.] *London*, [1876.] 8°.
No. 349 of the "Alliance Musicale. Album Bijou".
f. 406.

— La coquette, Schottisch. [P. F.] *London*, [1856.] fol.
h. 856. (19.)

— Le cor magique d'Oberon, Redowa sur l'Opera de C. M. von Weber, pour le Piano. Op. 292. *London*, [1858.] fol.
h. 856. (22.)

LAMOTTE (NICOLAS ANTONY)

— La couronne artistique, quadrille pour le piano-forte. Op. 193. *London*, [1855.] fol.
h. 856. (13.)

— La Couronne artistique, quadrille. Op. 193. *Paris*, [1855.] *obl.* fol.
e. 38. (5.)

— The Crown Diamonds quadrille. [P. F.] *London*, [1876.] 8°.
No. 102 of the "Alliance Musicale. Album Bijou".
f. 406.

— Darling Redowa. [Orchestral parts.] *London*, [1880.] 8°. fol.
Part of the "Alliance Musicale".
f. 400. x. (15.)

— Darling. Redowa. [Conductor's P. F. part.] *London*, [1881.] 8°.
No. 656 of the "Alliance Musicale, Album Bijou".
f. 406.

— "Les délices de Valentino," Schottisch pour Piano. Op. 301. *London*, [1858.] fol.
h. 856. (25.)

— Les Emigrans d'Amérique, overture-fantaisie. [P. F.] *London*, [1873.] 8°.
No. 28 of the "Alliance Musicale. Album Bijou".
f. 406.

— "L'Enfant du tour de France," Quadrille, pour Piano [on Darcier's music to the drama of that name]. Op. 300. *London*, [1858.] fol.
h. 856. (24.)

— Entre Paris et Lyon. (Quadrille sur des chansonnettes de Devillebichot, Darcier et Hervé.) Op. 642 ... Piano, *etc.* pp. 5. *Ph. Feuchot: Paris*, [c. 1875.] *obl.* fol.
f. 502. g. (3.)

— L'Étoile de France ... polka de concert, with variations for the Cornet. *London*, [1877.] fol.
h. 2284. a. (7.)

— "Expansion," polka-mazurka pour le piano. Op. 177. *London*, [1855.] fol.
h. 856. (10.)

— Expansion, polka-mazurka. [P. F.] *Paris*, [1855.] fol.
h. 3213. c. (12.)

— The Fairest Rose, valse sentimentale. [P. F. with cornet accompaniment.] *London*, [1860.] fol.
h. 1460. u. (30.)

— Falstaf, musique d'A. Adam, quadrille et valse, pour piano. Oeuvre 238 et 239. 2 pt. *Paris*, [1856.] fol.
e. 38. (6.)

— Falstaf, musique d'A. Adam, quadrille et valse, pour piano à 4 mains. Oeuvre 238 et 239. *Paris*, [1856.] fol.
e. 38. (7.)

— "Fanchon la Vieilleuse," polka savoyarde pour le piano-forte. Op. 194. *London*, [1855.] fol.
h. 856. (15.)

— Fanchon la Vieilleuse, polka. [P. F.] Op. 194. *Paris*, [1855.] fol.
h. 856. (14.)

— Fandar quadrille. [P. F.] *London*, [1874.] 8°.
No. 186 of the "Alliance Musicale. Album Bijou".
f. 406.

— Farewell to Jullien, valse sentimentale. [P. F. with cornet accompaniment.] *London*, [1861.] fol.
h. 1460. u. (31.)

— La fée des roseaux, 20ᵐᵉ Polka-Mazurka, pour le Piano. Op. 290. *London*, [1858.] fol.
h. 856. (21.)

— La Fête des Lilas Quadrille. *See* BOOSEY AND CO. Boosey's Orchestral Journal, *etc.* No. 9. [1860, *etc.*] 8°.
e. 69.

— La fête des lilas, quadrille, pour le Piano Forte. *London*, [1853.] fol.
h. 975. e. (13.)

— La fête des lilas, quadrille. (Arrangé pour piano par J. Mootz.) *London*, [1854.] fol.
h. 975. e. (12.)

— La Fête des Lilas quadrille. [P. F.] *London*, [1859.] fol.
No. 1404, 1405 of the "Musical Bouquet".
H. 2345.

— "Fleur de Grenade," Varsoviana élégante pour le piano forte. Op. 170. *London*, [1854.] fol.
h. 856. (7.)

— Fleur de Grenade, Varsoviana élégante, pour piano ... Op. 170. *Paris*, [1854.] fol.
h. 975. e. (19.)

LAMOTTE (Nicolas Antony)

— La Flûte Enchantée, schottisch sur l'opéra de Mozart. [P. F.]
Paris, [1856.] fol. **h. 3213. c. (15.)**

— "La Folle." Redowa, sur la romance de Grisar, pour Piano.
London, [1858.] fol. **h. 856. (31.)**

— Fra Diavolo quadrille. [P. F.] *London*, [1876.] 8°.
No. 314 of the "Alliance Musicale, Album Bijou". **f. 406.**

— Franklin polka. [Octet band parts.] *London*, [1877.] 8°.
f. 411. b. (9.)

— Franklin polka with Cornet solo. *London*, [1877.] fol.
h. 2284. a. (9.)

— Les Gloires artistiques de la Flandre. [P. F.] *London*, [1879.]
8°.
No. 580 of the "Alliance Musicale. Album Bijou". **f. 406.**

— Grand Irish fantasia. [Orchestral parts.] *London*, [1880.] 8°.
Part of the "Alliance Musicale". **f. 400. x. (16.)**

— Grand Irish Fantasia, *etc.* [Cornet, clarinet or violin and
P. F.] *J. R. Lafleur & Son: London*, [1881.] fol.
Part of the "Alliance Musicale". **h. 2915. d. (11.)**

— Grand Selection from ... The Daughter of the Regiment.
Arrd. by A. Lamotte. [Orchestral parts.] [1874.] 8°. *See*
Donizetti (D. G. M.) [La Fille du Régiment.–Selections.]
f. 400. c. (15.)

— Grand selection from G. Donizetti's opera La Fille du
Régiment. [P. F.] *London*, [1874.] 8°.
No. 161 of the "Alliance Musicale. Album Bijou". **f. 406.**

— Grande fantaisie sur La Vestale de Mercadante. [P. F.]
London, [1874.] 8°.
No. 125 of the "Alliance Musicale. Album Bijou". **f. 406.**

— "La guerre d'Orient," quadrille ... pour le pianoforte.
Op. 166. *London*, [1854.] fol. **h. 856. (4.)**

— Handsome Knights quadrilles. [P. F.] *London*, [1878.] 8°.
No. 278 of the "Alliance Musicale. Album Bijou". **f. 406.**

— Highlanders quadrille. [P. F.] *London*, [1876.] 8°.
No. 354 of the "Alliance Musicale. Album Bijou". **f. 406.**

— Honey Moon mazurka. [Fife and drum band parts.] *London*,
[1877.] 8°. **f. 414. (36.)**

— The Huntsman's Polka. [P. F.] Op. 509. *London*, [1860.] fol.
h. 1460. u. (28.)

— Idylle du Cœur, suite de valses sympathiques pour Piano.
Paris, [1881.] *obl.* fol. **e. 272. k. (22.)**

— Invocation à Ste. Cécile. [P. F.] *London*, [1873.] 8°.
No. 19 of the "Alliance Musicale. Album Bijou". **f. 406.**

— Joseph Barra, ou le Héros Republicain de 1793, quadrille
héroïque. [Orchestral parts.] *Paris*, [1883.] 8°.
f. 245. f. (11.)

— "Juaniska," Schottisch sur les motifs de la guerre d'Orient
pour le piano. Op. 168. *London*, [1854.] fol. **h. 856. (5.)**

— Juaniska, Schottisch, sur des motifs de la guerre d'Orient,
musique de A. Fessy. Op. 168. No. 1. *Paris*, [1854.] fol.
h. 975. e. (18.)

— The Last Rose of Summer, air varié for B Clarionet. *See*
Celebrated. Celebrated Clarinette Solos. No. 11. [1877.] fol.
h. 2190.

— La Malibran. Polka. 1st Cornet [part]. *London*, [1874.] 8°.
*Part of the "Alliance Musicale". Imperfect; wanting the other
parts.* **f. 402. f. (14.)**

— "Malvina," Schottisch pour le piano forte. Op. 169. *London*,
[1855.] fol. **h. 856. (6.)**

LAMOTTE (Nicolas Antony)

— Masaniello, artistic Schottische. [P. F.] *London*, [1876.] 8°.
No. 311 of the "Alliance Musicale. Album Bijou". **f. 406.**

— La médaille d'or impériale, grande valse. Pour piano. *Paris*,
[1854.] *obl.* fol. **e. 38. (8.)**

— La médaille d'or impériale, grande valse. [P. F.] *London*,
[1855.] fol. **h. 856. (8.)**

— Mignonne. Polka. 1st Cornet [part]. *London*, [1874.] 8°.
*Part of the "Alliance Musicale". Imperfect; wanting the other
parts.* **f. 402. f. (12.)**

— The Minstrel overture. [Orchestral parts.] *London*, [1877.] 8°.
Part of the "Alliance Musicale". **f. 400. n. (15.)**

— The Minstrel overture, arranged by J. Hecker. [Reed band
parts.] *London*, [1879.] 8°.
Part of the "Alliance Musicale". **f. 401. m. (12.)**

— Le Minstrel overture. [P. F.] *London*, [1877.] 8°.
No. 400 of the "Alliance Musicale. Album Bijou". **f. 406.**

— Musique de danse. [P. F.] No. 5, 8, 16. *Paris*, [1855.] fol.
Imperfect; wanting all the other no. **h. 3213. c. (10.)**

— Nozze di Figaro quadrille [on W. A. Mozart's opera.
Orchestral parts]. *London*, [1879.] 8°.
Part of the "Alliance Musicale". **f. 400. s. (12.)**

— Nozze de Figaro quadrille. [P. F.] *London*, [1879.] 8°.
No. 546 of the "Alliance Musicale. Album Bijou". **f. 406.**

— Oberon, Quadrille brillant, sur l'opéra de C. M. von Weber,
pour Piano. Op. 301. *London*, [1858.] fol. **h. 856. (26.)**

— Olivier Cromwel [*sic*]. Overture-Fantasia ... Op. 995.
[Orchestral parts.] 17 pt. *J. R. Lafleur & Son: London*, [1888.]
4°.
"Alliance Musicale." Nouveau répertoire des concerts. no. 11.
g. 1800. (187.)

— "Orage du cœur" (The heart's emotion), suite de Valses
sympathiques, pour le Piano. Op. 303. *London*, [1858.] fol.
h. 856. (27.)

— Orage du Cœur. (The Heart's Emotion.) Suite de valses
sympathiques pour le Piano. Op. 303. *London*, [1859.] fol.
h. 1460. u. (27.)

— Oreste et Pylade polka. [Brass band parts.] *London*, [1873.]
8°.
Part of the "Alliance Musicale". **f. 402. c. (21.)**

— "Le Palais de l'Alcazar quadrille pour le pianoforte. Op. 143.
London, [1854.] fol. **h. 975. e. (15.)**

— "Pauvre fleur fanée," schottisch pour le piano forte. Op. 175.
London, [1855.] fol. **h. 856. (9.)**

— Pauvre Fleur Fanée schottisch. [P. F.] *Paris*, [1855.] fol.
h. 3213. c. (11.)

— Le Père Coucou quadrille. [P. F.] *London*, [1874.] 8°.
No. 221 of the "Alliance Musicale, Album Bijou". **f. 406.**

— La Perle de Madrid, Spanish valse. [Orchestral parts.]
London, [1880.] 8°.
Part of the "Alliance Musicale". **f. 400. w. (8.)**

— La Perle de Madrid. Spanish valse. Op. 894. [P. F.] *London*,
[1881.] 8°.
No. 613 of the "Alliance Musicale, Album Bijou". **f. 406.**

— La Perle de Valentino, Varsoviana élégante pour piano.
Op. 195. *Paris*, [1855.] fol. **h. 856. (16.)**

— "La Perle de Valentino" Varsoviana élégante pour le piano.
Op. 195. *London*, [1855.] fol. **h. 856. (17.)**

— La Perle du Mexique polka pour le Piano. *Paris*, [1878.] fol.
h. 1493. n. (8.)

LAMOTTE (Nicolas Antony)

— Les premières "Gloires du quadrille". Grand quadrille caractéristique pour le piano-forte. Op. 136. *London*, [1854.] fol. **h. 975. e. (14.)**

— Pretty Pet schottische. [Orchestral parts.] *London*, [1883.] 8°. *Part of the "Alliance Musicale".* **f. 400. cc. (8.)**

— Pretty Pet. Schottische. Op. 878. [P. F.] *London*, [1883.] 8°. *No.* 806 *of the "Alliance Musicale, Album Bijou".* **f. 406.**

— Les Pupilles de la Garde, fantaisie-march. [Octet band parts.] *London*, [1877.] 8°. **f. 411. b. (10.)**

— Quadrille sur le Billet de Marguerite, opéra de F. A. Gevaert. No. 1. Piano avec accomp. No. 2. Piano à quatre mains. 2 pt. *Paris*, [1855.] obl. fol. **e. 38. (4.)**

— 4 Quadrilles. No. 2. La Perruche en Goguette. No. 3. Le Franc Picard. [P. F.] *Paris*, [1856.] obl. fol. *Imperfect; wanting no.* 1 *and* 4. **e. 272. o. (6.)**

— Quand Même. Quadrille résolu. Op. 987. [Orchestral parts.] *London*, [1885.] 8°. *Part of the "Alliance Musicale".* **f. 400. gg. (11.)**

— Queen of Beauty polka mazurka. [Fife and drum band parts.] *London*, [1876.] 8°. *Part of the "Alliance Musicale".* **f. 403. c. (43.)**

— Queen of Beauty polka mazurka. [Reed band parts.] *London*, [1879.] 8°. *Part of the "Alliance Musicale".* **f. 401. c. (27.)**

— [Queen of Beauty.] Reine de Beauté polka-mazurka. [P. F.] *London*, [1873.] 8°. *No.* 109 *of the "Alliance Musicale. Album Bijou".* **f. 406.**

— "Le refrain des canotiers," quadrille, (avec chœur ad libitum,) pour le pianoforte. Op. 186. *London*, [1855.] fol. **h. 856. (12.)**

— Le refrain des canotiers, quadrille avec chœurs, ad libitum. Pour piano. Op. 186. *Paris*, [1855.] obl. fol. **e. 38. (9.)**

— Reine de Beauté. *See* supra: [Queen of Beauty.]

— Le roi du pastel, quadrille artistique … pour piano. Oeuv. 163. *Paris*, [1854.] fol. **e. 38. (10.)**

— "Le roi du pastel," (hommage à Latour) quadrille artistique pour le piano forte. Op. 163. *London*, [1855.] fol. **h. 856. (3.)**

— Severn Bank valses. [P. F.] *London*, [1860.] fol. **h. 1460. u. (29.)**

— "Simple chant des montagnes," 16ᵉ. Redowa pour le pianoforte. Op. 151. *London*, [1855.] fol. **h. 856. (2.)**

— Sophia schottisch, arranged by C. Dubois. [Reed band parts.] *London*, [1877.] 8°. **f. 412. c. (32.)**

— Souvenir de Cremorne quadrille. [P. F.] *London*, [1875.] 8°. *No.* 169 *of the "Alliance Musicale. Album Bijou".* **f. 406.**

— Spanish Serenade. Bolero. [Orchestral parts.] *London*, [1878.] 8°. *Part of the "Alliance Musicale".* **f. 400. q. (1.)**

— Spanish Serenade. Bolero. [P. F.] *London*, [1878.] 8°. *No.* 497 *of the "Alliance Musicale. Album Bijou".* **f. 406.**

— Star of England polka. [P. F.] *London*, [1873.] 8°. *No.* 96 *of the "Alliance Musicale. Album Bijou".* **f. 406.**

— Star of England polka. [P. F.] *London*, [1879.] fol. **h. 1494. p. (9.)**

— Star of France. Grand Polka. [Solo cornet part.] *London*, [1874.] 8°. *Part of the "Alliance Musicale". Imperfect; wanting the other parts.* **f. 402. f. (13.)**

LAMOTTE (Nicolas Antony)

— The Sylph of the Glen, set of quadrilles. [Orchestral parts.] *London*, [1877.] 8°. *Part of the "Dance Music Orchestral Journal".* **f. 415. d. (2.)**

— Téléphone. Galop. Op. 986. [Orchestral and P. F. parts.] *J. R. Lafleur & Son: London*, [1887.] 8°. *Part of the "Alliance Musicale".* **f. 400. kk. (15.)**

— Thirst of Love. Valse. Op. 949. [Orchestral and P. F. parts.] *J. R. Lafleur & Son: London*, [1887.] 8°. *Part of the "Alliance Musicale".* **f. 400. kk. (17.)**

— Tramway-Polka. Polka caractéristique. Op. 851. [P. F.] *Paris*, [1883.] 8°. *No.* 710 *of the "Alliance Musicale, Album Bijou".* **f. 406.**

— "La Traviata." ⟨Galop.⟩ [Based on themes from F. G. F. Verdi's opera. Military band parts.] 20 pt. *In:* BRIGHT (M. D.) L'Enfant de France, *etc.* [1858.] fol. [*C. Boosé's supplemental military Journal. no.* 172.] **h. 1544.**

— Galop de la Traviata (arrangé pour Piano par R. Nordmann). Op. 316. *London*, [1858.] fol. **h. 856. (29.)**

— La Trompette, polka. [P. F.] *London*, [1856.] fol. **h. 856. (18.)**

— Le Trompette Major, polka chevalresque. [P. F.] *Paris*, [1856.] fol. **h. 3213. c. (14.)**

— Unknown Flower redowa. [Brass band parts.] *London*, [1873.] 8°. *Part of the "Alliance Musicale".* **f. 402. c. (20.)**

— Le Vaillant Belle Rose quadrille. [P. F.] *London*, [1877.] 8°. *No.* 399 *of the "Alliance Musicale. Album Bijou".* **f. 406.**

— The Village Ball quadrille. [P. F.] *London*, [1877.] 8°. *No.* 427 *of the "Alliance Musicale. Album Bijou".* **f. 406.**

— The Volunteer of '92, fantaisie héroique. [Orchestral parts.] *London*, [1880.] 8°. *Part of the "Alliance Musicale".* **f. 400. x. (18.)**

— The Volunteer of '92. Fantaisie héroïque. [P. F.] *London*, [1881.] 8°. *No.* 621 *of the "Alliance Musicale, Album Bijou".* **f. 406.**

— The Wedding Presents Valse. [Orchestral parts.] *London*, [1880.] 8°. *Part of the "Alliance Musicale".* **f. 400. x. (17.)**

— Wedding Presents. Valse. [P. F.] *London*, [1881.] 8°. *No.* 641 *of the "Alliance Musicale, Album Bijou".* **f. 406.**

— William Tell quadrille. [P. F.] *London*, [1875.] 8°. *No.* 103 *of the "Alliance Musicale. Album Bijou".* **f. 406.**

— *See* AUBER (D. F. E.) [Le Cheval de Bronze.] Fantasia from [the] Bronze Horse. Arrᵈ. by A. Lamotte. [1887.] 8°. **f. 400. ii. (5.)**

— *See* DONIZETTI (D. G. M.) [La Favorite.—Selections.] La Favorita. Selection … arrd. by A. Lamotte, *etc.* [1880.] 8°. **f. 400. w. (5.)**

— *See* DONIZETTI (D. G. M.) [La Favorite.—Selections.] La Favorita. Selection arrᵈ by A. Lamotte. [1881.] 8°. *No.* 629 *of the "Alliance Musicale, Album Bijou".* **f. 406.**

— *See* MERCADANTE (S.) [La Vestale.] Grand Selection. By A. Lamotte. Op. 768. [For orchestra.] [1888.] 4°. **g. 1800. (222.)**

— *See* REYLOFF (E.) The Knight Belle Rose quick step, from Lamotte's melodies, *etc.* [1873.] 8°. **f. 402. d. (5.)**

LAMOTTE (Pascal)

— Annie Laurie … Scotch ballad [by Lady J. Scott]. (Arranged by P. Lamotte.) *London*, [1876.] fol. **H. 1778. x. (16.)**

LAMOTTE (PASCAL)

— The Big Sunflower. Song & chorus [begins: "There is a charm"]. (Arranged by P. Lamotte.) *London*, [1876.] fol.
H. 1778. x. (15.)

— Birdies' Musical Moments ... for the Pianoforte. 6 no. *London*, [1876.] fol.
h. 1494. p. (10.)

— God save the Queen, arranged for the Pianoforte. *London*, [1876.] fol.
h. 1482. y. (25.)

— Grandmother's Watch. [Song.] *London*, [1881.] fol.
H. 1787. j. (7.)

— Robin Adair ... Scotch ballad. (Arranged by P. Lamotte.) *London*, [1876.] fol.
H. 1778. x. (17.)

— The Starlight schottische. [P. F.] *London*, [1876.] fol.
h. 1482. y. (24.)

— *See* BOCCHERINI (L.) [Quintet. Op. 13. No. 5.] Celebrated Minuet, transcribed ... by P. Lamotte. [1881.] fol.
h. 3275. b. (12.)

LAMOTTE (PHILIPPE)

— S'il faut vieillir. Romance. Paroles de Mr Alf^e Goy. *J. Maho: Paris*, [1845?] fol.
Hirsch M. 1298. (14.)

LAMOUR (FRANÇOIS)

— Madelon. Menuet pour Piano. *Leonard & Co.: London*, [1910.] fol.
g. 606. n. (33.)

LAMOUREUX (ALFRED)

— Cor Jesu. (Chants sacrés.) Op. 2. No. 1. Solo ou choeur à l'unisson. No. 2. Solo et choeur. *A. J. Boucher: Montreal*, 1914. 8°.
F. 274. q. (10.)

— Fleurs de mon Pays. Mélodies à une voix, avec accompagnement. Op. 1. No. 1. Les Lilas, *etc.* (Poésie de Chapman.) *A. J. Boucher: Montreal*, (1914.) fol. *Wanting no.* 2–8.
H. 1793. r. (48.)

— Les Lilas. *See* supra: Fleurs de mon Pays ... Op. 1. No. 1.

LAMOUREUX (CHARLES)

— *See* HAENDEL (G. F.) Judas Machabée ... Partition Piano et Chant réduite par C. Lamoureux. [1875.] 8°.
E. 452. e.

LAMOURIE

— Lamourie Fair. [Part-song.] *See* WEBBER (William S. L.)

LAMOURY (PHILIPPE)

— Berceuse pour Violoncelle avec accompagnement de Piano. *Paris*, [1878.] fol.
h. 198. (3.)

— École d'accompagnement. Transcriptions de morceaux classiques pour piano et violon par Ph. Lamoury, *etc.* [Score and part.] no. 2. *E. Minier: Paris*, [1878?] fol. *Imperfect; wanting all the other numbers.*
h. 1729. x. (3.)

— École d'Accompagnement. Transcriptions de morceaux classiques pour Piano et Violon. no. 9–14. *Paris*, [1879.] fol. *Imperfect; wanting no.* 1–8.
h. 1608. h. (9.)

— Ecole d'Accompagnement. Transcriptions de morceaux classiques pour Piano & Violoncelle. 14 no. *Paris*, [1878.] fol.
h. 198. (6.)

— Le Rêve, première pensée musicale pour Violon avec accompagnement de Piano. *Paris*, [1879.] fol.
h. 1609. m. (3.)

— Le Rêve, première pensée musicale pour Violoncelle avec accompagnement de Piano. *Paris*, [1878.] fol. **h. 198. (4.)**

LAMOURY (PHILIPPE)

— Rêverie pour Violon avec accompagnement de Piano. *Paris*, [1879.] fol.
h. 1609. m. (4.)

— Rêverie pour Violoncelle avec accompagnement de Piano. *Paris*, [1879.] fol.
h. 198. (7.)

— Romance sans paroles pour Violoncelle. *Bruxelles*, [1880.] fol.
h. 1849. k. (11.)

— 6 Sonatines pour Piano et Violon. *Mayence*, [1878.] fol.
h. 1751. c. (10.)

— Sonatine pour Violon et Piano. Op. 19. 3 no. *Paris*, [1878.] fol.
h. 1728. (8.)

— Six Sonatines pour Piano & Violoncelle. 6 no. *Paris*, [1877.] fol.
h. 198. (1.)

— [Another edition.] Six Sonatines pour Piano et Violoncelle. 6 no. *Mayence*, [1878.] fol.
h. 198. (2.)

— Sonatine pour Violoncelle et Piano. Op. 18. 3 no. *Paris*, [1878.] fol.
h. 198. (5.)

— *See* BEETHOVEN (Ludwig van) [Sonatas. P. F. Op. 13.] Adagio cantabile. Bearbeitet von P. Lamoury. [Violin or violoncello and P. F.] [c. 1920.] fol.
h. 4090. o. (1.)

— *See* MOZART (W. A.) [Quartets. K. 575.] Andante. Bearbeitet von Ph. Lamoury, *etc.* [Violin and P. F.] [c. 1920.] fol.
h. 321. rr. (2.)

LAMP

— The Lamp. [Song.] *See* HILL (M. W.) Four Poems, *etc.* [No. 3.]

— The Lamp. [Song.] *See* SANDERSON (W. E.) [Songs of Homage. No. 3.]

— The Lamp in the West. [Part-song.] *See* PARKER (H. W.)

— The Lamp in the West. Sacred Song. *See* SPEAKS (O.)

— The Lamp of Hope. [Song. By William Shield.] *See* SPRIGS. Sprigs of Laurel.

— The Lamp of Life. Song. *See* LOGÉ (H.)

— The Lamp of Love. [Song.] *See* SALTER (M. T.) Three Love-Songs. No. 3.

— Lamp of my life. Song. *See* BISHOP (*Sir* H. R.)

— The Lamp of Night. Song. *See* GOULD (W. M.)

— Lamp of the Night. [Song.] *See* LENZ (L.) An den Abendstern.

— A Lamp unto my Feet. [Anthem.] *See* LEKBERG (S.)

LAMP (J. BODEWALT)

— *See* LAMPE.

LAMPADA

— Лампада. Романсъ. *See* SHISHOV (N. A.)

LAMPADARIOS (JOANNES)

— *See* JOANNES, *Lampadarios.*

LAMPADARIOS (PETROS)

— *See* PETROS, *Lampadarios.*

LAMPARD (G. R.)

— May Blossoms. 6 songs. 6 no. *Chicago*, 1864. fol.
H. 1780. f. (6.)

LAMPARD (G. R.)

— Our Beautiful Gems for the Parlor. [P. F.] 4 no. *Chicago*, 1864. fol.   **h. 1459. g. (4.)**

LAMPARD (J. DE)

— Dear little Flora … [Song.] Written & composed by J. de Lampard. *Howard & Co.: London*, [1883.] fol.
     H. 1260. f. (20.)

LAMPARELLI (ANTONIO)

— L'Age d'or. Romance. Parole [*sic*] de ***. Musique et accompagnement de f. piano … par Lamparelli. pp. 3. *Chez Mᵐᵉ Duhan et compagnie:* [*Paris*, 1802?] obl. fol.
[*Nouveau journal d'Apollon. année* 1. *livr.* 32. *no.* 64.]
     E. 271. z. (2.)

— Le Buisson. Romance. Paroles de Mʳ Authenac. Musique et accompagnement de f. piano … par Lamparelli. pp. 3. *Chez Mᵐᵉ Duhan et compagnie:* [*Paris*, 1802?] obl. fol.
[*Nouveau journal d'Apollon. année.* 1. *livr.* 29. *no.* 58.]
     E. 271. z. (2.)

— L'Heureuse Attente. Romance [begins: "Il n'est de bonheur"]. Paroles de Mr. Lor ***. *Paris*, [1810?] fol.   **G. 548. (31.)**

— Le Mal d'amour. Romance. Paroles de ***. Musique et accompagnement de f. piano par Lamparelli. pp. 3. *Chez Mᵐᵉ Duhan et compagnie:* [*Paris*, 1802?] obl. fol.
[*Nouveau journal d'Apollon. année* 1. *livr.* 34. *no.* 68.]
     E. 271. z. (2.)

— La Montagne d'Amour. [Song.] [*B. Viguerie: Paris*, 1800?] fol.
No. 21, 2ᵉ *Année of the 'Journal de la Lyre d'Orphée'.*
     G. 548. (55.)

— [O doux réveil.] Chanson, de la bergère de philosie [*sic*]. Paroles de ***. pp. 3. *Chez Mᵐᵉ Duhan et compagnie:* [*Paris*, 1802?] obl. fol.
[*Nouveau journal d'Apollon. année* 1. *livr.* 30. *no.* 60.]
     E. 271. z. (2.)

— Le Pauvre Henri. Romance. Paroles de ***. pp. 3. *Chez Mᵐᵉ Duhan et compagnie:* [*Paris*, 1802?] obl. fol.
[*Nouveau journal d'Apollon. année* 1. *livr.* 26. *no.* 52.]
     E. 271. z. (2.)

— Sept romances avec accompagnement de forte-piano. Paroles de divers auteurs … 7ᵉᵐᵉ recueil. pp. 15. *Chez [J. H.] Naderman: Paris*, [c. 1800.] fol.   **H. 346. g. (5.)**

— Romances de Zilia, roman pastoral, paroles de la Cᵉⁿⁿᵉ Beaufort, musique et accompagement de forte-piano par Lamparelli. pp. 19. *Chez l'auteur, etc.: Paris*, [c. 1800.] fol.
     H. 346. g. (4.)

— Romances nouvelles avec accompagnement de forte piano, *etc.* pp. 19. *Chez Mʳ Lobry: Paris*, [1815?] obl. fol.
     E. 1717. f. (5.)

— Tu m'aimes encor, ma Lesbie! *Romance. Chez B. Viguerie: Paris*, [1800?] fol.
No. 21, 2ᵉ *Année of the 'Journal de la Lyre d'Orphée'.*
     G. 548. (54.)

— Les vœux. Romance. Paroles de Mʳ ***. Musique et accompagnement de f. piano … par Lamparelli. pp. 3. *Chez Mᵐᵉ Duhan et compagnie:* [*Paris*, 1802?] obl. fol.
[*Nouveau journal d'Apollon. année* 1. *livr.* 31. *no.* 62.]
     E. 271. z. (2.)

LAMPARELLI (J.)

— *See* LAMPARELLI (A.)

LAMPE

— La Lampe d'Argile. Drame. *See* MARESCOTTI (André F.)

LAMPE

— La Lampe du ciel. [Cantata.] *See* KOECHLIN (Charles)

LAMPE (CARL)

— Trio (E dur) für Pianoforte, Violine und Violoncell. Op. 1. *Leipzig*, [1882.] fol.   **h. 2850. g. (7.)**

LAMPE (CHARLES JOHN FREDERICK)

— Britannia's Invitation to her Sons, to partake of the Glory of the intended Expedition. [Song.] The words by Mr. Wignell, *etc. Printed for M. Whitaker: London*, [1760?] fol.
     G. 316. (94.)

— Six English Songs as sung by Mr. Lowe & Mrs. Lampe Junʳ at Mary-bone Gardens. *Printed for C. Jones: London*, 1764. fol.   **G. 808. g. (21.)**

— *See* CATCH. The Catch Club … Selected by C. I. F. Lampe. Book I. [1765?] obl. fol.   **E. 155.**

— *See* CATCHES. A Second Collection of Catches by … Dr. Arne … Mr. Lampe, *etc.* [1766?] obl. 4°.   **A. 756. a. (2.)**

LAMPE (J. BODEWALT)

— Creole Belles. Rag-Time March. [P. F.] *Lampe Music Co.: Buffalo, N. Y.*, 1900. fol.   **h. 3286. y. (26.)**

— Creole Belles. ⟨March—Two-step.⟩ [P. F.] pp. 3. *B. Feldman & Co.: London*, [c. 1905.] fol.   **h. 925. k. (2.)**

— Daffo down dilly. Characteristic song. Words by George Sidney. *Whitney Warner Pub. Co.: Detroit*, [1902.] fol.
     H. 3985. h. (2.)

— Daughters of the American Revolution. National march. [P. F.] pp. 5. *Jerome H. Remick & Co.: Detroit, New York*, [1909.] fol.   **h. 4120. mm. (1.)**

— Dixie Girl. Characteristic march two step. [P. F.] *Whitney Warner Pub. Co.: Detroit*, [1903.] fol.   **h. 4120. mm. (2.)**

— Dream Sprites. A Lullaby, text by F. Archer. *Whitney Warner Pub. Co.: Detroit, Mich.*, 1902. fol.
     H. 1799. vv. (18.)

— Dreamy Eyes. Characteristic march song. Words & music by J. B. Lampe. pp. 5. *Whitney Warner Pub. Co.: Detroit*, [1902.] fol.   **H. 3985. h. (3.)**

— Dreamy Eyes … March and Two Step. [P. F.] *Whitney Warner Pub. Co.: Detroit, Mich.*, 1902. fol.   **h. 3286. y. (27.)**

— Dreamy Eyes. Characteristic march and two-step. [P. F.] pp. 5. *Francis, Day & Hunter: London*, [1902.] fol.
     h. 4120. mm. (3.)

— "Dreamy Eyes." ⟨Characteristic march and two-step. Arr. [for military band] by M. Retford.⟩ [Parts.] 31 pt. *In:* PHELPS (Bernard) *pseud.* "The Old Belfry," *etc.* 1904. obl. 8°. [*Boosey & Co.'s new supplemental Journal for military Bands. no.* 9.]
     h. 1544.

— The Enterpriser. Military march and two step. [P. F.] pp. 5. *Jerome H. Remick & Co.: Detroit, New York*, [1909.] fol.
     h. 4120. mm. (4.)

— Happy-go-lucky. March and two step. [P. F.] pp. 5. *Jerome H. Remick & Co.: Detroit, New York*, [1908.] fol.
     h. 4120. mm. (5.)

— Happy-go-lucky. March two-step. [P. F.] pp. 4. *Francis, Day & Hunter: London*, [1908.] fol.   **h. 4120. mm. (6.)**

— "Happy-go-lucky." ⟨March & two-step. Conductor [and military band parts].⟩ 33 pt. *In:* DAREWSKI (Herman E.) "Down in Jungle Town." ⟨Two-step⟩, *etc.* 1911. fol. [*Boosey's military Journal. ser.* 131. *no.* 1.]
     h. 1549.

LAMPE (J. BODEWALT)

— Happy Heinie. A characteristic march-two step. [P. F.] pp. 6.
Jerome H. Remick & Co.: Detroit, New York, [1905.] fol.
h. 4120. mm. (7.)

— Happy Heine. Characteristic march, two-step. [P. F.] pp. 4.
Francis, Day & Hunter: London, [1905.] fol.
h. 4120. mm. (8.)

— "I'm afraid to come Home in the Dark." ⟨Humoresque.
Conductor [and military band parts].⟩ 33 pt. *In*:
MENDELSSOHN-BARTHOLDY (J. L. F.) [6 zweistimmige Lieder.
Op. 63. No. 1. Ich wollt' meine Liebe.] "I would that my
Love," *etc.* 1910. fol. [*Boosey & Co.'s new supplemental
Journal for military Bands. no.* 84.] **h. 1544. a.**

— If you could sing this Song to me. [Song.] *J. H. Remick &
Co.: Detroit, New York*, 1909. fol. **H. 1794. uu. (61.)**

— The Manhattan Club. A Musical Sketch in one act adapted
to a Male Quartette, words and music by J. B. Lampe.
M. Witmark & Sons: New York, etc., 1903. 8°.
F. 163. b. (20.)

— Moonlight on the old Plantation. Characteristic piece ... Arr.
by Karl L. Hoschna. [P. F.] pp. 2–5. *M. Witmark & Sons:
[New York*, 1903.] fol. **h. 4120. mm. (9.)**

— My Dixie Girl. Characteristic two-step march. [P. F.] pp. 4.
Francis, Day & Hunter: London, [1903.] fol.
h. 4120. mm. (10.)

— Nokomis. March two step. [P. F.] pp. 5. *M. M. Leidt: Buffalo*,
[1903.] fol. **h. 4120. mm. (11.)**

— Paddy Whack. Characteristic march and two-step. [P. F.]
pp. 6. *Jerome H. Remick & Co.: Detroit*, [1907.] fol.
h. 4120. mm. (12.)

— Piggy-Back. Grotesque intermezzo two step. [P. F.] pp. 5.
Jerome H. Remick & Co.: Detroit, New York, [1909.] fol.
h. 4120. mm. (13.)

— Piggy-Back. Grotesque intermezzo two-step. [P. F.] pp. 4.
Francis, Day & Hunter: London, [1909.] fol.
h. 4120. mm. (14.)

— Songs of Scotland ... Selection of Scottish Folk Songs and
Dances. Compiled & edited by J. B. Lampe. [P. F.]
J. H. Remick & Co.: New York, Detroit, (1913.) fol.
h. 3284. f. (35.)

— Songs of the Nation. Selection of American national songs.
[P. F.] pp. 9. *Jerome H. Remick & Co.: Detroit, New York*,
[1907.] fol. **h. 4120. mm. (15.)**

— Stein Song. For Alto or Bass, words by H. Carlton.
M. Witmark & Sons: [New York, etc.,] 1904. fol.
H. 1799. vv. (19.)

— Taps. [Song.] Words by J. O'Dea. *J. H. Remick & Co.:
Detroit, New York*, 1908. fol. **H. 1794. uu. (62.)**

— Twilight. Serenade. [P. F.] pp. 5. *Jerome H. Remick & Co.:
Detroit, New York*, [1909.] fol. **h. 4120. mm. (16.)**

— A Vision of Salome. Descriptive fantasie. [P. F.] pp. 9.
Jerome H. Remick & Co.: Detroit, New York, [1908.] fol.
h. 4120. mm. (17.)

— Wanda from Anaconda. Cow boy song. [Composed by
Frederic Chapin.] Arr. by J. B. Lampe. pp. 3. *Jerome
H. Remick & Co.: Detroit, New York*, [1906.] fol.
H. 3982. uu. (8.)

— Wanda from Anaconda. (Cowboy song.) ... ⟨Arranged by
J. B. Lampe.⟩ [1906.] fol. *See* CHAPIN (Frederic)
H. 3982. uu. (9.)

— What the Wires tell to me. [Song.] Words by R. Clark.
M. Witmark & Sons: New York, 1893. fol. **H. 1798. u. (13.)**

LAMPE (J. BODEWALT)

— Yankee Dude. Characteristic march and two step. [P. F.]
pp. 7. *Jerome H. Remick & Co.: Detroit, New York*, [1907.]
fol. **h. 4120. mm. (18.)**

— Yankee Girl. ⟨Song.⟩ Words by Florence M. Cooke. pp. 5.
Shapiro, Remick & Co.: New York, [1904.] fol.
H. 3985. h. (4.)

— Yankee Girl. Characteristic march and two-step. [P. F.] pp. 6.
Shapiro, Remick & Co.: Detroit, New York, [1904.] fol.
h. 4120. mm. (19.)

— *See* GILLESPIE (Arthur) Broncho Buster Jim, *etc.* [Song.] ⟨Arr.
by J. B. Lampe.⟩ [1906.] fol. **H. 3984. (40.)**

— *See* HAND (C.) The Bolivar Cadets ... Arr. by J. B. Lampe.
1906. 8°. **F. 637. dd. (15.)**

— *See* HAND (C.) Jolly little Johnnies at the old Stage Door ...
Arr. by J. B. Lampe. 1906. 8°. **F. 637. dd. (16.)**

— *See* HAND (C.) Nance ... [Song.] Arr. by J. B. Lampe. [1906.]
fol. **H. 3984. j. (33.)**

— *See* HEIMERLE (M.) Popular Band ... Arr. by J. B. Lampe.
1902. fol. **h. 3286. x. (44.)**

— *See* KOVEN (H. Le R. de) The Wedding Trip. Selection ...
Arranged by J. B. Lampe. [P. F.] 1912. fol. **h. 3284. e. (43.)**

— *See* LILIUOKALANI, *Queen of Hawaii*. Aloha oe ... Arr. by
J. B. Lampe. (1912.) fol. **G. 806. mm. (37.)**

— *See* NEVIN (E. W.) Mighty lak' a Rose. Fox Trot, *etc.* (Arr. by
J. B. Lampe.) 1923. 4°. **g. 1127. j. (20.)**

— *See* STRAUS (O.) [Der tapfere Soldat.] The Chocolate Soldier.
Selection ... Arr. by J. B. Lampe. 1909. fol. **h. 4265. (14.)**

— *See* VAN ALSTYNE (Egbert A.) Shy-try ... Arr. by J. B. Lampe.
[P. F.] [1906.] fol. **h. 4121. o. (35.)**

— *See* VELASQUEZ (J.) Evangeline ... Arr. [for orchestra] by
J. B. Lampe. [1904.] 8°. **f. 800. a. (467.)**

LAMPE (JOHANN FRIEDRICH)

— Advice to the Unwary, *etc.* [Song.] [*London*, 1738.] 8°.
Gentleman's Magazine, Vol. VIII., p. 430. **249. c. 8.**

— [Amelia.] Amelia wishes when she dies. A favourite song in
the opera of Amelia. [By J. F. Lampe, words by Henry Carey.
Score.] Set for yᵉ German fl[ute]. [1732?] *s. sh.* fol. *See* AMELIA.
G. 316. q. (11.)

— The Art of Musick. *Printed for C. Corbett: London*, 1740. 8°.
1042. h. 6. (4.)

— The Batchelor's Advantage. [Song.] *See* As. As Thomas and
Harry one Midsummer Day, *etc.* [Music by J. F. Lampe.]
[1730?] *s. sh.* fol. **G. 306. (36.)**

— Bright Cynthia's Pow'r. *See infra*: [Oroonoko.]

— British Melody; or, the Musical Magazine. Consisting of a
large Variety of ... English and Scotch Songs Airs, &c. ...
Set to Musick by the most Eminent Masters ... The Whole
curiously Engrav'd on Three-score Folio Copper Plates; ...
revis'd and corrected and one Fourth Part of them set to
Musick by J. F. Lampe ... each Plate ... Embellish'd with a
New Head-Piece, *etc.* *Printed for ... B. Cole: London*, 1739.
fol.
*The composers named in this collection are: Lampe,
Ramondon, Philips, C. Young, M. Greene, S. Mabbat or
Mobbot, Carey, Stanley, R. Graves, Pepusch, Galliard,
Hatchdosam and Handel.* **H. 1364.**

— [Another copy.] **K. 11. b. 4.**

LAMPE (JOHANN FRIEDRICH)

—[British melody.] [*London*, 1739.] fol.
An imperfect copy; wanting the titlepage, dedication, and
address to the reader, and containing only ff. 14–16, 19, 20,
22–24, 28–35, 37, 38–45, 47–51, 53. **H. 1364. a.**

— But shall I go mourn for that my Dear. [Song.] *Set by Mr.*
Lampe from Shakespear['s 'Winter's Tale']. [*London*, 1745?]
s. sh. fol. **G. 306. (251.)**

— By the Beer as brown as a Berry. *See* infra: [The Dragon of
Wantley.]

— A Cantata and Four English Songs. *Printed for I. Walsh:*
London, [1746.] fol. **G. 221. (5.)**

— Chaconne. *See* infra: [Columbine Courtezan.]

—[Columbine Courtezan.] A Collection of all the Aires,
Pastorells, Chacoons, Entre, Jiggs, Minuets and Musette's in
Columbine Courtezan, and all the late Entertainments ... To
which is Prefix'd, the Original Violin, German Flute, &
Harpsicord, *etc. Printed for I. Walsh: London*, [1735.] obl. fol.
c. 60. (1.)

—[Another copy.]
Imperfect; wanting the titlepage and ff. 1, 2, 4, 6, 13–15.
e. 5. k. (3*.)

—[Columbine Courtezan.] Chaconne. For violins, pianoforte &
descant recorders (bamboo pipes & treble recorders optional)
... Arr. by Kenneth Finlay. [Score and parts.] 6 pt.
A. Weekes & Co.: London, [1951.] 8°.
School Orchestra Series. no. 5. **h. 3210. i. (110.)**

— The Complaint. *See* infra: [The Despairing Shepherd.]

— The Cuckoo, a Celebrated Concerto: in Five Parts, viz.
Traversa, Violin 1, Violin 2, Tenor, Violencella, and Bass.
[Harpsichord part.] *Printed for J. Wilcox: London*, [1740?]
fol. **G. 221. (1.)**

— The Celebrated Cuckoo Concerto. Composed by C. F. [or
rather, F. J.] Lampe. [1798.] *See* PERIODICAL PUBLICATIONS.—
London. The Piano-Forte Magazine. Vol. IV. [No. 6.]
[1797–1802.] 8°. **D. 854.**

— The Declaring Lover. [Song.] [*London*, 1740?] *s. sh.* fol.
G. 310. (133.)

—[Another copy.] **G. 305. (168.)**

— The Despairing Shepherd. [Also known as "The Complaint".
For editions of this song published anonymously:] *See*
CLEON. Cleon, whose heart foretold despair, *etc.*

The Dragon of Wantley

— Songs and Duetto's in the Burlesque Opera, call'd, The
Dragon of Wantley. [Written by H. Carey] ... Composed and
Carefully Corrected by Mr. J. F. Lampe, *etc.* [Full score.]
Printed for J. Wilcox: London, 1738. fol.
Engraved by B. Cole. **F. 5.**

— Songs and Duetto's in ... The Dragon of Wantley, in Score,
etc. Printed for I. Walsh: London, [1746?] fol.
This is the same as the edition of 1738, *with a new titlepage.*
G. 221. (2.)

— The Songs, Duettos and Trio in the Dragon of Wantley ...
Dispos'd properly for the Harpsicord & Voice, and may be
accompanied with a Violin or German Flute & Violoncello.
W. Smith: London, [1752.] obl. fol. **F. 5. a.**

— By the Beer as brown as a Berry ... Music freely arranged by
Geoffrey Bush. pp. 5. *Elkin & Co.: London*, [1958.] 4°.
[*Songs from the Ballad Operas. no.* 6.] **G. 1408. b.**

— Zeno, Plato, Aristotle. [Song, by J. F. Lampe.] *Sung by M*^r
Salway in the Dragon of Wantley. [c. 1740.] *s. sh.* fol. *See*
DRAGON. **G. 425. rr. (7.)**

LAMPE (JOHANN FRIEDRICH)

—[Fatal Falsehood.] Whilst endless Tears and Sighs declare. *A*
Song in the new Tragedy [by J. Hewitt] *of Fatal Falsehood* ...
Sung by Mrs. Clive. [*London*, 1734.] *s. sh.* fol. **I. 530. (82.)**

— Female Advice. [Song.] [*London*, 1750?] *s. sh.* fol.
G. 307. (161.)

— Female Advice. [Song.] [*London*, c. 1760.] *s. sh.* fol.
H. 1601. u. (140.)

— Flavia. [Song.] [*London?* c. 1760.] *s. sh.* fol.
H. 1601. u. (142.)

— Fly Care to the Winds, *etc.* [Duet, music by J. F. Lampe.]
[1740?] *s. sh.* fol. *See* FLY. **G. 307. (238.)**

— Go lovely Rose. [Song.] *The Words by Mr. Waller.* [*London*,
1740?] fol. **G. 308. (19.)**

—[Another copy.] **G. 305. (162.)**

— The Happy Man. Arietta. [*London*, c. 1740.] *s. sh.* fol.
H. 1601. r. (5.)

— The Inconstant. *See* WHEN. When fading Beauty does decay.
The Inconstant. [Song, music by J. F. Lampe.] [1730?] *s. sh.* fol.
G. 313. (150.)

— Kirchen-Music, die am Dank-Feste wegen der unterdrückten
Rebellion ... auffgeführet wurde. *See* infra: The Musick in
Score of the Thanksgiving Anthem, *etc.*

— Ladies' Amusement: being a new Collection of Songs,
Ballads, &c. With Symphonies and Thorough-Bass. *J. Hoey,*
for the Author: Dublin, [1748?] fol.
Imperfect; wanting pp. 19–22. **H. 1625. b.**

— The Lady's Lamentation for ye absence of Capt John. *See* As.
As near to Rosamonda's stream. [1740.] *s. sh.* fol.
G. 306. (114.)

— A Lass there lives upon the green. *See* infra: [Oroonoko.]

— The Lion's song. *See* infra: [Pyramus and Thisbe.]

— Love and Honour. [Song.] *See* I. I wish and long for that
which I, *etc.* [Music by J. L. Lampe.] [1740?] *s. sh.* fol.
G. 309. (115.)

— Lovely Fair. Song ... arranged by J. Greenhill. *Boosey &*
Co.: London & New York, 1895. fol. **H. 1798. u. (14.)**

— The Lover's Address. [Song.] *See* CHARMER. Charmer permit
me to make a Surrender, *etc.* [Music by J. F. Lampe.] [1730?]
s. sh. fol. **G. 307. (47.)**

— The Maid's Request, *etc.* [Song.] *See* GLIDE. Glide swiftly on
thou Silver Stream, *etc.* [By J. F. Lampe.] [1735?] *s. sh.* fol.
G. 316. d. (159.)

—[Another edition.] The Maid's Request, *etc. See* GLIDE. Glide
Swiftly on thou Silver stream, *etc.* [1740?] *s. sh.* fol.
G. 310. (200.)

—[Margery.] [Overture and Chorus's in the Burlesque Opera
called Margery, being a Sequel to the Dragon of Wantley,
etc.] [Words by H. Carey. Full score.] [*Printed for J. Wilcox:*
London, 1739.] fol.
Wanting the titlepage. **G. 221. (3.)**

—[Margery.] Songs and Duetto's in the burlesque Opera, call'd
Margery, being a sequel to the Dragon of Wantley, *etc.* [Full
score.] pp. 101. *Printed for John Wilcox: London*, 1739. fol.
Hirsch II. 503.

— The Modest Concealment. [Song.] *See* DEAR. Dear Collin
prevent my warm Blushes, *etc.* [1733?] *s. sh.* fol.
G. 307. (130.)

— The Musick in Score of the Thanksgiving Anthem perform'd
at the Protestant-Lutheran-German Church in the Savoy,

LAMPE (JOHANN FRIEDRICH)

Octr 1746, for the Suppression of the Rebellion. *Eng. & Ger.*
pp. 46. *Printed for the author: London,* [1747.] fol.
With an additional titlepage reading "Kirchen-Music, die am
Dank-Feste wegen der unterdrückten Rebellion ... auffgeführt
wurde," and bearing the imprint "Hannover und Göttingen bey
Johann Wilhelm Schmidt".   **H. 1364. b.**

— Lampe's Original Medley Overture. [Orchestral parts.]
[*London*, 1740?] fol.   **g. 474. a. (14.)**

— [Oroonoko.] Bright Cynthia's Pow'r, divinely great. *A Song in*
Oroonoko. [Words by T. Cheek.] [*London*, 1730?] *s. sh.* fol.
                                                  G. 306. (244.)

— [Another copy.]   **I. 530. (80.)**

— [Oroonoko.] A Lass there lives upon the green. *Song in*
Oroonoko, Sung by Mrs. Lampe. [*London*, 1730?] *s. sh.* fol.
                                                  G. 316. c. (25.)

— The Parent Bird. *See* infra: Paternal Love.

Paternal Love

— Paternal Love. [Song.] *See* PARENT. The Parent Bird whose
little Nest, *etc.* [Music by J. F. Lampe.] [1745?] *s. sh.* fol.
                                                  H. 1994. b. (64.)

— [Another edition.] The Parent Bird whose little Nest, *etc.*
[Music by J. F. Lampe.] [1745?] *s. sh.* fol. *See* PARENT.
                                                  G. 305. (240.)

— The Parent Bird. A Song, *etc.* [*London*, 1747.] 8°.
Universal Magazine, Vol. I., p. 184.   **P. P. 5439.**

— The Parent Bird. [Song.] [*London?* c. 1750.] *s. sh.* fol.
                                                  H. 1652. hh. (8.)

— The Parent Bird. [Song.] [*London?* c. 1750.] *s. sh.* fol.
Followed by an arrangement for the guitar.   **G. 426. rr. (26.)**

— [A reissue.] The Parent Bird. [Song.] *L & B* [*Longman &*
Broderip: London, c. 1780.] *s. sh.* fol.   **G. 426. kk. (65.)**

— The Perfections of true Love. [Song.] *See* THERE. There liv'd
long ago in a Country place, *etc.* [Music by J. F. Lampe.]
[1730?] *s. sh.* fol.   **G. 312. (86.)**

— A Plain and Compendious Method of Teaching Thorough
Bass ... With Proper Rules for Practice. The Examples and
Lessons ... Engraved on Copper Plates. *Printed for*
J. Wilcox: London, 1737. 4°.   **558*. c. 22.**

— [Another copy.]
Imperfect; wanting pl. 68.   **Hirsch I. 301.**

— A Preservative against Love. [Song.] *See* HOW. How frail
alas! we mortals are, *etc.* [By J. F. Lampe.] [1740.] *s. sh.* fol.
                                                  G. 308. (97.)

— Pyramus and Thisbe: a Mock-Opera. The words taken from
Shakespeare, *etc.* [Full score.] pp. 39. *Printed for I. Walsh:*
London, [1745.] fol.   **G. 193. (5.)**

— [Another copy.]
In this issue the verso of p. 39 is blank.   **Hirsch II. 504.**

— [Another edition.] Pyramus and Thisbe: a Mock-Opera. The
Words taken from Shakspeare['s 'Midsummer Night's
Dream,' as altered in 1716 by R. Leveridge. Full score], *etc.*
Printed for I. Walsh: London, [1746?] fol.
The verso of p. 39 bears a song sung by Mr. Beard.
                                                  G. 221. (4.)

— [Pyramus and Thisbe.] The Lion's song. [Begins: "Ladies
don't fright ye".] *See* ROFFE (A.) Twelve English base songs,
etc. Bk. 1. No. 5. [1854.] fol.   **H. 1771. p. (30.)**

LAMPE (JOHANN FRIEDRICH)

— Ruscelletto Infidele, or, The false Shepherd. [Song.]
[*London*, 1740?] *s. sh.* fol.
This is No. v. of 'British Melody,' with alterations in Cole's
engraving.   **G. 360. (59.)**

— [The Sham Conjurer.] The Grand Concerto, Favourite Songs,
Dueto's, Trio & Chorus in the New Masque call'd the Sham
Conjurer, *etc.* [Full score.] *Printed for I. Simpson: London,*
[1741.] fol.   **G. 221. (6.)**

— The Shepherd's Invitation. [Song.] Sung by Mr. Sullivan ...
The Words by Mr. Ayre. [*London*, 1730?] *s. sh.* fol.
                                                  I. 530. (81.)

— The Shepherd's Invitation. [Song.] Sung by Mr. Sullivan ...
The Words by Mr. Ayre. [*London*, 1744.] 8°.
London Magazine, 1744, *p.* 510.   **157. l. 6.**

— The Shepherd's Invitation. [Song.] ... The Words by Mr.
Ayre. [*London*, 1745.] 8°.
Gentleman's Magazine, Vol. XV., p. 217.   **249. c. 15.**

— The Shepherd's Invitation, *etc.* [*London*, 1750?] *s. sh.* 4°.
Plate LXXIX of the Agreeable Amusement.   **H. 1994. c. (53.)**

— The Spring Wish. [Song.] [*London*, 1730?] *s. sh.* fol.
                                                  I. 530. (83.)

— [Another edition.] The Spring Wish, *etc.* [*London?* 1740?]
s. sh. fol.   **G. 316. d. (87.)**

— This Love is a Joker. *Sung by Mr Mullart.* [c. 1740.] *s. sh.* fol.
                                                  G. 316. q. (6.)

— Tho' rude Rebellion rears its Head. *The occasional Song* as it
is now perform'd at the Theatre Royal in Covent Garden,
etc. [*London*, 1745.] fol.   **G. 312. (15.)**

— To Sylvia. [Song.] Sung by Mr. Sullivan at the Theatre in
Drury Lane ... the Words by Mr. Garrick. [*London*, 1745?]
s. sh. fol.   **G. 309. (25.)**

— [Tom Thumb.] The Most Celebrated Aires in the opera of
Tom Thumb. ⟨Cross sculp.⟩ ff. 18. [By J. F. Lampe.] [1733.] fol.
See TOM.   **G. 226. c.**

— [Tom Thumb.—To have my bold Actions.] Tom Thumb. By
Master Arne. [Song, by J. F. Lampe, sung by Richard Arne.]
[1733?] *s. sh.* fol. *See* TOM.   **H. 1994. c. (12.)**

— The True Briton. A Two Part Song, *etc.* [*London*, 1740?]
s. sh. fol.   **I. 530. (84.)**

— [Another edition.] The True Britton. A two part Song. *See*
COME. Come Drawers more Wine, *etc.* [By J. F. Lampe.]
[1740?] *s. sh.* fol.   **G. 307. (73.)**

— Upon the Taking of Chagre Castle by Adm^l Vernon. [Song.]
See YE. Ye Brittons draw near, *etc.* [Music by J. F. Lampe.]
[1740.] *s. sh.* fol.   **G. 314. (56.)**

— Whilst endless Tears and Sighs declare. *See* supra: [The Fatal
Falsehood.]

— The Wish. [Song.] Sung by Mr. Sullivan, *etc.* [*London*, 1740?]
s. sh. fol.   **G. 307. (20.)**

— [Another copy.]   **I. 530. (85.)**

— Wit Musically Embellish'd. Being a Collection of Forty New
English Ballads; the Words by divers Eminent Hands, set to
Musick with a Thorough Bass for the Harpsichord ... The
Tunes all Transpos'd for the Flute. *Engraved & Printed for*
the Author: London, [1731.] fol.
Engraved by T. Cobb, with an engraved titlepage.
                                                  H. 1625. a.

— [Another copy.]
This work appeared in parts of eight Ballads each. It was
advertised in the Grub Street Journal for 5 Aug., 1731. *This*

LAMPE (Johann Friedrich)

copy is complete, but has no preface nor list of subscribers, and the titlepage is the printed one issued with the first part.

H. 1625.

— Wit Preferable to Beauty. [Song.] *See* Though. Tho' here at Bath you make a Rout, *etc.* [Music by J. F. Lampe.] [1730?] *s. sh.* fol. **G. 312. (87.)**

— *See* Hymns. [*English.*] Hymns on the Great Festivals, *etc.* [Music by J. F. Lampe.] 1746. 4°. **F. 5. b.**

— *See* Hymns. [*English.*] Hymns on the Great Festivals ... The Second Edition. [Music by J. F. Lampe.] 1753. 4°.

E. 1498. j.

— *See* Overtures. Six Medley or Comic Overtures in Seven Parts ... by Dr. Arne, Lampe, *etc.* [1763.] fol. **g. 100. c.**

— *See* Summer. The Summer's Tale. A Musical Comedy ... The Music by Abel ... Lampe, *etc.* [1765.] *obl.* fol. **D. 273. (1.)**

— *See* Thesaurus. Thesaurus Musicus. A Collection of ... Part Songs ... by ... Lampe, *etc.* [1745.] fol. **H. 73.**

LAMPE (Johann Friedrich) and **HOWARD** (Samuel)

— The Vocal Musical Mask. A Collection of English Songs never before printed, set to Musick by Mr. Lampe, Mr. Howard, &c. [Book IV.] *Printed for I. Walsh: London,* [1746?] fol.
With additional items in manuscript. **H. 39.**

LAMPE (Walther)

— *See* Beethoven (L. van) Sonaten für Klavier und Violine ... herausgegeben von W. Lampe und K. Schäffer. [1949.] 4°.
g. 249. ww. (1.)

— *See* Mozart (W. A.) Klavier-Sonaten ... Herausgegeben von W. Lampe, *etc.* [1948.] 4°. **g. 1018. dd. (1.)**

— *See* Mozart (W. A.) Klaviersonaten ... Herausgegeben und mit Fingersatz versehen von W. Lampe. ⟨Urtext.⟩ Neue, verbesserte Ausgabe. [1965.] 4°. **g. 382. bb.**

— *See* Volkmann (F. R.) Variationen über ein Thema von Händel. Herausgegeben von W. Lampe. [1927.] fol.
h. 3865. q. (7.)

LAMPEL (Otto)

— The Astronauts. March ... Military band arrangement by W. J. Duthoit. ⟨Conductor [and parts].⟩ 43 pt. *Chappell & Co.: London,* [1963.] 8°.
Various parts are in duplicate. **h. 3210. i. (827.)**

LAMPEN (Charles Dudley)

— Magnificat in vocal score with accompaniment ... for Piano or Organ. *London,* [1883.] 8°. **B. 597. k. (16.)**

— A Wedding Hymn. "Father supreme, Creator divine." Words and music by C. D. Lampen. *Novello and Co.: London,* [1909.] 8°. **C. 799. p. (19.)**

LAMPEN (Margaret Whitlocke)

— Sanctus, Psalms, Chants, Kyrie eleeson, and Doxology. The music in vocal score, with an accompaniment for the organ or pianoforte, *etc.* pp. 66. *London Sacred Music Warehouse:* [*London,*] 1851. 8°. **F. 1122. j.**

LAMPERN (M. van)

— Les Lutins. Chœur à 2 voix égales [begins: "Voici l'heure"] avec accompt. de Piano à quatre mains, d'après les Danses de Goldmark. Op. 22. Paroles de Mlle. L. H. *Mayence,* [1881.] fol. **H. 1786. e. (7.)**

LAMPERT (Ernst Ludwig)

— *See* S., E. H. Z. Tonij ... Vollständiger Clavierauszug ... eingerichtet von E. Lampert. [1853.] fol. **H. 644. a.**

LAMPERT (J. F.)

— The Celebrated Tyrolian Wastel, Lampert's Grand German March, Miss Jameson & Miss Carmichael's Waltzes, and a much admir'd Bohemian Air for the Piano Forte. *Muir, Wood & Co.: Edinburgh,* [1805?] fol. **g. 443. j. (4.)**

LAMPERT (Vera)

— *See* Koželuch (Leopold) Konzert für Klarinette und Orchester Es-dur ... Herausgegeben von G. Balassa und V. Lampert. [1975.] 8°. **f. 388. f. (6.)**

LAMPERTI (Francesco)

— The Art of Singing. *See infra:* [Guida teorico-pratica-elementare per lo studio del canto.]

— Bravura Studies for Trumpet. *See infra:* [Studi di bravura.]

— Daily Exercises in Singing. *See infra:* [Esercizi giornalieri di canto.]

— Esercizi giornalieri di canto. pp. 17. *Carl Blosfeld: Riga; Moscou* [printed, c. 1900.] 4°.
Bibliothèque de musique internationale. no. 260.
G. 295. ii. (11.)

— [Esercizi giornalieri di canto.] Daily Exercises in Singing. pp. 19. *Chappell & Co.: London,* [1951.] 8°.
Schirmer's Library of musical Classics. vol. 570.
F. 1692. e. (4.)

Guida teorico-pratica-elementare per lo studio del canto

— Guida teorico-pratica-elementare per lo studio del Canto. *Milano, Napoli,* [1865.] fol. **H. 2235.**

— The Singer's Guide, theoretical, practical and elementary. *London,* [1868.] fol. **H. 1775. t. (13.)**

— A treatise on the art of singing ... translated ... by ... J. C. Griffith. *Milan,* [1877.] 4°. **F. 481.**

— The Art of Singing. Revised edition with translation by J. C. Griffith. pp. 62. *G. Schirmer: New York; Chappell & Co.: London;* [*London* printed, 1951.] 8°.
Schirmer's Library of musical Classics. vol. 1587.
F. 1692. e. (5.)

— Osservazioni e consigli sul Trillo.—Observations & directions on the Trillo. *Ital. & Eng. Milano,* [1878.] 8°. **F. 481. a.**

— Prime lezioni di canto per lo studio degli intervalli secondo lo stile moderno. 2 pt. *F. Lucca: Milano,* [1886.] fol.
H. 2245. f. (2.)

— The Singer's Guide, *etc. See supra:* [Guida teorico-pratica-elementare per lo studio del canto.]

— 8 Solfeggi ... per Soprano e Mezzo-Soprano. *Milano,* [1877.] 8°. **F. 481. b.**

— [Studi di bravura.] Vocal Studies in Bravura. Provided with explanatory text of a pedagogical nature [and revised and edited] by Estelle Liebling. pp. 48. *G. Schirmer: New York; Chappell & Co.: London;* [*London,* printed, 1951.] 8°.
Schirmer's Library of musical Classics. vol. 1633.
F. 1692. e. (6.)

— [Studi di bravura.] Bravura Studies for Trumpet. Melodic etudes in articulation ... Trumpet and piano. ⟨Transcribed by Robert Weatherley.⟩ [Score and part.] 2 pt. *G. Schirmer: New York,* [1970.] 4°. **g. 1105. m. (13.)**

LAMPERTI (Francesco)

— A treatise on the art of singing. *See* supra: [Guida teorico-pratica-elementare per lo studio del canto.]

— Vocal Studies in Bravura. *See* supra: [Studi di bravura.]

LAMPERTI (G. B.)

— Vocalizzi preparatorii per la scuola di canto. 5 pt. *Milano*, [1881.] fol. **H. 3509.**

LAMPLIGHTER

— [The Lamplighter.] Songs from the American story the Lamplighter. The words by J. E. Carpenter, the music by S. Glover, H. Farmer, E. L. Hine and G. Linley. 6 no. *London*, [1854.] fol. **H. 1467. (4.)**

— The Lamplighter. [Song.] *See* DIBDIN (C.) [The Oddities.]

— The Lamplighter. [Song.] *See* EDWARDS (Henry J.)

— The Lamplighter. Song. *See* MACDONALD (R. H.)

— The Lamplighter. [Song.] *See* MACNAMERA (Lizzie)

— The Lamp Lighter. [Two-part song.] *See* MOY (E.)

— The Lamp-Lighter. Cantata. *See* MOZE (J. H.)

— The Lamplighter. Unison Song. *See* ROWLEY (A.)

— The Lamplighter. Unison song. *See* WHITFIELD (John B. R.)

LAMPLIT

— The Lamplit Hour. [Song.] *See* BARNETT (A.) Three Love-Songs, *etc.* [No. 1.]

— The Lamplit Hour. Song. *See* PENN (A. A.)

LAMPORT (Thomas)

— Twenty-four original Psalm Tunes in Score, with the Thorough Bass figured for the Organ or Piano-Forte. *Printed for the Author: London*, [1812?] *obl.* 4°. **A. 1033.**

LAMPORT-SMITH (L.)

— *See* SMITH (L. Lamport)

LAMPRECHT (Frances)

— Liedjies vir klein mensies. pp. 19. *J. L. van Schaik: Pretoria*, 1954. 4°. **F. 1196. h. (3.)**

LAMPS

— The Lamps of Faerie-Land. Part-Song. *See* HUTCHINSON (T.)

— The Lamps of Heaven. Song. *See* KEEN (A.)

— The Lamps of Hope. Song. *See* ROECKEL (J. L.)

— Lamps of Memory. [Song.] *See* PINSUTI (C. E.)

— The Lamps of Night. Hymn. *See* CHALLINOR (F. A.)

— The Lamps of old Broadway. [Song.] *See* SOLOMON (Frederic)

— The Lamps of Paradise. Song. *See* SQUIRE (W. H.)

— Lamps of the Dusk. Song. *See* NEVIN (G. B.)

LAMPTEY (C. Mills)

— Ghana Independence March ... Written and composed by C. Mills-Lamptey, *etc.* [S. A. T. B. Staff and tonic sol-fa notation.] pp. 5. *E. Chebib Bros.: Accra*, [1957.] 8°. **F. 1744. t. (5.)**

LAMPUGNANI (Giovanni Battista)

— [Alceste.] The Favourite Songs in the Opera call'd Alceste, *etc. Printed for I. Walsh: London*, [1744.] fol. **G. 206. a. (4.)**

— [Alessandro nell' Indie.] The Favourite Songs in the Opera call'd Alexander in India. pp. 25. *Printed for I. Walsh: London*, [1746.] fol. **G. 811. e. (2.)**

— Alessandro nell' Indie. [A Pasticcio, chiefly by G. B. Lampugnani and G. Cocchi.] *See* DELIZIE. Le Delizie dell' Opere, *etc.* Vol. 4, 11, 12. [1776.] fol. **G. 159.**

— [Alfonso.] The Favourite Songs in the Opera call'd Alfonso, *etc. Printed for I. Walsh: London*, [1744.] fol. **G. 190. (6.)**

— [Songs in L'Ingratitudine Punita. A Pasticcio, by Hasse, Lampugnani, *etc.*] *See* DELIZIE. Le Delizie dell' Opere, *etc.* Vol. 5. [1776.] fol. **G. 159.**

— [Songs in Semiramide. A Pasticcio, by Hasse and Lampugnani.] *See* DELIZIE. Le Delizie dell' Opere, *etc.* Vol. 5. [1776.] fol. **G. 159.**

— [Siroe.] The Favourite Songs in the Opera call'd Siroe, *etc.* (The Two favourite Songs in ... Siroe, sung by Sign^{ra} Mingotti.) [Short score.] 2 no. *Printed for I. Walsh: London*, [1755.] fol. **G. 201. (3.)**

— [Another copy.] **H. 348. e. (1, 10.)**

— [Another copy.] **R. M. 13. c. 22. (5.)**

— Six Sonatas for Two Violins, with a Through Bass for the Harpsicord or Violoncello ... Opera Prima. [Parts.] *Printed for I. Walsh: London*, [1745?] fol. **g. 420. c. (8.)**

— [Another copy.] **R. M. 17. c. 5. (11.)**

— Six Sonatas for two Violins and a Thorough Bass ... Opera prima. [Parts.] 3 pt. *John Simpson: [London*, c. 1745.] fol. *No. 1–4 of this set are the same as no. 6, 3, 2, 1 of the preceding.* **h. 1728. p. (2.)**

— [Another copy.] *The violino primo part only.* **g. 271. m. (6.)**

— Six Sonatas for two Violins and a Thorough Bass. [Parts.] *Printed for C. & S. Thompson: London*, [1765?] fol. *The same set as the preceding.* **g. 409. (7.)**

— *See* EZIO. The Favourite Songs in ... Ezio. With some Songs [by J. A. Hasse and G. B. Lampugnani] in Ipermestra, *etc.* [1755.] fol. **G. 173.**

— *See* SONGS. Farinelli's Celebrated Songs, *etc.* (Galuppi, Hasse, Vinci, Lampugnani ... & Pescetti's Chamber Aires ... Collected out of all their late Operas.) [1736–1756?] fol. **g. 444.**

— *See* SUMMER. The Summer's Tale. A Musical Comedy ... The Music by Abel ... Lampugnani, *etc.* [1765.] *obl.* fol. **D. 273. (1.)**

LAMPUGNANI (Giovanni Battista) and SAN MARTINI (Giovanni Battista)

— Six Sonatas for Two Violins with a Through Bass for the Harpsicord or Violoncello. Composed by Sig^r G. B. Lampugnani and St. Martini of Milan. Opera Prima. *Printed for J. Walsh: London*, [1744.] fol. *This work is the same as the Six Sonatas published by Walsh under Lampugnani's name alone as Op. 1.* **g. 480. (1.)**

LAMPUGNANI (Giovanni Battista) and **SAN MARTINI** (Giovanni Battista)

— Six Sonatas for Two Violins, with a Through Bass for the Harpsicord or Violoncello. Compos'd by Sig^r G. B. Lampugnani and St Martini of Milan. Opera Seconda. [Parts.] *Printed for I. Walsh: London,* [1745.] fol.

g. 480. (2.)

— [Another copy.] **R. M. 17. d. 3. (3.)**

LAMSDALE (Sam A.)

— Rosie Doon. ⟨Song.⟩ Written and composed by S. A. Lamsdale, *etc.* [Staff and tonic sol-fa notation. Voice part.] *Francis, Day & Hunter: London,* [1904.] *s. sh.* fol.

H. 3985. h. (5.)

— Rosie Doon, *etc.* ⟨Song.⟩ [With separate voice part.] 2 pt. *Francis, Day & Hunter: London,* [1904.] fol. **H. 3985. h. (6.)**

LAMSON (Georgie)

— Because it's you. [Song.] Words and music by G. Lamson. *H. S. Gordon: New York,* 1896. fol. **H. 1798. u. (15.)**

— If that high World. Sacred Song ... ([Words by] Byron.) *Phelps Music Co.: New York,* 1896. fol. **H. 1187. u. (1.)**

— A Life's Regret. [Song.] *H. S. Gordon: New York,* 1900. fol.

H. 1799. g. (65.)

— My Girl Jean. ⟨Song and chorus.⟩ Words and music by G. Lamson. pp. 5. *Chas. W. Held: Brooklyn,* [1895.] fol.

H. 3980. oo. (50.)

— The Song of the Brooklet. [Song.] Words and Music by G. Lamson. *H. S. Gordon: New York,* 1900. fol.

H. 1799. g. (64.)

— Summer Swing Song. For piano without octaves. pp. 3. *Hamilton S. Gordon: New York,* [1905.] fol.

h. 4120. mm. (20.)

LA MURE (Pierre)

— The Lord's Prayer. [Song.] pp. 5. *Ehlem Music Co.: Los Angeles,* [1970.] 4°. **G. 295. nn. (13.)**

LAMY (   )

— Pay your Debts polka. [Orchestral parts.] *London,* [1873.] 8°. *Part of the "Alliance Musicale".* **f. 400. c. (16.)**

— Pay your Debts polka. [P. F.] *London,* [1873.] 8°. *No.* 128 *of the "Alliance Musicale. Album Bijou".* **f. 406.**

— The Two Brass Men. Polka. [Reed band parts.] *London,* [1885.] 8°. **f. 412. q. (13.)**

L'AMY (J. Alexander R. Ramsay)

— Two Songs. a. Come buy. b. May Song. Words by P. B. Marston and E. Nesbit, *etc. West & Co.: London,* 1914. fol.

H. 1793. r. (49.)

LAN (Mei-jui)

— Farmer's Song ... Chinese work song arranged for 4-part chorus by Maryette Lum ... English words by Berta Metzger and M. Lum ... Second edition. Chin. & Eng. pp. 8. [*Peiping,* 1932.] 4°.
The titlepage, which is in Chinese and English, bears a dedication in the arranger's autograph. **G. 1363. w. (2.)**

— Songs of Chinese Children. Translated and arranged by Maryette H. Lum. Illustrated by Lin Yü Ts'ang. *Eng. & Chin.* pp. 23. *Printed by Peking Institute of Photography: Peiping,* [1936.] 4°. **G. 1363. k. (10.)**

LANAF

— Y Lanaf Oriana. [Part-song.] *See* Wilbye (J.) [The Lady Oriana.]

LANAGAN

— Lanagan's Log. Song. *See* Loehr (H.)

LANCASHIRE

— The Lancashire and Yorkshire Harmonist. Anthems and Tunes. *See* Lister (G.)

— The Lancashire Appeal. [Part-song.] *See* Hendy (H.)

— The Lancashire Lad. [Song.] *See* Delavanti (P.)

— A Lancashire Lullaby. Song. *See* Clarke (S. H.)

— The Lancashire Sands by the Sea. Song. *See* Gressler (C.)

— The Lancashire Witches, or King Jamie's Frolic. Opera. *See* Stanilaus (F.)

LANCASHIRE (Alfred James)

— Hameland. Song, words by J. Donnan. *Agate & Co.: London,* (1908.) fol. **H. 1794. uu. (63.)**

— Sons of Galloway. Song, words by J. Donnan. *Agate & Co.: London,* (1908.) fol. **H. 1794. uu. (64.)**

— Sons of Galloway—Part Song—, *etc. See* Paterson, Sons and Co. Paterson's Part Music, *etc.* No. 83. [1890? *etc.*] 8°.

F. 1686.

LANCASTER (   ) *Professor*

— *See* Milton (J. L.) Souvenir of the Rev. J. L. Milton, arranged by Professor Lancaster. [1839.] fol. **H. 1676. (51.)**

LANCASTER (E.)

— Gilpin's galop. [P. F.] *London,* [1875.] fol. **h. 1482. y. (26.)**

LANCASTER (E. L.)

— *See* Stecher (Melvin) Keyboard Strategies ... By M. Stecher, N. Horowitz, C. Gordon, R. F. Kern, and E. L. Lancaster. ⟨Master text.⟩ [1980.] 4°. **g. 652. a.**

LANCASTER (Edmund)

— *See* Kevin (Alexander) Jubilee Girl, *etc.* ⟨Piano selection. Arranged by E. Lancaster.⟩ [1956.] 4°. **f. 133. uu. (27.)**

LANCASTER (Edward)

— Six Christmas Carols. Words by F. St. John Corbett. *Novello, Ewer and Co.: London & New York,* [1892.] 8°.

F. 1171. j. (25.)

LANCASTER (Fanny Connable)

— Suffrage Marching Song. [Song.] Words by F. L. Lent, *etc. Massachusetts Woman's Suffrage Association: Boston, Mass.,* (1914.) fol. **G. 806. ll. (42.)**

LANCASTER (John)

— *See* Ferry (H. E.) and Lancaster (J.) Benedicite, *etc.* [1899.] 8°. **C. 799. e. (8.)**

LANCASTER (Joseph)

— Annie, valse for the Pianoforte. *London,* [1867.] fol.

h. 3102. (1.)

LANCASTER (JOSEPH)

— L'Enchanteresse, mazurka pour Piano. *London*, [1866.] fol.
h. 3102. (3.)

— Evening Service in G. *London*, [1875.] 8°. **E. 605. d. (30.)**

— The Featherstone Quadrilles, composed and arranged for the Piano Forte, *etc. Leeds*, [1857.] fol. **h. 977. f. (22.)**

— For these and all Thy Mercies given. Grace for four Voices. 1867. *See* PERIODICAL PUBLICATIONS.— *London*. The Musical Times, *etc.* No. 292. [b.] 1844, *etc.* 8°. **P. P. 1945. aa.**

— Impromptu in A flat. [P. F.] *London*, [1867.] fol.
h. 3102. (2.)

— The Leeds Tune Book. A collection of 232 ... Hymn Tunes ... Compiled ... by J. Lancaster. *London*, 1868. 8°.
D. 693.

— The Leeds Tune Book, with supplement. A collection of 274 congregational hymn tunes, *etc. London*, 1875. 8°.
D. 693. a.

— Little Kate's quadrille, for the Pianoforte. *London*, [1866.] fol. **h. 3102. (4.)**

— The Neighbours don't know. Ballad [begins: "Of all the braw lads"] ... written by J. Robertshaw. *London*, [1874.] fol.
H. 1778. x. (18.)

— Oh! wert thou a flower so gay. Ballad, written by Mrs. A. Sykes. *London*, [1876.] fol. **H. 1778. x. (20.)**

— The Primrose waltz, for the Pianoforte. *London*, [1866.] fol.
h. 3102. (5.)

— Silvery Dewdrops, caprice for the Pianoforte. *London*, [1868.] fol. **h. 3102. (6.)**

— Trust in God and do the right. Song [begins: "Courage brother"]. *London*, [1868.] fol. **H. 1775. t. (14.)**

— Where the harebells grow. Ballad [begins: "Oh! faded are the lilies"]. Words by Mrs. A. Sykes. *London*, [1876.] fol.
H. 1778. x. (19.)

— *See* SLADEN (J.) Britannia's Call ... Harmonised by J. Lancaster. [1878.] fol. **H. 1783. y. (56.)**

LANCASTER (LILLIAN MAY)

— Laura. [Song.] Words and music by L. M. Lancaster (Maude Leota Byrd). pp. 5. *Victor Kremer Co.: Chicago, etc.*, [1907.] fol. **H. 3985. h. (7.)**

LANCASTER (LILLIE TURLEY)

— *See* BUTLER (S. T.) The Coming of Santa Claus and other original Songs, *etc.* (Arranged for the Piano by L. T. Lancaster.) [1911.] 4°. **F. 637. oo. (1.)**

— *See* BUTLER (S. T.) The Land of Nod ... My Black Dolly ... Arranged ... by L. T. Lancaster. 1910. fol. **H. 1792. e. (43.)**

LANCASTER (MAY E.)

— Hymn for Peace, 1914. Words & Music by M. E. Lancaster. *Hime & Addison: Manchester*, [1914.] 4°. **F. 607. ee. (11.)**

LANCASTER (WALTER J.)

— As pants the Hart. Anthem. *Novello & Co.: London*, [1939.] 8°. **E. 442. v. (41.)**

— Collect for the Second Sunday after Easter. Short Anthem for four voices. *Phillips & Page: London*, [1903.] 8°.
E. 442. o. (36.)

— If ye love me. Anthem, *etc. Novello and Co.: London*, 1939. 8°. **E. 442. v. (42.)**

LANCASTER (WALTER J.)

— Magnificat and Nunc Dimittis ... for four voices. *Novello, Ewer and Co.: London and New York*, [1891.] 8°.
E. 597. n. (20.)

— Prayer. [1894.] *See* BROADHOUSE (J.) English Organ Music, *etc.* No. 49. [1883, *etc.*] obl. fol. **e. 1151.**

— Six Songs. *J. Williams: London*, [1902.] 4°. **F. 637. j. (4*.)**

— To Blossoms. [Part-song.] Words by R. Herrick. *J. Vickers: Bolton*, [1900.] 8°. **F. 321. o. (21.)**

— Up-Hill. Words by C. G. Rossetti set to music for Baritone Solo and Chorus with Pianoforte accompaniment. *Novello and Co.: London*, [1904.] 8°. **F. 321. r. (22.)**

LANCASTRE SALDANHA (ADELINE LOUISE MARIA)
Countess of Cardigan and Lancastre

— La Papillon et la Rose. Song, *etc. J. B. Cramer & Co.: London*, [1879.] fol.
Autograph of Queen Alexandra. **R. M. 26. g. 13. (4.)**

LANCE

— Lance or Love. Song. *See* HARRIS (C.)

LANCE (E. A.)

— An Epiphany Carol. *Novello and Co.: London*, [1932.] s. sh. 8°. **D. 835. (5.)**

LANCEL (ANATOLE)

— Je vois tout rose ... Chansonnette. Paroles de Lemercier de Nauville. *Paris*, [1880.] fol. **H. 1786. e. (8.)**

LANCELL (FRANZ)

— Night, song [begins: "Night is the time to rest"], the words by J. Montgomery. *London*, [1857.] fol. **H. 1771. l. (8.)**

LANCELOT

— Lancelot. Opera. *See* HENTSCHEL (T.)

— Lancelot. Drame lyrique. *See* JONCIÈRES (F. L.)

— Lancelot and Elaine. [Song.] *See* FAVARA (A.) Two Lyrics ... I.

LANCELOT (CECILIA)

— Allegro scherzando for the pianoforte. *S. Lucas, Weber & Co.: London*, [1882.] fol. **h. 1484. s. (8.)**

LANCELOT (J.)

— *See* DEVIENNE (F.) Première sonate pour clarinette si♭ et piano-forte. Réalisation par J. P. Dautel. Révision et annotation par J. Lancelot. [1962.] 4°. **h. 2189. m. (2.)**

LANCELOTT (F.)

— The Anna Maria galop. [P. F.] *London*, [1855.] fol.
No. 100 of the "Musical Bouquet". **H. 2345.**

— The Bells, a Cantata [begins: "Hear the sledges with the bells"], the poetry by E. A. Poe. *London*, [1857.] fol.
H. 1771. l. (9.)

— Beware ... Song [begins: "I know a maiden"] ... translated from the German by Longfellow. *Leeds*, [1874.] fol.
H. 1778. x. (21.)

— British Navy quadrilles. [P. F.] *London*, [1846.] fol.
No. 59 of the "Musical Bouquet". **H. 2345.**

LANCELOTT (F.)

— Chase from thine eye love that bright starting tear. [Song, begins: "Fair maiden believe me".] *London*, [1846.] fol.
No. 55 of the "Musical Bouquet". **H. 2345.**

— Come away to the glen. Cavatina, written by A. Koyne. *London*, [1846.] fol.
No. 24 of the "Musical Bouquet". **H. 2345.**

— The Composer's Dream [quadrille. P. F.] *London*, [1846.] fol.
No. 49 of the "Musical Bouquet". **H. 2345.**

— The Cottage Girl. Ballad [begins: "How fair, how meek"]. *London*, [1855.] fol.
No. 101 of the "Musical Bouquet". **H. 2345.**

— The Cricket on the Hearth ... quadrille. [P. F.] *London*, [1846.] fol.
No. 57 of the "Musical Bouquet". **H. 2345.**

— The Drawing Room mazurka. [P. F.] *London*, [1846.] fol.
No. 1 of the "Musical Bouquet". **H. 2345.**

— The Ethiopian polka ... for the Pianoforte. *London*, [1845?] fol. **h. 1480. n. (29.)**

— Fairy Polkas. [P. F.] *London*, [1846.] fol.
No. 15 of the "Musical Bouquet". **H. 2345.**

— La Favorite, valse à deux temps. [P. F.] *London*, [1846.] fol.
No. 12 of the "Musical Bouquet". **H. 2345.**

— Fun quadrilles. [P. F.] *London*, [1870.] fol. **h. 1485. s. (15.)**

— Fun quadrilles. [P. F.] *London*, [1877.] fol. **h. 1482. y. (27.)**

— If we say that we have no sin, and the Easter Hymn, arranged ... by F. Lancelott. *London*, [1846.] fol.
No. 75 of the "Musical Bouquet". **H. 2345.**

— Let us quaff the cup of joy. [Duet, begins: "Why should we".] Words by Mrs. Hemans. *London*, [1846.] fol.
No. 34 of the "Musical Bouquet". **H. 2345.**

— Merry Christmas mazurka. [P. F.] *London*, [1846.] fol.
No. 56 of the "Musical Bouquet". **H. 2345.**

— The Old Lawn Hall. [Song, begins: "How well I remember".] Written by W. Wilson. *London*, [1846.] fol.
No. 69 of the "Musical Bouquet". **H. 2345.**

— The Reaper and the Flowers. [Song, begins: "There is a reaper".] The poetry by H. W. Longfellow. *See* FISHER (B. W.) The Day is done, *etc.* [1872.] fol. **H. 1778. m. (35.)**

— The Redowa and Polish polkas. [P. F.] *London*, [1846.] fol.
No. 13 of the "Musical Bouquet". **H. 2345.**

— The rose had been washed. [Song.] Poetry by Cowper. *London*, [1856.] fol.
No. 60 of a series entitled: "Cyclopedia of Music. Miscellaneous series of songs". **H. 2342.**

— The Rose of old England is king. [Song, begins: "Of all the sweet nosegays".] Written by J. Neal. *London*, [1846.] fol.
No. 60 of the "Musical Bouquet". **H. 2345.**

— A Rose Tree in full bearing. [Song.] *London*, [1858.] fol.
No. 4 of the "Cyclopedia of Music. Select Songs, Ladies' Series". **H. 2342. b.**

— The Royal Bal Masqué quadrille. [P. F.] *London*, [1846.] fol.
No. 21 of the "Musical Bouquet". **H. 2345.**

— The Song of Steam [begins: "Harness me down"]. *London*, [1846.] fol.
No. 51 of the "Musical Bouquet". **H. 2345.**

— La Sonnambula quadrille [on V. Bellini's opera. P. F.]. *London*, [1846.] fol.
No. 30 of the "Musical Bouquet". **H. 2345.**

LANCELOTT (F.)

LANCELOTT (F.)

— The Spring Quadrilles ... Arranged for one or two performers on the piano-forte by F. Lancelott. ⟨As solos.⟩ pp. 8. *B. Williams: London*, [c. 1845.] fol. **h. 61. aa. (24.)**

— The steam aerial party. Words by B. Miles. [Song, begins: "As aerostation's all the rage".] *London*, [1856.] fol.
No. 66 of a series entitled: "Cyclopedia of Music. Miscellaneous series of songs". **H. 2342.**

— Take, oh! take those lips away. [Round.] Words from Shakespeare. *London*, [1858.] fol.
No. 12 of the "Cyclopedia of Music. Select Glees, etc.". **H. 2342. c.**

— The Victoria and Albert minuet, the Royal mazurka, and the Minuet de la Cour ... for the Pianoforte. *London*, [1846.] fol.
No. 33 of the "Musical Bouquet". **H. 2345.**

— The Village Boy, [song] written by B. Miles. pp. 5. *L. Williams & Son: London*, [1845?] fol. **H. 1654. vv. (28.)**

— *See* BOIELDIEU (F. A.) [Le Calife de Bagdad.] Overture ... arranged ... by F. Lancelott. [1846.] fol. **H. 2345.**

— *See* DIBDIN (Charles) [A Tour to the Land's End.] The Anchorsmiths ... Newly arranged by F. Lancelott. [1850?] fol. [*Musical Bouquet. no. 81.*] **H. 2345. a.**

— *See* HAYDEN (G.) As I saw fair Clora ... The pianoforte accompaniment by F. Lancelott. [1866.] fol. **H. 1772. r. (12.)**

— *See* HOY (J. A.) Thames tunnel ... arranged by F. Lancelott. [1846.] fol. **H. 1756. (46.)**

— *See* PHELPS, afterwards PHELPS MACDONNELL (E.) Rest, Holy Pilgrim ... The Pianoforte accompaniment by F. Lancelott. [1866.] fol. **H. 1772. z. (2.)**

— *See* ROSSINI (G. A.) [Il Barbiere di Siviglia.] Overture ... arranged ... by F. Lancelott. [1846.] fol. **H. 2345.**

LANCELOTT (WILLIAM FRANCIS)

— Always do to others as you wish they'd do to you. Motto song [begins: "Man's faith in Man"]. Words by S. Smith. *London*, [1878.] fol. **H. 1783. o. (6.)**

— Belle Vue. Gavotte for the pianoforte. *J. Guest: London*, [1886.] fol. **h. 1484. s. (9.)**

— Bless the Bonnie Bride. [Song.] Words by Nora. *A. Bertini: London*, [1883.] fol. **H. 1788. u. (34.)**

— La Bonne bouche Lancers. [P. F.] pp. 4. *John Guest: London*, [c. 1885.] fol. **h. 3870. yy. (11.)**

— The Briton's Island Home ... Song [begins: "'Gainst threatening foes"]. Words by S. Smith. *London*, [1877.] fol. **H. 1778. x. (23.)**

— Cough, John, cough, and make the baby laugh. [Song, begins: "You see that I'm a married man".] Words by T. Pinder. *London*, [1878.] fol. **H. 1783. o. (5.)**

— England's Royal Navy. Song [begins: "Oh! search the most glorious records"]. Words by J. Orton. *London*, [1879.] fol. **H. 1783. o. (7.)**

— The Erin Waltzes ... founded on J. Guest's ... melody, "Father says it's wrong," *etc.* [P. F.] *J. Guest: London*, [1884.] fol. **h. 975. u. (23.)**

— [A reissue.] The Erin Waltzes, *etc.* *F. Pitman Hart & Cº: London*, [c. 1910.] fol. **h. 62. o. (16.)**

— Fleur de Lys mazurka. [Fife and drum band parts.] *London*, [1883.] 8°.
Part of the "Alliance Musicale". **f. 403. f. (36.)**

LANCELOTT (William Francis)

— Fleur de Lys. Polka Mazurka. [P. F.] *J. Guest: London*, [1886.] fol. **h. 975. u. (24.)**

— Forest Echoes. Waltz. [P. F.] pp. 7. *F. Pitman Hart & Cᵒ: London*, [c. 1900.] fol. **h. 3870. hh. (5.)**

—- Happy Days in store. Ballad [begins: "Loving hearts with joys"] written by S. Smith. *London*, [1876.] fol. **H. 1778. x. (22.)**

— Have you seen my doll? Humorous song [begins: "If you please I am almost distracted"] written by E. Cympson. *London*, [1880.] fol. **H. 1783. o. (8.)**

— I'll twine for thee a Wreath of Flowers. [Song.] Poetry by Lord Byron. *J. Guest: London*, [1886.] fol. **H. 1788. u. (35.)**

— The Jug Polka. [P. F.] *Howard & Co.: London*, [1882.] fol. **h. 975. u. (25.)**

— Leaving all to Jesus. A Sacred Song, written by R. J. Holloway. *J. Guest: London*, [1886.] fol. **H. 879. e. (7.)**

— Mignonette, polka-mazurka for the Piano. *London*, [1881.] fol. **h. 3275. j. (8.)**

— Oh, that we two were maying. Song, poetry by C. Kingsley. pp. 3. *J. Guest: London*, [1886.] fol. **H. 1788. u. (36.)**

— [A reissue.] Oh, that we two were maying, *etc. Hart & Cᵒ: London*, [1887?] fol. **H. 1650. oo. (15.)**

— The Parade March ... for the Piano Forte. *J. Guest: London*, [1884.] fol. **h. 1484. s. (10.)**

— The Phrenologic Professor. [Song, begins: "Ah! once I was jolly".] Words by S. Smith. *London*, [1877.] fol. **H. 1778. x. (24.)**

— The Postillion polka. [P. F.] *London*, [1881.] fol. **h. 3275. j. (9.)**

— Ruby polka for the Piano. *London*, [1880.] fol. **h. 1494. p. (12.)**

— The Scramble Galop, for the pianoforte. *J. Guest: London*, [1883.] fol. **h. 975. u. (26.)**

— The Sea Shells Waltz, for the pianoforte. *J. Guest: London*, [1883.] fol. **h. 975. u. (27.)**

— Somebody whispered so sweetly. Ballad [begins: "Where is the harm"]. Words by G. Cooper. *London*, [1880.] fol. **H. 1783. o. (9.)**

— Strangers yet. Song, words by Lord Houghton. *J. Guest: London*, [1883.] fol. **H. 1788. u. (37.)**

— The Sweet Kiss. Waltz ... for the pianoforte. *J. Guest: London*, [1884.] fol. **h. 975. u. (28.)**

— Three Fishers went sailing. [Song.] Poetry by C. Kingsley. *J. Guest: London*, [1883.] fol. **H. 1788. u. (38.)**

— Tick Tack polka. [P. F.] *London*, [1880.] fol. **h. 1494. p. (11.)**

— Tick Tack polka. [P. F.] *London*, [1881.] fol. **h. 3275. j. (10.)**

— The Tiptoe Schottische, for the pianoforte. *J. Guest: London*, [1886.] fol. **h. 975. u. (29.)**

LANCEN (Serge)

— Andante et tyrolienne pour deux flûtes. [Score and parts.] 3 pt. *Chappell: Paris*, [1970.] 4°. **h. 2140. z. (1.)**

— Berceuse for Baby Hippopotamus. For double bass and piano. ⟨Score [and part].⟩ 2 pt. *Yorke Edition: London*, [1978.] 4°. **g. 867. h. (7.)**

LANCEN (Serge)

— Cap Kennedy. Pour harmonie-fanfare. ⟨Conducteur C.⟩ pp. 40. *Éditions Chappell: Paris*, [1971.] 4°. **h. 1568. v. (10.)**

— Cavatine. Pour 4 contrebasses à cordes. [Score and parts.] 5 pt. *Chappell: Paris*, [1970.] 4°. **h. 1845. e. (1.)**

— Cavatine. For four double basses. [Score and parts.] 5 pt. *Yorke Edition: London*, [1978.] fol. **g. 867. h. (8.)**

— Trois chansons dans un style français. ⟨Words by Jean Courçay.⟩ I. La forêt normande. II. Les jardins à la française. III. Les filles de Picardie. (French words, and English translations added.) pp. 16. *Hinrichsen Edition & Peters Edition: New York, etc.;* [*London* printed, 1953.] 4°. **G. 1276. m. (26.)**

— Trois chansons dans un style français. English words and adaptation by Thomas B. Pitfield, *etc.* [Voice part only.] *Eng. Hinrichsen Edition: London*, [1955.] 8°. **E. 1501. i. (2.)**

— Concert à six. 1 petite clarinette E♭, 2 clarinettes B♭, 1 clarinette alto E♭ (ou 3ᵉᵐᵉ clarinette B♭), 1 clarinette basse B♭, 1 clarinette contrabasse E♭ (ou 2ᵉᵐᵉ clarinette basse B♭). [Score.] pp. 54. *Chappell: Paris*, [1971.] fol. **h. 141. u. (2.)**

— Concertino pour piano et orchestre. ⟨Two pianos, four hands.⟩ pp. 32. *Hinrichsen Edition: London*, [1953.] 4°. **g. 1122. o. (1.)**

— Concerto pour contrebasse et cordes. (Violons, altos, violoncelles), *etc.* [Double bass and P. F. Score and part.] 2 pt. *Éditions francaises de musique: Paris*, [1962.] 4°. **h. 1568. v. (1.)**

— Concerto da camera. Pour flûte solo et orchestra à cordes. [P. F. score and part.] 2 pt. *Éditions françaises de musique: Paris*, [1963.] 4°. **g. 70. aa. (5.)**

— Concerto pour guitare et orchestre. Réduction guitare et piano. [Score and part.] 2 pt. *Éditions Chappell: Paris*, [1973.] 4°. **h. 259. ll. (3.)**

— Concerto pour guitare et orchestre. Guitare. pp. 12. *Éditions Chappell: Paris*, [1973.] 4°. **h. 259. gg. (11.)**

— Crépuscule. Pièce pour 2 harpes ou 2 pianos ou 1 harpe et 1 piano. [Score.] pp. 9. *Chappell: Paris*, [1973.] 4°. **g. 1098. c. (9.)**

— Croquis. ⟨Sketches.⟩ For double bass and piano. ⟨Score [and part].⟩ 2 pt. *Yorke Edition: London*, [1978.] 4°. **g. 867. h. (9.)**

— Domino. Suite fantasque ... Piano. pp. 15. *Hinrichsen Edition: London*, [1952.] 4°. **g. 1128. q. (4.)**

— Duo concertant pour flûte et harpe ou flûte et piano et orchestre à cordes non obligé. Flûte & harpe. [Score and part.] 2 pt. *Éditions Chappell: Paris*, [1972.] 4°. **h. 1568. vv. (1.)**

— Fantaisie concertante n° 1. Pour hautbois et piano, *etc.* [Score and part.] 2 pt. *Chappell: Paris*, [1971.] fol. **g. 1078. o. (3.)**

— Fantaisie sur un thème ancien pour piano. pp. 8. *Hinrichsen Edition: London, New York*, [1959.] 4°. **g. 1126. s. (7.)**

— Foursomes. "Quatre par quatre." 10 petites pièces pour jouer à 4 instruments de même nature ... Conducteur en ut. pp. 20. *Éditions Chappell: Paris*, [1973.] 4°. **h. 1568. vv. (10.)**

— Trois impromptus, *etc.* ⟨Piano.⟩ pp. 12. *Hinrichsen Edition: London*, [1953.] 4°. **g. 1128. q. (5.)**

— Miniatures. Pièces progressives pour petites mains. Progressive pieces for small hands, *etc.* 2 pt. *Hinrichsen Edition: London, New York*, [1960.] 4°. **g. 272. uu. (5.)**

— Moins que rien. Weniger als nichts. Less than nothing. Piano. pp. 4. *Peters Edition & Hinrichsen Edition: New York, etc.;* [*London* printed, 1955.] 4°. **g. 1128. x. (10.)**

LANCEN (Serge)

— Monologues. 3 pieces for flute alone. pp. 7.   *Hinrichsen Edition: London, New York*, [1960.] 4°.   **g. 70. ee. (1.)**

— Old French Songs. For three or more treble-clef instruments of equal pitch. Arranged by S. Lancen ... Score and parts. 4 pt.   *Hinrichsen Edition: London*, [1966.] 4°.   **g. 271. kk. (9.)**

— Ouverture texane. Pour harmonie-fanfare. Conducteur C. pp. 14.   *Éditions Chappell: Paris*, [1971.] 4°.   **h. 1568. nn. (17.)**

— Printanières. 5 vocalises de concert pour voix élevée. 5 pièces pour flûte avec accompagnement de piano. [5 pieces for flute or voice, with P. F. accompaniment.] [Score and part.] 2 pt.   *Hinrichsen Edition: London*, [1954.] 4°.   **g. 70. p. (7.)**

— Quatre flûtes en balade. Pour quatre flûtes. [Score and parts.] 5 pt.   *Chappell: Paris*, [1971.] 4°.   **g. 70. qq. (5.)**

— The Twins. Les Jumeaux ... 5 pieces for 2 part treble-clef instruments of equal pitch, *etc.* [Score.] pp. 7.   *Hinrichsen Edition: London*, [1964.] 4°.   **g. 271. kk. (2.)**

— Valse 1900 ... Piano. pp. 7.   *Peters Edition & Hinrichsen Edition: New York, etc.; [London* printed, 1955.] 4°.   **g. 1128. x. (11.)**

— Vocalises. I. Ombre. ⟨II. Lumière. III. Clair-obscur.⟩ [Voice and P. F.] 3 no.   *Chappell: Paris*, [1972.] fol.   **G. 295. oo. (4.)**

— Zweifache. A la mémoire de Franz Schubert, *etc.* [P. F.] pp. 19.   *Hinrichsen Edition: London*, [1957.] 4°.   **g. 1126. m. (5.)**

LANCERO

— El Lancero. Zarzuela. *See* GAZTAMBIDE (J.)

LANCERS

— The Lancers quadrilles. *See* QUADRILLES.

LANCES

— Lances of Gold. [Song.] *See* FOULDS (J. H.)

— Lances of the Free. [Chorus.] *See* FOULDS (J. H.) Three Marching Songs ... Op. 5. No. 2.

LANCETTE

— La Lancete. [Song.] *See* JE. Je suis excellent chirurgien, *etc.* [1780?] 8°.   **B. 362. j. (17.)**

LANCETTI (Salvador)

— *See* LANZETTI.

LANCHBERY (John)

— Peter Rabbit and the Tales of Beatrix Potter. *See* infra: [Tales of Beatrix Potter.]

— Tales of Beatrix Potter ... ⟨Selection from the ballet.⟩ Arranged for brass band by Edrich Siebert. ⟨Conductor in B♭ [and parts.]⟩ 25 pt.   *EMI Film Music: London*, [1971.] 8°.   *With several copies of various parts.*   **e. 1330. (12.)**

— Tales of Beatrix Potter. Music from the film. Arranged for the piano by J. Lanchbery, *etc.* pp. 17.   *EMI Film Music: London*, [1971.] 4°.   **g. 352. y. (14.)**

— [Tales of Beatrix Potter.] Peter Rabbit and the Tales of Beatrix Potter. Music from the film ... Arranged for easy piano by John Brimhall, *etc.* pp. 23.   *EMI Film Music: London*, [1971.] 4°.   **f. 760. r. (11.)**

LANCHBERY (John)

— Three Girls for five Brass ... A suite for brass quintet. ⟨Score.⟩ pp. 17.   *Novello: Borough Green*, [1974.] 4°.   **f. 390. rr. (4.)**

— *See* ADAM (A. C.) Giselle ... An album of pieces arranged for the piano by J. Lanchbery. [1959.] 4°.   **g. 230. nn. (8.)**

— *See* DELIBES (C. P. L.) Coppelia ... Arranged for the piano by J. Lanchbery. [1957.] 4°.   **g. 941. (1.)**

— *See* DELIBES (C. P. L.) Sylvia ... Arranged for the piano by J. Lanchbery. [1957.] 4°.   **g. 941. (2.)**

— *See* HÉROLD (L. J. F.) La Fille mal gardée. Ballet suite ... arranged by J. Lanchbery. [1960.] 8°.   **f. 502. e. (6.)**

— *See* HÉROLD (L. J. F.) [La Fille mal gardée.] Two Dances ... Arranged by J. Lanchbery. [Orchestra.] [1964.] 4°.   **h. 3210. i. (891.)**

— *See* HÉROLD (L. J. F.) [La Fille mal gardée.] Clog Dance. Arranged by J. Lanchbery, *etc.* [For orchestra.] [1973.] 4°.   **g. 860. gg. (7.)**

— *See* HÉROLD (L. J. F.) [La Fille mal gardée.] Clog Dance ... Arranged for piano solo by J. Lanchbery. [1962.] 4°.   **g. 1128. gg. (8.)**

— *See* HÉROLD (L. J. F.) [La Fille mal gardée.] Flute Dance ... [Arranged by J. Lanchbery.] Arranged for band by R. O'Brien, *etc.* [1970.] 4°.   **g. 1071. b. (9.)**

— *See* HÉROLD (L. J. F.) [La Fille mal gardée.] Flute Dance. Arranged by J. Lanchbery, *etc.* [For orchestra.] [1973.] 4°.   **g. 860. gg. (8.)**

— *See* KHACHATURYAN (A. I.) [Gayaneh.—Dance of young Maidens.] Dance of the Flower Girls ... Arr. J. Lanchbery. [1947.] 8°.   **h. 3210. i. (32.)**

— *See* KHACHATURYAN (A. I.) [Gayaneh.] Gopak ... Arr. J. Lanchbery. [1948.] 8°.   **h. 3210. i. (33.)**

LANCIA (Florence)

— Hymn "Christopher" [begins: "Thy way O Lord"]. Words ... by ... N. Hall.   *London*, [1878.] 8°.   **E. 1498. b. (17.)**

LANCIANI (Pietro)

— Aubade ... Paroles de F. A. Steenackers.   *A. Mertens: Bruxelles*, 1888. 4°.   Pp. 111–115 *of the "Album illustré ... du Grand Concours International des Sciences," etc.*   **7957. g. 9.**

— Bruxelles Kermesse. Marche officielle. Pour piano. pp. 4.   *J. B. Katto: Bruxelles, Anvers: Colombier: Paris*, [c. 1895.] fol.   **h. 1226. l. (9.)**

— Pierrot Macabre. Ballet-Pantomime en un acte et deux tableaux. Scénario de MM. T. Hannon et J. Hansen. Réduction pour piano par l'auteur.   *Hambourg*, 1886. 8°.   **f. 540. a. (2.)**

— Pierrot Macabre ... Morceaux détachés. [P. F.] 3 no.   *A. Cranz: Hambourg*, [1886.] fol.   **h. 3281. l. (1.)**

LANCIE (John de)

— Three Cadenzas for the Mozart Oboe Concerto (K. 314). pp. 3.   *Boosey & Hawkes: New York*, [1966.] 4°.   **g. 1078. k. (11.)**

L'ANCIEN (Bernard)

— L'Étudiant. Chansonnette [begins: "Être un Jeudi"]. Poésie ... de Mr. E. Bourget.   *Paris*, [1835?] fol.   **G. 543. (1.)**

LANCIER (A.)

— Bootle's Baby. Waltz. [P. F.] *C. Jefferys: London,* [1886.] fol.
h. 975. u. (30.)

— The Pleasures of Spring. Polka. [P. F.] *C. Jefferys: London,*
[1888.] fol. **h. 975. u. (31.)**

LANCKENAU (K.)

— Eagle wings … Duett, *etc. New York,* [1850?] fol.
H. 1780. p. (28.)

LAND

— The Land. [Song.] *See* NEUKOMM (S.)

— The Land across the Sea. Song. *See* BARNARD (D'A.)

— Land Ahead. [Song.] *See* CLINTON (J.)

— Land ahead! Song. *See* MARRIOTT (C. H. R.)

— Land and Sea. Song. *See* BOND (C. H.) *of Brighton.*

— Land and sea. [Song.] *See* DUERNER (J.)

— Land at last. Song. *See* SAINT QUENTIN (E.) *pseud.*

— The Land at the Back of the Moon. Song. *See* OLIVER (H.)

— The Land between the Seas. Song. *See* EDEN (R.)

— The Land beyond. Sacred Song. *See* HAYWOOD (A.)

— The Land beyond. Song. *See* PINSUTI (C. E.)

— The Land beyond. Cantata. *See* WITTY (J. S.)

— The Land beyond the Sea. Sacred Song. *See* ADAMS (T.)
Organist of St. Alban's, Holborn.

— The Land beyond the Sea. [Part-song.] *See* CALDICOTT (A. J.)

— The Land beyond the Sea. [Hymn.] *See* FETHERSTON (*Sir*
G. R.) *Bart.*

— The Land beyond the sea. Sacred song. *See* HENRY (H. F.)

— The Land beyond the setting Sun. Sacred Song. *See* WILHELM
(S. F.)

— Das Land der Liebe. Operette. *See* EYSLER (Edmund)

— Das Land des Lächelns. Operette. *See* LEHÁR (F.)

— Land Dirge. Part Song. *See* EDMUNDS (C. M.)

— A Land Dirge. [Song.] *See* ROBBINS (R. C.) Songs, *etc.* 114,
114a.

— A Land Dirge. Chorus. *See* WARRELL (A. S.)

— A Land Dirge. Part-Song. *See* WOOD (C.) *Mus. Doc.*

— Land, ever calm and peaceful. [Song.] *See* DONAUDY (S.)
[Luoghi sereni e cari.]

— Land Ho! [Song.] *See* GLOVER (S.)

— Land-ho. Part-Song. *See* LESLIE (H. D.) [Six Four-part Songs.
Op. 23. No. 5.]

— Land ho! [Song.] *See* RUSSELL (H.)

— The Land immortal. [Sacred song.] *See* BREWER (J. H.)

— The Land Immortal. Sacred Solo. *See* GEIBEL (A.)

— The Land immortal. Sacred Song. *See* MILLER (W. T.)

— The Land immortal! Song. *See* MOIR (F. L.)

— The Land in the Ocean. Song. *See* DIBDIN (Charles)

— Land, land, land. Song. *See* RUSSELL (H.)

LAND

— Land meiner seligsten Gefühle. Song. *See* KELLER (C.)

— Land o' Dreams. Song. *See* KENSWORTH (J. H.)

— Land o' Dreams. [Part-song.] *See* RICHARDSON (Lilian)

— Land o' Hame and purple Heather. Song. *See* DAVIES (W. W.)

— Land o' mine. Song. *See* NUTTING (G.)

— Land o' my Dreams. [Song.] *See* BRUNELL (M.)

— The Land o' the Leal. Song. *See* I. I'm wearin' awa', Jean.
[1876.] fol. **H. 1791. b. (30.)**

— The Land o' the Leal. Song. *See* I. I'm wearin' awa', John.
[1877.] fol. **H. 2324.**

— The land o' the leal … arranged … for the pianoforte, *etc.*
[1823.] fol. *See* HOLDER (J. W.) **h. 112. (35.)**

— The Land o' the Leal. Part-Song. *See* BOLTWOOD (J. B.)

— The Land o' the Leal. [Part-song.] *See* BUTTON (H. E.)

— The Land o' the Leal. [Song.] *See* DEWAR (J. R.) Dewar's
New Edition of the Songs of Scotland. [No. 1.]

— The Land o' the Leal. [Song.] *See* GOULD (W. M.) The New
Accompaniment Series, *etc.* No. 7.

— The Land o' the Leal. Song. *See* HAIGH (T.) *Mus. Doc.*

— The Land o' the Leal. [Song.] *See* HAWES (W.) [Scottish Airs.
First Series. No. 2.]

— The Land o' the Leal. Song. *See* HENSCHEL (*Sir* G.)

— The Land o' the Leal. Song. *See* LITTLE (A. E.)

— The Land o' the Leal. [Song.] *See* METCALF (J. W.) Five
Songs. [No. 2.]

— The Land o' the Leal. [Part-song.] *See* OULD (S. G.)

— The Land o' the Leal. Part-Song. *See* PROTHEROE (D.)

— The Land o' the Leal. [Part-song.] *See* SIMPSON (Kenneth)

— The Land o' the Leal. Song. *See* TURNER (A. T.)

— The Land o' the North. Song. *See* HARLAND (H.)

— The Land o'er the Sea. Song. *See* THOMSON (B.)

— Land of beautiful Dreams. Song. *See* BLAKE (Charlotte)

— Land of Beauty. Part-Song. *See* MENDELSSOHN-BARTHOLDY
(J. L. F.) [Vier Lieder. Op. 120. No. 3. Im Süden.]

— Land of Beauty, fair Savoy. [Song.] *See* BUCHANAN (R.)

— The Land of Biscay. Unison Song. *See* SUMSION (C. C.)

— The Land of By-and-by. [Part-song.] *See* HILLER (F.)
[8 volksthümliche Gesänge. Op. 176. No. 2.]

— The Land of Contrairy. Song. *See* ELLIOTT (L.)

— The Land of Counterpane. Unison chorus. *See* ROFF (Joseph)

— The Land of Day. Song. *See* SIVRAI (J. de) *pseud.*

— The Land of Delight. Song. *See* As. As you mean to set sail,
etc. 1895. fol. **H. 3441. (22.)**

— Land of Delight. Song. *See* SANDERSON (W. E.)

— The Land of Dream. Song. *See* IDLE (F.)

— The Land of Dreams. Song. *See* BARRI (O.)

— The Land of Dreams. [Song.] *See* BENNETT (M. E.)

— The Land of Dreams. Song. *See* BRIAN (H.)

LAND

— The Land of Dreams. Two-Part Song. *See* CHALLINOR (F. A.)

— The Land of Dreams. Song. *See* DENZA (L.)

— The Land of Dreams. Song. *See* FRYE (F. R.)

— The Land of Dreams. Song. *See* HEINS (N.)

— The Land of Dreams. Song. *See* HOLLOWAY (A. S.)

— The Land of Dreams. Song. *See* LOEHR (R. H.)

— The Land of Dreams. [Song.] *See* MACGLENNON (F.)

— The Land of Dreams. Part-Song. *See* MARZO (E.) Two Three-Part Songs, *etc.* [No. 1.]

— The Land of Dreams. [Song.] *See* SHEPPERD (F. N.)

— The Land of Dreams. [Song.] *See* STUART (S.)

— The Land of Dreams. Song. *See* WATSON (M. G.)

— Land of each dear and joyous feeling. Song. *See* KELLER (C.) [Land meiner seligsten Gefühle.]

— Land of each pure & happy feeling. [Song.] *See* KELLER (C.) [Land meiner seligsten Gefühle.]

— Land of Enchantment. Song. *See* LEYBACH (J.)

— Land of eternal Light. Song. *See* GRAY (H.) *pseud.*

— The Land of Eternal Light. Song. *See* KANE (L.)

— The Land of Exile. Part-Song. *See* LYON (J.) Part-Songs ... Op. 57. No. 1.

— The Land of Fancy. Song. *See* PHILP (J. E.)

— The Land of Flowers. Song. *See* RUBENS (P. A.) [My Mimosa Maid.]

— Land of Freedom. [Song.] *See* DUNAEVSKY (I. O.) [Песня о родине.]

— Land of Freedom. [Song.] *See* FERRARI (G.)

— The Land of Glory. Sacred Cantata. *See* MACBETH (A.)

— The Land of Gold. Song. *See* GLASS (D.)

— The Land of Gold. Song. *See* SANDERSON (J.) [Harlequin Mariner.]

— The Land of golden Dreams. [Song.] *See* DUSENBERRY (E. F.)

— Land of golden Dreams. [Song.] *See* FREEBORN (Cass. M.)

— Land of golden Sunshine. Song. *See* ADAMS (A. E.)

— The Land of Good Hope. Song. *See* HYDE (J.)

— The Land of Gra-Ma-chree. Song. *See* BARNES (Lewis)

— Land of happy Dreams. Song. *See* KENNEDY (N.)

— The Land of happy Dreams. Song. *See* SLAUGHTER (W. A.) [Marjorie.]

— The Land of happy Hearts. Song. *See* MEALE (A.)

— Land of Heart's Delight. Part Song. *See* EDMONDS (P. N.)

— The Land of Heart's Delight. Two part Song. *See* MARSHALL (Charles) *Songwriter.*

— Land of Heart's Delight. Song. *See* NEIDLINGER (W. H.)

— The Land of Heart's Delight. [Song.] *See* WINDSOR (M.)

— Land of Heart's Desire. [Song.] *See* FRASER (M. K.) [Songs of the Hebrides. Vol. II.]

— The Land of Heart's Desire. Song. *See* MOORE (E. C.)

LAND

— The Land of Heart's Desire. [Song.] *See* SHAW (M. F.)

— The Land of Heart's Desire. [Song.] *See* TALBOT (H.) [Monte Carlo.]

— Land of Heart's Desire. Chorus. *See* THOMAS (C. L. A.) [Mignon.—Connais-tu le pays.]

— The Land of Heather Bells. Song. *See* FISHER (B. W.)

— The Land of Home. Song. *See* GRAY (H.) *pseud.*

— Land of Home. Part Song. *See* LÜTGEN (B.)

— The Land of Home, sweet Home. [Song.] *See* L'ESTRANGE (B.)

— The Land of Hope. Song. *See* COWEN (*Sir* F. H.)

— Land of Hope and Glory. Song. *See* ELGAR (*Sir* E. W.) *Bart.* [Pomp and Circumstance. Op. 39. No. 1.]

— The Land of Joy. Part Song. *See* BARNETT (J. M.)

— The Land of Joy. Review. *See* VALVERDE (J.) *the Younger.*

— Land of Joy and Liberty. Chorus. *See* SMALLMAN (C. S.)

— The Land of Joys. Song. *See* ELLIOTT (L.)

— Land of Laughter. Opening Chorus. *See* OLIVER (H.)

— The Land of Let's pretend. Song. *See* LA TOUCHE (E. D.)

— The Land of Liberty. Operetta. *See* LERMANN (J. W.)

— The Land of Light. Song. *See* GOLDSTEIN (H. M.)

— The Land of Light. Cantata. *See* PEARSON (A.)

— The Land of Little Children. Song. *See* BONHEUR (T.) *pseud.*

— The Land of Little People. Song. *See* MARSHALL (Charles) *Songwriter.*

— The Land of Little People. Song. *See* MOIR (F. L.)

— The Land of Little People. Part-Song. *See* NAYLOR (E. W.)

— The Land of long ago. Song. *See* CRIMP (H. E.)

— Land of Long ago. Song. *See* DAVIS (L.)

— The Land of long ago. Song. *See* DOLORES, *pseud.*

— The Land of Long Ago. Song. *See* LOEHR (F. N.)

— The Land of Long Ago. Song. *See* MAXWELL (K. H.)

— The Land of Lost Content. Song. *See* GREGG (H. P.)

— The Land of Lost Content. Songs. *See* IRELAND (J. N.)

— The Land of lost Toys. Play with music. *See* SIMMONS (Constance)

— The Land of Love. Song. *See* BROOKS (Vivian)

— The Land of Love. Ballad. *See* CARYLL (I.) *pseud.* [Little Christopher Columbus.]

— The Land of Love. Song. *See* DUNCAN (E.)

— The Land of Love. Duet. *See* EDWARDS (Julian)

— The Land of Love. Song. *See* MOIR (F. L.)

— The Land of Love. [Song.] *See* MOZART (W. A.) [Symphonies. K. 504.—Andante.]

— Land of Love. Song. *See* NORTON (F. W.)

— The Land of Love. Song. *See* OLIVER (H.)

— The Land of Love. Song. *See* PINSUTI (C. E.)

LAND

— The Land of Love. Song. *See* RUBENS (P. A.) [Dear little Denmark.]

— The Land of Love. Ballad. *See* WEST (W.)

— Land of Love and Smiles. Song. *See* COVERLEY (R.)

— Land of Love's Sunshine. Song. *See* FRASER (R.)

— The Land of lovely Ladies. [Song.] *See* STRICKLAND (L. T.)

— The Land of Make-believe. [Song.] *See* CHAMBERLIN (Bob)

— The Land of Make-Believe. Song. *See* KEMBLE (J.)

— Land of Memory. [Song.] *See* MARSCHAL-LOEPKE (G.)

— The Land of Memory. [Song.] *See* RONALD (*Sir* L.)

— The Land of Might-have-been. Song. *See* NOVELLO (I.)

— Land of Mighty Heroes. Song. *See* READ (Ethel)

— Land of mine. [Song.] *See* GOULD (W. M.) The New Accompaniment Series, *etc.* [No. 21.]

— Land of mine. [Song.] *See* MACDERMID (J. G.)

— Land of mine. Song. *See* WILSON (H. J. L.)

— The Land of my best Girl. [Song.] *See* CARROLL (Harry)

— The Land of my Birth. [Song.] *See* BISHOP (*Sir* Henry R.) [Home, sweet Home.]

— The Land of my birth. Song. *See* HARGREAVES (G.)

— The Land of my birth. Trio. *See* WALKER (T.)

— The Land of my Birth. [Song.] *See* YOUNG (T.)

— Land of my dearest happiest Feelings. Arietta. *See* KELLER (C.) [Land meiner seligsten Gefühle.]

— Land of my Dreams. Song. *See* HARRIS (C.)

— The Land of my Dreams. Song. *See* TREVELYAN (A.)

— The Land of my Dreams and you. [Song.] *See* BROOKE (Hubert S.)

— Land of my early happy feelings. Song. *See* KELLER (C.) [Land meiner seligsten Gefühle.]

— Land of my Fathers. Song. *See* BARRI (O.)

— Land of my Fathers. Song. *See* JAMES (J.)

— Land of my Fathers. [Song.] *See* PHIPPS (Osmond G.)

— Land of my Fathers. Part-song. *See* PICKLES (W.) Récréations musicales. No. 3.

— Land of my first and best affections. [Song.] *See* KELLER (C.) [Land meiner seligsten Gefühle.]

— Land of my Heart. Song. *See* COATES (E.)

— The Land of my Heart. Song. *See* ELLIOTT (P.)

— Land of my Heart. Song. *See* EVILLE (V. M.)

— Land of my Heart. Song. *See* GRAYLING (G.)

— The Land of my Heart's Desire. Song. *See* LAMBERT (E. F.)

— The Land of my Home. [Song.] *See* SHELLEY (H. R.)

— The Land of my love. [Song.] *See* KNIGHT (J. P.)

— Land of my own. Song. *See* LOUGHBOROUGH (R.)

— Land of my Sires. [Song.] *See* ALMAN (S.) Four Hebrew Songs. [No. 2.]

LAND

— Land of my Youth. Song. *See* KELLER (C.) [Land meiner seligsten Gefühle.]

— The Land of Never-a-care. Song. *See* COVER (L.)

— The Land of Nevermore. Song. *See* SHAW (S.)

— The Land of Nicotine. [Song.] *See* HIRSCH (Louis A.)

— The Land of Nod. [Song.] *See* ARCHER (C.)

— The Land of Nod. Song. *See* ARMSTRONG (A. E.)

— The Land of Nod. [Song.] *See* CLIFFORD (Nat)

— The Land of Nod. Song. *See* EDWARDS (A. M.)

— The Land of Nod. Musical comedy. *See* HOWARD (Joseph E.)

— The Land of Nod. Song. *See* LANSING (A. W.)

— The Land of Nod. [Song.] *See* NORRIS (H. A.)

— The Land of Nod. [Song.] *See* PHELAN (E. G.)

— The Land of Nod. [Two-part song.] *See* ROFF (Joseph)

— The Land of Nod. Musical Play. *See* SHERRINGTON (C.)

— The Land of Nod. Musical Play. *See* WEST (A. H.)

— Land of Orange Trees. Duet. *See* MOSS (K.)

— The Land of Otherwhere. [Song.] *See* HUNT (N. A. B.) Three Songs. [No. 1.]

— Land of our Birth. [Unison song.] *See* BRAHMS (J.) [Symphony No. 4. Op. 98.—Andante moderato.]

— The Land of our Birth. Song. *See* DACRE (H.) *pseud.*

— Land of our Birth. Song. *See* WILLIAMS (R. Vaughan) [Thanksgiving for Victory.]

— The Land of our Fathers. Part Song. *See* DONIZETTI (D. G. M.) [Lucrezia Borgia.—Maffio Orsini, signora, son'io.]

— Land of our Hearts. Chorus. *See* CHADWICK (G. W.)

— Land of our Love. [Hymn.] *See* PETTMAN (J.)

— The Land of our Loved. [Song.] *See* LINTER (R.)

— The Land of Peace. [Song.] *See* RITA.

— The Land of Potatoes. Song. *See* O. Oh had I in the clear, *etc.* [c. 1800.] *s. sh.* fol.   **H. 1653. j. (46.)**

— Land of Potatoes. Song. *See* REEVE (William)

— Land of Promise. [Song.] *See* BANTOCK (*Sir* G.) Hebridean Songs. 3.

— The Land of Promise. Song. *See* BARRI (O.)

— The Land of Promise. Song. *See* COLBORN (A. G.)

— The Land of Promise. Song. *See* COOPER (Florry)

— The Land of Promise. Oratorio. *See* HOWELL (F.)

— The Land of Promise. [Song.] *See* RIMBAULT (Edward F.)

— The Land of Rest. Song. *See* BROOME (E.)

— The Land of Rest. Song. *See* PINSUTI (C. E.)

— The Land of Right. [Part-song.] *See* WILKINS (F. W.)

— Land of Romance. Part Song. *See* CONVERSE (F. S.)

— The Land of Romance. Song. *See* CORRI (C. C.) [The Dandy Fifth.]

— The Land of Roses. [Part-song.] *See* GLOVER (S.)

LAND

— A Land of Roses. Song. *See* RIEGO (T. del)

— A Land of Shadows. [Part-song.] *See* REDMAN (Reginald)

— The Land of Sleep. Unison Song. *See* CHAIKOVSKY (P. I.) [16 Chansons pour la Jeunesse. Op. 54. No. 16. Petite chanson d'enfant.]

— The Land of Sleep. Two-Part Song. *See* WHITEHEAD (P. A.)

— Land of Sleep. [Unison song.] *See* WILKINSON (Philip G.)

— The Land of Sleepy-Bye. Song. *See* BENJAMIN (C. T.)

— The Land of Smiles. Musical Play. *See* LEHÁR (F.) [Das Land des Lächelns.]

— The Land of Someday. [Song.] *See* THEA (D.)

— The Land of Sometime. Song. *See* OLLERENSHAW (T. R.)

— The Land of Song. Romance. *See* CONCONE (J.)

— Land of Song. [Song.] *See* HERZ (Henri) [A First Set of six Songs and two Duets.]

— The Land of Song. Song. *See* LEIDERITZ (F.)

— The Land of Summer. Song. *See* ROLT (B.)

— The Land of Sun. Song. *See* NOEL (J.)

— Land of sunny beauty. National hymn of Navarre. *See* SPERANZA, *pseud.*

— Land of Sunshine. Duettino. *See* BORDÈSE (L.)

— The Land of Sunshine. [Song.] *See* BROWNE (Raymond A.)

— The Land of the Almond Blossom. Cycle of Songs. *See* ARUNDALE (C.)

— Land of the Almond Blossom. Song. *See* GREGORIO (G. de)

— Land of the Americas. [Part-song.] *See* REED (William L.)

— Land of the Blest. Duetto. *See* ROOT (G. F.)

— Land of the brave and free. [Song.] *See* PLUMLEY (G. S.)

— The Land of the Christmas Stocking. Musical play. *See* BUCHANAN (Mabel)

— The Land of the emerald green. Song. *See* ELLIS (Charles T.)

— The Land of the Free. [Song.] *See* ELLIS (W. C.)

— Land of the Free. Operetta. *See* PEACE (F. W.)

— Land of the Free. [Song.] *See* RODWELL (G. H.)

— The Land of the Free. Song. *See* TILBURY (Walter)

— Land of the Gaël. Song. *See* CHAMBERLAIN (H. R.)

— Land of the Gael. Song. *See* JAMES (J.)

— Land of the golden Day. Song. *See* HEWITT (T. J.)

— The Land of the Harlequinade. [Song.] *See* OLIVER (H.)

— The Land of the Heart. [Song.] *See* ROMA (C.)

— The Land of the Heart's Desire. [Song.] *See* MORSE (Theodore F.)

— Land of the Iris. [Song.] *See* CHAPPELLE (Frederick W.)

— The Land of the Leal. Song. *See* BULMER (J.)

— The Land of the Little People. [Song.] *See* FRASER (M. K.) From the Hebrides.

— Land of the lonely Pines. Song. *See* LEMON (L. G.)

LAND

— The Land of the long ago. Song. *See* ASHTON (A.)

— Land of the long ago. Song. *See* RAY (L.)

— Land of the Long Ago. Ballad. *See* TENNIS (D. W.)

— Land of the Maple. Song. *See* BUCKLEY (R. R.)

— The Land of the Maple. Song. *See* GODFREY (H. H.)

— The Land of the Maple. Song. *See* GROUNDS (H. C.)

— The Land of the Might-have-been. [Musical monologue.] *See* HARRIS (L.)

— Land of the Minstrel and Bard. Song and chorus. *See* THOMAS (J.) *Pencerdd Gwalia.*

— Land of the Mountain. Duet. *See* ROSENBERG (S. T.)

— The Land of the Never-End. Operetta. *See* KRENKEL (G.)

— The Land of the North. Song. *See* BARNETT (J.)

— The Land of the Past. Song. *See* GERMAN (*Sir* E.)

— The Land of the Puppy-Dogs. [Song.] *See* FORD (J. S.) Funnyland.

— Land of the red, red Rose. Song. *See* LYND (S.)

— The Land of the Setting Sun. Duettino. *See* SMART (H.)

— The Land of the Shamrock. [Song.] *See* ROSSITER (L. W.)

— The Land of the Stranger. Ballad. *See* FITZGERALD (E. M.)

— Land of the Sun. Part Song. *See* TAYLOR (S. C.)

— Land of the sunny South. *New Zealand Song of Empire.* [Words by] A. Hampden. [1907.] *s. sh.* 4°.   I. 600. c. (171.)

— The Land of the Sunset Glow. Song. *See* FORTESCUE (Edith) *pseud.*

— Land of the Veld. [Part-song.] *See* BUTTON (H. E.)

— Land of the waving Maple Leaf. [Song.] *See* SIMS (F. L. H.)

— The Land of the West. Ballad. *See* LOVER (Samuel) [Songs of Rory O'More. No. 5.]

— The Land of the West. Song. *See* TOMLYN (A. W.)

— The Land of To-morrow. [Song.] *See* WITTMANN (T.)

— The Land of Twilight Shadows. Song. *See* TREHARNE (B.)

— The Land of which I dream. Sacred Song. *See* GAUL (A. R.)

— The Land of Wonders. Part-Song. *See* SMART (H.)

— A Land of wondrous oriental Treasures. [Part-song.] *See* RIMSKY-KORSAKOV (N. A.) [Sadko.—Song of India.]

— The Land of Yesterday. Song. *See* MASCHERONI (A.)

— The Land of Youth. Romance. *See* VOGEL (A.)

— The Land St. Patrick loved. Song. *See* KELLY (C.)

— Land so fair. Sacred Song. *See* WOOLER (A.)

— The Land Song. [Song.] *See* SOUND. Sound a Blast for Freedom, Boys. *The Land Song.*—Air—"Marching through Georgia." [1910.] *s. sh.* 8°.   I. 600. d. (97.)

— Land Song of the West Country. [Song.] *See* BRYAN (G.)

— The Land that calls me. Song. *See* BAIRD (A.)

— Land that I love. Song. *See* ROECKEL (J. L.)

— The Land that I love. [Duet.] *See* RUBINSTEIN (A. G.)

LAND

— The Land that we all love the best. [Song.] *See* NATHAN (J. S.)

— The Land to which we go. Hymn Anthem. *See* TROWBRIDGE (J. E.)

— The Land we live in. [Song.] *See* REEVE (William) [Harlequin and Oberon.]

— The Land we Love. Song. *See* BREARLEY (H.)

— The Land we love. Part song. *See* DACE (J.)

— The Land we love. Song. *See* MACGREGOR (D. C.)

— Land we love, Australia. Part Song. *See* MITCHELL (E. E.) [Land we love the best of all.]

— The Land we love for ever! Chorus. *See* LISZT (F.) [Vierstimmige Männergesänge. No. 1. Rheinweinlied.]

— Land we love the best of all. Part-Song. *See* MITCHELL (E. E.)

— The Land where I was born. *See* PICTON (Nina) Beautiful Songs. 2.

— The Land where my Fathers died is good enough for me. [Song.] *See* AYER (Nat. D.)

— Land where my fondest Hopes are dwelling. [Song.] *See* KELLER (C.) [Land meiner seligsten Gefühle.]

— Land where my forefathers rest. [Song.] *See* WALLERSTEIN (F.)

— The Land where partings are unknown. [Song.] *See* GLOVER (C. W.)

— The Land where roses bloom. [Song.] *See* ENDERSSOHN (M.)

— The Land where the Angels are. Song. *See* LONG (John P.)

— The Land where the Angels stay. [Song.] *See* DONALDSON (Charles A.)

— The Land where the Children play. Song. *See* LLOYD (C. F.)

— The Land where the Shamrock grows. Song. *See* GLOVER (Alfred)

— The Land which no mortal may know. Ballad. *See* SAFFERY, *afterwards* SHELTON (E.)

— The Land which no mortal may know. Song. *See* WRIGLEY (F.)

— The Land which no one knows. *See* DOLORES, *pseud.*

— Land without Music. [Film.] *See* STRAUS (O.)

LAND (EDWARD)

— Alice Gray ... English melody [by V. Millard] arranged as a Part song. *London*, [1862.] fol. **H. 1559. a. (14.)**

— Angel forms will guard us there. Ballad [begins: "Soon the bird will quit the bowers"] written by J. E. Carpenter. *London*, [1873.] fol. **H. 1559. b. (2.)**

— The Angels watch. Song. (Words by E. J. Gill.) [Begins: "Mother! the Angels they say keep watch".] *London*, [1853.] fol. **H. 1735. (3.)**

— Auld Lang Syne, arranged as a Four-part song. *London*, [1862.] fol. **H. 1559. a. (4.)**

— Auld Lang Syne. Arranged as a Four-part Song by E. Land. *See* NOVELLO AND CO. Novello's Part-Song Book. Second Series. No. 582. [1869, *etc.*] 8°. **F. 280. b.**

— Auld Lang Syne. Arranged as a four-part Song, by E. Land. [1884.] *See* NOVELLO AND CO. Novello's Tonic Sol-fa Series. No. 215. [1876, *etc.*] 4°. **B. 885.**

LAND (EDWARD)

— Away! to the fairies' well, cavatina ... the words by J. P. Douglas. *London*, [1859.] fol. **H. 1559. (2.)**

— [Away to the fairies' well.] The Fairies' Well. [Two-part song.] [1893.] *See* SONGS. Two-Part Songs for Classes. No. 16. [1892–5.] 8°. **F. 1530. e.**

— "Better late than never." Ballad written by E. J. Gill. *London*, [1852.] fol. **H. 1735. (8.)**

— Binnorie, an old ... ballad [begins: "There were twa sisters"] arranged ... by E. Land. *Edinburgh*, [1876.] fol. **H. 1559. b. (14.)**

— Bird of beauty wing thy flight, words by J. E. Carpenter. *London*, [1852.] fol. **H. 1735. (9.)**

— Bird of the Wilderness. [Song.] ... Words by the Ettrick Shepherd [J. Hogg]. *London*, [1863.] fol. **H. 1559. a. (8.)**

— Bird of the Wilderness. [Duet.] *London*, [1863.] fol. **H. 1559. a. (9.)**

— Bird of the Wilderness, *etc.* [Two-part chorus.] *Hutchings & Romer: London*, [1902.] 8°.
Two-Part Choruses for treble voices, No. 16. **E. 263. f. (22.)**

— Bird of the Wilderness. (The Skylark.) *See* HIME (E. L.) E. Land's song ... for the Pianoforte. [1863.] fol. **h. 983. (17.)**

— Birds of the sea. Song, written by J. E. Carpenter. *London*, [1858.] fol. **H. 1559. (3.)**

— Blessed are the merciful, the poetry by A. Fricker. [Begins: " 'Tis ev'ning on the battle day".] *London*, [1856.] fol. **H. 1758. (6.)**

— Blessed are the Merciful. [Song, begins: "Oh! Mercy".] Poetry by A. Fricker. *London*, [1862.] fol. **H. 1559. a. (6.)**

— Bring hither flowers! Song, the words by J. P. Douglas. *London*, [1857.] fol. **H. 1559. (4.)**

— Cherry Ripe [by C. E. Horn], arranged as a Four-part song. *London*, [1862.] fol. **H. 1559. a. (3.)**

— Cherry Ripe [by C. E. Horn], arranged as a Four-part Song by E. Land. [1890.] *See* NOVELLO AND CO. Novello's Part-Song Book. Second Series. No. 583. [1869, *etc.*] 8°. **F. 280. b.**

— Classical Lyrics, selected from the words of eminent composers ... Edited by E. Land. 4 no. *London*, [1871.] fol. **H. 1559. b. (1.)**

— La Contadina. The Italian flower-girl's song [begins: "Buy my flowers"] written by E. J. Gill. *London*, [1850.] fol. **H. 1717. (4.)**

— The Desert Spring. Song [begins: "There's a murmuring spring"]. *London*, [1876.] fol. **H. 1559. b. (12.)**

— Do I not weep for thee? Canzonetta, the words by E. Fitzball. *London*, [1853.] fol. **H. 1758. (8.)**

— Du, du, liegst mir im Herzen. (Thee, thee, dearest believe me.) A popular German song [by Carl Eduard Pax], with an English translation, arranged as a duet by Edward Land. pp. 6. *Addison, Hollier & Lucas: London*, [1859.] fol. **H. 1559. (11.)**

— The Fairies' Well. *See supra*: [Away to the fairies' well.]

— Flowers we love thee ... Duet [begins: "Our happy isle"] ... The words by E. J. Gill. *London*, [1876.] fol. **H. 1559. b. (13.)**

— Gavotte for the Pianoforte. *London*, [1874.] fol. **h. 1482. y. (28.)**

LAND (EDWARD)

— Gentle Bessie, Scottish ballad [begins: "Come my gentle Bessie"], the words by J. Duff. *London*, [1863.] fol.
H. 1559. a. (10.)

— The golden Sun. Cavatina by E. J. Gill. [Begins: "Over hills".] *London*, [1852.] fol.
H. 1735. (7.)

— "Grieve not over earthly care," the words by Miss M. A. Stodart. *London*, [1855.] fol.
H. 1758. (7.)

— Home, sweet Home [by Sir H. R. Bishop] ... harmonized as a Part song. *London*, [1862.] fol.
H. 1559. a. (2.)

— Home, sweet Home [by Sir H. R. Bishop] ... harmonized as a Four-part Song by E. Land. [1890.] *See* NOVELLO AND CO. Novello's Part-Song Book. Second Series. No. 581. [1869, *etc.*] 8°.
F. 280. b.

— I'm waiting for thee, Serenade [begins: "Mid all the sad moments"], written by G. Hodder. ⟨In D.⟩ *London*, [1857.] fol.
H. 1559. (7.)

— I've been roaming ... English melody [by C. E. Horn], arranged as a Part song. *London*, [1862.] fol.
H. 1559. a. (15.)

— If thou must sing to-night. Song, words by J. E. Carpenter. *R. Cocks & Co.: London*, [1850?] fol.
G. 805. t. (16.)

— The isle of flowers, duet for Soprano and Contralto [begins: "Our happy isle"] the words by E. J. Gill. *London*, [1849.] fol.
H. 1717. (6.)

— Jock o'Hazledean. Border ballad ... newly arranged by E. Land. *London*, [1870.] fol.
H. 1559. a. (30.)

— Lady Nairn's Lays from Strathearn, arranged as songs without words by E. Land. [Based on the vocal arrangements by Finlay Dun. P. F.] pp. 14. *Paterson & Sons: Edinburgh*, [1867.] fol.
h. 1460. u. (32.)

— Lady Nairn's Lays from Strathearn, arranged as songs without words by E. Land. [Based on the vocal arrangements by Finlay Dun. P. F.] pp. 14. *Paterson & Sons: Edinburgh*, [1870.] fol.
h. 1485. w. (42.)

— Lady Nairn's Lays from Strathearn. Arranged as songs without words by E. Land. [Based on the vocal arrangements by Finlay Dun. P. F.] pp. 14. *Paterson & Sons: London*, [1899.] fol.
h. 3282. i. (24.)

— The Last Rose of Summer, Irish melody [begins: "Tis the last"], the poetry by T. Moore, newly arranged by E. Land. *London*, [1868.] fol.
H. 1559. a. (25.)

— Let by-gones be by-gones, written by H. W. Challis. *London*, [1859.] fol.
H. 1559. (6.)

— Lord Ullin's Daughter. [Song, begins: "A Chieftain".] (Words by T. Campbell.) *London*, [1866.] fol. H. 1559. a. (20.)

— The lovely summer flowers, cavatina, written by A. Park. *London*, [1853.] fol.
H. 1735. (12.)

— A loving Heart. Song [begins: "O! give me but a loving heart"] written by J. P. Douglas. *London*, [1859.] fol.
H. 1559. (8.)

— The Meeting of the Waters. Irish melody [begins: "There is not"]. (The poetry by T. Moore.) *London*, [1868.] fol.
H. 1559. a. (26.)

— The Mermaid's Cave. Four-part song [begins: "Come mariner"]. *London*, [1875.] 8°.
No. 30 of the "Choristers' Album". E. 1708.

— Mine Love! Yes or No? Song [begins: "Wilt thou be mine"]. *London*, [1864.] fol.
H. 1559. a. (16.)

LAND (EDWARD)

— My gentle Elodie. Romanza [begins: "O first love"] ... The poetry by Mrs. Crawford. *London*, [1864.] fol.
H. 1559. a. (18.)

— [My old Friend John.] "When we were Boys, merry, merry Boys," or My old Friend John, song, written by John Legge, *etc.* pp. 7. *Addison, Hollier & Lucas: London*, [c. 1860.] fol.
H. 1654. oo. (12.)

— My old friend John. ⟨In B flat.⟩ *London*, [1876.] fol.
H. 1559. b. (16.)

— E. Land's popular song My Old Friend John ... arranged for two voices by M. Watson. *London*, [1880.] fol.
H. 1787. j. (8.)

— My old friend John ... for the Pianoforte. [1880.] fol. *See* LEMOINE (F.)
h. 1494. q. (26.)

— My old Friend John. [Violin and P. F.] *See* VOLTI (C.) Modern Gems, *etc.* No. 14. [1889–92.] fol.
h. 3236. (5.)

— [My old Friend John.] *See* VANDERVELL (W.) My Old Friend John polka. [1862.] fol.
h. 869. (11.)

— The New Moon. Ballad [begins: " 'Twas in beautiful midsummer weather"]. Words by J. E. Carpenter. *London*, [1874.] fol.
H. 1559. b. (5.)

— "O could my Spirit fly to thee," song, words by J. P. Douglas. pp. 5. *Cramer, Beale & Cº: London*, [c. 1855.] fol.
H. 1654. zz. (12.)

— "O could my Spirit fly to thee," song, words by J. P. Douglas. pp. 5. *Cramer, Beale & Chappell: London*, [c. 1860.] fol.
H. 1650. oo. (16.)

— Oh! say when we again shall meet, ballad, written by L. M. Thornton. *London*, [1855.] fol. H. 1758. (5.)

— O! weel may the keel row, Northumbrian ballad ... arranged with chorus by E. Land. *London*, [1873.] fol.
H. 1559. b. (4.)

— Oft in the stilly night, Scottish melody, newly arranged by E. Land. *London*, [1875.] fol. H. 1559. b. (10.)

— The Old Tree blossoms still. Ballad [begins: "There the old tree"], the words by E. M. Aldridge. *London*, [1861.] fol.
H. 1559. a. (1.)

— The Old Tree blossoms still. Ballad. The words by E. M. Aldridge. *London*, [1874.] fol. H. 1559. b. (7.)

— Pilgrims passing onward. Song [begins: "We are pilgrims"]. Words by W. Maynard. *London*, [1876.] fol.
H. 1559. b. (15.)

— The Queen of the Fays. Song [begins: "Over valley over fountain"] the words by E. J. Gill. *London*, [1849.] fol.
H. 1717. (5.)

— Book 1 (2) Reminiscences of the Jacobite Airs, sung by Mr. Wilson in his ... Scottish Entertainment entitled "The Adventures of Prince Charles". Arranged as a Fantasia for the Piano Forte ... by E. Land. *Duff & Hodgson: London*, [1847.] fol.
h. 708. (17.)

— Saviour, sail with me. Sacred ballad, the poetry by M. Farningham. *London*, [1874.] fol. H. 1559. b. (8.)

— Saviour, wehn I wake. Sacred ballad, the poetry by M. Farningham. ⟨In D. In F.⟩ 2 no. *London*, [1874.] fol.
H. 1559. b. (9.)

— Scotch Songs, newly arranged, with Symphonies & Accompaniments by E. Land ... Transposed editions. 13 no. *C. Lonsdale: London*, [1861.] fol. H. 1559. a. (23.)

— The Scottish exile, Ballad written by E. J. Gill. *London*, [1851.] fol.
H. 1717. (8.)

LAND (Edward)

— Scottish Melodies arranged as Songs without words by
E. Land. [P. F.] 2 bk. *Paterson & Sons: Edinburgh, etc.*, [1876.]
fol.   **h. 1482. y. (29.)**

— Sighs that only love can share. Song [begins: "There's an
hour"]. Words by C. Swain. *London*, [1871.] fol.
                                                        H. 1559. a. (32.)

— "The Slave-girl's Love," ballad, the words by J. E. Carpenter,
etc. pp. 5. *Cramer, Beale & Cᵒ: London*, [c. 1855.] fol.
                                                        H. 1601. n. (22.)

— So sweet is Love's young spring. Ballad [begins: "When
Nature"]. Words by T. Oliphant. *London*, [1869.] fol.
                                                        H. 1559. a. (27.)

— Somebody thinking of me. Ballad [begins: "I know there is
somebody"] written by L. M. Thornton. ⟨In C. In D. In E
flat.⟩ 3 no. *London*, [1876.] fol.   **H. 1559. b. (11.)**

— The spirit dream. Song written by E. J. Gill. [Begins: "I've
watch'd for thee".] *London*, [1852.] fol.   **H. 1735. (11.)**

— Star of Eternity ... Song [begins: "Darkness upon the sea"].
London, [1871.] fol.   **H. 1559. a. (31.)**

— Star of Eternity. Pilgrim's Song, with choral refrain, ad
libitum. *S. Lucas, Weber & Co.: London*, [1882.] fol.
                                                        H. 879. e. (9.)

— Stars of the Summer night. Serenade by Longfellow.
London, [1851.] fol.   **H. 1735. (5.)**

— The sunny dreams of childhood. [Song.] Written by E. J. Gill.
London, [1849.] fol.   **H. 1717. (7.)**

— There's nae luck about the house ... Scotch melody, arranged
as a Part song, *etc. London*, [1862.] fol.   **H. 1559. a. (13.)**

— Thou whom to love is all my Care, romance. pp. 5. *Cramer,
Beale & Wood: London*, [1862.] fol.   **H. 1650. ii. (5.)**

— [Another issue.] Thou whom to love is all my care. Romance.
London, [1862.] fol.   **H. 1559. a. (5.)**

— Through the Wood ... English melody [by C. E. Horn],
arranged as a Part song. *London*, [1862.] fol.
                                                        H. 1559. a. (12.)

— Thy Guardian never sleeps. Song [begins: "Go forth my
boy"] written by J. E. Carpenter. ⟨In E flat. In F.⟩ 2 no.
London, [1874.] fol.   **H. 1559. b. (6.)**

— Trespassers beware! Song [begins: "Four girls were
walking"]. Words by H. Spicer. *London*, [1873.] fol.
                                                        H. 1559. b. (3.)

— The vesper dream. Written by E. J. Gill. Prize song. [Begins:
"At vesper hour".] *London*, [1851.] fol.   **H. 1735. (4.)**

— Vocal duets ... from Wilson's songs of Scotland ... arranged
... by E. Land. *London*, [1846.] fol.   **H. 1717. (3.)**

— Waiting for thee. Serenade [begins: "Mid all the sad
moments"], written by G. Hodder. *London*, [1864.] fol.
                                                        H. 1559. a. (17.)

— Serenade, Coralie, "Waiting for thee". [Begins: "When
fortune".] *London*, [1867.] fol.   **H. 1559. a. (21.)**

— Wha'll buy caller herring ... Scotch melody [by N. Gow],
arranged as a Part song, *etc. London*, [1862.] fol.
                                                        H. 1559. a. (11.)

— What can the heart want more. Song [begins: "To feel the
grasp"] ... Words by J. Ellison. *London*, [1862.] fol.
                                                        H. 1559. a. (7.)

— When night is darkest, Dawn is nearest. Song [begins: "The
flower that droops"]. (Words by J. Wilce.) *London*, [1867.]
fol.   **H. 1559. a. (22.)**

LAND (Edward)

— When Night is darkest, Dawn is nearest. [Two-part song.] ...
Words by J. Wilce. *See* STARK (H. J.) Morley's School Songs,
etc. No. 2. [1901, *etc.*] 8° & 4°.   **F. 1180.**

— When Night is darkest ... Arranged by B. Tours. [Violin and
P. F.] [1887.] *See* MORLEY AND CO. Morley's Melodious Gems,
etc. No. 2. [1887, *etc.*] fol.   **h. 1685.**

— When Sorrow sleepeth, wake it not. Song written by Miss
M. A. Stodart. [With German words beginning: "Lass
Thränen ruh'n" by L. J. Lardner.] *London*, [1852.] fol.
                                                        H. 1735. (6.)

— When Sorrow sleepeth, wake it not. ⟨In D flat.⟩ *London*,
[1870.] fol.   **H. 1559. a. (29.)**

— When sorrow sleepeth, wake it not. E. Land's popular Song
arranged for the Piano forte by I. Gibsone. *London*, 1852.
fol.   **h. 1304. (1.)**

— When Sorrow sleepeth wake it not ... transcribed for the
harp by C. Oberthür ... Op. 349. *E. Ashdown: London, etc.*,
[1895.] fol.   **h. 3200. b. (19.)**

— When we were Boys, merry, merry Boys. *See* supra: [My old
Friend John.]

— "Why art thou sad?" Song. The words by Edward J. Gill.
pp. 7. *Addison & Hollier: London*, [1853.] fol.
                                                        H. 1601. nn. (4.)

— [A reissue.] Why art thou sad? Song ... (the words by E. J.
Gill), *etc. L. Cock, Addison & Co.: London*, [c. 1868.] fol.
                                                        H. 2815. m. (1.)

— Why linger so long? Song, words by J. E. Carpenter.
London, [1852.] fol.   **H. 1735. (10.)**

— Why should thy voice still follow me? Ballad, written by
C. Swain. *London*, [1859.] fol.   **H. 1559. (13.)**

— Willie's gane to Melville Castle ... Scottish ballad ... The
symphonies & accompaniments by E. Land. *London*, [1866.]
fol.   **H. 1559. a. (19.)**

— Willie's gane to Melville Castle, old Scottish ballad ... The
symphonies & accompaniments by E. Land. *London*, [1876.]
fol.   **H. 1559. b. (17.)**

— Woodland fairies. [Song, begins: "Dancing in the
moonlight," words by J. E. Carpenter.] *London*, [1858.] fol.
                                                        H. 1559. (5.)

— You know not how I've missed you, Song, written by H. W.
Challis. *London*, [1858.] fol.   **H. 1559. (9.)**

— *See* ABT (F. W.) [7 Lieder. Op. 39. No. 1. Agatha.] "When the
swallow homeward flies" ... arranged as a Duet for two
voices by E. Land. [1858.] fol.   **H. 1559. (12.)**

— *See* As. "As I came in by Sandgate" ... Ballad arranged with
harmonized Burden by E. Land. [1860.] fol.   **H. 1559. (1.)**

— *See* BEETHOVEN (L. van) [Sonata. Op. 27. No. 2. Adagio
sostenuto.] Unto Thee, O Lord ... Adapted by E. Land.
[1861.] fol.   **H. 2430. a. (5.)**

— *See* CLARKE, afterwards CLARKE WHITFELD (J.) Dr. J. Clarke's
... scena, The Last Words of Marmion ... Revised by
E. Land. [1866.] fol.   **H. 1559. a. (28.)**

— *See* LEEVES (W.) Auld Robin Gray ... arranged by E. Land.
[1868.] fol.   **H. 1559. a. (24.)**

— *See* PRAY. Pray Goody, old English song ... newly arranged
by E. Land. [1859.] fol.   **H. 1559. (10.)**

— *See* STEVENSON (*Sir* J. A.) [The Patriot.] See our oars ...
arranged by E. Land. [1848.] fol.   **H. 1723. (38.)**

— *See* TRIOS. Chamber Trios. No. 61. See the star of queenly
beauty. Arranged ... by E. Land. [1844, *etc.*] fol.   **H. 2260.**

LAND (EDWARD)

— See TRIOS. Chamber trios. No. 64. Here in cool grot, *etc.* Arranged ... by E. Land. [1844, *etc.*] fol. **H. 2260.**

LAND (JAN PIETER NICOLAAS)

— See HUYGENS (C.) Musique et musiciens au XVIIᵉ siècle. Correspondance et œuvre musicales de C. Huyghens publiées par ... J. P. N. Land. 1882. 4°. [*Vereeiniging voor Nederlandsche Muziekgeschiedenis. Uitgave. no.* 11.] **G. 12. a.**

LANDAETA (JUAN JOSÉ)

— Himno nacional de Venezuela. ⟨Vicente Salias, autor de la letra. Arreglo para piano y canto ó piano solo. Partitura de banda arreglada al uso de las Bandas nacionales. Edición oficial del centenario de la independencia.⟩ pp. 18. *S. N. Llamozas & Cᵃ: Caracas; Leipzig* printed, [1911.] fol. **H. 1248. z. (13.)**

— Himno national de Venezuela. Letra de Vicente Salias. ⟨Reducción para canto y piano.⟩ ⟨Arreglo para 4 voces mixtas.—Arreglo para 3 voces oscuras.⟩ Edición oficial. pp. vi. 6. [1950?] 4°. *See* VENEZUELA.— *Ministerio de Relaciones Interiores.— Dirección de Politica.* **G. 981. cc. (12.)**

— Himno Nacional de Venezuela. Letra de Vicente Salias ... Edición oficial. [1950?] *s. sh.* fol. *See* VENEZUELA.— *Ministerio de Relaciones Interiores.— Dirección de Información y Publicaciones.* **I. 600. e. (504.)**

— Himno nacional de la República de Venezuela. Letra de Vicente Salias ... Arreglo para piano y canto o piano solo. ⟨Partitura de banda arreglado al uso de las Bandas nacionales.⟩ *In:* VENEZUELA.— *Imprenta nacional.* ... Calendario para 1956, *etc.* [1955.] 4°. **G. 1310. c.**

— Pésame a la virgen. Partitura para voces y orquesta. ⟨Revisión por Juan B. Plaza.⟩ pp. 32. *Instituto interamericano de musicología: Montevideo*, 1943. 4°. [*Archivo de música colonial venezolana. no.* 1.] **H. 2596.**

— Pésame a la Virgen. *In:* MOREIRA (Sergio) Música religiosa de seis maestros venezolanos, *etc.* 1973. fol. **H. 1028. z. (1.)**

— Salve regina. Partitura para voces y orquesta. ⟨Revisión por Juan B. Plaza.⟩ pp. 28. *Instituto interamericano de musicología: Montevideo*, 1943. 4°. [*Archivo de música colonial venezolana. no.* 11.] **H. 2596.**

LANDAIS (EUGÈNE)

— Prélude. *See* RÉPERTOIRE. Répertoire moderne de Musique ... d'Orgue, *etc.* No. 11. [1896, *etc.*] fol. **H. 1048.**

LANDARZT

— Ein Landarzt. Oper. *See* HENZE (H. W.)

LANDAU (S. V.)

— The Springbokken Waltz. [P. F.] pp. 8. *L. Shapiro & Co.: Port Elizabeth*, [1907.] fol. **i. 138. (1.)**

LANDAU (SIEGFRIED)

— Or zarua latsadik. For cantor (tenor or baritone) and mixed voices (S. A. T. B.) a cappella. pp. 7. *Mills Music: New York*, [1961.] 8°. **E. 1499. r. (1.)**

LANDAU (VICTOR)

— See CHOPIN (F. F.) [17 polnische Lieder. Op. 74. No. 1. Mädchens Wunsch.] The Maiden's Wish. For women's voices (S. S. A.) with piano accompaniment ... Arranged by V. Landau. [1962.] 8°. **F. 217. t. (11.)**

LANDAU (WILHELM)

— Italienische Träumereien. Fantasie für das Pianoforte. *Breslau*, [1879.] fol. **h. 1493. n. (9.)**

LANDAUER (WALTER)

— See KHACHATURYAN (A. I.) [Маскарад.] Waltz ... Arranged for two pianos by Rawicz and Landauer. [1955.] 4°. **g. 1548. a. (23.)**

LANDE

— Aus Allen Landen. [Music for military band.] Lieferung IV. Tenorhorn. *L. Oertel: Hannover*, [1884.] 8°. *Imperfect; wanting all the other parts.* **c. 120. a. (1.)**

LANDE (KAY)

— See TIMMENS (Jim) and LANDE (K.) My true Love's Hair ... Music and lyrics by J. Timmens & K. Lande. [1977.] 8°. **F. 1874. cc. (20.)**

LANDECK (BEATRICE)

— Echoes of Africa in Folk Songs of the Americas ... Instrumental arrangements by Milton Kaye. English version of foreign lyrics by Margaret Marks. Drawings by Alexander Dobkin. pp. viii. 184. *David McKay Co.: New York*, [1961.] 4°. **G. 935. k.**

— Folk Songs of the Americas. From Echoes of Africa. ⟨This edition compiled and edited by Harold C. Fields and Frederick Harper.⟩ pp. 55. *Phoenix Music Publishing Co.: London*, [1964.] 8°. **E. 1885. j. (5.)**

— "Git on Board." Collection of Folk Songs, arranged for Mixed Chorus. Compiled and edited by B. Landeck ... Vocal arrangements by Charity Bailey, Ernest Gold, Felix Guenther, J. Rosamond Johnson and others. *Edward B. Marks Music Corporation: New York*, 1944. 8°. **F. 1834.**

— "Git on Board" ... Enlarged and revised edition, *etc.* pp. 86. *Edward B. Marks Music Corporation: New York*, [1950.] 8°. **F. 1771. k. (14.)**

— Songs my true Love sings. Compiled by B. Landeck. Piano settings by Charity Bailey. [With illustrations.] pp. 64. *Edward B. Marks Music Corporation: New York*, 1946. 4°. **F. 1834. a.**

LANDEGHEM (HIPPOLITE VAN)

— Apple Blossoms ... Duet [begins: "Oh! the merry merry time"]. Words by Mrs. H. van Landeghem. *London*, [1876.] fol. **H. 1778. x. (34.)**

— Around the Christmas tree. [Song.] Words by Mrs. H. van Landeghem. *London*, [1876.] 8°. *No. 69 of A. Bertini & Co's "Presentation Music".* **E. 1702.**

— Around the Christmas Tree quadrille. [P. F.] *London*, [1876.] fol. **h. 1482. y. (30.)**

— Ave Maria. [Solo.] *London*, [1876.] fol. **H. 1129. a. (26.)**

— Beautiful breeze of the sea. Ballad, words by Mrs. H. van Landeghem. *London*, [1875.] fol. **H. 1778. x. (28.)**

— Bright Skies. Song [begins: "Beam on"]. The words by M. A. Dunham. *London*, [1862.] fol. **H. 1775. t. (16.)**

— Bright Skies. Ballad. Words by Mrs. H. van Landeghem. *London*, [1875.] fol. **H. 1778. x. (30.)**

— Dreaming again. Ballad [begins: "O sing that dear familiar song"]. Words by Mrs. H. van Landeghem. *London*, [1875.] fol. **H. 1778. x. (29.)**

— Golden Bloom. Ballad, words by Mrs. H. van Landeghem. *London*, [1873.] fol. **H. 1778. x. (26.)**

LANDEGHEM (HIPPOLITE VAN)

— The Golden Sheaf. A Cantata, written by Mrs. Van Landeghem. [1872.] *See* TONIC. The Tonic Sol-fa Times, *etc.* No. 94, 95, 96. [1864–73.] 4°.　　　　**B. 559. f.**

— I think of thee in the silent night, song. (Words by Miss S.) *London*, [1857.] fol.　　　　**H. 1771. l. (10.)**

— The Mistletoe quadrille for the Pianoforte. *London*, [1862.] fol.　　　　**h. 1460. u. (33.)**

— The Mountain and the Vale ... Duet [begins: "Mine by the mountains height"]. (Words by Mrs. H. van Landeghem.) *London*, [1878.] fol.　　　　**H. 1783. o. (10.)**

— The New Moon of love. Song [begins: "When tempests were wildest"]. (Words by Mrs. H. van Landeghem.) *London*, [1876.] fol.　　　　**H. 1778. x. (33.)**

— Our Roads must lie apart. Song [begins: "Oh! fairest star"]. Words by Mrs. H. van Landeghem. *London*, [1876.] fol.　　　　**H. 1778. x. (32.)**

— Over the heather ... Duet. (Words by Mrs. H. van Landeghem.) *London*, [1876.] fol.　　　　**H. 1778. x. (31.)**

— There are angels dwelling with us. Ballad, words by Mrs. H. van Landeghem. *London*, [1876.] fol.　　　　**H. 1778. x. (27.)**

— Weep not, my gentle Mary. Ballad, the poetry by M. A. D. *London*, [1861.] fol.　　　　**H. 1775. t. (15.)**

— The Whisper on the Stair. Ballad [begins: "I am waiting"], written by Mrs. van Landeghem. *London*, [1869.] fol.　　　　**H. 1775. t. (17.)**

— Words of hope. Ballad, written by Mrs. H. van Landeghem. *London*, [1872.] fol.　　　　**H. 1778. x. (25.)**

LANDELLE (GUILLAUME JOSEPH GABRIEL DE LA)

— *See* LA LANDELLE.

LANDEN (　　　　)

— The Hazel-ey'd Maid, *etc.* [Song.] [*London*, 1753.] 8°. The Gentleman's Magazine, Vol. XXIII., p. 191.　　　　**249. c. 23.**

LANDER (BARBARA)

— Music for Mime. [P. F.] pp. 118. *Methuen & Co.: London*, [1958.] 4°.　　　　**g. 230. v. (7.)**

— *See* LONDON.— *Imperial Society of Teachers of Dancing.— National Dance Branch.* Music Album, *etc.* ⟨[Re-edited by] B. Lander.⟩ [P. F.] [1979.] 4°.　　　　**g. 839. (4.)**

— *See* WINGRAVE (Helen) and HARROLD (R.) Regional Dances of Europe, *etc.* [The music edited by B. Lander. P. F.] [1970.] 4°.　　　　**X. 435/109.**

LANDER (G. H.)

— Waves of the Sea. Song, *etc.* *West & Co.: London*, 1914. fol.　　　　**H. 1793. s. (1.)**

LANDER (J. M.)

— Five O'Clock in the Morning galop. [P. F.] *London*, [1874.] fol. No. 3982 *of the "Musical Bouquet".*　　　　**H. 2345.**

LANDERGAN (A.)

— Ballad for the Pianoforte. *London*, [1863.] fol.　　　　**h. 1460. u. (34.)**

— I'm thinking of the pleasant days. Song. The poetry by C. G. Phillipson. *London*, [1865.] fol.　　　　**H. 1772. r. (13.)**

LANDERKENNUNG

— Landerkennung. [Part-song.] *See* GRIEG (E. H.) [Landkjending.]

LANDEROIN (JOSEPH)

— Andromaque. ⟨Tragédie lyrique en 4 actes d'après Racine. Poème et musique de J. Landeroin. Op. 105. Partition pour piano et chant.⟩ pp. 230. *David Bontoux: Majunga*, 1910. fol. *No.* 14 *of an edition of twenty copies.*　　　　**H. 233. j.**

LANDERS (JAMES)

— Ave verum, for four voices. *London*, [1854.] fol.　　　　**H. 1129. (11.)**

— O gloriosa Virginum, for four voices. *London*, [1853.] fol.　　　　**H. 1128. (5.)**

— O salutaris and Tantum ergo. No. 5. [Words by St. Thomas Aquinas.] *London*, [1854.] fol.　　　　**H. 1129. (17.)**

— Sub tuum praesidium, motett for four voices. *London*, [1856.] fol.　　　　**H. 1129. (12.)**

LANDERS (R. C.)

— In the Land of Yesterday. [Song.] Words and music by R. C. Landers. pp. 5. *Victor Kremer Co.: Chicago, etc.*, [1908.] fol.　　　　**H. 3985. h. (8.)**

LANDES (R. W.)

— *See* BLOCH (Ernest) [Poems of the Sea. No. 2.] Chanty ... Transcribed for brass sextet by R. W. Landes. [1962.] 4°. [*Brass in Concert. ser.* 1. *no.* 3.]　　　　**g. 1110. m.**

LANDESEN (THÉRÈSE VON)

— *See* POLONASKI (Thérèse) afterwards LANDESEN (Thérèse von)

LANDFRIEDE

— Der Landfriede. Oper. *See* BRUELL (I.)

LANDGRAF

— Landgraf Ludwig. [Song.] *See* REITER (J.) Balladen. N° 14.

LANDGRAVE (PHILLIP)

— Peace I leave with you. For S. A. T. B. chorus. Text: Jozhn 14. 27. pp. 5. *Walton Music Corporation: North Hollywood*, [1962.] 8°.　　　　**E. 335. ee. (27.)**

LANDI (BARTOLOMEO GRASSI)

— *See* GRASSI-LANDI.

LANDI (CLAUDE P.)

— If ye then be risen.—Response.— [S. A. T. B.] *B. F. Wood Music Co.: Boston, Mass.*, (1908.) 8°. Choir Journal, No. 219 *b.*　　　　**F. 986.**

— The Lord is good.—Response.— [S. A. T. B.] *B. F. Wood Music Co.: Boston, Mass.*, (1908.) 8°. Choir Journal, No. 228 *b.*　　　　**F. 986.**

— Solitude. Song ... words by Chrystabel, *etc.* *J. Williams: London*, 1914. fol.　　　　**G. 806. ll. (43.)**

— Tarry with me, O my Saviour. Evening Hymn-Anthem for mixed voices. [Words by] C. L. Smith. *O. Ditson Co.: [Boston,]* 1907. 8°.　　　　**F. 281. h. (22.)**

LANDI (CLAUDE P.)

— Eight Unaccompanied Responses—First Set—for mixed voices. *B. F. Wood Music Co.: Boston, etc.*, (1907.) 8°.

F. 281. i. (20.)

— *See* MASCAGNI (P.) [Iris.—Introduction.] Hymn to the Sun ... Arranged for the Organ by C. P. Landi. 1912. fol.

h. 2731. t. (34.)

LANDI (STEFANO)

— Arie a Una Voce, *etc. Appresso Bartholomeo Magni. Stampa del Gardano: Venetia*, 1620. fol. **K. 8. g. 14.**

— La Morte d'Orfeo. Tragicomedia Pastorale con le Musiche ... Opera Seconda. *Appresso Bartolomeo Magni. Stampa del Gardano: Venetia*, 1619. fol. **K. 8. g. 10.**

— La Morte d'Orfeo, *etc.* [Extracts.] [*Leipzig*, 1901.] 8°. *Anhang F of H. Goldschmidt's "Studien zur Geschichte der italienischen Oper".* **2268. c. 4.**

— Il S. Alessio. Dramma Musicale, *etc.* [Full score.] *Apresso Paolo Masotti: Roma*, 1634. fol. **K. 8. g. 8.**

— [Il S. Alessio.] Lampi e lumi egregi. Squarcio d'un Coro nel Prologo ... a 5 voci (Poca voglia di far bene. Arietta a 2 Voci) (Coro di Demonij nell' Atto I, Scena IV ... a tre voci) (Coro nell' Atto III, Scena V ... a 4 voci), col Basso continuo dell' A. e l'accompagnamento di Pianoforte di L. Torchi. *See* TORCHI (L.) L'Arte Musicale in Italia, *etc.* Vol. V. pp. 43–58. [1898–1907.] 4°. **G. 413.**

— Il S. Alessio, *etc.* [Extracts.] [*Leipzig*, 1901.] 8°. *Anhang G of H. Goldschmidt's "Studien zur Geschichte der italienischen Oper".* **2268. c. 4.**

LANDING

— The Landing of the Pilgrim Fathers. Ballad. *See* BROWNE, afterwards HUGHES ( )

— The Landing of the Pilgrims. Chorus. *See* POWELL (J.)

— The Landing of the Pilgrims. [Part-song.] *See* TALMADGE (Charles L.)

LANDINI (FRANCESCO)

— The Works of Francesco Landini. Edited by Leonard Ellinwood. *The Mediaeval Academy of America: Cambridge, Mass.*, 1939. 4°. *The Mediaeval Academy of America, Publication No. 36.* **F. 53.**

— [Another copy.] **Ac. 2684/2.**

— The Works of Francesco Landini. ⟨Edited by Leo Schrade.⟩ pp. 122. *Édition de l'oiseau-lyre: Monaco*, [1959.] fol. [*Polyphonic Music of the fourteenth Century. vol.* 4.]

— Commentary, *etc.* pp. xi. 162. *Monaco*, [1959.] fol. **H. 4012.**

LANDINI (GIOVANNI BATTISTA DE)

— [Gaudeamus omnes.] Introit for the Feast of the Assumption of the Blessed Virgin Mary. [S. A. T. B.] *In:* GUARNERUS (Bernardus) [Contrapunctus seu figurata musica.] The Lyons Contrapunctus (1528), *etc.* pt. 2. pp. 97–100. [1976.] 4°. [*Recent Researches in the Music of the Renaissance. vol.* 22.] **G. 1490. a.**

LANDKJENDING

— Landkjending. [Solo and chorus.] *See* GRIEG (E. H.)

LANDLADY

— The Landlady's Daughter. [Song.] *See* WINCOTT (Harry)

LANDLER (THEODORE W.)

— Three Progressive Pieces for the Violin with accompaniments for the pianoforte. No. 1. Reverie. No. 2. Elfen-Tanz. No. 3. Romance. 3 no. *H. Beresford: London, Birmingham*, [1890.] fol. **h. 1608. x. (35.)**

LANDLESS

— Landless serfs, and homeless slaves. *Foreward!* A Marching Song, by an English Yeoman. *F. Hunt:* [*London*, 1893.] *s. sh.* fol. **H. 1797. z. (38.)**

LANDLORD

— The Landlord cries Pat. *Posting in Ireland.* A new Comic Song, the words by Major General Sir Charles Doyle, *etc. T. Williams, for the Author: London*, [1820?] fol. **H. 1846. pp. (9.)**

— The Landlord he looks very big. *A good Ale thou art my Darling.* [Song.] [L]*ongman and* [B]*roderip: London*, 1785?] *s. sh.* fol. **G. 312. (118.)**

— The Landlord of the old Ship Inn. Song. *See* LOUGHBOROUGH (R.)

LANDMANN (ARNO)

— Sechs Choral-Improvisationen für Orgel. Opus 4 b. *B. Schott's Söhne: Mainz, etc.*, 1923. 4°. **g. 575. ee. (24.)**

— Fantasie über den Choral "Herzliebster Jesu, was hast du verbrochen," für Orgel. Opus 4 a. *B. Schott's Söhne: Mainz, etc.*, 1923. 4°. **g. 575. ee. (25.)**

— Sonate für Orgel, B moll. Opus 9. *B. Schott's Söhne: Mainz*, 1923. fol. **h. 2732. n. (21.)**

— Traugesang, von Pfarrer Klein-Mannheim, für eine Singstimme mit Orgel- Harmonium- oder Klavierbegleitung (Cello, Soloquartett, oder gem. Chor ad libitum) ... Op. 8. Orgel, zugleich Cello- u. Gesangsst. *B. Schott's Söhne: Mainz, Leipzig*, [1925.] fol. **H. 1846. ll. (15.)**

— Vier Vortragsstücke für Orgel. Opus 10. *B. Schott's Söhne: Mainz, etc.*, 1923. 4°. **g. 575. ee. (26.)**

LANDON (AGNES)

— The bridge, "I stood on the bridge at midnight," written by H. W. Longfellow. *London*, [1855.] fol. **H. 1758. (9.)**

— The old clock on the stairs, [begins: "Somewhat back from the village street"] the words by H. W. Longfellow. *London*, [1855.] fol. **H. 1758. (10.)**

LANDON (CHARLES W.)

— Playing two notes against three. Explanations, Illustrations and Studies ... Written and compiled by C. W. Landon. [P. F.] *T. Presser Co.: Philadelphia*, (1911.) fol. **h. 3820. z. (2.)**

— *See* BATCHELLOR (D.) and LANDON (C. W.) Musical Kindergarten Method, *etc.* (1909.) 8°. **F. 1674.**

LANDON (CHRISTA)

— *See* HAYDN (F. J.) Concerto D major. For horn and orchestra ... Hob. VII d. 3. Edited ... by C. Landon. [c. 1960.] 8°. [*Edition Eulenburg. no.* 1232.] **b. 212.**

— *See* HAYDN (F. J.) [Concertos. Violin. Hob. VII a/4.] Concerto G major. For violin and string orchestra ... ⟨Hob. VII a. 4.⟩ Edited ... by C. Landon. [c. 1960.] 8°. [*Edition Eulenburg. no.* 1228.] **b. 212.**

LANDON (Christa)

— *See* HAYDN (F. J.) [Masses. Hob. XXII/7.] Missa brevis Stⁱ Joannis de Deo. "Kleine Orgelmesse," *etc.* [Edited by H. C. R. Landon in association with K. H. Füssl and C. Landon.] [1978.] fol.   **H. 2120. m. (3.)**

— *See* HAYDN (F. J.) [Sonatas. Hob. XVI. Large Collections.] Sämtliche Klaviersonaten ... Revidiert von ... C. Landon, *etc.* [1966, 64.] 4°.   **g. 127.**

— *See* HAYDN (F. J.) Symphony No. 13. D major ... Edited by C. Landon. [1964?] 8°. [*Edition Eulenburg. no.* 563.]   **b. 212.**

— *See* HAYDN (F. J.) Symphony No. 21. A major ... Edited by C. Landon. [1963.] 8°. [*Edition Eulenburg. no.* 561.]   **b. 212.**

— *See* HAYDN (F. J.) Symphony No. 29. E major ... Edited by C. Landon. [1963.] 8°. [*Edition Eulenburg. no.* 562.]   **b. 212.**

— *See* HAYDN (F. J.) Symphony No. 35. B♭ major ... Edited by C. Landon. [1964?] 8°. [*Edition Eulenburg. no.* 564.]   **b. 212.**

— *See* HAYDN (F. J.) Symphony No. 42. D major ... Edited by C. Landon. [1965?] 8°. [*Edition Eulenburg. no.* 568.]   **b. 212.**

— *See* HAYDN (F. J.) [Symphonies. Hob. I/105.] Concertante (Sinfonia concertante) B♭ major ... (Original-Fassung.) Edited by C. Landon. [1968.] 8°. [*Edition Eulenburg. no.* 790*.]   **b. 212.**

— *See* MOZART (W. A.) [*Collected Works.— e.*] Werke für Klavier zu vier Händen. Nach den Autographen und Erstdrucken revidiert von ... C. Landon, *etc.* [1963.] *obl.* 4°.   **e. 57. ee.**

— *See* MOZART (W. A.) Serenade No. 9. D major. [K. 320] ... Two Marches ... [K. 335.] Edited by C. Landon. [1961.] 8°. [*Edition Eulenburg. no.* 1311.]   **b. 212.**

— *See* SCHUBERT (F. P.) [*Collected Works.— d.*] "Vollendung." "Die Erde." Zwei Lieder ... Herausgegeben von ... C. Landon. [1970.] 8°.   **F. 409. qq. (8.)**

— *See* SCHUBERT (F. P.) Sechs Menuette für Bläser ... Herausgegeben von ... C. Landon. [1970.] 4°.   **g. 567. dd. (4.)**

— *See* SCHUBERT (F. P.) Sinfonie in D. Nr. 1. D 82. ⟨Edited by A. Feil and C. Landon.⟩ [1968.] 4°.   **h. 3183. l. (1.)**

— *See* SCHUBERT (F. P.) Sinfonie in B. Nr. 2. D 125. ⟨Edited by A. Feil and C. Landon.⟩ [1968.] 4°.   **h. 3183. l. (2.)**

— *See* SCHUBERT (F. P.) Sinfonie in D. Nr. 3. D 200. ⟨Edited by A. Feil and C. Landon.⟩ [1968.] 4°.   **h. 3183. l. (3.)**

— *See* SCHUBERT (F. P.) Sinfonie in h-Moll. [No. 8.] "Die Unvollendete." Vollständiges Faksimile ... Mit einem Nachwort von W. Dürr und C. Landon. [1978.] *obl.* fol. [*Publikationen der Sammlungen der Gesellschaft der Musikfreunde in Wien. Bd.* 3.]   **X. 0439/112.**

— *See* SIEGMEISTER (E.) The Joan Baez Songbook. Arrangements ... by E. Siegmeister ... Music editors: C. Landon & Jack Lothrop. [1966.] 4°.   **F. 1196. qq.**

LANDON (Howard Chandler Robbins)

— *See* BACH (J. Christian) Temistocle. Dramma per musica ... Revisione di E. O. D. Downes e H. C. R. Landon, *etc.* [1965.] 4°.   **H. 740. b.**

— *See* BECK (F.) [Sei sinfonie. Op. 3. No. 5.] Sinfonia D-moll ... Herausgegeben von ... H. C. R. Landon. [1959.] 4°.   **g. 420. jj. (5.)**

— *See* GASSMANN (F. L.) [L'Issipile.] Sinfonia dall'opera "L'Issipile," *etc.* ⟨Erstdruck, herausgegeben von H. C. R. Landon.⟩ [1966.] 4°.   **g. 420. ff. (4.)**

— *See* HAYDN (F. J.) [*Collected Works.— a.*] Kritische Gesamtausgabe, *etc.* ⟨Ser. 1. Bd. 9, 10. Symphonien. Herausgegeben von H. C. R. Landon.⟩ [1950, 51.] fol.   **N. 9.**

LANDON (Howard Chandler Robbins)

— *See* HAYDN (F. J.) [*Collected Works.— e.*] 13 Arien für Sopran ... Herausgegeben von H. C. R. Landon, *etc.* [1961.] 4°.   **G. 339. g.**

— *See* HAYDN (F. J.) [*Collected Works.— e.*] Arien für Sopran. Herausgegeben von H. C. R. Landon ... Klavierauszug von K. H. Füssl. [1961.] 4°.   **G. 339. c. (10.)**

— *See* HAYDN (F. J.) [*Collected Works.— e.*] 3 Arien für Bariton (Bass) ... Herausgegeben von H. C. R. Landon, *etc.* [1964.] 4°.   **G. 339. i. (3.)**

— *See* HAYDN (F. J.) [*Collected Works.— e.*] Arien für Bariton (Bass). Herausgegeben von H. C. R. Landon. Klavierauszug von K. H. Füssl. [1964.] 4°.   **G. 339. i. (4.)**

— *See* HAYDN (F. J.) [*Collected Works.— e.*] 4 Arien für Tenor ... Herausgegeben von H. C. R. Landon, *etc.* [1964.] 4°.   **G. 339. i. (1.)**

— *See* HAYDN (F. J.) [*Collected Works.— e.*] Arien für Tenor. Herausgegeben von H. C. R. Landon. Klavierauszug von K. H. Füssl. [1964.] 4°.   **G. 339. i. (2.)**

— *See* HAYDN (F. J.) [*Collected Works.— e.*] Arien mit Orchester für Sopran/Tenor/Bass (Bariton). Revisionsberichte. H. C. R. Landon. [c. 1970.] 8°.   **F. 426. z. (2.)**

— *See* HAYDN (F. J.) Acide e Galatea. Sinfonia. (Overtura) ... Erstdruck herausgegeben von H. C. R. Landon, *etc.* [1959.] 4°.   **g. 75. g. (9.)**

— *See* HAYDN (F. J.) Six Allemandes ... Herausgegeben von H. C. R. Landon, *etc.* [1960.] 4°.   **g. 455. rr. (2.)**

— *See* HAYDN (F. J.) Applausus. Cantata. Erstdruck, *etc.* ([Edited by] H. C. R. Landon.) [1969.] 4°.   **G. 339. m. (3.)**

— *See* HAYDN (F. J.) Cantilena pro Adventu. "Ein' Magd, ein' Dienerin" ... herausgegeben von ... H. C. R. Landon. Partitura, *etc.* [1957.] 4°.   **G. 339. c. (6.)**

— *See* HAYDN (F. J.) Cantilena pro Adventu. "Ein' Magd, ein' Dienerin." Erste Veröffentlichung herausgegeben von ... H. C. R. Landon. Klavierauszug, *etc.* [1957.] 4°.   **G. 339. c. (5.)**

— *See* HAYDN (F. J.) Cassatio in D für 4 Hörner, Violine, Viola und Bass ... herausgegeben von H. C. R. Landon, *etc.* [1960.] 4°.   **g. 75. g. (13.)**

— *See* HAYDN (F. J.) Concertino per il cembalo. (Hoboken XIV: 11) ... herausgegeben von H. C. R. Landon. [1959.] 4°.   **g. 75. g. (3.)**

— *See* HAYDN (F. J.) [Concertos. Keyboard.] Concerto per l'organo no. 2. ⟨Hoboken XVIII. 8.⟩ Erstdruck herausgegeben von H. C. R. Landon, *etc.* [1962.] 4°.   **g. 75. k. (12.)**

— *See* HAYDN (F. J.) Concerto per il clavicembalo. F-Dur. (Hob. XVIII: F2.) Erstdruck (⟨hrsg. von⟩ H. C. R. Landon.) [1969.] 4°.   **g. 75. f. (3.)**

— *See* HAYDN (F. J.) [Concertos. 2 lire organizzate. Hob. VII h/1–5.] Sämtliche Konzerte für König Ferdinand IV. von Neapel ... herausgegeben von H. C. R. Landon, *etc.* [1959–60.] 4°.   **g. 75. r. (8.)**

— *See* HAYDN (F. J.) [Concertos. Violin. Hob. VII a/1.] Concerto, C major, for Violin and String Orchestra ... Edited, and with foreword, by R. Landon. [1953.] 8°. [*Edition Eulenburg. no.* 1202.]   **b. 212.**

— *See* HAYDN (F. J.) [Divertimenti. Hob. II.] I. ⟨—VIII.⟩ Divertimento ... ⟨Für Blasinstrumente.⟩ Herausgegeben von H. C. R. Landon. [1959, 60.] 4°.   **g. 75. f. (1.)**

— *See* HAYDN (F. J.) Divertimento a sei ... (Hoboken II: 11) ... Erstdruck, herausgegeben von H. C. R. Landon, *etc.* [1961.] 4°.   **g. 75. k. (6.)**

LANDON (HOWARD CHANDLER ROBBINS)

— *See* HAYDN (F. J.) [Divertimento. Hob. II/20.] Cassatio. (Divertimento a nove stromenti) ... Erstdruck, herausgegeben von H. C. R. Landon, *etc.* [1962.] 4°. **g. 75. r. (1.)**

— *See* HAYDN (F. J.) [Divertimenti.] Cassatio ... in G ... (Hoboken II: G. 1.) Erstdruck, herausgegeben von H. C. R. Landon. [1959.] 4°. **g. 75. g. (2.)**

— *See* HAYDN (F. J.) [Divertimenti. Hob. XIV/12.] Concerto per il cembalo C-Dur ... Erstdruck (⟨hrsg. von⟩ H. C. R. Landon.) [1969.] 4°. **g. 75. f. (2.)**

— *See* HAYDN (F. J.) Divertimento per il clavicembalo ⟨con due violini e basso⟩. C-Dur. (Hob. XIV: C2.) Ersdruck, *etc.* ⟨Hrsg. von H. C. R. Landon.⟩ [1969.] 4°. **g. 75. hh. (1.)**

— *See* HAYDN (F. J.) [2 Duette. Hob. XXVa/2, 1.] Zwei italienische Duette (1796), für Sopran, Tenor und Pianoforte ... herausgegeben von H. C. R. Landon. [1960.] 4°. **G. 339. e. (3.)**

— *See* HAYDN (F. J.) La Fedeltà premiata. Sinfonia (Ouvertüre). [Edited by] H. C. R. Landon, *etc.* [1963.] 4°. **g. 75. r. (2.)**

— *See* HAYDN (F. J.) L'incontro improvviso ... Sinfonia, *etc.* ⟨Herausgegeben von H. C. R. Landon.⟩ [1964.] 4°. **g. 75. r. (7.)**

— *See* HAYDN (F. J.) L'Infedeltà delusa ... Burletta per musica in due atti ... A cura di ... H. C. R. Landon, *etc.* [1968.] 8°. **B. 550. d.**

— *See* HAYDN (F. J.) L'Infedeltà delusa ... Burletta per musica ... A cura di ... H. C. R. Landon, *etc.* [1961.] 4°. **G. 339. f.**

— *See* HAYDN (F. J.) L'Infedeltà delusa. Overtura. Herausgegeben von H. C. R. Landon. [1962.] 4°. **g. 75. u. (4.)**

— *See* HAYDN (F. J.) [L'Isola disabitata.] Overture to the Azione teatrale L'Isola disabitata ... Edited by H. C. R. Landon. [1959.] 8°. [*Edition Eulenburg. no.* 1124.] **b. 212.**

— *See* HAYDN (F. J.) Libera. Responsorium ad absolutionem, *etc.* ⟨Herausgegeben von H. C. R. Landon.⟩ [1969.] 4°. **G. 339. l. (3.)**

— *See* HAYDN (F. J.) Märsche. Erstdruck. Herausgegeben von H. C. R. Landon. ⟨Für Blasinstrumente⟩, *etc.* [1960.] 4°. **g. 75. g. (7.)**

— *See* HAYDN (F. J.) March ... (Hoboken VIII: 3bis.) Erstdruck herausgegeben von H. C. R. Landon, *etc.* [1961.] 4°. **g. 75. g. (6.)**

— *See* HAYDN (F. J.) [Masses. Hob. XXII/6.] Missa Sancti Nicolai ... Edited by H. C. R. Landon, *etc.* [Score.] [1976.] 8°. [*Edition Eulenburg. no.* 1099.] **b. 212.**

— *See* HAYDN (F. J.) [Masses. Hob. XXII/6.] Missa Sancti Nicolai. Mass for four part chorus, four solo voices and orchestra. Edited by H. C. R. Landon, *etc.* ⟨Vocal score.⟩ 1969. 8°. **F. 274. kk. (4.)**

— *See* HAYDN (F. J.) [Masses. Hob. XXII/7.] Missa brevis St^i Joannis de Deo. "Kleine Orgelmesse." Partitur. [Edited by H. C. R. Landon in association with K. H. Füssl and C. Landon.] [1978.] fol. **H. 2120. m. (3.)**

— *See* HAYDN (F. J.) [Masses. Hob. XXII/7.] Missa brevis Sancti Joannis de Deo ... For four-part chorus of mixed voices with piano or organ accompaniment. Edited by H. C. R. Landon. [1972.] 8°. **F. 426. ee. (1.)**

— *See* HAYDN (F. J.) [Masses. Hob. XXII/8.] Missa Cellensis. "Mariazellermesse." Herausgegeben von ... H. C. R. Landon. [1963.] 8°. **B. 550. c. (3.)**

LANDON (HOWARD CHANDLER ROBBINS)

— *See* HAYDN (F. J.) [Masses. Hob. XXII/8.] Missa Cellensis in C. "Mariazellermesse." For four-part chorus of mixed voices with piano or organ accompaniment. Edited by H. C. R. Landon. [1972.] 8°. **F. 426. ee. (2.)**

— *See* HAYDN (F. J.) [Masses. Hob. XXII/9.] Missa in tempore belli ... Herausgegeben von H. C. R. Landon. [1962.] 8°. **B. 550. c. (2.)**

— *See* HAYDN (F. J.) [Masses. Hob. XXII/10.] Missa St^i Bernardi von Offida ... Herausgegeben von H. C. R. Landon. [1962.] 8°. **B. 550. c. (1.)**

— *See* HAYDN (F. J.) [Masses. Hob. XXII/10.] Missa Sancti Bernardi de Offida. "Heiligmesse." For four-part chorus of mixed voices with piano or organ accompaniment. Edited by H. C. R. Landon. [1972.] 8°. **F. 426. ee. (3.)**

— *See* HAYDN (F. J.) [Masses. Hob. XXII/11.] Missa in angustiis. (Mass in D minor.) ⟨Nelson Mass⟩ ... Edited by H. C. R. Landon. [Score.] [1965?] 8°. [*Edition Eulenburg. no.* 995.] **b. 212.**

— *See* HAYDN (F. J.) [Masses. Hob. XXII/11.] Mass in D minor ... Edited by ... H. C. R. Landon, *etc.* [1963.] 8°. **F. 426. i. (10.)**

— *See* HAYDN (F. J.) [Masses. Hob. XXII/13.] Creation Mass in B♭ major ... Edited by H. C. R. Landon. [1975.] 8°. **F. 426. x. (11.)**

— *See* HAYDN (F. J.) [Minuets.] Raccolta de menuetti ballabili, *etc.* ⟨Herausgegeben von H. C. R. Landon.⟩ [1970.] 4°. **g. 75. ii. (1.)**

— *See* HAYDN (F. J.) [Minuets.] 24 Menuetti. Hoboken IX: 16, *etc.* ⟨Hrsg. von H. C. R. Landon.⟩ [1974.] 4°. **g. 75. ii. (2.)**

— *See* HAYDN (F. J.) "Miseri noi, misera patria" ... Erstdruck, herausgegeben von H. C. R. Landon. [1960.] 4°. **G. 339. e. (4.)**

— *See* HAYDN (F. J.) Non nobis domine ... (⟨Herausgegeben von⟩ H. C. R. Landon). Orgelpartitur, *etc.* [1978.] 4°. **G. 339. o. (2.)**

— *See* HAYDN (F. J.) [Notturnos. Hob. II/25.] Notturno No. 1 in C ... herausgegeben von H. C. R. Landon, *etc.* [1961.] 4°. **g. 75. g. (14.)**

— *See* HAYDN (F. J.) [Notturnos. Hob. II/26.] Notturno No. 2 in F ... (⟨Hrsg. von⟩ H. C. Robbins Landon.) Partitur, *etc.* [1979.] 4°. **f. 460. c. (1.)**

— *See* HAYDN (F. J.) [Notturnos. Hob. II/27.] Notturno No. 8 in G ... (⟨Hrsg. von⟩ H. C. R. Landon.) Partitur, *etc.* [1980.] 4°. **g. 75. ii. (5.)**

— *See* HAYDN (F. J.) [Notturnos. Hob. II/28.] Notturno No. 7 in F ... (⟨Hrsg. von⟩ H. C. R. Landon.) Partitur, *etc.* [1980.] 4°. **g. 75. ii. (4.)**

— *See* HAYDN (F. J.) [Notturnos. Hob. II/29.] Notturno No. 5 in C ... (⟨Hrsg. von⟩ H. C. Robbins Landon.) Partitur, *etc.* [1979.] 4°. **f. 460. c. (4.)**

— *See* HAYDN (F. J.) [Notturnos. Hob. II/30.] Notturno No. 6 in G ... (⟨Hrsg. von⟩ H. C. R. Landon.) Partitur, *etc.* [1980.] 4°. **g. 75. ii. (3.)**

— *See* HAYDN (F. J.) [Notturnos. Hob. II/31.] Notturno No. 4 in C ... (⟨Hrsg. von⟩ H. C. Robbins Landon.) Partitur, *etc.* [1979.] 4°. **f. 460. c. (3.)**

— *See* HAYDN (F. J.) [Notturnos. Hob. II/32.] Notturno No. 3 in C ... (⟨Hrsg. von ⟩ H. C. Robbins Landon.) Partitur, *etc.* [1979.] 4°. **f. 460. c. (2.)**

— *See* HAYDN (F. J.) [Orfeo e Euridice.] Overture for an English Opera, *etc.* [Edited by H. C. Robbins Landon.] [1953.] 4°. **h. 656. u. (5.)**

LANDON (HOWARD CHANDLER ROBBINS)

— *See* HAYDN (F. J.) Orlando Paladino. Sinfonia. (Overtura) . . . herausgegeben von H. C. R. Landon, *etc.* [1960.] 4°.
        g. 75. g. (8.)

— *See* HAYDN (F. J.) [Overture. Hob. ɪa/4.] Ouvertüre in D . . . Nach dem Erstdruck herausgegeben von H. C. R. Landon, *etc.* [1959.] 4°.
        g. 75. g. (5.)

— *See* HAYDN (F. J.) [Overture. Hob. ɪa/7.] Sinfonia in D . . . herausgegeben von H. C. R. Landon, *etc.* [1959.] 4°.
        g. 75. g. (12.)

— *See* HAYDN (F. J.) Le Pescatrici . . . (ed. H. C. R. Landon.) [Score.] [1965?] fol.
        H. 2120. s.

— *See* HAYDN (F. J.) Le Pescatrici. Dramma giocoso in tre atti . . . Prima edizione in cura di H. C. R. Landon, *etc.* [1971.] 4°.
        G. 339. n.

— *See* HAYDN (F. J.) [Quartets.—Collections.] Streichquartette . . . herausgegeben von R. Barrett-Ayres and H. C. R. Landon, *etc.* [1977, *etc.*] 8°.
        b. 200. c.

— *See* HAYDN (F. J.) Salve regina . . . Partitur, *etc.* ⟨Hrsg. von H. C. R. Landon.⟩ [1964.] 4°.
        G. 339. e. (5.)

— *See* HAYDN (F. J.) Scena di Berenice . . . Herausgegeben von H. C. R. Landon. Partitur, *etc.* [1965.] 4°.   **G. 339. e. (8.)**

— *See* HAYDN (F. J.) Scena di Berenice . . . Herausgegeben von H. C. R. Landon . . . Klavierauszug. [1965.] 4°.
        G. 339. e. (9.)

— *See* HAYDN (F. J.) Scherzando No. 1 ⟨–6⟩ . . . (Hoboken ɪɪ. 33⟨–38⟩.) Erstdruck herausgegeben von H. C. R. Landon, *etc.* [1961.] 4°.
        g. 75. k. (7.)

— *See* HAYDN (F. J.) "Son pietosa, son bonina" . . . Herausgegeben von H. C. R. Landon, *etc.* [1959.] 4°.
        G. 339. e. (2.)

— *See* HAYDN (F. J.) Lo Speziale. Dramma giocoso in tre atti . . . In cura di H. C. R. Landon, *etc.* [1970.] 4°.   **G. 339. l. (5.)**

— *See* HAYDN (F. J.) Lo Speziale. Dramma giocoso. Sinfonia . . . Herausgegeben von H. C. R. Landon. [1959.] 4°.
        g. 75. r. (6.)

— *See* HAYDN (F. J.) Stabat mater . . . Edited by H. C. R. Landon. Full score. 1977. fol.
        I. 605. p.

— *See* HAYDN (F. J.) Stabat mater. For four part chorus, four solo voices and orchestra. Edited by H. C. R. Landon. Piano reduction by R. Biss. 1977. 8°.   **F. 426. gg. (1.)**

— *See* HAYDN (F. J.) [Symphonies.—Collections.] Kritische Ausgabe sämtlicher Symphonien . . . Herausgeber . . . H. C. R. Landon, *etc.* [1963, *etc.*] 8°.   **d. 96.**

— *See* HAYDN (F. J.) [Symphonies.—Collections.] Sinfonia No. 1, [*etc.*] ([Edited by] H. C. R. Landon), *etc.* [1962, *etc.*] 4°.
        g. 75. q.

— *See* HAYDN (F. J.) [Symphonies.—Collections. Hob. ɪ/93–104.] Die Salomon-Symphonien zum ersten Male nach Autographen, authentischen Kopien und Frühdrucken herausgegeben von H. C. R. Landon, *etc.* [1962, *etc.*] fol.
        h. 656. uu.

— *See* HAYDN (F. J.) [Symphonies.—Collections. Hob. ɪ/2, 16, 17, 27, 33, 37, 57, 98.] [Instrumental parts omitted from most printed editions. Edited by H. C. R. Landon.] 1955. 8°. [*LANDON (H. C. R.) The Symphonies of Joseph Haydn.* pp. 781–794.]
        7900. d. 105.

— *See* HAYDN (F. J.) Symphony, No. 6 (La Matin), D major . . . Edited . . . by H. C. R. Landon. [1956.] 8°. [*Edition Eulenburg. no.* 536.]
        b. 212.

LANDON (HOWARD CHANDLER ROBBINS)

— *See* HAYDN (F. J.) Symphony, No. 8, G major . . . Edited and with foreword by R. Landon. [1954.] 8°. [*Edition Eulenburg. no.* 515.]   **b. 212.**

— *See* HAYDN (F. J.) Symphony No. 26. D minor (Lamentatione) . . . Edited . . . by H. C. R. Landon. [c. 1960.] 8°. [*Edition Eulenburg. no.* 550.]   **b. 212.**

— *See* HAYDN (F. J.) Symphony No. 39. G minor . . . Edited . . . by H. C. R. Landon. [c. 1960.] 8°. [*Edition Eulenburg. no.* 551.]
        b. 212.

— *See* HAYDN (F. J.) Symphony no. 44, E minor . . . Edited . . . by H. C. R. Landon. [1958.] 8°. [*Edition Eulenburg. no.* 544.]
        b. 212.

— *See* HAYDN (F. J.) Symphony No. 44 . . . Edited . . . by H. C. R. Landon. [1959.] 4°.   **g. 455. kk. (10.)**

— *See* HAYDN (F. J.) Symphony, No. 49 (La Passione), F minor . . . Edited . . . by H. C. R. Landon. [1955.] 8°. [*Edition Eulenburg. no.* 535.]   **b. 212.**

— *See* HAYDN (F. J.) Symphony No. 53, D major, (L'Imperiale) . . . Edited from the original edition by H. C. R. Landon. [1956.] 8°. [*Edition Eulenburg. no.* 537.]   **b. 212.**

— *See* HAYDN (F. J.) Sinfonia No. 58. Herausgegeben von . . . H. C. R. Landon, *etc.* [1958.] 4°.   **h. 656. oo. (1.)**

— *See* HAYDN (F. J.) Sinfonia No. 59. Herausgegeben von . . . H. C. R. Landon, *etc.* [1958.] 4°.   **h. 656. oo. (2.)**

— *See* HAYDN (F. J.) Sinfonia No. 60. Herausgegeben von . . . H. C. R. Landon, *etc.* [1959.] 4°.   **h. 656. oo. (3.)**

— *See* HAYDN (F. J.) Sinfonia No. 61. Herausgegeben von . . . H. C. R. Landon, *etc.* [1959.] 4°.   **h. 656. oo. (4.)**

— *See* HAYDN (F. J.) Sinfonia No. 65. Herausgegeben von . . . H. C. R. Landon, *etc.* [1958.] 4°.   **h. 656. oo. (5.)**

— *See* HAYDN (F. J.) Symphony No. 70 in D major . . . Edited . . . by H. C. R. Landon. [1963.] 8°. [*Edition Eulenburg. no.* 559.]
        b. 212.

— *See* HAYDN (F. J.) Symphony, No. 84. (Paris No. 3) . . . Edited . . . by R. Landon. [1954.] 8°. [*Edition Eulenburg. no.* 534.]
        b. 212.

— *See* HAYDN (F. J.) Symphony, No. 87 (Paris No. 6), A major . . . Edited from the original MS. by R. Landon. [1954.] 8°. [*Edition Eulenburg. no.* 533.]   **b. 212.**

— *See* HAYDN (F. J.) Symphony No. 89 in F major (1787) . . . Edited from the autograph by H. C. R. Landon. [1963.] 8°. [*Edition Eulenburg. no.* 558.]   **b. 212.**

— *See* HAYDN (F. J.) [Symphonies. Hob. ɪ/107.] Sinfonia. First publication, *etc.* [In B flat. The original version of the work published as the String Quartet, op. 1, no. 5. Edited by H. C. R. Landon.] 1955. 8°. [*LANDON (H. C. R.) The Symphonies of Joseph Haydn.*]   **7900. d. 105.**

— *See* HAYDN (F. J.) [Symphonies. Hob. ɪ/107.] Sinfonia "A" . . . ([Edited by] H. C. R. Landon), *etc.* [1965.] 4°.   **g. 75. u. (7.)**

— *See* HAYDN (F. J.) Sinfonia (Parthia) in B. (Hob. ɪ: 108.) Herausgegeben von H. C. R. Landon, *etc.* [1960.] 4°.
        g. 75. g. (10.)

— *See* HAYDN (F. J.) Te Deum [Hob. XXIIIc/1] für Fürst Nicolaus Esterházy . . . Erstdruck (⟨Hrsg. von⟩ H. C. R. Landon). Partitur, *etc.* [1967.] 4°.   **G. 339. m. (1.)**

— *See* HAYDN (F. J.) Te Deum [Hob. XXIIIc/1] für Fürst Nicolaus Esterházy . . . Erstdruck (⟨hrsg. von⟩ H. C. R. Landon) . . . Klavierauszug, *etc.* [1967.] 4°.   **G. 339. m. (2.)**

LANDON (HOWARD CHANDLER ROBBINS)

— *See* HAYDN (F. J.) Te Deum. [Hob. XXIIIC/2.] Für die Kaiserin Marie Thérèse ... Herausgegeben von H. C. R. Landon. Partitur, *etc.* [1959.] 4°. **G. 339. c. (9.)**

— *See* HAYDN (F. J.) Te Deum [Hob. XXIIIC/2] für die Kaiserin Marie Thérèse ... Herausgegeben von H. C. R. Landon ... Klavierauszug, *etc.* [1959.] 4°. **G. 339. c. (7.)**

— *See* HAYDN (F. J.) [Trios. Horn, violin and violoncello. Hob. IV/5.] Divertimento à tre per il corno da caccia ... Nach dem Autograph herausgegeben von H. C. R. Landon, *etc.* [1957.] 4°. **g. 455. x. (11.)**

— *See* HAYDN (F. J.) Klaviertrios. Urtext-Ausgabe ... herausgegeben von H. C. R. Landon, *etc.* [1977, 1970, *etc.*] 4°. **g. 75. gg.**

— *See* HAYDN (F. J.) [Trios.] Divertimento in E. Klaviertrio. (Hoboken XV: 34.) Erstdruck herausgegeben von H. C. R. Landon. [1959.] 4°. **g. 75. g. (1.)**

— *See* HAYDN (F. J.) [*Doubtful and Supposititious Works.*] Die Feuersbrunst ... Opera in two acts ... Edited by H. C. R. Landon, *etc.* [1963.] 8°. **G. 339. h.**

— *See* HAYDN (F. J.) [*Doubtful and Supposititious Works.*] [Die Feuersbrunst.] Overture ... Edited and with foreword by H. C. R. Landon. [1963.] 8°. [*Edition Eulenburg. no.* 1128.] **b. 212.**

— *See* HAYDN (F. J.) [*Doubtful and Supposititious Works.*] Litaniae de Beata Maria Virgine in C ... Erstdruck herausgegeben von H. C. R. Landon, *etc.* [1960.] 4°. **G. 339. c. (8.)**

— *See* HAYDN (F. J.) [*Doubtful and Supposititious Works.*] [Masses.] Missa brevis alla capella "Rorate coeli desuper" ... Erstmalige Veröffentlichung vorgelegt von ... H. C. R. Landon ... Partitur, *etc.* [1958.] fol. **H. 2120. h. (1.)**

— *See* HAYDN (F. J.) [*Doubtful and Supposititious Works.*] [Masses.] Missa brevis alla capella "Rorate coeli desuper" ... Erstmalige Veröffentlichung vorgelegt von ... H. C. R. Landon ... Klavierauszug, *etc.* [1957.] 4°. **G. 339. c. (4.)**

— *See* HAYDN (J. M.) Der büssende Sünder. Introduzione, *etc.* ⟨Hrsg. von H. C. R. Landon.⟩ [1968.] 4°. **g. 420. ff. (10.)**

— *See* HAYDN (J. M.) Concerto per il flauto traverso. Erste Veröffentlichung ... herausgegeben von ... H. C. R. Landon. Partitur, *etc.* [1959.] 4°. **g. 65. b. (7.)**

— *See* HAYDN (J. M.) Concerto per il flauto traverso ... Herausgegeben von H. C. R. Landon. Klavierauszug, *etc.* [1959.] 4°. **g. 65. b. (3.)**

— *See* HAYDN (J. M.) Rebekka als Braut. Intrada, *etc.* ⟨Hrsg. von H. C. R. Landon.⟩ [1968.] 4°. **g. 420. ff. (9.)**

— *See* HAYDN (J. M.) Sinfonia in C-Dur. [Perger 31.] Erstdruck, *etc.* ⟨Herausgegeben von H. C. R. Landon.⟩ [1966.] 4°. **g. 420. ff. (5.)**

— *See* HAYDN (J. M.) Sinfonia in D-dur. [Perger 42.] Erstdruck, herausgegeben von H. C. R. Landon, *etc.* [1962.] 4°. **g. 65. b. (8.)**

— *See* MOZART (J. G. L.) Cassatio ex G (mit der "Kindersinfonie"), *etc.* ⟨Hrsg. von H. C. R. Landon.⟩ [1974.] 4°. **g. 934. s. (8.)**

— *See* MOZART (J. G. L.) Sinfonia in B für Streicher. Erstdruck, *etc.* ⟨Hrsg. von H. C. R. Landon.⟩ [1970.] 4°. **g. 1780. hh. (10.)**

— *See* MOZART (J. G. L.) Sinfonia, G major, for String Orchestra ... Edited by H. C. R. Landon. [1957.] 8°. [*Edition Eulenburg. no.* 539.] **b. 212.**

LANDON (HOWARD CHANDLER ROBBINS)

— *See* MOZART (J. G. L.) Sinfonia in G für Streicher. [A different work from the preceding.] Erstdruck. ([Edited by] H. C. R. Landon), *etc.* [1970.] 4°. **g. 934. v. (2.)**

— *See* MOZART (W. A.) Kyrie (K. 322). For four-part chorus ... Edited by H. C. R. Landon. [1977.] 8°. **F. 307. hh. (6.)**

— *See* MOZART (W. A.) Kyrie (K. 323). For four-part chorus ... Edited by H. C. R. Landon. [1977.] 8°. **F. 307. hh. (7.)**

— *See* MOZART (W. A.) Kyrie. (K. 341) ... Edited by H. C. R. Landon. [1977.] 8°. **F. 307. hh. (8.)**

— *See* MOZART (W. A.) [Masses. K. 257.] Credo Mass ... Mixed chorus with piano or organ accompaniment. Edited by H. C. R. Landon. [1974.] 8°. **F. 240. s. (1.)**

— *See* MOZART (W. A.) [Masses. K. 258.] Piccolomini Mass. (Missa brevis in C) ... Mixed chorus with piano or organ accompaniment. Edited by H. C. Robbins Landon. [1974.] 8°. **F. 240. s. (4.)**

— *See* MOZART (W. A.) [Masses. K. 259.] Organ Solo Mass. (Missa brevis in C.) ... Mixed chorus with piano or organ accompaniment. Edited by H. C. R. Landon. [1974.] 8°. **F. 240. s. (3.)**

— *See* MOZART (W. A.) [Masses. K. 337.] Missa for Archbishop Colloredo ... Four-part chorus ... Edited by H. C. R. Landon. [1973.] 8°. **F. 240. t. (1.)**

— *See* MOZART (W. A.) Missa C-moll für Soli, Chor, Orchester und Orgel ... K. V. 427 (417ª) ... Nach der Gesamtausgabe und dem Andre'schen Erstdruck revidiert bzw. rekonstruiert und mit einer Einführung versehen von H. C. R.Landon. [1956.] 8°. [*Edition Eulenburg. no.* 983.] **b. 212.**

— *See* MOZART (W. A.) Symphony in D, K. 385. 'Haffner' symphony. Edited ... by doctoral students of the City University of New York under the supervision of H. C. R. Landon. 1971. 8°. **f. 67. dd. (1.)**

— *See* MOZART (W. A.) [Symphonies. K. 543.] Sinfonie in Es ... Herausgegeben von ... H. C. R. Landon. [1958.] fol. **h. 321. qq. (2.)**

— *See* MOZART (W. A.) [Symphonies. K. 550.] Sinfonie in g ... Herausgegeben von ... H. C. R. Landon. [1958.] fol. **h. 321. qq. (3.)**

— *See* MOZART (W. A.) [Symphonies. K. 550.] Sinfonie in g ... (1. Fassung.) [Edited by H. C. R. Landon.] [1976.] fol. **h. 405. cc. (2.)**

— *See* ORDOÑEZ (C. d') Sinfonia per tre cori. Partitura. Prima edizione a cura di H. C. R. Landon. 1972. 4°. [*Accademia musicale.* 16.] **H. 4029.**

— *See* SALOMON (J. P.) Romance. Für Solo-Violine und Streicher. Erstdruck. ([Edited by] H. C. R. Landon.) [1970.] 4°. **g. 934. v. (3.)**

— *See* VIVALDI (A.) Magnificat. Ossecensis. Per soli, coro ed orchestra. Prima edizione a cura di H. C. R. Landon. Partitura. [1961.] 4°. **G. 518. f. (1.)**

— *See* VIVALDI (A.) Magnificat. Ossecensis. Per soli, coro ed orchestra. Prima edizione a cura di H. C. R. Landon, *etc.* [Vocal score.] [1961.] 4°. **G. 1271. k. (1.)**

— *See* WANHAL (J. B.) Sinfonia g-moll. Herausgegeben von H. C. R. Landon, *etc.* [1965.] 4°. **g. 860. m. (1.)**

LANDON (JAMES F.)

— Gavotte de Concert for piano. *R. Maynard: London,* [1889.] fol. **h. 1489. s. (1.)**

LANDON (ROBBINS)
— *See* LANDON (Howard C. R.)

LANDONO (FRANCESCO)
— *See* SPOGLIA. Spoglia Amorosa. Madrigali, *etc.* [With a dedication by F. Landono.] 1584. 4°. **D. 202.**

— *See* SPOGLIA. Spoglia Amorosa. Madrigali, *etc.* [With a dedication signed by F. Landono.] 1588. 4°.
R. M. 15. e. 1. (14.)

LANDOR (PAUL)
— "Fleurs d'Amour." Valse. [P. F.] *Hopwood & Crew: London,* 1905. fol. **h. 3286. ll. (20.)**

— Papillon rouge. Valse. [P. F.] *Ascherberg, Hopwood & Crew: London,* 1908. fol. **h. 3286. uu. (37.)**

LANDOWSKA (WANDA)
— Cadenza for the Keyboard Concerto in B-flat major, Opus 4, No. 6 by G. F. Handel. Second movement. *Broude Bros.: New York,* [1959.] 4°. **g. 1126. ii. (7.)**

— Cadenzas for the Keyboard Concerto in D major, Opus 21 by Joseph Haydn. First and second movements. pp. 6. *Broude Bros.: New York,* [1960.] 4°. **g. 1126. ii. (6.)**

— Cadenzas for the Piano Concerto No. 9 in E-flat major, K. 271, by W. A. Mozart. First and second movements. pp. 7. *Broude Bros.: New York,* [1963.] 4°. **g. 1126. ii. (8.)**

— Cadenzas for the Piano Concerto No. 11, in F major, K. 413, by W. A. Mozart. First and second movements. pp. 5. *Broude Bros.: New York,* [1963.] 4°. **g. 1126. ii. (14.)**

— Cadenzas for the Piano Concerto No. 12, in A major, K. 414, by W. A. Mozart. First movement. pp. 5. *Broude Bros.: New York,* [1959.] 4°. **g. 1126. ii. (13.)**

— Cadenzas for the Piano Concerto No. 20, in D minor, K. 466, by W. A. Mozart. First and third movements. pp. 9. *Broude Bros.: New York,* [1963.] 4°. **g. 1126. ii. (12.)**

— Cadenzas and Ornamentations for the Piano Concerto No. 22, in E-flat major, K. 482, by W. A. Mozart. First and third movements. pp. 12. *Broude Bros.: New York,* [1963.] 4°. **g. 1126. ii. (11.)**

— Cadenzas and Ornamentation for the Piano Concerto No. 26, in D major, K. 537, by W. A. Mozart. First and second movements. pp. 5. *Broude Bros.: New York,* [1963.] 4°. **g. 1126. ii. (10.)**

— Cadenzas for the Piano Sonata in B-flat major, K. 333 by W. A. Mozart. Third movement. pp. 4. *Broude Bros.: New York,* [1959.] 4°. **g. 1126. ii. (9.)**

— Rêverie d'automne. Pour piano. ⟨Op: 6.⟩ pp. 5. *Enoch & co.: Paris,* [1901.] fol. **h. 3870. dd. (4.)**

— *See* LANNER (J. F. C.) [*Smaller Collections.*] Valses Viennoises ... Réunies et doigtées par W. Landowska. 1925. 4°.
g. 1127. dd. (2.)

— *See* LANNER (J. F. C.) [*Smaller Collections.*] Valses Viennoises ... Réunies et doigtées par W. Landowska. 1926. 4°.
g. 1127. gg. (19.)

LANDOWSKI (MARCEL)
— Les Adieux. Drame lyrique en un acte et un tableau. Paroles et musique de M. Landowski. Partition chant et piano. pp. 59. *Éditions Choudens: Paris,* [1960.] 4°. **G. 1269. k. (3.)**

— Concerto pour basson et orchestre. Réduction pour basson et piano. [Score and part.] 2 pt. *Éditions Choudens: Paris,* [1959.] 4°. **g. 1083. d. (5.)**

LANDOWSKI (MARCEL)
— Concerto pour ondes martenot, orchestre à cordes et percussion. Partition d'orchestre. pp. 66. *Éditions Choudens: Paris,* [c. 1970.] 8°. **e. 667. i. (1.)**

— Concerto pour ondes martenot, orchestre à cordes et percussion. Réduction pour piano. [Score and part.] 2 pt. *Éditions Choudens: Paris,* [1957.] fol. **h. 1568. k. (1.)**

— 2me concerto pour piano et orchestre. (Réduction pour deux pianos.) pp. 66. *Éditions Choudens: Paris,* [1963.] 4°.
h. 3865. dd. (6.)

— L'Opéra de poussière. Drame lyrique. 1 prologue—2 actes—4 tableaux. Livret de Gérard Gaillet et Marcel Landowski ... Partition chant et piano. pp. 201. *Éditions Choudens: Paris,* [1964.] 4°. **G. 1268. hh. (2.)**

— Symphonie N°. 1, "Jean de la Peur," *etc.* [Score.] pp. 112. *Choudens: Paris,* [1949.] 8°. **c. 156. ff. (3.)**

— Deuxième symphonie en trois mouvements ... Partition d'orchestre. pp. 117. *Éditions Choudens: Paris,* [1965.] 8°.
d. 145. s. (1.)

—— Troisième symphonie en deux mouvements ... Partition d'orchestre. pp. 73. *Éditions Choudens: Paris,* [c. 1965.] 8°.
d. 145. s. (2.)

LANDPARTHIE
—— Ein Landparthie. Liederspiel. *See* KOEHLER (C.)

LANDRAM (W. J.)
— At home our friends are dying. [Song, begins: "Soft the fall winds"]. Words by Miss V. R. Moser. *Chicago,* 1864. fol.
H. 1780. f. (7.)

— I spare that aged tree, or Woodman's reply ... [song,] written by S. Dyer. *New York,* 1855. fol. **H. 1780. p. (29.)**

LANDRÉ (GUILLAUME LOUIS FRÉDÉRIC) *the Elder*
— Requiem. In memoriam uxorsis (1930). Voor gemengd koor, soli en orkest. [With a portrait.] Klavieruittreksel. pp. 66. *W. F. Lichtenauer: Rotterdam,* [1934.] 4°. **H. 1125. d.**

LANDRÉ (GUILLAUME LOUIS FRÉDÉRIC) *the Younger*
— Suite pour orchestre à cordes et piano (1936). [Score and parts.] 6 pt. *Éditions de l'oiseau lyre: Paris,* [1939.] 4°.
h. 3210. i. (435.)

— Trio pour piano, violon et violoncelle. [Score and parts.] 3 pt. *Éditions de l'oiseau lyre: Paris,* [1934.] 4°. **g. 409. p. (5.)**

LANDRÉ (WILLEM)
— *See* LANDRÉ (G. L. F.) *the Elder.*

LANDRIN (   ) *Fils*
— La Léon. [Contredanse.] *Landrin: Paris,* [1785?] 8°.
Hirsch I. 294. (27.)

LANDRIN (   ) *Maître de Danse*
— [A collection of "contre-danses" from a series edited by Landrin.] no. 10–12, 24–27, 34, 36, 40, 42–45, 60, 62, 68, 69, 80, 81, 83, 87, 88, 100, 110, 113, 114, 116, 117, 119–121, 123, 126, 128, 129, 133, 134, 141, 144, 145, 152, 155, 165, 183, 188–191, 193, 196, 197, 199–203, 205–208, 211, 213–217, 254. 68 pt. *Paris,* [1765?] 8°.
With the arms of King Louis XV of France impressed in gold on the covers. **Hirsch I. 302**
& Hirsch I. 302. a. (4.)

LANDRIN (   ) *Maître de Danse*

— [A collection of "contre-danses" from the same series as the preceding, edited by Landrin.] no. 82–84, 86–88, 90, 93–101, 103–106, 108–115. 28 pt. *Paris*, [1765?] 8°.   **c. 57. a. (1.)**

— [1ᵉ, 2ᵉ] Feuille de menuet avec accompagnement. Mis au jour par Mʳ Landrin. 2 no. *Paris*, [1785?] 8°.
Hirsch I. 302. a. (5.)

— Potpourri François des Contre-danse Ancienne, tel, qu'il se danse chez la Reine. Arrangé, et mis au Jour, par Mʳ Landrin, *etc.* (Potpourri Nouveau avec l'Explication des Figures, vû et corrigé, telle que je les enseigne au public.) 24 no. *Chez Landrin: Paris*, [1785? *etc.*] 8°.
Engraved throughout. There is a MS. index of the contredanses.   **c. 57. (1.)**

— [Another copy.]
With the arms of King Louis XV of France impressed in gold on the covers.   **Hirsch I. 302. a. (1.)**

— 1ᵉʳ Recueil d'Airs Figurée [*sic*] tel qu'il se joue aux Woxhall de la foire Sᵗ Germain, *etc.* (2ᵐᵉ Recueil de Menuet mêlée de Petit Airs, avec les Préludes dans les tons les plus usités, *etc.*) (3ᵐᵉ Recueil de Menuet mêlée de Petit Airs, *etc.*) (4ᵐᵉ Receuil de Menuet de Mʳ Lahante ... Mis au Jour par Mʳ Landrin, *etc.*) (5ᵉᵐᵉ Recueil d'Anglaise arrangées avec leurs Traits, *etc.*) 5 no. *Chez Landrin: Paris*, [1785?] 8°.
Engraved throughout. The following composers' names occur in this collection: Denis, Lahante, La Loyeau, Dſichere [Fisher?], Dauvergne, Canavase and Fauveau.   **c. 57. (3.)**

— [Another copy.] 1ᵉʳ Recueil d'airs figurée [*sic*], *etc.* ⟨4ᵐᵉ Recueil de menuet—[5ᵉᵐᵉ] Recueil d'anglaise.⟩ 3 no. *Paris*, [1785?] 8°.
Hirsch I. 302. a. (3.)

LANDROCK (GUSTAVE)

— L'Oiseau de Paradis (Paradies Vogel) valse pour le Piano. *Mayence*, [1869.] fol.   **h. 1462. r. (4.)**

LANDRY (ALBERT)

— À travers Prés. Deux Paysanneries pour Piano, *etc.* (Op. 292.) *Schott & Co.: London*, 1909. fol.   **g. 606. f. (17.)**

— Auréoline. Mazurka élégante. (Op. 181.) [P. F.] *Au Ménestrel: Paris*, 1902. fol.
Supplement to "Le Ménestrel," September 14th, 1902.
h. 3284. f. (36.)

— Barcarolle, for the Pianoforte. *Ascherberg, Hopwood & Crew: London*, 1911. fol.   **h. 3284. f. (37.)**

— Bergers Louis XV. Air à danser pour piano. *A. Lissarrague: Paris*, [1887.] fol.   **h. 3281. l. (2.)**

— Cendrillonnette. Deux petites Valses pour Piano, *etc.* (Op. 293.) *Schott & Co.: London*, 1909. fol.   **g. 606. f. (18.)**

— Les Échos du Lac. Valse brillante pour piano. *Chelu: Paris*, [1887.] fol.   **h. 3281. l. (3.)**

— 6 Morceaux très faciles pour Piano à 4 mains ... 1. Premier Sourire. Petite Valse. 2. Premier Jouet. 3. Premier Pas. Gavotte. 4. Bébé calin. Berceuse. 5. Premier Babillage. Galop. 6. Bébé joyeux. Tarentelle. 6 no. *Schott & Co.: London*, 1907. fol.   **g. 545. m. (11.)**

— Réveil d'Avril. Valse de Salon. (Op. 180.) [P. F.] *Au Ménestrel: Paris*, 1902. fol.
Supplement to "Le Ménestrel," October 12th, 1902.
h. 3284. f. (38.)

LANDSBERG (LUDWIG)

— Novena cantata dai Pifferari e accompagnata dalla loro Cornamusa ... messa in musica per Piano-forte e canto ad libitum. *Martelli: Roma*, [1850?] fol.   **G. 424. c. (3.)**

LANDSBERG (SIGMUND)

— Caste. Song. *J. Church Co.: Cincinnati, etc.*, 1903. fol.
H. 1799. vv. (20.)

— Dry yo' Eyes. [Song.]—F. L. Stanton, *etc. Boston Music Co.: Boston, Mass.*, (1904.) fol.   **G. 807. ff. (27.)**

— Lines. [Song.] *Boston Music Co.: Boston, Mass.*, (1905.) fol.
G. 807. jj. (28.)

— Paolo. Capricietto-Burlesque for Piano Solo. *C. Fischer: New York, Boston*, (1911.) fol.   **h. 3284. f. (39.)**

— A Song Memory. Song for medium voice. (H. B. Linsley.) *O. Ditson Co.: Boston*, 1904. fol.   **H. 1799. vv. (21.)**

— The Symphony. [Song.] Poem by R. H. Schauffler. *Boston Music Co.: Boston, Mass.*, (1904.) fol.   **G. 807. jj. (29.)**

LANDSBERGIS (VYTAUTAS)

— *See* ČIURLIONIS (Mikalojus K.) Album per pianoforte. Ed.: V. Landsbergis. 1978. 4°.   **f. 791. (1.)**

— *See* GRUODIS (J.) Kūriniai fortepijonui. ⟨Paruošė V. Landsbergis.⟩ 1961. 4°.   **g. 442. ff.**

LANDSCAPE

— The Landscape. [Song.] *See* HOW. How pleas'd within my native bowers, *etc.* [1761.] 8°.   **P. P. 5441.**

— Landscape. [Song.] *See* SCHERER (F. H.) Four Songs. II.

— The Landscape. [Song.] *See* YATES (W.)

LANDSCAPES

— Landscapes. Song cycle. *See* HODDINOTT (Alun)

— Landscapes. [Songs.] *See* HOLD (Trevor J.)

— Landscapes. Choral suite. *See* PAYNTER (John)

— Landscapes. [Song.] *See* WILLEBY (C.)

LANDSCHAFT

— Landschaft. [Song.] *See* SCHILLINGS (M. von) Vier Lieder. N° 4.

LANDSCHAFTSBILDER

— Landschaftsbilder. [6 songs.] *See* DRAESEKE (F.)

LANDSEER (LAURA)

— Federation. Waltz. [P. F.] *Weekes & Co.: London*, [1891.] fol.
h. 3285. p. (51.)

LANDSHOFF (LUDWIG)

— Alte Meister des bel canto. Eine Sammlung von Arien aus Opern und Kantaten, von Kanzonen, Kanzonetten, Opern-und Kammerduetten, für den praktischen Gebrauch herausgegeben von L. Landshoff. pp. 223. *C. F. Peters: Leipzig*, [1915.] 4°.
Edition Peters. no. 3348.   **Hirsch M. 211.**

— Alte Meister des Bel Canto. Arien für eine Singstimme, ein obligates Streichinstrument und Basso continuo (Klavier). Für den praktischen Gebrauch herausgegeben von L. Landshoff. pp. 76. *C. F. Peters: Leipzig*, [c. 1915.] 8°.
F. 1196. n. (1.)

— *See* BACH (C. P. E.) [6 concerti per il cembalo. Wq. 43. No. 2.] Concerto D-dur ... für Cembalo (Klavier), zwei Flöten, zwei Hörner und Streicher ... Herausgegeben von L. Landshoff, *etc.* [1967.] 4°.   **g. 48. q. (1.)**

LANDSHOFF (Ludwig)

— *See* Bach (C. P. E.) [Zwey Trio. Wq. 161. No. 2.] Trio in B-dur ... Bearbeitet von L. Landshoff. [1936.] 4°.　　**g. 48. h. (11.)**

— *See* Bach (J. Christian) [*Collections.*] [Konzert- und Opernarien. Edited, with P. F. accompaniment, by L. Landshoff.] [1923.] 8°.　　**Hirsch M. 11.**

— *See* Bach (J. Christian) [*Collections.*] 12 Konzert- und Opernarien zum praktischen Gebrauch herausgegeben von L. Landshoff. [c. 1950.] 8°.　　**F. 89.**

— *See* Bach (J. Christian) [La Clemenza di Scipione.— Overture.] Sinfonia (D dur) für Orchester ... [The overture to "La Clemenza di Scipione" with the andante from the Overture, Op. 18, No. 6.] Eingerichtet und herausgegeben von L. Landshoff, *etc.* [c. 1960.] 4°.　　**h. 423. j. (7.)**

— *See* Bach (J. Christian) [A Third Sett of Six Concertos. Op. 13. No. 2.] Konzert (D dur) für Cembalo oder Klavier und Orchester ... Herausgegeben von L. Landshoff, *etc.* [1955.] 4°.　　**h. 423. e. (3.)**

— *See* Bach (J. Christian) [A Third Sett of Six Concertos. Op. 13. No. 4.] Konzert (B dur) für Cembalo oder Klavier und Orchester ... Herausgegeben von L. Landshoff, *etc.* [1955.] 4°.　　**h. 423. e. (4.)**

— *See* Bach (J. Christian) Zehn Klavier-Sonaten ... Herausgegeben von L. Landshoff. [1925.] 4°.　　**Hirsch M. 672.**

— *See* Bach (J. Christian) Sonatas ... (Opera x.) Edited ... by L. Landshoff. [1938.] 4°.　　**h. 423. d. (3.)**

— *See* Bach (J. S.) Aria, "Bekennen will ich seinen Namen" ... herausgegeben und eingerichtet von L. Landshoff, *etc.* 1935. fol.　　**H. 911. k.**

— *See* Bach (J. S.) [Inventionen und Sinfonien.] Die 15 zweistimmigen Inventionen und 15 dreistimmigen Sinfonien im Urtext. Herausgegeben von L. Landshoff. [1933.] 4° & 8°.　　**g. 548. dd.**

— *See* Bach (J. S.) [A reissue.] Die 15 zweistimmigen Inventionen und die 15 dreistimmigen Sinfonien im Urtext. Herausgegeben von L. Landshoff. [1935.] 4° & 8°.　　**g. 548. ii.**

— *See* Bach (J. S.) [Inventionen und Sinfonien.] Die 15 zweistimmigen Inventionen und die 15 dreistimmigen Sinfonien im Urtext. Herausgegeben von L. Landshoff. [1978.] 4°.　　**g. 1700. h. (5.)**

— *See* Bach (J. S.) [Zweistimmige Inventionen.] Fifteen 2-part Inventions ... ([Edited by] L. Landshoff.) [1972?] 4°.　　**g. 699. ss. (9.)**

— *See* Bach (J. S.) [Dreistimmige Inventionen (Sinfonien).] Fifteen 3-part Inventions (Sinfonias) ... ([Edited by] L. Landshoff.) [1972?] 4°.　　**g. 699. ss. (10.)**

— *See* Bach (J. S.) Musikalisches Opfer ... herausgegeben von L. Landshoff. [1937.] 4° & 8°.　　**g. 548. jj.**

— *See* Bach (J. S.) Sonate, F dur, für Violine und Cembalo. [BWV 1022.] Herausgegeben von L. Landshoff, *etc.* 1936. 4°.　　**g. 548. kk. (18.)**

— *See* Bach (J. S.) Trio-Sonaten (i. ii.) Neue Urtext-Ausgabe von L. Landshoff. [B. G. Jahrg. 9 & 31.] 1936, 37. 4°.　　**g. 548. kk. (17.)**

— *See* Gabrielli (D.) Sonata No. 1 (2) ... Einrichtung für den praktischen Gebrauch von L. Landshoff. 1930. 4°.　　**g. 510. j. (15.)**

— *See* Haydn (F. J.) [*Collected Works.— e.*] Songs for Schools ... Edited by L. Landshoff, *etc.* [1965.] 4°.　　**G. 339. e. (6.)**

LANDSHOFF (Ludwig)

— *See* Haydn (F. J.) [Battle of the Nile.] Nelson-Arie ... Herausgegeben und instrumentiert von L. Landshoff. Partitur. [1931.] fol.　　**I. 525. b. (2.)**

— *See* Haydn (F. J.) [Battle of the Nile.] Nelson-Arie ... Herausgegeben ... von L. Landshoff. Klavierausgabe. 1931. fol.　　**H. 2120.**

— *See* Haydn (F. J.) [Canzonets. Set 1.] Englische Canzonetten. Eingeleitet und herausgegeben von L. Landshoff, *etc.* 1924. 8°.　　**Hirsch M. 178.**

— *See* Mozart (W. A.) [Sechs dreistimmige Fugen von J. S. und W. F. Bach mit je einem einleitenden langsamen Satz versehen. K. 404 a. No. 1–3, 6.] Four Preludes and Fugues. For violin, viola and violoncello. The preludes composed by W. A. Mozart; the fugues by J. S. and W. F. Bach, transcribed by Mozart ... Edited by L. Landshoff. [1951.] 4°.　　**g. 1018. ii. (8.)**

— *See* Rossini (G. A.) Signor Bruschino ... Klavier-Auszug von L. Landshoff. 1931. 4°.　　**H. 385. q.**

— *See* Vivaldi (A.) [*Collections.*] Zwei kleine Sinfonien für Streichorchester. [Ryom 719, 146.] Zum praktischen Gebrauch eingerichtet und mit einer Cembalostimme versehen von L. Landshoff, *etc.* [1935.] fol.　　**h. 43. b. (2.)**

— *See* Vivaldi (A.) Violin-Konzert (A dur). [Ryom 340.] Nach dem Autograph herausgegeben und für den Konzertgebrauch eingerichtet von L. Landshoff, *etc.* [1935.] fol.　　**h. 43. b. (1.)**

— *See* Zelter (C. F.) Fünfzig Lieder ... herausgegeben von L. Landshoff. 1932. 8°.　　**Hirsch M. 658.**

— *See* Zumsteeg (J. R.) Ausgewählte Lieder. Eingeleitet und herausgegeben von L. Landshoff. [1902.] *obl.* fol.　　**F. 1196. ww. (3.)**

LANDSKNECHT

— Der Landsknecht. [Song.] *See* Bruch (M. C. F.) 4 Gesänge ... Op. 18. No. 2.

— Der Landsknecht. [Song.] *See* Flotow (F. F. A. von) *Baron.* Vier Lieder ... No. 4.

— Der Landsknecht. Lieder-Cantate. *See* Taubert (C. G. W.)

— Der Landsknecht unter Georg von Frondsberg. [Song cycle.] *See* Lenz (Leopold)

LANDSKNECHTLIED

— Landsknechtlied. [Four-part song.] *See* Zenger (M.) Fünf ... Männergesänge. Op. 27. No. 2.

— Landsknechtlied beim wälschen Wein. [Part-song.] *See* Zoellner (H.) Vier Lieder, *etc.* No. 4.

LANDSKRON (Leopold)

— Die Wasserfee. Gedicht von H. Lingg für Sopran-Solo, gemischten Chor und Orchester. Clavier-Auszug. *Offenbach a. M.,* [1875.] fol.　　**H. 1777. h. (9.)**

LANDSMAN

— A Landsman's Life for Me. Ballad. *See* MacCarthy (C.)

LANDSTREICHER

— Die Landstreicher. Operette. *See* Ziehrer (C. M.)

LANDTAG

— Der Landtag von Wolkenkukuksheim. Singspiel. *See* Engelsberg (E. S.)

LANDTMANSON (SAMUEL)

— Folkmusik i Västergötland. (Musikbilaga.) 2 pt. *L. Norblads Bokhandel: Uppsala*, 1911 [1930]. 8°& 4°.
Vastergötland. Ser. A. No. 1. **010281. t. 1/1a.**

LANDU

— Landû. Ein Portugisischer Nationaltanz mit Chitarrenbegleitung. [Score.] *In:* Berlinische musikalische Zeitung. Jahrg. 2. Beilage 5. 1806. *obl.* 4°.
Hirsch IV. 1131. (1.)

— The Landu. *See* HOWARD (W.) *of London.*

LANDUISHI

— Ландыши, лютики. [Song.] *See* IPPOLITOV-IVANOV (M. M.) Шесть романсовъ. Соч. 14а.

LANDWEHR (FREDERICK)

— *See* KING (Godfré R.) Great divine Director. [Song.] Arranged by F. Landwehr, *etc.* [1941.] 4°. **G. 1277. l. (2.)**

— *See* KING (Godfré R.) Leto, blessed Leto. [Song.] Arranged by F. Landwehr, *etc.* [1940.] 4°. **G. 1277. l. (3.)**

— *See* KING (Godfré R.) Mighty Victory. [Song.] Arranged by F. Landwehr, *etc.* [1940.] 4°. **G. 1277. l. (4.)**

— *See* KING (Lotus R.) Great Hercules—thou Elohim. [Song.] Arranged by F. Landwehr, *etc.* [1948.] 4°. **G. 1277. l. (5.)**

— *See* KING (Lotus R.) "I am" here. [Song.] Arranged by F. Landwehr, *etc.* [1942.] 4°. **G. 1277. l. (6.)**

LANDWEHR (JOHANN)

— Trio pour Piano, Violon et Violoncelle. *Leipzig*, 1860. fol.
h. 2900. a. (6.)

LANDWEHR-MELNICKI (MARGARETA)

— Die Gesänge des altrömischen Graduale. Vat. lat. 5319. Einführung von Bruno Stäblein. Notenteil, kritischer Bericht und Verzeichnisse von Margareta Landwehr-Melnicki. [With facsimiles.] pp. viii. 164. 724. *Bärenreiter: Kassel, etc.,* 1970. 8°.
[*Monumenta monodica medii aevi. Bd.* 2.] **E. 1321.**

LANE

— Lane o' the Thrushes. Song. *See* HARTY (*Sir* H. H.)

— A Lane of Roses. Song. *See* DAWSON (S.)

— The Lane that leads to Drowsy Land. [Song.] *See* BALL (Ernest R.)

— The Lane that leads to Loveland. [Song.] *See* WITT (Max S.)

— The Lane to Ballybree. Song. *See* SPEAKS (O.)

LANE (ARTHUR)

— Highfield. [Anthem. Tonic sol-fa and staff notation.] Third Prize Tune. 1895. *See* NATIONAL. The National Choralist. No. 29. 1892, *etc.* 4°. **F. 1527.**

LANE (BURTON)

Finian's Rainbow

— Finian's Rainbow. A new musical, lyrics by E. Y. Harburg ... Book by E. Y. Harburg and Fred Saidy. Vocal score. pp. 133. *Chappell & Co.: London*, [1947.] 4°. **F. 943. w. (3.)**

LANE (BURTON)

— Finian's Rainbow ... Lyrics by E. Y. Harburg. Book by E. Y. Harburg and Fred Saidy. Vocal score. Revised edition, *etc.* pp. 137. *De Sylva, Brown & Henderson: New York*, [1967.] 4°.
G. 1282. u. (1.)

— Finian's Rainbow. Song album. Lyrics by E. Y. Harburg, *etc.* pp. 32. *De Sylva, Brown & Henderson: New York; Chappell & Co.: London; London* [printed, 1968.] 4°. **G. 809. u. (11.)**

— Finian's Rainbow. Selection. Orchestrated by Geo. L. Zalva. [Parts.] 20 pt. *Chappell & Co.: London*, [1947.] 4°.
[*Chappell & Co.'s Orchestral Works. no.* 400.] *The* 1st *violin part is in duplicate.* **f. 424.**

— Finian's Rainbow. Selection. Arranged for military band by W. J. Duthoit. ⟨Conductor [and parts].⟩ 32 pt. *Chappell & Co.: London*, [1947.] fol.
[*Chappell's Army Journal. no.* 736.] **h. 1562.**

— Finian's Rainbow. Selection ... Arranged for brass and reed band by Allan Street. ⟨Solo B♭ cornet (conductor) [and parts].⟩ 26 pt. *Chappell & Co.: London*, [1968.] 8°.
Brass and Reed Band Journal. no. 227. *Various parts are in duplicate.* **h. 3210. j. (237.)**

— Finian's Rainbow. Selection for descant recorder(s) (or flute/oboe/violin) and piano with voice and guitar optional, *etc.* [Score and parts.] 3 pt. *Chappell: London; De Sylva, Brown & Henderson:* [*New York*, 1968.] 4°.
With two copies of the recorder part, differently imposed.
G. 809. u. (10.)

— Finian's Rainbow. Easy-to-play piano or organ selection. Lyrics by E. Y. Harburg ... Arranged by Mischa Portnoff. pp. 16. *Chappell & Co.: London*, [1968.] *obl.* 4°.
e. 1093. ee. (11.)

— Finian's Rainbow. Selection for all organs ... Arranged by Mark Laub, *etc.* pp. 19. *DeSylva, Brown & Henderson: New York; Chappell & Co.: London; London* [printed, 1970.] 4°.
g. 1378. kk. (13.)

— How are things in Glocca Morra? ... S. A. T. B. ⟨Three part women's voices. S. S. A.⟩ Arranged by William Stickles. 2 no. *Chappell & Co.: London*, [1968.] 8°. **F. 321. aa. (31.)**

— If this isn't Love. Three part women's voices. (S. S. A.) Arranged by William Stickles, *etc.* pp. 4. *Chappell & Co.: London*, [1968.] 8°. **F. 217. dd. (28.)**

— Look to the Rainbow. Arranged for S. S. A. ... by Stephen Duro, *etc.* [Staff and tonic sol-fa notation.] pp. 4. *Chappell & Co.: London*, [1968.] 8°. **F. 217. dd. (29.)**

— How are Things in Glocca Morra? *See supra:* [Finian's Rainbow.]

— If this isn't Love. *See supra:* [Finian's Rainbow.]

— Look to the Rainbow. *See supra:* [Finian's Rainbow.]

— On a clear Day you can see forever. Book & lyrics by Alan Jay Lerner ... Vocal score ... Piano reduction by Robert H. Noeltner. pp. 114. *Chappell & Co.: New York*, [1967.] 4°.
G. 1282. o. (1.)

— On a clear Day you can see forever. Vocal selection. Screenplay and lyrics by Alan Jay Lerner, *etc.* pp. 40. *Chappell & Co.: New York*, [1970.] 4°. **G. 1271. zz. (3.)**

— On a clear Day you can see forever. Piano selection. Arranged by Walter Paul, *etc.* pp. 16. *Chappell: London, New York*, [1971.] 4°. **f. 760. r. (10.)**

— *See* JACOBI (Victor) [The Gay City.] Selection from the Film "The Gay City". [By] V. Jacobi, B. Lane & Louis Alter. ⟨Arranged for military band by W. J. Duthoit.⟩ [1942?] fol. [*Chappell's Army Journal. no.* 687.] [KERN (*Jerome* D.) [*One Night in the Tropics.*] *Two Songs, etc.*] **h. 1562.**

LANE (CUTHBERT)

— Softly whispers the Wind. Song, words by P. J. O'Reilly. 3 no. [In C, D flat and E flat.] *Gould & Co.: London*, 1910. fol.
H. 1792. r. (16.)

—— Speak, my Beloved. Song, words by P. J. O'Reilly. 2 no. [In B and C.] *Gould & Co.: London*, 1911. fol. **H. 1792. r. (17.)**

LANE (E. I.)

— Virginia. Two step. [P. F.] pp. 3–5. *M. Witmark & Sons: [New York*, 1904.] fol. **h. 4120. mm. (21.)**

LANE (EASTWOOD)

— The Blue-Robed Mandarins. *See infra:* [Mongoliana.]

— [Eastern Seas.] Sea Burial. (Piano.) *J. Fischer & Bro.: New York, Birmingham*, 1925. 4°. **g. 1127. gg. (18.)**

— [Mongoliana.] The Blue-Robed Mandarins, from "Mongoliana," a Suite for Piano. *J. Fischer & Brother: New York, Birmingham*, 1922. 4°. **g. 1127. gg. (16.)**

— Persimmon Pucker. (Piano.) *J. Fischer & Bro.: New York, Birmingham*, 1926. 4°. **g. 1127. gg. (17.)**

— Sea Burial. *See supra:* [Eastern Seas.]

— Sold down the River. Ballet Suite for Piano, *etc. J. Fischer & Bro.: New York, Birmingham*, 1928. 4°. **g. 230. f. (11.)**

LANE (EDGAR A.)

— Dreaming of you. Song, words and music by E. A. Lane. *J. H. Larway: London*, (1913.) fol. **H. 1793. s. (2.)**

— "England." This England never did. Unison Song, words by Shakespeare. *Novello and Co.: London*, 1927. 8°.
E. 1830. (27.)

— Fight the good Fight. Hymn, words by J. S. B. Monsell. *Novello and Co.: London*, [1925.] 8°. **D. 619. vv. (42.)**

— For sixty Years our Queen. Patriotic Song and Chorus written and composed by E. A. Lane. *Novello, Ewer & Co.: London & New York*, [1897.] fol. **F. 321. j. (24.)**

— For the Empire. Song, written and composed by E. A. Lane, *etc. Novello and Co.: London*, [1913.] fol. **G. 806. ll. (44.)**

— Men who march away. Song, words by T. Hardy, *etc. E. Ashdown, for the Author: London*, 1914. fol.
G. 806. ll. (45.)

— O Jesu! Thou art standing. Song. Words by Bishop W. How. *Weekes & Co.: London*, [1899.] fol. **H. 1187. z. (13.)**

— Stand up for the old, old Country! Patriotic Song, written & composed by E. A. Lane, *etc. J. H. Larway: London*, (1913.) fol. **H. 1793. s. (3.)**

LANE (EDITH M.)

— A Child's Request. Unison Song, words and music by E. M. Lane. *Novello and Co.: London*, 1927. 8°. [*Novello's School Songs. No.* 1462.] **F. 280. d.**

— Six Irish Tunes. Arranged for:—Descant & treble or tenor recorders with piano, guitar, tuned & untuned percussion by Edith M. Lane. [Score.] pp. 10. *Alfred Lengnick & Co.: South Croydon*, [1975.] 4°. **g. 109. y. (3.)**

LANE (ELIHU BURRITT)

— "All hail!" [Hymn.] Words by E. Perronet. *See infra:* Original Tunes, *etc.* No. 8.

— Calm me, my God. [Hymn.] Words by ... H. Bonar. *See infra:* Original Tunes, *etc.* No. 10.

LANE (ELIHU BURRITT)

— Eternal Light. [Hymn.] Words by Rev. T. Binney. *See infra:* Original Tunes, *etc.* No. 4.

— Heal us, Emmanuel! [Hymn.] Words by W. Cowper. *See infra:* Original Tunes, *etc.* No. 9.

— Six Settings of the Kyrie Eleison. *Composers & Authors Press: London*, 1897. 8°. **F. 1171. x. (27.)**

— The Lord's Table. [Hymn.] Words by Dr. P. Doddridge. *See infra:* Original Tunes, *etc.* No. 5.

— O Lord, how happy should we be. [Hymn.] Words by J. Anstice, *etc. See infra:* Original Tunes, *etc.* No. 3.

— Original Tunes to favourite Hymns. 10 no. *Vincent Music Co.: London*, [1903.] *s. sh.* 8°. **D. 619. ff. (12.)**

— Our Refuge. [Hymn.] Words by H. F. Lyte, *etc. See supra:* Original Tunes, *etc.* No. 7.

— Sometimes a Light surprises. [Hymn.] Words by W. Cowper. *See supra:* Original Tunes, *etc.* No. 2.

— "Sweet Hosannas." [Hymn.] Words by Theodulph of Orleans ... Translated by J. M. Neale, *etc. See supra:* Original Tunes, *etc.* No. 1.

— Te Deum ... in ... F. 1893. *See* NOVELLO AND CO. Novello's Parish Choir Book ... No. 131. [1866, *etc.*] 8°. **E. 618.**

— Unto us is born a Saviour! A Christmas Carol, words by ... G. W. Keesey. *Vincent Music Co.: London*, [1905.] 8°.
F. 538. c. (28.)

— Vesper Hymn. Words and music by E. B. Lane. *Vincent Music Co.: London*, [1905.] *q card.* **I. 600. c. (37.)**

— Vesper Hymn. Words and music by E. B. Lane. Second Setting. *Vincent Music Co.: London*, [1905.] *a card.*
I. 600. c. (57.)

— The Wondrous Cross. [Hymn.] Words by Dr. I. Watts. *See supra:* Original Tunes, *etc.* No. 6.

LANE (FREDERICK)

— L'Amour Vainqueur Valse. [P. F.] *Weekes & Co.: London*, 1910. fol. **h. 3286. uu. (38.)**

LANE (G. G.)

— Constance, Violet, Margaret. Three Gavottes, *etc.* [P. F.] *West & Co.: London*, 1916. fol. **h. 3284. nn. (6.)**

— A Song of the King's Navee. Song, words by M. Wadham. *Parker-Charles Music Publishing Co.: London*, 1919. fol.
H. 1846. x. (11.)

LANE (GERALD M.)

— Songs. [1903.] *See* MUSICAL. Musical Fragments, *etc.* Book 112. [1888, *etc.*] fol. **h. 3295.**

— Abiding Words. Song, the words and music by G. Lane. *Enoch & Sons: London*, 1903. fol. **H. 3600. a. (6.)**

— Asking the Way. Song, the words and music by G. M. Lane. 2 no. [In C and A.] *R. Cocks & Co.: London*, [1886.] fol.
H. 1788. u. (39.)

— At the Dance. Song. Written & composed by Gerald M. Lane. pp. 5. *Marriott & Williams: London*, [c. 1885.] fol.
H. 1650. oo. (17.)

— Autumn Gold. Song, words and music by G. Lane. 3 no. [In E flat, F and G.] *Gould & Co.: London*, 1906. fol.
H. 3600. a. (13.)

LANE (GERALD M.)

— Autumn Gold. [Song.] Words and music by G. Lane. *Gould & Co.: London*, [1916.] 4°.
No. 8 of 'The Royal 6d. edition'. **G. 805. zz. (15.)**

— Baby-Girl. [Song.] Words and music by G. Lane. *Francis, Day & Hunter: London*, 1905. fol. **H. 3600. a. (14.)**

— [Another copy.]
With a different titlepage. **H. 3600. a. (15.)**

— Benediction. Song, words and music by G. Lane. *Boosey & Co.: London and New York*, 1904. fol. **H. 3600. a. (16.)**

— Ben-ma-Chree ... Song, the words and music by G. Lane.
Enoch & Sons: London, 1898. fol. **H. 3600. (28.)**

— Blue-Eyes. Song. Words and Music by G. Lane. *Enoch & Sons: London*, 1896. fol. **H. 3600. (11.)**

— Carmencita. Song, words and music by G. Lane.
J. & J. Hopkinson: London, 1893. fol. **H. 3600. (1.)**

— Carmencita Waltz. Arranged ... on the ... Song ... by
G. Lane. [1900.] fol. *See* LACOSTE (L.) **h. 3286. q. (71.)**

— Carmencita Waltz.—L. Lacoste.—Founded on G. Lane's ...
Song. [P. F.] *See* GODARD (F.) Sunny Rays, *etc.* No. 2. [1901.]
fol. **h. 3499. (12.)**

— Children's Ways. Song, the words and music by G. Lane.
Enoch & Sons: London, 1898. fol. **H. 3600. (29.)**

— A City by the Sea. Song, the words & music by G. M. Lane.
Cary & Co.: London, 1893. fol. **H. 3600. (30.)**

— A City by the Sea ... Easily arranged for the Pianoforte, *etc.*
See GAUTIER (L.) Golden Thoughts, *etc.* No. 9. [1905?] fol.
h. 3483. d. (13.)

— [A City by the Sea.] *See* FARE (F.) *pseud.* A City by the Sea.
Waltz on G. Lane's ... Song. [1898.] fol. **h. 2945. (23.)**

— The Crown of Life. Song, written and composed by G. Lane.
W. Morley & Co.: London, 1892. fol. **H. 3600. (2.)**

— Daisies in the Grass. Song, words and music by G. Lane.
Ascherberg, Hopwood & Crew: London, 1907. fol.
H. 3600. a. (22.)

— A Dance and a Dream. Song, the words and music by
G. Lane. *Enoch & Sons: London*, 1898. fol. **H. 3600. (31.)**

— Donovan O'Dare. Song, written & composed by G. Lane.
J. & J. Hopkinson: London, 1892. fol. **H. 3600. (3.)**

— Down by the Sea. Song, the words and music by G. Lane.
2 no. [In D and E flat.] *W. Morley & Co.: London*, [1891.] fol.
H. 3600. (4.)

— Down by the Sea. Waltz, *etc.* [P. F.] *W. Morley & Co.:
London*, 1891. fol. **h. 3285. p. (52.)**

— The Dream-Boat. Song, the words and music by G. Lane.
Enoch & Sons: London, 1903. fol. **H. 3600. a. (7.)**

— Dreamy June. Song. The Words and Music by G. Lane.
Enoch & Sons: London, 1896. fol. **H. 3600. (12.)**

— Easter Morn. Sacred Song, the words & music by G. M. Lane.
Boosey & Co.: London, [1886.] fol. **H. 879. e. (10.)**

— Fairyland. [Song.] Written and composed by G. M. Lane.
J. & J. Hopkinson: London, [1889.] fol. **H. 1788. u. (40.)**

— Fairyland. Song, written and composed by G. M. Lane.
Phillips & Page: London, [1890.] fol. **H. 3600. (32.)**

— Fairyland. Song, *etc.* 3 no. [In E flat, F and G.] *Gould & Co.:
London*, [1901.] fol. **H. 3600. (33.)**

LANE (GERALD M.)

— The Fall of the Dew. Song, words and music by G. Lane.
Ascherberg, Hopwood & Crew: London, 1907. fol.
H. 3600. a. (23.)

— Firelight Faces. Song, words and music by G. Lane. *Elkin & Co., for C. A. Pearson: London*, 1905. fol. **H. 3600. a. (17.)**

— The Fisher's Lullaby. Song, words and music by G. Lane.
Elkin & Co.: London, 1905. fol. **H. 3600. a. (18.)**

— Florentia. Waltz. [P. F.] *Enoch & Son: London*, [1884.] fol.
h. 975. u. (32.)

— For old Time's Sake. Song, written & composed by G. M.
Lane. *J. B. Cramer & Co.: London*, [1887.] fol.
H. 1788. u. (41.)

— Garden of Dreams. Song, the words and music by G. Lane.
Enoch & Sons: London, 1899. fol. **H. 3600. (34.)**

— The Golden Promise. Song ... The words & music by Gerald
Lane. pp. 7. *W. Morley & Cº: London*, [1894.] fol.
H. 1601. mm. (17.)

— Golden Summer. Song, words and music by G. Lane.
J. & J. Hopkinson: London, 1891. fol. **H. 3600. (5.)**

— Harvest. Song, the words and music by G. Lane. *Enoch & Sons: London*, 1902. fol. **H. 3600. a. (1.)**

— Homeward. [Song.] Words and music by G. Lane. *Elkin & Co., for C. A. Pearson: London*, 1904. fol. **H. 3600. a. (19.)**

— Homeward, *etc.* *Elkin & Co.: London*, 1918. fol.
H. 1846. x. (12.)

— Hush-a-bye. Song. With Violin or Violoncello Accpt. ad lib.
The Words and Music by G. Lane. *Enoch & Sons: London*,
1897. fol. **H. 3600. (13.)**

— Hush-a-bye. Two-Part Song, *etc.* 1900. *See* JACKMAN (P.)
Two-Part Songs, *etc.* No. 19. 1896, *etc.* 8°. **E. 806. a.**

— I crown you Queen. Song, the words and music by G. Lane.
Enoch & Sons: London, 1903. fol. **H. 3600. a. (8.)**

— If ever. Song, written and composed by G. Lane. *W. Morley & Co.: London*, 1891. fol. **H. 3600. (6.)**

— June Roses. Waltz, with vocal refrain ad lib. *Francis Bros. & Day: London*, [1885.] fol. **h. 975. u. (33.)**

— June Roses. Waltz. [Orchestral parts.] *See* FRANCIS AND DAY.
Francis & Day's String Band Journal ... No. 71. [1886? *etc.*]
8°. **e. 1341.**

— The Life of a Soldier. Song, the words and music by G. Lane.
Enoch & Sons: London, 1898. fol. **H. 3600. (35.)**

— Life's All in All! Song, the words and music by G. Lane.
Enoch & Sons: London, 1899. fol. **H. 3600. (36.)**

— Life's Lullaby. Song. The Words and Music by G. Lane.
Enoch & Sons: London, 1895. fol. **H. 3600. (14.)**

— Life's Lullaby. Song, *etc.* ⟨In A♭.⟩ [c. 1900.] fol.
A pirated edition. **H. 1848. b. (7.)**

— Life's Lullaby ... in G. *Enoch & Sons: London*, [1910.] fol.
H. 3600. a. (30.)

— Life's Lullaby. Two-Part Song, *etc.* 1897. *See* JACKMAN (P.)
Two-Part Songs, *etc.* No. 12. 1896, *etc.* 8°. **E. 806. a.**

— Life's Lullaby. Arranged for S. C. T. B., *etc.* (1913.) *See*
METCALFE (R. D.) Enoch & Sons' Church Choral Series, *etc.*
No. 17. (1908, *etc.*) 8°. **F. 1097.**

— Life's Lullaby ... Transcribed for the Pianoforte by B. Smith.
Enoch & Sons: London, 1902. fol. **h. 3282. kk. (20.)**

LANE (GERALD M.)

—[Life's Lullaby.] *See* BUCALOSSI (E.) Life's Lullaby. Waltz on the ... Song by G. Lane. 1896. fol.   **h. 3356. a. (8.)**

— Listen! Song, words and music by G. Lane. *Ascherberg, Hopwood & Crew: London*, 1907. fol.   **H. 3600. a. (24.)**

— Three Little quiet Pieces for the Piano, *etc. A. Weekes & Co.: London*, 1928. 4°.   **g. 1125. w. (21.)**

— Love is everywhere. Valse Song, words and music by G. Lane. 3 no. [In A, B flat and C.] *Chappell & Co.: London, etc.*, 1906. fol.   **H. 3600. a. (20.)**

— The Love of Angels. [Song.] Words and music by G. Lane. *C. Woolhouse: London*, 1908. fol.   **H. 3600. a. (25.)**

— The Love of Old, song, written and composed by Gerald M. Lane. pp. 7. *Marriott & Williams: London*, [c. 1885.] fol.   **H. 1650. oo. (18.)**

— Love that slumbered. Song, words and music by G. Lane. *J. B. Cramer & Co.: London*, [1891.] fol.   **H. 3600. (7.)**

— Love, the Rover. Song. The Words and Music ... by G. Lane. 3 no. [In D, E flat, and F.] *R. Cocks & Co.: London*, 1896. fol.   **H. 3600. (15.)**

— 5 Morceaux caractéristiques for the Pianoforte. [No. 1.] Chant du Sommeil. [No. 2.] Jeu d'Esprit. [No. 3.] Chant sans Paroles. [No. 4.] Tristesse d'Amour. Valse Lente. [No. 5.] Grande Valse. 5 no. *Enoch & Sons: London*, 1902. fol.   **h. 3282. kk. (21.)**

— 3 Morceaux de Salon for the Pianoforte ... [1.] Bonsoir. Berceuse. [2.] Sous les Etoiles. Rêverie. [3.] Joie de Vivre. Valse Caprice. 3 no. *Enoch & Sons: London*, 1901. fol.   **h. 3282. w. (26.)**

— My Heart and Thine. Song. The Words and Music by G. Lane. *W. Morley & Co.: London*, 1893. fol.   **H. 3600. (16.)**

— My little Lass. Song. The Words and Music by G. Lane. *Enoch & Sons: London*, 1897. fol.   **H. 3600. (17.)**

— Not mine be Monarch's Throne. Song. Words and Music by G. M. Lane. 2 no. [In B flat and C.] *W. Morley & Co.: London*, 1895. fol.   **H. 3600. (18.)**

— O Heart divine. Song, words and music by G. Lane. *Elkin & Co.: London*, 1905. fol.   **H. 3600. a. (21.)**

— O hush me to a dreamless Sleep. Song, the words and music by G. Lane. *Enoch & Sons: London*, 1902. fol.   **H. 3600. a. (9.)**

— The Old Highland Home. Song. The Words and Music by G. Lane. *Enoch & Sons: London*, 1896. fol.   **H. 3600. (19.)**

— The Old Oak Stair. Vocal Gavotte, written and composed by G. Lane. *J. & J. Hopkinson: London*, [1891.] fol.   **H. 3600. (8.)**

— The Old, old Songs, Song, written and composed by Gerald M. Lane. pp. 7. *Marriott & Williams: London*, [c. 1890.] fol.   **H. 1860. mm. (18.)**

— The Old Sundial. [Song.] Written and composed by G. M. Lane. *J. & J. Hopkinson: London*, [1886.] fol.   **H. 1788. u. (42.)**

— The Old Sundial. *See* COOKE (S.) The Old Sundial. Waltz on G. M. Lane's ... Song. [1888.] fol.   **h. 3285. j. (16.)**

— The Old World and the new. Song, the words and music by G. Lane. *Enoch & Sons: London*, 1902. fol.   **H. 3600. a. (10.)**

— Onward Christian Soldiers. [Part-song.] [1897.] *See* UNION. The Union Choralist, *etc.* No. 41. [1882, *etc.*] 8°.   **F. 687.**

LANE (GERALD M.)

— Our Day. Words and Music by G. Lane. *Enoch & Sons: London*, 1897. fol.   **H. 3600. (20.)**

— Paddy. Song. The Words and Music by G. Lane. *Enoch & Sons: London*, 1896. fol.   **H. 3600. (21.)**

— Peace! Song, written and composed by G. Lane. *Enoch & Sons: London*, 1899. fol.   **H. 3600. (37.)**

— Peace on Earth. Song, with organ or harmonium accompaniment ad lib., the words and music by G. Lane. *Enoch & Sons: London*, 1901. fol.   **H. 3600. a. (2.)**

— Pierrette. Song, the words and music by G. Lane. *Enoch & Sons: London*, 1900. fol.   **H. 3600. (38.)**

— Pipistrello. Song, the words and music by G. Lane. *Enoch & Sons: London*, 1898. fol.   **H. 3600. (39.)**

— Remember yet! Song, the words and music by G. Lane. *Enoch & Sons: London*, 1900. fol.   **H. 3600. (40.)**

— River Dreams. Song, the words and music by G. Lane. *Enoch & Sons: London*, 1898. fol.   **H. 3600. (41.)**

— The Rocking Chair. Song, words and music by G. Lane. *Elkin & Co.: London*, 1908. fol.   **H. 3600. a. (26.)**

— Roses of June. Song. Words and Music by G. Lane. *Enoch & Sons: London*, 1895. fol.   **H. 3600. (22.)**

— Sanctuary. Song with Pianoforte & Harmonium or Organ ... accompaniment, the words & music by G. Lane. *Boosey & Co.: London*, [1889.] fol.   **H. 1788. u. (33.)**

— The Seasons. Four ... Pieces for the Pianoforte. 1. Spring. 2. Summer. 3. Autumn. 4. Winter. *Elkin & Co.: London*, 1904. 4°.   **g. 442. n. (21.)**

— Serenade, written and composed by G. Lane. *J. B. Cramer & Co.: London*, [1890.] fol.   **H. 3600. (9.)**

— The Shepherd and the Star. Song, words and music by G. Lane. *J. B. Cramer & Co.: London*, 1919. 4°.   **G. 390. z. (29.)**

— Singing to you. Song, the words & music by G. Lane. 3 no. [In C, E flat and F.] *Ascherberg, Hopwood & Crew: London*, 1912. fol.   **H. 1793. s. (3*.)**

— So Robin sang. Song, the words and music by G. Lane. *Enoch & Sons: London*, 1901. fol.   **H. 3600. (43.)**

— So Robin sang. Two-Part Song, *etc.* 1905. *See* JACKMAN (P.) Two-Part Songs, *etc.* No. 29. 1896, *etc.* 8°.   **E. 806. a.**

— A Song of April. Song, words by L. G. *C. Woolhouse: London*, 1907. fol.   **H. 3600. a. (27.)**

— A Song of Flowers. Song, the words and music by G. Lane. *Enoch & Sons: London*, 1901. fol.   **H. 3600. a. (3.)**

— A Song of Flowers. Two-Part Song ... words and music by G. Lane. 1903. *See* JACKMAN (P.) Two-Part Songs, *etc.* No. 25. 1896, *etc.* 8°.   **E. 806. a.**

— Song of the Contadino.—Italian Peasant's Song.— Words and music by G. Lane. 2 no. [In G and A.] *Ascherberg, Hopwood & Crew: London*, 1908. fol.   **H. 3600. a. (28.)**

— A Song of Welcome. Song, written and composed by G. Lane. *Enoch & Sons: London*, 1899. fol.   **H. 3600. (42.)**

— Souvenir d'Eté. Valse. [P. F.] *Enoch & Sons: London*, [1885.] fol.   **h. 975. u. (34.)**

— The Star of Eternity. Song. With Violin or Violoncello Accpt. ad lib. The Words and Music by G. Lane. *Enoch & Sons: London*, 1895. fol.   **H. 3600. (23.)**

LANE (Gerald M.)

— The Story of the Year. Song, words and music by G. Lane. 3 no. [In E flat, F and G.] *Elkin & Co.: London,* 1904. fol.
H. 3600. a. (11.)

— Story-Time. Song, the words and music by G. Lane. *Enoch & Sons: London,* 1900. fol.
H. 3600. (44.)

— Summer comes To-morrow. Song, words and music by G. Lane. 2 no. [In C and E flat.] *Ascherberg, Hopwood & Crew: London,* 1908. fol.
H. 3600. a. (29.)

— Summer Shade. Song. The Words and Music by G. Lane. *Enoch & Sons: London,* 1897. fol.
H. 3600. (24.)

— Sunbeams. Intermezzo. [P. F.] *Francis, Day & Hunter: London,* 1912. fol.
h. 3284. f. (40.)

— "Sunbeams." ⟨Dance intermezzo.⟩ G. Lane ... "Love's Prayer". ⟨Waltz.⟩ Bernard Phelps ... "My little Jap". ⟨Two-step.⟩ Bernard Phelps. [Military band parts.] 33 pt. *Boosey & Co.: London,* 1913. fol.
[*Boosey's military Journal. ser.* 134. *no.* 4.]
h. 1549.

— Sweet long ago. Song, the words & music by G. M. Lane. *Boosey & Co.: London,* [1883.] fol.
H. 1788. u. (43.)

— Tatters. Song. The Words and Music Composed by G. Lane. 3 no. [In D, E, and F.] *R. Cocks & Co.: London,* 1895. fol.
H. 3600. (25.)

— Tatters. Song, *etc. Gould & Co.: London,* 1901. fol.
H. 3600. a. (4.)

— Tatters. [Song.] Words and music by G. Lane. *Gould & Co.: London,* [1916.] 4°.
No. 7 *of 'The Royal* 6*d. edition'.*
G. 805. zz. (14.)

— Tatters. [P. F.] 1900. *See* GREVILLE (M.) Sunbeams, *etc.* No. 23. [1900–1.] fol.
h. 3507. a.

— Tatters. [P. F.] [1900.] *See* WEST (S.) and SMALLWOOD (W.) Echoes of Home. No. 16. [1899, *etc.*] fol.
h. 3808.

— Tell me, Swallow! Song, the words and music by G. Lane. *Enoch & Sons: London,* 1900. fol.
H. 3600. (45.)

— Tipperary. Irish Ballad, words & music by G. Lane. 2 no. [In C and E flat.] *R. Cocks & Co.: London,* [1890.] fol.
H. 3600. (10.)

— 'Tis Thine. Song, the words and music by G. Lane. *Boosey & Co.: London,* [1889.] fol.
H. 1788. uu. (34.)

— Toys. Song, the words and music by G. Lane. *Enoch & Sons: London,* 1901. fol.
H. 3600. (46.)

— Trust and believe. Song. The Words and Music by G. Lane. *Enoch & Sons: London,* 1897. fol.
H. 3600. (26.)

— Under the Flag. Song, the words and music by G. Lane. *Enoch & Sons: London,* 1899. fol.
H. 3600. (47.)

— Under the Flag, *etc.* [Voice part and words only.] *Enoch & Sons: London,* [1909.] *s. sh.* 8°.
Part of "Enoch & Sons' Class-Singing Series".
E. 1766. p. (5.)

— Under the Flag. [Song.] Words & music by G. Lane. *See* METCALFE (R. D.) Enoch & Sons' Class-Singing Series, *etc.* No. 1. [1910.] 8°.
E. 1766. v. (10.)

— The Unseen Kingdom. Song. With Organ or Harmonium Accompt. ad lib. The Words and Music by G. Lane. *Enoch & Sons: London,* 1895. fol.
H. 3600. (27.)

— The Unseen Kingdom, *etc.* [Anthem.] (1909.) *See* METCALFE (R. D.) Enoch & Sons' Church Choral Series, *etc.* No. 9. (1908, *etc.*) 8°.
F. 1097.

— Viva España! Song, the words and music by G. Lane. *Enoch & Sons: London,* 1902. fol.
H. 3600. a. (5.)

LANE (Gerald M.)

— The Voice of London. Song, words and music by G. Lane. *Keith, Prowse & Co.: London,* 1920. fol.
H. 1846. x. (13.)

— Wedding Bells. Waltz, with voice parts ad lib. [P. F. solo, duet, and voice part.] 3 no. *Chappell & Co.: London,* [1885.] fol.
h. 975. u. (35.)

— Wedding Bells. Waltz. [Orchestral parts.] *See* CHAPPELL AND Co. Popular Quadrilles, *etc.* No. 182. [1886.] 8°.
e. 249.

— Welcome Home! Song, the words and music by G. Lane. *Enoch & Sons: London,* 1900. fol.
H. 3600. (48.)

— What have I to give? Song, words and music by G. Lane. *Boosey & Co.: London and New York,* 1913. fol.
H. 1793. s. (4.)

— When falls the Night. Song, the words and music by G. Lane. *Enoch & Sons: London,* 1903. fol.
H. 3600. a. (12.)

— When the Lights are low. [P. F. solo and duet.] 2 no. [1901–2.] *See* SMALLWOOD (W.) Home Treasures, *etc.* No. 105. [1872, *etc.*] fol.
h. 1412. o.

— When the Lights are low. [P. F.] [1902.] *See* SMALLWOOD (W.) Little Buds, *etc.* No. 97. [1874, *etc.*] fol.
h. 1412. p.

— [When the lights are low.] *See* BONHEUR (Theodore) *pseud.* When the Lights are low. Valse (on Gerald Lane's popular song). [c. 1890.] fol.
h. 61. q. (6.)

— Wooden Shoes. Song, the words and music by G. Lane. *Enoch & Sons: London,* 1899. fol.
H. 3600. (49.)

— Woodman Will. Song, the words and music by G. Lane. *Enoch & Sons: London,* 1901. fol.
H. 3600. (50.)

— The World's Fair. Song, the words and music by G. Lane. *Enoch & Sons: London,* 1899. fol.
H. 3600. (51.)

LANE (Harry)

— In the Isle of Sicily. ⟨Song.⟩ Written by Stanley J. Damerell. [Staff and tonic sol-fa notation. Voice part.] *Francis, Day & Hunter: London,* [1909.] *s. sh.* fol.
H. 3985. h. (9.)

— In the Isle of Sicily, *etc.* ⟨Song.⟩ [With separate voice part.] 2 pt. *Francis, Day & Hunter: London,* [1909.] fol.
H. 3985. h. (10.)

— "Won't you come for a Sail in my Yacht?" ⟨Song.⟩ Written by Stanley J. Damerell, *etc.* [Staff and tonic sol-fa notation. Voice part.] *Francis, Day & Hunter: London,* [1908.] *s. sh.* fol.
H. 3985. h. (11.)

— "Won't you come for a Sail in my Yacht?" *etc.* ⟨Song.⟩ [With separate voice part.] 2 pt. *Francis, Day & Hunter: London,* [1908.] fol.
H. 3985. h. (12.)

— *See* DAMERELL (Stanley J.) The Mirror of your Eyes. [Song.] Written and composed by S. J. Damerell, H. Lane, *etc.* [1910.] 4°.
H. 3990. qq. (2.)

LANE (Herbert)

— Benedicite, omnia opera. An easy setting in Chant form. *Weekes & Co.: London,* [1904.] 8°.
F. 1169. c. (16.)

— The Happy Bird of Blue. [Song.] Words and H. F. Simpson. [In E flat and G.] 2 no. 1913. *See* SERIES. A Series of Little Encore Songs. No. 5. 1912–14. fol.
H. 2273.

— If there were Dreams to sell. [Song.] Words by T. L. Beddoes. 1914. *See* SERIES. A Series of Little Encore Songs. No. 13. 1912–14. fol.
H. 2273.

— The Kerchief. [Song.] Words by G. Gaston. [In F and G.] 2 no. 1913. *See* SERIES. A Series of Little Encore Songs. No. 6. 1912–14. fol.
H. 2273.

LANE (HERBERT)

— My Garden of Posies. [Song.] Words by G. Gaston. 1914. *See* SERIES. A Series of Little Encore Songs. No. 14. 1912–14. fol.
H. 2273.

LANE (HILDA)

— Collection of Russian Songs with Russian and English words ... [Collected and translated by] H. Lane, *etc. J. Albert & Son: Sydney*, [1944.] 4°.
G. 981. v. (10.)

LANE (J. M.)

— Ten Preludes for piano. 2 bk. *Stainer & Bell: London*, 1921. 4°.
g. 1125. c. (24.)

LANE (JAIME)

— Album di sei valses per pianoforte. pp. 20. *Jaime Lane: Napoli*, [1924.] fol.
The titlepage bears a MS. dedication in the composer's autograph.
h. 3870. nn. (2.)

LANE (JASPER VALE)

— Apollonia. Festival Dance. [P. F.] *Francis, Day & Hunter: London and New York*, [1891.] fol.
h. 3574. (1.)

— Barn Dance ... Arranged by W. H. Nicholls. [Violin and P. F.] 1892. *See* MORLEY AND CO. Morley's Melodious Gems, *etc.* No. 12. [1887, *etc.*] fol.
h. 1685.

— Vale-Lane's Second ... Barn Dance. Piano Solo. *W. Morley & Co.: London*, 1892. fol.
h. 3574. (3.)

— Berlina. Intermezzo-Gavotte for the pianoforte. *Ransford & Son: London*, 1892. fol.
h. 3574. (2.)

— Coquetterie. Intermezzo. [P. F.] *Jefferys: London*, 1900. fol.
h. 3574. (19.)

— The Dear old Motherland. [Song.] Words and Music by J. V. Lane. *Jeffreys: London*, [1899.] fol.
H. 1799. h. (1.)

— The Dear old Motherland, *etc. Vale-Lane: Banstead*, 1917. fol.
H. 1846. x. (14.)

— The Egyptian Patrol passes, for piano solo. *Jefferys: London*, [1899.] fol.
h. 3574. (17.)

— The Egyptian Patrol. J. V. Lane ... "The Veleta". ⟨New round dance.⟩ Arthur Morris ... Arr. [for military band] by M. Retford. [Parts.] 29 pt. *Boosey & Co.: London*, 1904. fol.
[*Boosey & Co.'s new supplemental Journal for military Bands. no.* 11.]
h. 1544. a.

— Eternal Light. Song. Words and music by J. V. Lane. 2 no. [In D and F.] *Jefferys: London*, 1900. fol.
H. 1187. z. (14.)

— For Thee. Valse. [P. F.] *W. Morley & Co.: London*, 1891. fol.
h. 3574. (4.)

— Home again. March. [P. F.] *R. Cocks & Co.: London*, [1890.] fol.
h. 3574. (5.)

— Infanta. Spanish Waltz. [P. F.] *Ransford & Son: London*, 1891. fol.
h. 3574. (6.)

— The King-Emperor's Call. To Arms! March with vocal trio, for the pianoforte ... Words & music by J. Vale-Lane. *Vale-Lane: Banstead*, 1915. fol.
h. 3284. nn. (7.)

— Leben ein Traum.—Life's a Dream.—Walzer. [P. F.] *Jefferys: London*, [1900.] fol.
h. 3574. (20.)

— Lord of Light ... Sacred Song ... Words and music by J. Vale-Lane. *Vale-Lane: Banstead*, 1917. fol.
H. 1186. c. (37.)

— Lyric. Intermezzo. [P. F.] *Marshall's: London*, [1889.] fol.
h. 3574. (7.)

LANE (JASPER VALE)

— Madame Sans-Gêne. Valse. [P. F.] *Jefferys: London*, [1899.] fol.
h. 3574. (18.)

— O, Canada for ever. New Canadian National Anthem or Toast Song ... Words and music by J. Vale-Lane, *etc. Vale-Lane: Banstead*, 1916. fol.
H. 1846. x. (15.)

— Sabrina. Intermezzo. [P. F.] *H. Beresford: London*, [1891.] fol.
h. 3574. (8.)

— Sabrina. Waltz. [P. F.] *Metzler & Co.: London*, [1892.] fol.
h. 3574. (9.)

— Shall we remember. Waltz. [P. F.] *H. Beresford: London*, [1891.] fol.
h. 3574. (10.)

— Summer Roses. Valse. [P. F.] *Francis, Day & Hunter: London*, [1890.] fol.
h. 3574. (11.)

— Sweet Maiden. Valse. [P. F.] *W. Morley & Co.: London*, 1892. fol.
h. 3574. (12.)

— Three Girls in a Boat. Waltz. [P. F.] *E. Ascherberg & Co.: London*, 1891. fol.
h. 3574. (13.)

— Woodland Echoes. Cuckoo Polka. [P. F.] *H. Beresford: London*, [1890.] fol.
h. 3574. (14.)

— Zarita. Intermezzo or Gavotte. [P. F.] *W. Morley & Co.: London*, [1891.] fol.
h. 3574. (15.)

— [Another edition.] Zarita, *etc. W. Morley & Co.: London*, [1891.] fol.
h. 3574. (16.)

— Zarita. Intermezzo ... arranged by P. Dale. [P. F.] *E. Ashdown: London*, [1901.] fol.
h. 3574. (21.)

LANE (JOHN)

— Great TV Themes. Compiled and arranged by J. Lane. ⟨Vocal and piano edition.⟩ pp. 41. *Robbins Music Corp.: New York*, [1966.] 4°.
G. 809. y. (2.)

— A Raggedy Ann Song Book. Easy piano arrangements by J. Lane. pp. 41. *Miller Music Corp.: New York*, [1971.] 4°.
G. 1487. m. (1.)

— *See* GROFÉ (Ferde) World's Fair Suite, *etc.* ⟨Piano arrangement by J. Lane.⟩ [1964.] 4°.
g. 1126. x. (18.)

— *See* MACCARTNEY (Paul) The Best of McCartney. For easy piano. Music arrangement by J. Lane. [1977.] 4°.
g. 1529. u. (4.)

LANE (O. W.)

— College Boys. March and Two-Step, *etc.* [P. F.] *O. W. Lane: Gloucester, Mass.*, 1901. fol.
h. 3286. q. (72.)

— College Boys. March and two step ... Arr. by Max von Lenz. ⟨Solo B♭ cornet (conductor) [and wind band parts].⟩ 36 pt. *O. W. Lane: Gloucester, Mass.*, [1901.] 8°.
Various parts in duplicate.
f. 800. (780.)

LANE (PHILIP)

— American Lullaby. For S. S. A. unaccompanied. Words traditional. pp. 4. *Edwin Ashdown: London*, [1980.] 8°.
Vocal Trios. no. 75.
E. 812. k. (50.)

— Angels from the Realms of Glory ... [Carol. Words by] James Montgomery. pp. 4. *Edwin Ashdown: London*, [1977.] 8°.
Unison Songs. no. 105.
F. 1892. e. (24.)

— A Babe is born. ⟨S. S. A. (unacc.).⟩ [Words] 15th century. pp. 2. *Banks Music Publications: York*, [1975.] 8°.
[*Eboracum choral Series.* 54.]
F. 1874. x.

LANE (PHILIP)

— Balulalow. Carol for SATB and organ or piano. Words 16th century (adapted). pp. 4. *Basil Ramsey: Eastwood*, [1977.] 8°. *Part of "Choral Music Leaflets".* **B. 742. ii. (6.)**

— Caribbean Chorale. [Words from] The Oxford Book of Carols ... Arranged by Philip Lane. [Voice, P. F. and optional flute part. Score.] pp. 4. *Edwin Ashdown: London*, [1977.] 8°. *Unison Songs. no.* 104. **E. 352. a. (8.)**

— Three Carols. My dancing day.—De Virgin Mary.—Deck the hall. Arranged and orchestrated by Philip Lane. ⟨Piano score.⟩ *Galliard: Great Yarmouth; Galaxy:* [*New York*, 1972.] 4°. **G. 950. g. (2.)**

— Celebration Overture. [Orchestra.] Full score. pp. 26. *Edwin Ashdown: London*, [1977.] 4°. **f. 641. ss. (2.)**

— Concertino. [Brass band.] ⟨Full score.⟩ pp. 42. *R. Smith & Co.: Watford*, [1979.] obl. 4°. **d. 290. b. (6.)**

— Five Diversions. Soft Shoe Solitaire. Romanza. Bru up. Sarabandina. Burleske. For melody instrument and piano. [Score and part.] 2 pt. *Stainer & Bell: London*, [1973.] 4°. **g. 270. ii. (8.)**

— The Huron Carol. ⟨Traditional carol of the Huron Indians.⟩ For SSA and piano (optional tom-tom). English words: Philippa Frischmann. French words: Anon. Arranged by Philip Lane. *Eng. & Fr.* pp. 8. *Roberton Publications:* [*Wendover*, 1980.] 8°. **F. 1892. q. (21.)**

— Joy to the World. A nativity sequence of 5 carols, arranged for SSA and piano or organ. pp. 21. *Basil Ramsey: Eastwood*, [1977.] 8°. **F. 1892. q. (22.)**

— Lady Mary. For SA and piano. Traditional English arr. Philip Lane. pp. 8. *Roberton Publications:* [*Wendover*, 1980.] 8°. **E. 263. t. (6.)**

— The Lourdes Carol. Pyreneean folk tune arranged for three-part female voice choir and organ by Philip Lane. ⟨[Words by] The Venerable Bede (adapted).⟩ pp. 7. *Roberton Publications:* [*Wendover*, 1980.] 8°. **E. 1501. yy. (20.)**

— Prestbury Park. [Brass band.] ⟨Score.⟩ pp. 12. *R. Smith & Co.: Watford*, [1977.] obl. 4°. **d. 290. (16.)**

— A spotless Rose. ⟨S. A. (unacc.).⟩ [Words] 15th century. pp. 2. *Banks Music Publications: York*, [1975.] 8°. [*Eboracum choral Series.* 48.] **F. 1874. x.**

— A Spring Overture. [Brass band.] ⟨Full score.⟩ pp. 30. *R. Smith & Co.: Watford*, [1976.] obl. 4°. **g. 1795. (6.)**

— Suite of Cotswold Folkdances. [Orchestra.] Full score. pp. 38. *Edwin Ashdown: London*, [1978.] 4°. **g. 861. k. (4.)**

— There is no Rose. [Carol. S. A. T. B. Words:] Anon 15th cent. *Oecumuse: Ryde*, [1977.] *s. sh.* 4°. *Part of "Canticum novum choral Series".* **G. 954. a. (2.)**

— Versicles, Responses, and the Lord's Prayer. [S. A. T. B.] pp. 7. *Basil Ramsey: Eastwood, Essex*, [1977.] 8°. *Part of "Choral Music Leaflets".* **C. 799. cc. (7.)**

— A Wedding Album ... ⟨Five pieces.⟩ Arranged for organ by Philip Lane. pp. 22. *Edwin Ashdown: London*, [1978.] 4°. **g. 1378. dd. (6.)**

— What sweeter Music. Carol for SSATBB unaccompanied. Words by Robert Herrick. *Oecumuse: Ryde*, [1978.] *s. sh.* 8°. *Part of "Canticum novum choral Series".* **C. 950. a. (36.)**

— *See* CHAIKOVSKY (Petr I.) [16 chansons pour la jeunesse. Op. 54. No. 5. Légende.] Legend. Arranged for S. S. A. unaccompanied by P. Lane, *etc.* [1980.] 8°. **F. 906. cc. (2.)**

— *See* LEUNER (Karl) The Shepherds' Cradle Song ... For SSA & organ (or piano) ... arr. P. Lane. [1980.] 8°. **F. 1874. ff. (9.)**

LANE (PHILIP)

— *See* PRAETORIUS (Michael) [Terpsichore.] Dances from Terpsichore. Arranged [for orchestra] by P. Lane. [1977.] 4°. **f. 641. ss. (5.)**

LANE (POWLETT) *Mrs*

— The Pumpkin Polka. [P. F.] pp. 3. *Boosey & Sons: London*, [c. 1860.] fol. **h. 723. dd. (5.)**

LANE (RICHARD)

— A Hymn to the Night. Words by Henry Wadsworth Longfellow ... For mixed voices (S. A. T. B.) a cappella, *etc.* pp. 7. *Mills Music: New York*, [1962.] 8°. **E. 335. ii. (12.)**

— Suite for Saxophone. For E♭ alto saxophone and piano. [Score and parts.] 2 pt. *Boosey & Hawkes: New York*, [1962.] 4°. **g. 1112. d. (5.)**

LANE (STUART)

— Little Mary ... Song, written and composed by S. Lane, *etc.* *Francis Bros. & Day: London*, [1889.] fol. **H. 1260. m. (42.)**

— Nothing like it. [Song.] Written and composed by S. Lane, *etc.* ⟨Arranged by John S. Baker.⟩ pp. 4. *Francis, Day & Hunter: London*, [1891.] fol. **H. 3980. pp. (1.)**

— Sailors of Her Majesty Victoria. Written by James Rolmaz, *etc.* [Song. Staff and tonic sol-fa notation. Voice part.] *Francis, Day & Hunter: London*, [1899.] *s. sh.* fol. **H. 3980. pp. (2.)**

— There's my little Missis in the old Arm-chair. ⟨Song.⟩ Written by Fred. Riley. [With separate voice part.] 2 pt. *Francis, Day & Hunter: London*, [1901.] fol. **H. 3985. h. (13.)**

— Yarmouth Pier. [Comic song.] Written by H. Hudson, *etc.* *Francis Bros. & Day: London*, [1888.] 4°. **F. 636. k. (5.)**

LANE (THOMAS FREDERICK)

— Harmonized Gregorian Canticles. The Magnificat ... and the Nunc Dimittis, *etc. Beaconsfield*, [1883.] 8°. **B. 835. b. (10.)**

LANE (URIAH)

— "Our hearts are both loyal and true," [song,] written, composed, and sung by U. Lane on Sept. 3, 1830; the accompaniment by M. Newcombe. *Brighton*, [1830.] fol. **H. 1675. (8.)**

LANE (VIRGINIA)

— The "Aurora" Barn Dance, for Pianoforte. *E. Donajowski: London*, [1904.] fol. **h. 3286. dd. (52.)**

LANEARE (NICHOLAS)

— *See* LANIER.

LANE-KEMPEL (HENRY)

— *See* KEMPEL.

LANES

— Lanes in Summer. Unison song. *See* BROOK (Harry)

LANES (MATHIEU)

— Petites pièces d'orgue ... Transcrites et restituées par Norbert Dufourcq, Janine Alaux, Roger Hugon, Roberte Machard.

LANES (Mathieu)

— [With facsimiles.] pp. xvi. 91. pl. iii. *Heugel et c^{ie}: Paris*, 1970. fol.
[*Publications de la Société française de musicologie. ser.* 1. tom. 18.] **g. 1.**

LANESBOROUGH, George John Danvers Butler, *Earl of*
— *See* Danvers.

LANEUVILLE (Legros de)
— *See* Legros de Laneuville .

LANEY (Kate)
— By the Streamlet. [P. F.] *H. G. Bensted & Sons: London*, [1899.] fol.
The Kindergarten Series, etc. No. 2. **h. 727. a. (4.)**

LANG
— Lang lang syne. Ballad. *See* Inglis (J.)
— Lang Syne. Ballad. *See* Hawes (W.)

LANG (A. S.)
— College Boys. March & two-step. [P. F.] pp. 3. *A. Cox & Co.: [Toronto*, 1906.] fol. **h. 4120. mm. (22.)**

LANG (Agnes Mary)
— The Child's Face. Song, *etc. Elkin & Co.: London*, 1913. fol.
H. 1793. s. (4*.)

— Two Eastern Songs. 1. Before the Dawn. Words from "The Garden of Kama" by L. Hope. 2. Salsam, *etc. Elkin & Co.: London*, 1910. fol. **H. 1792. r. (18.)**

— Two Eastern Songs ... Arranged by F. H. Howard. [P. F. and strings.] *Elkin & Co.: London*, 1921. 4°.
[*Elkin & Co.'s Piano & String Series. No.* 11.] **g. 945.**

— Two Little Songs. 1. My wife and I. Words by A. Tennyson. 2. The gift. Words by S. T. Fresinger. *Elkin & Co.: London*, 1920. fol. **H. 1846. x. (16.)**

— Marigolds. Song, words by A. Sullivan. *Elkin & Co.: London*, 1918. fol. **H. 1846. x. (17.)**

— Ode to Sorrow. Song, words by J. Keats. *Elkin & Co.: London*, 1912. fol. **H. 1792. r. (19.)**

— The Poem. Song, words by T. Hood. *Elkin & Co.: London*, 1920. fol. **H. 1846. x. (18.)**

— Songs of the Heart. 1. Heart o' the North. 2. Heart of gold. Words by R. Service. *Elkin & Co.: London*, 1919. fol.
H. 1846. x. (19.)

LANG (Benjamin J.)
— Youthful Voices, a collection of hymns and tunes for the use of Sunday Schools. *Boston*, 1862. 8°. **B. 217.**

LANG (C. A.)
— Te Deum laudamus ... in ... F. *Novello, Ewer & Co.: London & New York*, [1891.] 8°. **F. 1170. h. (16.)**

LANG (C. Tilghman)
— The Earth is the Lord's. For four-part chorus of mixed voices and solos with organ accompaniment. Psalm XXIV. pp. 12.
G. Schirmer: [New York, 1963.] 8°. **E. 335. kk. (33.)**

LANG (C. Tilghman)
— On that first bright Easter Day. Carol for children's voices. Unison. Based on St. Matthew 18: 1–6. pp. 3. *G. Schirmer: New York*, [1966.] 8°. **E. 812. d. (7.)**

LANG (Charles)
— Love at first sight. Song [begins: "I looked from my window"]. The words by L. Gray. *London*, [1879.] fol.
No. 6 *of "London Ballads".* **H. 1783. o. (11.)**

LANG (Craig Sellar)
— Basso ostinato in A. [P. F.] *J. Williams: London*, 1930. 4°.
Public School Series, No. 8. **g. 1400.**

— De Battle ob Jerico. Negro Spiritual. Traditional Melody. Arranged for S. A. T. B. by C. S. Lang. Op. 32. *Novello & Co.: London*, 1939. 8°.
[*The Musical Times. No.* 1159.] **P. P. 1945. aa.**

— Benedictus ... in ... C♯ minor. Op. 29. *Novello & Co.: London*, 1939. 8°.
[*Novello's Services, Anthems, etc., for Men's Voices. No.* 112.]
F. 280. g.

— Benedictus ... in ... A. Op. 36. *Novello & Co.: London*, 1940. 8°.
[*Novello's Services, Anthems, etc., for Men's Voices. No.* 116.]
F. 280. g.

— Benedictus ... in ... F for S. A. T. B. and organ ... Op. 62. pp. 8. *Novello & Co.: London*, [1952.] 8°.
[*Parish Choir Book*, 1302.] **E. 618.**

— Butterflies. (Op. 75. No. 3.) [P. F.] pp. 3. *Elkin & Co.: London*, [1958.] 4°.
Part of the Elkin Series of short Piano Pieces.
g. 1126. n. (23.)

— Four Canons for Violin and Piano. (Op. 4.) (Op. 8.) (Op. 11.) 3 set. *Stainer & Bell: London*, 1925–29. 4°. **g. 505. pp. (9.)**

— Three Choral Preludes. Opus 77. [Organ.] pp. 11. *Oxford University Press: London*, [1957.] 4°. **g. 1380. ff. (8.)**

— Chorale Prelude, Come, Holy Spirit, for organ. *Stainer & Bell: London*, 1916. fol. **h. 2731. x. (1.)**

— Christ the Lord hath risen. Anthem ... Founded on a XIIth century melody ... Op. 18. *Novello and Co.: London*, 1930. 8°.
[*The Musical Times. No.* 1044.] **P. P. 1945. aa.**

— Christ the Lord hath risen. (Christ ist erstanden.) Easter anthem for S. A. T. B. and organ. Words from the German of the XII century, trans. by G. R. W. ... Op. 79. pp. 8. *Elkin & Co.: London*, [1959.] 8°.
Elkin Anthem Series. no. 2554. **E. 442. z. (44.)**

— The Office of the Holy Communion ... in ... E♭ for Unison Voices and Organ. Op. 30. *Novello & Co.: London*, 1939. 8°.
F. 1158. i. (5.)

— The Office of the Holy Communion ... in ... C♯ minor for Men's Voices. Op. 39. *Novello & Co.: London*, 1941. 8°.
[*Novello's Services, Anthems, etc., for Men's Voices. No.* 122.]
F. 280. g.

— The Office of the Holy Communion ... in ... A for Men's Voices ... Op. 45. *Novello & Co.: London*, 1945. 8°.
[*Novello's Services, Anthems, etc., for Men's Voices. No.* 124.]
F. 280. g.

— Communion Service ... in F ... Opus 78. [S. A. T. B.] pp. 24. *Novello & Co.: London*, [1959.] 8°.
[*Parish Choir Book.* 1369.] **E. 618.**

— A Cradle Hymn. Carol for Treble Voices and Organ, words by I. Watts ... Op. 43. *Novello and Co.: London*, 1943. 8°.
[*The Musical Times. No.* 1209.] **P. P. 1945. aa.**

LANG (CRAIG SELLAR)

—— A Cradle Hymn. Carol for S. A. T. B. (unaccompanied) . . .
Op. 59. ⟨Arranged from the original version for treble voices
and organ.⟩ pp. 4. *Novello & Co.: London*, [1950.] 8°.
[*Musical Times. no.* 1292.]   **P. P. 1945. aa.**

—— Six Easy Dances. For piano, *etc.* pp. 11. *Augener: London*,
[1955.] 4°.   **g. 1126. g. (18.)**

—— An Endless Alleluia. Motet for two choirs (S. A. T. B.), words
from the Latin, 10th cent. Translated by J. Ellerton. Op. 56.
pp. 19. *J. Curwen & Sons: London*, [1950.] 8°.
[*Church Choralist. no.* 795.]   **E. 1330.**

—— Everyone suddenly burst out singing. Part-Song for Mixed
Voices, words by S. Sassoon. Op. 26. *Novello and Co.:
London*, 1936. 8°.
[*Novello's Part-Song Book. No.* 1490.]   **F. 280. b.**

—— Everyone suddenly burst out singing . . . for Mixed Voices . . .
Op. 26. *Novello and Co.: London*, 1936. 8°.
[*Novello's Tonic Sol-fa Series. No.* 2689.]   **B. 885.**

—— Everyone suddenly burst out singing. Part-Song for Male
Voices . . . Op. 27. *Novello and Co.: London*, 1936. 8°.
[*The Orpheus. No.* 649.]   **E. 1748.**

—— Everyone suddenly burst out singing . . . for Male Voices . . .
Op. 27. *Novello and Co.: London*, [1939.] 8°.
[*Novello's Tonic Sol-fa Series. No.* 2725.]   **B. 885.**

—— Exercises for Organists, *etc.* 2 bk. *Novello and Co.: London*,
[1952.] 8°.
[*Primer. no.* 128, 129.]   **W. P. A. 900.**

—— Fireflies ⟨Op. 75, No. 1⟩ and Grotesque Dance. ⟨Op. 75, No. 2.⟩
[P. F.] pp. 3. *Elkin & Co.: London*, [1958.] 4°.
Part of the Elkin Series of short Piano Pieces.
       g. 1126. n. (2.)

—— Fugue-Triology on E. G. B. ⟨Op. 58.⟩ For organ. pp. 21.
Novello and Co.: London, [1952.] 4°.
[*Original Compositions. new ser. no.* 215.]   **g. 1270.**

—— Glorious the Sun in mid career. Song for unison voices and
orchestra (or piano). Words by Christopher Smart
(1722–1771). [Voices and P. F.] pp. 4. *Joseph Williams:
London*, [1953.] 8°.
Unison Song Series. 6. no. 28.   **E. 1830. e. (78.)**

—— Grotesque Dance. *See* supra: Fireflies, *etc.*

—— Hail, gladdening Light. Hymn . . . Words by J. Keble from a
Hymn of the 4th century. Op. 28. *Novello and Co.: London*,
1936. 8°.
[*Novello's Octavo Anthems. No.* 1208.]   **E. 618. a.**

—— Hail, gladdening Light. Anthem for unison voices. Translated
from the Greek by John Keble, 1792–1866 . . . Op. 67. pp. 4.
Novello & Co.: London, [1953.] 8°.
[*Octavo Anthems.* 1304.]   **E. 618. a.**

—— Hail thee, festival Day. Anthem for unison voices . . . Words
by Bishop Fortunatus (503–609), translated by P. D. and
G. G. . . . Op. 68. pp. 4. *Novello & Co.: London*, [1953.] 8°.
[*Octavo Anthems.* 1305.]   **E. 618. a.**

—— Harmonic and melodic Dictation Tests, *etc.* 2 bk. *Novello
and Co.: London*, [1952.] 8°.
[*Primer. no.* 125, 126.]   **W. P. A. 900.**

—— He shall give his Angels Charge over thee. Anthem for Five
Voices, unaccompanied . . . Op. 38. *Novello & Co.: London*,
1941. 8°.
[*Novello's Octavo Anthems. No.* 1247.]   **E. 618. a.**

—— 20 Hymn-tune Descants. pp. 17. *Novello and Co.: London*,
[1953.] 8°.   **E. 602. yy. (13.)**

—— Twenty Hymn-tune Preludes. ⟨Op. 90.⟩ [Organ.] For manuals
only, with optional pedals. pp. 19. *Oxford University Press:
London*, [1963.] 4°.   **g. 1378. q. (4.)**

LANG (CRAIG SELLAR)

—— Twenty Hymn-tune Preludes. (Second set.) ⟨Op. 91.⟩ For
manuals only, with optional pedals. pp. 20. *Oxford
University Press: London*, [1966.] 4°.   **g. 1378. r. (2.)**

—— I loved a Lass. Canon for two Sopranos, words by G. Wither
. . . Op. 17. *Novello & Co.: London*, 1930. 8°.
[*Novello's Octavo Edition of Two-part Songs. No.* 252.]
       F. 280. e.

—— I loved a Lass. Madrigal for four voices S. A. T. B., words by
George Wither, 1588–1667 . . . Op. 50. pp. 12. *Novello & Co.:
London*, [1949.] 8°.
[*Part-Song Book.* 1544.]   **F. 280. b.**

—— Introduction and Fugue on 'Redhead No. 46'. ⟨Op. 83.⟩
[Organ.] pp. 8. *Oxford University Press: London*, [1959.] fol.
       g. 1380. oo. (14.)

—— Introduction and Passacaglia A minor. ⟨Op. 51.⟩ For organ.
pp. 11. *Novello and Co.: London*, [1952.] 4°.
[*Original Compositions. new ser. no.* 208.]   **g. 1270.**

—— The Jackdaw of Rheims. Ballad for Chorus and Orchestra,
the poem by T. Ingoldsby. Op. 14. [Vocal score.] *Boosey &
Co.: London and New York*, 1929. 8°.   **E. 1592. kk. (2.)**

—— Jesu, the very Thought of Thee. Words c. 12th century.
Tr. E. Caswall . . . Op. 88, No. 2. ⟨Two-part.⟩ pp. 4. *Oxford
University Press: London*, [1962.] 8°.
[*Oxford easy Anthems. E* 95.]   **F. 1001.**

—— Jubilate Deo . . . in G . . . Op. 19. *Novello & Co.: London*,
1930. 8°.
[*Novello's Parish Choir Book. No.* 1160.]   **E. 618.**

—— Jubilate Deo . . . in . . . G . . . Op. 19. [Voice part only.]
Novello & Co.: London, [1954.] s. sh. 8°.   **F. 1158. n. (10.)**

—— The King of Love. Words by H. W. Baker (1821–1877) . . .
Op. 88. No. 1. ⟨Two-part.⟩ pp. 4. *Oxford University Press:
London*, [1962.] 8°.
[*Oxford easy Anthems. E* 96.]   **F. 1001.**

—— Let all the World in every Corner sing. For S. A. T. B. Chorus
and Orchestra, words by G. Herbert, *etc.* (Op. 28.) [Vocal
score.] *Boosey & Co.: London*, 1938. 8°.   **F. 1176. l. (34.)**

—— Let all the World in every Corner sing . . . For treble voices
and organ or piano. [Words by] George Herbert . . . Op. 82.
⟨Two-part.⟩ pp. 4. *Oxford University Press: London*, [1959.]
8°.
[*Oxford easy Anthems. E* 86.]   **F. 1001.**

—— Let the Words of my Mouth. Anthem for S. A. T. B.
(unaccompanied), *etc.* Op. 61. pp. 3. *J. Curwen & Sons:
London*, [1951.] 8°.
[*Church Choralist. no.* 800.]   **E. 1330.**

—— Let us drink and be merry. Coronemus nos rosis antequam
marcescant. Part-song for S. A. T. B. (unaccompanied), words
by Thomas Jordan (1612?–1685) . . . Op. 65. pp. 8. *Novello &
Co.: London*, [1951.] 8°.
[*Musical Times. no.* 1306.]   **P. P. 1945. aa.**

—— Let us now praise famous Men. Anthem for Men's Voices . . .
Op. 42. *Stainer & Bell: London*, 1942. 8°.
Church Choir Library, No. 545.   **F. 1137. b.**

—— Lochinvar. Ballad for Chorus and Orchestra, the poem by Sir
W. Scott. Op. 7. [Vocal score.] *Novello and Co.: London*,
1927. 8°.   **E. 1592. ff. (6.)**

—— Lochinvar . . . Op. 7. [String parts.] *Novello & Co.: London*,
1928. fol.   **h. 3210. h. (229.)**

—— The Lord's Prayer . . . in . . . D minor for S. A. T. B.
(unaccompanied). pp. 3. *J. Curwen & Sons: London*, [1951.]
8°.
[*Church Choralist. no.* 796.]   **E. 1330.**

LANG (CRAIG SELLAR)

— Love is a Babel. Unaccompanied part song for S. A. T. B., words from Robert Jones' Second Book of Airs (1601) ... Op. 46. pp. 4. *Novello & Co.: London*, [1947.] 8°.
[*Musical Times. no.* 1252.]   **P. P. 1945. aa.**

— Magnificat. (Nunc dimittis.) Op. 13. *J. B. Cramer & Co.: London*, 1931. 8°.
[*Cramer's Library of Church Music. No.* 12.]   **F. 157. e.**

— Magnificat and Nunc dimittis ... in ... B♭ for men's voices ... Op. 16. *Novello & Co.: London*, 1929. 8°.
[*Novello's Services, Anthems, etc., for men's voices. No.* 105.]
    F. 280. g.

— Magnificat and Nunc dimittis ... in ... B flat. (Opus 16.) For SATB and organ. pp. 11. *Novello & Co.: London*, [1962.] 8°.
[*Parish Choir Book.* 1400.]   **E. 618.**

— Magnificat and Nunc dimittis ... D ... Op. 20. *Novello & Co.: London*, 1930. 8°.
[*Novello's Parish Choir Book. No.* 1162.]   **E. 618.**

— Magnificat and Nunc dimittis ... in ... F ... Op. 25. *Novello & Co.: London*, 1933. 8°.
[*Novello's Parish Choir Book. No.* 1186.]   **E. 618.**

— Magnificat and Nunc dimittis ... in C♯ minor. Op. 33. *Novello & Co.: London*, 1940. 8°.
[*Novello's Services, Anthems, etc., for Men's Voices. No.* 113.]
    F. 280. g.

— Magnificat and Nunc dimittis ... in ... A. Op. 37. *Novello & Co.: London*, 1940. 8°.
[*Novello's Services, Anthems, etc., for Men's Voices. No.* 117.]
    F. 280. g.

— Magnificat and Nunc dimittis ... For unaccompanied voices in ... A minor ... Op. 48. pp. 16. *Novello & Co.: London*, [1948.] 8°.
[*Parish Choir Book.* 1282.]   **E. 618.**

— Magnificat and Nunc dimittis ... in ... B flat for two choirs (S. A. T. B.) unaccompanied ... Op. 52. pp. 15. *Novello & Co.: London*, [1952.] 8°.
[*Parish Choir Book.* 1286.]   **E. 618.**

— Magnificat and Nunc dimittis ... in ... E♭ for A. T. B. and organ. Op. 57. pp. 12. *J. Curwen & Sons: London*, [1951.] 8°.
[*Church Choralist. no.* 797.]   **E. 1330.**

— Magnificat and Nunc dimittis ... in ... E♭ for congregation, choir and organ ... Op. 63. pp. 11. *Novello & Co.: London*, [1953.] 8°.
[*Parish Choir Book.* 1311.]   **E. 618.**

— Magnificat and Nunc dimittis ... in ... E♭. For congregation, choir and organ ... Op. 63. [Congregational part.] pp. 3. *Novello & Co.: London*, [1953.] 8°.   **F. 1158. m. (25.)**

— Magnificat and Nunc dimittis ... in ... F ... Op. 71. pp. 19. *J. Curwen & Sons: London; G. Schirmer: New York*, [1955.] 8°.
[*Church Choralist. no.* 817.]   **E. 1330.**

— Melodies and Basses to be harmonized in four Parts at the Keyboard, *etc.* pp. 20. *Novello and Co.: London*, [1952.] 8°.
[*Primer. no.* 127.]   **W. P. A. 900.**

— A Miniature 48. Two books of short preludes & fugues in all keys, *etc.* (Op. 64. Piano solo.) 2 bk. *Augener: London*, [1953.] 4°.   **g. 1126. e. (1.)**

— [A Miniature 48. Op. 64.] Ten Short Preludes & Fugues. Op. 70 ... Organ. 2 bk. *Augener: London*, [1956.] 4°.
    g. 1380. cc. (7.)

— Miniature Suite. Seven short Pieces for Pianoforte. Op. 3. *Stainer & Bell: London*, 1924. 4°.   **g. 543. ee. (11.)**

— Miniature Suite. (Op. 89. Piano solo.) pp. 9. *Oxford University Press: London*, [1962.] 4°.   **g. 1128. ii. (21.)**

LANG (CRAIG SELLAR)

— Miniature Suite for Violin & Piano. Op. 10, *etc. Augener: London*, 1928. 4°.   **g. 500. n. (20.)**

— Miserere Domine. Anthem for Men's Voices, unaccompanied, words from a paraphrase of the 14th cent. hymn "Anima Christi sanctifica me" ... Op. 44. *Novello and Co.: London*, 1945. 8°.
[*Services and Anthems for Men's Voices. No.* 123.]   **F. 280. g.**

— Miserere Domine. Anthem for S. A. T. B. (unaccompanied) ... Op. 49. pp. 4. *Novello & Co.: London*, [1948.] 8°.
[*Musical Times. no.* 1264.]   **P. P. 1945. aa.**

— My Spirit longs for Thee. Anthem for S. A. T. B. and organ, words by J. Byrom 1692–1763. Op. 53. pp. 6. *J. Curwen & Sons: London*, [1951.] 8°.
[*Church Choralist. no.* 793.]   **E. 1330.**

— The Nativity. Words by W. Dunbar ... For Unison Voices, Choir and Organ. Op. 21. *Novello & Co.: London*, 1931. 8°.
[*Novello's Octavo Anthems. No.* 1175.]   **E. 618. a.**

— O let my Wish be crowned. Words by J. Byrom (1691–1763) ... Op. 88, No. 3. (Two-part.) pp. 4. *Oxford University Press: London*, [1962.] 8°.
[*Oxford easy Anthems. E*97.]   **F. 1001.**

— O Lord, support us all the Day long. Anthem for S. A. T. B. (unaccompanied), words 16th century. pp. 4. *Novello & Co.: London*, [1950.] 8°.
[*Musical Times. no.* 1286.]   **P. P. 1945. aa.**

— Paper-work Tests, *etc. Novello and Co.: London*, [1954.] 8°.
[*Primer. no.* 136, 137.]   **W. P. A. 900.**

— Passacaglia in G minor for four Violins. Op. 22. Score. *Novello and Co.: London*, 1932. 8°.   **e. 668. g. (1.)**

— Prelude and Fugue in G minor. For organ. (Opus 84.) pp. 7. *Novello & Co.: London*, [1960.] 4°.
[*Original Compositions. new ser. no.* 307.]   **g. 1270.**

— Prelude, Pastorale and Fugue. For organ. pp. 11. *Novello & Co.: London*, [1962.] 4°.
[*Novello's Organ Music Club. no.* 28.]   **g. 1023. f.**

— Psalm VIII ... for Unison Voices, Choir and Organ. *Novello & Co.: London*, [1939.] 8°.   **F. 1176. m. (33.)**

— Rejoice in the Lord alway. Anthem for Men's Voices and Organ. Op. 34. *Novello & Co.: London*, 1940. 8°.
[*Novello's Services, Anthems, etc., for Men's Voices. No.* 114.]
    F. 280. g.

— Remember, O thou Man. Carol for unison voices, Chorus ad lib. ... Words from Ravenscroft's Melismata ... Op. 12. *Novello & Co.: London*, 1928. 8°.
[*Novello's Octavo Anthems. No.* 1158.]   **E. 618. a.**

— Remember, O thou Man ... Op. 12, *etc. Novello and Co.: London*, 1928. 4°.
[*Novello's Tonic Sol-fa Series. No.* 2586.]   **B. 885.**

— Save us, O Lord, waking. Anthem for S. A. T. B. (unaccompanied), words from The Order for Compline ... Op. 60. pp. 4. *Novello & Co.: London*, [1951.] 8°.
[*Musical Times. no.* 1298.]   **P. P. 1945. aa.**

— Score Reading Exercises, *etc.* 2 bk. *Novello and Co.: London*, [1949, 51.] 8°.
[*Primer. no.* 123, 124.]   **W. P. A. 900.**

— Morning and Evening Service ... in ... A. *H. F. W. Deane & Sons: London*, 1925. 8°.
[*The Year Book Press Series of Anthems and Church Music. No.* 33.]   **H. 802.**

— Set up Thyself, O God. Words from Ps. 57. v. 6 and 9. Ps. 40. v. 1–2. Ps. 57. v. 10–12. Anthem for SATB and organ ... Op. 80. pp. 12. *Elkin & Co.: London*, [1960.] 8°.
Elkin Anthem Series. no. 2562.   **E. 442. dd. (17.)**

LANG (CRAIG SELLAR)

— The Seven Joys. Christmas Carol, *etc. Novello and Co.: London*, 1928. 8°.
[*Novello's Christmas Carols. No.* 441.]   **C. 754.**

— Ten Short Preludes & Fugues. Op. 70. *See* supra: [A Miniature 48. Op. 64.]

— Six Short Sketches for the piano ... Op. 2. *Stainer & Bell: London*, 1920. 4°.   **g. 1129. w. (16.)**

— Sing Alleluia forth in duteous Praise. Alleluia piis edite laudibus. Anthem for treble voices and organ. Words from the Latin of the 10th century, tr. by J. Ellerton, 1826–1893 ... Opus 74. pp. 7. *Novello & Co.: London*, [1957.] 8°.
[*Chorister Series.* 97.]   **F. 280. i.**

— Sketches for Piano. First ⟨–Third⟩ book of five easy pieces. 3 bk. *Novello and Co.: London*, [1955.] 4°.   **g. 1126. h. (11.)**

— Sonata in D minor for Organ. ⟨Op. 47.⟩ pp. 50. *Novello and Co.: London*, [1948.] 4°.
[*Original Compositions. New series. no.* 202.]   **g. 1270.**

— Te Deum and Jubilate ... in ... F ... Op. 23. *J. B. Cramer & Co.: London*, [1933.] 8°.   **F. 1158. f. (25.)**

— Te Deum laudamus ... in ... C♯ minor. Op. 29. *Novello & Co.: London*, 1939. 8°.
[*Novello's Services, Anthems, etc., for Men's Voices. No.* 111.]   **F. 280. g.**

— Te Deum laudamus ... for unaccompanied Voices in ... A minor. Op. 35. *Novello & Co.: London*, 1940. 8°.
[*Novello's Parish Choir Book. No.* 1236.]   **E. 618.**

— Te Deum laudamus ... in ... A. Op. 36. *Novello & Co.: London*, 1940. 8°.
[*Novello's Services, Anthems, etc., for Men's Voices. No.* 115.]   **F. 280. g.**

— Te Deum Laudamus ... in ... D ... Op. 41. *Novello & Co.: London*, 1941. 8°.
[*Novello's Parish Choir Book. No.* 1251.]   **E. 618.**

— Te Deum laudamus ... in ... F for S. A. T. B. and organ ... Op. 62. pp. 12. *Novello & Co.: London*, [1952.] 8°.
[*Parish Choir Book.* 1301.]   **E. 618.**

— Te Deum laudamus ... in ... E flat for congregation, choir and organ ... Op. 73. pp. 14. *Novello & Co.: London*, [1958.] 8°.
[*Parish Choir Book.* 1341.]   **E. 618.**

— This joyous Day. Anthem ... Words by E. Spenser ... Op. 24. *Novello and Co.: London*, 1933. 8°.
[*Novello's Short Anthems. No.* 267.]   **F. 280. f.**

— The Time draws near the Birth of Christ. Carol ... Words from Tennyson's In Memoriam ... Op. 31. *Novello & Co.: London*, 1939. 8°.
[*Novello's Octavo Anthems. No.* 1242.]   **E. 618. a.**

— Toccata in C minor. ⟨Opus 81.⟩ [Organ.] pp. 8. *Oxford University Press: London*, [1959.] 4°.   **g. 1380. ff. (18.)**

— Six Tone Pictures ... for the pianoforte. Op. 1. *Stainer & Bell: London*, 1920. 4°.   **g. 1129. w. (17.)**

— Tres magi de gentibus. Carol for unison voices, eight-part chorus and organ, words from the Latin text, XV century. (Voice Part only.) 2 no. *H. F. W. Deane & Sons: London*, 1925. 8°.
[*The Year Book Press Series of Unison and Part-Songs. No.* 260.]   **F. 223.**

— Tuba Tune in D major. Op. 15. (Organ.) *J. B. Cramer & Co.: London*, 1929. 4°.
[*Cramer's Library of Organ Music. Set* 3. *No.* 1.]   **g. 1353.**

LANG (CRAIG SELLAR)

— Two Hundred Tunes for Sight Singing ... together with twelve Rounds. *H. F. W. Deane & Sons: London*, 1927. 8°.   **E. 769.**

— 100 Tunes for sight-singing in the Treble Clef. ⟨In the Bass Clef. Book II.⟩ 2 bk. *Novello and Co.: London*, [1954.] 8°.   **E. 763. g. (4.)**

— Six Vesper Hymns ... Op. 76. 1. Jesus Christ, Thou Child so wise. (Unison.) Hilaire Belloc. ⟨2. Christ was the Word. (Unison.) Ascribed to Queen Elizabeth I. 3. God's two Dwellings. (S. S.) Thomas Washbourne. 1606–1687. 4. Save us, O Lord, waking. (S. S.) Words from the Order for Compline. 5. I will lay me down in Peace. (S. S. A.) Psalm IV, v.9. 6. The Duteous Day now closeth. (S. S. A.) Paul Gerhardt, 1607–1676. Tr. Robert Bridges.⟩ 3 no. *Novello & Co.: London*, [1958.] 8°.
[*Chorister Series.* 102–104.] *Each no. contains two Hymns.*   **F. 280. i.**

— Voluntary on 'Winchester new'. For organ. pp. 3. *Novello & Co.: London*, [1959.] 4°.
[*Original Compositions. new ser. no.* 268.]   **g. 1270.**

— Wake, little Bees! Two-part Song, words by W. H. Ogilvie. *H. F. W. Deane & Sons: London*, 1926. 8°.
[*The Year Book Press Series of Unison and Part-Songs. No.* 266.]   **F. 223.**

— When Johnny come down to Hilo. Windlass and Capstan Shanty. Arranged [for S. A. T. B.] by C. S. Lang. Op. 9. *Stainer & Bell: London*, 1928. 8°.
Choral Library, No. 241.   **F. 1137. d.**

— Wind of the Night. Unison Song ... Words by W. H. Ogilvie. *H. F. W. Deane & Sons: London*, 1925. 8°.
[*The Year Book Press Series of Unison and Part Songs. No.* 255.]   **F. 223.**

— Wine and Water. Part-Song for Mixed Voices, words by G. K. Chesterton. Op. 40. *Novello & Co.: London*, 1941. 4°.
[*Novello's Part-Song Book. No.* 1522.]   **F. 280. b.**

— Ye Men of Galilee. (God is gone up with a merry Noise.) Anthem. Op. 54. pp. 7. *J. Curwen & Sons: London*, [1951.] 8°.
[*Church Choralist. no.* 794.]   **E. 1330.**

— *See* ALBRECHTSBERGER (J. G.) [Douze fugues pour le clavecin ou l'orgue. Op. 1. No. 2, 4, 11.] Three Fugues ... Arranged for organ by C. S. Lang. [1952.] 4°.   **g. 575. nn. (2.)**

— *See* ALBRECHTSBERGER (J. G.) [Douze fugues pour le clavecin ou l'orgue. Op. 1. No. 6.] Fugue in D minor on the chorale "Christus ist erstanden" ... Arranged by C. S. Lang. [1953.] 4°. [*Cramer's Library of Organ Music by British & foreign Composers. no.* 46.]   **g. 1353. a.**

— *See* ALBRECHTSBERGER (J. G.) Fugue in E flat ... Arranged by C. S. Lang. [1952.] 4°. [*Cramer's Library of Organ Music by British & foreign Composers. no.* 39.]   **g. 1353. a.**

— *See* BACH (J. E.) Fugue in F ... Arranged by C. S. Lang. [1952.] 4°. [*Cramer's Library of Organ Music by British & foreign Composers. no.* 40.]   **g. 1353. a.**

— *See* BACH (J. S.) [Die Kunst der Fuge.—Contrapunctus No. 1.] Fugue in D minor ... Arranged for organ by C. S. Lang. [1954.] 4°. [*Cramer's Library of Organ Music by British & foreign Composers. no.* 52.]   **g. 1353. a.**

— *See* BACH (J. S.) [Die Kunst der Fuge.—Contrapunctus No. 5.] Fugue in D minor. (In contrary motion) ... Arranged for organ by C. S. Lang. [1954.] 4°. [*Cramer's Library of Organ Music by British & foreign Composers. no.* 53.]   **g. 1353. a.**

— *See* BACH (J. S.) [Die Kunst der Fuge.—Contrapunctus No. 11.] Triple Fugue in D minor ... Arranged for organ by C. S. Lang. [1954.] 4°. [*Cramer's Library of Organ Music by British & foreign Composers. no.* 51.]   **g. 1353. a.**

LANG (CRAIG SELLAR)

— *See* BAIRSTOW (*Sir* Edward C.) Magnificat and Nunc dimittis ... in ... D ... Arranged for use with the original edition ... by C. S. Lang. [1952.] 8°.   **F. 1158. m. (13.)**

— *See* CHARPENTIER (J. J. B.) [Journal d'orgue. No. 2. Six fugues. No. 1.] Fugue in G minor ... Arranged by C. S. Lang. [1953.] 4°. [*Cramer's Library of Organ Music by British & foreign Composers. no.* 44.]   **g. 1353. a.**

— *See* CHRIST'S HOSPITAL. A Shortened Psalter. For use in Christ's Hospital Chapel. [The editor's preface signed: H. L. O. F., i. e. H. L. O. Flecker; C. S. L., i. e. C. S. Lang; E. D. D., i. e. E. D. Deane.] [1931.] 8°.   **D. 605. r.**

— *See* CORELLI (A.) [Concerti grossi. Op. 6. No. 1.] Largo and Fugue, *etc.* ⟨Arranged for organ by C. S. Lang.⟩ [1956.] 4°. [*Cramer's Library of Organ Music by British & foreign Composers. no.* 70.]   **g. 1353. a.**

— *See* EBERLIN (J. E.) [IX. toccate e fughe. No. 2.] Fugue in G minor ... Arranged by C. S. Lang. [1953.] 4°. [*Cramer's Library of Organ Music by British & foreign Composers. no.* 45.]   **g. 1353. a.**

— *See* EBERLIN (J. E.) [IX. toccate e fughe. No. 3.] Fugue in A minor ... Arranged by C. S. Lang. [1952.] 4°. [*Cramer's Library of Organ Music by foreign & British Composers. no.* 41.]   **g. 1353. a.**

— *See* FRANCK (C. A. J. G. H.) [*Collections.*] Five Pieces ... Arranged for organ by C. S. Lang. [1951.] 4°.   **h. 2693. f. (3.)**

— *See* GIBBONS (Orlando) In nomine. Arranged for organ by C. S. Lang. [1952.] 4°. [*Cramer's Library of Organ Music by British Composers. set* 10. 7.]   **g. 1353.**

— *See* HAENDEL (G. F.) [*Collected Works.—g.*] Six Selected Pieces (Six Selected Pieces from "The Water Music") (Six Selected Marches) (Six Selected Minuets) for Piano. Arranged ... by C. S. Lang. 1928–31. 4°.   **g. 74. b. (11.)**

— *See* HAENDEL (G. F.) [*Collected Works.—h.*] Handel Album for Violin & Piano. Select Movements arranged from the figured bass by C. S. Lang, *etc.* 1928. 4°.   **g. 74. b. (4.)**

— *See* HAENDEL (G. F.) [*Collected Works.—h.*] Five Overtures ... Arranged for organ by C. S. Lang. 1951. 4°.   **g. 74. uu. (1.)**

— *See* HAENDEL (G. F.) [*Collected Works.—h.*] Fourteen Pieces. Arranged for organ by C. S. Lang. [1955.] 4°.   **g. 74. yy. (1.)**

— *See* HAENDEL (G. F.) [Alcina.] Musette and Minuet ... Arranged for Violin and Piano by C. S. Lang, *etc.* 1926. 4°. [*The Year Book Press Series of Instrumental Music. No.* 10.]   **g. 1383.**

— *See* HAENDEL (G. F.) [Berenice.—Overture.] Minuet ... Arranged for Violin & Piano by C. S. Lang. 1928. 4°.   **g. 74. b. (8.)**

— *See* HAENDEL (G. F.) [Chandos Anthems. H. G. 35. No. 10.] Overture ... Arranged for organ by C. S. Lang. [1952.] 4°.   **g. 74. oo. (11.)**

— *See* HAENDEL (G. F.) Organ Concertos. Op. 4 ... Edited and arranged for organ by C. S. Lang and J. Dykes Bower. [1958.] 4°.   **g. 74. uu. (16.)**

— *See* HAENDEL (G. F.) [Messiah.—Selections, vocal.] The Messiah. A Unison Part ... Arranged for use with the Choir by C. S. Lang. 1938. 8°.   **E. 146. q. (14.)**

— *See* HARWOOD (Basil) Magnificat and Nunc dimittis in A flat ... A unison part for men's voices, arranged for use with the original edition ... by C. S. Lang. [1956.] 8°.   **F. 1158. p. (2.)**

— *See* HYMNS. [*English.*] The Public School Hymn Book, *etc.* The music edited by C. S. Lang. [1949.] 8°.   **C. 550. p.**

LANG (CRAIG SELLAR)

— *See* MOZART (W. A.) Fugue in G minor. ⟨K. 401.⟩ ... Arranged by C. S. Lang. [1953.] 4°. [*Cramer's Library of Organ Music by British & foreign Composers. no.* 43.]   **g. 1353. a.**

— *See* NARES (James) [Six Fuges with Introductory Voluntary's. No. 2.] Fugue in G minor ... Arranged by C. S. Lang. [1953.] 4°. [*Cramer's Library of Organ Music by British Composers. set.* 11. *no.* 3.]   **g. 1353.**

— *See* PARRY (*Sir* Charles H. H.) *Bart.* Blest Pair of Sirens ... Arranged for Four-part, S. A. T. B., Chorus by C. S. Lang. 1938. 8°.   **F. 585. zz. (34.)**

— *See* PARRY (*Sir* Charles H. H.) *Bart.* [Blest Pair of Sirens.] O sanctaidd swynwyr, *etc.* ⟨Arr. by C. S. Lang. Tonic sol-fa.⟩ [1957.] 8°.   **C. 745. k. (1.)**

— *See* PARRY (*Sir* Charles H. H.) *Bart.* Magnificat and Nunc dimittis ... in ... D ... Arranged for use with the original edition ... by C. S. Lang. [1952.] 8°.   **F. 1158. m. (17.)**

— *See* PURCELL (Henry) [Ode for Queen Mary's Birthday, 1694.] Sound the Trumpet ... Accompaniment arranged by C. S. Lang. 1931. 8°. [*The Musical Times. no.* 1060.]   **P. P. 1945. aa.**

— *See* RUBRA (Edmund D.) Festival Te Deum ... ⟨Op. 71.⟩ Vocal score with organ reduction by Dr. C. S. Lang. [1951.] 8°.   **F. 1191. a. (4.)**

— *See* STANFORD (*Sir* Charles V.) [Morning and Evening Service in B flat. Op. 10.] Benedictus in B flat ... A unison part for men's voices, arranged ... by C. S. Lang. [1949.] *s. sh.* 8°.   **F. 1158. j. (39.)**

— *See* STANFORD (*Sir* Charles V.) [Morning and Evening Service in B flat. Op. 10.] Jubilate in B flat ... A unison part for men's voices, arranged ... by C. S. Lang. [1948.] *s. sh.* 8°.   **F. 1158. j. (40.)**

— *See* STANFORD (*Sir* Charles V.) [Morning and Evening Service in B flat. Op. 10.] Magnificat and Nunc dimittis in B flat ... A Unison Part for Men's Voices, arranged ... by C. S. Lang. 1929. 8°.   **F. 1158. e. (30.)**

— *See* STANFORD (*Sir* Charles V.) [Morning and Evening Service in B flat. Op. 10.] Te Deum laudamus in B flat ... Arranged ... by C. S. Lang. [1928.] 8°.   **F. 1158. d. (40.)**

— *See* STANFORD (*Sir* Charles V.) [Morning and Evening Service in A. Op. 12.] Te Deum laudamus ... in ... A ... Arranged for use with the original edition ... by C. S. Lang. [1952.] 8°.   **F. 1158. m. (18.)**

— *See* STANFORD (*Sir* Charles V.) [Morning, Communion and Evening Service in C. Op. 115.] Te Deum Laudamus ... arranged ... by C. S. Lang. 1933. 8°. [*Modern Church Services. No.* 7 *a.*]   **F. 1137.**

— *See* TALLIS (T.) [Nine psalm tunes. No. 8.] Tallis' Canon. Arranged as an Organ Prelude [by] C. S. Lang. 1926. 4°. [*The Year Book Series of Instrumental Music. No.* 11.]   **g. 1383.**

— *See* WALMISLEY (T. A.) [Service in D minor.] Magnificat and Nunc dimittis in D minor ... Arranged ... by C. S. Lang. [1931.] 8°.   **F. 1158. f. (6.)**

— *See* WOOD (Charles) *Mus. Doc.* Magnificat and Nunc dimittis ... in ... C minor ... Arranged for use with the original edition ... by C. S. Lang. [1952.] 8°.   **F. 1158. m. (20.)**

— *See* WOOD (Charles) *Mus. Doc.* Magnificat and Nunc dimittis ... in ... D ... Arranged for use with the original edition ... by C. S. Lang. [1952.] 8°.   **F. 1158. m. (21.)**

LANG (EDDIE)

— Eddie Lang Modern advanced Guitar Method. Edited by
D. Berend. *Robbins Music Corporation: New York*, 1935. 4°.
g. 660. e. (8.)

LANG (EDITH)

— A Crystal Stream of Folk-Lore, a compendium for beginners
in piano-playing, compiled and edited by E. Lang. *Boston
Music Co.: Boston*, 1916. 4°.
g. 442. z. (13.)

— Elevation in G major. [Organ.] *H. W. Gray Co.: [New York,]*
1916. 4°.
St. Cecilia Series, No. 66.
g. 1380. a. (17.)

— Gaelic Song. Words by M. O'Neill ... Song with Pianoforte
accompaniment. *Boston Music Co.: Boston, Mass.*, (1909.)
fol.
H. 1794. uu. (65.)

— God is my strong Salvation. [Sacred song.] For baritone
voice, text from hymn by J. Montgomery and the Psalms.
H. W. Gray Co.: [London,] 1916. 4°.
G. 519. c. (12.)

— The Heavenly Message ... Christmas Cantata for soli and
chorus of mixed voices, with organ accompaniment. Vocal
score. *Boston Music Co.: Boston*, 1917. 8°.
F. 1269. z. (1.)

— I hear Thy Voice. Anthem ... [Words by] M. F. Ham. *Boston
Music Co.: Boston, Mass.*, (1915.) 8°.
F. 281. ss. (25.)

— I hear Thy Voice. [Sacred song, words by] M. F. Ham, *etc.*
Boston Music Co.: Boston, Mass., (1915.) fol.
H. 1187. xx. (9.)

— It was a Lover and his Lass. Trio for women's voices. [Words
by] W. Shakespeare, *etc. Boston Music Co.: Boston, Mass.*,
(1915.) 8°.
F. 328. v. (23.)

— A Morning in Munich. Four easy and instructive Pieces for
the Pianoforte. 1. Peasant's Dance. 2. Soldier's March. 3. In
the Cathedral. 4. Student's Song. *Boston Music Co.: Boston,
Mass.*, 1912. 4°.
g. 232. r. (8.)

— National Anthems of the Allies, simply arranged for young
Americans by E. Lang, *etc.* (Piano.) *Boston Music Co.:
Boston*, 1919. 4°.
g. 1129. j. (19.)

— Romanesque, for the Pianoforte. *Boston Music Co.: Boston,
Mass.*, (1913.) fol.
h. 3284. f. (41.)

LANG (EDWIN R.)

— The Hebrew Fancy Ball. [Song.] Words and music by E. R.
Lang. pp. 5. *Willis Woodward & Co.: New York*, [1892.] fol.
H. 3980. pp. (3.)

LANG (HANS)

— Fröhliches Handwerk. Kleine Kantate nach einem Text von
Max Mumenthaler für dreistimmigen gemischten Chor und
Instrumente (Blockflöte, zwei Geigen und Violoncello) oder
Klavier ... Partitur (zugl. Klavierstimme), *etc.* pp. 16.
B. Schott's Söhne: Mainz, [1952.] 8°.
F. 1267. cc. (6.)

— Glückwunsch-Kantate nach Worten von Ludwig Schuster für
Solo-Sopran, Chor und Instrumente. Opus 44 ... Partitur.
B. Schott's Söhne: Mainz, 1938. 8°.
E. 1500. a. (3.)

— In dulci jubilo. Weihnachtskantate nach geistlichen
Volksliedern und Worten der heiligen Schrift für Sopran-und
Bariton-Solo, gemischten Chor, Kinder- oder Frauenchor,
kleines Orchester und Klavier (oder Cembalo, Orgel,
Harmonium) ... Opus 51. Klavierauszug. pp. 35. *B. Schott's
Söhne: Mainz*, [1951.] 4°.
G. 976. a. (4.)

— Der Sonnengesang des heiligen Franziskus für dreistimmigen
Jugendchor, vier- bis sechsstimmigen gemischten Chor und
Blechbläser (3 Trompeten in B, 3 Hörner in F, 3 Posaunen,
Tuba, Pauken und Schlagzeug ad lib.). Deutsche Textfassung

LANG (HANS)

nach dem Original vom Komponisten. Opus 52. Klavier-
Partitur, *etc.* pp. 23. *B. Schott's Söhne: Mainz*, [1957.] 8°.
F. 1195. k. (3.)

— *See* HAAS (J.) Festgabe Joseph Haas, *etc.* (Herausgegeben von
... H. Lang.) 1939. fol.
G. 1410.

— *See* REIN (W.) and LANG (H.) Der Wundergarten ...
Herausgegeben und gesetzt von W. Rein und H. Lang, *etc.*
[1953, *etc.*] 8°.
F. 1771. t. (2.)

LANG (HENRY ALBERT)

— Gavotte. Concertstück für Pianoforte. Op. 8. *Leipzig*, 1884.
fol.
h. 3280. k. (22.)

— Fünf kleine Tonstücke für die Jugend ... für Pianoforte.
Op. 1. *Leipzig u. Winterthur*, [1884.] fol.
h. 3280. k. (21.)

— Sonate für Pianoforte und Violoncello oder Violine. Op. 12.
Leipzig u. Winterthur, [1883.] fol.
h. 1866. (9.)

— Traum und Nebelbilder. Fünf kleine Phantasien für
Pianoforte. Op. 11. *Leipzig*, 1884. fol.
h. 3280. k. (23.)

LÁNG (ISTVÁN)

— Concerto bucolico. For horn and orchestra. Piano reduction.
[Score and part.] 2 pt. *Boosey & Hawkes: London, etc.; Editio
musica: Budapest*, 1972. 4°.
g. 1138. bb. (11.)

— Duo. For trumpets in C. [Score.] pp. 5. *Boosey & Hawkes
Music Publishers: London, etc.; Editio Musica: Budapest;
printed in Hungary*, [1973.] 4°.
g. 1105. s. (6.)

— Fúvósötös, vagy amit akartok ... or, what you will
(Shakespeare). ⟨Quintetto per fiati.⟩ pp. 21. *Zeneműkiadó
vállalat: Budapest*, 1965. 8°.
Kispartitúrák 183.
b. 346. i. (5.)

— In memoriam N. N. Cantata to poems by János Pilinszky.
Score. pp. 68. *Boosey & Hawkes Music Publishers: London,
etc.; Editio Musica: Budapest; printed in Hungary*, [1973.] 8°.
F. 1257. qq. (2.)

— Symphony No. 2. ⟨Orchestra.⟩ Score. pp. 42. *Editio Musica:
Budapest*, [1977.] fol.
i. 174. w.

LANG (J. B.)

— *See* SULLIVAN (M. D.) Bible Songs ... harmonized by J. B.
Lang. 1856. *obl.* 8°.
A. 979.

LANG (J. C.)

— Three Sonatas, for the Piano Forte or Harpsichord, with
Accompagniment for a Violin ... Opera 3. *The Author:
London*, [1787.] *obl.* fol.
e. 100. (2.)

— Three Sonatas for the Piano Forte or Harpsichord, with an
accompaniment for a violin ... Opera VI. [Score.] pp. 17. *The
Author: London*, [1795?] fol.
Hirsch M. 1423.

LANG (J. D.)

— Rondo à la chasse for the Piano Forte. *London*, [1815?] fol.
h. 117. (5.)

LANG (J. P.)

— *See* LONG.

LANG (JOHANN GEORG)

— Concerto per il cembalo obligato con due violini, due oboe, due corni, viola e basso. ⟨Opera IV.⟩ [Parts.] *Presso Giovanni André: Offenbach; presso l'Autore: Coblenz*, [1776.] fol.
Plate number 15. Imperfect; wanting the viola part, supplied in photographic facsimile. **h. 2782. oo. (1.)**

— Concerto Pastorale per il Cembalo, due Violini, Viola e Basso, Due Flauti, due Corni ad libitum … Opera V. [Parts.] *Presso G. André: Offenbach*, [1780?] fol. **g. 79. a. (2.)**

— Concerto per il Cembalo, Due Violini, Due Flauti traversi obligati, Due Corni ad libitum, Viola e Basso, *etc. Longman and Broderip: London*, [1785?] fol.
The cembalo part only. **h. 82. a.**

— Concerto per il cembalo due violini due flauti traversi obligati due corni ad libitum viola è basso. [Parts.] 9 pt. *Sold by W. Forster:* [*London*, c. 1785.] fol. **h. 82. b.**

— A Favorite Quartet, composed for a Harpsichord, Violin, Flute & Tenor … now properly adapted as a Harpsichord Lesson. pp. 11. *Birchall and Andrews: London*, [c. 1785.] fol. **g. 443. s. (10.)**

— Two Excellent Solos for the Violin, con Violoncello obligato. *Longman, Lukey and Co.: London*, [1775?] fol. **g. 422. h. (3.)**

— [Another copy.] **g. 420. b. (3.)**

— [Two … Solos. No. 2.] Andante and Minuet for violin with piano accompaniment. *See* PEINIGER (O.) O. Peiniger's Edition of Old English Music. No. 2. [1885.] fol. **h. 3657. (1.)**

— Sei Sonate per il Cembalo Violino e Violoncello … Opera VI. [Parts.] *Presso G. André: Offenbach*, [1780?] fol. **h. 82.**

LANG (JOHN)

— Joy and Peace, an orchestral prelude … arranged as a duet for the Pianoforte. *London*, [1871.] fol. **h. 1485. s. (16.)**

LANG (JOSEPHINE)

— Abschied. *See* MAYER (C.) Transcriptionen, *etc.* No. 2. [1862.] fol. **h. 531. a. (5.)**

— Ballad. [Begins: "Let the flash split Heav'n asunder". "Mag da draussen Schnee sich thürmen".] *See* ROCKSTRO (W. S.) Lyra Anglo-Germanica, *etc.* Vol. 1. [1853, *etc.*] fol. **H. 2265.**

— Sechs Deutsche Lieder von L. Uhland und J. Kerner für eine Singstimme mit Begleitung des Pianoforte … Op. 11. *F. Kistner: Leipzig*, [1850?] fol. **H. 2134. a. (17.)**

— In die Ferne. *See* LIEDER-REPERTORIUM. Lieder Repertorium, *etc.* No. 103. [1847, *etc.*] fol. **H. 2274.**

— Liederbuch für eine Singstimme mit Begleitung des Pianoforte. 2 Hft. *Leipzig*, [1882.] 8°. **F. 651.**

— Das Traumbild, von H. Heine. [Song.] [1838.] *See* PERIODICAL PUBLICATIONS.— *Leipzig.*— Neue Zeitschrift für Musik. [Sammlung von Musik-Stücken, *etc.*] Hft. 13. [1838, *etc.*] fol. **Hirsch M. 1134.**

LANG (LEON M.)

— Coast Defense March. [P. F.] pp. 5. *Sherman, Clay & Co.: San Francisco*, [1905.] fol. **h. 4120. mm. (23.)**

LANG (MARGARET RUTHVEN)

— Betrayed. *See* infra: Four Songs. Op. 9. No. 4.

— Chimes. *See* infra: Two Songs. Op. 54. II.

— Christmas Lullaby. *See* infra: Three Songs … Op. 8. No. 2.

LANG (MARGARET RUTHVEN)

— A Cradle Song of the War. [Song, words by] N. S. D. Op. 55. *O. Ditson Co.: Boston*, 1916. fol. **H. 1846. x. (20.)**

— Day is gone. Song, the words by J. V. Cheney.—Op. 40. No. 2. *Boosey & Co.: London*, [1907.] fol. **H. 1794. uu. (66.)**

— An Even Psalm. *See* infra: Three Songs. Op. 46. [No. 1.]

— A Garden is a lovesome thing. *See* infra: Four Songs. Op. 50. No. 1.

— Grandmama's Song Book for the Children. Words taken from "The Daisy" & "The Cowslip," printed in 1807, cautionary stories in verse … Op. 44, *etc. A. P. Schmidt: Boston, etc.*, 1909. 4°. **G. 809. e. (9.)**

— Grant, we beseech Thee, merciful Lord … [Anthem.] Op. 51. *A. P. Schmidt: Boston, etc.*, (1912.) 8°. **F. 281. ff. (21.)**

— Heliotrope. *See* infra: Four Songs … Op. 9. No. 1.

— Into my Heart. *See* infra: Two Songs. Op. 54. I.

— Irish Love-Song. The Words Anon. Op. 22. *Enoch & Sons: London*, 1895. fol. **H. 1799. cc. (44.)**

— Irish Love Song.—Trio.— Op. 22. *A. P. Schmidt: Boston, etc.*, [1912.] 8°. **F. 328. o. (32.)**

— An Irish Mother's Lullaby. Song, the words by M. E. Blake. Op. 34. *Enoch & Sons: London*, 1900. fol. **H. 1799. cc. (45.)**

— An Irish Mother's Lullaby.—Trio.— … Op. 34. *A. P. Schmidt: Boston, etc.*, 1912. 8°. **F. 328. o. (33.)**

— Lydia. [Song.] Words by L. W. Reese. Op. 32. No. 2. *J. Church Co.:* [*Cincinnati*,] 1899. fol. **H. 1799. h. (3.)**

— The Night of the Star … A Cycle for Christmas, for Soli, Chorus, and Organ. Text by D. A. McCarthy. Op. 52. *O. Ditson Co.: Boston*, (1913.) 8°. **F. 1269. m. (3.)**

Nonsense Rhymes and Pictures. Op. 42

— The Old Lady of France. [Part-song for S. S. A. A., words by] E. Lear. *A. P. Schmidt: Boston, etc.*, (1909.) 8°. **F. 328. j. (20.)**

— The Old Man in a Tree. [Part-song for men's voices.] Words by E. Lear. *A. P. Schmidt: Boston, etc.*, (1909.) 8°. **F. 163. h. (6.)**

— The Old Man with a Gong. [Part-song for men's voices.] Words by E. Lear. *A. P. Schmidt: Boston, etc.*, (1907.) 8°. **F. 163. h. (7.)**

— The Old Person of Cassel. [Part-song for S. A. T. B., words by] E. Lear. *A. P. Schmidt: Boston, etc.*, (1909.) 8°. **F. 328. j. (21.)**

— The Old Person of Skye. [Part-song for S. S. A. A., words by] E. Lear. *A. P. Schmidt: Boston, etc.*, 1909. 8°. **F. 328. j. (22.)**

— The Person of Filey. [Part-song for S. S. A. A., words by] E. Lear. *A. P. Schmidt: Boston, etc.*, 1909. 8°. **F. 328. j. (23.)**

— There was an old Man who said, "Well!" [Part-song for men's voices.] Words by E. Lear. *A. P. Schmidt: Boston, etc.*, 1909. 8°. **F. 163. h. (9.)**

More Nonsense Rhymes and Pictures. Op. 43

— More Nonsense Rhymes and Pictures, by E. Lear … [Songs.] Op. 43, *etc. A. P. Schmidt: Boston, etc.*, 1907. 4°. **G. 385. dd. (3.)**

— [No. 1.] The Old Man of Dumbree, *etc.* [Part-song for S. S. A. A.] *A. P. Schmidt: Boston, etc.*, 1909. 8°. **F. 328. j. (24.)**

LANG (Margaret Ruthven)

— [No. 2.] The Old Man with a Beard, *etc.* [Part-song for S. A. T. B.] *A. P. Schmidt: Boston, etc.*, (1909.) 8°.

F. 321. x. (20.)

— [No. 4.] The Old Person of Ware, *etc.* [Part-song for men's voices.] *A. P. Schmidt: Boston, etc.*, (1909.) 8°.

F. 163. h. (8.)

— The Old Lady of France. *See* supra: [Nonsense Rhymes and Pictures. Op. 42.]

— The Old Man in a Tree. *See* supra: [Nonsense Rhymes and Pictures. Op. 42.]

— The Old Man of Dumbree. *See* supra: [More Nonsense Rhymes and Pictures. Op. 43. No. 1.]

— The Old Man with a Beard. *See* supra: [More Nonsense Rhymes and Pictures. Op. 43. No. 2.]

— The Old Man with a Gong. *See* supra: [Nonsense Rhymes and Pictures. Op. 42.]

— The Old Person of Cassel. *See* supra: [Nonsense Rhymes and Pictures. Op. 42.]

— The Old Person of Skye. *See* supra: [Nonsense Rhymes and Pictures. Op. 42.]

— The Old Person of Ware. *See* supra: [More Nonsense Rhymes and Pictures. Op. 43. No. 4.]

— One Summer Day, for the pianoforte. [No. 1.] Hide and seek in the barn. [No. 2.] Morning lessons. [No. 3.] Picnic in the woods. [No. 4.] Knitting for the soldiers. [No. 5.] Driving to the blacksmith. 5 no. *T. Presser Co.: Philadelphia*, 1919. 4°.

g. 1129. h. (27.)

— Oriental Serenade. *See* infra: Three Songs ... Op. 8. No. 1.

— Out of the Night. *See* infra: Three Songs. Op. 46. [No. 3.]

— The Person of Filey. *See* supra: [Nonsense Rhymes and Pictures. Op. 42.]

— Three Pianoforte Pieces for young players. (Op. 60. No. 1.) Happy days. (No. 2.) Day dreams. (No. 3.) Rondoletto. 3 no. *T. Presser Co.: Philadelphia*, 1919. 4°. **g. 1129. h. (28.)**

— A Poet gazes on the East. *See* infra: Three Songs ... Op. 8. No. 3.

— Revery ... Opus 31. [P. F.] *J. Church Co.:* [*Cincinnati,*] 1899. fol. **h. 3282. w. (27.)**

— The Sky-Ship. *See* infra: Four Songs ... Op. 9. No. 3.

— Snowflakes. *See* infra: Four Songs. Op. 50. No. 3.

— Sometimes. *See* infra: Three Songs. Op. 46. [No. 2.]

— A Song of May. [Song.] Words by L. W. Reese. Op. 32. No. 1. *J. Church Co.:* [*Cincinnati,*] 1899. fol. **H. 1799. h. (2.)**

— A Song of the Spanish Gypsies. *See* infra: Four Songs. Op. 50. No. 2.

— Song of the three Sisters. [Part-song for S. S. A. A., words by] J. V. Cheney. *A. P. Schmidt: Boston, etc.*, 1909. 8°.

F. 328. j. (25.)

— Three Songs of the East. Op. 8. No. 1. Oriental Serenade. No. 2. Christmas Lullaby. (Words by J. A. Symonds.) No. 3. A Poet gazes on the Moon. (After Tang-go-Su. Translated by S. Merrill.) 3 no. *A. P. Schmidt: Boston & London*, 1892. fol.

G. 807. h. (2.)

— Four Songs. Op. 9. 1. Heliotrope (F. D. Sherman.) 2. Spinning-Song (L. W. Reese.) 3. The Sky-Ship (F. D. Sherman.) 4. Betrayed (L. W. Reese.) 4 no. *A. P. Schmidt: Boston & London*, 1892. fol. **G. 807. h. (3.)**

LANG (Margaret Ruthven)

— Six Songs for medium voice. Op. 37. [No. 1.] A Thought. [No. 2.] Out of the Past. [No. 3.] The Hills o' Skye. [No. 4.] Summer Noon. [No. 5.] Tryste Noël. (Words by L. I. Guiney.) [No. 6.] Northward. *A. P. Schmidt: Boston, etc.*, 1902. fol. *No. 5 only.* **G. 807. jj. (30.)**

— Three Songs. Op. 46. [No. 1.] An Even Psalm. (Words by M. Radclyffe-Hall.) [No. 2.] Sometimes. (Words by T. S. Jones.) [No. 3.] Out of the Night. 3 no. *A. P. Schmidt: Boston, etc.*, 1909. fol. **H. 1794. uu. (67.)**

— Four Songs. (Op. 50. No. 1.) A Garden is a lovesome thing. (T. E. Brown.) (No. 2.) A Song of the Spanish Gypsies. (Translated from the Spanish by A. Strettell.) (No. 3.) Snowflakes. (J. V. Cheney.) (No. 4.) There would I be. (J. V. Cheney.) 4 no. *A. P. Schmidt: Boston, etc.*, (1912.) fol.

G. 806. ll. (46.)

— Two Songs. Op. 54. i. Into my Heart. (A. E. Housman.) ii: Chimes. (A. Meynell.) 2 no. *A. P. Schmidt: Boston, etc.*, 1915. fol. **G. 806. ll. (47.)**

— Spinning-Song. *See* supra: Four Songs ... Op. 9. No. 2.

— The Spirit of the old House. An Elegy for the pianoforte. Op. 58. *A. P. Schmidt & Co.: Boston, etc.*, 1917. fol.

h. 3284. nn. (8.)

— Spring. Song. Op. 47. *A. P. Schmidt: Boston, etc.*, 1909. fol.

H. 1794. uu. (68.)

— A Spring Idyll ... Opus 33. [P. F.] *J. Church Co.:* [*Cincinnati,*] 1899. fol. **h. 3282. w. (28.)**

— There was an old Man who said, "Well!" *See* supra: [Nonsense Rhymes and Pictures. Op. 42.]

— There would I be. *See* supra: Four Songs. Op. 50. No. 4.

— Tryste Noël. *See* supra: Six Songs ... Op. 37. [No. 5.]

— The Wild-Brier. [Part-song for S. S. A. A., words by] J. V. Cheney. *A. P. Schmidt: Boston, etc.*, 1909. 8°.

F. 328. j. (26.)

LANG (Oscar)

— The Serpentine Dance Caprice for pianoforte. *O. Ditson Company: Boston, etc.*, 1892. fol. **h. 1489. s. (2.)**

LANG (Paul H.)

— Mass "Exult in the Lord". For congregational use with organ accompaniment. pp. 10. *Gregorian Institute of America: Toledo, Ohio*, [1965.] 8°. **F. 274. ss. (2.)**

— Four Pieces. For organ. pp. 11. *Gregorian Institute of America: Toledo, Ohio*, [1963.] 4°. **g. 1378. j. (19.)**

LANG (Phil)

— *See* LOEWE (Frederick) ... My Fair Lady ... Musical arrangements by R. R. Bennett and P. Lang, *etc.* [1956.] 4°.

G. 760. kk. (1.)

— *See* LOEWE (Frederick) ... My fair Lady ... Musical arrangements by R. R. Bennett and P. Lang, *etc.* [1958.] 4°.

F. 943. oo. (1.)

LANG (Philip J.)

— Carnival Suite. For band, *etc.* (Full score.) pp. 32. *Edwin H. Morris & Co.: New York*, [1953.] 4°. **g. 1072. (8.)**

— Thunderbird. Overture ... for band, *etc.* (Score printed from the composer's original manuscript.) pp. 47. *Edwin H. Morris & Co.: New York*, [1953.] 4°. **g. 1072. (9.)**

LANG (PHILIP J.)

— *See* BACH (J. S.) [Overture for Orchestra in D. No. 1.] Air ... transcribed for band by P. J. Lang. [1958.] 4°.
h. 3210. i. (509.)

— *See* BARNBY (*Sir* Joseph) Sweet and low ... Arranged by P. J. Lang. Full band, *etc.* [1957.] 4°.
h. 3210. i. (361.)

— *See* BENJAMIN (Arthur L.) Jamaican Rumba ... Arranged [for military band] by P. J. Lang. [1955.] 4°. [*Q. M. B. Edition. no.* 221.]
h. 3211. b.

— *See* COPLAND (A.) [Billy the Kid.] Celebration ... Arranged ... by P. J. Lang. 1945. 8°.
h. 3210. h. (915.)

— *See* COPLAND (A.) [Billy the Kid.] Waltz ... Arranged ... by P. J. Lang. 1944. 4°.
h. 3210. h. (916.)

— *See* FRANCK (C. A. J. G. H.) [Messe. Op. 12.] Panis angelicus. Clarinet choir ... Edited by P. J. Lang, *etc.* [1953.] 4°.
h. 2693. d. (1.)

— *See* HAENDEL (G. F.) [Joshua.—March.] Solemn March ... Arranged by P. J. Lang. [1958.] 4°.
h. 3210. i. (534.)

— *See* PROKOF'EV (S. S.) [Symphonie classique. Op. 25.] Gavotte ... Transcribed ... by P. J. Lang, *etc.* 1943. 8°.
h. 3210. h. (887.)

— *See* SARASATE Y NAVASCUÉS (P. M. M. de) Zigeunerweisen ... [Op. 20.] Transcribed by P. J. Lang for B♭ clarinet solo with piano accompaniment. [1950.] 4°.
g. 1104. s. (18.)

— *See* SCHUMANN (R. A.) [Kinderscenen. Op. 15. No. 7.] Träumerei ... Trans. by P. J. Lang, *etc.* [1953.] 4°.
g. 715. t. (9.)

— *See* SCOTT (Raymond) March of the Slide Trombones ... Military band arrangement by P. J. Lang. [1966.] 8°.
h. 3210. i. (993.)

— *See* SHOSTAKOVICH (D. D.) [Золотой вѣкъ. Op. 22.] Danse ... Transcribed ... by P. J. Lang, *etc.* 1943. 8°.
h. 3210. h. (888.)

— *See* SHOSTAKOVICH (D. D.) [Золотой вѣкъ. Op. 22.] Polka ... Transcribed ... by P. J. Lang, *etc.* 1943. 8°.
h. 3210. h. (889.)

LANG (VIOLA)

— *See* PURCELL (H.) [Dido and Æneas.—When I am laid in Earth.] Aria ... Freely arranged ... by V. Lang. 1942. 4°.
g. 25. e. (12.)

LANG (WALKER M.)

— Love's Gifts. [Song. Words by] Roy Dickinson Welch. pp. 5. *Jerome H. Remick & Co.: Detroit, New York*, [1908.] fol.
H. 3985. h. (14.)

LANG (WALTER)

— Suite für Violoncello und Klavier. Opus 20. *B. Schott's Söhne: Mainz und Leipzig*, 1933. 4°.
g. 514. s. (18.)

LÅNGA

— Den långa dagen. [Song.] *See* KAJANUS (A.) Vier Lieder. No. 2.

— Den långa Dagen. Sång. *See* VALENTIN (C.)

LANGAGE

— Le Langage des baisers. [Song.] *See* CLARK (Kenneth S.)

— Le Langage des Fleurs. Ariette. *See* MASINI (F.)

LANGAGE

— Le Langage des Fleurs. [Song.] *See* VIAULT (E.) 12 Mélodies. No. 1.

— Le Langage des Yeux. [Song.] *See* LECOCQ (J.)

LANGALERIE (DE) *Marquis*

— L'Entretrainante, grand valse pour Piano. *Paris*, [1850?] fol.
h. 1480. o. (16.)

— Les Rivales. Recueil, *etc. London*, [1850.] fol. **h. 947. (38.)**

— Trois Walses brillantes pour le Pianoforte. *Paris*, [1830?] *obl.* fol.
e. 368. (10.)

— Trois Valses et une Sauteuse Galop pour le Piano. *Paris*, [1830?] *obl.* fol.
e. 368. (11.)

LANGBECKER (EMANUEL CHRISTIAN GOTTLIEB)

— *See* CRUEGER (J.) J. Crüger's ... Choral-Melodien ... mit einem ... Abrisse des Lebens ... dieses geistlichen Lieder-Componisten begleitet von E. C. G. Langbecker. 1835. 4°.
E. 1375.

LANGBRIDGE (FREDERICK)

— Caleb's Curse. A Temperance Story with Song. Staff notation (Tonic Sol-fa) edition. 2 no. *J. Curwen & Sons: London*, [1889.] 8°.
D. 675. m. (7.)

— Dan Dabberton's Dream, *etc.* [Service of song.] Staff Notation (Tonic Sol-fa) Edition. 2 no. *United Kingdom Band of Hope Union: London*, [1894.] 8°.
No. 8 *of "Temperance Stories with Song".*
D. 698. a.

LANGDALE (BERNARD)

— Teach me Thy Way. Anthem, *etc. J. Blackburn: Leeds*, [1923.] 8°.
The Classic Series, No. 141.
E. 1624.

— Teach me Thy Way ... Tonic Sol-fa edition. *J. Blackburn: Leeds*, [1923.] 4°.
"Phlox" Sol-fa Series, No. 95.
C. 418.

LANGDALE (VIVIAN)

— The Green Vales of Antrim. Song, words by E. Teschemacher. *Warren & Phillips: London*, 1914. fol.
H. 1793. s. (5.)

— In the Hush of God's Morning. Song, words by F. G. Bowles, *etc. Warren & Phillips: London*, 1913. fol.
H. 1793. s. (6.)

LANGDON (CHRISTOPHER S.)

— [Rhapsody.] Piano Selection from the M-G-M Film Rhapsody. Arranged by Chris. Langdon. pp. 11. *Chappell & Co.: London*, [1955.] 4°.
g. 1425. d. (1.)

— Sixteen Standard Songs of Shakespeare. Music by Purcell, Arne, Bishop, Schubert, etc. Accompaniments revised and edited by C. S. Langdon. *Chappell & Co.: London, etc.*, 1939. 4°.
One of "Chappell's Popular Albums".
G. 440. c. (2.)

— *See* ADDINSELL (Richard S.) [Greengage Summer.] Joss, *etc.* (Arranged [for P. F.] by C. Langdon.) [1962.] 4°.
g. 1425. d. (15.)

— *See* ADDISON (John) *A. R. C. M.* [I was Monty's Double.] ... Monty's Double. (March) ... Arranged for piano solo by C. Langdon. [1958.] 4°.
g. 1425. c. (32.)

— *See* ALWYN (W.) March. The True Glory ... Arranged ... by C. S. Langdon. 1945. 4°.
g.1425. a. (9.)

LANGDON (CHRISTOPHER S.)

— *See* BERNSTEIN (Leonard) ... Candide ... ⟨Piano selection.⟩
Arranged by C. Langdon. [1959.] 4°.   **g. 1128. ee. (4.)**

— *See* BERNSTEIN (Leonard) Wonderful Town. Selection ...
Arranged for piano solo by C. Langdon. [1955.] 4°.
                                              f. 133. ss. (20.)

— *See* BLACKBURN (Tom) [Westward ho the Wagons.] Piano
Selection, *etc.* ⟨Arranged by C. Langdon.⟩ [1957.] 4°.
                                              g. 1425. c. (11.)

— *See* BLANE (Ralph) and BARNES (W.) Quillow and the Giant
... ⟨Piano selection (with lyrics).⟩ Arranged by C. Langdon,
etc. [1962.] 4°.   **g. 272. zz. (7.)**

— *See* ELLIS (Vivian) Big Ben. Selection. Arranged by
C. Langdon. 1946. 4°.   **f. 133. ii. (7.)**

— *See* ELLIS (Vivian) Charles B. Cochran's Bless the Bride, *etc.*
⟨Arranged by C. Langdon.⟩ 1947. 4°.   **f. 133. ii. (30.)**

— *See* ELLIS (Vivian) "Half in Earnest," *etc.* ⟨Piano selection.
Arranged by C. Langdon.⟩ [1958.] 4°.   **F. 1196. g. (10.)**

— *See* ELLIS (Vivian) "Listen to the Wind," *etc.* ⟨Piano selection.
Arranged by C. Langdon.⟩ [1955.] 4°.   **f. 133. uu. (24.)**

— *See* ELLIS (Vivian) Tough at the Top. A light opera, *etc.*
⟨Piano selection. Arranged by C. Langdon.⟩ [1949.] 4°.
                                              f. 133. mm. (17.)

— *See* ELLIS (Vivian) The Water Gipsies ... Arranged by
C. Langdon. [P. F.] [1955.] 4°.   **f. 133. ss. (25.)**

— *See* FRANCK (C. A. J. G. H.) [Messe. Op. 12.—Panis angelicus.]
Heavenly Bread, *etc.* ⟨Arranged by C. Langdon.⟩ [1950.] 4°.
                                              F. 1176. q. (19.)

— *See* FRANCK (C. A. J. G. H.) [Messe. Op. 12.—Panis angelicus.]
Heavenly Bread, *etc.* ⟨Arranged by C. Langdon.⟩ [1961.] 8°.
                                              E. 442. dd. (11.)

— *See* GREEN (Philip) Wildfire ... Arranged by C. Langdon.
[P. F.] [1955.] 4°.   **f. 133. ss. (31.)**

— *See* HENEKER (David) Half a Sixpence ... ⟨Piano selection.⟩
Arranged by C. Langdon. [1963.] 4°.   **g. 352. a. (7.)**

— *See* HENEKER (David) Half a Sixpence. Film selection. [P. F.]
Arranged by C. Langdon. [1967.] 4°.   **g. 1138. s. (1.)**

— *See* HERBERT (Victor) The Red Mill. Selection. Arranged by
C. Langdon. 1947. 4°.   **f. 133. ii. (38.)**

— *See* JOCHEMS (J.) Cape Kennedy March ... Piano solo.
⟨Arranged by C. Langdon.⟩ [1965.] 4°.   **g. 1129. ee. (7.)**

— *See* NORMAN (Monty) Belle (or The Ballad of Dr. Crippen).
Arranged by C. Langdon. [1961.] 4°.   **g. 1128. mm. (9.)**

— *See* NORMAN (Monty) and HENEKER (D.) Make me an Offer,
etc. ⟨Piano selection (with lyrics). Arranged by C. Langdon.⟩
[1959.] 4°.   **f. 770. h. (28.)**

— *See* NOVELLO (I.) [Arc de Triomphe.] Selection, Arc de
Triomphe. Arranged by C. Langdon. 1943. 4°.
                                              f. 133. hh. (35.)

— *See* NOVELLO (I.) Crest of the Wave. Selection. Arranged by
C. S. Langdon. 1937. 4°.   **g. 1125. qq. (34.)**

— *See* NOVELLO (I.) The Dancing years. (Pianoforte) Selection.
Arranged by C. Langdon. 1939. 4°.   **g. 1125. rr. (22.)**

— *See* NOVELLO (I.) The Dancing Years ... Arranged by
C. Langdon. [P. F.] [1955.] 4°.   **f. 133. uu. (4.)**

— *See* ORNADEL (Cyril) Pickwick ... ⟨Piano selection.⟩ Arranged
by C. Langdon. [1963.] 4°.   **g. 352. b. (18.)**

— *See* ORNADEL (Cyril) Turn again Whittington ... ⟨Piano
selection.⟩ Arranged by C. Langdon. [1961.] 8°.   **f. 65. (20.)**

LANGDON (CHRISTOPHER S.)

— *See* ROBERTS (Henry S.) The Harvey Memorial grand March
... Arranged for piano by C. S. Langdon. [1963.] 4°.
                                              g. 443. oo. (12.)

— *See* SPRINGFIELD (Tom) and BORZA (P.) O holy Child. [Song.]
Arranged by C. Langdon. [1964.] 4°.   **G. 503. m. (1.)**

— *See* SPRINGFIELD (Tom) and DIAMOND (M.) The Man in the
Moon ... ⟨Piano selection.⟩ Arranged by C. Langdon. [1964.]
4°.   **g. 352. g. (15.)**

— *See* STANFORD (Trevor H.) and NEWELL (Norman) ... Mister
Venus, *etc.* ⟨Piano selection. Arranged by C. Langdon.⟩
[1958.] 4°.   **f. 770. h. (1.)**

— *See* WILSON (Sandy) The Boy Friend ... Arranged by
C. Langdon. [P. F.] [1954.] 4°.   **f. 133. ss. (19.)**

— *See* WILSON (Sandy) The Buccaneer ... Arranged by
C. Langdon. [P. F.] [1955.] 4°.   **f. 133. uu. (20.)**

— *See* ZWAR (Charles) Marigold ... Piano selection. ⟨Arranged
by C. Langdon.⟩ [1959.] 4°.   **g. 1128. aa. (32.)**

LANGDON (J. A.)

— Aye she kaimed her yellow Hair. [Four-part song.] Words by
... H. Johnston. *Stainer & Bell: London*, 1920. 8°.
Choral Library, No. 161.   **F. 1137. d.**

— Meditation in the Synagogue at the Feast of Tabernacles, for
Organ. *Oxford University Press: London*, 1930. 4°.
                                              g. 575. ii. (25.)

LANGDON (JOHN)

— A Short Setting of the Service for Holy Communion, *etc.* (In
A.) *A. Weekes & Co.: London*, 1930. 8°.
Services, No. 166.   **F. 1158. e. (8.)**

— Love me if I live, for Voice and Pianoforte. (Words by
B. Cornwall.) *J. & W. Chester: London*, 1929. fol.
                                              H. 1860. g. (29.)

— Magnificat. On the traditional Hebrew Yigdal Hymn of
Faith. (Nunc dimittis. On a traditional Hebrew melody
Duchon for Maskir-Něschamoth.) *J. B. Cramer & Co.:*
[London,] 1929. 8°.
[*Cramer's Library of Church Music. No.* 9.] **F. 157. e.**

LANGDON (JOHN DAVID)

— *See* TYE (Christopher) Give Almes of thy Goods ... Full
anthem for SATB ... Edited by J. Langdon. [1969.] 8°.
[*Novello early Church Music.* 11.]   **E. 618. g.**

— *See* TYE (Christopher) I will exalt thee ... Full anthem for
four voices ... Edited by J. Langdon. [1970.] 8°. [*Novello
Early Church Music.* 10.]   **E. 618. g.**

— *See* TYE (Christopher) O God be merciful unto us. (Deus
misereatur.) Edited by J. Langdon. ⟨Version I. S. A. T. B.
(full.)-Version II. S. A. T. B. (full) with verse for S. A. T. B.⟩
[1971.] 8°. [*Tudor Church Music.* 73 *a, b.*]   **F. 1140. j.**

— *See* TYE (Christopher) Peccavimus cum patribus nostris
Motet for SATTBar.BB(unaccompanied) ... Edited by
J. Langdon. [1972.] 8°.   **E. 1439. ff. (2.)**

LANGDON (LLOYD)

— The Homeland of my Heart. ⟨Song.⟩ Written by Herbert
Shelley, *etc.* [Staff and tonic sol-fa notation. Voice part.]
Francis, Day & Hunter: London, [1906.] *s. sh.* fol.
                                              H. 3985. h. (15.)

— The Homeland of my Heart. Song, *etc.* [With separate voice
part.] 2 pt. *Francis, Day & Hunter: London*, [1906.] fol.
                                              H. 3985. h. (16.)

LANGDON (RICHARD)

— *See also* L., R.

— Cantate Domino & Deus Misereatur. *See* infra: Te Deum and Jubilate Deo.

— A Collection of Songs, *etc.* [Op. 2.] *Printed for J. Johnson: London*, [1755?] fol.   **G. 805. a. (8.)**

— [Another edition.] A Second Collection of Songs, *etc.* [Op. 2.] *Printed for J. Johnson: London*, [1755?] fol.
This is the same as 'A Collection of Songs,' with an altered titlepage.   **G. 424. d. (5.)**

— Cupid and Chloe. A Cantata. [*J. Johnson: London*, 1755?] fol.
Printed from the plates of pp. 34–43 of Langdon's 'Ten Songs and a Cantata'.   **G. 808. c. (18.)**

— Divine Harmony; being a Collection in Score of Psalms and Anthems, with several other Pieces of Sacred Music composed by the most eminent Masters … Selected and … revised by R. Langdon, *etc.* [Op. 5.] *Longman, Lukey & Compy., for the Editor: London*, 1774. fol.
The composers named are: Morley, Ravenscroft, Milton, W. Harrison, Wainwright, J. Tomkins, Croft, W. Cranfield, Handel, J. Bennet, E. Blanks, J. Farmer, R. Palmer, R. Allison, M. Pierson, M. Cavendish, Courteville, Dowland, R. Langdon, Farnaby, Tallis, Kerby, Hooper, T. Tomkins, Carissimi, M. Wise, W. Blake, C. King, Aldrich and T. Langdon.   **H. 879. a. (1.)**

— [A reissue.] Divine Harmony … In II parts … Part [MS II.]
Printed for J. Bland: London, [c. 1780.] fol.
Imperfect; wanting Part I.   **H. 1652. ff. (9.)**

— Ev'ry Bliss that Heav'n can give. *A Favorite Rondo.* [Song.] Sung by Miss Marshall at the Grotto Gardens. Adapted for the harpsichord German Flute and Guittar. [*London*, 1770?] fol.   **578. i. 10.**

— Twelve Glees for three and four Voices … Op. VI. *J. Bland: London*, [1780?] fol.   **G. 424. d. (4.)**

— I told my nymph. An admired Song of Mr. Shenstone's … sung at Ranelagh by Mr. Hudson. *R. Falkener: London*, [1775?] *s. sh.* fol.   **H. 1994. a. (38.)**

— Lord Thou hast been our Refuge. Anthem. *E. Ashdown: London*, [1902?] 8°.
No. 24 of the "Collegiate Series".   **E. 758.**

— The Lord's Prayer. [For four voices.] Adapted from R. Langdon, *etc.* [Staff and tonic sol-fa notation.] *J. Curwen & Sons: London*, [1906.] *a card.*   **I. 600. c. (113.)**

— The Lord's Prayer, adapted from R. Langdon, *etc. J. Curwen & Sons: London*, [1920.] 8°.
[*Anthems of Praise. No.* 165.]   **E. 336.**

— O Lord our Governour. Anthem. *E. Ashdown: London*, [1902?] 8°.
No. 39 of the "Collegiate Series".   **E. 758.**

— Six Sonatas for the Harpsichord … Opera Terza. *Printed for Cha⁵ and Sam¹ Thompson: London*, [1765.] *obl.* fol.   **e. 5. f. (6.)**

— Ten Songs and a Cantata, *etc.* [Op. 1.] pp. 43. *J. Johnson, for the Author: London*, [1759.] fol.   **G. 805. e. (2.)**

— Twelve Songs and Two Cantatas … Opera IV. pp. 67. *Messrs. Thompson, for the Author: London*, [1769.] fol.   **I. 376.**

— Sweet are the banks when Spring perfumes. *A Glee, etc.* *L[ongman], L[ukey] & B[roderip]: London*, 1775?] *s. sh.* fol.   **G. 311. (138.)**

LANGDON (RICHARD)

— Te Deum and Jubilate Deo (Cantate Domino & Deus Misereatur). Chanting Service. 2 no. *Novello, Ewer & Co.: London*, [1874.] 8°.
No. 1 of the Collegiate … Edition of Church Services.   **E. 597. n. (21.)**

— Turn thee unto me. Anthem. *London*, [1874.] 8°.   **E. 758.**

— *See* ARNE (T. A.) The Fond Appeal. Quartetto … Harmonized by R. Langdon. [1800?] fol.   **G. 353. (22.)**

— *See* ARNE (T. A.) [The Merchant of Venice.—To keep my gentle Jessy.] Quartetto … harmonized by R. Langdon, *etc.* [1800?] fol.   **G. 353. (21.)**

— *See* ARNE (T. A.) [To Delia.] Trio … Harmonized by R. Langdon, *etc.* [1800?] fol.   **G. 352. (28.)**

LANGDON-DAVIES (OLIVE)

— *See* DAVIES.

LANGE

— Lange nachher. [Song.] *See* BOHM (C.)

— Der lange Tag. [Song.] *See* KAJANUS (R.) Vier Lieder. No. 2.

— Lange vorden. [Song.] *See* WEYERMANN (M.) Sechs Gesänge … Op. 14. No. 5.

LANGE ( )

— *See* BENSON (Carver) Keep jazzin' it Ras'. [Song.] By Benson … and Lange. [1918.] fol.   **H. 3989. l. (54.)**

LANGE (A.)

— *See* LANGE (L.)

LANGE (ARTHUR)

— A Gosling in Gotham. A Symphonic Narrative in one movement. [Full score.] *Robbins Music Corp.: New York*, [1937.] fol.   **h. 1509. ww. (9.)**

— *See* BRANEN (Jeffrey T.) Always be Honey to me. [Song.] By J. Branen, A. Lange, *etc.* [1915.] fol.   **H. 3989. hh. (7.)**

— *See* BRANEN (Jeffrey T.) In the Valley of the Moon, *etc.* [Song. Followed by an arrangement of the chorus for male or mixed quartet by A. Lange.] [1913.] fol.   **H. 3989. hh. (10.)**

— [For editions and arrangements of songs written and composed by A. Lange in sole collaboration with Jeffrey T. Branen:] *See* BRANEN (Jeffrey T.) and LANGE (A.)

— *See* DILLON (William A.) That Girl of mine. [Song.] By W. A. Dillon … and A. Lange. [1916.] fol.   **H. 3991. i. (13.)**

— *See* FRANKLIN (Melvin A.) and LANGE (A.) Hot Chocolate Rag. [1908.] fol.   **h. 4120. t. (40.)**

LANGE (ARTHUR W.)

— *See* LEHÁR (F.) [Die lustige Witwe.—Waltz.] When your Lips pressed mine … Arr. by A. W. Lange. (1907.) fol.   **H. 3616. (13.)**

LANGE (DANIEL DE)

— Cantate. Woorden van J. A. Böhringer. [Composed for the 25th yearly assembly of the Netherlands Protestantenbond.] *De Erven J. J. Tyl: Zwolle*, [1896.] fol.
Printed in facsimile throughout.   **H. 2815. q. (4.)**

LANGE (Daniel de)

— Gedicht van Albert Verwey, *etc. van Holkema & Warendorf: Amsterdam*, [1893.] fol.
Appendix to the biography of D. de Lange in H. Viotta's "Onze hedendaagsche Toonkunstenaars". **1761. b. 16.**

— Nederlandsch Volksliederenboek. Samengesteld door Daniel de Lange ... J. C. M. van Riemsdijk, D[r] G. Kalff. 134 liederen voor zang en klavier. Uitgave van de Maatschappij tot Nut van 't Algemeen. *S. L. van Looy: Amsterdam*, 1896. 8°. **F. 1585.**

— Nederlandsch Volksliederenboek. Samengesteld door D. de Lange ... J. C. M. van Riemsdyk, Dr. G. Kalff. 143 Liederen voor zang en Klavier. Uitgave van de Maatschappij tot nut van 't algemeen. Vierde Druk. *S. L. van Looy: Amsterdam*, 1900. 8°. **F. 1585. b.**

— Nederlandsch Volksliederenboek. Samengesteld door D. de Lange ... J. C. M. van Riemsdijk, Dr. G. Kalff. Eerste Bundel. 144 Liederen voor zang en piano. Uitgave van de Maatschappij tot Nut van 't Algemeen. Negende herziene druk, *etc. S. L. van Looy: Amsterdam*, 1913. 8°. **F. 1585. a.**

— Passio Domini Nostri Jesu Christi secundum Matthæum ... van Jacob Obrecht. [Edited by D. de Lange.] 1894. *See* AMSTERDAM.— *Vereeniging voor Noord-Nederlands Muziekgeschiedenis, etc.* Uitgave van oudere Noordnederlandsche Meesterwerken. No. XVIII. 1896, *etc.* 8° & fol. **G. 12. a.**

— Vor einer Genziane. Gedicht von R. Hamerling [begins: "Die schönste der Genzianen"] in Musik gesetzt für eine tiefere Singstimme mit Begleitung des Pianoforte. *Leipzig u. Winterthur*, 1881. fol. **H. 1786. e. (9.)**

LANGE (Diana Baddeley)

— *See* DOCUMENTARY. Documentary Dance Materials ... Editors: R. Lange, D. Baddeley-Lange, J. Lee. [1976, *etc.*] 4°. **g. 822. aa.**

LANGE (F.)

— Königs-Husaren. Op. 29. [P. F.] *J. Bauer: Braunschweig*, [1879.] fol.
No. 3 of 'Im Salon'. **h. 3281. l. (4.)**

LANGE (Fr. Gustav)

— *See* LANGE (Gustav Fr.)

LANGE (Francisco Curt)

— *See* MENDOZA.— *Universidad nacional de Cuyo.* Archivo de música religiosa de la Capitanía Geral das Minas Gerais (Brasil). (Siglo XVIII.) Hallazgo, restauración y prólogo por F. C. Lange. 1951, *etc.* 4°. **G. 1267.**

LANGE (Georg)

— Mondnacht. Salonstück für Pianoforte. *Berlin*, [1881.] fol. **h. 3272. j. (9.)**

— Sonnenuntergang. Nordisches Lied von J. G. Conradi. Improvisation für Pianoforte. Op. 8. *C. Simon: Berlin*, [1887.] fol. **h. 3281. l. (5.)**

— Türkische Scharwache ... für Pianoforte. *Berlin*, [1880.] fol. **h. 3272. j. (8.)**

— *See* JAEGER (F.) and LANGE (G.) Aus dem In- und Auslande, *etc.* [1878.] fol. **h. 1448. a. (11.)**

LANGE (Gustav)

COLLECTIONS

— Compositions for the Pianoforte. no. 1–204, 208, 210–217, 220, 221. *A. Hammond & Co: London*, [1876–1903.] fol. *Wanting no. 205–207, 209, 218, 219.* **h. 3101. d.**

— Pianoforte Works. 4 no. *Augener & Co.: London*, [1879–86.] fol. **h. 3101. i. (1.)**

— Compositions ... arranged as Pianoforte duets by J. Rummel. 14 no. *London*, [1880.] fol. **h. 3101. a. (36.)**

— Lange-Album. Favorite pianoforte pieces. Herzeleid. Blumenlied. Edelweiss. Feen-Märchen. *London*, [1886.] 4°. *Augener & Co.'s edition, No. 6220.* **g. 543. g. (7.)**

— Lange's three Pieces. Blumenlied. Edelweiss. Herzeleid. (Arranged [for violin and P. F.] by L. Diehl.) [1888.] *See* BOOSEY AND CO. Boosey's Violin Miscellany, *etc.* No. 45. [1886, *etc.*] fol. **h. 1653.**

— Six Pieces ... arranged for Violin & Pianoforte by O. J. Stimpson. 6 no. *E. Ashdown: London*, [1891.] fol. **h. 3101. j. (15.)**

— Lange's Album of Favourite Pieces for the Pianoforte. *R. Cocks & Co.: London*, [1894.] 4°. *No. 322 of the Philharmonic Edition.* **g. 1450.**

— 3 Favorite Pieces ... for Violin & Pianoforte. 1. An der Wiege ... 2. Fischerlied. 3. By the Meadow Brook. *A. Hammond & Co.: London*, [1896.] 4°. *The Academic Edition, No. 23.* **g. 1130. h. (1.)**

— "Die Sennerin." ⟨Swiss idyll.⟩ [Op. 63.] Gustav Lange ... "The Hussars come!" ⟨Cavalry piece.⟩ [Op. 124.] R. Eilenberg ... "In der Waldschenke." ⟨Rustic dance.⟩ [Op. 377.] Gustav Lange. [Military band parts.] 29 pt. *Boosey & Co.: London*, 1905. fol.
[*Boosey's new supplemental Journal for military Bands. no. 15.*] **h. 1544. a.**

— 5 Most popular Pieces. 1. Longing ... 2. An der Wiege ... 3. Blumenlied ... 4. Dein Eigen ... 5. Edelweiss. [P. F.] *A. Hammond & Co.: London*, [1913.] 4°. *The Academic Edition, No. 510.* **g. 1130. y. (7.)**

— Six Celebrated Pieces for pianoforte, *etc. A. Lengnick & Co.: London*, [1921.] 4°. **g. 1127. g. (13.)**

— À la Cosaque. Morceau caractéristique. [P. F.] Op. 365. *N. Simrock: Berlin*, [1886.] fol. **h. 3101. i. (20.)**

— Abendständchen. Melodie für Pianoforte. *Leipzig*, [1875.] fol. **h. 3101. c. (30.)**

— Abendständchen. Melodie für Pianoforte. Op. 224. Vierhändig. *Leipzig*, [1883.] fol. **h. 3101. h. (13.)**

— Abendständchen. Melodie. Op. 224 [for zither]. [1880.] *See* GUTMANN (F.) Compositionen für Zither ... No. 21. [1880–86.] *obl.* 4°. **b. 244.**

— Abendstille. Méditation für das Pianoforte. *Frankfurt a. O.*, [1875.] fol. **h. 3101. c. (35.)**

— Abschied von der Alm. Idylle für das Pianoforte. Op. 334. *Berlin*, 1885. fol. **h. 3101. h. (44.)**

— Les Adieux. Op. 375. [P. F.] *N. Simrock: Berlin*, [1887.] fol. **h. 3101. i. (30.)**

— Aeolsharfen. Tonstück für das Pianoforte. *Berlin & Posen*, [1874.] fol. **h. 3101. b. (32.)**

— Albumblatt für das Piano. *Berlin*, [1882.] fol. **h. 3101. h. (8.)**

— Albumblatt. Album Leaf for the pianoforte. Op. 293. *E. Ashdown: London*, [1890.] fol. **h. 3101. j. (1.)**

LANGE (GUSTAV)

— [Albumblatt.] Album Leaf . . . Pianoforte Duet. *E. Ashdown: London, etc.*, [1896.] fol.   **h. 3101. j. (21.)**

— Alte Liebe. Ländler. Op. 335. [P. F.]   *Berlin*, [1885.] fol.   **h. 3101. h. (45.)**

— Am Felsenquell . . . Characteristisches Tonstück. Op. 376. [P. F.]   *N. Simrock: Berlin*, [1887.] fol.   **h. 3101. i. (31.)**

— Am Scheidewege. Tonstück für das Pianoforte. *Berlin und Dresden*, [1875.] fol.   **h. 3101. c. (25.)**

— Among the Pines. Improvisation on Carinthian Melodies for the Pianoforte. Op. 408. 2 no. [Solo and duet.] *E. Ashdown: London*, [1888–93.] fol.   **h. 3101. j. (2.)**

— Amoretten. Tonstück für Pianoforte. Op. 306. *Leipzig*, [1883.] fol.   **h. 3101. h. (21.)**

— An den Sonnenschein, Lied von R. Schumann. Fantasiestück für Pianoforte. *Berlin*, [1871.] fol.   **h. 3101. (52.)**

— An der Wiege. Tonstück für das Pianoforte. *Berlin & Posen*, [1874.] fol.   **h. 3101. b. (42.)**

— An der Wiege. Cradle song. [P. F.]   *London*, [1879.] fol.   **h. 3101. a. (31.)**

— [An der Wiege.] Cradle Song . . . Lange . . . "The Little Trumpeter". [Op. 228.] ⟨Polka.⟩ Gung'l . . . "Thine alone". ⟨Valse.⟩ Meissler. [Military band parts.] 26 pt. *Boosey & Co.: London*, 1882. fol. [*C. Boosé's supplemental military Journal. no.* 316.]   **h. 1544.**

— An der Wiege.—Cradle song.— For full orchestra. [Separate parts.]   *A. Hammond & Co.: London*, [1888.] 8°.   **e. 1342. (8.)**

— [An der Wiege.] Cradle Song. Lange. *See* DUNN (Matthew S.) Six Two-part Songs . . . 6. [1892.] 8°.   **E. 263. b. (5.)**

— Angelina. Notturno. Op. 319. [P. F.]   *Berlin*, [1884.] fol.   **h. 3101. h. (33.)**

— Antiquités Musicales. Transcriptionen für das Pianoforte. Op. 241. No. 1, 2.   *Offenbach a. M.*, [1876.] fol.   **h. 3101. c. (42.)**

— Antiquités Musicales . . . Op. 241. No. 3–6.   *Offenbach a. M.*, [1878–9.] fol.   **h. 3101. h. (15.)**

— Aquarellen. Vier kleine Tonbilder für das Pianoforte. 4 no. *Offenbach a. M.*, [1877.] fol.   **h. 3101. e. (21.)**

— Aquarelles . . . Morceaux de moyenne force, *etc.* [P. F.] no. 16. *Paris*, [1870.] fol. *Imperfect; wanting the other no.*   **h. 3101. h. (12.)**

— Arabesken. Beliebte Volkslieder für Piano frei übertragen. 6 no. *Berlin*, [1870.] fol.   **h. 3101. (31.)**

— Au Bivouac, grand galop militaire pour le Piano. Op. 47. *Berlin & Posen*, [1868.] fol.   **h. 3101. (22.)**

— Au clair de la lune. Mélodie rêveuse. Op. 338. [P. F.] *Berlin*, [1885.] fol.   **h. 3101. h. (48.)**

— Au Printemps. Mélodie de C. Gounod. Transcription pour Piano. *Paris*, [1880.] fol.   **h. 3101. g. (1.)**

— Auf Bergeshohen. Idylle. Op. 321. [P. F.]   *Berlin*, [1885.] fol.   **h. 3101. h. (35.)**

— Auf blauer Fluth. Barcarole. Op. 359. [P. F.]   *N. Simrock: Berlin*, [1886.] fol.   **h. 3101. i. (14.)**

— Auf brauner Haide. Idylle. Op. 360. [P. F.]   *N. Simrock: Berlin*, [1886.] fol.   **h. 3101. i. (15.)**

— Auf dem Kirchwege. Tonstück für das Pianoforte. *Berlin & Posen*, [1873.] fol.   **h. 3101. b. (29.)**

LANGE (GUSTAV)

— Auf der Blumli-Alp. Tonbild für das Pianoforte. *Dresden*, [1880.] fol.   **h. 3101. g. (20.)**

— Auf der Blümli-Alp . . . Tonbild für das Pianoforte. *London*, [1882.] fol.   **h. 3101. h. (3.)**

— Auf der Blümli-Alp. On the Alps. Tonbild. Pianoforte Duet. *E. Ashdown: London, etc.*, [1894.] fol.   **h. 3101. j. (17.)**

— Auf der Heimwehfluh. Eine Schweizer-Idylle für das Pianoforte. *Berlin & Posen*, [1875.] fol.   **h. 3101. c. (10.)**

— Auf der Höhe. Tanz Idylle für das Pianoforte. *Berlin*, [1880.] fol.   **h. 3101. g. (21.)**

— Aus dem deutschen Liederhain. Fantasiestücke über berühmte Lieder für das Pianoforte. 6 no.   *Berlin*, [1872.] fol.   **h. 3101. b. (14.)**

— Aus der Heimath. Home Thoughts. Morceau de Salon for the pianoforte. 2 no. [Solo and duet.]   *E. Ashdown: London*, [1891–4.] fol.   **h. 3101. j. (14.)**

— Aus des Lebens Mai. Sechs leichte Clavierstücke. 6 no. *Berlin*, [1882.] fol.   **h. 3101. h. (7.)**

— Aus meinem Liederbuche. Lyrische Tonstücke für das Pianoforte. *Berlin*, [1877.] fol.   **h. 3101. e. (18.)**

— Aus schöner Zeit. Tonstück. [P. F.]   *Berlin & Posen*, [1872.] fol.   **h. 3101. b. (7.)**

— Aus tiefster Seele. Melodie. [P. F.]   *Berlin & Posen*, [1872.] fol.   **h. 3101. b. (3.)**

— Aus treuen Herzen. Melodisches Tonstück für das Pianoforte. *Frankfurt a. O.*, [1876.] fol.   **h. 3101. c. (38.)**

— Ballerinen. Sechs leichte Tänze . . . für das Pianoforte. *Offenbach a. M.*, [1876.] fol.   **h. 3101. c. (41.)**

— Sechs beliebte Lieder von F. Curschman. Fantasie-Transcriptionen für das Pianoforte. 6 no.   *Berlin & Posen*, [1874.] fol.   **h. 3101. c. (7.)**

— Beliebte Lieder von O. Tiehsen. Fantasie-Transcriptionen für das Pianoforte. 7 no.   *Berlin & Posen*, [1875.] fol.   **h. 3101. c. (9.)**

— La belle Paysanne. Polka-Mazurka de Salon. Op. 368. [P. F.] *N. Simrock: Berlin*, [1886.] fol.   **h. 3101. i. (23.)**

— Bergblümlein. Mountain Flowers. Idyl for the pianoforte. Op. 411. 2 no. [Solo and duet.]   *E. Ashdown: London*, [1890–3.] fol.   **h. 3101. j. (6.)**

— Blätter im Winde. 4 leichte Tonstücke für das Pianoforte. 4 no.   *Berlin & Posen*, [1873.] fol.   **h. 3101. b. (16.)**

— Blätter im Winde. 4 leichte Tonstücke für das Pianoforte. Op. 138.   *A. Hammond & Co.: London*, [1896.] 4°. *The Academic Edition, No. 46.*   **g. 1130. a. (5.)**

— [Blätterrauschen. Op. 294.] Rustling Leaves . . . Pour piano, *etc.* pp. 7.   *F. Amos & Cᵒ: London*, [c. 1885.] fol.   **h. 60. zz. (24.)**

— [Blätterrauschen.] Rustling Leaves . . . Op. 294. ⟨For pianoforte.⟩ pp. 7.   *Cary & Co.: London*, [c. 1910.] fol. *One of "Three original Compositions for Pianoforte".*   **h. 60. zz. (25.)**

— Blumen am Wege. [P. F.]   *Berlin & Posen*, [1871.] fol.   **h. 3101. (41.)**

— Blumen am Wege—Flowers by the Wayside—für Pianoforte. Op. 87.   *A. Hammond & Co.: London*, [1896.] 4°. *The Academic Edition, No. 2.*   **g. 1130.**

— [Blumen am Wege.] Wayside Flowers . . . For piano. Op. 87. *W. Paxton & Co.: London*, 1924. 4°.   **g. 1125. k. (8.)**

LANGE (Gustav)

— [Blumen am Wege. Op. 87. No. 2. Am Wiesenbach.] Song without Words. "By the Meadow-brook." Lange ... Polka. "Bellona." (For cornet solo.) Faust.—Polonaise "Hofball". Gung'l. [Military band parts.] 26 pt. *Boosey & Co.: London,* [1882.] fol.
[*Boosé's military Journal. ser. 72. no. 2.*] **h. 1549.**

— [Blumen am Wege. Op. 87. No. 2. Am Wiesenbach.] By the Meadow Brook. For full orchestra. [Parts.] *A. Hammond & Co.: London,* [1888.] 8°. **e. 1342. (9.)**

— [Blumen am Wege. Op. 87. No. 2. Am Wiesenbach.] The Meadow Brook. Lange. *See* DUNN (Matthew S.) Six Two-part Songs ... 1. [1892.] 8°. **E. 263. b. (5.)**

— Blumenlied, mélodie for Pianoforte. *London,* [1878.] fol. **h. 3101. a. (23.)**

— [Blumenlied.] Song of the Flowers ... for the Pianoforte. *London,* [1878.] fol. **h. 3101. a. (24.)**

— Blumenlied, mélodie for the Pianoforte. *London,* [1879.] fol. **h. 3101. a. (25.)**

— [Another edition.] Blumenlied, mélodie. *London,* [1879.] fol. **h. 3101. a. (26.)**

— [Another edition.] Blumenlied ... pour Piano. *London,* [1879.] fol. **h. 3101. a. (27.)**

— [Another edition.] Blumenlied ... pour le Piano. *London,* [1879.] fol. **h. 3101. a. (28.)**

— [Another edition.] Blumenlied. Piano. *London,* [1879.] fol. **h. 3101. a. (29.)**

— [Another edition.] Blumenlied ... pour Piano. *London,* [1879.] fol. **h. 3101. a. (30.)**

— Blumenlied. Mélodie. [P. F.] *London,* [1880.] fol. **h. 3101. a. (33.)**

— Blumenlied. Morceau pour Piano. *London,* [1880.] fol. **h. 3101. a. (34.)**

— Blumenlied. Morceau pour piano. *C. Sheard: London,* [1880.] fol.
No. 6305 of the Musical Bouquet. **H. 2345.**

— Blumenlied. Mélodie pour piano. *Howard & Co.: London,* [1883.] fol. **h. 3101. i. (3.)**

— Blumenlied. Melodie für Pianoforte. Op. 39. Revised ... by L. Schumann. *Ransford & Son: London,* [1884.] fol. **h. 3101. a. (40.)**

— Blumenlied. [P. F.] *See* BAPTISTE (A.) Swallow Flights ... No. 7. [1888.] fol. **h. 3329. (3.)**

— Blumenlied ... Op. 39. Für Pianoforte zu zwei Händen, *etc.* pp. 9. *L. Massute: Frankfurt a/O.,* [c. 1890.] fol. **g. 1129. rr. (2.)**

— Blumenlied. Mélodie pour piano. pp. 4. *W. Paxton: London,* [c. 1900.] fol. **h. 61. xx. (44.)**

— Blumenlied. Mélodie. [P. F. solo and duet.] 2 no. [1901.] *See* PERCIVAL (F.) Sweet Memories, *etc.* No. 20. [1897, *etc.*] fol. **h. 3168. g.**

— Blumenlied. Mélodie pour Piano ... Edited and fingered by R. Stephens. *J. Green & Co.: Colne,* [1902.] fol. **h. 3282. ww. (29.)**

— Blumenlied. [P. F.] [1909.] *See* PEARSON (A.) The Eddystone Edition, *etc.* No. 2. [1903–09.] fol. **h. 3283. mm. (26.)**

— Blumenlied. [P. F.] *Chappell & Co.: London,* (1910.) fol.
Chappell Edition of Popular Pianoforte Works, No. 16. **h. 3369.**

LANGE (Gustav)

— Blumenlied. Op. 39. [P. F.] *Rowland's: London,* [1928.] 4°.
[*Rowland's Popular Series. No. 14.*] **g. 1258. a.**

— [Blumenlied.] Flower Song ... Transcription by H. Frey. [P. F.] *Robbins Music Corporation: New York,* 1935. 4°. **g. 1127. ss. (34.)**

— Blumenlied. [Violin and P. F.] *See* WEEKES (F.) Favorite Melodies, *etc.* No. 30. [1878, *etc.*] fol. **h. 1677.**

— Blumenlied ... arranged as a Violin Solo with Pianoforte accompaniment, by J. Pridham. *B. Williams: London,* [1884.] fol. **h. 210. d. (33.)**

— Blumenlied. [Violin and P. F.] *See* STIMPSON (O. J.) Six Popular Pieces, *etc.* No. 3. [1887.] fol. **g. 505. h. (15.)**

— Blumenlied. [Violin and P. F.] *See* VOLTI (C.) Modern Gems, *etc.* No. 7. [1889–92.] fol. **h. 3236. (5.)**

— Blumenlied ... Arrangiert von L. Artok. [Parts.] *B. Schott's Söhne: Mainz und Leipzig,* 1931. 4°.
[*Schott & Co.'s Domesticum Salon-Orchestra. No. 79.*] **g. 1053. a.**

— Blumenmährchen. [P. F.] *Berlin & Posen,* [1871.] fol. **h. 3101. (44.)**

— Blumenreigen. Salon-Walzer für das Pianoforte. *Berlin,* [1877.] fol. **h. 3101. e. (11.)**

— La Bouquetière. Polka de Salon. Op. 361. [P. F.] *N. Simrock: Berlin,* [1886.] fol. **h. 3101. i. (16.)**

— Brillantfeuer. Salonstück für Pianoforte. Op. 308. *Berlin,* [1883.] fol. **h. 3101. h. (23.)**

— [Brillantfeuer.] Glistening Diamonds. Caprice for the pianoforte. Op. 308. *E. Ashdown: London,* [1884.] fol. **h. 3101. a. (45.)**

— Bunte Blätter. Sechs leichte melodische Tonstücke für das Pianoforte. 6 no. *Berlin & Posen,* [1874.] fol. **h. 3101. c. (6.)**

— Bunte Blätter. Sechs leichte melodische Tonstücke für das Pianoforte. Op. 194. *A. Hammond & Co.: London,* [1896.] 4°.
The Academic Edition, No. 7. **g. 1130.**

— Bunte Schmetterlinge. Idylle für das Pianoforte. *Berlin & Posen,* [1876.] fol. **h. 3101. c. (15.)**

— By the Meadow-brook. *See* supra: [Blumen am Wege. Op. 87. No. 2. Am Wiesenbach.]

— La Cascade, morceau de concert pour Piano. Op. 21. *Berlin & Posen,* [1866.] fol. **h. 3101. (7.)**

— Centi-Folie. 100 Fantasien über beliebte Volkslieder in leichtem ... Stile für das Pianoforte. Op. 232. no. 65–67, 75, 76, 80–83. *Offenbach a/M.,* [1879, *etc.*] fol.
Imperfect; wanting no. 1–64, 68–74, 77–79. **h. 3101. h. (14.)**

— Six Characteristic Pieces for the pianoforte. Op. 292. 6 no. *E. Ashdown: London,* [1882.] fol. **h. 3101. a. (43.)**

— [Six Characteristic Pieces. No. 3.] In Ball-Costume. Valse ... Op. 292. No. 3. Edited and fingered by P. Gallico. [P. F.] *J. W. Stern & Co.: New York,* (1912.) fol. **g. 606. n. (34.)**

— Der Cid. Oper von J. Massenet. Transcriptionen ... Op. 369. [P. F.] 2 no. *A. Fürstner: Berlin,* [1886.] fol. **h. 3101. i. (24.)**

— Der Cid. Oper von J. Massenet. Fantasie. Op. 370. [P. F.] *A. Fürstner: Berlin,* [1886.] fol. **h. 3101. i. (25.)**

— Les Contes d'Hoffmann, opéra fantastique de J. Offenbach, fantaisie brillante pour Piano. *Paris,* [1881.] fol. **h. 3101. g. (23.)**

— Coppélia, Ballet von L. Delibes, grosse Fantasie für das Pianoforte. *Berlin und Dresden,* [1878.] fol. **h. 3101. e. (23.)**

LANGE (Gustav)

— La Course au Clocher. *See* infra: [Steeple-Chase.]

— Dahin! Elegie. [P. F.] *Berlin & Posen,* [1872.] fol.
h. 3101. (6.)

— Dein Bildniss ... Tonstück für Pianoforte. *Leipzig,* [1880.] fol.
h. 3101. g. (13.)

— Dein Eigen, Melodie für Piano. *Berlin & Posen,* [1870.] fol.
h. 3101. (29.)

— [Dein eigen. Op. 54.] Thine own ... Revised and fingered by M. Gould, *etc.* [P. F.] *M. Witmark & Sons: New York, etc.,* (1910.) fol.
h. 3283. jj. (33.)

— Deutsche Kriegsbilder. Op. 95. [P. F.] *N. Simrock: Bonn & Berlin,* [1871.] fol.
Part of "Beliebte Compositionen für das Pianoforte".
h. 3101. (48.)

— Diavolina. Morceau de salon pour piano. Op. 310. *Berlin,* [1883.] fol.
h. 3101. h. (25.)

— Diavolina. Morceau de salon pour piano. Op. 310. *E. Ashdown: London,* [1884.] fol.
h. 3101. a. (47.)

— Diavolina. Morceau de Salon pour piano à quatre mains. *E. Ashdown: London,* [1892.] fol.
h. 3101. j. (13.)

— Dolorosa, méditation pour le Piano. Op. 28. *Berlin & Posen,* [1867.] fol.
h. 3101. (15.)

— Dornröschen ... Idylle. Op. 378. [P. F.] *N. Simrock: Berlin,* [1887.] fol.
h. 3101. i. (33.)

— Dreaming Flowers ... Op. 70. *See* infra: [Träumende Blumen.]

— Du meine Seele, du mein Herz. Fantasiestück nach R. Schumann's Widmung für Pianoforte. *Berlin,* [1871.] fol.
h. 3101. (49.)

— Edelweiss, idylle für Piano. *London,* [1878.] fol.
h. 3101. a. (15.)

— [Another edition.] Edelweiss ... für Piano. *London,* [1878.] fol.
h. 3101. a. (16.)

— [Another edition.] Edelweiss ... pour Piano. *London,* [1878.] fol.
h. 3101. a. (17.)

— [Another edition.] Edelweiss ... für Piano. *London,* [1878.] fol.
h. 3101. a. (18.)

— [Edelweiss.] Flowers on the Rocks ... for the Pianoforte. *London,* [1878.] fol.
h. 3101. a. (19.)

— Edelweiss, Idylle für Piano. *London,* [1879.] fol.
h. 3101. a. (20.)

— [Another edition.] Edelweiss ... pour Piano. *London,* [1879.] fol.
h. 3101. a. (21.)

— Edelweiss. Idylle pour le Piano. *London,* [1880.] fol.
h. 3101. a. (35.)

— Edelweiss. Morceau pour piano. *C. Sheard: London,* [1880.] fol.
No. 6306 of the Musical Bouquet. **H. 2345.**

— Edelweiss. Idylle pour piano. (Op. 31.) *Howard & Co.: London,* [1883.] fol.
h. 3101. i. (4.)

— Edelweiss. Idylle. (Op. 31.) [P. F.] Edited ... by A. H. Brown. *F. Pitman: London,* [1884.] fol.
h. 1246. d. (18.)

— Edelweiss. Idylle für Pianoforte. Op. 31. Revised ... by L. Schumann. *Ransford & Sons: London,* [1884.] fol.
h. 3101. a. (38.)

— Edelweiss. [P. F.] *See* DUFAURE (A.) Crotchets and Quavers, *etc.* No. 34. [1892–1904.] fol.
h. 3416. c.

LANGE (Gustav)

— Edelweiss. Idylle. [P. F. solo and duet.] 2 no. [1901.] *See* PERCIVAL (F.) Sweet Memories, *etc.* No. 22. [1897, *etc.*] fol.
h. 3168. g.

— Einsame Thränen, Nocturne für Pianoforte. Op. 52. *Berlin & Posen,* [1870.] fol.
h. 3101. (26.)

— Engelwacht ... Romanze. Op. 374. [P. F.] *N. Simrock: Berlin,* [1887.] fol.
h. 3101. i. (29.)

— Er ist gekommen. (Lied von R. Franz.) Fantasie für Pianoforte. *Berlin,* [1871.] fol.
h. 3101. (50.)

— Erika ... Tonstück für das Pianoforte. *Leipzig,* [1879.] fol.
h. 3101. g. (5.)

— Erika. Tonstück für das Pianoforte. Op. 265. Vierhändig. *Leipzig,* [1883.] fol.
h. 3101. h. (17.)

— Erika. Tonstück. Op. 265 [for zither]. [1880.] *See* GUTMANN (F.) Compositionen für Zither ... No. 26. [1880–86.] *obl.* 4°.
b. 244.

— Erinnerung, Melodie für das Pianoforte. Op. 49. *Berlin & Posen,* [1869.] fol.
h. 3101. (24.)

— Erinnerung an Wien. Zwei Valse-Capricen nach Melodieen von J. Strauss. 2 no. *Berlin,* [1880.] fol. **h. 3101. g. (10.)**

— Erinnerung an Wien ... Zwei Valse-Capricen nach Melodeen von J. Strauss für das Pianoforte. 2 no. *London,* [1882.] fol.
h. 3101. h. (1.)

— Erinnerungsblätter ... Melodisches Tonstück für Pianoforte. *Leipzig,* [1880.] fol.
h. 3101. g. (12.)

— Fantaisies brillantes sur des opéras les plus favoris ... pour le piano. No. 1–4. *Leipzig,* [1885.] fol. **h. 3101. h. (43.)**

— Fantaisie brillante pour Piano sur des motifs de l'opéra Aida de Verdi. *Milano,* [1873.] fol. **h. 3101. e. (12.)**

— Fantasien über Brüll's Opern: Das goldene Kreuz, Der Landfriede, für das Pianoforte. 2 no. *Berlin & Posen,* [1877.] fol.
h. 3101. e. (22.)

— Zwei Fantasien über beliebte Lieder für das Pianoforte. *Leipzig,* [1873.] fol. **h. 3101. b. (30.)**

— Drei Fantasien über beliebte Lieder für das Pianoforte. 3 no. *Berlin & Posen,* [1874.] fol. **h. 3101. c. (1.)**

— Fantasien über beliebte Lieder ... für das Pianoforte. Op. 172. no. 3, 4. *Leipzig,* [1880.] fol.
These are a continuation of the Zwei Fantasien, etc., published in 1873. **h. 3101. h. (10.)**

— Fantaisie über Motive der Oper Tannhäuser ... von R. Wagner, für das Pianoforte. *Berlin und Dresden,* [1875.] fol.
h. 3101. c. (36.)

— Fantaisie über das Wiegenlied von J. Brahms für das Pianoforte. *Berlin,* [1875.] fol. **h. 3101. c. (2.)**

— Lullaby, Wiegenlied, by Brahms. Fantasie for Pianoforte by G. Lange. *W. Paxton & Co.: London,* [1936.] fol.
h. 3870. i. (24.)

— Fantasie-Ballade (E moll) für Pianoforte. *Berlin,* [1877.] fol.
h. 3101. e. (9.)

— Fantasie-Polonaise nach Motiven von B. Bilse's beliebter Königs-Polonaise. [P. F.] *Berlin,* [1877.] fol. **h. 3101. e. (2.)**

— Vier Fantasiestücke aus Gounod's Faust. 4 no. *Berlin & Posen,* [1874.] fol. **h. 3101. b. (39.)**

— Fantasiestücke nach beliebten Motiven für Pianoforte. 8 no. *Adolph Fürstner: Berlin,* [1872.] fol. **h. 3101. b. (15.)**

LANGE (GUSTAV)

— Fantasiestücke nach Liedern von Mendelssohn-Bartholdy. 22 no. *Berlin*, [1877.] fol.   **h. 3101. e. (14.)**

— Fantasiestücke nach Liedern von R. Schumann für Pianoforte. 12 no. *Breslau*, [1872.] fol.   **h. 3101. b. (10.)**

— Fantasie-Transcriptionen über drei Lieder von F. Abt für das Pianoforte. 3 no. *Berlin & Posen*, [1876.] fol.   **h. 3101. c. (23.)**

— Drei Fantasie-Transcriptionen über Lieder und Arien von W. A. Mozart für das Pianoforte. 3 no. *Berlin & Posen*, [1877.] fol.   **h. 3101. e. (15.)**

— Farewell, méditation pour le Piano. Op. 15. *Berlin & Posen*, [1864.] fol.   **h. 3101. (2.)**

— Farewell, méditation for the Pianoforte. *London*, [1867.] fol.   **h. 3101. a. (1.)**

— [Farewell. Op. 15.] Song without Words, *etc.* ([Followed by] Polka—"Bric-à-brac". C. Coote Junr.— Gavotte—"Stella". Kappey.) [Military band parts.] 25 pt. *Boosey & Co.: London*, [1878.] fol. [*Boosé's military Journal. ser.* 63. *no.* 2.]   **h. 1549.**

— Faublas-Polonaise von R. Wüerst für das Pianoforte frei übertragen von G. Lange. *Berlin & Posen*, [1873.] fol.   **h. 3101. b. (38.)**

— Felice notte! Notturno für das Pianoforte. Op. 305. *Leipzig*, [1883.] fol.   **h. 3101. h. (20.)**

— Festklänge. Grosser Marsch für das Pianoforte. *Berlin & Posen*, [1873.] fol.   **h. 3101. b. (27.)**

— Fête Militaire, grand galop de concert, pour Piano. Op. 18. *Berlin & Posen*, [1865.] fol.   **h. 3101. (5.)**

— Fischerlied, Tonstück für das Pianoforte. Op. 43. *Berlin & Posen*, [1868.] fol.   **h. 3101. (19.)**

— [Fischerlied. Op. 43.] Barcarole, *etc.* ([Followed by] Queen Victoria—Vocal galop.—Polka Mazurka—"Die Tanzende Muse ... Joh. Strauss [or rather, Josef Strauss. Op. 266].) [Military band parts.] 25 pt. *Boosey & Co.: London*, [1879.] fol. [*Boosé's military Journal. ser.* 60. *no.* 4.]   **h. 1549.**

— Fleurs Fanées, mélodie pour Piano. Op. 48. *Berlin & Posen*, [1868.] fol.   **h. 3101. (23.)**

— Flower Song. *See* supra: [Blumenlied.]

— Frohe Spiele. Tonstück für Pianoforte. *Berlin & Posen*, [1874.] fol.   **h. 3101. b. (36.)**

— Frohes Erwachen. Tonstück für Piano. *Berlin & Posen*, [1871.] fol.   **h. 3101. (35.)**

— Frühlingsläuten ... Tonstück für Pianoforte. Op. 313. *Leipzig*, [1884.] fol.   **h. 3101. h. (28.)**

— Frühlingssänger. Birds of Spring. Caprice for the pianoforte. Op. 426. *E. Ashdown: London*, [1890.] fol.   **h. 3101. j. (12.)**

— Für dich. Melodisches Tonstück. [P. F.] *Berlin & Posen*, [1874.] fol.   **h. 3101. b. (35.)**

— La Gavotte de la Reine. Op. 352. [P. F.] *N. Simrock: Berlin*, [1886.] fol.   **h. 3101. i. (7.)**

— La Gazelle. Mazurka brillante. Op. 336. [P. F.] *Berlin*, [1885.] fol.   **h. 3101. h. (46.)**

— Gedenkblätter. Lyrisches Tonstück für das Pianoforte. *Berlin & Posen*, [1873.] fol.   **h. 3101. b. (23.)**

— Ein Gedenkblatt. Méditation. [P. F.] *Berlin*, [1880.] fol.   **h. 3101. g. (3.)**

LANGE (GUSTAV)

— Gelübde. Melodisches Tonstück. [P. F.] *Berlin & Posen*, [1876.] fol.   **h. 3101. b. (4.)**

— Glockenblumen. Idylle. Op. 317. [P. F.] *Berlin*, [1884.] fol.   **h. 3101. h. (31.)**

— Glöckchen-Mazurka für das Pianoforte componirt. Op. 14. *Berlin u. Posen*, [1864.] fol.   **h. 3101. (1.)**

— Glöckchen mazurka. [P. F.] Op. 14. *London*, [1870.] fol.   **h. 3101. a. (9.)**

— Graziella. Valse brillante. [P. F.] *Berlin & Posen*, [1875.] fol.   **h. 3101. c. (11.)**

— Le Grillon. Morceau caractéristique. Op. 367. [P. F.] *N. Simrock: Berlin*, [1886.] fol.   **h. 3101. i. (22.)**

— Grosse Fantasie über Motive der Operette "Die Fledermaus" von J. Strauss, für das Pianoforte. *Offenbach a./M.*, [1876.] fol.   **h. 3101. c. (32.)**

— [Grossmütterchen.] Ländler—Grossmütterchen ... Arr. for military band by M. Retford. [Parts.] 25 pt. *S. A. Chappell: London*, [1889.] fol. [*Army Journal. no.* 193.]   **h. 1562.**

— Grüss Gott, du schöner Wald. Tonstück für das Pianoforte. *Berlin & Posen*, [1874.] fol.   **h. 3101. c. (4.)**

— Gruss in Tönen. Tonstück für das Pianoforte. *Berlin & Posen*, [1875.] fol.   **h. 3101. c. (12.)**

— Habanera aus dem Bizet'schem Oper Carmen. [P. F.] *Berlin*, [1880.] fol.   **h. 3101. g. (8.)**

— Die Harfnerin ... Tonstück für Pianoforte. *Leipzig*, [1880.] fol.   **h. 3101. g. (16.)**

— Harzelied. Melody for Pianoforte. *London*, [1879.] fol.   **h. 3101. a. (32.)**

— Heimathsgrüsse. Thüringer-Idylle für das Pianoforte. *Frankurt a./O.*, [1876.] fol.   **h. 3101. c. (37.)**

— Heimweh ... Elegisches Tonstück. Op. 373. [P. F.] *N. Simrock: Berlin*, [1887.] fol.   **h. 3101. i. (28.)**

— Herbstblüthen. Tonstück für das Pianoforte. *Francfort a./O.*, [1876.] fol.   **h. 3101. c. (39.)**

— Herzblättchen. Melodie für das Piano. *Berlin*, [1881.] fol.   **h. 3101. g. (27.)**

— Herzblättchen ... Melodie für das Piano. *London*, [1882.] fol.   **h. 3101. h. (4.)**

— Herzblättchen. The Leaflet. Melody. Pianoforte Duet. *E. Ashdown: London, etc.*, [1895.] fol.   **h. 3101. j. (16.)**

— Herzeleid. Melodie. Edited ... by F. Berger. [P. F.] *London*, [1881.] fol.   **h. 3101. a. (37.)**

— Herzeleid ... Edited by G. Rolande. *London*, [1881.] fol.   **h. 3101. a. (39.)**

— Herzeleid. Mélodie pour piano. *R. Cocks & Co.: London*, [1883.] fol.   **h. 3101. i. (5.)**

— Herzeleid. Mélodie pour piano. (Edited ... by A. Meyer.) *W. H. Broome: London*, [1897.] fol.   **h. 3101. j. (23.)**

— Herzeleid ... Op. 38. Transcribed on the Keyboard System, *etc.* [1897.] *See* TYSSEN (A. D.) Keyboard Music Series. No. 26. [1890, *etc.*] fol.   **h. 3287.**

— Herzeleid ... for the piano. Op. 38. Edited and fingered by C. Ross. *Ross, Grey & Co.: London*, [1923.] fol.   **h. 3865. f. (1.)**

— Herzensfrühling. Tonstück für das Pianoforte. *Berlin & Posen*, [1874.] fol.   **h. 3101. b. (34.)**

LANGE (GUSTAV)

— Herzensgrüsse. Tonstück für das Pianoforte. *Frankfurt a./O.*, [1875.] fol.   **h. 3101. c. (33.)**

— Herzensstimmen. Nocturne für Piano. *Berlin & Posen*, [1871.] fol.   **h. 3101. (34.)**

— Herzenstöne. Melodisches Tonstück für das Pianoforte. *Berlin*, [1877.] fol.   **h. 3101. e. (20.)**

— Herzenstöne. For full orchestra. [Parts.] *A. Hammond & Co.: London*, [1888.] 8°.   **e. 1342. (10.)**

— [Hirtenleben im Gebirge.] Mountain Life. [P. F.] Op. 72. *London*, [1870.] fol.   **h. 3101. a. (8.)**

— Hirtenleben im Gebirge. Tongemälde für Piano. *Berlin & Posen*, [1871.] fol.   **h. 3101. (33.)**

— Die Hochländerin. Idylle für das Pianoforte. *Dresden*, [1880.] fol.   **h. 3101. g. (19.)**

— Die Hochländerin ... Idylle für das Pianoforte. *London*, [1882.] fol.   **h. 3101. h. (2.)**

— Die Hochländerin. The Mountain Naiad. Idyll. Pianoforte Duet. *E. Ashdown: London, etc.*, [1895.] fol.   **h. 3101. j. (18.)**

— Hortensia, valse de concert. [P. F.] Op. 53. *Berlin & Posen*, [1870.] fol.   **h. 3101. (27.)**

— Ich kann wohl manchmal singen. (Gedicht von Frhr. von Eichendorff.) Lied für Mezzo-Sopran oder Baryton mit Begleitung des Pianoforte. *Berlin & Dresden*, [1876.] fol.   **H. 1777. h. (10.)**

— Im Böhmerwald. Bohemia. Improvisation on Slavonic melodies for the pianoforte. Op. 412. *E. Ashdown: London*, [1889.] fol.   **h. 3101. j. (7.)**

— [Im Böhmerwald.] Bohemia ... Improvisation on Slavonic Melodies. Pianoforte Duet. *E. Ashdown: London*, [1897.] fol.   **h. 3101. j. (22.)**

— Im Freien. Tanz-Idylle. [P. F.] *Berlin & Posen*, [1872.] fol.   **h. 3101. b. (8.)**

— Im frohen Kreise. Tanzscene. [P. F.] *Berlin & Posen*, [1872.] fol.   **h. 3101. b. (1.)**

— "Im grünen Hain." ⟨Song without words.⟩ Gustav Lange ... "Nadeshda". ⟨Prelude to the opera.⟩ A. Goring Thomas ... "Loreley". ⟨Polka.⟩ Piefke. [Military band parts.] 26 pt. *Boosey & Co.: London*, 1885. fol. [*Boosey's supplemental military Journal. no. 334.*]   **h. 1544.**

— Im grünen Hain. For full orchestra. [Parts.] *A. Hammond & Co.: London*, [1888.] 8°.   **e. 1342. (12.)**

— Im Kloster. Legende. Op. 345. [P. F.] *Berlin*, [1886.] fol.   **h. 3101. h. (55.)**

— Im Traume ... Tonstück für Pianoforte. *Leipzig*, [1880.] fol.   **h. 3101. g. (15.)**

— Immortellen. Elegie. [P. F.] *Berlin & Posen*, [1871.] fol.   **h. 3101. (45.)**

— In a strange Land. Loin du pays. Op. 36. Edited by A. Cooper. [P. F.] *G. Schirmer: New York*, 1916. 4°.   **g. 442. z. (14.)**

— In Ball-Costume. *See* supra: [Six Characteristic Pieces. No. 3.]

— In bunter Reihe. Erste Polonaise für das Pianoforte. *Berlin & Posen*, [1873.] fol.   **h. 3101. b. (24.)**

— In der Alpenhütte. Schweizer Idylle für das Pianoforte. *Frankfurt a./O.*, [1876.] fol.   **h. 3101. e. (4.)**

LANGE (GUSTAV)

— In der Czarda. Hungary. Fantasia on Hungarian melodies for the pianoforte. Op. 413. *E. Ashdown: London*, [1889.] fol.   **h. 3101. j. (8.)**

— In der Mühle. Genrestück. Op. 348. [P. F.] *Berlin*, [1886.] fol.   **h. 3101. h. (58.)**

— In der Sennhütte. Tonbild für das Pianoforte. Op. 314. *Leipzig*, [1884.] fol.   **h. 3101. h. (29.)**

— In der Sennhütte. Tonbild. Op. 314. [For zither.] [1886.] *See* GUTMANN (F.) Compositionen für Zither ... No. 46. [1880–86.] *obl.* 4°.   **b. 244.**

— In der Spinnstube. Genrestück. Op. 344. [P. F.] *Berlin*, [1886.] fol.   **h. 3101. h. (54.)**

— In der Waldschenke ... Bauerntanz ... Op. 377. [P. F.] *N. Simrock: Berlin*, [1887.] fol.   **h. 3101. i. (32.)**

— In dunkler Nacht. (Lied von G. Luther.) Fantasie-Transcription für Pianoforte. *Berlin*, [1871.] fol.   **h. 3101. (51.)**

— In einsamen Stunden. Zwei melodische Tonstücke für das Pianoforte. 2 no. *Berlin & Posen*, [1876.] fol.   **h. 3101. c. (19.)**

— In jungen Jahren. Leichte und gefällige Clavierstücke zum Vorspielen. Op. 316. 6 no. *Berlin*, 1884. fol.   **h. 3101. h. (30.)**

— In süssen Traum. Méditation. Op. 322. [P. F.] *Berlin*, [1885.] fol.   **h. 3101. h. (36.)**

— In trauter Hütte. Tonstück für das Pianoforte. *Berlin und Dresden*, [1875.] fol.   **h. 3101. c. (26.)**

— In Trauter Stunde ... Melodisches Tonstück. Op. 371. *N. Simrock: Berlin*, [1887.] fol.   **h. 3101. i. (26.)**

— Innere Stimmen. Lyrisches Tonstück. [P. F.] *Berlin & Posen*, [1872.] fol.   **h. 3101. b. (9.)**

— In's Herz geschlossen. Lyrisches Tonstück. [P. F.] *Berlin & Posen*, [1872.] fol.   **h. 3101. b. (5.)**

— Irrlichter. Fantasie Mazurka für das Pianoforte. *Berlin & Posen*, [1873.] fol.   **h. 3101. b. (21.)**

— Jägerfahrt, Clavierstück. Op. 26. *Berlin & Posen*, [1867.] fol.   **h. 3101. (13.)**

— Jean et Jeannette. Gavotte. Op. 362. [P. F.] *N. Simrock: Berlin*, [1886.] fol.   **h. 3101. i. (17.)**

— Klänge aus der Alpenwelt. Alpine Echoes ... Ländler on Austrian melodies for the pianoforte. Op. 410. 2 no. [Solo and duet.] *E. Ashdown: London*, [1889, 92.] fol.   **h. 3101. j. (4.)**

— [Klänge aus der Alpenwelt.] Brise des Alpes, *etc.* *A. Leduc: Paris*, 1890. fol.   **h. 3101. j. (5.)**

— Kleine Welt. Neun kleine Tonbilder aus dem Kinderleben für das Pianoforte. 3 Hft. *Berlin & Posen*, [1873.] fol.   **h. 3101. b. (17.)**

— Kleine Welt, neun kleine Tonbilder aus dem Kinderleben für das Pianoforte ... Op. 139. *A. Hammond & Co.: London*, [1886.] 4°. *The Academic Edition, No. 4.*   **g. 1130.**

— Krieger's Ständchen ... Tonstück. Op. 350. [P. F.] *Berlin*, [1886.] fol.   **h. 3101. h. (60.)**

— Langage d'Amour, Tonstück. [P. F.] Op. 45. *Berlin & Posen*, [1868.] fol.   **h. 3101. (20.)**

— Langage du Cœur. Méditation. Op. 325. [P. F.] *Berlin*, [1885.] fol.   **h. 3101. h. (39.)**

LANGE (GUSTAV)

— Leaves from the Shamrock. Fantasia on Irish Melodies for the pianoforte. Op. 409. *E. Ashdown: London*, [1888.] fol.
h. 3101. j. (3.)

— Legende. Tonstück für das Pianoforte. *Berlin & Posen*, [1876.] fol.
h. 3101. c. (16.)

— Zwei leichte Jagdstücke für das Pianoforte. 2 no. *Berlin & Posen*, [1874.] fol.
h. 3101. b. (40.)

— 5 leichte Sonatinen für das Pianoforte componirt. [Op. 114.] 5 no. *Berlin & Posen*, [1871.] fol.
h. 3101. (46.)

— [Fünf leichte Sonatinen.] Five Sonatines for the Pianoforte. Op. 114. *A. Hammond & Co.: London*, [1896.] 4°.
The Academic Edition, No. 1.
g. 1130.

— Lenzeswonne. Tonstück für das Pianoforte. *Frankfurt a. O.*, [1875.] fol.
h. 3101. c. (34.)

— Die Libelle, Idylle für Pianoforte componirt. Op. 24. *Berlin & Posen*, [1866.] fol.
h. 3101. (8.)

— Liebesahnung. Melodisches Tonstück für Piano. *Berlin & Posen*, [1871.] fol.
h. 3101. (36.)

— Der Liebesbote ... Gavotte. Op. 372. [P. F.] *N. Simrock: Berlin*, [1887.] fol.
h. 3101. i. (27.)

— Liebesreigen. Salon-Walzer. Op. 337. [P. F.] *Berlin*, [1885.] fol.
h. 3101. h. (47.)

— Liebesständchen. Love's Serenade. Characteristic Piece for the pianoforte. Op. 423. 2 no. [Solo and duet.] *E. Ashdown: London*, [1890, 94.] fol.
h. 3101. j. (9.)

— Lied der Sehnsucht. Tonstück für das Pianoforte. *Frankfurt a. Oder*, [1876.] fol.
h. 3101. e. (3.)

— Vier Lieder von A. Rubinstein, für das Pianoforte frei bearbeitet, *etc.* 4 no. *Berlin & Posen*, [1876.] fol.
h. 3101. c. (22.)

— Lieder von E. Lassen für Pianoforte frei übertragen. 12 no. *Breslau*, [1881.] fol.
h. 3101. g. (26.)

— Lieder von F. Schubert für das Pianoforte. 20 no. *Berlin*, [1877.] fol.
h. 3101. e. (17.)

— Zwei Lieder von R. Schumann, für das Pianoforte frei bearbeitet, *etc.* 2 no. *Berlin & Posen*, [1876.] fol.
h. 3101. c. (14.)

— 2 Lieder von W. Westmeyer für das Pianoforte frei übertragen, *etc.* 2 no. *Dresden*, [1873.] fol. **h. 3101. b. (31.)**

— Liederblüthen. Drei leichte Fantasiestücke nach beliebten Liedern für Pianoforte. Op. 149. 3 no. *Breslau*, [1872.] fol.
h. 3101. b. (19.)

— Lieder Blüthen. Fantasien über beliebte Lieder für das Pianoforte. Op. 171. *Offenbach a. M.*, [1873, *etc.*] fol.
h. 3101. f.

— [Lieder Blüthen.] Waldandacht. Lied v. F. Abt. Fantasie. Op. 171. No. 11. [P. F.] *Metzler & Co.: London*, [1883.] fol.
h. 3101. i. (6.)

— [Lieder Blüthen.] Waldandacht.—Abt.—Meditation ... Op. 171. No. 11. [Organ.] [1896.] fol. *See* ABT (F. W.) [5 Lieder. Op. 383. No. 2.]
h. 2709. (12.)

— Liederreigen. Walzer. [P. F.] *Berlin & Posen*, [1871.] fol.
h. 3101. (43.)

— Lockung. Salon Walzer für das Pianoforte. *Berlin & Posen*, [1873.] fol.
h. 3101. b. (25.)

— Lorbeer und Rose. Fantasiestück über das Duett von A. E. Grell für das Pianoforte. *Berlin*, [1872.] fol.
h. 3101. b. (13.)

LANGE (GUSTAV)

— Die Loreley singt. Gondellied für das Pianoforte. *Berlin & Posen*, [1874.] fol.
h. 3101. b. (41.)

— Lose Blätter. Drei lyrische Tonstücke für das Pianoforte. 3 no. *Berlin & Posen*, [1872.] fol.
h. 3101. b. (11.)

— Lose Blätter. Drei lyrische Tonstücke. Op. 125. [P. F.] *A. Hammond & Co.: London*, [1896.] 4°.
The Academic Edition, No. 42.
g. 1130. a. (2.)

— Die Maccabäer. Oper von A. Rubinstein. Grosse Fantasie für Pianoforte. *Berlin & Posen*, [1875.] fol.
h. 3101. c. (40.)

— Maddalena. Mazurka brillante. Op. 364. [P. F.] *N. Simrock: Berlin*, [1886.] fol.
h. 3101. i. (19.)

— Das Mädchen aus den Bergen ... Idylle für das Pianoforte. *Leipzig*, [1879.] fol.
h. 3101. a. (14.)

— Das Mädchen aus den Bergen. Idylle. Op. 262 [for zither]. [1883.] *See* GUTMANN (F.) Compositionen für Zither ... No. 34. [1880–86.] *obl.* 4°.
b. 244.

— Das Mädchen aus der Fremde. Fantasie-Mazurka für das Pianoforte. *Berlin & Posen*, [1874.] fol.
h. 3101. b. (43.)

— [Mädchen Traum.] A Maiden's Dream. Nocturne ... for the Pianoforte. Op. 62. *London*, [1870.] fol.
h. 3101. a. (5.)

— Marcella. Valse de salon ... Op. 432. [P. F.] ⟨Edited by O. B. Boise.⟩ pp. 7. *Ed. Bote & G. Bock: Berlin, Posen*, [1890.] fol.
h. 721. y. (2.)

— Marie am Fenster setzest du. Lied von G. Piefke. Salon-Fantasie für das Pianoforte. *Frankfurt a. Oder*, [1881.] fol.
h. 3101. g. (24.)

— Mary's Traum. Melodisches Tonstück für das Pianoforte. *Offenbach a. M.*, [1877.] fol.
h. 3101. e. (7.)

— Massliebchen. Lyrisches Tonstück für das Pianoforte. Op. 303. *Leipzig*, [1883.] fol.
h. 3101. h. (18.)

— Mazeppa. Grand Galop de Bravoure. Op. 327. [P. F.] *Berlin*, [1885.] fol.
h. 3101. h. (41.)

— Mein Heimaths-dörfchen ... Idylle für das Pianoforte. *Leipzig*, [1879.] fol.
h. 3101. a. (13.)

— Mein Himmel (Lied von F. Abt) für Pianoforte. *Berlin & Posen*, [1872.] fol.
h. 3101. b. (20.)

— Mein Lied. Lied von F. Gumbert. Fantasie. [P. F.] *Berlin*, [1879.] fol.
h. 3101. a. (11.)

— Zwei melodische Tonstücke für das Pianoforte. 2 no. *Hannover*, [1880.] fol.
h. 3101. g. (2.)

— Der Mikado. Operette von A. Sullivan. Grosse Fantasie für das Pianoforte. Op. 416. *Chappell & Co.: London*, [1889.] fol.
h. 3101. j. (24.)

— Mimosen. 16 leichte melodische Klavierstücke für Kinder. 4 Hft. *Offenbach a. M.*, [1877.] fol.
h. 3101. e. (5.)

— Minnelied. Melodie. [P. F.] Op. 51. *Berlin & Posen*, [1870.] fol.
h. 3101. (25.)

— Minnesang. Mélodie. Op. 328. [P. F.] *Berlin*, [1885.] fol.
h. 3101. h. (42.)

— Mit fliegenden Fahnen. Militairisches Tonstück für das Pianoforte. Op. 318. *Berlin*, 1884. fol.
h. 3101. h. (32.)

— Morgenwanderung im Walde. Tonstück. [P. F.] *Berlin & Posen*, [1871.] fol.
h. 3101. (40.)

— [Morgenwanderung im Walde. Op. 86.] Wanderung im Walde. Wanderings in the Wood. ⟨Tonstück.⟩ [P. F.] pp. 7. *A. Hammond & Cº: London*, [c. 1880.] fol.
h. 722. v. (4.)

LANGE (GUSTAV)

— Nachklänge. Melodisches Tonstück für Pianoforte. *Leipzig,*
[1875.] fol. **h. 3101. c. (28.)**

— Nachtlied. Tonstück. [P. F.] *Berlin & Posen,* [1872.] fol.
h. 3101. b. (12.)

— Nachtschatten. Salon-Walzer für das Pianoforte. *Berlin,*
[1880.] fol. **h. 3101. g. (22.)**

— La Napolitana ... Tonstück für das Pianoforte. Op. 323.
Berlin, [1885.] fol. **h. 3101. h. (37.)**

— Neue Tonstücke für das Pianoforte. 3 no. *Leipzig,* [1882.] fol.
h. 3101. h. (9.)

— Neues Blumenlied für das Piano. *Berlin,* [1881.] fol.
h. 3101. h. (6.)

— Neues Blumenlied für das Piano. Op. 291. *E. Ashdown:
London,* [1882.] fol. **h. 3101. a. (42.)**

— Nordische Romanze ... Tonstück für Pianoforte. *Leipzig,*
[1880.] fol. **h. 3101. g. (11.)**

— Nordisches Lied. Melodie für das Pianoforte. *Berlin &
Posen,* [1873.] fol. **h. 3101. b. (22.)**

— O frage nicht. Lyrisches Tonstück für Pianoforte. *Berlin &
Posen,* [1874.] fol. **h. 3101. c. (3.)**

— Offenbach-Fantasien. Fantasien und Transcriptionen über ...
Motiven aus Offenbach's Opern für das Pianoforte. 4 no.
Berlin & Posen, [1876.] fol. **h. 3101. c. (18.)**

— L'Ondine. Mazurka ... Op. 341. [P. F.] *Berlin,* [1885.] fol.
h. 3101. h. (51.)

— Drei Opern Arien von Meyerbeer. Fantasie-Transcriptionen
für das Pianoforte. 3 no. *Berlin & Posen,* [1876.] fol.
h. 3101. c. (17.)

— Le Papillon, mazurka de concert. [P. F.] *London,* [1867.] fol.
h. 3101. a. (2.)

— Paraphrase über die Romanze der Ines aus der Oper: "Die
Africanerin," von Meyerbeer. [P. F.] *Berlin,* [1877.] fol.
h. 3101. e. (1.)

— Paraphrase über die Schlummer-Arie aus der Oper: Die
Stumme von Portici, von Auber, für das Pianoforte. *Berlin
& Posen,* [1876.] fol. **h. 3101. c. (24.)**

— Perles de Fantaisie. Fantaisies brillantes sur des thèmes
favoris pour le piano. Op. 256. No. 1. Der Carneval von
Venedig. *Offenbach s. M.,* [1879.] fol. **h. 3101. h. (16.)**

— Perles et Diamants, valse brillante pour Piano. Op. 27. *Berlin
& Posen,* [1867.] fol. **h. 3101. h. (14.)**

— Prière à la Madonne [*sic*], mélodie sérieuse pour Piano.
Op. 17. *Berlin & Posen,* [1865.] fol. **h. 3101. (6.)**

— Prière à la Madonne [*sic*] ... G. Lange. ([Followed by]
Amusement Quadrille. [Op. 52.] Zikoff—"Unter Kreuzband
Galop. F. Roth.) [Military band parts.] 24 pt. *Boosey & Co.:
London,* [1876.] fol.
[*Boosé's supplemental military Journal. no.* 281.] *Without
titlepage. The title is taken from the head of p. 1 of the first
clarinet part.* **h. 1544.**

— Reigen im Grünen, Tanz-Idylle für Pianoforte. Op. 23.
Berlin & Posen, [1866.] fol. **h. 3101. (11.)**

— La Reine du Bal, mazurka de concert. [P. F.] Op. 16. *Berlin
& Posen,* [1865.] fol. **h. 3101. (3.)**

— Le Reine du Bal, mazurka de concert. [P. F.] *London,* [1867.]
fol. **h. 3101. a. (3.)**

— Le Retour du Printemps, pièce caractéristique pour le Piano.
Op. 34. *Berlin & Posen,* [1867.] fol. **h. 3101. (17.)**

LANGE (GUSTAV)

— Le Retour du Soldat, grande marche triomphale pour le
Piano. Op. 19. *Berlin & Posen,* [1865.] fol. **h. 3101. (4.)**

— Le Retour du Soldat, grand march triomphale for the
Pianoforte. *London,* [1867.] fol. **h. 3101. a. (4.)**

— Le Réveil des Oiseaux. Idylle. Op. 356. [P. F.] *N. Simrock:
Berlin,* [1886.] fol. **h. 3101. i. (11.)**

— Rococo. Menuet. Op. 349. [P. F.] *Berlin,* [1886.] fol.
h. 3101. h. (59.)

— La Ronde militaire. Marche caractéristique. Op. 363. [P. F.]
N. Simrock: Berlin, [1886.] fol. **h. 3101. i. (18.)**

— Vier Rondinos ... nach Motiven beliebter Lieder für das
Pianoforte. 4 no. *Breslau,* [1872.] fol. **h. 3101. b. (18.)**

— Rose Marie. Fantaisie-Mazurk pour piano. Op. 424. 2 no.
[Solo and duet.] *E. Ashdown: London,* [1890–2.] fol.
h. 3101. j. (10.)

— Rosen ohne Dornen. 6 Sonatinen über Motive von Mozart &
Beethoven. *A. Hammond & Co.: London,* [1896.] 4°.
The Academic Edition, No. 11. **g. 1130.**

— Rustling Leaves, idylle ... for the Pianoforte. Op. 68.
London, [1870.] fol. **h. 3101. a. (6.)**

— Rustling Leaves ... Op. 294. [P. F.] *See* supra:
[Blätterrauschen.]

— Sänger in den Zweigen. Idylle. [P. F.] *Berlin & Posen,* [1871.]
fol. **h. 3101. (42.)**

— La Sainte Vierge. Méditation pour Piano. *Leipzig,* [1875.] fol.
h. 3101. c. (31.)

— Santa Maria. Mélodie sacrée. Op. 357. [P. F.] *N. Simrock:
Berlin,* [1886.] fol. **h. 3101. i. (12.)**

— Schalmeienklänge. Idylle. [P. F.] *Berlin & Posen,* [1871.] fol.
h. 3101. (39.)

— Schaumperlen. Tonstück für das Pianoforte. Op. 312.
Leipzig, [1884.] fol. **h. 3101. h. (27.)**

— Schlaf wohl du süsser Engel du! Lied von F. Abt. Fantasia
für das Pianoforte. *London,* [1878.] fol. **h. 3101. a. (22.)**

— Schlummerlied. Tonstück für Pianoforte. *Berlin & Posen,*
[1874.] fol. **h. 3101. c. (5.)**

— Schnitterlied. Idylle für Piano. *Berlin & Posen,* [1871.] fol.
h. 3101. (37.)

— Schottische Weisen für Pianoforte. 6 no. *Berlin,* [1877.] fol.
h. 3101. e. (16.)

— [Schottische Weisen. Op. 89.] Six favourite Scotch Songs
arranged for Piano by G. Lange, *etc. A. Hammond & Co.:
London,* [1903.] 4°.
The Academic Edition, No. 238. **g. 1130. i. (5.)**

— [Seerosen. Op. 296.] Sea-flowers. Morceau caractéristique
pour piano. pp. 11. *The London Music Publishing Cᵒ:
London; Leipzig printed,* [c. 1895.] fol. **h. 62. x. (14.)**

— Sehnsuchtsklänge, melodisches Tonstück für Piano. Op. 20.
Berlin & Posen, [1866.] fol. **h. 3101. (9.)**

— Selige Tage. Tonstück für das Pianoforte. *Berlin & Posen,*
[1874.] fol. **h. 3101. b. (37.)**

— Senners Ständchen. Idylle. Op. 340. [P. F.] *Berlin,* [1885.] fol.
h. 3101. h. (50.)

— Separation. Andante for the Pianoforte. *London,* [1880.] fol.
h. 3101. g. (17.)

— Serena, polka brillante pour Piano. Op. 50. *Berlin & Posen,*
[1870.] fol. **h. 3101. (28.)**

LANGE (GUSTAV)

— Silvana ... Tonstück. Op. 326. [P. F.] *Berlin*, [1885.] fol.
h. 3101. h. (40.)

— Sirenen. Charakterstück. [P. F.] *Berlin & Posen*, [1873.] fol.
h. 3101. b. (28.)

— Seven Sonatinas ... for Violin & Pianoforte. *A. Hammond & Co.: London*, [1896.] 4°.
The Academic Edition, No. 61. **g. 1130. a. (2.)**

— Die Spieluhr (Le Carillon) für das Pianoforte. *Berlin*, [1877.] fol.
h. 3101. e. (10.)

— Spieluhr als Echo. Humoreske. Op. 366. [P. F.] *N. Simrock: Berlin*, [1886.] fol.
h. 3101. i. (21.)

— Steeple-Chase. Galop de Bravoure pour le piano. Op. 309. *Berlin*, [1883.] fol.
h. 3101. h. (24.)

— [Steeple-Chase.] La Course au Clocher ... Galop de Bravoure pour piano. Op. 309. *E. Ashdown: London*, [1884.] fol.
h. 3101. a. (46.)

— Steyrische Lieder. Op. 342. [P. F.] *Berlin*, [1886.] fol.
h. 3101. h. (52.)

— Stille Liebe, Tonstück für das Pianoforte componirt. Op. 46.
Berlin & Posen, [1868.] fol. **h. 3101. (21.)**

— Stimmen aus der Kinderwelt. 12 leichte Vortragsstücke für das Pianoforte. *Berlin & Posen*, [1871.] fol. **h. 3101. (32.)**

— Stimmen aus der Kinderwelt. 12 leichte Vortragsstücke für das Pianoforte. Op. 78. *A. Hammond & Co.: London*, [1896.] 4°.
The Academic Edition, No. 8. **g. 1130.**

— Stücke aus der Oper Tannhäuser ... von R. Wagner für das Pianoforte frei übertragen. 6 no. *Berlin und Dresden*, [1875.] fol.
h. 3101. e. (13.)

— Sturmfanfaren—Cavalry Charge—for piano. Op. 425. 2 no. [Solo and duet.] *E. Ashdown: London*, [1890, 93.] fol.
h. 3101. j. (11.)

— Première suite d'orchestre. [Orchestral parts.] 18 pt. *J. R. Lafleur & Son: London*, [1887.] 4°.
"Alliance Musicale." Nouveau répertoire des concerts. no. 4.
g. 1800. (188.)

— Deuxième suite d'orchestre. [Orchestral parts.] 17 pt. *J. R. Lafleur & Son: London*, [1887.] 4°.
"Alliance Musicale." Nouveau répertoire des concerts. no. 5.
g. 1800. (189.)

— Troisième suite d'orchestre. [Orchestral parts.] 17 pt. *J. R. Lafleur & Son: London*, [1887.] 4°.
"Alliance Musicale." Nouveau répertoire des concerts. no. 6.
g. 1800. (190.)

— Sunny Woods, melody by Truhn, transcribed for the Pianoforte. *London*, [1873.] fol. **h. 3101. a. (10.)**

— La Sylphide. Morceau de salon pour Piano. *Berlin & Posen*, [1870.] fol. **h. 3101. (30.)**

— Ein Tag in der Schweiz. Tonbild für das Pianoforte. *Berlin*, [1882.] fol. **h. 3101. h. (5.)**

— Ein Tag in der Schweiz ... Tonbild für das Pianoforte.
Op. 290. *E. Ashdown: London*, [1882.] fol. **h. 3101. a. (41.)**

— Ein Tag in der Schweiz ... Tonbild. Pianoforte Duet.
E. Ashdown: London, etc., [1894.] fol. **h. 3101. j. (19.)**

— Tausendschön. (Lied von P. Eckert.) Fantasie für Pianoforte.
Berlin, [1871.] fol. **h. 3101. (53.)**

— Tausendschön ... Tonstück für das Pianoforte. *Leipzig*, [1879.] fol. **h. 3101. g. (4.)**

LANGE (GUSTAV)

— [Thauperlen.] Pearls of Dew. [P. F.] Op. 77. *London*, [1870.] fol. **h. 3101. a. (7.)**

— Thauperlen. Tonstück für Piano. *Berlin & Posen*, [1871.] fol.
h. 3101. (38.)

— Thine own. *See* supra: [Dein eigen. Op. 54.]

— [Träumende Blumen.] Dreaming Flowers ... melodious piece for the pianoforte. Op. 70. *W. Czerny: London*, [1882.] fol.
h. 3101. i. (2.)

— Traumesstimmen. Tonstück. [P. F.] *Berlin & Posen*, [1872.] fol. **h. 3101. b. (2.)**

— Traumglück. Tonstück für das Pianoforte. *Berlin*, [1880.] fol.
h. 3101. g. (9.)

— "Traumglück." 〈Song without words.〉 [Op. 268. Military band parts.] 26 pt. *In:* WALDTEUFEL (E.) "Sentiers fleuris," *etc.*
1884. fol. [*Boosey's supplemental military Journal. no.* 327.]
h. 1544.

— Traumglück. (Op. 268.) For full orchestra. [Parts.]
A. Hammond & Co.: London, [1888.] 8°. **e. 1342. (13.)**

— Treue Liebe. Melodie für Pianoforte. Op. 29. *Berlin & Posen*, [1867.] fol. **h. 3101. (18.)**

— Treues Gedenken, Melodie für Pianoforte. Op. 22. *Berlin & Posen*, [1866.] fol. **h. 3101. (10.)**

— Le Tribut de Zamora, opéra de C. Gounod, fantaisie brillante pour Piano. *Paris*, [1881.] fol. **h. 3101. g. (25.)**

— Trinklied ... Tonstück. Op. 343. [P. F.] *Berlin*, [1886.] fol.
h. 3101. h. (53.)

— Trost in Tönen. Melodisches Tonstück für das Pianoforte.
Berlin und Dresden, [1875.] fol. **h. 3101. c. (27.)**

— Ueber Land und Meer. Salon-Polka für das Pianoforte.
Offenbach a. M., [1877.] fol. **h. 3101. e. (8.)**

— [Zwei ungarische Tänze.] Two Hungarian Dances transcribed for the Pianoforte. 2 no. *London*, [1879.] fol.
h. 3101. g. (6.)

— Zwei ungarische Tänze ... für das Piano gesetzt. 2 no.
Berlin, [1880.] fol. **g. 3101. g. (7.)**

— [Zwei ungarische Tänze.] Two Hungarian Dances transcribed for Violin and Piano. 2 no. *London*, [1880.] fol.
h. 1609. q. (5.)

— Unter Blüthenbäumen. Tonstück für Pianoforte. *Leipzig*, [1875.] fol. **h. 3101. c. (29.)**

— Unter Liebchens Fenster. Serenade. Op. 339. [P. F.] *Berlin*, [1885.] fol. **h. 3101. h. (49.)**

— Valse Champêtre pour le piano. Op. 307. *Berlin*, [1883.] fol.
h. 3101. h. (22.)

— Valse Champêtre pour piano. Op. 307. *E. Ashdown: London*, [1884.] fol. **h. 3101. a. (44.)**

— Valse champêtre pour piano à quatre mains. *E. Ashdown: London, etc.*, [1895.] fol. **h. 3101. j. (20.)**

— Valse des Grâces. Op. 320. [P. F.] *Berlin*, [1884.] fol.
h. 3101. h. (34.)

— Valse mélancolique pour le Piano. *Berlin & Posen*, [1876.] fol. **h. 3101. c. (20.)**

— Vergiss mein nicht! Melodisches Tonstück für das Pianoforte.
Berlin, [1877.] fol. **h. 3101. e. (19.)**

— La Vivandière. Marche Militaire. Op. 346. [P. F.] *Berlin*, [1886.] fol. **h. 3101. h. (56.)**

LANGE (GUSTAV)

— Vive le Soldat! Galop militaire pour piano ... Op. 295. pp. 11. *Amos & Shuttleworth: London; Leipzig* [printed, 1883?] fol.
h. 925. k. (14.)

— Vive le soldat! Galop militaire ... Op. 295. ⟨For pianoforte.⟩ pp. 11. *Cary & Co.: London*, [c. 1910.] fol.
One of "Three original Compositions for Pianoforte".
h. 60. zz. (26.)

— Von Herzen ... Lyrisches Tonstück für das Pianoforte. *Leipzig*, [1879.] fol.
h. 3101. a. (12.)

— Von Herzen. Lyrisches Tonstück. Op. 260 [for zither]. [1884.] *See* GUTMANN (F.) Compositionen for Zither ... No. 37. [1880–86.] *obl.* 4°.
b. 244.

— Vor deinem Bilde. Meditation für das Pianoforte. *Berlin & Posen*, [1874.] fol.
h. 3101. b. (33.)

— Die Wacht am Rhein. Militairische Fantasie über C. Wilhelm's patriotisches Lied, für das Pianoforte. *Berlin*, [1871.] fol.
h. 3101. (47.)

— Waldandacht ... Op. 171. No. 11. *See* supra: [Lieder Blüthen.]

— Waldglocken. Idylle. Op. 324. [P. F.] *Berlin*, [1885.] fol.
h. 3101. h. (38.)

— Zwei Wald-Idyllen für das Pianoforte. 2 no. *Berlin & Posen*, [1876.] fol.
h. 3101. c. (21.)

— Waldlieder. Zehn Lyrische Tonstücke für das Pianoforte. 10 no. *Berlin & Posen*, [1875.] fol.
h. 3101. c. (13.)

— Waldlieder. Zehn lyrische Tonstücke für das Pianoforte. Op. 203. *A. Hammond & Co.: London*, [1896.] 4°. *The Academic Edition, No. 17.*
g. 1130.

— Walzer und Soldatenchor aus der Oper Margarethe (Faust) von C. Gounod für das Pianoforte. 2 no. *Berlin & Posen*, [1874.] fol.
h. 3101. c. (8.)

— Wanda, mazurka brillante pour Piano. Op. 25. *Berlin & Posen*, [1866.] fol.
h. 3101. (12.)

— Wanderung im Walde. *See* supra: [Morgenwanderung im Walde. Op. 86.]

— Wayside Flowers. *See* supra: [Blumen am Wege.]

— Weisst du noch? Lyrisches Tonstück für das Pianoforte. *Berlin & Posen*, [1873.] fol.
h. 3101. b. (26.)

— Welke Blätter ... Melodisches Tonstück für Pianoforte. *Leipzig*, [1880.] fol.
h. 3101. g. (14.)

— Wenn ich dein gedenke. Meditation für Pianoforte. *Offenbach a. M.*, [1877.] fol.
h. 3101. e. (6.)

— Wenn sich zwei Herzen scheiden. Melodie für das Piano. *Berlin*, [1880.] fol.
h. 3101. g. (18.)

— Wildrose. Tonstück für das Pianoforte. Op. 304. *Leipzig*, [1883.] fol.
h. 3101. h. (19.)

— Zepherine, mazurka brillante pour Piano. Op. 30. *Berlin & Posen*, [1867.] fol.
h. 3101. (16.)

— Die Zillerthalerin ... Tonstück für das Pianoforte. Op. 311. *Leipzig*, [1884.] fol.
h. 3101. h. (26.)

— Die Zillerthalerin. Op. 311 [for zither]. [1885.] *See* GUTMANN (F.) Compositionen für Zither. ... No. 42. [1880–86.] *obl.* 4°.
b. 244.

— Zitherklänge. For full orchestra. [Parts.] *A. Hammond & Co.: London*, [1888.] 8°.
e. 1342. (11.)

— Zu Weihnachten. Fantaisie für Pianoforte. Op. 172. No. 5. *Leipzig*, [1885.] fol.
This is a continuation of the Fantasien über beliebte Lieder, etc., published in 1880.
h. 3101. h. (11.)

LANGE (GUSTAV)

— Zu Zweien. Liebes-Ländler. Op. 354. [P. F.] *N. Simrock: Berlin*, [1886.] fol.
h. 3101. i. (9.)

— Zur Laute. Charakteristisches Tonstück. Op. 353. [P. F.] *N. Simrock: Berlin*, [1886.] fol.
h. 3101. i. (8.)

— Zur Nacht. Lyrisches Tonstück. Op. 347. [P. F.] *Berlin*, [1886.] fol.
h. 3101. h. (57.)

— Zur Strohzither. Burleske. Op. 355. [P. F.] *N. Simrock: Berlin*, [1886.] fol.
h. 3101. i. (10.)

— Zwergglöckchen. Genrestück. Op. 358. [P. F.] *N. Simrock: Berlin*, [1886.] fol.
h. 3101. i. (13.)

— Zwischen Frankreich und dem Böhmerwald, Lied von Thurn. Fantasiestück für Pianoforte. *Berlin*, [1871.] fol.
h. 3101. (54.)

— *See* BLUMENLIED. Blumenlied Album ... for the piano. [By G. Lange, and others.] [1898.] 4°.
g. 603. d. (2.)

— *See* GLUCK (C. W. von) [Paride ed Elena.] Gavotte ... übertragen von G. Lange. [1872.] fol.
h. 1493. i. (31.)

— *See* MENDELSSOHN-BARTHOLDY (J. L. F.) [*Collected Works.—j.*] Favorite Melodies ... arranged for the Pianoforte by G. Lange. [1896.] 4°.
g. 1130. (3.)

— *See* MOZART (W. A.) [*Collected Works.—e.*] Favorite Melodies arranged for the Pianoforte by G. Lange. [1896.] 4°.
g. 1130. a. (4.)

— *See* SCHUBERT (F. P.) [*Collected Works.—e.*] Favorite Melodies ... arranged for the Pianoforte by G. Lange. [1896.] 4°.
g. 1130. (5.)

LANGE (GUSTAV F.)

— Gondelfahrt. Salonstück für Piano. Op. 14. *A. Prinz: Hamburg*, [1865?] fol.
g. 442. e. (21.)

LANGE (GUSTAV FR.)

— Albumleaf. Op. 14. No. 3. (Violin and Piano.) *C. Fischer: New York, etc.*, (1906.) fol.
h. 1612. p. (18.)

— Chanson. Op. 14. No. 1. (Violin and Piano.) *C. Fischer: New York, etc.*, (1906.) fol.
h. 1612. p. (16.)

— Norwegian Humoreske. Op. 14. No. 4. (Violin and Piano.) *C. Fischer: New York, etc.*, (1906.) fol.
h. 1612. p. (19.)

— Norwegian Song. Op. 14. No. 2. (Violin and Piano.) *C. Fischer: New York, etc.*, (1906.) fol.
h. 1612. p. (17.)

LANGE (HIERONYMUS GREGOR)

— Eine ausgewählte Sammlung Motetten zu 4, 5, 6 und 8 Stimmen. In Partitur gesetzt und mit einer Klavierpartitur versehen von R. Starke. 1901. *See* BERLIN.—*Gesellschaft für Musikforschung.* Publikation aelterer ... Musik-Werke, *etc.* Bd. XXV. 1873, *etc.* fol.
Ac. 5144/2.

LANGE (JOHANN HEINRICH)

— An Sie. Lied. Glücklich bin ich nur bey Dir, von C. Beils, mit Pianoforte Begleitung. pp. 3. *Bei J. G. Stock: Bremen*, [c. 1830.] *obl.* fol.
A slip bearing the imprint "C. G. Herrig: Braunschweig," has been pasted over the original imprint.
E. 271. dd. (13.)

— Choralbuch zu dem neuen bremischen Gesangbuch ... Vierstimmig gesetzt und herausgegeben von J. H. Lange, *etc.* *C. A. Steuber: Rinteln*, [1821.] *obl.* 8°.
c. 123.

LANGE (JULIUS)

— Alpenveilchen. Salonstück für Pianoforte. *Berlin*, [1884.] fol.
h. 3280. k. (24.)

— Marietta. Salonstück für das Pianoforte. *Berlin*, [1884.] fol.
h. 3280. k. (25.)

LANGE (L.)

— Fleurs de Printemps. Poésies musicales au Piano. *Paris*, [1884.] 8°.
f. 133. g. (5.)

— Mazurka di [sic] Concert. [P. F.] *Church, Paxson and Co.: New York*, (1912.) fol.
h. 3284. f. (42.)

LANGE (O. H.)

— Der Abschied des Jägers. Gedicht von Schütz, [begins: "Das Mühlrad brauset"] für Bariton mit Begleitung des Pianoforte und des Waldhorns (ad libitum). *Hannover*, [1880.] fol.
H. 1786. e. (10.)

— Altdeutsche Lieder für eine Singstimme mit Pianoforte-Begleitung eingerichtet von O. H. Lange. *H. Litolff: Braunschweig*, [1879.] 8°.
[Collection Litolff, No. 897.]
g. 375.

— Aus Volkes Mund und Herz. Alte deutsche Volkslieder für eine Singstimme mit Begleitung des Pianoforte, bearbeitet von O. H. Lange. 2 Hft. *Hannover*, [1880.] 4°.
G. 385. a. (7.)

— Heimkehr, von H. Lingg [begins: "In meine Heimath kam ich wieder"] für eine Tenorstimme componirt. *Hannover*, [1880.] fol.
H. 1786. e. (11.)

— In der Sommernacht. Nocturne für Violine und Pianoforte. *Hannover*, [1880.] fol.
h. 1609. q. (7.)

— J'y pense. Nocturne pour le Violon et Pianoforte. *Hannover*, [1880.] fol.
h. 1609. q. (6.)

— Meditation über ein Präludium in C moll von J. S. Bach (No. 7 der kleinen Präludien) für Pianoforte oder Harfe und obligate Violine nebst Orgel oder Harmonium ad lib. *Hannover*, [1884.] fol.
h. 1609. y. (15.)

— Zwei Salonstücke für das Pianoforte. 2 no. *Hannover*, [1880.] fol.
h. 3272. j. (10.)

LANGE (OSCAR)

— See DELIBES (C. P. L.) Coppélia ... Valse lente. [Violin and violoncello parts arranged by O. Lange.] 1935. fol.
h. 3870. h. (24.)

— See HAENDEL (G. F.) [Serse.—Ombra mai fù.] Largo, *etc.* (Arranged by O. Lange.) 1933. fol.
h. 435. l. (6.)

— See HÉROLD (L. J. F.) Zampa. Selection, *etc.* (Violin, Violoncello. Arranged by O. Lange.) 1934. fol.
h. 3870. h. (26.)

— See OFFENBACH (J.) [Les Contes d'Hoffmann.] Selection from the Tales of Hoffmann, *etc.* (Arranged by O. Lange.) [1935.] fol.
h. 3870. i. (26.)

— See OFFENBACH (J.) [Les Contes d'Hoffmann.—Belle nuit.] Barcarolle ... Arranged for Piano Solo by O. Lange. [1934.] 4°.
g. 1125. ll. (7.)

— See OFFENBACH (J.) [Les Contes d'Hoffmann.—Belle nuit.] Barcarolle, *etc.* (Arranged by O. Lange.) [1935.] fol.
h. 3870. i. (27.)

— See ROSSINI (G. A.) [Guillaume Tell.] William Tell. Selection ... Violin & Cello parts. (Arranged by O. Lange.) 1934. fol.
h. 3870. h. (27.)

LANGE (OTTO)

— Down the Lanes—Zu Zweien, im Freien—Pianoforte Duet. *E. Ashdown: London*, [1890.] fol.
g. 545. d. (23.)

— Stay, stay at home my heart and rest. Song, words from Longfellow's "Keramos". *London*, [1880.] fol.
H. 1783. o. (12.)

LANGE (RICHARD)

— Träumerei ... von R. Schumann ... für die Orgel bearbeitet von R. Lange. [1894.] See ALBUM. Album für Orgel-Spieler ... Lief. 107. [1880? *etc.*] obl. fol.
e. 119.

— See FERRATA (G.) A Night on the Island of Amalasunta, *etc.* (Transcribed ... by R. Lange.) 1914. fol.
h. 3284. ee. (5.)

— See OEHME (R.) [Was die Blumen sagten. Op. 10. No. 4. Männertreue.] La Véronique ... Édition par R. Lange. (1908.) fol.
h. 3625. (3.)

— See OEHME (R.) [Was die Blumen sagten. Op. 10. No. 7.] Myrthe ... Édition ... par R. Lange. (1908.) fol.
h. 3625. (7.)

— See OEHME (R.) [Was die Blumen sagten. Op. 10. No. 8. Vergissmeinnicht.] Ne m'oubliez pas ... Édition ... par R. Lange. (1908.) fol.
h. 3625. (9.)

— See RAKHMANINOV (S. V.) [Morceaux de Fantaisie. Op. 3. No. 2.] Prélude ... arrangé par R. Lange. [1911.] fol.
h. 3984. b. (5.)

— See ROMANOFF (E.) 4 Intermezzi ... Édition ... par R. Lange. 1908. fol.
g. 505. x. (18.)

— See SCOTT (C. M.) Two Alpine Sketches. Pianoforte duet. (Arranged by R. Lange.) 1914. fol.
h. 3640. a. (14.)

— See SCOTT (C. M.) Intermezzo. Violin and pianoforte. (Arranged by R. Lange.) 1914. fol.
h. 3640. a. (23.)

— See SCOTT (C. M.) Three Little Waltzes. No. 1. Allegro poco scherzando. Pianoforte duet. (Arranged by R. Lange.) 1914. fol.
h. 3640. a. (40.)

— See SCOTT (C. M.) Three Little Waltzes. No. 2. Andante languido. Violin and pianoforte. (Arranged by R. Lange.) 1914. fol.
h. 3640. a. (41.)

— See SCOTT (C. M.) Mazurka. Pianoforte duet. (Arranged by R. Lange.) 1914. fol.
h. 3640. a. (27.)

— See SCOTT (C. M.) Vesperale. Violin and pianoforte. (Arranged by R. Lange.) 1914. fol.
h. 3640. a. (39.)

LANGE (RODERYK)

— Dances from Cuiavia. Kinetograms & music. *Centre for Dance Studies: St. Peter, Jersey*, 1976. 4°.
[Documentary Dance Materials. no. 1.] Printed on one side of the leaf only.
g. 822. aa.

— See DOCUMENTARY. Documentary Dance Materials ... Editors: R. Lange, D. Baddeley-Lange, J. Lee. [1976, *etc.*] 4°.
g. 822. aa.

LANGE (SAMUEL DE)

— Adagio und Tarantelle. Concertstück für Violoncell mit Orchesterbegleitung. Op. 38. Clavierauszug. *Bremen*, [1885.] fol.
h. 204. c. (35.)

— Andante für Cello und Orgel. Op. 16^b. [1892.] See ALBUM. Album für Orgel-Spieler ... Lief 103. [1880? *etc.*] obl. fol.
e. 119.

— Zwei Andante für die Orgel. Op. 30. 2 no. *Leipzig u. Winterthur*, 1880, 87. fol.
h. 2732. d. (12.)

LANGE (SAMUEL DE)

— Ave Maria für eine Singstimme mit Begleitung von Orgel und Violoncell. Op. 52. *J. Rieter-Biedermann: Leipzig*, 1888. fol. **H. 1187. k. (17.)**

— Brautwerbung. *See* infra: Vier Lieder ... Op. 42. No. 3.

— Concerto pour le Violon avec accomp. de Piano. Op. 22. *Mayence*, [1878.] fol. **h. 1729. (7.)**

— [Concerto for Violin. Op. 22.] Moderato, *etc.* [Violin and P. F.] *See* KROSS (E.) Sammlung characteristischer Stellen aus Violin-Concerten, *etc.* No. 4. [1890.] fol. **h. 1732. (3.)**

— Durch Erd' und Himmel. *See* infra: Vier Lieder ... Op. 42. No. 4.

— Dutch Serenade. Song with Piano accompaniment (poem by Fiore della Neve), English words by G. Harris ... Arranged by C. V. Bos. *G. Schirmer: New York, London*, (1915.) fol. **G. 806. ll. (48.)**

— Fantasie und Fugue in C moll für die Orgel. Op. 53. *J. Rieter-Biedermann: Leipzig*, 1888. fol. **h. 2731. i. (5.)**

— 5 Gesänge für Männerchor. Op. 24. *Mainz*, [1877.] 8°. **E. 308. b. (13.)**

— Vier Impromptus für Pianoforte. 4 no. *Leipzig*, [1873.] fol. **h. 1487. o. (30.)**

— Käferlied. *See* infra: Vier Lieder ... Op. 42. No. 2.

— Lieder und Gesänge für dreistimmigen Frauenchor mit Pianofortebegleitung. Op. 35. *Leipzig u. Winterthur*, 1881. fol. **H. 1786. e. (12.)**

— Vier Lieder und Gesänge für dreistimmigen Frauenchor mit Pianofortebegleitung. Op. 42. (1. Der Pilger [begins: "Es zieht ein Pilger mit Mantel und Stab"], E. R. Neubauer. 2. Käferlied [begins: "Es waren einmal drei Käferknaben"], R. Reinick. 3. Brautwerbung [begins: "Einzige Eine!"], E. R. Neubauer. 4. "Durch Erd' und Himmel." E. Geibel.) Partitur. *Leipzig*, 1886. fol. **H. 1795. a. (7.)**

— Märchenbilder. Clavierstücke. 2 Hft. *Leipzig*, [1876.] fol. **h. 1487. o. (31.)**

— Mein Herz ist im Urwald, von E. R. Neubauer, für vierstimmigen Männerchor mit willkürlicher Begleitung von 2 Hörner und 2 Posaunen. Op. 54. Partitur. *J. Rieter-Biedermann: Leipzig*, 1888. 8°. **E. 308. r. (21.)**

— Out of the Depth ... [Anthem] Arranged ... by W. Sparger. *G. Schirmer: New York*, 1901. 8°. *G. Schirmer's Octavo Church Music, No.* 1061. **F. 231. o. (59.)**

— Pedalstudien. Ein Supplement zu jeder Orgelschule, zusammengestellt von S. de Lange. *Leipzig*, 1885. *obl.* 8°. **e. 174. p. (8.)**

— Der Pilger. *See* supra: Vier Lieder ... Op. 42. No. 1.

— Quartett in E moll für zwei Violinen, Viola und Violoncello. Op. 15. *Leipzig*, [1874.] fol. **h. 2830. c. (7.)**

— Quartett No. 2 in C dur für zwei Violinen, Viola und Violoncello. Op. 18. *Leipzig*, [1875.] fol. **h. 2830. c. (8.)**

— Romance pour violon avec accomp. de piano. Op. 39. *Mayence*, [1884.] fol. **h. 1609. u. (12.)**

— Sonate über Luther's Choral Ein' feste Burg ist unser Gott, für die Orgel. *Leipzig u. Winterthur*, [1872.] fol. **h. 2732. a. (11.)**

— Sonate (No. 4 in D dur) für die Orgel. *Leipzig u. Winterthur*, [1879.] fol. **h. 2732. c. (1.)**

— Sonate No. 5 in C moll für die Orgel. Op. 50. *Leipzig*, 1887. fol. **h. 2732. e. (10.)**

LANGE (SAMUEL DE)

— Sonate für Pianoforte und Violine. Op. 19. *Leipzig*, [1875.] fol. **h. 1728. d. (3.)**

— Sonate (No. 2 in C moll) für Pianoforte und Violine. Op. 29. *Leipzig u. Winterthur*, 1880. fol. **h. 1728. d. (4.)**

— Sonate—No. 3, in D dur—für Pianoforte und Violine. Op. 48. *J. Rieter-Biedermann: Leipzig*, 1888. fol. **h. 1728. d. (5.)**

— Variationen über das Volkslied "God save the Queen" für die Orgel. Op. 34. *Leipzig u. Winterthur*, 1883. fol. **h. 2732. e. (9.)**

— Verbeidend. [Song, words by] J. P. Heije. *van Holkema & Warendorf: Amsterdam*, [1893.] fol. *Appendix to the biography of S. de Lange in H. Viotta's "Onze hedendaagsche Toonkunstenaars".* **1761. b. 16.**

— *See* BACH (J. S.) [*Collected Works.—f.*] Selected Organ Compositions ... fingered by S. de Lange. [1910.] *obl.* 4°. **e. 113. d.**

— *See* FRESCOBALDI (G.) Fuga und Canzona für die Orgel ... Herausgegeben von S. de Lange. 1872. fol. **h. 1487. h. (22.)**

— *See* HAENDEL (G. F.) [Organ Concertos. Op. 4.] Concerte ... Für Orgel allein bearbeitet von S. de Lange ... Op. 4, No. 3 ... No. 4. 1887. fol. **h. 435. c. (14.)**

— *See* HAENDEL (G. F.) [Organ Concertos. Op. 7.] Concerte für Orgel ... bearbeitet von S. de Lange. [1878.] fol. **h. 2732. b. (16.)**

— *See* HAENDEL (G. F.) [Organ Concertos. Op. 7.] Conzerte für Orgel mit Orchester ... für Orgel allein bearbeitet von S. de Lange, *etc.* [1884.] fol. **h. 2732. f. (14.)**

— *See* HAENDEL (G. F.) [Organ Concertos. Op. 7. No. 1–3, 5.] Konzerte für Orgel und Orchester. Für Orgel allein bearbeitet von S. de Lange. [1930.] 4°. **g. 74. y. (13.)**

— *See* MUFFAT (G.) Apparatus musico-organisticus ... herausgegeben ... von S. de Lange. 1888. *obl.* fol. **e. 461. a.**

— *See* PSALMS. [*Dutch.*] De Psalmen en Evangelische Gezangen der Hollandsche Gereformeerde Kerk, *etc.* [With a preface by S. de Lange.] 1895. 8°. **A. 647. c.**

LANGE (WILLIAM A.)

— America. Hymn, *etc. Angeles Music House: Port Angeles, Washington*, 1912. *s. sh.* 8°. **F. 1176. d. (22.)**

LANGELLE (RAE)

— *See* CHAIKOVSKY (P. I.) [Quatuor. Op. 11. — Andante cantabile.] Theme ... Arranged by R. Langelle. 1941. 4°. **g. 557. f. (37.)**

LANGEMARCK

— Langemarck. [Song.] *See* BIRKETT (Cecil J. A.)

LANGE-MUELLER (PETER ERASMUS)

— Songs. Lieder. (English words by P. Pinkerton.) 3 no. *F. Harris Co.: London*, (1907.) fol. **H. 1794. uu. (69.)**

— Sange. [With a portrait.] 3 Bd. *Wilhelm Hansen: Kjøbenhavn, Leipzig; Nordisk Musik-forlag: Kjøbenhavn*, [1913.] fol. **H. 1980. k.**

— Udvalgte Klaverstykker. (Danse og Intermezzi, Op. 49. Syv Skovstykker, Op. 56. Dæmpede Melodier, Op. 68.) pp. 119. *Wilhelm Hansen: København, Leipzig*, [1926.] fol. **h. 722. g. (10.)**

LANGE-MUELLER (PETER ERASMUS)

— [Agnete og Havmanden.] Prolog og Epilog til "Agnete og Havmanden" af Edv. Blaumüller, componeret for Chor og Orchester ... Op. 73. Klaveerudtog med Text. 1910. *See* COPENHAGEN.—*Samfundet til Udgivelse af dansk Musik.* [Publications of the Society.] 2. Række. No. 28. 1872, *etc.* fol. **G. 728.**

— "Arion." Digt af Ernst von der Recke, komponeret for Tenorsolo, Chor og Orchester ... Op. 62. Klaveerudtog. pp. 27. *Nordisk Musik-Forlag: København,* [c. 1930.] fol. **H. 1850. w. (10.)**

— "1848." Kantate ved Veteranfesten 1898. Tekst af Ernst von der Recke ... Op. 60. For Mandskor, Baryton-Solo og Blæserorkester. Klaverudtog af Komponisten. [1919.] *See* COPENHAGEN.—*Samfundet til Udgivelse af dansk Musik.* [Publications of the Society.] 3. Række. No. 2. 1872, *etc.* fol. **G. 728.**

— The Birch Tree. *See* supra: Songs, *etc.* No. 2.

— De profundis [begins: "Ingens Frelse." Danish words by Alexis Tolstóy and Thor Lange]. In Extremis [begins: "Efte Skriftemaa lets Tröst." Danish words by Alexis Tolstóy and Thor Lange]. In te Domine speramus [begins: "Der Kommer en Konge." Danish words after Psalm 72 by B. S. Ingemann]. Drei Gesänge für Chor und Orchester ... Op. 21. [With German words by Jens Christensen.] Clavierauszug. *Breslau,* [1885.] fol. **H. 1187. e. (16.)**

— [Der var engang. Op. 25.] Musik til Holger Drachmanns Eventyrkomedie: "Der var engang". no. 1–4, 14. *Kgl. Hofmusikhandels Forlag: Kjöbenhavn,* [1887.] fol. *Imperfect; wanting no.* 5–13. **H. 2025. e. (8.)**

— "Der var engang—." (Forkortet Klaverudtog), *etc.* ⟨Op. 25.⟩ pp. 27. *Wilhelm Hansen: København,* [1949.] 4°. **G. 1276. oo. (17.)**

— En Efteraarsfantasi. For piano ... Op. 66. pp. 17. *Nordisk Musik-Forlag: København,* [1921?] fol. **h. 722. g. (8.)**

— Tre Fantasistykker for Violin og Piano ... Op. 39. [Score and part.] 2 pt. *Kgl. Hofmusikhandel (Henrik Hennings): Kjøbenhavn,* [1891?] fol. **h. 210. y. (4.)**

— Fru Jeanna. Tragisk Opera in 4 Akter. Text af E. v. d. Recke ... ⟨Übersetzt von E. Klingenfeld⟩ Op. 30. [Vocal score.] *Dan. & Ger.* pp. 279. *Kgl. Hofmusikhandel (Henrik Hennings): Copenhague,* [1891?] fol. **H. 231. bb.**

— Kantate ved den nordiske Industri-, Landbrugs- og Kunst-Udstellings Aabningsfest den 18ᵈᵉ Maj, 1888, for Solo, Chor og Orchester. Op. 37. Klaverudtog med Text. 1889. *See* COPENHAGEN.—*Samfundet til Udgivelse af dansk Musik.* [Publications of the Society.] 2. Række. No. 1. 1872, *etc.* fol. **G. 728.**

— Kantate ved Festen i Odense paa Hundredaarsdagen for H. C. Andersen's Fødsel ... Op. 71. Klaverudtog af Komponisten. [1907.] *See* COPENHAGEN.—*Samfundet til Udgivelse af dansk Musik.* [Publications of the Society.] 2. Række. No. 22. 1872, *etc.* fol. **G. 728.**

— Kantate ved Universitetets Fest i Anledning af Hundredaarsdagen for Stavnsbaandets Løsning, Juni 1888. Text af H. Drachmann. Op. 36. Klaverudtog med Text. 1911. *See* COPENHAGEN.—*Samfundet til Udgivelse af dansk Musik.* [Publications of the Society.] 2. Række. No. 29. 1872, *etc.* fol. **G. 728.**

— Lamentation. [P. F.] *Daily Telegraph: London,* 1914. 4°. *Pp.* 156–158 *of "King Albert's Book".* **K. T. C. 104. b. 3.**

— The Lotus Flower. *See* supra: Songs, *etc.* No. 3.

— Meraner Reigen für Klavier zu vier Händen ... Op. 26. *J. Hainauer: Breslau,* [1886.] fol. **h. 3290. h. (18.)**

LANGE-MUELLER (PETER ERASMUS)

— [Middelalderlig.] Musik til H. Drachmanns Melodrama 'Middelalderlig' ... Op. 55. Klaveerudtog. [1903.] *See* COPENHAGEN.—*Samfundet til Udgivelse af dansk Musik.* [Publications of the Society.] 2. Række. No. 16. 1872, *etc.* fol. **G. 728.**

— Niels Ebbesen ... Op. 9. ⟨Af C. Gandrup, for Baryton solo, Mandskor og Orkester. Klaveerudtog.⟩ pp. 23. *Wilhelm Hansen: København, Leipzig,* [c. 1910.] fol. **H. 1980. cc. (4.)**

— Serenade. *See* supra: Songs, *etc.* No. 1.

— Spanske Studenter. Opera i 2 Akter. Text af Villiam Faber ... Op. 22. [Vocal score.] pp. 214. *Kgl. Hof-Musikhandels: Kjöbenhavn,* [1883?] 8°. **E. 1598. o. (8.)**

— Tove. Syngespil. Op. 7. Forkortet Klaver-Udtog af Komponisten. (Text og Musik af P. E. Lange-Müller.) 1879. *See* COPENHAGEN.—*Samfundet til Udgivelse af dansk Musik.* [Publications of the Society.] XII. 1879, *etc.* fol. **G. 728.**

— Trio für Pianoforte, Violine und Violoncello ... Op. 53. [Score and parts.] 3 pt. *D. Rahter: Hamburg, Leipzig,* [1899.] fol. **g. 1000. (5.)**

— Vikingeblod. Opera i fire Akter. ⟨Op. 50.⟩ Tekst af Einar Christiansen ... Fuldstændigt Klaveerudtog med Tekst. pp. 219. *Det Nordiske Forlag: Kjøbenhavn,* [1897.] fol. **H. 2025. g.**

LANGE-MUELLER (PETER ERASMUS) and SJÖGREN (JOHANN GUSTAV EMIL)

— Vier Klavierstücke über das Motiv B. H. *J. Hainauer: Breslau,* [1885.] fol. **h. 3280. h. (26.)**

LANGE-MÜLLER (PETER ERASMUS)

— *See* LANGE-MUELLER.

LANGEN (MATHILDE)

— Ever thine. (Ewig dein.) *See* SONGS. Gems of German Song. Book 32. No. 3. [1843, *etc.*] fol. **H. 2123.**

— Ever thine, Ewig Dein, song. *London,* [1855.] fol. **H. 1758. (11.)**

— Kœnigl. Preussischer Galopp. Royal Prussian galop, *etc.* [P. F.] *London,* [1854.] fol. **h. 975. e. (21.)**

LANGENAU (JOHANN LEONHARD DE)

— *See* LEICHTENTRITT (H.) Mehrstimmige Lieder alter deutscher Meister, *etc.* (Heft v. Leonard de Langenau, *etc.*) [1906–08.] 8°. **F. 1724.**

LANGENBECK (GEORG)

— Walzer. Serenade für Orchester. Op. 23. [Orchestral parts.] *Berlin und Leipzig,* [1883.] fol. **h. 3210. b. (7.)**

— Walzer-Serenade für Klavier. *Berlin und Leipzig,* [1883.] fol. **h. 3276. g. (6.)**

LANGENDORFF (WILLY)

— Amoretten. Op. 6. [P. F.] 2 no. *C. Simon: Berlin,* [1880.] fol. **h. 3281. l. (6.)**

LANGENHAN (ANNA HIRZEL)

— *See* HIRZEL-LANGENHAN.

LANGENHOVEN (C. J.)

— Ou-Liedjies. Aangevul deur C. J. Langenhoven. Met wysie-musiek. *Nasionale Pers: Kaapstad*, 1928. 4°.
F. 607. mm. (8.)

LANGENUS (GUSTAVE)

— Fingered Scale Studies for the Boehm Clarinet. *Cundy Bettoney Co.: Boston, Mass.*, 1912. 4°.
g. 761. l. (4.)

— Modern Clarinet Playing. A Method ... for players contemplating a change from the old to the Boehm System, etc. *C. Fischer: New York, etc.*, (1913.) 4°.
g. 761. b. (4.)

— Table of Fingerings for the Boehm Clarinet, with ... examples illustrating their practical use. *C. Fischer: New York*, 1913. s. sh. fol.
I. 600. e. (48.)

— *See* BEETHOVEN (L. van) [Sonatas. Op. 22.] Adagio ... Transcribed for B♭ clarinet and piano by G. Langenus. [1950.] 4°.
g. 249. oo. (6.)

— *See* BEETHOVEN (L. van) [Sonatas. Op. 22.] Menuetto ... Transcribed for B♭ clarinet and piano by G. Langenus. [1950.] 4°.
g. 249. oo. (7.)

— *See* BRAHMS (J.) Sonata in F minor. Op. 120, No. 1. Transcribed for two clarinets by G. Langenus. [1950.] 4°.
g. 609. p. (9.)

— *See* BRAHMS (J.) Sonata in E♭ major. Op. 120, No. 2. Transcribed for two clarinets by G. Langenus. [1950.] 4°.
g. 609. p. (10.)

— *See* KREISLER (F.) Caprice Viennois ... Arranged ... by G. Langenus. 1941. 4°.
g. 1104. c. (2.)

— *See* KREISLER (F.) [Klassische Manuskripte. No. 2.] Andantino. In the style of Martini. Arranged ... by G. Langenus. 1941. 4°.
g. 1104. c. (3.)

— *See* KREISLER (F.) [Klassische Manuskripte. No. 5.] Praeludium and Allegro. (In the style of Pugnani.) Arranged ... by G. Langenus. 1941. 4°.
g. 1104. c. (4.)

— *See* SCHUBERT (F.) of Dresden. [Bagatellen. Op. 13. No. 9. L'Abeille.] The Bee ... Transcribed for B♭ clarinet and piano by G. Langenus. [1950.] 4°.
g. 1104. f. (7.)

— *See* WEBER (C. M. F. E. von) Concertino for Clarinet. Op. 26. Transcribed for two clarinets by G. Langenus. [1950.] 4°.
h. 1336. j. (6.)

LANGER (A.)

— Frühlingseinkehr. Capriccio. Op. 9. Erinnerung an Interlaken. Fantaisie. Op. 11, für Pianoforte. 2 no. *Leipzig*, [1875.] fol.
h. 1487. o. (32.)

LANGER (ADOLF)

— Základní škola hry na pianovou harmoniku. pp. 121. *Státní nakladatelství krásné literatury, hudby a umění: Praha*, 1959. 4°.
g. 761. nn. (1.)

LANGER (CURT)

— Gavotte d'Amour, morceau de salon pour Piano. *R. Cocks & Co.: London*, [1881.] fol.
h. 1484. s. (11.)

— Gavotte d'Amour. [P. F.] *C. F. Kahnt: Leipzig*, [1885.] fol. *No. 1 of 'Telephon-Klänge'.*
h. 3281. l. (7.)

LANGER (EDUARD)

— *See* CHAIKOVSKY (P. I.) [La Belle au Bois dormant.] Suite du ballet "La Belle au bois dormant," *etc.* ⟨Arr. pour le piano simplifié par E. Langer.⟩ [c. 1900.] fol.
h. 2988. s. (2.)

LANGER (EDUARD)

— *See* CHAIKOVSKY (P. I.) "Буря" ... Фантазія. Соч. 18. ⟨Переложенная для 4 рукъ Э. Лангеромъ.⟩ [1873.] fol.
h. 2988. u. (5.)

— *See* CHAIKOVSKY (P. I.) [Casse-Noisette.] Suite tirée de la partition du ballet "Casse-noisette," *etc.* ⟨Arr. à 4 mains par E. Langer.⟩ [1893?] fol.
h. 2988. aa. (6.)

— *See* CHAIKOVSKY (P. I.) [Casse-Noisette.] The Nutcracker Suite ... ⟨Op. 71 a.⟩ Arranged for piano duet by E. Langer, *etc.* [1950.] 4°.
g. 557. k. (2.)

— *See* CHAIKOVSKY (P. I.) Hamlet. Phantasie-Ouverture für grosses Orchester ... Op. 67 ... Für Pianoforte zu zwei Händen. ⟨Arr. par E. Langer.⟩ [1895.] fol.
h. 2988. o. (3.)

— *See* CHAIKOVSKY (P. I.) Hamlet ... Ouverture, mélodrames, fanfares, marches et entr'actes ... Op. 67ᵇ ... Compl. pour piano à 2/ms. ⟨Arr. par E. Langer.⟩ [1895.] 8°.
f. 234. t. (1.)

— *See* CHAIKOVSKY (P. I.) [Hamlet. Op. 67b.] Marche funèbre ... Переложеніе для фортепіано въ 2 руки, *etc.* [Arranged by E. Langer.] [1895.] fol.
h. 2988. v. (7.)

— *See* CHAIKOVSKY (P. I.) Le Lac des cygnes. Grand ballet en 4 actes ... Op. 20. Partition pour piano à 2 mains. ⟨Arr. par E. Langer.⟩ [c. 1920.] 4°.
g. 557. y. (1.)

— *See* CHAIKOVSKY (P. I.) Marche slave. Slavonic march. ⟨Op. 31.⟩ For two pianos, eight-hands. Arranged by E. Langer. [1951.] 4°.
g. 557. m. (3.)

— *See* CHAIKOVSKY (P. I.) "Mozartiana." Suite N° 4 ... Op. 61 ... Arr. à 4/ms. (E. Langer.) [1887.] fol.
h. 2988. o. (5.)

— *See* CHAIKOVSKY (P. I.) Mozartiana. Suite N° 4 ... Op. 61 ... Für Pianoforte zu 4 Händen von E. Langer. [1889.] fol.
h. 2988. q. (1.)

— *See* CHAIKOVSKY (P. I.) [Symphony No. 3. Op. 29.] Третья симфонія для большаго оркестра ... Соч. 29. ⟨Arrangée par E. Langer. Переложеніе въ 4 руки.⟩ [c. 1890.] fol.
h. 2988. a. (3.)

— *See* KOCHETOV (N. R.) [Die schreckliche Rache.] Potpourri ... Арр. Э. Лангера. [1915?] fol.
h. 1426. m. (6.)

LANGER (FERDINAND)

— *See* WEBER (C. M. F. E. von) Silvana ... Vollständiger Klavierauszug von F. Langer. [1885.] 8°.
F. 665. e.

LANGER (GUSTAV)

— Cradle Song. Op. 8. Piano Solo. *C. Fischer: New York, etc.*, (1908.) fol.
h. 3283. p. (11.)

Grossmütterchen

— Grossmütterchen, für Pianoforte und Violoncell. *Dresden*, [1880.] fol.
h. 1849. k. (12.)

— Little Granny ... Ländler. Op. 20 ... for pianoforte & flute, with 2ⁿᵈ. flute ad lib. *S. Lucas, Weber & Co.: London*, [1884.] fol.
h. 250. f. (14.)

— Little Granny ... Ländler. Op. 20. For pianoforte & violin, with 2ⁿᵈ. violin ad lib. *S. Lucas, Weber & Co.: London*, [1884.] fol.
h. 210. d. (34.)

— Grossmütterchen. Little Granny. Ländler. Op. 20. [P. F.] *S. Lucas, Weber & Co.: London*, [1884.] fol. **h. 1484. s. (12.)**

— Grossmütterchen, *etc.* [P. F.] *R. Cocks & Co.: London*, [1887.] fol.
h. 1484. s. (13.)

— Grossmütterchen. Ländler. For 2 solo Violins, 1ˢᵗ & 2ⁿᵈ Violins, Viola, Cello & Bass. [Parts.] *A. Hammond & Co.: London*, [1888.] 8°.
e. 1342. (7.)

LANGER (Gustav)

— Grossmütterchen. Op. 20. [Violin and P. F.] [1888.] *See* BOOSEY AND CO. Boosey's Violin Miscellany, *etc.* No. 43. No. 3. [1886, *etc.*] fol.   **h. 1653.**

— Grossmütterchen ... Ländler, *etc.* [Violin and P. F.] *See* FARMER (H.) Select Pieces, *etc.* No. 17. [1892.] fol.   **h. 211. g.**

— Grossmütterchen ... Ländler. Op. 20. 1. Pianoforte solo. 2. Pianoforte & Violin with 2nd Violin ad lib. 2 no.   *Augener & Co.: London*, [1894.] fol.   **g. 605. f. (4.)**

— Grossmütterchen. Granny. Ländler. Op. 20 ... Pianoforte & Violin, with 2nd Violin ad lib. [1904.] *See* HERMANN (F.) Morceaux Favoris, *etc.* No. 137. [1886, *etc.*] fol.   **h. 1621. b.**

— Grossmütterchen ... Op. 20. Arrangiert von L. Artok. [Parts.] *B. Schott's Söhne: Mainz*, 1928. 4°. [*Domesticum Salon-Orchester. No.* 254.]   **g. 1053. a.**

— [Grossväterchen.] The Little Grandfather. Ländler. [P. F.] *London*, [1880.] fol.   **h. 1494. p. (13.)**

— Grossväterchen, für Pianoforte und Violoncell.   *Dresden*, [1880.] fol.   **h. 1849. k. (13.)**

LANGER (Hermann)

— Der erste Unterricht im Gesänge für Schule und Haus. Erster (zweiter) Cursus. 2 no.   *Leipzig*, [1875–6.] 8°.   **A. 868. c. (5.)**

— Musikalische Gartenlaube. Hausmusik für Pianoforte und Gesang. Herausgegeben von Dr. H. Langer. 8 Bd.   *Leipzig*, [1870–73.] 4°.   **G. 451.**

— Volkslieder und volksthümliche Lieder für vier Männerstimmen. Op. 11. Partitur. 2 Hft.   *F. Kistner: Leipzig*, [1874.] 8°.   **F. 585. q. (18.)**

LANGER (Leopold)

— Air bohémien "Дружбы нѣжное волненье," transcrit et varié pour le piano forte ... Op. 12. Nr 2. pp. 7.   *Chèz Müller & Grotrian: Moscou*, [c. 1840.] fol.   **h. 1426. aa. (4.)**

— Air bohémien Ночинька, transcrit et varié pour le piano forte ... Op. 11. N° 1. pp. 5.   *Chèz Müller & Grotrian: Moscou*, [c. 1840.] fol.   **h. 1426. aa. (3.)**

LANGER (Max)

— *See* MOZART (J. G. L.) Sinfonia di caccia. Jagdsymphonie. G. dur ... herausgegeben ... von Dr. M. Langer. 1935. 4°.   **g. 727. j. (4.)**

LANGER (Victor)

— Gyászhangok Deák Ferencz halálára. Zongorára szerzé Langer Victor.   *Budapest*, [1876.] fol.   **h. 1493. n. (10.)**

— Kurucz nóták. Irta Endrődi Sándor. Zenéjét énekhangra zongorakisérettel szerzé Ögyek (Langer Victor). pp. 25.   *Pesti könyvnyomda részvény társaság: Budapest*, [c. 1900.] fol.   **H. 1403. d. (4.)**

LANGERFELD (Wallie)

— The Ivory City. Waltzes. [P. F.]   *F. B. Haviland Publishing Co.: New York*, (1904.) fol.   **h. 3286. dd. (53.)**

LANGERT (August)

— Die Fabier, grosse dramatische Oper in 5 Akten. Text ... von G. v. Meyern. Klavierauszug.   *Berlin & Posen*, [1868.] fol.   **H. 639. a.**

— Hochzeitsmarsch für grosses Orchester componirt. 4 hand. Arrangement.   *Coburg*, [1874.] fol.   **h. 1487. o. (34.)**

LANGERT (August)

— Melodies de l'opéra Faust de C. Gounod, transcrites pour le Piano.   *Berlin & Posen*, [1872.] fol.   **h. 1487. o. (33.)**

— Des Sängers Fluch (nach Uhland). Grosse Oper in drei Akten. Vollständiger Klavier-Auszug, mit Text.   *Berlin u. Posen*, [1864.] 8°.   **H. 639.**

LANGEY (Otto)

— Arabische Serenade für Orchester. Op. 24. Partitur.   *Berlin*, [1882.] fol.   **h. 1509. k. (10.)**

— Banjolina. Ethiopian serenade [for strings]. Op. 42. [Parts.] *London*, [1883.] 8°.   **f. 410. j. (10.)**

— Biondina. Gavotte. Op. 50. [Orchestral parts.]   *London*, [1885.] 8°.   **f. 410. j. (11.)**

— Bravura. Op. 59. [Violin and P. F.]   *Rivière & Hawkes: London*, [1887.] fol. *No.* 10 *of The Concert Edition.*   **g. 790. (1.)**

— But why? [Song.] Words by W. Browne. Op. 138. *M. Witmark & Sons:* [*New York, etc.,*] 1901. fol.   **H. 1799. cc. (46.)**

— Chanson sans Paroles. Op. 58. [Violoncello and P. F.]   *Rivière & Hawkes: London*, [1887.] fol. *No.* 17 *of The Concert Edition.*   **g. 790. (14.)**

— The Dancer of Bagdad. An oriental scene ... Op. 118. [Orchestral parts.] 16 pt.   *Oliver Ditson Co.: Boston, London*, [1896.] 4°.   **g. 1800. (191.)**

— Dream Shadows. A Tone Picture. Op. 140. [P. F.] *M. Witmark & Sons:* [*New York, etc.,*] 1901. fol.   **h. 3282. kk. (22.)**

— English Maypole Dance ... Op. 105. [Orchestral parts.] 16 pt. *Oliver Ditson Co.: Boston, London*, [1893.] 4°.   **g. 1800. (192.)**

— L'Estafette, or: A Wild Ride. Op. 55. [Orchestral parts.]   *J. R. Lafleur & Son: London*, [1887.] 8°. *Part of the "Alliance Musicale".*   **f. 400. ee. (1.)**

— L'Estafette ... Descriptive Piece. Op. 55. [P. F.]   *J. R. Lafleur & Son: London*, [1887.] 8°. *Part of the "Alliance Musicale. Album Bijou".*   **f. 406. a. (12.)**

— Evening Breeze. An Idyl. For string quartett. Op. 60. [Parts.] *J. R. Lafleur & Son: London*, [1887.] 8°. *Part of the "Alliance Musicale".*   **f. 400. mm. (2.)**

— Evening Breeze. An Idyl ... for the piano. (Op. 60.)   *J. R. Lafleur & Son: London*, [1887.] fol.   **h. 1484. s. (14.)**

— Fanfare militaire. Marche caractéristique ... Op. 106. [Orchestral parts.] 16 pt.   *Oliver Ditson & Co.: Boston, London*, [1893.] 4°.   **g. 1800. (193.)**

— Felice. Canzonetta. Op. 124. Piano Solo.   *Roeder & O'Hara: New York*, 1896. fol.   **h. 3282. f. (9.)**

— Flirtation. Gavotte. [Orchestral parts.]   *J. R. Lafleur & Son: London*, [1887.] 8°. *Part of the "Alliance Musicale".*   **f. 400. mm. (3.)**

— Flirtation Gavotte. Arr. by Charles George Godfrey. (Conductor [and military band parts].) 26 pt. *In:* FAHRBACH (P.) *the Younger.* Esprit viennois, *etc.* [1887.] fol. [*Orpheus. no.* 51.]   **h. 1548.**

— Flirtation. Gavotte. Pianoforte solo. Op. 54.   *Enoch & Sons: London*, [1885.] fol.   **h. 1484. s. (15.)**

— Flirtation. Gavotte. Op. 54. Pianoforte Duet.   *Enoch & Sons: London*, [1885.] fol.   **h. 3290. f. (37.)**

LANGEY (OTTO)

— Flirtation. Gavotte. Op. 54. Piano & Violin,—or Cello, or Flute, *etc. Enoch & Sons: London*, [1885.] fol.
h. 210. e. (20.)

— Flirtation. Gavotte. Op. 54. Pianoforte with vocal part. *Enoch & Sons: London*, [1885.] fol. **H. 1795. e. (1.)**

— Gavotte. Op. 43. [Violoncello and P. F.] *L. Oertel: Hannover*, [1884.] fol. **h. 1847. (39.)**

— Gavotte de la cour du roi Henri IV. Op. 48. [Orchestral parts.] *London*, [1885.] 8°. **f. 410. k. (1.)**

— Gavotte de la cour du roi Henri Quatre. (Op. 48.) [P. F.] *Rivière & Hawkes: London*, [1885.] fol. **h. 1484. s. (16.)**

— Gondolier and Nightingale. Barcarolle. Op. 49. [Orchestral and P. F. parts.] *J. R. Lafleur & Son: London*, [1888.] 8°. *Part of the "Alliance Musicale".* **f. 400. ll. (2.)**

— Grand Fantasia on "Dixie". Op. 130. [P. F. and orchestra. Parts.] *O. Ditson Co.: Boston*, 1898. fol. **h. 1508. e. (12.)**

— Grand Fantasia on V. Herbert's Opera, Natoma. (For full Orchestra.) Arranged ... by O. Langey. (Score.) *G. Schirmer: New York*, (1911.) fol. **h. 1567. (6.)**

— Grand Fantasia on V. Herbert's Opera, Natoma, *etc.* (Parts.) *G. Schirmer: New York*, (1911.) fol. **h. 3210. h. (125.)**

— Graziella. Morceau de salon. Op. 35. [P. F.] *Rivière & Hawkes: London*, [1882.] fol. **h. 1484. s. (17.)**

— Her first Dance. Waltz caprice. *See infra:* Old German Clog Dance.

— "In the Bungalow." Intermezzo ... Op. 143. [Orchestral parts.] 18 pt. *Carl Fischer: New York*, [1906.] 4°. *The 1st violin part is in duplicate.* **g. 1800. (194.)**

— Inez. Spanish Minuet. Op. 119. [P. F. and orchestral parts.] *O. Ditson Company:* [*Boston, etc.*,] 1896. fol. **h. 3212. i. (6.)**

— Instructor for Zobo Brass Instruments, for Soloists, Quartettes and Zobo Bands. *W. H. Frost & Co.: New York*, 1896. 8°. **f. 759. c. (3.)**

— Leila. Valse. [Orchestral parts.] *See* CHAPPELL AND CO. Popular Quadrilles, *etc.* No. 173. [1885.] 8°. **e. 249.**

— Leila. Valse. (Op. 36.) [P. F.] *Chappell & Co.: London*, [1885.] fol. **h. 975. u. (36.)**

— Malva, set of valses. [Orchestral parts.] *London*, [1880.] 8°. *Part of the "Dance Music Orchestral Journal".* **f. 415. e. (13.)**

— Malva. Set of Valses. Op. 20. [P. F. and orchestra.] *London*, [1880?] 8°. *Part of "Dance Music, Orchestral Journal". The P. F. part only.* **f. 415. f. (13.)**

— Mandolina. (Mexican serenade.) [Orchestral parts.] *London*, [1882.] 8°. **f. 410. e. (12.)**

— Mexican Beauties. Serenata ... Op. 142. [P. F.] pp. 7. *M. Witmark & Sons: New York, etc.*, [1904.] 4°. **h. 4120. mm. (24.)**

— Mi Querida. Spanish Dance. Op. 53. [Orchestral parts.] *J. B. Cramer & Co.: London*, [1885.] 8°. **e. 665. f. (4.)**

— Mi querida. Spanish dance. Op. 53. [P. F.] *J. B. Cramer & Co.: London*, [1885.] fol. **h. 1484. s. (18.)**

— Musical Scenes from Italy. Fantasia ... Op. 120. [Orchestral parts.] 16 pt. *Oliver Ditson Co.: Boston, London*, [1896.] 4°. **g. 1800. (195.)**

— The Nautch Girls' Polka, on melodies from H. Pontet's opera, "Melita". [P. F.] *W. D. Cubitt, Son & Co.: London*, [1883.] fol. **h. 975. u. (37.)**

LANGEY (OTTO)

— A Night with the Bogies. Descriptive Fantasia. Op. 125. [P. F. and orchestral parts.] *O. Ditson Co.:* [*Boston*,] 1897. fol.
h. 1508. e. (11.)

— Oasis. A Caravan Episode ... Op. 134. [P. F.] *M. Witmark & Sons:* [*New York, etc.*,] 1901. fol. **h. 3282. w. (29.)**

— Old German Clog Dance ... Op. 104. ⟨Her first Dance. Waltz caprice ... Op. 103.⟩ [Orchestral parts.] 32 pt. *Oliver Ditson Co.: Boston, London*, [1893.] 4°. **g. 1800. (196.)**

— Three Oriental Sketches for the pianoforte. Op. 158. 3 no. *G. Schirmer: New York, Boston*, 1917. 4°. **g. 442. z. (15.)**

— Our Babies polka. [Orchestral parts.] *London*, [1880.] 8°. *Part of the "Dance Music Orchestral Journal".*
f. 415. e. (12.)

— Our Babies. Polka. (Op. 22.) [P. F. and orchestra.] *London*, [1880.] 8°. *Part of "Dance Music, Orchestral Journal". The P. F. part only.* **f. 415. f. (14.)**

— Our Babies polka. [Reed band parts.] *London*, [1882.] 8°. **f. 412. m. (25.)**

— Paraphrase on Adeste Fideles. Op. 52. [Orchestral parts.] *London*, [1885.] 8°. **f. 410. j. (9.)**

— Péché Mignon. Overture. Op. 44. [P. F. and orchestral parts.] *London*, [1883.] 8°. **f. 410. k. (2.)**

— Restored. Song [begins: "All day long I'm weeping"]. Words by S. Bellamy. *London*, [1881.] fol. **H. 1787. j. (9.)**

— A Russian Pansy. Flower Song for violin and piano. Op. 160. *G. Schirmer: New York, Boston*, 1917. 4°. **g. 223. dd. (18.)**

— Saragossa. Spanish waltz ... Op. 72. [Orchestral parts.] 17 pt. *J. R. Lafleur & Son: London; Paris* [printed, 1892.] 8°.
f. 800. (781.)

— Saragossa. Spanish waltz. [Op. 72.] ... Arrd. by A. Morelli. Solo conductor & 1st B♭ cornet [and military band parts]. 28 pt. *J. R. Lafleur & Son: London*, [1892.] 8°. *Part of "Alliance Musicale". The conductor part is in duplicate.*
f. 800. (782.)

— Saragossa. Spanish valse ... [Op. 72.] Arrd. by A. Morelli. [Parts for fife and drum band.] 8 pt. *J. R. Lafleur & Son: London*, [1892.] 8°. **f. 800. (783.)**

— Saragossa. Spanish Waltz. Op. 72. [P. F.] *Lafleur & Son: London*, [1892.] fol. **h. 3285. p. (53.)**

— Zwei schottische Tänze. Two Scottish Dances. N° 1. Highland. N° 2. Tullochgorum. Für Orchester ... Op. 21. Partitur, *etc.* pp. 47. *Carl Simon: Berlin*, 1881. 8°.
e. 666. qq. (2.)

— Selected Studies from B♭ and BBB♭ Bass Tutor. *See infra:* [Tutor for the B♭ and BBB♭ Bass.]

— Selection from Millöcker's opera "The Beggar Student," arranged by O. Langey. [Orchestral parts.] *London*, [1885.] 8°. **f. 410. j. (12.)**

— Selection from Weber's opera "Euryanthe," arranged by O. Langey. [P. F. and orchestral parts.] *London*, [1883.] 8°.
f. 410. k. (3.)

— Selection from Weber's opera "Preciosa," arranged by O. Langey. [P. F. and orchestral parts.] *London*, [1883.] 8°.
f. 410. k. (4.)

— A Siamese Wedding. An oriental sketch ... Op. 141. [Orchestral parts.] 17 pt. *Hawkins & Son: London, Leipzig* [printed, 1905.] 4°. **g. 1800. (197.)**

— Sweet Caresses, *etc.* [P. F. and orchestral parts.] *O. Ditson Co.:* [*Boston*,] 1901. fol. **h. 1508. i. (2.)**

LANGEY (Otto)

— Sweet Caresses. Valse mélodique. Op. 136. [P. F.] *O. Ditson Co.: Boston,* 1901. fol.   **h. 3282. w. (31.)**

— "Sweet Ponderings." A melodic sentiment ... Op. 144. [Orchestral parts.] 18 pt. *Carl Fischer: New York,* [1907.] 4°. *Various parts are in duplicate.*   **g. 1800. (198.)**

— [Tutor for the B♭ and BB♭ Bass.] Selected Studies from B♭ and BB♭ Bass Tutor. In the treble clef. pp. 20. *Boosey & Hawkes: London, etc.,* [1969.] 4°.   **g. 761. zz. (4.)**

— Tutor for the Bassoon. *London,* [1885.] 4°.   **f. 744. c. (2.)**

— Tutor for the Bassoon. Selected, arranged & composed by O. Langey. *Hawkes & Son: London,* [1900?] 4°.   **f. 744. f.**

— Tutor for the Bombardon in E♭. *London,* [1885.] 4°.   **f. 744. c. (4.)**

— Practical Tutor for the E♭ Bombardon—in the Bass-Clef—. New edition, revised & enlarged. *Hawkes & Son: London,* [1911.] 4°.   **g. 1135. j.**

— Practical Tutor for the E♭ Bombardon, in the Treble-clef. New edition, revised & enlarged. *Hawkes & Son: London,* 1921. 4°.   **g. 1135. n.**

— Tutor for the Clarinette. *London,* [1885.] 4°.   **f. 744. c. (3.)**

— Practical Tutor for the Clarinet in the Simple and the Boehm Systems, and the Corno di Bassetto. New edition, revised & enlarged. *Hawkes & Son: London,* [1908.] 4°.   **g. 1135. a. (1.)**

— Tutor for the Cornet. *London,* [1885.] 4°.   **f. 744. d. (3.)**

— Otto Langey's Tutor for the Cornet. Revised, re-arranged & many studies added ... by W. Morrow. *Hawkes & Son: London,* [1911.] 4°.   **g. 1135. d.**

— Practical Tutor for the Cornet or Trumpet. New edition revised and enlarged by E. Hall. *Hawkes & Son: London,* 1937. 4°.   **g. 1135. p.**

— Tutor for the Three String Double Bass. *London,* [1885.] 4°.   **f. 744. b. (2.)**

— Practical Tutor for the Double-Bass—with Three Strings— ... New edition, revised & enlarged by J. Reynolds. *Hawkes & Son: London,* [1908.] 4°.   **g. 1135. (1.)**

— Tutor for the Four String Double Bass. *London,* [1885.] 4°.   **f. 744. b. (3.)**

— Practical Tutor for the Double-Bass—with Four Strings— ... New edition, revised & enlarged by J. Reynolds. *Hawkes & Son: London,* [1908.] 4°.   **g. 1135. (2.)**

— Practical Tutor for the B♭ Euphonium with Four Valves, Bass-Clef. New edition, revised & enlarged. *Hawkes & Son: London,* [1912.] 4°.   **g. 1135. i.**

— Practical Tutor for the B♭ Euphonium with Four Valves, Treble Clef. New edition, revised & enlarged. *Hawkes & Son: London,* 1913. 4°.   **g. 1135. m.**

— Tutor for the Flageolet. Selected, arranged & composed by O. Langey. *Rivière & Hawkes: London,* [1890?] 4°.   **f. 744. e.**

— Tutor for the Flute. *London,* [1885.] 4°.   **f. 744. d. (2.)**

— Practical Tutor for the Flute in four systems. New edition, revised & enlarged. *Hawkes & Son: London,* [1909.] 4°.   **g. 1135. b. (1.)**

— Practical Tutor for the Flute in four systems ... New and revised edition. *Hawkes & Son: London,* 1934. 4°.   **g. 1135. o.**

LANGEY (Otto)

— Practical Tutor for the French-Horn.—With and without Valves.— New edition, revised & enlarged. *Hawkes & Son: London,* [1910.] 4°.   **g. 1135. g.**

— Tutor for the Oboe. *London,* [1885.] 4°.   **f. 744. c. (1.)**

— Practical Tutor for the Oboe and the Cor Anglais. New edition, revised & enlarged. *Hawkes & Son: London,* 1911. 4°.   **g. 1135. e.**

— Tutor for the Piccolo. *London,* [1885.] 4°.   **f. 744. d. (1.)**

— Practical Tutor for the Piccolo in the Simple and the Boehm Systems. New edition, revised & enlarged. *Hawkes & Son: London,* [1911.] 4°.   **g. 1135. k.**

— Practical Tutor for the Tenor Saxhorn and the Tenor Cor. New edition, revised & enlarged. *Hawkes & Son: London,* [1910.] 4°.   **g. 1135. h.**

— Tutor for the Side Drum. Selected, arranged & composed by O. Langey. *Hawkes & Son: London,* 1909. 4°.   **g. 1135. l.**

— Tutor for the Tenor Slide Trombone. *London,* [1885.] 4°.   **f. 744. d. (4.)**

— Practical Tutor for the B♭ Slide-Trombone—in the Bass-Clef—. New edition, revised & enlarged. *Hawkes & Son: London,* [1909.] 4°.   **g. 1135. b. (2.)**

— Practical Tutor for the B♭ Slide Trombone. In the treble clef ... Edited by G. Savage. pp. 118. *Boosey & Hawkes: London, etc.,* [1966.] 4°.   **g. 761. zz. (2.)**

— Practical Tutor for the B♭ Valve-Trombone, and the B♭ Baritone. New edition, revised & enlarged. *Hawkes & Son: London,* [1908.] 4°.   **g. 1135. a. (2.)**

— Tutor for the Tenor or Viola. *London,* [1885.] 4°.   **f. 744. b. (1.)**

— Practical Tutor for the Viola. New edition, revised & enlarged. *Hawkes & Son: London,* [1912.] 4°.   **g. 1135. f.**

— Tutor for the Violin. *London,* [1884.] 4°.   **f. 744.**

— Tutor for the Violin. New edition, revised & enlarged. *Hawkes & Son: London,* 1903. 4°.   **g. 1135. c.**

— Tutor for the Violoncello. *London,* [1884.] 4°.   **f. 744. a.**

— Practical Tutor for the Violoncello. New edition, revised & enlarged. *Hawkes & Son: London,* 1909. 4°.   **g. 1135. b. (3.)**

— Two little Comrades. ... Op. 62. [For two solo violins, with string quintet accompaniment.] *Rivière & Hawkes: London,* [1887.] fol. *Part of The Concert Edition.*   **g. 790. (8.)**

— Two little Comrades. Landler [for two violins and P. F.] Op. 62. *Rivière & Hawkes: London,* [1887.] fol. *No. 83 of The Concert Edition.*   **g. 790. (7.)**

— Two little comrades. Landler. Op. 62. Piano solo. *Rivière & Hawkes: London,* [1887.] fol.   **h. 1484. s. (19.)**

— Verona. Tuscan Serenade. Op. 135. [P. F.] *J. W. Stern & Co.: New York,* 1901. fol.   **h. 3282. w. (30.)**

— *See* BREIL (J. C.) [The Birth of a Nation.] The Perfect Song ... Arranged (for violin and piano) by O. Langey. 1915. fol.   **h. 1612. dd. (45.)**

— *See* CERVANTES (Ignacio) 3 Cuban Dances. Arr. for orch. by O. Langey. [1909.] 8°.   **f. 800. (245.)**

— *See* CHILVERS (Thomas H.) The Little Host. Arr. [for orchestra] by O. Langey. [1899.] 8°.   **f. 800. (255.)**

LANGEY (Otto)

— *See* Donizetti (D. G. M.) Selection from ... Linda di Chamouni. Arranged by O. Langey. [1883.] 8°.
f. 410. j. (13.)

— *See* Flotow (F. F. A. von) *Baron*. [Martha.—Ach! So fromm.] How so fair ... Arr. by O. Langey. [1887.] fol.　**g. 790. (18.)**

— *See* Friml (R.) [*Collections*.] Suite of four selected Pieces, *etc.* Arr. for orchestra by O. Langey. [1909.] 8°.
f. 800. (446.)

— *See* Friml (R.) [The Firefly.] March and Two-Step ... Arranged by O. Langey. (1912.) fol.　**h. 3477. a. (18.)**

— *See* Friml (R.) [The Firefly.] Waltzes ... Arr. by O. Langey. (1912.) fol.　**h. 3477. a. (19.)**

— *See* Gounod (C. F.) Bells across the Snow. Christmas Carol. Arranged by O. Langey. [1887.] 8°.　**f. 400. kk. (1.)**

— *See* Grainger (P. A.) Shepherd's Hey ... Arranged by O. Langey. 1922. 4°.　**g. 1212. d. (4.)**

— *See* Hammerstein (O.) Mia cara ... Arr. for orchestra by O. Langey. [1909.] 8°.　**f. 800. (578.)**

— *See* Herbert (Victor) American Fantasie ... Arr. [for orchestra] by O. Langey. [1898.] 4°.　**g. 1800. (133.)**

— *See* Herbert (Victor) American Fantasie ... Arr. [for military band] by O. Langey. [1898.] 4°.　**g. 1800. (134.)**

— *See* Herbert (Victor) Badinage. Arr. [for orchestra] by O. Langey. [1897.] 4°.　**g. 1800. (135.)**

— *See* Herbert (Victor) Badinage ... Arr. [for military band] by O. Langey. [1898.] 4°.　**g. 1800. (136.)**

— *See* Herbert (Victor) Columbia. Anthem ... Arr. [for orchestra] by O. Langey. [1898.] 8°.　**f. 800. (636.)**

— *See* Herbert (Victor) Columbia ... Arr. [for military band] by O. Langey. [1898.] *obl.* 8°.　**f. 800. (637.)**

— *See* Herbert (Victor) "Gate City Guard" ... Arr. [for orchestra] by O. Langey. [1897.] 8°.　**f. 800. (638.)**

— *See* Herbert (Victor) [The Idol's Eye.] Selection ... Arr. [for orchestra] by O. Langey. [1898.] 4°.　**g. 1800. (137.)**

— *See* Herbert (Victor) [The Idol's Eye.] Selection ... Arr. [for military band] by O. Langey. [1898.] 4°.　**g. 1800. (138.)**

— *See* Herbert (Victor) The Idol's Eye. Lancers. (Waltzes.) Arr. by O. Langey. 1898. fol.　**h. 3286. d. (35.)**

— *See* Herbert (Victor) The Idol's Eye. March ... Arr. [for orchestra] by O. Langey. [1897.] 8°.　**f. 800. (639.)**

— *See* Herbert (Victor) The Idol's Eye: March ... Arr. [for military band] by O. Langey. [1898.] *obl.* 8°.　**f. 800. (640.)**

— *See* Herbert (Victor) The Idol's Eye. Waltzes ... Arr. [for orchestra] by O. Langey. [1898.] 8°.　**f. 800. (641.)**

— *See* Herbert (Victor) The Idol's Eye. Waltzes ... Arr. [for military band] by O. Langey. [1898.] 4°.　**g. 1800. (139.)**

— *See* Herbert (Victor) Inauguration March ... Arr. [for orchestra] by O. Langey. [1897.] 8°.　**f. 800. (642.)**

— *See* Herbert (Victor) Ocean Breezes ... Arr. [for orchestra] by O. Langey. [1898.] 8°.　**f. 800. (643.)**

— *See* Herbert (Victor) Ocean Breezes ... Arr. [for military band] by O. Langey. [1898.] 4°.　**g. 1800. (140.)**

— *See* Herbert (Victor) The President's March ... Arr. [for orchestra] by O. Langey. [1898.] 8°.　**f. 800. (644.)**

— *See* Herbert (Victor) The President's March ... Arr. [for military band] by O. Langey. [1898.] *obl.* 8°.　**f. 800. (645.)**

LANGEY (Otto)

— *See* Herbert (Victor) [The Serenade.] Selection ... Arr. [for orchestra] from the original score by O. Langey. [1897.] 4°.
g. 1800. (141.)

— *See* Herbert (Victor) [The Serenade.] Selection ... Arr. [for military band] by O. Langey. [1897.] 4°.　**g. 1800. (142.)**

— *See* Herbert (Victor) 22nd Regiment March ... Arr. [for orchestra] by O. Langey. [1898.] 8°.　**f. 800. (649.)**

— *See* Herbert (Victor) 22nd Regiment March ... Arr. [for military band] by O. Langey. [1898.] *obl.* 8°.　**f. 800. (650.)**

— *See* Herbert (Victor) The Veiled Prophet. March ... Arr. [for orchestra] by O. Langey. [1897.] 8°.　**f. 800. (651.)**

— *See* Herbert (Victor) [The Wizard of the Nile.] Oriental march ... Arr. [for orchestra] by O. Langey. [1897.] 8°.
f. 800. (652.)

— *See* Miller (Charles) The Hocus-Pocus Dance ... Arr. [for orchestra] by O. Langey. [1898.] 8°.　**f. 800. (972.)**

— *See* Milloecker (C.) [Der Bettelstudent.] Gavotte ... arranged ... by O. Langey. [1884.] fol.　**h. 1429. (17.)**

— *See* Moya, *pseud*. [Chanson du Cœur brisé.] The Song of Songs ... Arranged for violin solo ... by O. Langey. 1915. fol.
h. 1612. hh. (51.)

— *See* Schirmer (G.) Schirmer's Photoplay Series ... By O. Langey ... and others. 1915, *etc.* 4°.　**g. 1466.**

— *See* Schmid (F.) Queen Christina. Gavotte ... arrd. by O. Langey. [1887.] fol.　**g. 790. (32.)**

— *See* Silèsu (L.) Un Peu d'Amour ... Arranged for Violin and Piano by O. Langey. (1913.) fol.　**h. 1612. cc. (3.)**

— *See* Silèsu (L.) Un Peu d'Amour ... Arranged for Violoncello and Piano by O. Langey. 1913. fol.　**h. 1851. g. (35.)**

— *See* Stults (Robert M.) The Birds and the Brook ... Arr. [for orchestra] by O. Langey. [1901.] 8°.　**f. 800. a. (394.)**

— *See* Weber (C. M. F. E. von) [Euryanthe.] Selection ... arranged by O. Langey. [1882.] 8°.　**f. 410. f. (10.)**

— *See* Wilkins (H. P.) "Gilly, Gally, Gee" ... Arr. [for orchestra] by O. Langey. [1898.] 8°.　**f. 800. a. (501.)**

— *See* Wilkins (H. P.) "Gilly, Gally, Gee" ... Arr. [for wind band] by O. Langey. [1899.] *obl.* 8°.　**f. 800. a. (502.)**

— *See* Wilkins (H. P.) Oceanic ... Arr. [for orchestra] by O. Langey. [1899.] 8°.　**f. 800. a. (503.)**

— *See* Wolf-Ferrari (E.) [I Gioielli della Madonna.— Benedicimi tu.] Prayer ... transcribed by O. Langey. 1912. fol.
h. 1851. g. (51.)

— *See* Wolf-Ferrari (E.) [I Gioielli della Madonna.] Intermezzo II. ... Arranged (for Violin and Piano) by O. Langey. (1912.) fol.　**h. 1612. cc. (33.)**

LANGFORD (Alan)

— Blue Dreams. [P.F.] *Mozart Edition: London*, [1963.] 4°.
g. 1138. bb. (12.)

— Irish Coffee ... Arr. Peter Hope. [For orchestra. Score.] pp. 11. *Mozart Edition:* [*London*, c. 1965.] 4°.
g. 860. mm. (9.)

— Petite promenade. [For orchestra. Score.] pp. 11. *Mozart Edition:* [*London*, c. 1965.] 4°.　**g. 860. ll. (5.)**

— Scherzetto. For clarinet in B♭ and piano. [Score and part.] 2 pt. *Arcadia Music Publishing Co.: London*, [1962.] 4°.
g. 1104. z. (7.)

LANGFORD (ALAN)

— Suite international. [For orchestra. Score.] pp. 75. *Mozart Edition:* [*London*, c. 1965.] 4°.　　　　　　　**g. 860. jj. (3.)**

— Travelling Light. [For orchestra. Piano-conductor.] pp. 4. *Mozart Edition:* [*London*, c. 1965.] 4°.　　　　**g. 860. ll. (4.)**

— Trio. Three dance contrasts. [For orchestra. Score.] pp. 71. *Mozart Edition:* [*London*, c. 1965.] 4°.　　　**g. 860. ll. (6.)**

— Valse de la jeunesse. [For orchestra. Score.] pp. 23. *Mozart Edition:* [*London*, c. 1965.] fol.　　　　　**g. 860. mm. (7.)**

LANGFORD (E.)

— The Runaway. Two-Step. [P. F.] *Boosey & Co.: London and New York*, 1910. fol.　　　　　　　　**h. 3286. uu. (39.)**

LANGFORD (FRANK)

— The Hymns my Mother used to sing. [Song.] Written by F. Gee-Fort. *Star Music Publishing Co.: London*, 1911. fol.　　　　　　　　　　　　　　　　　**H. 1792. r. (20.)**

LANGFORD (GORDON)

— Ballade for Violin and Piano. [Score and part.] 2 pt. *Chandos Music: London*, [1969.] 4°.　　　**g. 223. uu. (5.)**

— *See* HART (Marion) [Gentlemen's Pastime.] Album of Songs from Gentlemen's Pastime ... Orchestrations by G. Langford. [1958.] 4°.　　　　　　　　　　　**F. 1196. j. (19.)**

— *See* NIVELLI (G.) Gypsy Tango. Bearbeitung: G. Langford. [1969.] 4°.　　　　　　　　　　　**h. 3210. j. (783.)**

LANGFORD (L. J.)

— Gavotte Pompadour ... Dance, *etc.* [P. F.] *M. Witmark & Sons: New York, etc.*, 1899. fol.　　　　**h. 3282. f. (10.)**

— *See* WILSON (Al. H.) Nightingale Song. [Song.] Arr. by L. J. Langford. [1909.] fol.　　　　　　**H. 3988. a. (24.)**

LANGFORD (LILIE)

— Come to my Heart. Song, words by S. A. Fitz-Gerald. *C. King: London*, [1887.] fol.　　　　　**H. 1788. u. (44.)**

LANGFORD-JAMES (RICHARD LLOYD)
— *See* JAMES.

LANGGAARD (RUDOLF IMMANUEL)

— Sanct Hansaften Spil ... Fragment af Slutningsscenen komponeret ... af N. W. Gade ... Instrumentation ... samt Komposition af den ufuldendte Hymne (Nr. 1 og 5) foretaget af R. I. Langgaard. Klaverudtog, *etc. See* COPENHAGEN.— *Samfundet til Udgivelse af dansk Musik.* [Publications of the Society.] 2. Række. Nr. 37. 1872, *etc.* fol.　　**G. 728.**

LANGGAARD (RUED)

— Strygekvartet Nr. 3 ... Partitur. pp. 26. *Fr. Kistner & C. F. W. Siegel: Leipzig*, [1931.] 8°. [*Samfundet til Udgivelse af dansk Musik. ser.* 3. *no.* 34.]　　　　　　　　　　　　　　　　**G. 728.**

LANGGAARD (SIEGFRIED)

— Romantisk Fantasi for Pianoforte. pp. 11. *Wilhelm Hansens Musik-Forlag: Kjöbenhavn*, [1881.] fol.　**h. 1226. a. (12.)**

LANGHAM (ALONZO)

— School Slates. An Action Song for five Girls, words and music by A. Langham. *J. Curwen & Sons: London*, [1909.] fol.　　　　　　　　　　　　　　　**H. 1984. e. (19.)**

LANGHANS (FRIEDRICH WILHELM)

— Zwanzig Studien für Violine in der ersten Lage. Zur Ausbildung der Finger insbesondere der Bogenführung ... Op. 5, durchgesehen von C. Nowotny. *Friedrich Hofmeister: Leipzig*, [1936?] 4°.　　　　　　　**g. 498. gg. (4.)**

LANGHANS (LOUISE)

— Danse guerrière pour le Piano. *Paris*, [1868.] fol.　　　　　　　　　　　　　　　　　　**h. 1462. r. (5.)**

— Nocturne pour le Piano. *Paris*, [1868.] fol.　**h. 1462. r. (6.)**

LANGHANS (WILHELM)

— Sonate für Violine mit Begleitung des Pianoforte. *Berlin*, [1878.] fol.　　　　　　　　　　**h. 1609. m. (5.)**

LANGI

— Langi rivolgo. *Venetian Ballad* [for two voices], *etc.* [*London*, 1776.] *s. sh.* 4°. *Lady's Magazine, Feb.*, 1776.　　　　**P. P. 5141.**

LÄNGIN

— [For the German surname of this form:] *See* LAENGIN.

LANGIUS (GREGOR)
— *See* LANGE (H. G.)

LANGLAIS (JEAN)

— American Suite. For organ, *etc.* pp. 64. *H. W. Gray Co.: New York*, [1962.] 4°.　　　　　**g. 1378. e. (14.)**

— [American Suite.] Troisième symphonie, *etc.* ⟨Pour orgue (1959/1979). Version révisée de l'"American suite" de 1959.⟩ [With a portrait.] pp. 47. *Universal Edition: Wien*, [1980.] fol. *Part of "Universal Orgel Edition".*　　**g. 1378. xx. (12.)**

— Carillons. For handbells alone. [Score.] pp. 8. *H. W. Gray Co.: New York*, [1968.] 8°. *Handbell Choir Series. no.* 15.　　　　**f. 246. o. (3.)**

— Huit chants de Bretagne. Pour orgue, *etc.* pp. 38. *Éditions Bornemann: Paris*, [1975.] fol.　　**h. 2732. cc. (5.)**

— Three Characteristic Pieces. For organ. pp. 13. *Novello and Co.: London*, [1957.] 4°. [*Novello's Organ Music Club. no.* 10.]　　　**g. 1023. f.**

— Essai (Trial). Pour orgue. pp. 9. *Éditions Bornemann: Paris*, [1962.] fol.　　　　　　　**h. 2732. cc. (6.)**

— Trois implorations. N°. 1—Pour la joie. ⟨N°. 2—Pour l'indulgence. N°. 3—Pour la croyance.⟩ Pour orgue. 2 bk. *Éditions Bornemann: Paris*, [1970.] fol.　　**h. 2732. cc. (7.)**

— Livre œcuménique. Pour orgue. pp. 42. *Éditions Bornemann: Paris*, [1968.] fol.　　　　　**g. 1376. j. (1.)**

— Cinq méditations sur l'Apocalypse pour orgue. pp. 47. *Éditions Bornemann: Paris*, [1974.] fol.　**h. 2732. dd. (9.)**

— Miniature. For organ. pp. 12. *H. W. Gray Co.: New York*, [1959.] 4°.　　　　　　　　**g. 1380. jj. (11.)**

— Missa dona nobis pacem. For voices in unison. pp. 16. *H. W. Gray Co.: New York*, [1963.] 8°. *Church Music Review. no.* 2836.　　　　　**F. 274. ll. (6.)**

LANGLAIS (JEAN)

— Missa misericordiae Domini. For soprano, tenor and bass and organ. pp. 53. *Gregorian Institute of America: Toledo, Ohio*, [1959.] 8°.
Part of "Connoisseur's Catalog. ser. 2".   **F. 1175. ff. (14.)**

— Piece in free Form. For string quartet (or orchestra) and organ. [Score and parts.] 5 pt. *H. W. Gray Co.: New York*, [1960.] 4°.   **g. 420. nn. (2.)**

— Prelude on 'Coronation'. [Organ.] *In:* WILLCOCKS (*Sir* David V.) Modern Organ Music. Book 2, *etc.* pp. 16–18. [1967.] 4°.   **g. 1376. bb. (1.)**

— Sonate en trio pour orgue. pp. 12. *Éditions Bornemann: Paris*, [1968.] fol.   **g. 1376. i. (3.)**

— Suite médiévale en forme de messe basse. Pour orgue. pp. 18. *Rouart, Lerolle & cⁱᵉ: Paris*, [1950.] fol.   **h. 2732. o. (13.)**

— Première symphonie pour orgue. pp. 44. *Philippo: Paris*, [c. 1970.] fol.   **g. 1376. j. (3.)**

— Deuxième symphonie. Pour orgue. pp. 6. *Éditions M. Combre: Paris*, [1977.] 4°.   **g. 1376. j. (2.)**

— Troisième symphonie. *See* supra: [American Suite.]

— Triptyque. [Organ.] pp. 24. *Novello & Co.: London*, [1958.] 4°.
[*International Series of contemporary Organ Music. no. 1.*]   **g. 1023. g.**

— Triptyque grégorien. Für Orgel, *etc.* ⟨1. Rosa mystica. 2. In Paradisum. 3. Alléluia.⟩ [With a portrait.] pp. 24. *Universal Edition: Wien*, [1979.] fol.
Part of "Universal Orgel Edition".   **g. 1378. xx. (10.)**

LANGLÉ (HONORÉ FRANÇOIS MARIE)

— IIIᵐᵉ. Canon à deux voix égales [begins: "Quanto mai felici siete"]. Paroles ... de Métastase. *Paris*, [1805?] fol.   **G. 808. a. (16.)**

— Corisandre, ou les Foux par Enchantement. Opéra Ballet. Paroles de *** [i.e. de Linières and A. F. Lebailly. Full score.] *Chés Le Duc: Paris*, [1791.] fol.   **G. 143.**

— [Another copy.]   **Hirsch ii. 505.**

— Nouvelle méthode pour chiffrer les accords. *Paris, An ix.* [1801.] 8°.   **557*. d. 35. (4.)**

— Solfèges. *See* BATISTE (A. E.) Solfèges du Conservatoire, *etc.* [1866, *etc.*] 8°.   **F. 470.**

— Traité d'Harmonie et de Modulation. *Chez Boyer: Paris*, [1793.] fol.   **G. 835. a.**

— Traité de la Basse sous le Chant, précédé de toutes les Règles de la Composition, *etc. Chez Naderman: Paris*, [1798.] fol.   **H. 2186.**

— Traité de la Fugue. *Paris*, [1805.] fol.   **G. 835.**

— Triomphe! de nos droits célébrons la conquête. *Hymne à la Liberté*, par T. Desorgues. *Du Magazin de Musique à l'usage des fêtes Nationales: Paris*, [1795.] 8°.   **E. 1717. b. (17.)**

— *See* AGUS (J. F.) Solféges pour servir à l'étude dans le Conservatoire de Musique à Paris par ... Agus ... Langlé, *etc.* [1795?] fol.   **H. 2851.**

— *See* MENGOZZI (B.) Méthode de chant du Conservatoire de musique, *etc.* [Edited by H. F. M. Langlé.] [1804.] fol.   **H. 2240. a.**

LANGLEY

— Langley Dale. Song. *See* BENNETT (J. L.)

LANGLEY

— Langley Fair. [Part-song.] *See* MARTIN (E.) [Four Songs of the Fair. No. 2.]

LANGLEY (   )

— The Dance. [P. F.] *S. Brainard's Sons Co.: New York, Chicago*, 1900. fol.
Part of "Brainard's Graded Studies in Rhythm," etc.   **h. 3820. o. (3.)**

— Gathering Flowers ... Contrary Motion. T. G. Boettger. [P. F.] *S. Brainard's Sons Co.: New York, Chicago*, 1900. fol.
Part of "Brainard's Graded Studies in Rhythm," etc.   **h. 3820. o. (4.)**

— The Mill ... Melody for the left Hand. T. G. Boettger. [P. F.] *S. Brainard's Sons Co.: New York, Chicago*, 1900. fol.
Part of "Brainard's Graded Studies in Rhythm," etc.   **h. 3820. o. (7.)**

— Pastime. [P. F.] *S. Brainard's Sons Co.: New York, Chicago*, 1900. fol.
Part of "Brainard's Graded Studies in Rhythm," etc.   **h. 3820. o. (6.)**

LANGLEY (ARTHUR)

— The jolly waggoner [song, begins: "Oh! when I drove my waggon"], written and composed by A. Langley, *etc. London*, [1858.] fol.   **H. 1771. l. (11.)**

LANGLEY (C. J.)

— The Star of Love. Song. Words by A. W. Oram, *etc.* pp. 7. *C. Barth & Cᵒ: London*, [c. 1895.] fol.   **H. 2184. d. (24.)**

LANGLEY (E. C. R.)

— A Service of Song illustrative of early Wesleyan enterprise in the Fiji and Friendly Isles by J. Hunt. Musical arrangements by E. C. R. Langley. *London*, [1873.] 8°.   **D. 675. c. (11.)**

LANGLEY (GEORGE)

— Examination Scales & Arpeggios ... arranged for the requirements of the various local Examinations ... Compiled and edited by G. Langley. [P. F.] *Augener: London*, (1912.) 4°.   **g. 337. cc. (8.)**

— Helen. Song [begins: "I wish I were where Helen lies"]. *London*, [1877.] fol.   **H. 1778. x. (35.)**

— Pianoforte Student's Chart of Technique and Theory. *Augener & Co.: London*, [1902.] 4°.   **f. 745.**

— *See* BACHE (F. E.) Compositions for the Pianoforte, *etc.* (Second Series. Revised ... by G. Langley.) [1898–1905.] 4°.   **g. 1145.**

— *See* BACHE (F. E.) L'Irrésistible ... Revised ... by G. Langley. [1903.] fol.   **g. 605. hh. (18.)**

— *See* BENNETT (*Sir* W. S.) 3 Musical Sketches ... Edited by G. Langley. [1904.] 4°.   **g. 442. n. (6.)**

— *See* CZERNY (C.) [École Préliminaire de Vélocité. Op. 636.] Preparatory School of Velocity ... revised ... by G. Langley. [1909.] 4°.   **g. 371. a. (6.)**

— *See* CZERNY (C.) [Die Schule der Geläufigkeit. Op. 299.] School of Velocity for Pianoforte ... revised ... by G. Langley. [1908–11.] 4°.   **g. 371. a. (5.)**

— *See* MAYER (C.) Select Works for the Pianoforte ... edited by G. Langley. [1906.] fol.   **g. 606. g. (14.)**

— *See* POTTER (P. C. H.) [Pezzi di Bravura. Op. 15. No. 2.] Allegretto ... Revised ... by G. Langley. [1906.] fol.   **h. 1424.**

LANGLEY (George)

— *See* WOLLENHAUPT (H. A.) [5 Morceaux caractéristiques ... Op. 22.] 5 Characteristic Pieces ... Edited by G. Langley. [1903.] fol.　　　　　　　　　　　　　**h. 1433. b. (8.)**

— *See* WOLLENHAUPT (H. A.) [5 Morceaux caractéristiques ... Op. 22.] 5 Characteristic Pieces ... Edited by G. Langley, *etc.* [1904.] 4°.　　　　　　　　　　　　　**g. 442. o. (20.)**

— *See* WOLLENHAUPT (H. A.) Le Ruisseau ... Revised ... by G. Langley. [1903.] 4°.　　　　　　　　**g. 603. j. (13.)**

LANGLEY (George A.)

— Ma little Sue. [Solo and chorus.] Words and music by G. A. Langley. [1909.] *See* CHORAL. The Choral Handbook. No. 825. [1885, *etc.*] 8°.　　　　　　　　　　　**E. 862.**

— The Piccaninnies' Lullaby. [Solo and chorus.] Words and music by G. A. Langley. [1909.] *See* CHORAL. The Choral Handbook. No. 824. [1885, *etc.*] 8°.　　　　**E. 862.**

LANGLEY (Hubert)

— *See* ARNE (T. A.) [*Collections, Vocal.*] Arias and Songs selected from the Works of Dr. Arne by H. Langley, *etc.* 1927, *etc.* 4°.　　　　　　　　　　　**G. 320. b. (1.)**

— *See* ARNE (T. A.) [Judith.] Here, Sons of Jacob, let us rest ... Edited by H. Langley. 1932. 8°.　　　**E. 602. qq. (31.)**

LANGLEY (James W.)

— Autumn. Part song for S.A.T.B. Words by Walter de la Mare. [Staff and tonic sol-fa notation.] pp. 6. *Ascherberg, Hopwood & Crew: London*, [1960.] 8°. [*Mortimer Series of modern Part-songs. no. 536.*]　　**F. 1659. a.**

— Chansonette. For oboe and piano. [Score and part.] 2 pt. *Hinrichsen Edition: London*, [1963.] 4°.　　**g. 1078. f. (10.)**

— Green Belt Suite. Flute, oboe, clarinet. [Parts.] 3 pt. *New Wind Music Co.: London*, [1969.] 4°.　　**g. 1067. s. (4.)**

— Invocation and Dance. For flute, oboe and piano. [Score and parts.] 3 pt. *Edition Peters; Hinrichsen Edition: London, etc.*, [1969.] 4°.　　　　　　　　　　**g. 1067. j. (2.)**

— Maestoso and Allegro (for trombone quartet), *etc.* ⟨Score, parts for trombones (concert) and trombones (in B♭).⟩ 5 pt. *Studio Music Company: London*, [1976.] 8°. *The alternative parts for trombones in B flat are printed on the verso of the parts for concert trombones.*　　**h. 3210. j. (857.)**

— Overture and Beginners. [For orchestra. Score.] pp. 31. *Mozart Edition:* [*London*, c. 1965.] 4°.　　**g. 860. hh. (5.)**

— Quartet. For 4 horns ... Score and parts. 5 pt. *Hinrichsen Edition: London*, [1963.] 4°.　　**g. 1094. i. (12.)**

— Quartet for four Horns ... Horn IV (alternative part for tenor horn). pp. 4. *Hinrichsen Edition: London*, [1965.] 4°.　　　　　　　　　　　　**g. 1094. l. (2.)**

— Scherzo. For four cornets ... Score & parts. 5 pt. *Studio Music Co.: London*, [1966.] 8°.　　**h. 3210. j. (41.)**

— Suite ... 4 trombones or 3 trombones & tuba. [Score.] pp. 12. *Hinrichsen Edition: London*, [1961.] 4°.　　**g. 1110. l. (9.)**

— Trio. Fanfare, waltz, berceuse, tarantella. Four pieces for three or more treble-clef instruments of equal pitch ... either ... descant recorders or flutes or oboes or violins ... or ... clarinets in B♭ or trumpets or cornets ... Score, *etc.* pp. 6. *Hinrichsen Edition: London*, [1966.] 4°.　　**g. 271. kk. (8.)**

LANGLEY (Lionel)

— Two Short Pieces. Prelude and Theme. [Organ.] *Enoch & Sons: London*, 1936. 4°. [*The Enoch Organ Library. No. 29.*]　　**g. 1283.**

LANGLEY (Mildred)

— King of the Land, King of the Sea. Patriotic Song, words & music by M. Langley, *etc. Weekes & Co.: London*, [1914.] fol.　　　　　　　　　　　　**H. 1793. s. (7.)**

— Waiting for you. Ballad, words and music by M. Langley. *West & Co.: London*, 1915. fol.　　**H. 1793. s. (8.)**

LANGLEY (Paul)

— Yo' ah ma Sunshine. [Song.] Words and music by P. Langley. pp. 6. *S. Brainard's Sons Co.: New York, Chicago*, [1899.] fol.　　　　　　　　　　　　**H. 3980. pp. (4.)**

LANGLEY (Percival)

— Don't you worry over me. ⟨Song.⟩ Written and composed by P. Langley, *etc.* [Staff and tonic sol-fa notation. Voice part.] *Francis, Day & Hunter: London*, [1903.] *s. sh.* fol.　　　　　　　　　　　　**H. 3985. h. (17.)**

— Don't you worry over me, *etc.* ⟨Song.⟩ [With separate voice part.] 2 pt. *Francis, Day & Hunter: London*, [1903.] fol.　　　　　　　　**H. 3985. h. (18.)**

— I'm coming back to London Town. ⟨Song. Arranged by Mark Archer. With tonic sol-fa.⟩ Written & composed by P. Langley, *etc.* pp. 3. *E. Marks & Son: London*, [1907.] fol. *Champion Edition. no. 31.*　　**H. 3985. h. (19.)**

— I've been over the Sea ... ⟨Song.⟩ Written and composed by P. Langley. [Staff and tonic sol-fa notation. Voice part.] *Francis, Day & Hunter: London*, [1907.] *s. sh.* fol.　　　　　　　　　　　　**H. 3985. h. (20.)**

— I've been over the Sea, *etc.* [With separate voice part.] 2 pt. *Francis, Day & Hunter: London*, [1907.] fol.　　　　　　　　　　　　**H. 3985. h. (21.)**

— The Old Coxwain. ⟨Song. With tonic sol-fa.⟩ Written by Charles Hayes, *etc.* pp. 3. *E. Marks & Son: London*, [1907.] fol. *Champion Edition. no. 23.*　　**H. 3985. h. (22.)**

— The Sweetest Song on Earth. Song. ⟨Arranged by Mark Archer. With tonic sol-fa.⟩ Written and composed by P. Langley. pp. 3. *E. Marks & Son: London*, [1907.] fol. *Champion Edition. no. 21.*　　**H. 3985. h. (23.)**

— There's always a Bit for you. Song. Written and composed by P. Langley, *etc.* ⟨With tonic sol-fa. Arranged by Mark Archer.⟩ *E. Marks & Son: London*, [1909.] fol. *Champion Edition. no. 67.*　　**H. 3985. h. (24.)**

— *See* BECKETT (Harry) By the sweet Seaside, *etc.* ⟨Song. Arranged by P. Langley.⟩ [1912.] fol.　　**H. 3989. j. (2.)**

— *See* BECKETT (Harry) Come out for the Moon don't shine, *etc.* ⟨Song. Arranged by P. Langley.⟩ [1912.] fol.　　**H. 3989. j. (3.)**

— *See* BECKETT (Harry) My Starlight Sue, *etc.* ⟨Song. Arranged by P. Langley.⟩ [1912.] fol.　　**H. 3989. j. (7.)**

— *See* BECKETT (Harry) My Wife is waiting up for me, *etc.* ⟨Song. Arranged by P. Langley.⟩ [1912.] fol.　　**H. 3989. j. (8.)**

— *See* BECKETT (Harry) Over there in Donegall [*sic*], *etc.* ⟨Song. Arranged by P. Langley.⟩ [1912.] fol.　　**H. 3989. j. (10.)**

— *See* BECKETT (Harry) Promise me, *etc.* ⟨Song. Arranged by P. Langley.⟩ [1912.] fol.　　**H. 3989. j. (11.)**

— *See* DONNELLY (Robert) Alexandra Day, *etc.* ⟨Song. Arranged by P. Langley.⟩ [1912.] fol.　　**H. 3991. k. (4.)**

LANGLEY (PERCIVAL)

— See DONNELLY (Robert) The Band was playing as the Ship went down, *etc.* ⟨Song. Arranged by P. Langley.⟩ [1912.] fol.
H. 3991. k. (5.)

— See DONNELLY (Robert) Gather round Boys, *etc.* ⟨Song. Arranged by P. Langley.⟩ [1911.] fol.
H. 3991. k. (7.)

— See DONNELLY (Robert) Sally from Paradise Alley, *etc.* ⟨Song. Arranged by P. Langley.⟩ [1911.] fol.
H. 3991. k. (8.)

— See DONNELLY (Robert) We are parted from each other, *etc.* ⟨Song. Arranged by P. Langley.⟩ [1911.] fol.
H. 3991. k. (10.)

— See DONNELLY (Robert) When next Summer's Sun is sinking Evelyn, *etc.* ⟨Song. Arranged by P. Langley.⟩ [1912.] fol.
H. 3991. k. (11.)

— See LESTER (George) and LANGLEY (P.) It's a Wonder what Money will do ... ⟨Song.⟩ Written and composed by G. Lester and P. Langley. [1905.] *s. sh.* fol.
H. 3985. x. (35.)

— See LESTER (George) and LANGLEY (P.) It's a Wonder what Money will do, *etc.* ⟨Song.⟩ [1905.] fol.
H. 3985. x. (36.)

— See ROBSON (T. F.) and LANGLEY (P.) I do love myself, don't I! ⟨Song.⟩ Written & composed by T. F. Robson & P. Langley, *etc.* [1900.] *s. sh.* fol.
H. 3986. tt. (62.)

— See ROBSON (T. F.) and LANGLEY (P.) I do love myself, don't I! *etc.* ⟨Song.⟩ [1900.] fol.
H. 3986. tt. (63.)

LANGLEY (ROBIN)

— See CHILCOT (Thomas) [Six Concertos. Op. 2. No. 2.] Concerto in A major ... For harpsichord, two violins, and violoncello ... Edited by R. Langley. [1975.] fol. [*Musica da camera.* 32.]
g. 935.

— See CHILCOT (Thomas) [Six Concertos. Op. 2. No. 5.] Concerto in F major ... For harpsichord, two oboes, bassoon, and strings ... Edited by R. Langley. [1975.] fol. [*Musica da camera.* 33.]
g. 935.

LANGLOIS (EDMOND)

— Les Souvenirs du Jeune Age. Romance [begins: "Entendez vous"]. [*Paris*, 1835?] fol.
G. 551. (28.)

LANGLOIS (ERNEST)

— See BARON (V.) Souvenez-vous ... Accompagnement de E. Langlois. 1914. fol.
H. 1187. tt. (30.)

LANGLOIS (H. G.)

— Holy Lord God Almighty. Motet, *etc. H. W. Gray Co.: New York*, 1926. 8°.
E. 335. d. (19.)

— Souls of the Righteous. Anthem for S.A.T.B. ... From the Book of Wisdom, verse tr. by ... Dr Stubbs. pp. 4. *H. W. Gray: New York*, [1959.] 8°.
E. 335. x. (27.)

LANGLY (PAUL)

— I look into thine Eyes. A Ballad. Words and Music by P. Langly. *American Composers' Assoc.: Chicago*, 1898. fol.
H. 1799. h. (4.)

LANGO

— Lango Lee. Song. *See* THERE. There lives a sweet lovely dear Girl, *etc.* [1775?] *s. sh.* fol.
G. 316. j. (12.)

— Lango Lee. Irish song. *See* THERE. There lives a sweet lovely dear Girl, *etc.* [c. 1775.] *s. sh.* fol.
H. 1648. f. (33.)

LANGO

— Lango Lee. Song. *See* YOU. You Lads of Hybernia that's fond of true pleasure. [1775?] *s. sh.* fol.
G. 314. (108.)

— New words to Lango Lee. [Song.] *See* I. I'm an Irish young Fellow. [1777?] *s. sh.* fol.
H. 1601. a. (83.)

— Lango Lee. [Song.] *In:* LIFE. Life's like a Ship, *etc.* p. 3. [WM1822.] fol.
G. 425. ss. (20.)

LANGRAN (JAMES)

— Abide with me; fast falls the Eventide. Evening hymn, for four voices, with an accompaniment for the organ or pianoforte. ⟨Fourth edition.⟩ *Novello & Co.: London*, [c. 1870.] 8°.
F. 1124. t. (7.)

— A Short Setting of the Office for the Holy Communion—with Benedictus and Agnus Dei—for parochial and general use. *Novello and Co.: London*, [1905.] 8°.
E. 597. r. (24.)

— Hark! the Sound of holy Voices. Hymn for four voices. Written by the ... Bishop of Lincoln. pp. 3. *Novello, Ewer & Co: London*, [c. 1865.] 8°.
B. 1179. ii. (2.)

— Magnificat and Nunc Dimittis. Easy setting for parish choirs. *London*, [1883.] 8°.
E. 597. d. (21.)

— The New Mitre Hymnal adapted to the Services of the Church of England. With accompanying tunes. [Music editor: J. Langran.] 1875. 8°. *See* HYMNS. [*English*.]
E. 619.

— O God of Glory, King of Kings most high. National Thanksgiving Hymn, words by Rev. A. Newns. [1902.] *See* NOVELLO AND CO. Novello's Parish Choir Book, *etc.* No. 611. [1866, *etc.*] 8°.
E. 618.

— Te Deum and Benedictus. Easy setting in chant form. *Novello, Ewer and Co.: London & New York*, [1888.] 8°.
E. 597. k. (17.)

— See HYMNS. [*English*.] Eight Original Harvest Hymns ... Music by Dr. Dykes ... J. Langran, *etc.* [1880?] 8°.
B. 507. (21.)

— See MACCLUER (W. L. R.) Ten Hymns ... by ... J. Langran, *etc.* [1901.] 8°.
D. 620. y. (17.)

— See NEVIN (G. B.) Two Funeral Hymns ... [No. 1.] Welcome the Rest to weary pilgrim Feet.—Arr. from J. Langran, *etc.* (1906.) 8°.
F. 1529. e. (31.)

LANGREDER (MARTIN)

— Canticum Gloriosæ Deiparæ Virginis Mariæ, Sex Vocibus, super varia—ut vocant—Madrigalia, non ita pridem artificiosissimè modulatum, à R. F. Martino Langreder ... Iam verò post immaturum illius obitum typis evulgatum, operâ & studio R. D. Michaelis Hererii, *etc.* Quinta (Sexta) Vox. 2 pt. *Matthæus Nenninger: Pataviæ*, 1602. 4°. **C. 261.**

— Honora Medicum [Motet for 5 voices] ... Nobili ... Viro Ioanni Hiltprando ... dedicatum. 5 pt. *Matthæus Nenninger: Pataviæ*, 1602. 4°.
B. 293.

LANGRIDGE (ROY)

— See WHARTON (Patricia M.) Brighton Belle ... Music arranged by R. Langridge. 1975. 4°.
F. 1199. g. (5.)

LANGRISH (HUGO)

— Benedicite. For unison voices and organ or piano, *etc.* pp. 4. *Ascherberg, Hopwood & Crew: London*, [1969.] 8°. [*Year Book Press Music Series. A* 171.]
H. 802.

— Communion Service. For unison voices and organ or piano, *etc.* pp. 8. *Ascherberg, Hopwood & Crew: London*, [1969.] 8°. [*Year Book Press Music Series. A* 173a.]
H. 802.

LANGRISH (Hugo)

— Eighty easy Pieces. For horn and piano. Arranged by
H. Langrish. [The music by] Byrd, Couperin, Farnaby, [and
others] etc. [Score and part.] 2 pt. *Oxford University Press:
London*, [1972.] 4°.   **g. 1780. uu. (4.)**

LANGRISH (Vivian)

— See BACH (J. S.) [*Collected Works.—g.*] Organ Choral Preludes
... Arranged as pianoforte duo by V. Langrish. 1924. fol.
                                              h. 3007. e. (11.)

— See BACH (J. S.) [Übrige Choralvorspiele. B. G. Jahrg. XL.
Herzlich thut mich verlangen.] My Soul longeth for Thee, O
Lord ... transcribed for the Pianoforte by V. Langrish. 1940.
4°.   **g. 548. pp. (10.)**

— See BACH (J. S.) [Notenbuch der Anna Magdalena Bach ...
1725.] Eighteen Selected Pieces from A Little Notebook for
Anna Magdalena Bach ... Revised ... by V. Langrish. [1935.]
4°.   **g. 548. bb. (26.)**

— See BACH (J. S.) [Praeludien and Fugen für Orgel. Zweite
Folge. No. 10.] Organ Toccata in F. Arranged for two pianos
by V. Langrish. [1947.] 4°. [*Two-Piano Series. no.* 31.]
                                              g. 1393.

— See BACH (J. S.) Organ Prelude and Fugue in G major. [B. G.
Jahrg. XXXVIII. No. 2.] Arranged for Two Pianos by
V. Langrish. 1938. 4°.   **g. 548. ff. (14.)**

— See BACH (J. S.) [Das wohltemperirte Clavier. Th. 1. Prelude
7.] Prelude in E flat ... Arranged by V. Langrish for
S. A. T. B., etc. 1929. 4°.   **G. 136. i. (19.)**

— See BEETHOVEN (L. van) [*Collected Works.—c.*] Beethoven
Album ... Edited by V. Langrish. [1936.] 4°.
                                              g. 249. dd. (12.)

— See BRAHMS (J.) [Clavierstücke. Op. 118. No. 5.] Romance in
F. Freely arranged for clarinet and piano by V. Langrish.
[1965.] 4°.   **g. 609. v. (4.)**

— See SCARLATTI (D.) Scarlatti Album. Twelve Sonatas for
Pianoforte ... Edited by V. Langrish. 1936. 4°.
                                              g. 1127. xx. (24.)

— See WEBER (C. M. F. E. von) [Sonatas. Op. 24.] Rondo in C ...
Freely transcribed for two pianofortes by V. Langrish. [1950.]
4°.   **h. 1336. j. (10.)**

LANGRISH (W. E.)

— See L., W. E.

LANGS (John Pierce)

— The Blueing of the Day. A Welsh Folk-Poem. [Song.]
G. Schirmer: New York, etc., 1916. 4°.   **G. 383. bb. (18.)**

LANGSDALE (Edwin)

— L'Adorée. Waltz. [P. F.] *R. Cocks & Co.: London*, 1895. fol.
                                              h. 3285. p. (54.)

— Bal poudré, waltz-lancers, introducing the following popular
waltzes:—"La Gitana," "Innamorata," "Zuleika" &
"Braganza". Arranged by Edwin Langsdale. ⟨Orchestra,
[arranged] by Carl Kiefert.⟩ [Parts.] *Robert Cocks & Cᵒ:
London*, [c. 1895.] 8°.
Imperfect; the P.F. and 1st violin parts only. **g. 1797. k. (7.)**

— Bal Poudré. Waltz-Lancers, etc. [P. F.] *R. Cocks & Co.:
London*, [1895.] fol.   **h. 3285. p. (55.)**

— "The Bric-à-brac Will." Lancers. ⟨Polka. Waltz.⟩ On airs from
Emilio Pizzi's successful comedy-opera. Orchestra [arranged]
by Herman Finck. 3 no. *Robert Cocks & Cᵒ: [London*, 1896.]
8°.
Imperfect; the P.F. and 1st violin parts only. **g. 1797. l. (7.)**

LANGSDALE (Edwin)

— The Bric-à-Brac Will. Lancers (Polka) (Waltz). On airs from
E. Pizzi's ... Opera. Arranged by E. Langsdale. 3 no.
R. Cocks & Co.: London, 1896. fol.   **h. 2386. g. (5.)**

— Cigarette. Barn Dance on Airs from J. H. Parry's ... Opera.
[P. F.] *R. Cocks & Co.: London*, 1894. fol. **h. 3285. p. (56.)**

— Easy Fantasias on Plantation Melodies for the Pianoforte.
Arranged and fingered by E. Langsdale. See LONDON. The
London Album. No. 19. [1900.] fol.   **H. 1983. a.**

— The Lady Cyclists. Waltz-Lancers ... (arranged by
E. Langsdale.) [P. F.] *R. Cocks & Co.: London*, [1896.] fol.
                                              h. 3286. g. (6.)

— R. Cocks & Co.'s National and Patriotic Song Album, edited
by E. Langsdale. *R. Cocks & Co.: London*, [1896.] 4°.
                                              G. 385. m. (6.)

— Sir Reynard. Lancers ... arranged by E. Langsdale. [P. F.]
R. Cocks & Co.: London, 1894. fol.   **h. 3285. p. (57.)**

— The United Kingdom Lancers, on popular airs, arranged by
E. Langsdale. [P. F.] *R. Cocks & Co.: London*, [1892.] fol.
                                              h. 3285. p. (58.)

— See ASCHER (J.) Alice, where art thou, etc. (Arrangement by
E. Langsdale.) [1904.] fol.   **H. 1799. kk. (26.)**

— See BLACK (J. M.) When the Roll is called up yonder. ...
Arrangement by E. Langsdale. [1903.] fol.   **H. 1187. bb. (19.)**

— See BOGERT (L.) La Tosca ... arranged by E. Langsdale.
[1894.] fol.   **h. 3285. h. (11.)**

— See COBB (G. F.) A Drinking Song. Arranged ... by
E. Langsdale, etc. 1898. 8°.   **F. 156. a.**

— See EXCELL (E. O.) Count your Blessings ... Arrangement by
E. Langsdale. 1903. fol.   **H. 1187. bb. (50.)**

— See FARBAN (R.) The Yaller Gal. Barn Dance. Arranged ...
by E. Langsdale. 1896. fol.   **h. 188. e. (5.)**

— See GODFREY (A. E.) The Boston Belle ... Barn Dance,
arranged ... by E. Langsdale. 1894. fol.   **h. 2930. (3.)**

— See GODFREY (A. E.) Happy Darkies ... Barn Dance,
arranged ... by E. Langsdale. 1894. fol.   **h. 2930. (11.)**

— See GODFREY (A. E.) The Piccaninnies, etc. (Arranged for
Mandoline (Violin) & Piano by E. Langsdale.) 1895. fol.
                                              h. 2930. (19.)

— See MASCHERONI (A.) A Soldier's Song. Arranged ... by
E. Langsdale, etc. [1898.] 8°.   **F. 156. a.**

— See SCOTT (Bennett) Somebody's Sailor Boy ... Orchestra by
E. Langsdale. [1903.] 8°.   **f. 800. a. (328.)**

— See SOUSA (J. P.) The Liberty Bell. March ... simplified ... by
E. Langsdale. [1898.] fol.   **h. 3662. (23.)**

— See SOUSA (J. P.) The Washington Post March ... Simplified
... by E. Langsdale. [1898.] fol.   **h. 3662. (30.)**

— See STUDENT. The Student's Cabinet, etc. [Book 11 arranged
by E. Langsdale.] [1902, etc.] fol.   **h. 1718.**

— See TCHAKOFF (I.) pseud. Cossack Dance ... Arranged for
Mandoline & Piano by E. Langsdale. [1895.] fol.
                                              h. 188. b. (25.)

LANGSHAW (Gifford)

— A Maid of Sicily. Song, words by E. Oxenford. *Ransford &
Son: London*, 1892. fol.   **G. 807. h. (4.)**

— The Sweetest Music. Song, words by E. Oxenford. *Ransford
& Son: London*, 1892. fol.   **G. 807. h. (5.)**

LANGSHAW (JOHN)

— Air with Variations for the Harp, or piano-forte. pp. 7. *Printed by Goulding, Phipps & D'Almaine: London,* [WM1802.] fol. **h. 61. h. (8.)**

— *See* PLEYEL (I. J.) The Flow'r that's unvalu'd ... air ... adapted ... by J. Langshaw. [c. 1805.] fol. **G. 295. q. (3.)**

LANGSHAW (W.)

— Dear boy, throw that icicle down. Ballad with an accompaniment for the piano forte, or harp ... the poetry by R. Bloomfield. *London,* [WM1801.] fol. **H. 2818. f. (7.)**

— [Another copy.] *On this copy the composer's name has been altered in ink to "Jnº Langshaw".* **H. 2401. f. (9.)**

LANGSTAFF (A. M.)

— With thee. [Song.] *M. Witmark & Sons:* [*New York, etc.,*] 1904. fol. **H. 1799. vv. (22.)**

LANGSTAFF (ARTHUR)

— Beryl. Gavotte. [P. F.] *W. H. Broome: London,* [1897.] fol. **h. 3282. f. (11.)**

— Elvera. Entr'acte. 2 no. [P. F. solo and duet.] *W. H. Broome: London,* [1896.] fol. **h. 3282. f. (12.)**

— Elvera. Entr'acte. [P. F.] *See* PLAYTIME. Playtime Melodies, *etc.* [No. 3.] 1902. fol. **h. 3283. d. (42.)**

— In golden Days. Waltz. [P. F.] *W. H. Broome: London,* [1897.] fol. **h. 3286. g. (7.)**

— Regulation. Quick March. [P. F.] *W. H. Broome: London,* [1897.] fol. **h. 3286. g. (8.)**

— Rosemary. Gavotte. [P. F.] *W. H. Broome: London,* 1899. fol. **h. 3282. f. (13.)**

LANGSTAFF (JOHN)

— Hot Cross Buns, and other old street cries. Chosen especially for children by John Langstaff. Pictures by Nancy Winslow Parker. [Melodies only.] pp. 26. *Angus & Robertson: London,* 1980. 8°. **E. 353. bb.**

— On Christmas Day in the Morning! Carols gathered by J. Langstaff ... Piano settings by Marshall Woodbridge, *etc. World's Work: Tadworth; Haarlem* [printed, 1959.] 8°. **11663. s. 39.**

— Skin and Bones, and other folk songs for group singing. Selected by John Langstaff, with piano settings by John Edmunds, Seymour Barab, Phil Merrill, Marshall W. Barron. With guitar chords suggested by Happy Traum. Illustrated by Robin Jacques. pp. 112. *Harcourt, Brace & World: New York; Oxford University Press: London; Amersham* printed, [1976.] 4°. **E. 1885. ii.**

— Skin and Bones, and other folk-songs for group singing. ⟨Melody edition.⟩ pp. 67. *Harcourt, Brace & World: New York; Oxford University Press: London; Amersham* printed, [1976.] 8°. **D. 485. ff.**

— *See* LANGSTAFF (Nancy) and LANGSTAFF (J.) Jim along, Josie. A collection of folk songs and singing games ... Compiled by N. and J. Langstaff, *etc.* [1975.] 8°. **E. 1885. gg.**

LANGSTAFF (NANCY) and LANGSTAFF (JOHN)

— Jim along, Josie. A collection of folk songs and singing games for young children. Compiled by Nancy and John Langstaff. Piano arrangements by Seymour Barab. Guitar chords by Happy Traum. Optional percussion accompaniments for children. Illustrated by Jan Pienkowski.

LANGSTAFF (NANCY) and LANGSTAFF (JOHN)

pp. 127. *Harcourt Brace Jovanovich: New York; Oxford University Press: London; Amersham* printed, [1975.] 8°. **E. 1885. gg.**

LANGSTON (ASTLEY)

— *See* VOLUNTARIES. The Cathedral Voluntaries, *etc.* Book 13 ... by A. Langston. [1901, *etc.*] 4°. **f. 316. a.**

LANGSTON (HORACE)

— Pansies. Pianoforte solo. *Reid Bros.: London,* 1916. fol. **h. 3284. nn. (9.)**

— Sleigh Bells. [P. F.] *Westbrook & Co.: Birmingham,* [1901.] fol. *Miniature Recreations, etc. No. 5.* **H. 727. a. (12.)**

— Sleigh Bells. [P. F.] *See* MINIATURE. Miniature Recreations, *etc.* No. 5. [1904.] fol. **h. 3283. d. (41.)**

— The Waterfall. Pianoforte solo. *Reid Bros.: London,* 1916. fol. **h. 3284. nn. (10.)**

LANGSTON (W. STEFF)

— Home Dreams. Song, words by H. J. Brandon. *Kibble & Co.: London,* 1918. fol. **H. 1846. x. (21.)**

— Severed. Song, the words ... by W. C. Tetley. *Novello and Co.: London,* [1900.] fol. **G. 807. o. (41.)**

— Stand to your Guns. Song, words by P. J. Grace, *etc. Kibble & Co.: London,* 1915. fol. **H. 1793. s. (9.)**

LANGSTROTH (IVAN SHED)

— At the Cradle. For organ. ⟨Opus 34, No. 1.⟩ pp. 4. *Novello and Co.: London,* [1956.] 4°. [*Original Compositions. new ser. no.* 278.] **g. 1270.**

— Three Chorale Preludes for Organ. pp. 7. *Novello & Co.: London,* [1957.] 4°. [*Original Compositions. new ser. no.* 292.] **g. 1270.**

— Chorale-Toccata and Fugue. For organ. ⟨Opus 30.⟩ pp. 25. *Novello and Co.: London,* [1956.] 4°. [*Original Compositions. new ser. no.* 242.] **g. 1270.**

— Fantasy and Fugue for Organ. ⟨Opus 22, No. 1.⟩ pp. 21. *Novello and Co.: London,* [1956.] 4°. [*Original Compositions. new ser. no.* 240.] **g. 1270.**

— God be merciful unto us. Anthem for S.A.T.B. with soprano and tenor solos. Psalm 67 ... Op. 32. No. 1. pp. 16. *H. W. Gray & Co.: New York,* [1961.] 8°. **E. 335. dd. (3.)**

— Introduction and Fugue. For organ. pp. 15. *H. W. Gray Co.: New York,* [1962.] 4°. **g. 1378. f. (11.)**

— Love at Christmas Time. Christmas carol for mixed voices. [With bells or chimes and organ. Words by] Kathleen Norris. [Score.] pp. 7. *The H. W. Gray Co.: New York,* [1955.] 8°. *Church Music Review. no.* 2386. **F. 260. mm. (13.)**

— Soldier's Song 1915. Soldatenlied 1915. — Oesterreichisches Reiterlied. — Poem by Zuckermann. — Fallen in battle. — (Engl. version by G. Harris.) Op. 12. No. 1. *G. Schirmer: New York, London,* 1915. fol. **H. 1846. x. (22.)**

— Sonatina. For piano. ⟨Opus 29.⟩ pp. 14. *Novello & Co.: London,* [1960.] 4°. **g. 272. tt. (7.)**

— Theme with Variations. For organ. Opus 43. pp. 20. *Novello & Co.: London,* [1961.] 4°. [*International Series of contemporary Organ Music. no.* 6.] **g. 1023. g.**

LANGSTROTH (Ivan Shed)

— Toccata in A major. [Organ.] pp. 8. *H. W. Gray Co.: New York*, [1959.] 4°. **g. 1380. jj. (12.)**

— Toccata on 'Wir pflügen' [by J. A. P. Schulz]. For organ. pp. 7. *Novello & Co.: London*, [1958.] 4°.
[*Original Compositions. new ser.* 263.] **g. 1270.**

LANGSYNE

— Langsyne. Song. *See* Needham (A. A.)

LÄNGTAN

— Längtan. [Part-song.] *See* Söderman (J. A.)

— Längtan heter min arfvedel. [Song.] *See* Sibelius (J.) Sex Sänger. Op. 86. Nr. 2.

LANGTON (   )

— *See* Wallis (W. H.) and Langton (   ) Now he's climbing up the golden Stairs, *etc.* (Song.) [1891.] fol.
H. 3981. nn. (10.)

LANGTON (Stephen)

— The Army. Song. *W. Paxton: London*, 1902. fol.
H. 1799. vv. (23.)

— The Army. Song. *Whaley, Royce & Co.: Toronto*, 1902. fol.
G. 807. z. (28.)

— The Navy; or The Sailors of the King. [Song.] *W. Paxton: London*, 1901. fol. **H. 1799. vv. (24.)**

— The Navy; or The Sailors of the King. [Song.] *Whaley, Royce & Co.: Toronto*, 1901. fol.
G. 807. z. (29.)

LANGTON (Thomas)

— Hymn Tunes. *T. Langton:* [*Toronto*,] 1909. *s. sh.* 8°.
F. 538. e. (28.)

LANGTRY, afterwards MALCOLM (Jeanne)

— Golden Leaves. *See* infra: Two Songs. [No. 2.]

— The Heart of a Maid. Song, words by R. Lucas. *Chappell & Co.: London, etc.*, 1911. fol. **H. 1792. u. (26.)**

— It can't be wrong! Song, the words by I[on] Z[achary] M[alcolm]. *Enoch & Sons: London*, 1904. fol.
H. 1799. vv. (25.)

— Keeper of my Heart. Song, the words by M. S. MacMullan. *Enoch & Sons: London*, 1906. fol. **H. 1794. xx. (39.)**

— My Rose. Song, the words and music by J. Langtry. *Enoch & Sons: London*, 1902. fol. **H. 1799. vv. (26.)**

— Shall I not wake? Song, the words by B. Deane-Freeman. *Boosey & Co.: London and New York*, 1906. fol.
H. 1794. m. (13.)

— Soldier and Slave. Song, words by I[on] Z[achary] M[alcolm]. *Chappell & Co.: London*, 1904. fol. **H. 1799. vv. (27.)**

— Two Songs. [No. 1.] Tell me. [No. 2.] Golden Leaves. [Words by E. B.] 2 no. *J. Church Co.: Cincinnati, etc.*, (1908.) fol.
H. 1794. xx. (40.)

— Tell me. *See* supra: Two Songs. [No. 1.]

— To the Fairies. Song, the words by I[on] Z[achary] M[alcolm]. *Enoch & Sons: London*, 1904. fol. **H. 1799. vv. (28.)**

— Viking Hearts. Song, the words by I[on] Z[achary] M[alcolm]. *Boosey & Co.: London and New York*, 1905. fol.
H. 1794. m. (14.)

LANGTRY, afterwards MALCOLM (Jeanne)

— Viking Hearts. Military March. [P. F.] *Boosey & Co.: London and New York*, 1905. fol. **h. 3283. q. (9.)**

LANGUAGE

— Language failed him. Song. *See* Henry (Roland)

— Language of Flowers. Song. *See* Carr (F. O.) [Blue-Eyed Susan.]

— The Language of Flowers. Song. *See* Gounod (C. F.) [Faust.—Faites-lui mes aveux.]

— The Language of Flowers. Song-Cycle. *See* Moss (R. A.)

— The Language of Flowers. Song. *See* Schubert (F. P.) [Der Blumenbrief.]

— The Language of Flowers. Song. *See* Wood (Haydn)

— The Language of London Town. Song. *See* Rogers (E. W.)

— The Language of Love. Song. *See* Diabelli (A.)

— The Language of Love. Ballad. *See* Farnie (H. B.)

— The Language of Love. Canzonet. *See* Jarvis (C.)

— The Language of Love. Song. *See* Leo (Frank)

— The Language of Lover's Smiles. [Song.] *See* Barratt (W. A.)

— The Language of popular Songs. Song. *See* Perry (Albert)

— The Language of Song. Canzona. *See* Donizetti (D. G. M.) [La Fille du Régiment.—Chacun le sait.]

— The Language of the Bells. [Part-song.] *See* Nixon (C.)

— The Language of the Eye. [Song.] *See* Dorn (C. J.)

— The Language of the Eye. Ballad. *See* Hodgson (C.)

— The Language of the Eye. Song. *See* Payn (G. H.)

— The Language of the Eyes. [Song.] *See* Words. Words but faintly can impart, *etc.* [1770?] *s. sh.* fol. **G. 313. (245.)**

— The Language of the Eyes. Song. *See* Meyder (C.)

— The Language of the Eyes. [Song.] *See* Ware (N. H.)

— The Language of the Flowers. Song. *See* Monckton (L.) [The Toreador.]

— The Language of the Heart. Song. *See* Blockley (J. J.)

— The Language of the Heart. [Song.] *See* Eulenstein (C.)

— The Language of the Heart. Ballad. *See* Matthews (J. A.)

— The Language of the Heart. Song. *See* Miles (R. E.)

— The Language of the Rose. Song. *See* Turner (K. W.)

LANGUE

— La Langue musicale. Opéra. *See* Halévy (J. F. F. É.)

LANGUENTIBUS

— Languentibus in Purgatorio. [Duet.] *See* G., G.

LANGUID

— The Languid Swell. *See* I. I've always been a languid swell. [1872.] fol. **H. 1791. (59.)**

LANGUIDEZZE

— Languidezze Amorose. Cantate a voce sola. *See* Bassani (G. B.)

LANGUIR

— Languir d'amore. Ariette. *See* CRESCENTINI (G.)

— Languir d'amore. Cavatina. *See* MIGLIORUCCI (Vincenzo)

— Languir d'Amore. Venetian Ballad. *See* SOLARI (C. H.)

— Languir me fais. Chanson. *See* SERMISY (C. de)

— Languir mi sento il core. Duett. *See* ZINGARELLI (N. A.) [Il Conte di Saldagna.]

— Languir per una bella. Cavatina. *See* ROSSINI (G. A.) [L'Italiana in Algieri.]

LANGUIRÒ

— Languirò sempre. Song. *See* COSTA (P. M.)

LANGUISH

— Languish and dispair, my Heart. [Song.] *See* WILSON (John) *Mus. Doc.*

LANGUISHING

— The Languishing Lady. [Ballad.] *See* WELCOME. Welcome Death, *etc.* [1695?] *s. sh.* fol.   **Case 39. k. 6. (52.)**

— The Languishing Shepherd. [Ballad.] *See* WHEN. When my kids and my lambs, *etc.* [1695?] *s. sh.* fol.   **Case 39. k. 6. (5.)**

— The Languishing Swain. Song. *See* HAPPY. Happy's the Man that's free from love, *etc.* [1690?] *s. sh.* fol.
Case 39. k. 6. (62.)

LANGUISHMENT

— Languishment. [Part-song.] *See* NOBLE (H.)

LANGUOR

— Languor. [Song.] *See* CRIST (L. B.)

LANGUORE

— Languore. Romanza. *See* MATTEI (T.)

LANGWORTHY (BEATRICE)

— *See* GATTY, afterwards SCOTT-GATTY (*Sir* A. S.) Six Plantation Songs, *etc.* (The accompaniment arranged for Banjo by B. Langworthy.) 1893–96. fol.   **H. 2542. d. (5.)**

LANHAM (AUGUSTUS)

— Off to Blackpool. Action Song ... words and music by A. Lanham. *J. Curwen & Sons: London,* [1893.] fol.
H. 1984. (23.)

LANHAM (GUY)

— Valse Impromptu, for the Pianoforte. *Metzler & Co.: London,* 1911. fol.   **h. 3284. f. (43.)**

LANIER (NICHOLAS)

— Six Songs by Nicholas Lanier. Edited by Edward Huws Jones. [With a portrait.] pp. 15. *Galliard; Stainer & Bell: London; Galaxy Music Corporation: New York,* [1976.] 8°.
E. 271. k. (4.)

— Hero and Leander. [Cantata. Edited by Vincent Duckles.] *In:* DUCKLES (Vincent) and ZIMMERMAN (Franklin B.) Words to Music, *etc.* pp. 28–42. 1967. 8°.   **X. 431/492.**

LANIER (NICHOLAS)

— The Lilly ... [Song.] Extrait de: Select Ayres and Dialogues ... John Playford, Second Book, 1669, *etc. F. Alcan: Paris,* 1912. 8°.
Pp. 531 *and* 532 *of "Robert Herrick," etc., by F. Delattre.*
011853. dd. 1.

— Though I am young. [Three-part song.] From Select Musical Ayres and Dialogues, Playford, 1653 ... Arr. by E. Rowland. *J. B. Cramer & Co.: London,* 1942. 4°.
[*Cramer's Library of School Classics. No.* 13.]   **F. 157. f.**

— *See* PLAYFORD (J.) Select Musicall Ayres and Dialogues ... by ... Mr. Nicholas Lanneare, *etc.* 1653. fol.   **K. 7. i. 18.**

— *See* PLAYFORD (J.) Select Ayres and Dialogues ... Composed by ... N. Laneare ... and other Masters of Musick. 1659. fol.
K. 7. i. 19. (1.)

— *See* ROWLAND (E.) Ayres from Playford ... by ... N. Laniere, *etc.* 1935. 8°.   **F. 217. g. (7.)**

— *See* SABOL (Andrew J.) [Lovers made Men.] A Score for "Lovers made Men". A masque by Ben Jonson. The music adapted and arranged ... from compositions by N. Lanier, A. Ferrabosco and their contemporaries ... by A. J. Sabol. 1963. 4°.   **G. 1306.**

LANIERE (NICHOLAS)

— *See* LANIER.

LANIGAN

— Lanigan's Ball. Song. *See* GLOVER (C. W.)

LANIGER (W. D.)

— "After" (H. Millard) transcribed for the Pianoforte. *London,* [1872.] fol.   **h. 1485. s. (17.)**

— Graziella, fantaisie mazurka for Pianoforte. *London,* [1876.] fol.   **h. 1482. y. (31.)**

— Minuet & Trio in D for the Pianoforte. *London,* [1876.] fol.
h. 1482. y. (32.)

LANKASTER (YORKE A.)

— England calls, To Arms! Song, words by E. Trevelyan. *Weekes & Co.: London,* [1914.] fol.   **H. 1793. s. (10.)**

LANKAU (C.)

— *See* EISOLAT (C. A.) Sérénade ... arr. par C. Lankau. [1878.] fol.   **h. 1609. l. (3.)**

LANKFORD (GRACE WARD)

— Classics for the young Pianist. Compiled and edited by G. W. Lankford. *G. Schirmer: New York,* [1960, *etc.*] 4°.
g. 1126. aa.

— [A reissue.] Classics for the young Pianist. Compiled and edited by G. W. Lankford. *Chappell & Co., etc.: London, etc.,* [1960.] 4°.   **g. 1126. bb.**

LANKY

— Lanky Lucy Lister. Songs. *See* MENDOZA (Anne)

— The Lanky Yankee Boys in blue. Song. *See* MORSE (Theodore F.)

LANLA

— Les Lanla. [Song.] *See* FOURNIER (   )

LANNEARE (NICHOLAS)

— *See* LANIER.

LANNER (A.)

— Pensez à moi, Impromptu Polka. *See* ALBUM. [Ewer's] Album de Piano. 1858. No. 21. 1858. fol.　　　　　**h. 1211.**

LANNER (AUGUST JOSEPH)

— Ballnachts-Träume. Walzer für das Pianoforte ... Op. 15. pp. 11.　*C. A. Spina: Wien,* [1854?] *obl.* 4°.　　**d. 161. j. (10.)**

— Brabanter-Klänge. Walzer für das Pianoforte ... Op. 7. pp. 11. *C. A. Spina: Wien,* [1854?] *obl.* fol.　　**f. 65. l. (4.)**

— Die Drei und zwanziger, Fest-Walzer zur Feier des 23. Allerhöchsten Geburts-Festes S^r. K. K. Apostol. Majestät Franz Josef I ... Op. 11. [P. F.] pp. 11.　*C. A. Spina: Wien,* [1854.] *obl.* fol.　　　　**f. 770. cc. (13.)**

— Elisabeth-Bürger-Balltänze. Walzer für das Pianoforte ... Op. 17. pp. 11.　*C. A. Spina: Wien,* [1854?] *obl.* fol.　　　　　　　　　　**f. 65. l. (5.)**

— D'ersten Gedanken. Walzer für das Pianoforte ... Op. 1. pp. 11.　*C. A. Spina: Wien,* [1853.] *obl.* fol.　　**f. 541. g. (2.)**

— Festgedichte. Walzer für das Pianoforte. ⟨Op. 21.⟩ pp. 11. *C. A. Spina: Wien,* [1855.] *obl.* fol.　　**f. 790. c. (4.)**

— Frühlingsknospen. Walzer für das Pianoforte ... Opus 3. pp. 11.　*C. A. Spina: Wien,* [1854?] *obl.* fol.　　**f. 65. l. (3.)**

— Die gemüthlichen Wiener. Walzer ... Op. 19. [P. F.] pp. 11. *C. A. Spina: Wien,* [1857?] *obl.* fol.　　**f. 790. c. (6.)**

— Gruss an Steiermark. Steirische Tänze für das Pianoforte ... Op. 5. pp. 8.　*C. A. Spina: Wien,* [1853.] *obl.* fol.　　　　　　　　　　　**f. 790. c. (2.)**

— Die Gunstwerber. Walzer ... op. 33. ⟨Für das Pianoforte.⟩ pp. 11.　*C. A. Spina: Wien,* [1855.] *obl.* fol.　**e. 282. bb. (10.)**

— Heiligenstädter-Souvenir-Quadrille ... 6tes Werk. [Violin and P. F. Parts.] 2 pt.　*C. A. Spina: Wien,* [1853.] fol.　　　　　　　　　　　　　**g. 443. zz. (13.)**

— Isar Klänge. Walzer für das Pianoforte ... Op. 25. pp. 11. *C. A. Spina: Wien,* [1855.] *obl.* fol.　　**f. 790. c. (3.)**

— Kränzchen-Fest-Quadrille, für das Pianoforte ... Op. 23. pp. 7.　*C. A. Spina: Wien,* [1855.] fol.　　**g. 443. zz. (12.)**

— Kränzchen Stammblätter. Walzer für das Pianoforte ... Op. 13. pp. 11.　*C. A. Spina: Wien,* [1854.] *obl.* 4°.　　　　　　　　　　　　　　**d. 161. j. (9.)**

— Die Orientalen. Walzer für das Pianoforte ... Op. 26. pp. 11. *C. A. Spina: Wien,* [1854?] *obl.* fol.　　**d. 161. j. (8.)**

— Prinzessin Sophie-Dorothea's Wiegenlieder. Walzer für das Pianoforte ... Op. 24. pp. 11.　*C. A. Spina: Wien,* [1855.] *obl.* fol.　　　　　　　　　**f. 770. cc. (14.)**

— Scherz-Polka für das Pianoforte ... Op. 16. pp. 5.　*C. A. Spina: Wien,* [1854.] fol.　　　　**g. 545. jj. (6.)**

— Sofien-Klänge. Walzer für das Pianoforte ... Opus 9. pp. 11. *C. A. Spina: Wien,* [1853.] *obl.* fol.　　**f. 790. d. (1.)**

— Sperl-Polka ... Opus 2 ... Für Pianoforte allein, *etc.* pp. 5. *C. A. Spina: Wien,* [1853.] fol.　　**g. 545. jj. (7.)**

— Der Tanz durch's Leben. Polka mazurka ... Op. 30. ⟨Für das Pianoforte.⟩ pp. 5.　*C. A. Spina: Wien,* [c. 1860.] fol. *The titlepage reads "Brucker Jux-Polka. Op. 29. Der Tanz durch's Leben. Polka-Mazurka. Op. 30".*　　**h. 722. h. (5.)**

— Wiener Tanzeln aus der guten Zeit. Walzer für das Pianoforte ... Opus 32. pp. 11.　*C. A. Spina: Wien,* [1857?] *obl.* fol.　　　　　　　　　　　　　　**f. 790. c. (5.)**

LANNER (FRANZ)

— Dinorah-Quadrille nach Motiven aus der Oper Dinorah oder die Wallfahrt nach Ploermel von G. Meyerbeer. Für Pianoforte ... Op. 12, *etc.* pp. 5.　*F. E. C. Leuckart: Breslau,* [1860?] 4°.　　　　　**h. 977. j. (13.)**

— Dragoner-Galopp über Motive aus A. Maillart's "Das Glöckchen des Eremiten," für das Pianoforte ... Op. 22. pp. 5.　*F. E. C. Leuckart: Breslau,* [1860.] 4°.　　**h. 977. j. (20.)**

— Kuss-Polka. (Nach Arditi's "Il Bacio".) ... Op. 26. [P. F.] pp. 3.　*F. E. C. Leuckart: Breslau,* [1861?] 4°.　　**h. 977. j. (17.)**

— Luftschiffer. Galop für Pianoforte ... Op. 37.　*F. E. C. Leuckart: Breslau,* [c. 1865.] 4°.　　**h. 977. j. (18.)**

— Saba-Quadrille nach Motiven aus der Oper La Reine de Saba von Ch. Gounod ... Op. 40. Für Pianoforte zu 2 Händen, *etc.* pp. 14–19.　*F. E. C. Leuckart: Breslau,* [c. 1865.] 4°.　　　　　　　　　　　　　**h. 977. j. (14.)**

— Tambour-Polka für das Pianoforte ... Op. 17. pp. 3.　*F. E. C. Leuckart: Breslau,* [1860.] 4°.　　**h. 977. j. (19.)**

— Wiegenlieder. Walzer ... Op. 20. [P. F.] pp. 9.　*F. E. C. Leuckart: Breslau,* [1860.] 4°.　　**h. 977. j. (15.)**

— *See* GOUNOD (C. F.) [Faust.—Selections, instrumental.] Waltz ... March. [Arranged by] F. Lanner. 1864. fol.　　　　　　　　　　　**h. 1459. d. (16.)**

LANNER (FREDERICK)

— Palm Leaves valse. [P. F.]　*London,* [1882.] fol.　　　　　　　　　　　　　　**h. 3275. j. (11.)**

— The Telegram polka. [P. F.]　*London,* [1882.] fol.　　　　　　　　　　　　　　**h. 3275. j. (12.)**

LANNER (JOSEF FRANZ CARL)

COMPLETE WORKS

— Josef Lanner's Werke. (Neue Gesammtausgabe ... herausgegeben von E. Kremser.) 8 Bd. 36 Lfg. 　　Bd. 1–5. Walzer. 　　Bd. 6. Ländler, Polkas und Mazurkas. 　　Bd. 7. Galoppe. 　　Bd. 8. Quadrillen, Märsche und andere Werke. *Breitkopf & Härtel: Leipzig,* [1889–91.] fol.　　**h. 860. a.**

— [A reissue.] Josef Lanner's Werke. ⟨Neue Gesammtausgabe ... herausgegeben von Eduard Kremser.⟩ 8 Bd.　*Leipzig,* [1895?] fol.　　　　　　　　　　　　**Hirsch** IV. **977.**

SMALLER COLLECTIONS

— The Beauties of Lanner. Three elegant sets of waltzes, for the piano forte. First set. Prometheus-Funken Walzer. Op. 123 ... Second set. Die Aelpler Walzer. Op. 124 ... Third set. Pesth-Walzer, *etc.* set 1, 2.　*R. Cocks & C°: London,* [1838.] fol. *Imperfect; wanting set 3.*　　**h. 860. (16.)**

— Hommage aux dames. Two ⟨[^MS Three]⟩ sets of new German waltzes for two performers on one piano forte. 1st set. Prometheus-Funken Walzer. Op. 123 ... 2nd set. Die Aelpler-Walzer. Op. 124. ⟨[^MS 3rd set. Orpheus-Klange Walzer. Op. 126.]⟩ 3 no.　*R. Cocks & C°: London,* [1838.] fol.　　　　　　　　　　　　**h. 860. (17.)**

— Valses favorite [*sic*] de Lanner, arrangés pour harpe, et piano, avec accompagnement de flute et violoncelle ... par N. C. Bochsa. [Parts.] 2 bk. 4 pt.　*Chez T. Boosey & C°: Londres,* [1838?] fol. *Without the accompaniments.*　　**h. 2605. ff. (18.)**

— Album für das Piano-Forte ... mit dem Portrait des Compositeurs. pp. 34.　*Bei Pietro Mechetti: Wien,* [1839.] fol. *Imperfect; wanting the portrait.*　　**h. 860. d. (1.)**

LANNER (JOSEF FRANZ CARL)

— Taglioni-Walzer. Tourbillon- u. Gitana-Galoppe. 141. 142stes Werk. ⟨Für die Violine mit Begleitung des Pianoforte.⟩ [Parts.] 2 pt. *Bei Pietro Mechetti: Wien,* [1839.] fol. **h. 860. f. (8.)**

— Beauties of Lanner. A collection of the most favorite waltzes, galops, marches, &c. for the piano forte. no. 8. *George Ward: London,* [c. 1840.] fol. *Imperfect; wanting no. 1–7, 9.* **h. 860. c.**

— Der Kinder-Ball. Album der beliebtesten Walzer etc. für das Pianoforte, im leichten Style mit Hinweglassung der Octaven für die Jugend. Hft. 2, 4. *Bei Pietro Mechetti: Wien,* [1840.] *obl.* fol. *Imperfect; wanting Hft. 1, 3.* **Hirsch M. 216. (1.)**

— [MS Lanner's Royal Waltzes arranged in a familiar style for the pianoforte by C. Czerny.] bk. 7. [MS *Printed by R. Cocks & Cº: London,*] [1840.] fol. *The titlepage is in MS. Imperfect; wanting all the other bk.* **h. 860. (18.)**

— Tarantelle and Gartenfest, galops. Op. 114 & 125. [P. F.] pp. 7. *Wessel & Cº, for the proprietor: London,* [1840.] fol. *Lannerina. no. 32.* **h. 1458. d. (7.)**

— Lanner's Nachlass Walzer. [Hft. 1.] The last waltzes for the piano forte. 3 bk. *Printed by R. Cocks & Cº: London,* [1843.] fol. **h. 862. (15.)**

— Lascito di Giuseppe Lanner. Valzer per pianoforte. Fascicolo I della raccolta de' valzer postumi del suddetto defunto autore. pp. 15. *Giovanni Ricordi: Milano,* [c. 1845.] *obl.* 4°. **e. 284. e. (5.)**

— Quadrillen für das Pianoforte zu 4 Händen ... N°. 1. La Victoire de la danse ... 2. Souvenir des artistes ... 3. Jagd-Quadrille ... 4. Rouge et noire, *etc.* no. 4. *Bei Tobias Haslinger: Wien,* [c. 1845.] fol. *Imperfect; wanting no. 1–3.* **h. 860. e. (1.)**

— Lanner-Album. 20 valses pour violon seul. Arrangées par Franz Görner. pp. 41. *Henry Litolff's Verlag: Braunschweig,* [1874.] 4°. [*Collection Litolff. no.* 390.] **g. 375.**

— Ausgewählte Walzer. Mit einer Einleitung herausgegeben von ... Oskar Bie. [With a portrait.] pp. xii. 79. *Drei Masken Verlag: München,* 1920. 8°. *One of the "Musikalische Stundenbücher".* **Hirsch M. 212.**

— Valses Viennoises ... Réunies et doigtées par W. Landowska. [P. F.] *G. Schirmer: New York,* 1925. 4°. **g. 1127. dd. (2.)**

— Ländler und Walzer. Bearbeitet von A. Orel. Nebst Anhang: "Die Schönbrunner" für Klavier gesetzt von I. Friedman. *Universal-Edition A.G.: Wien,* 1926. fol. [*Denkmäler der Tonkunst in Österreich. XXXIII. Jahrgang. 2. Teil. Bd.* 65.] **H. 988.**

— Valses Viennoises ... Réunies et doigtées par W. Landowska. [P. F.] *G. Schirmer: New York,* 1926. 4°. **g. 1127. gg. (19.)**

— Abendsterne. Walzer für das Pianoforte ... 180tes Werk. pp. 11. *Bei Tobias Haslinger: Wien,* [1841.] *obl.* fol. **e. 284. e. (6.)**

— [Another copy.] **R. M. 26. c. 12. (4.)**

— Abend-Sterne Walzer. (Evening Stars.) Op. 180. ⟨For the piano forte.⟩ pp. 9. *Printed by R. Cocks & Cº: London,* [1841.] fol. *Les Élégants du beau monde. no.* 33. **h. 861. (28.)**

— [Abendsterne.] Le Stelle della sera ... Valzer per pianoforte ... Op. 180. pp. 9. *Giovanni Ricordi: Milano,* [c. 1845.] *obl.* 4°. **e. 284. e. (3.)**

LANNER (JOSEF FRANZ CARL)

— Die Abenteurer. Walzer, für das Pianoforte ... 91stes Werk. pp. 11. *Bei Pietro Mechetti: Wien,* [1834.] *obl.* fol. **Hirsch M. 213. (1.)**

— Die Abenteurer. Walzer für das Pianoforte ... 2te. Ausgabe. 91stes Werk. pp. 11. *Bei Pietro Mechetti: Wien,* [c. 1835.] *obl.* fol. **e. 563. (2.)**

— Abschied von Pesth. Monument-Walzer, für das Pianoforte ... 95stes Werk. pp. 11. *Bei Pietro Mechetti: Wien,* [1835.] *obl.* fol. **Hirsch M. 216. (2.)**

— Abschied von Pesth. Monument-Walzer für das Piano-Forte zu vier Händen ... 95stes Werk. pp. 15. *Bei Pietro Mechetti: Wien,* [1835.] *obl.* fol. **e. 563. (1.)**

— Les Adieux. Walzer für das Pianoforte ... 185tes Werk. pp. 11. *Bei Tobias Haslinger: Wien,* [1841.] *obl.* fol. **e. 282. bb. (9.)**

— Les Adieux-Walzer. Op. 185. ⟨For the piano forte.⟩ pp. 9. *Printed by R. Cocks & Cº: London,* [1842.] fol. *Les Élégants du beau monde. no.* 44. **h. 861. (33.)**

— Die Aelpler. Walzer für das Piano-Forte ... 124stes Werk. pp. 11. *Bei Pietro Mechetti: Wien,* [1837.] *obl.* fol. **e. 283. b. (1.)**

— Die Aelpler. Walzer. ⟨Op. 124.⟩ [P. F.] pp. 9. *R. Cocks & Cº.: London,* [1838.] fol. *La Mode à la cour de la Grande Bretagne. no.* 25. **h. 860. e. (3.)**

— Aeskulap ... Walzer für das Pianoforte ... 113tes Werk. pp. 11. *Bei Pietro Mechetti: Wien,* [1837.] *obl.* fol. **Hirsch M. 213. (2.)**

— Aeskulap-Walzer. 113tes Werk. ⟨Für die Violine mit Begleitung des Pianoforte.⟩ [Parts.] 2 pt. *Bei Pietro Mechetti: Wien,* [1837.] fol. **h. 860. f. (4.)**

— Air de ballet. ⟨Op. 159.⟩ [P. F.] pp. 9. [MS *Printed by R. Cocks & Cº: London,*] [1840.] fol. *Les Élégants du beau monde. no.* 12. *The titlepage is in MS. The title is taken from the head of p. 1.* **h. 861. (10.)**

— Almacks-Tänze, für das Piano-Forte ... 205tes Werk. pp. 11. *Bei Tobias Haslinger: Wien,* [1843.] *obl.* fol. **Hirsch M. 213. (3.)**

— Almacks-Walzer for the Piano-Forte ... Op. 205. pp. 9. *R. Cocks & Co.: London,* [1848.] fol. **h. 862. (14.)**

— Almacks-Tänze. Walzer. Op. 205. [P. F. trio.] *See* BORSCHITZKY (J. F.) Concordia, *etc.* No. 8. [1900.] fol. **h. 2772. a.**

— Alpen-Rosen. Walzer für das Pianoforte ... 162stes Werk. pp. 11. *Bei Pietro Mechetti: Wien,* [1840.] *obl.* fol. **Hirsch M. 216. (3.)**

— Alpen-Rosen. Walzer. ⟨Op. 162.⟩ [P. F.] pp. 9. [MS *Printed by R. Cocks & Cº: London,*] [1841.] fol. *Les Élégants du beau monde. no.* 17. *The titlepage is in MS. The title is taken from the head of p. 1.* **h. 861. (15.)**

— Amazonen-Galoppe. *See infra:* [Malapou- und Amazonen-Galoppe. Op. 148.]

— Amoretten Walzer für das Pianoforte ... 53stes Werk. pp. 11. *Bei Pietro Mechetti: Wien,* [1831.] *obl.* fol. **f. 133. ww. (5.)**

— Amors-Flügel. Walzer für das Pianoforte ... 120stes Werk. pp. 11. *Bei Pietro Mechetti: Wien,* [1837.] *obl.* fol. **Hirsch M. 213. (4.)**

— Amors Flügel Walzer ... [Op. 120.] Arranged by T. Valentine. [P. F.] *In:* The Musical Bijou ... for MDCCCXL. pp. 53–56. [1840.] fol. **H. 2330.**

— L'Anima Waltzes. *See infra:* [Die Lebenswecker Walzer. Op. 104.]

LANNER (JOSEF FRANZ CARL)

— Ankunfts-Walzer für das Pianoforte ... 34stes Werk. pp. 7.
Bei Pietro Mechetti: Wien, [1829.] *obl.* fol.   **e. 563. a. (1.)**

— Annen-Einladungs-Walzer für das Pianoforte ... 48stes Werk.
pp. 7. *Bei Pietro Mechetti: Wien,* [1831.] *obl.* fol.
e. 563. (3.)

— Aurora. Künstler-Ball-Taenze für das Piano-Forte ... 156stes
Werk. pp. 11. *Bei Pietro Mechetti: Wien,* [1840.] *obl.* fol.
e. 563. b. (8.)

— Aurora. Künstler-Ball-Tänze. ⟨Op. 156.⟩ [P. F.] pp. 9.
[^{MS} *R. Cocks & Co: London,*] [1840.] fol.
Les Élégants du beau monde. no. 10. *The titlepage is in MS.*
The title is taken from the head of p. 1.   **h. 861. (8.)**

— Die Badner Ring'ln, Walzer; fürs Pianoforte, *etc.* [Op. 64.]
pp. 11. *Bei Pietro Mechetti: Wien,* [1833?] *obl.* fol.
e. 283. d. (1.)

— Ball-Contouren. Walzer für das Pianoforte ... 193tes Werk.
pp. 11. *Bei Tobias Haslinger: Wien,* [1842.] *obl.* fol.
Hirsch M. 216. (4.)

— Ball-Contouren. Walzer. ⟨Op. 193. For the piano forte.⟩ pp. 9.
Printed by R. Cocks & Co: London, [1842.] fol.
La Mode à la cour de la grande Bretagne. ser. 2. *no.* 8.
h. 862. (6.)

— Bankett-Polonaise. ⟨Op. 135.⟩ [P. F.] pp. 5. [^{MS} *R. Cocks & Co:*
London,] [1839.] fol.
The titlepage is in MS. The title is taken from the head of p. 2.
h. 860. (13.)

— Bankett-Polonaise. [Op. 135. P. F. duet.] pp. 7. [^{MS} *R. Cocks &*
C^o: London,] [1839.] fol.
The titlepage is in MS. The title is taken from the head of p. 2.
h. 860. (12.)

— Die Bestürmung von Constantine. Galoppe. 127tes Werk.
[Orchestral parts.] 20 pt. *Pietro Mechetti:* [*Vienna,* 1838.] 4°.
Part of "Beliebte Walzer und Galoppen für das Orchester von
Jos. Lanner".   **f. 416. a.**

— Die Bestürmung von Constantine. Galoppe für das
Pianoforte ... 127stes Werk. pp. 7. *Bei Pietro Mechetti: Wien,*
[1838.] *obl.* fol.   **e. 563. c. (4.)**

— [Die Bestürmung von Constantine.] The Storming of
Constantine, a new galop for the piano forte. pp. 5. *R. Cocks*
& Co: London, [1838.] fol.   **h. 860. (4.)**

— Blumen der Lust, Walzer für das Pianoforte ... 73stes Werk.
pp. 11. *Bei P. Mechetti: Wien,* [1833.] *obl.* fol.
Hirsch M. 213. (5.)

— Blumenfest Ländler für das Piano-Forte ... 23tes Werk. pp. 7.
Bei Tobias Haslinger: Wien, [1829.] *obl.* fol.   **e. 563. (4.)**

— Blumenfest Ländler für das Piano-Forte zu [^{MS} 4] Haenden ...
23tes Werk. pp. 13. *Bei Tobias Haslinger: Wien,* [1829?] *obl.*
fol.   **e. 282. ss. (10.)**

— Bolero für das Piano-Forte. ⟨J. Lanner's letzte Composition.⟩
pp. 11. *Bei Tobias Haslinger's Witwe & Sohn: Wien,* [1845.]
fol.   **h. 1203. e. (1.)**

— The Bride's Mazurkas. *See* infra: [Der Tanz um die Braut.
Op. 178.]

— [Bürger-Fest-Parademarsch. Op. 174.] Potpourri or The
Vienna Festival. A military pot-pourri. [P. F.] pp. 21.
[^{MS} *R. Cocks & Co: London,*] [1841.] fol.
Les Élégants du beau monde. no. 27. *The titlepage is in MS.*
The title is taken from the head of p. 1.   **h. 861. (22.)**

— Capricciosa. Grosses Potpourri für das Pianoforte ... 63stes
Werk. pp. 22. *Bei P. Mechetti: Wien,* [1833.] *obl.* fol.
e. 563. b. (3.)

— The Comet Waltz. *See* infra: [Komet-Walzer. Op. 87.]

LANNER (JOSEF FRANZ CARL)

— Dampf-Walzer, für das Pianoforte ... 94stes Werk. pp. 15. *Bei*
Pietro Mechetti: Wien, [1835.] *obl.* fol.   **Hirsch M. 213. (6.)**

— Le Danze della festa da ballo. *See* infra: [Kaiserl. Königl.
Kammerball-Tänze. Op. 177.]

— Defilir Marsch. *See* infra: [Märsche.] 3 Grand Marches. 1.

— Les Deux fleurs. Valse brillante. *Établissement Musical*
Parthénopéen: Naples, [1852?] fol.
Part of "Hommage à Therpsychore pour piano. Répertoire
dansant pour le carnaval 1852".   **h. 721. i. (4.)**

— Die Ein und Dreisiger. Walzer für das Pianoforte ... 55stes
Werk. pp. 9. *Bei Pietro Mechetti: Wien,* [1831.] *obl.* fol.
f. 541. g. (1.)

— Elite-Tänze für das Piano-Forte ... 182tes Werk. pp. 11. *Bei*
Tobias Haslinger: Wien, [1841.] *obl.* fol.   **e. 563. c. (9.)**

— Elite-Tänze. Op. 182. ⟨For the piano forte.⟩ pp. 9. *Printed by*
R. Cocks & Co: London, [1841.] fol.
Les Élégants du beau monde. no. 38.   **h. 861. (30.)**

— Eröffnungs-Walzer mit der Wilden-Jagd-Coda für das
Piano-Forte ... 24tes Werk. pp. 7. *Bei Tobias Haslinger:*
Wien, [1829.] *obl.* fol.   **e. 563. a. (3.)**

— Family Portraits. *See* infra: [Genre-Bilder. Op. 175.]

— Favorit-Polka für das Piano-Forte ... 201tes Werk. pp. 3. *Bei*
Tobias Haslinger: Wien, [1842.] fol.   **h. 925. i. (4.)**

— Fest-Marsch für das Piano-Forte ... 139stes Werk, *etc.* pp. 3.
Bei Pietro Mechetti: Wien, [1839.] *obl.* fol.   **f. 541. g. (3.)**

— Flora-Walzer, für das Piano-Forte ... 33tes Werk. pp. 6. *Bei*
Tobias Haslinger: Wien, [1830?] *obl.* fol.   **Hirsch M. 213. (7.)**

— Die Flotten. Walzer für das Pianoforte. 140stes Werk. *Wien,*
[1836?] *obl.* fol.   **e. 283. c. (11.)**

— Die Flotten Walzer. [Op. 140. P. F.] pp. 9. [^{MS} *R. Cocks & Co:*
London,] [1839.] fol.
The titlepage is in MS. The title is taken from the head of p. 2.
h. 860. (22.)

— Die Flotten Walzer. [Op. 140. P. F. duet.] pp. 17. [^{MS} *R. Cocks*
& Co: London,] [1839.] fol.
The titlepage is in MS. The title is taken from the head of p. 2.
h. 860. (23.)

— Flüchtige Lust. Walzer für das Pianoforte ... 46stes Werk.
pp. 10. *Bei Pietro Mechetti: Wien,* [1831.] *obl.* fol.
e. 563. a. (2.)

— Frohsinns Scepter. Walzer für das Pianoforte ... 131stes Werk.
pp. 11. *Bei Pietro Mechetti: Wien,* [1838.] *obl.* fol.
Hirsch M. 213. (8.)

— Frohsinns-Sceptre. Walzer für das Piano Forte ... Op. 131.
⟨No. 1. Piano solo.—No. 2. Piano duet.⟩ 2 no. *R. Cocks & Co:*
London, [1838.] fol.   **h. 860. (5.)**

— [Another copy.]   **g. 272. p. (1.)**

— Geistes-Schwingen. Walzer für das Piano-Forte zu 4 Händen
... 191tes Werk. pp. 19. *Bei Tobias Haslinger: Wien,* [1842.]
obl. fol.   **e. 563. b. (11.)**

— Geistes Schwingen Walzer. (Spirits Wings.) ⟨Op. 191. For the
piano forte.⟩ pp. 9. *Printed by R. Cocks & Co: London,* [1842.]
fol.
La Mode à la cour de la grande Bretagne. ser. 2. *no.* 3.
h. 862. (3.)

— Genre-Bilder. Künstler-Ball-Tänze für das Piano-Forte ...
175tes Werk. pp. 11. *Bei Tobias Haslinger: Wien,* [1841.] *obl.*
fol.   **e. 563. c. (8.)**

LANNER (JOSEF FRANZ CARL)

— [Genre-Bilder. Op. 175.] Family Portraits. Composed for the professors' ball. [P. F.] pp. 9. [^{MS} *R. Cocks & Co: London,*] [1841.] fol.
Les Élégants du beau monde. no. 28. The titlepage is in MS. The title is taken from the head of p. 1. **h. 861. (23.)**

— Gusto-Ländler, für das Pianoforte ... 69stes Werk. pp. 10. *Bei P. Mechetti: Wien,* [1833.] *obl.* fol. **Hirsch M. 213. (9.)**

— Die Haimbacher. Erinnerungs-Walzer für das Pianoforte ... 112tes Werk. pp. 12. *Bei Pietro Mechetti: Wien,* [1836.] *obl.* fol. **Hirsch M. 213. (10.)**

— Hans Jörgel Polka. Für das Pianoforte ... 194tes Werk. pp. 3. *Bei Tobias Haslinger: Wien,* [1842.] 4°. **h. 977. j. (16.)**

— [Hans Jörgel Polka. Op. 194.] John Bull's Polka, or Hans Jörge Polka. ⟨For the piano forte.⟩ pp. 3. *Printed by R. Cocks & Co: London,* [1842.] fol.
La Mode à la cour de la grande Bretagne. ser. 2. no. 2. **h. 862. (2.)**

— [Hans Jörgel Polka. Op. 194.] Polka. Danse nouvelle. [P. F.] pp. 3. *B. Girard et c^{ie}: Naples,* [c. 1850.] fol. **G. 691. l. (18.)**

— Hesperiens Echo. Cotillons, nach den beliebtsten Motiven der neuesten italienischen Opern, für das Pianoforte ... 98stes Werk. pp. 11. *Bei Pietro Mechetti: Wien,* [1835.] *obl.* fol. **Hirsch M. 213. (11.)**

— Hexentanz. Walzer für das Pianoforte ... 203tes Werk. pp. 11. *Bei Tobias Haslinger: Wien,* [1843.] *obl.* fol. **Hirsch M. 213. (12.)**

— Hexentanz-Walzer. Für das Piano Forte, *etc.* ⟨Op. 203.⟩ pp. 11. *R. Cocks & Co.: London,* [1843.] fol. **h. 862. (11.)**

— Hexen-Tanz. Walzer. 203tes Werk. ⟨Für Violine und Pianoforte.⟩ [Parts.] 2 pt. *Bei Tobias Haslinger: Wien,* [1843.] fol. **h. 860. f. (13.)**

— s' Hoamweh. Original Steyrer Ländler für das Piano-Forte ... 202tes Werk. pp. 9. *Bei Tobias Haslinger: Wien,* [1842.] *obl.* fol. **Hirsch M. 213. (13.)**

— s' Hoamweh. Steyrer. 202tes Werk. Guitare. pp. 7. *Bei Tobias Haslinger: Wien,* [1842.] fol. **h. 925. d. (9.)**

— s' Hoamweh Ländler. [P. F. trio.] *See* BORSCHITZKY (J. F.) Concordia, *etc.* No. 12. [1900.] fol. **h. 2772. a.**

— Hof-Ball-Tänze, für das Pianoforte ... 161stes Werk. pp. 11. *Bei Pietro Mechetti: Wien,* [1840.] *obl.* fol. **Hirsch M. 213. (14.)**

— Hof-Ball-Tänze. Op. 161. ⟨For the piano forte.⟩ pp. 11. *Printed by R. Cocks & Co: London,* [1840.] fol.
Les Élégants du beau monde. no. 16. The title is taken from the foot of p. 2. **h. 861. (14.)**

— Hofball-Tänze. Walzer. [P. F. trio.] *See* BORSCHITZKY (J. F.) Concordia, *etc.* No. 9. [1900.] fol. **h. 2772. a.**

— Hoffnungs-Strahlen. Walzer für das Pianoforte ... 158stes Werk. pp. 11. *Bei Pietro Mechetti: Wien,* [1840.] *obl.* fol. **Hirsch M. 213. (15.)**

— Hoffnungs Strahlen Walzer. ⟨Op. 158.⟩ [P. F.] pp. 11. [^{MS} *Printed by R. Cocks & Co: London,*] [1840.] fol.
Les Élégants du beau monde. no. 11. The titlepage is in MS. The title is taken from the head of p. 3. **h. 861. (9.)**

— Die Humoristiker, Walzer für das Pianoforte ... 92stes Werk. pp. 10. *Bei Pietro Mechetti: Wien,* [1834.] *obl.* fol. **e. 283. b. (2.)**

— The Huntsman's Quadrilles. *See* infra: [Jagd-Quadrille. Op. 190.]

LANNER (JOSEF FRANZ CARL)

— Hymens Feier-Klänge. Walzer für das Pianoforte ... 115tes Werk. pp. 11. *Bei Pietro Mechetti: Wien,* [1837.] *obl.* fol. **Hirsch M. 213. (16.)**

— Hymens Feier Klange. Walzer, for the Piano Forte. [Op. 115.] pp. 11. *Walker & Son: London,* [1840?] fol. **h. 1480. t. (25.)**

— Ideale. Künstler-Ball-Tänze für das Piano Forte zu 4 Händen ... 192tes Werk. pp. 18. *Bei Tobias Haslinger: Wien,* [1842.] *obl.* fol. **e. 563. b. (12.)**

— The Imperial and Royal Court Walzes. *See* infra: [Kaiserl. Königl. Kammerball-Tänze. Op. 177.]

— Isabella-Walzer, für das Pianoforte ... 74stes Werk. pp. 11. *Bei P. Mechetti: Wien,* [1833.] *obl.* fol. **Hirsch M. 214. (1.)**

— Isabella Walzer. The Isabella Waltzes ... Arranged for the piano forte ... Op. 74. pp. 11. *Metzler & Co., for the proprietors: London,* [c. 1850.] fol. **h. 860. e. (2.)**

— Jägers Lust. Jagd-Galoppe. ⟨82stes Werk.⟩ [P. F.] pp. 3. *Bei Pietro Mechetti: Wien,* [1834.] *obl.* fol.
Sammlung der neuesten und beliebtesten Galoppen. no. 35. Cropped. **e. 563. a. (4.)**

— Jagd-Quadrille für das Piano-Forte ... 190tes Werk. pp. 7. *Bei Tobias Haslinger: Wien,* [1842.] 4°. **h. 977. j. (10.)**

— [Jagd-Quadrille. Op. 190.] The Huntsman's Quadrilles. ⟨For the piano forte.⟩ pp. 7. *Printed by R. Cocks & Co: London,* [1842.] fol.
Les Élégants du beau monde. no. 48. **h. 861. (35.)**

— John Bull's Polka. *See* supra: [Hans Jörgel Polka. Op. 194.]

— Jubel-Fest-Tänze für das Piano-Forte zu 4 Händen ... 29tes Werk. pp. 11. *Bei Tobias Haslinger: Wien,* [1829.] *obl.* fol. **e. 563. b. (1.)**

— Jubel-Walzer, für das Pianoforte ... 100stes Werk. pp. 11. *Bei Pietro Mechetti: Wien,* [1835.] *obl.* fol. **Hirsch M. 216. (5.)**

— Die jüngsten Kinder meiner Laune. Ländler für das Pianoforte ... 65tes Werk. pp. 9. *Bei P. Mechetti: Wien,* [1833?] *obl.* fol. **Hirsch M. 214. (2.)**

— [Kaiserl. Königl. Kammerball-Tänze.] Le Danze della festa da ballo ... per pianoforte ... Op. 177. pp. 9. *Giovanni Ricordi: Milano,* [c. 1840.] *obl.* 4°. **e. 284. e. (1.)**

— Kaiserl. Königl. Kammer-Ball-Tänze, für das Piano-Forte ... 177tes Werk. pp. 14. *Bei Tobias Haslinger: Wien,* [1841.] *obl.* fol. **Hirsch M. 216. (6.)**

— [Kaiserl. Königl. Kammerball-Tänze. Op. 177.] The Imperial and Royal Court Waltzes. ⟨For the piano forte.⟩ pp. 9. *Printed by R. Cocks & Co: London,* [1841.] fol.
Les Élégants du beau monde. no. 30. **h. 861. (25.)**

— Karlsbader Sprudel-Walzer für das Pianoforte ... 50tes Werk. pp. 5. *Bei Tobias Haslinger: Wien,* [1831.] *obl.* fol. **e. 563. a. (7.)**

— Komet-Walzer, für das Pianoforte ... 87stes Werk. pp. 11. *Bei Pietro Mechetti: Wien,* [1834.] *obl.* fol. **Hirsch M. 216. (7.)**

— [Komet-Walzer. Op. 87.] The Comet Waltz. [Military band parts.] 23 pt. *In:* GUMBERT (F.) [O bitt' euch liebe Vögelein. Op. 43.] Song, *etc.* [1880.] fol. [*Boosé's military Journal. ser. 35. no. 4.*] **h. 1549.**

— Die Kosenden. Walzer für das Pianoforte ... 128stes Werk. pp. 11. *Bei Pietro Mechetti: Wien,* [1838.] *obl.* fol. **Hirsch M. 214. (3.)**

— Die Kosenden Walzer. [P. F.] pp. 9. *R. Cocks & Co: London,* [c. 1840.] fol.
La Mode à la cour de la Grande Bretagne. no. 2. **h. 722. bb. (16.)**

LANNER (Josef Franz Carl)

— [Die Kosenden. Op. 128.] Les Ramiers. Walses favorites pour piano, *etc.* pp. 9. *Chez S. Richault: Paris,* [c. 1845.] *obl.* fol.
e. 272. p. (8.)

— Die Kosenden, Walzer, for two performers on one piano forte ... Op. 128. pp. 15. *R. Cocks & Cᵒ: London,* [c. 1835.] fol. **h. 860. (2.)**

— Die Kosenden Walzer. [Harp and P. F. Parts.] *See* QUADRILLES. The Royal Quadrilles, *etc.* No. 3. [1840?] fol. **h. 1448. (15.)**

— Die Kosenden. Walzer. 128ˢᵗᵉˢ Werk. ⟨Für die Violine mit Begleitung des Pianoforte.⟩ [Parts.] 2 pt. *Bei Pietro Mechetti: Wien,* [1838.] fol. **h. 860. f. (6.)**

— Krönungs-Walzer, für das Pianoforte ... 133ˢᵗᵉˢ Werk. pp. 11. *Bei Pietro Mechetti: Wien,* [1838.] *obl.* fol.
Hirsch M. 216. (8.)

— Krönungs-Walzer ... Op. 133. [P. F.] pp. 11. [ᴹˢ *R. Cocks & Cᵒ: London,*] [1839.] fol.
The titlepage is in MS. The title is taken from the head of p. 2.
h. 860. (8.)

— Krönungs Walzer ... Op. 133. [P. F. duet.] pp. 21. [ᴹˢ *R. Cocks & Cᵒ: London,*] [1839.] fol.
The titlepage is in MS. The title is taken from the head of p. 2.
h. 860. (9.)

— Labyrinth-Walzer, für das Pianoforte ... 109ᵗᵉˢ Werk. pp. 11. *Bei Pietro Mechetti: Wien,* [1836.] *obl.* fol.
Hirsch M. 214. (4.)

— Labyrinth Walzer ... [Op. 109.] Arranged by E. F. Rimbault. [P. F.] *In:* The Musical Bijou ... for MDCCCXL. pp. 61–64. [1840.] fol. **H. 2330.**

— Lanner's Ankunft in Olymp. *See infra:* [Die Schönbrunner. Op. 200. No. 1.]

— Lebens-Pulse. — Walzer. ⟨Op. 172.⟩ [P. F.] pp. 11. [ᴹˢ *R. Cocks & Cᵒ: London,*] [1841.] fol.
Les Élégants du beau monde. no. 21. The titlepage is in MS. The title is taken from the head of p. 2. **h. 861. (19.)**

— Lebens-Pulse. Walzer. 172ˢ. Werk. ⟨Für Violine und Pianoforte.⟩ [Parts.] 2 pt. *Bei Tobias Haslinger: Wien,* [1841.] fol. **h. 860. f. (9.)**

— Die Lebenswecker. Walzer für das Pianoforte ... 104ᵗᵉˢ Werk. pp. 15. *Bei Pietro Mechetti: Wien,* [1835.] *obl.* fol.
Hirsch M. 214. (5.)

— [Die Lebenswecker Walzer. Op. 104.] L'Anima Waltzes, *etc.* [P. F.] pp. 9. *Wessel & Cᵒ, for the Proprietor: London,* [1839.] fol.
Lannerina. no. 21. **h. 62. bb. (13.)**

— Lemberger Mazur für das Pianoforte ... 60ˢᵗᵉˢ Werk. pp. 3. *Bei P. Mechetti: Wien,* [1832.] *obl.* fol. **e. 563. b. (2.)**

— Leopoldstädter Ländler für das Pianoforte ... 35ˢᵗᵉˢ Werk. pp. 7. *Bei Pietro Mechetti: Wien,* [1829.] *obl.* fol.
f. 541. g. (4.)

— Die Liebes-Tändler. Walzer für das Piano-Forte ... 105ᵗᵉˢ Werk. pp. 11. *Bei Pietro Mechetti: Wien,* [1835.] *obl.* fol.
f. 65. l. (6.)

— Die Liebes-Tändler. Walzer für das Pianoforte zu vier Händen ... 105ᵗᵉˢ Werk. pp. 15. *Bei Pietro Mechetti: Wien,* [1836.] *obl.* fol. **e. 563. (6.)**

— Liebes-Träume. Brünner-Walzer für das Piano-Forte ... 150ˢᵗᵉˢ Werk. pp. 11. *Bei Pietro Mechetti: Wien,* [1839.] *obl.* fol.
e. 283. d. (2.)

LANNER (Josef Franz Carl)

— Liebes Träume. Brünner Walzer. ⟨Op: 150.⟩ [P. F.] pp. 9. [ᴹˢ *R. Cocks & Cᵒ: London,*] [1840.] fol.
The titlepage is in MS. The title is taken from the head of p. 1.
h. 860. (24.)

— Lock-Walzer, für das Pianoforte ... 80ˢᵗᵉˢ Werk. pp. 11. *Bei P. Mechetti: Wien,* [1833.] *obl.* fol.
Imperfect; wanting pp. 5–8. **Hirsch M. 214. (6.)**

— Lock Walzer ... [Op. 80.] Arranged by T. Valentine. [P. F.] *In:* The Musical Bijou ... for MDCCCXL. pp. 49–52. [1840.] fol.
H. 2330.

— [Märsche.] 3 Grand Marches, for the piano forte ... 1. Defilir Marsch ... 2. Parade Marsch ... 3. Reise Marsch ... Op. 130. 3 no. *R. Cocks & Cᵒ: London,* [1838.] fol. **h. 860. (3.)**

— [Drei Märsche des zweiten Wiener Bürger Regimentes. Op. 157.] [1.] Defilir Marsch ⟨[2.] Reise-Marsch — [3.] Reise-Marsch⟩ des löbl. 2ᵗᵉⁿ Wiener Bürger-Regiments. [P. F.] pp. 7. [ᴹˢ *R. Cocks & Cᵒ: London,*] [1840.] fol. *Les Elegants du beau monde. no. 13. The titlepage is in MS. The title is taken from the head of p. 2.* **h. 861. (11.)**

— Malapou- und Amazonen-Galoppe für das Piano-Forte ... 148ˢᵗᵉˢ Werk. pp. 7. *Bei Pietro Mechetti: Wien,* [1839.] *obl.* fol.
e. 283. i. (1.)

— [Malapou- und Amazonen-Galoppe. Op. 148.] Amazonen-Galoppe. [P. F.] pp. 5. [ᴹˢ *R. Cocks & Co.: London,*] [1840.] fol.
Les Élégants du beau monde. no. 3. The titlepage is in MS. The title is taken from the head of p. 2. **h. 861. (1.)**

— [Malapou- und Amazonen-Galoppe. Op. 148.] Malapou-Galoppe. [P. F.] pp. 3. [ᴹˢ *R. Cocks & Cᵒ: London,*] [1840.] fol.
Les Elégants du beau monde. no. 4. The titlepage is in MS. The title is taken from the head of p. 2. **h. 861. (2.)**

— Marien-Walzer, für das Pianoforte ... 143ˢᵗᵉˢ Werk. pp. 11. *Bei Pietro Mechetti: Wien,* [1839.] *obl.* fol.
Hirsch M. 214. (7.)

— Marien-Walzer ... Op. 143. [P. F.] pp. 9. [ᴹˢ *R. Cocks & Cᵒ: London,*] [1839.] fol.
The titlepage is in MS. The title is taken from the head of p. 2.
h. 860. (26.)

— Marsch und Galoppe nach den beliebtesten Motiven der Oper von V. Bellini: Norma, für das Pianoforte ... 75ᵗᵉˢ Werk. pp. 6. *Bei P. Mechetti: Wien,* [1833.] *obl.* fol.
Hirsch M. 214. (8.)

— Masken-Bilder. Walzer für das Pianoforte ... 170ˢᵗᵉˢ Werk. pp. 11. *Bei Tobias Haslinger: Wien,* [1840.] *obl.* fol.
Hirsch M. 216. (9.)

— Masken-Bilder. Walzer. ⟨Op. 170.⟩ [P. F.] pp. 11. [ᴹˢ *Printed by R. Cocks & Cᵒ: London,*] [1841.] fol.
Les Élégants du beau monde. no. 18. The titlepage is in MS. The title is taken from the head of p. 2. **h. 861. (16.)**

— Vier Mazuren für das Piano-Forte ... 144ˢᵗᵉˢ Werk, *etc.* pp. 5. *Bei Pietro Mechetti: Wien,* [1839.] *obl.* fol. **f. 541. g. (5.)**

— Vier Maxuren. ⟨Op: 144.⟩ [P. F.] pp. 3. [ᴹˢ *R. Cocks & Cᵒ: London,*] [1839.] fol.
The titlepage is in MS. The title is taken from the head of p. 2.
h. 860. (25.)

— Mille-Fleurs-Walzer, für das Pianoforte ... 116ᵗᵉˢ Werk. pp. 11. *Bei Pietro Mechetti: Wien,* [1837.] *obl.* fol.
Hirsch M. 214. (9.)

— Minuten-Spiele. Grosses Potpourri für das Piano-Forte ... 208ᵗᵉˢ Werk. pp. 37. *Bei Tobias Haslinger: Wien,* [1843.] *obl.* fol. **e. 563. b. (13.)**

LANNER (Josef Franz Carl)

— Die Mozartisten. Walzer für das Pianoforte nach
Mozart'schen Melodien, aber nicht zum Tanze ... 196tes
Werk. pp. 15. *Bei Tobias Haslinger: Wien*, [1842.] obl. fol.
e. 563. b. (14.)

— Die Mozartisten Walzer. Nach Mozart'schen Melodien, *etc.*
⟨Op. 196. For the piano forte.⟩ pp. 15. *Printed by R. Cocks &
Cᵒ: London*, [1842.] fol.
La Mode à la cour de la grande Bretagne. ser. 2. no. 6.
h. 862. (5.)

— Musen-Klänge. Cotillon in Galoppen, für das Pianoforte ...
71stes Werk. pp. 9. *Bei P. Mechetti: Wien*, [1833.] obl. fol.
Hirsch M. 214. (10.)

— Nacht-Violen. Walzer für das Piano-Forte ... 160tes Werk.
pp. 11. *Bei Pietro Mechetti: Wien*, [1840.] obl. fol.
f. 541. g. (6.)

— Nacht-Violen. — Walzer. ⟨Op. 160.⟩ [P. F.] pp. 9. [^{MS} *R. Cocks
& Cᵒ: London*,] [1840.] fol.
*Les Élégants du monde. no. 14. The titlepage is in MS. The
title is taken from the head of p. 1.* **h. 861. (12.)**

— Die nächtlichen Wanderer. Walzer für das Pianoforte ...
171tes Werk. pp. 11. *Bei Tobias Haslinger: Wien*, [1840.] *obl.*
fol. **Hirsch M. 214. (11.)**

— Die nächtlichen Wanderer. Op. 171. [P. F.] pp. 9. [^{MS} *R. Cocks
& Cᵒ: London*,] [1841.] fol.
*Les Élégants du beau monde. no. 20. The titlepage is in MS.
The title is taken from the foot of p. 1.* **h. 861. (18.)**

— Les Nageurs. *See* infra: [Die Schwimmer. Op. 99.]

— National Oberoesterreicher-Ländler für das Piano-Forte. 11tes
Werk. pp. [7.] *Bey A. Diabelli u. Comp.: Wien*, [1827.] obl. fol.
e. 283. b. (3.)

— Die Neapolitaner. Walzer für das Pianoforte ... 107tes Werk.
pp. 11. *Bei Pietro Mechetti: Wien*, [1836.] obl. fol.
Hirsch M. 214. (12.)

— Nixen Tänze, für das Piano-Forte ... 198tes Werk. pp. 10. *Bei
Tobias Haslinger: Wien*, [1842.] obl. fol.
Hirsch M. 216. (10.)

— Nixen-Tänze. Walzer. ⟨Op. 198. For the piano forte.⟩ pp. 9.
Printed by R. Cocks & Cᵒ: London, [1842.] fol.
La Mode à la cour de la grande Bretagne. ser. 2. no. 10.
h. 862. (8.)

— Nord-Klänge. Mazur für das Pianoforte ... 66stes Werk. pp. 4.
Bei P. Mechetti: Wien, [1833?] obl. fol. **Hirsch M. 214. (13.)**

— Norwegische Arabesken. Potpourri. [Op. 145. For violin and
P. F. Score and part.] 2 pt. [^{MS} *Printed by R. Cocks & Cᵒ:
London*,] [1840.] fol.
*Les Élégants du beau monde. no. 9. The titlepage is in MS.
The title is taken from the head of p. 1 of the score.*
h. 861. (7.)

— Nymphen-Galoppe für das Piano-Forte ... 153stes Werk. pp. 3.
Bei Pietro Mechetti: Wien, [1840.] obl. fol. **e. 563. c. (5.)**

— Nymphen-Galoppe. [Op. 153. P. F.] pp. 3. [^{MS} *Printed by
R. Cocks & Co.: London*,] [1840.] fol.
*Les Élégants du beau monde. no. 5. The titlepage is in MS.
The title is taken from the head of p. 2.* **h. 861. (3.)**

— Olymp's Walzer, für das Pianoforte ... 67stes Werk. pp. 9. *Bei
P. Mechetti: Wien*, [1833?] obl. fol. **Hirsch M. 214. (14.)**

— Olymp's Walzer für das Pianoforte zu vier Händen ... 67stes
Werk. pp. 17. *Bei P. Mechetti: Wien*, [1833.] obl. fol.
e. 563. (7.)

— Olymp's Walzer für die Violine mit Begleitung des Pianoforte
... 67stes Werk. [Parts.] 2 pt. *Bei P. Mechetti: Wien*, [1833.] fol.
h. 860. f. (1.)

LANNER (Josef Franz Carl)

— Original Oberösterreicher Ländler für das Piano-Forte ...
186tes Werk. pp. 9. *Bei Tobias Haslinger: Wien*, [1841.] obl.
fol. **e. 283. d. (3.)**

— Orpheus-Klänge. Walzer für das Pianoforte. (Fortsetzung der
Olymps-Walzer.) ... 126stes Werk. pp. 10. *Bei Pietro Mechetti:
Wien*, [1838.] obl. fol. **Hirsch M. 214. (15.)**

— Orpheus-Klänge. Walzer. 126stes Werk. ⟨Für die Violine mit
Begleitung des Pianoforte.⟩ [Parts.] 2 pt. *Bei Pietro Mechetti:
Wien*, [1838.] fol. **h. 860. f. (5.)**

— Die Osmanen. Walzer für das Piano-Forte ... 146tes Werk.
pp. 11. *Bei Pietro Mechetti: Wien*, [1839.] obl. fol.
f. 541. g. (7.)

— Die Osmanen. Walzer. ⟨Op. 146.⟩ [P. F.] pp. 11. [^{MS} *R. Cocks
& Cᵒ: London*,] [1839.] fol.
The titlepage is in MS. The title is taken from the head of p. 2.
h. 860. (27.)

— [Die Osmanen. Op. 146.] Valse ... (The Osmanly.) ⟨[Followed
by] Quick March on Macdermott's war song "We don't want
to fight" by G. W. Hunt. Arr. by Kappey. — Quick March on
Stephen Adams' song "The Tar's Farewell". Arr. by
Kappey. — "Grüss an Ems." Quick March. Liebig. — "Aus
Freundschaft." Polka. Liebig.⟩ [Military band parts.] 140 pt.
Boosey & Co.: London, [1880.] obl. 8° & fol.
*[Boose's military Journal. ser. 64. no. 4.] The parts in obl.
octavo are printed on one side of the leaf only.* **h. 1549.**

— Ouverture aus dem Zaubermährchen: Der Preis einer
Lebensstunde ... 106tes Werk. Für Pianoforte ... zu vier
Händen. pp. 15. *Bei Pietro Mechetti: Wien*, [1836.] obl. fol.
e. 563. b. (4.)

— Panorama der beliebtesten Galoppen. Nᵒ 1. enthaltend:
italienische, spanische, ungarische und englische Galoppen
für das Piano-Forte zu vier Händen. ⟨97stes Werk.⟩ pp. 19. *Bei
Pietro Mechetti: Wien*, [1835.] obl. fol. **f. 134. g. (1.)**

— Drittes Panorama der beliebtesten Galoppen enthaltend:
Nᵒ. 1. Gartenfest Galoppe. Nᵒ. 2. Galoppe nach beliebten
Motiven der Oper: Die Hugenotten von Meyerbeer. Nᵒ. 3.
Champagner-Knall-Galoppe. Für das Piano-Forte ... 114tes
Werk. pp. 11. *Bei Mechetti: Wien*, [1838.] obl. fol.
e. 563. c. (3.)

— Parade Marsch. *See* supra: [Märsche.] 3 Grand Marches. 2.

— Paradies "Soirée" Walzer, für das Pianoforte ... 52stes Werk.
pp. 7. *Bei Pietro Mechetti: Wien*, [1831.] obl. fol.
The wrapper bears the title: "Paradies Garten-Musik".
Hirsch M. 215. (1.)

— Pesther-Walzer, für das Pianoforte ... 93tes Werk. pp. 11. *Bei
Pietro Mechetti: Wien*, [1833.] obl. fol. **Hirsch M. 215. (2.)**

— Pesther Walzer. [P. F.] pp. 9. *Printed by R. Cocks & Cᵒ:
London*, [c. 1845.] fol.
La Mode à la cour de la Grande Bretagne. no. 7.
h. 925. p. (6.)

— Pesther Waltzer for the Pianoforte. *London*, [1874.] fol.
No. 3967, 3968 of the "Musical Bouquet". **H. 2345.**

— Die Petersburger. Russische National-Walzer für das
Pianoforte ... 132stes Werk. pp. 11. *Bei Pietro Mechetti: Wien*,
[1838.] obl. fol. **Hirsch M. 215. (3.)**

— Die Petersburger. Russische National-Walzer, *etc.* [Op. 132.
P. F.] pp. 9. [^{MS} *R. Cocks & Cᵒ: London*,] [1839.] fol.
*Without titlepage. The imprint is given in MS. at the foot of
p. 1. The title is taken from the head of p. 1.* **h. 860. (6.)**

— Die Petersbourger-Walzer für das Piano Forte. [Op. 132. P. F.]
pp. 9. *Printed by Messʳˢ R. Cocks & Cᵒ: London*, [c. 1845.] fol.
h. 1480. t. (26.)

LANNER (JOSEF FRANZ CARL)

— Die Petersburger, Russische National Walzer, *etc.* ⟨Op: 132.⟩
[P. F. duet.] pp. 19. [^{MS} *R. Cocks & Co: London,*] [1839.] fol.
The titlepage is in MS. The title is taken from the head of p. 2.
h. 860. (7.)

— Die Petersburger. Walzer. 132stes Werk. ⟨Für die Violine mit
Begleitung des Pianoforte.⟩ [Parts.] 2 pt. *Bei Pietro Mechetti:*
Wien, [1839.] fol. **h. 860. f. (7.)**

— Petersburgh, set of valses. [Octet band parts.] *London,* [1877.]
8°.
One of "Celebrated German Valses". **f. 416. (5.)**

— Potpourri or The Vienna Festival. *See* supra: [Bürger-Fest-
Parademarsch. Op. 174.]

— Die Pressburger. Comité-Ball-Taenze für das Piano-Forte ...
155stes Werk. pp. 11. *Bei Pietro Mechetti: Wien,* [1840.] *obl.*
fol. **e. 283. b. (4.)**

— [^{MS} Die Pressburger. Comité-Ball Tänze für das Pianoforte.]
[Op. 155.] pp. 9. [^{MS} *R. Cocks & Co.: London,*] [1840.] fol.
Les Élégants du beau monde. no. 8. The titlepage is in MS.
h. 861. (6.)

— Prometheus-Funken. Graetzer Soirée-Walzer für das
Pianoforte ... 123stes Werk. pp. 11. *Bei Pietro Mechetti: Wien,*
[1837.] *obl.* fol. **Hirsch M. 215. (4.)**

— Quadrille pour le piano-forte ... Oeuvre 137. pp. 7. *Chez*
Pietro Mechetti: Vienne, [1839.] *obl.* fol. **e. 563. b. (5.)**

— Quadrille. [P. F.] ⟨Op. 137.⟩ pp. 9. [^{MS} *R. Cocks & Co.:*
London,] [1839.] fol.
The titlepage is in MS. The title is taken from the head of p. 2.
h. 860. (15.)

— Quadrille pour le piano-forte. *etc.* ⟨Livraison 3. Oeuvre 151.⟩
pp. 7. *Chez Pietro Mechetti: Vienne,* [1840.] *obl.* fol.
e. 563. c. (7.)

— Quadrille pour le piano-forte, *etc.* ⟨Livraison 4. Oeuvre 152.⟩
Chez Pietro Mechetti: Vienne, [1840.] *obl.* fol. **e. 563. b. (6.)**

— Quadrilles françaises, pour le pianoforte ... Oeuvre 68. pp. 7.
Chez P. Mechetti: Wien, [1833.] *obl.* fol. **Hirsch M. 215. (5.)**

— Les Ramiers. *See* supra: [Die Kosenden. Op. 128.]

— [Redout, Carneval, Tänze.] Zweite Lieferung der Redout,
Carneval, Tänze für das Pianoforte ... 42stes Werk. pp. 7. *Bei*
Pietro Mechetti: Wien, [c. 1830.] *obl.* fol. **f. 541. g. (8.)**

— Regata-Galoppe, für das Pianoforte ... 134stes Werk. pp. 7.
Bei Pietro Mechetti: Wien, [1838.] *obl.* fol.
Hirsch M. 215. (6.)

— Regata-Galoppe ... Op. 134. [P. F.] pp. 5. [^{MS} *R. Cocks & Co:*
London,] [1839.] fol.
The titlepage is in MS. The title is taken from the head of p. 1.
h. 860. (10.)

— Regata-Galoppe ... Op. 134. [P. F. duet.] pp. 7. [*R. Cocks &*
Co.: London, 1839.] fol.
Without titlepage. The title is taken from the head of p. 2.
h. 860. (11.)

— Reise Marsch. *See* supra: [Märsche.] 3 Grand Marches. 3.

— Roccoco-Walzer. Für das Piano-Forte ... 136stes Werk. pp. 11.
Bei Pietro Mechetti: Wien, [1839.] *obl.* fol. **e. 283. g. (5.)**

— [Another copy.] **e. 282. pp. (19.)**

— Roccoco-Walzer, *etc.* [Op. 136. P. F.] pp. 9. [^{MS} *R. Cocks &*
C^o: London,] [1839.] fol.
The titlepage is in MS. The title is taken from the head of p. 1.
h. 860. (14.)

LANNER (JOSEF FRANZ CARL)

— Roccoco-Walzer für das Piano-Forte zu vier Händen ...
136stes Werk. pp. 15. *Bei Pietro Mechetti: Wien,* [1839.] *obl.*
fol. **e. 282. pp. (20.)**

— Die Romantiker. Walzer für das Pianoforte ... 167tes Werk.
pp. 11. *Bei Pietro Mechetti: Wien,* [1841.] *obl.* fol.
Hirsch M. 215. (7.)

— Die Romantiker. Walzer. ⟨Op. 167.⟩ [P. F.] pp. 9. [^{MS} *Printed*
by R. Cocks & Co: London,] [1841.] fol.
Les Élégants du beau monde. no. 26. The titlepage is in MS.
The title is taken from the head of p. 1. **h. 861. (21.)**

— Der Romantiker, set of valses. [Orchestral parts.] *London,*
[1877.] 8°.
One of "Celebrated German Valses". **f. 416. (6.)**

— Die Romantiker. Waltzer. Op. 167. [Flute, violin and P. F.]
See BORSCHITSKY (J. F.) Concordia, *etc.* No. 7. [1876–97.] fol.
h. 2772.

— Die Rosensteiner. Walzer für das Pianoforte ... 204tes Werk.
pp. 11. *Bei Tobias Haslinger's Witwe u. Sohn: Wien,* [1843.]
obl. fol. **Hirsch M. 215. (8.)**

— Die Rosensteiner. Walzer für das Pianoforte ... 204tes Werk.
T. Haslinger's Witwe u. Sohn: Wien, [1843?] *obl.* fol.
R. M. 26. c. 12. (6.)

— Die Rosensteiner-Walzer. Für das Piano Forte, *etc.* ⟨Op. 204.⟩
pp. 9. *R. Cocks & Co.: London,* [1844.] fol. **h. 862. (12.)**

— Die Rosensteiner. Walzer. 204tes Werk. ⟨Für Violine und
Pianoforte.⟩ [Parts.] 2 pt. *Bei Tobias Haslinger: Wien,* [1844?]
fol. **h. 860. f. (14.)**

— Rouge et noire. Quadrilles. ⟨Op. 199. For the piano forte.⟩
pp. 7. *Printed by R. Cocks & Co: London,* [1842.] fol.
La Mode à la cour de la grande Bretagne. ser. 2. no. 9.
h. 862. (7.)

— Rouge et noire. Quadrille. 199^s Werk. ⟨Für Violine und
Pianoforte.⟩ [Parts.] 2 pt. *Tobias Haslinger: Wien,* [1842.] fol.
h. 860. f. (12.)

— The Royal Masque waltzes, for the Pianoforte. *London,*
[1840?] fol. **g. 270. b. (24.)**

— Sammlung der neuesten und beliebtesten Galoppen für die
Violine mit Begleitung des Pianoforte. [Parts.] Hft. 5. *Bei*
Pietro Mechetti: Wien, [1836.] fol.
Imperfect; wanting the other no. **h. 860. f. (3.)**

— Schnellsegler. Ländler für das Pianoforte ... 47stes Werk.
P. Mechetti: Wien, [1830?] *obl.* fol. **R. M. 26. c. 12. (1.)**

— Die Schönbrunner. Walzer für das Pianoforte ... 200tes Werk.
pp. 11. *Bei Tobias Haslinger: Wien,* [1842.] *obl.* fol.
Hirsch M. 216. (11.)

— [Another copy.] **R. M. 26. c. 12. (5.)**

— Die Schönbrunner-Walzer, für das Piano Forte, *etc.* ⟨Op. 200.⟩
pp. 9. *R. Cocks & Co.: London,* [1843.] fol. **h. 862. (10.)**

— Die Schönbrunner. Valse, *etc.* [P. F.] *Royal Aquarium ...*
Society: Westminster, [1887.] fol. **h. 975. u. (38.)**

— Die Schönbrunner set of valses. [Octet band parts.] *London,*
[1877.] 8°.
One of "Celebrated German Valses". **f. 416. (7.)**

— Die Schönbrunner. Walzer ... Op. 200. Arr. von M. Rhode.
[Parts.] *B. Schott's Söhne: Mainz und Leipzig,* 1937. 8°.
[*Schott & Co.'s Domesticum Salon Orchestra. No. 435.*]
g. 1053. a.

— [Die Schönbrunner. Op. 200. No. 1.] Lanner's Ankunft in
Olymp. Komisches Volkslied. [Melody only.] *Lampart &*
Comp.: Augsburg, [c. 1845.] 8°. **B. 880. f. (8.)**

LANNER (Josef Franz Carl)

— Schwechat-Ländler für das Pianoforte ... 32tes Werk. pp. 7.
Bei Pietro Mechetti: Wien, [1829.] *obl.* 4°.   **f. 541. g. (9.)**

— Die Schwimmer. Walzer für das Pianoforte ... 99stes Werk.
pp. 11. *Bei Pietro Mechetti: Wien*, [1835.] *obl.* fol.
    Hirsch M. 216. (12.)

— [Die Schwimmer. Op. 99.] "Les Nageurs," die Schwimmer
Walzer ... Arranged by E. F. Rimbault. [P. F.] *In:* The
Musical Bijou ... for MDCCCXL. pp. 68–70. [1840.] fol.
    H. 2330.

— Sehnsuchts-Mazur für das Pianoforte ... 89stes Werk. pp. 7.
Bei Pietro Mechetti: Wien, [1834.] *obl.* fol.   **e. 563. c. (2.)**

— Der Soirée-Plauderer. Grosses Potpourri für das Piano-Forte
... 149stes Werk. pp. 27. *Bei Pietro Mechetti: Wien*, [1840.] *obl.*
fol.   **e. 563. c. (6.)**

— Der Soirée Plauderer. Pot-pourri. [Op. 149. P. F.] pp. 25.
[^{MS} *Printed by R. Cocks & Co: London*, [1840.] fol.
*Les Élégants du beau monde. no. 15. The titlepage is in MS.
The title is taken from the head of p. 1.*   **h. 861. (13.)**

— Soldaten-Tänze für das Piano-Forte zu 4 Händen ... 173tes
Werk. pp. 19. *Bei Tobias Haslinger: Wien*, [1841.] *obl.* fol.
    e. 563. b. (9.)

— [Another copy.]   **R. M. 26. c. 12. (3.)**

— Soldaten-Tänze. (Military Waltzes.) ⟨Op. 173.⟩ [P. F.] pp. 9.
[^{MS} *R. Cocks & Co: London*,] [1841.] fol.
*Les Élégants du beau monde. no. 22. The titlepage is in MS.
The title is taken from the head of p. 1.*   **h. 861. (20.)**

— Sommernachts-Traum-Galoppen, für das Pianoforte ... 90stes
Werk. pp. 7. *Bei Pietro Mechetti: Wien*, [1834.] *obl.* fol.
    Hirsch M. 215. (9.)

— Die Sonderlinge. Walzer für das Pianoforte ... 183tes Werk.
pp. 10. *Bei Tobias Haslinger: Wien*, [1841.] *obl.*
Imperfect; wanting pp. 5–8.   **e. 563. (8.)**

— Die Sonderlinge. Walzer. (Strange Fellows.) Op. 183. ⟨For the
piano forte.⟩ pp. 11. *Printed by R. Cocks & Co: London*,
[1841.] fol.
Les Élégants du beau monde. no. 42.   **h. 861. (32.)**

— [Another copy.]   **g. 270. b. (23.)**

— Souvenir de Castellammare March. Op. 181. ⟨For the piano
forte.⟩ pp. 3. *Printed by R. Cocks & Co: London*, [1841.] fol.
Les Élégants du beau monde. no. 34.   **h. 861. (29.)**

— Souvenir des artistes. Quadrille pour le piano ... Ouevre 184.
pp. 7. *Chez Tobie Haslinger: Vienne*, [1841.] 4°.
    h. 977. j. (11.)

— Souvenirs des artistes, Quadrille. Op. 184. ⟨For the piano
forte.⟩ pp. 7. *Printed by R. Cocks & Co: London*, [1842.] fol.
Les Élégants du beau monde. no. 45.   **h. 861. (34.)**

— Souvenir des artistes. Quadrille. 184^s. Werk. ⟨Für Violine und
Pianoforte.⟩ [Parts.] 2 pt. *Bei Tobias Haslinger: Wien*, [1842.]
fol.   **h. 860. f. (10.)**

— Le Stelle della sera. *See* supra: [Abendsterne.]

— Steyrische Taenze, für das Pianoforte ... 165stes Werk. pp. 7.
Bei Pietro Mechetti: Wien, [1841.] *obl.* fol.
    Hirsch M. 215. (10.)

— [Another copy.]   **R. M. 26. c. 12. (2.)**

— Steyerische Tänze. ⟨Op. 165.⟩ [P. F.] pp. 7. [^{MS} *R. Cocks & Co:
London*,] [1841.] fol.
*Les Élégants du beau monde. no. 19. The titlepage is in MS.
The title is taken from the head of p. 3.*   **h. 861. (17.)**

— Steyrische Tänze. Ländler. [P. F. trio.] *See* BORSCHITZKY (J. F.)
Concordia, *etc.* No. 11. [1900.] fol.   **h. 2772. a.**

LANNER (Josef Franz Carl)

— [Steyrische Tänze.] Styrian Dances. (Op. 165.) ... Arranged
for Violin and Pianoforte. 1900. *See* WILHELMJ (A. E. D. F. V.)
and BROWN (J.) A Modern School for the Violin. No. 18.
1898, *etc.* 4°.   **h. 1748. a.**

— [Steyrische Tänze.] Five Styrian Dances.—Ländler.—Op. 165.
Arranged (as a Quintet) by C. E. Lowe. [1902.] *See* NOVELLO
AND CO. Novello, Ewer & Co.'s Albums for Pianoforte and
Stringed Instruments. No. 23. [1893, *etc.*] 4°.   **g. 1023.**

— The Storming of Constantine. *See* supra: [Die Bestürmung
von Constantine.]

— Styrian Dances. *See* supra: [Steyrische Tänze.]

— Taglioni-Walzer. [Op. 141. P. F.] pp. 5. [^{MS} *R. Cocks & Co:
London*,] [1839.] fol.
The titlepage is in MS. The title is taken from the head of p. 2.
    h. 860. (19.)

— Taglioni-Walzer. [Op. 141. P. F. duet.] pp. 7. *R. Cocks & Co:
[London*, 1839.] fol.
The titlepage is in MS. The title is taken from the head of p. 2.
    h. 860. (20.)

— Talismane. Walzer ... 176^s Werk. [Orchestral parts.] 20 pt.
Bei Tobias Haslinger: Wien, [1841.] fol.   **h. 860. b.**

— Talismane. Walzer für das Pianoforte ... 176tes Werk. pp. 11.
Bei Tobias Haslinger: Wien, [1841.] *obl.*
    Hirsch M. 215. (11.)

— Die Talismane Walzer ... 176tes Werk. ⟨For the piano forte.⟩
pp. 11. *Printed by R. Cocks & Co: London*, [1841.] fol.
Les Élégants du beau monde. no. 29.   **h. 861. (24.)**

— [Talismane.] I Talismani. Valzer per pianoforte ... Op. 176.
pp. 9. *Giovanni Ricordi: Milano*, [c. 1845.] *obl.* 4°.
    e. 284. e. (4.)

— [Der Tanz um die Braut. Op. 178.] The Bride's Mazurkas. ⟨For
the piano forte.⟩ pp. 5. *Printed by R. Cocks & Co: London*,
[1841.] fol.
Les Élégants du beau monde. no. 31.   **h. 861. (26.)**

— Tarantelle für das Piano-Forte ... 187tes Werk. pp. 7. *Bei
Tobias Haslinger: Wien*, [1842.] fol.   **h. 860. f. (11.)**

— Tarantel-Galoppe für das Pianoforte ... 125stes Werk, *etc.*
pp. 3. *Bei Pietro Mechetti: Wien*, [1838.] *obl.* fol.
    f. 541. g. (10.)

— Themis-Strahlen. Walzer für das Pianoforte ... 147stes Werk.
pp. 11. *Bei Pietro Mechetti: Wien*, [1839.] *obl.* fol.
    e. 282. bb. (8.)

— Themis-Strahlen Walzer, für das Piano Forte ... Op. 147.
pp. 9. *Printed by R. Cocks & Co: London*, [1840.] fol.
Les Élégants du beau monde. no. 7.   **h. 861. (5.)**

— Tourbillon-Galoppe ... Op. 142. [P. F.] pp. 3. [^{MS} *R. Cocks &
C^o: London*,] [1839.] fol.
The titlepage is in MS. The title is taken from the head of p. 1.
    h. 860. (21.)

— Der Traum. Londoner Saison-Potpourri für das Piano-Forte
... 188tes Werk. pp. 31. *Bei Tobias Haslinger: Wien*, [1842.]
obl. fol.   **e. 563. b. (10.)**

— Der Traum. (The Dream.) Londoner saison potpourri. Für
das Piano Forte ... Op. 188. pp. 33. *Printed by R. Cocks & Co:
London*, [1842.] fol.   **h. 862. (1.)**

— Trennungs-Walzer, für das Piano-Forte ... 19tes Werk. pp. [4.]
Bei Tobias Haslinger: Wien, [1828?] *obl.* fol.
    Hirsch M. 215. (12.)

— Die Troubadours. Walzer für das Pianoforte ... 197tes Werk.
pp. 11. *Bei Tobias Haslinger: Wien*, [1842.] *obl.* fol.
    Hirsch M. 216. (13.)

LANNER (JOSEF FRANZ CARL)

— Die Troubadours. Walzer für das Piano Forte ... Op. 197.
pp. 9.   R. Cocks & Co.: London, [1843.] fol.   **h. 862. (9.)**

— Die Troubadours. Walzer. [P. F. trio.] See BORSCHITZKY (J. F.)
Concordia, etc. No. 7. [1900.] fol.   **h. 2772. a.**

— Tyroler-Ländler für das Piano-forte ... 6tes Werk. pp. 5.   Bei
Ant. Diabelli u. Comp.: Wien, [1826.] obl. fol.   **e. 563. a. (8.)**

— Der Uhlane. (Le Lancier.) Mazur, für das Pianoforte ... 76stes
Werk. pp. 7.   Bei P. Mechetti: Wien, [1833.] obl. fol.
Hirsch M. 215. (13.)

— Ungarischer Nationaltanz. Op. 168. ⟨For the piano forte.⟩
pp. 5.   Printed by R. Cocks & Cº: London, [1841.] fol.
Les Élégants du beau monde. no. 41.   **h. 861. (31.)**

— Die Unwiderstehlichen. Walzer für das Pianoforte ... 81stes
Werk. pp. 11.   Bei P. Mechetti: Wien, [1834.] obl. fol.
e. 563. (9.)

— Valse pour le pianoforte ... Oeuvre 85. pp. 10.   Chez Pierre
Mechetti: Vienne, [1834?] fol.   **h. 721. w. (4.)**

— Die Vaterländischen. Harmonie-Ball-Taenze für das
Piano-Forte ... 154stes Werk. pp. 11.   Bei Pietro Mechetti:
Wien, [1840.] obl. fol.   **e. 563. b. (7.)**

— Die Vaterländischen. Harmonie-Ball-Tänze. ⟨Op 154.⟩ [P. F.]
pp. 9.   [MS Printed by R. Cocks & Co.: London,] [1840.] fol.
Les Élégants du beau monde. no. 6. The titlepage is in MS.
The title is taken from the head of p. 1.   **h. 861. (4.)**

— La Victoire de la danse. Quadrille pour le piano ...
Oeuvre 179. pp. 7.   Chez Tob. Haslinger: Vienne, [1841.] 4°.
h. 977. j. (12.)

— La Victoire de la danse quadrille. Op. 179. ⟨For the piano
forte.⟩ pp. 7.   Printed by R. Cocks & Cº: London, [1841.] fol.
Les Élégants du beau monde. no. 32.   **h. 861. (27.)**

— Victoria Quadrille, für das Piano Forte. ⟨Op. 207.⟩ pp. 7.
Printed by R. Cocks & Cº: London, [1844.] fol.   **h. 862. (13.)**

— Victoria-Walzer für das Piano-Forte ... 138stes Werk. pp. 11.
Bei Pietro Mechetti: Wien, [1839.] obl. fol.   **e. 282. pp. (22.)**

— Victoria-Walzer, etc. ⟨Op. 138. For the piano forte.⟩ pp. 12.
Printed by R. Cocks & Cº: London, [1839.] fol.
La Mode à la cour de la grande Bretagne. no. 1.   **h. 860. (1.)**

— Victoria-Walzer für das Piano-Forte zu vier Händen ... 138stes
Werk. pp. 15.   Bei Pietro Mechetti: Wien, [1839.] obl. fol.
e. 282. pp. (23.)

— Die Vorstädtler. Walzer für das Piano-Forte ... 195tes Werk.
pp. 10.   Bei Tobias Haslinger: Wien, [1842.] obl. fol.
Hirsch M. 216. (14.)

— Die Vorstädtler Walzer. ⟨Op. 195. For the piano forte.⟩ pp. 11.
Printed by R. Cocks & Cº: London, [1842.] fol.
La Mode à la cour de la grande Bretagne. ser. 2. no. 5.
h. 862. (4.)

— Walzer für das Pianoforte ... 101stes Werk. pp. 11.   Bei Pietro
Mechetti: Wien, [1835.] obl. fol.   **Hirsch M. 215. (15.)**

— Walzer für das Piano-Forte ... 111tes Werk, etc. pp. 11.   Bei
Pietro Mechetti: Wien, [1836.] obl. fol.   **f. 541. g. (11.)**

— Die Werber. Walzer für das Pianoforte ... 103tes Werk. pp. 15.
Bei Pietro Mechetti: Wien, [1835.] obl. fol.
Hirsch M. 215. (16.)

— Die Werber. Walzer. [Op. 103. P. F.] pp. 9.   Printed by
R. Cocks & Cº: London, [1839.] fol.
La Mode à la cour de la grande Bretagne. no. 13.
h. 721. xx. (8.)

LANNER (JOSEF FRANZ CARL)

— [Die Werber. Op. 103.] See ZIMMERMANN (Heinz W.) Drei
Nestroy-Collagen für gemischten Chor und zwei Klaviere,
etc. [No. 2 based on "Die Werber" by J. F. C. Lanner.] 1978.
fol.   **H. 2134. p. (3.)**

— Die Wiener. Ländler für das Pianoforte ... 59stes Werk. pp. 11.
Bei Pietro Mechetti: Wien, [1832.] obl. fol.   **f. 541. g. (12.)**

— Wiener-Juristen-Ball-Tänze, für das Pianoforte ... 70stes Werk.
pp. 10.   Bei P. Mechetti: Wien, [1833.] obl. fol.
Hirsch M. 215. (14.)

— Wiener-Juristen-Ball-Tänze für das Pianoforte zu vier
Händen ... 70stes Werk. pp. 15.   Bei P. Mechetti: Wien, [1833.]
obl. fol.   **e. 563. (10.)**

— [Wiener-Juristen-Ball-Tänze.] Zweite Lieferung der Wiener
Juristen-Ball-Tänze für das Pianoforte, etc. ⟨84stes Werk.⟩
pp. 10.   Bei Pietro Mechetti: Wien, [1833.] obl. 4°.
e. 284. e. (2.)

— [Wiener-Juristen-Ball-Tänze.] Zweite Lieferung der Wiener
Juristen-Ball-Tänze für das Pianoforte ... 84stes Werk. pp. 10.
Bei Pietro Mechetti: Wien, [1834.] obl. fol.   **e. 563. a. (5.)**

— Willkommen zum Sperl. Ländler für das Piano-Forte ... 28tes
Werk. pp. 5.   Bei Tobias Haslinger: Wien, [1829.] obl. fol.
f. 541. g. (13.)

— D'Wuarla. Ländler für das Pianoforte ... 49stes Werk. pp. 11.
Bei Pietro Mechetti: Wien, [1832?] obl. fol.   **e. 563. a. (6.)**

— Zeisel = Jux = Ländler für das Piano-Forte zu vier Haenden
... 25tes Werk. pp. 9.   Bei Tobias Haslinger: Wien, [1828.] obl.
fol.   **e. 563. c. (1.)**

— See CZERNY (C.) Bouquet royal des valses. A collection of
100 ... waltzes by Lanner, and Strauss ... arranged for the
piano forte by C. Czerny, etc. [1839.] fol.   **h. 504. (1.)**

— See CZERNY (C.) Rondeau ... sur waltzes ... de Lanner.
Op. 491. [1838.] fol.   **h. 494. (15.)**

— See CZERNY (C.) Variations brillantes sur une walse favorite
de Lanner ... Op. 324. [c. 1835.] fol.   **h. 514. n. (5.)**

— See CZERNY (C.) Variations brillantes sur une valse ... de
Lanner ... Op. 324. [1845?] fol.   **g. 270. a. (29.)**

— See GUMBERT (F.) Des Herzens Erwachen.
Walzer-Erinnerungen an ... J. Lanner, etc. [1882.] fol.
H. 1793. b. (29.)

— See GUTMANN (F.) Beliebte Tänze von Lanner, etc. [1881.] obl.
4°.   **b. 246. (2.)**

— See JAMES (W.) The Gems of Strauss & Lanner ... arranged
for the Flute by W. James, etc. [c. 1840.] 8°.   **b. 170. e. (3.)**

— See ROYAL. Royal State Marches, Galops, Polkas ... for the
Piano Forte ... by ... Lanner, etc. [1840?] obl. 8°.
c. 40. a. (1.)

— See SCHNETT (Eduard) Walzer-Momente. Nº 1 nach Lanner,
etc. [1908.] fol.   **h. 4090. o. (9.)**

— See TYRRELL (R. M.) Lanner Waltz Motifs ... Arranged by
R. M. Tyrrell. 1898. fol.   **h. 259. g. (54*.)**

— See WALTZES. One hundred German Waltzes for the
Pianoforte. By Strauss, Lanner, etc. [c. 1855.] fol. & 8°.
h. 721. oo.

LANNERS

— Lanner's Ankunft in Olymp. Komisches Volkslied. See
LANNER (J. F. C.) [Die Schönbrunner. Op. 200. No. 1.]

LANNIN (PAUL)

— See GERSHWIN (George) Stop flirting! ⟨Music by G. Gershwin, W. Daly and P. Lannin.⟩ Selection, etc. [1923.] 4°. [Chappell & Co.'s Operatic and popular Selections for Orchestra by various Composers. no. 160.] **f. 424.**

— See GERSHWIN (George) Stop flirting! Selection. Arranged for military band by Dan Godfrey ... Music by G. Gershwin, William Daly and P. Lannin. [1923.] fol. [Chappell's Army Journal. no. 511.] **h. 1562.**

LANNOY (HEINRICH EDUARD JOSEF VON)

— Odalisque aux doux yeux. [Song, begins: "Livre aux vents du Bosphore".] Paris, [1845?] fol. **G. 808. a. (17.)**

— Quintett Es-dur für Klavier, Oboe, Klarinette, Horn und Fagott. Op. 2. Herausgegeben von Georg Meerwein. [Score and parts.] 5 pt. Eulenburg: Zürich, [1977.] 4°. **g. 1667. g. (1.)**

— Grand Trio. For pianoforte, clarinet & violoncello. ⟨Op. 15. Edited by Wolfgang Suppan.⟩ [Score and parts.] 3 pt. Musica rara: London, [1970.] 4°. **g. 274. r. (2.)**

LANNOY (J. B. DE)

— La Fête du Village, pas redoublé à quatre voix d'hommes sans accompagnement. [Begins: "Amis, partons".] Paroles de X***. Paris, [1865.] 8°. **E. 600. b. (7.)**

— L'Hymne au Drapeau. Choeur [begins: "Noble étendard"] à quatre voix d'hommes sans accompagnement. Paroles de A. X. Paris, [1866.] 8°. **E. 600. b. (8.)**

— Polka des Fauvettes pour Piano. Paris, [1875.] fol. **h. 1487. o. (35.)**

LANO (C. S. DE)

— Instructions for playing the Hawaiian Steel Guitar. C. S. de Lano: Los Angeles, 1915. fol.

— [Another edition.] [1916.] fol. **h. 259. h. (27.)**

— Select Compositions for the Hawaiian Steel Guitar and Ukulele. Arrangements by C. S. de Lano. 8 no. W. A. Quincke & Co.: Los Angeles, 1916. fol. **h. 259. h. (28.)**

LANÓR (ARNOLD)

— Little Sweetheart. (Song.) Words by A. L. Muzzey. Arthur & Co.: Birmingham, [1908.] fol. **H. 1794. uu. (70.)**

LANS (M. J. A.)

— De Katholieke Organist. Onderricht in de Begeleiding van den Gregoriaanschen Zang en in het Kerkelijk Orgelspel, met een aantal speeloefeningen. J. W. van Leeuwen: Leiden, 1881. 4°. **f. 327.**

LANSA ( ) Frère

— Chansons originaires des Francs Maçons. ⟨Mises en musique par le Frère Lansa, et traduite de l'anglois par lui-mème et le Frère la Tierce.⟩ pp. 29. 1747. 8°. See CHANSONS. [5.] **C. 424. i.**

LANSAC (JOSÉ)

— La Guitarra flamenca. Método. Enseñanzas completas de rasgueos, percusiones y muchos otros efectos peculiares. pp. 87. Editóra musical Mills: São Paulo, [1962.] 8°. **g. 660. q. (4.)**

LANSDELL (CYRIL)

— Happy Thoughts, for Pianoforte. Warren & Phillips: London, [1913.] fol. **h. 3284. f. (44.)**

LANSDONN (EDMUND)

— Mind your own business. A new national song [begins: "There's a maxim in which all concur"], words and music by E. Lansdonn. London, [1856.] fol. **H. 1758. (12.)**

LANSDOWN (E. C.)

— The Children's Best Friend. [Hymn.] Words and music by E. C. Lansdown. J. Heywood: Manchester, etc., [1894.] s. sh. fol. **I. 600. (121.)**

LANSDOWNE (ETHEL)

— The Joy of Dancing. An allegro for the pianoforte. Independent Music Club: London, 1917. fol. **h. 3284. nn. (11.)**

— Minuet in F, for the pianoforte. Independent Music Club: London, 1917. fol. **h. 3284. nn. (12.)**

LANSDOWNE (HAROLD)

— Faithless. Song. 2 no. [In G flat and F.] Lyon & Hall: Brighton, [1893.] fol. **H. 1797. o. (29.)**

LANSEL ( )

— See BLIN DE LA CODRE (M. S.) Si l'Amour est peint volage ... Accompagnement de M. Lansel, etc. [1785?] 8°. **B. 362. g. (1.)**

LANSING (A. W.)

— Angelic Voices. Hymn Anthem. T. Presser: Philadelphia, (1909.) 8°. **F. 281. r. (21.)**

— Approach, my Soul. [Anthem.] Text by J. Newton. W. Maxwell Music Co.: New York City, (1910.) 8°. **F. 281. z. (23.)**

— As pants the Hart. Sacred Duet. Contralto and Tenor, etc. White-Smith Music Publishing Co.: Boston, etc., (1912.) fol. **H. 1187. rr. (5.)**

— Awake up, my Glory. Anthem. O. Ditson Co.: [Boston,] 1903. 8°. **F. 231. t. (21.)**

— Awake up, my Glory. [Anthem.] [1906.] See CHURCH. The Church Choralist. No. 351. [1886, etc.] 8°. **E. 1330.**

— Be at rest. [Anthem, words by] J. M. Neale. A. P. Schmidt: Boston, etc., 1915. 8°. **F. 281. uu. (27.)**

— Behold, I bring you good Tidings. [Anthem.] A. P. Schmidt: Boston, etc., (1911.) 8°. **F. 281. cc. (23.)**

— Blessed are the Merciful. [Anthem.] Sop. and Ten. Solo & Cho. A. Geibel Music Co.: Philadelphia, (1908.) 8°. **F. 281. n. (20.)**

— Boat Song, words by M. W. Dorman. O. Ditson Company: Boston, etc., 1894. fol. **H. 1798. u. (16.)**

— Bread of the World. Communion Hymn. [Words by] R. Heber. O. Ditson Co.: [Boston,] 1903. 8°. **F. 231. t. (22.)**

— Cantate Domino in F. Quartet or Chorus. O. Ditson Co.: [Boston, etc.,] 1896. 8°. **F. 1529. b. (26.)**

— Cast thy Burden upon the Lord. Sacred Song. A. P. Schmidt: Boston, etc., 1911. fol. **H. 1187. rr. (6.)**

— Christ being raised from the Dead. [Anthem.] A. P. Schmidt: Boston, etc., (1912.) 8°. **F. 281. dd. (29.)**

LANSING (A. W.)

— Christ our Passover. [Anthem.] *O. Ditson Co.: [Boston, etc.,]* 1897. 8°. **F. 1529. b. (27.)**

— Come unto Me, when Shadows darkly gather. [Anthem.] Words by C. H. Esling. *O. Ditson Co.: [Boston, etc.,]* 1897. 8°. **F. 1529. b. (28.)**

— Concert Polka for the Pianoforte ... Four Hands. *T. Presser Co.: Philadelphia,* (1913.) fol. **h. 3290. v. (26.)**

— Concert Valse, for the Pianoforte. *T. Presser Co.: Philadelphia,* (1911.) fol. **h. 3284. f. (45.)**

— The Day is past and over. Sacred Part-Song for men's voices. [Words by] Anatolius ... J. M. Neale, Jr. *O. Ditson Co.: [Boston,]* 1904. 8°. **F. 1529. d. (16.)**

— Dream on, dear Heart. Serenade. [Song, words by] W. H. Gardner. *J. H. Remick & Co.: Detroit, New York,* 1906. fol. **H. 1794. uu. (71.)**

— Earth hath no Sorrow but Heaven can remove. [Anthem.] *T. Pressser Co.: Philadelphia,* [1912.] 8°. **F. 281. ee. (56.)**

— The Earth is the Lord's. Sacred Song, *etc.* *O. Ditson Company: Boston, etc.,* 1893. fol. **H. 1187. u. (2.)**

— Eden of my Dreams. Song, words by J. R. Groves. *T. Presser Co.: Philadelphia,* 1918. 4°. **G. 390. u. (1.)**

— Evening Hymn. Men's voices, the poem by Mrs. S. Adams. *W. Maxwell Music Co.: New York City,* (1911.) 8°. **F. 281. bb. (19.)**

— Fear not ye, O Israel. Sacred Song. *A. P. Schmidt: Boston, etc.,* 1909. fol. **G. 517. v. (29.)**

— Festival March, for the organ. *A. P. Schmidt Co.: Boston, etc.,* 1917. fol. **h. 2731. x. (2.)**

— God is a Spirit. [Anthem.] *W. Maxwell Music Co.: New York,* (1909.) 8°. **F. 281. q. (22.)**

— God shall wipe away all Tears from their Eyes. Solo, *etc.* *H. W. Gray Co.: New York,* [1922.] 4°. **G. 519. k. (1.)**

— God so loved the World. [Anthem.] *A. Geibel Music Co.: Philadelphia,* (1908.) 8°. **F. 281. k. (21.)**

— God that madest Earth and Heaven. Hymn-Anthem. *T. Presser: Philadelphia,* (1906.) 8°. **F. 281. f. (27.)**

— Guide me, O thou great Jehovah. Sacred Duet. *O. Ditson Company: Boston,* 1895. fol. **H. 1187. u. (3.)**

— Hark, hark, my Soul. Male Quartette with Sopr. or Tenor obligato solo. [Words by] F. W. Faber. *O. Ditson Co.: Boston, etc.,* 1897. 8°. **F. 1529. b. (29.)**

— Hark! Hark my Soul. [Anthem, words by] F. W. Faber. *Tullar-Meredith Co.: New York, Chicago,* (1913.) 8°. **F. 281. ii. (34.)**

— He is risen. [Anthem.] *A. P. Schmidt: Boston, etc.,* 1914. 8°. **F. 281. ll. (14.)**

— He shall be great. Anthem for Christmas. *T. Presser Co.: Philadelphia,* (1912.) 8°. **F. 281. gg. (48.)**

— He shall give His Angels charge. (Anthem.) *T. Presser Co.: Philadelphia,* (1915.) 8°. **F. 281. ss. (26.)**

— Hear my Prayer. [Anthem.] *A. P. Schmidt: Boston, etc.,* (1912.) 8°. **F. 281. dd. (30.)**

— Heavenly Love. [Sacred duet.] *A. P. Schmidt Co.: Boston, New York,* 1922. 4°. **G. 519. k. (2.)**

— Holy Night! peaceful Night! [Anthem.] *A. P. Schmidt: Boston, etc.,* (1910.) 8°. **F. 281. x. (22.)**

LANSING (A. W.)

— The Homeland. Hymn Anthem. [Words by] H. R. Haweis. *O. Ditson Co.: [Boston,]* 1905. 8°. **F. 281. a. (22.)**

— I heard the Voice of Jesus say. Sacred Song. [Words by H. Bonar.] *A. P. Schmidt: Boston, etc.,* 1914. fol. **H. 1187. xx. (10.)**

— I'm a wee Lass. *See infra:* Two Scotch Songs, *etc.* No. 2.

— I think when I read that sweet Story of old. Sacred Song, *etc.* *T. Presser Co.: Philadelphia,* 1920. 4°. **G. 519. h. (26.)**

— I will lift up mine Eyes unto the Hills. [Anthem.] *A. P. Schmidt: Boston, etc.,* (1907.) 8°. **F. 281. g. (26.)**

— I will praise Thee, O God. [Song.] *O. Ditson Company: Boston, etc.,* 1896. fol. **H. 1187. u. (4.)**

— I will sing of Thy Power. [Anthem.] *A. P. Schmidt: Boston, etc,* 1912. 8°. **F. 281. ee. (57.)**

— If ye love Me. Anthem, *etc.* *T. Presser Co.: Philadelphia,* (1910.) 8°. **F. 281. v. (29.)**

— In the End of the Sabbath. Easter Anthem. *A. P. Schmidt: Boston, etc.,* (1910.) 8°. **F. 281. r. (22.)**

— Jesus, I my Cross have taken. Hymn Anthem. *T. Presser: Philadelphia,* (1907.) 8°. **F. 281. j. (27.)**

— Jesus my Savior, look on me. Quartet or Chorus. *T. Presser: Philadelphia,* (1907.) 8°. **F. 281. g. (27.)**

— Joy of Spring. Second concert polka for the pianoforte. *T. Presser Co.: Philadelphia,* 1917. 4°. **g. 603. mm. (33.)**

— The King of Love my Shepherd is. Sacred Duet for Soprano and Alto. [Words by] H. W. Baker. *T. Presser Co.: Philadelphia,* (1911.) fol. **H. 1187. rr. (7.)**

— The Land of Nod. Song, words by F. V. Hubbard. *T. Presser: Philadelphia,* (1906.) fol. **H. 1794. uu. (72.)**

— The Lord is exalted. [Anthem.] *A. P. Schmidt: Boston, etc.,* (1909.) 8°. **F. 281. p. (23.)**

— The Lord is my Light. [Anthem.] *O. Ditson Co.: [Boston, etc.,]* 1899. 8°. **F. 1529. b. (30.)**

— Lord, Thou art my God. [Anthem.] *A. P. Schmidt: Boston, etc.,* (1907.) 8°. **F. 281. g. (28.)**

— The Lord's Prayer. Mixed voices. *O. Ditson Co.: [Boston,]* 1904. 8°. **E. 335. (30.)**

— Love Divine, all Love excelling. Song. Words by C. Wesley. *O. Ditson Company: Boston,* 1897. fol. **H. 1187. u. (5.)**

— Marche fantastique, for organ. *H. W. Gray Co.: New York,* 1919. 4°. *No. 132 of the "St. Cecilia Series," etc.* **g. 1380. e. (39.)**

— Message of Christmas. Anthem, *etc.* *T. Presser Co.: Philadelphia,* (1911.) 8°. **F. 281. dd. (31.)**

— My Guardian. *See infra:* Two Scotch Songs, *etc.* No. 1.

— Now is Christ risen from the dead. [Anthem.] *A. P. Schmidt: Boston, etc.,* 1913. 8°. **F. 281. ii. (35.)**

— Now the Day is over. Hymn Anthem. [Words by] S. Baring-Gould. *T. Presser: Philadelphia,* (1909.) 8°. **F. 281. r. (23.)**

— O for a closer Walk with God. [Anthem.] *T. Presser Co.: Philadelphia,* (1911.) 8°. **F. 281. x. (23.)**

— O Maiden rare and lovely.—Du bist wie eine Blume.— Part-Song for men's voices. [Words by] H. Heine. *O. Ditson Co.: [Boston,]* 1905. 8°. **F. 163. e. (19.)**

LANSING (A. W.)

— O Mother dear, Jerusalem. Duet for Soprano and Contralto. [Words by] F. Baker. *T. Presser: Philadelphia*, (1906.) fol.
G. 517. v. (30.)

— O Paradise! [Anthem.] *A. P. Schmidt: Boston, etc.*, (1914.) 8°.
F. 281. ll. (15.)

— O Savior of the World. [Anthem.] *H. W. Gray Co.: New York*, 1924. 8°.
F. 281. zz. (27.)

— O Zion, that bringest good Tidings. Christmas Anthem. *A. P. Schmidt: Boston, etc.*, (1913.) 8°.
F. 281. jj. (29.)

— On such a Night as this. [Song, words by] W. H. Gardner. *J. H. Remick & Co.: Detroit, New York*, 1906. fol.
H. 1794. uu. (73.)

— The People that walked in Darkness. Christmas Anthem. *A. P. Schmidt: Boston, etc.*, 1908. 8°.
F. 281. l. (25.)

— Praise the Lord, O Jerusalem. [Anthem.] *A. P. Schmidt: Boston, etc.*, (1913.) 8°.
F. 281. jj. (30.)

— Praise the Lord, O my Soul ... Male Quartette or chorus with Soprano or Tenor Solo obligato. *O. Ditson Co.: [Boston, etc.,]* 1897. 8°.
F. 1529. b. (31.)

— A Red, red Rose. Part Song for men's voices. [Words by] R. Burns. *O. Ditson Co.: [Boston,]* 1907. 8°.
F. 163. f. (26.)

— Four Responses. 1. God of Mercy, God of Grace. (2. Hear my Prayer, O God. 3. Hear our Prayer. 4. Let the Words of my Mouth.) ... Women's voices (Mixed voices). 2 no. *A. P. Schmidt: Boston, etc.*, 1908. 8°.
F. 538. d. (21.)

— Three Responses. 1. God of Mercy, God of Grace. (2. Hear my Prayer, O God. 3. Let the Words of my Mouth.) ... Men's voices. *A. P. Schmidt: Boston, etc.*, (1908.) 8°.
F. 538. d. (22.)

— The Savior at the Door. [Anthem, words by] W. W. How. *T. Presser Co.: Philadelphia*, (1913.) 8°.
F. 281. ii. (36.)

— Two Scotch Songs, words by C. McIlvaine. 2 no. *O. Ditson Company: Boston, etc.*, 1896. fol.
H. 1798. u. (17.)

— Seek ye the Lord. Sacred Duet, *etc. O. Ditson Company: Boston, etc.*, 1895. fol.
H. 1187. u. (6.)

— The Shadows of the Evening Hours. [Anthem, words by] A. A. Proctor [or rather, Procter]. *T. Presser Co.: Philadelphia*, (1912.) 8°.
F. 281. ee. (58.)

— Show me Thy Ways, O Lord. [Sacred duet.] *A. P. Schmidt Co.: Boston, New York*, 1923. 4°.
G. 519. k. (3.)

— Softly now the Light of Day. Hymn Anthem. [Words by] C. W. Doane. *T. Presser: Philadelphia*, (1909.) 8°.
F. 281. r. (24.)

— The Star divine. Christmas Cantata, text by F. V. Hubbard. *A. P. Schmidt: Boston, etc.*, 1914. 8°.
F. 1269. q. (5.)

— Still, still with Thee. Hymn Anthem. [1908.] *See* CHURCH. The Church Choralist. No. 411. [1886, *etc.*] 8°.
E. 1330.

— Sun of my Soul. Hymn Anthem for Soprano and Tenor Solos and Quartet or Chorus. *T. Presser: Philadelphia*, (1907.) 8°.
F. 281. g. (29.)

— Sweet Saviour, bless us. Sacred Part-Song for men's voices. [Words by] F. W. Faber. *O. Ditson Co.: [Boston,]* 1904. 8°.
F. 1529. d. (17.)

— Te Deum in C. *A. P. Schmidt Co.: Boston, New York*, 1921. 8°.
F. 1158. (19.)

— Te Deum in E. *O. Ditson Co.: [Boston, etc.,]* 1900. 8°.
F. 1170. z. (20.)

— Te Deum in F. Soprano solo, Qut. & Ch. *O. Ditson Co.: [Boston, etc.,]* 1896. 8°.
F. 1529. b. (32.)

LANSING (A. W.)

— Ten thousand Times ten thousand. [Anthem, words by] H. Alford. *T. Presser Co.: Philadelphia*, (1913.) 8°.
F. 281. ll. (16.)

— Venite in A. Sop. and Alto Duet, Qut. or Ch. *O. Ditson Co.: [Boston, etc.,]* 1896. 8°.
F. 1529. b. (33.)

— Wait on the Lord. [Anthem.] *A. P. Schmidt: Boston, etc.*, (1911.) 8°.
F. 281. o. (18.)

— We come unto our Fathers' God. [Anthem.] *A. P. Schmidt: Boston, etc.*, (1907.) 8°.
F. 281. g. (30.)

— What are these that are arrayed in white Robes? [Anthem.] *A. P. Schmidt: Boston, etc.*, (1908.) 8°.
F. 281. l. (26.)

— When Shades of Night are falling. Sacred Part-Song for men's voices. *O. Ditson Co.: [Boston,]* 1904. 8°.
F. 1529. d. (18.)

— While the Earth remaineth. [Anthem.] *A. P. Schmidt: Boston, etc.*, 1915. 8°.
F. 281. uu. (28.)

— Ye shall find Rest. [Sacred song.] *A. P. Schmidt & Co.: Boston, New York*, 1921. 4°.
G. 519. i. (34.)

— Ye that love the Lord. Sacred Song. *A. P. Schmidt Co.: Boston, New York*, 1920. 4°.
G. 519. h. (27.)

LANSING (G. W.)

— *See* LANSING (A. W.)

LANSING (GEORGE L.)

— La Ballerina. Caprice. Banjo Solo. (Fingered and positioned by C. Essex.) *C. Essex: London*, [1904.] fol.
h. 1971. g. (33.)

— Banjo Etchings. Caprice. Banjo Solo. *Vega Co.: Boston, Mass.*, (1907.) fol.
h. 1971. j. (7.)

— The Cadet's Dream. Patrol ... Mandolin. *White-Smith Music Pub. Co.: Boston, etc.*, (1906.) fol.
h. 188. k. (15.)

— The Chieftain. March and two-step. [Mandolin orchestra parts.] 12 pt. *White-Smith Music Pub. Co.: Boston, etc.*, [1908.] 4°.
g. 1800. (199.)

— The Dancing Darkey. [P. F.] *Whaley, Royce & Co.: Toronto*, 1897. fol.
h. 3282. f. (14.)

— The Darkey's Dream. [P. F.] *A. Hammond & Co.: London*, [1892.] fol.
h. 1489. s. (3.)

— The Darkie's Dream ... Dance for the pianoforte. *Ransford & Son: London*, [1892.] fol.
h. 1489. s. (4.)

— The Darkie's Dream, *etc.* [P. F.] *Reynolds & Co.: London*, [1894.] fol.
h. 1489. s. (5.)

— The Darkie's Dream. Nigger Dance. [P. F.] [1895.] *See* MERRY. Merry Favorites, *etc.* No. 32. [1893–96.] fol.
h. 3293.

— The Darkey's Dream. Characteristic Piece for the pianoforte. *R. Cocks & Co.: London*, [1896.] fol.
h. 3282. f. (15.)

— The Darkie's Dream. Arranged for Banjo and Piano by C. Essex. *Essex & Cammeyer: London*, [1892.] fol. *No. 5 of "Banjo ... Solos".*
h. 1971. b. (5.)

— The Darkie's Dream. Arranged by E. Read. [Mandoline and P. F.] [1896.] *See* MANDOLINIST. The Mandolinist, *etc.* No. 13. [1896, *etc.*] fol.
h. 196.

— The Darkie's Patrol. Arranged for Banjo and Piano by C. Essex. *Essex & Cammeyer: London*, [1892.] fol. *No. 4 of "Banjo ... Solos".*
h. 1971. b. (4.)

LANSING (George L.)

— General Jasper Jones. Cakewalk-Two-Step. Banjo Solo. (Fingered and positioned by C. Essex.) *C. Essex: London,* [1904.] fol. **h. 1971. g. (34.)**

— Guardmount in Darktown. Characteristic Patrol. Banjo. *Essex & Cammeyer: London,* 1899. fol. **h. 1971. c. (28.)**

— March of the Pierrots. Banjo Solo. *Vega Co.: Boston, Mass.,* (1907.) fol. **h. 1971. j. (8.)**

— My dusky Belle. A Creole Intermezzo. Banjo Solo. *Vega Co.: Boston, Mass.,* (1907.) fol. **h. 1971. j. (9.)**

— Violetta Waltz. Banjo Solo. *Vega Co.: Boston, Mass.,* (1907.) fol. **h. 1971. j. (10.)**

— The Witmark Progressive Method for the Banjo. Written and compiled by G. L. Lansing. *M. Witmark & Sons: New York, etc.,* 1902. 4°. **g. 1103. (1.)**

— *See* WATSON (J. J.) Happy New Year. March ... arr. by G. L. Lansing. 1892. fol. **h. 1971. (38*.)**

LANT (Thomas)

— Seven Anonymous Elizabethan Rounds. Collected by T. Lant in the year 1580. From a manuscript in the library of King's College, Cambridge. Edited by Jill Vlasto, *etc.* pp. 4. *Stainer & Bell: [London,* 1954.] 8°. **F. 1744. n. (17.)**

LANTERN

— The Lantern. Trio. *See* ROWLAND (A.)

— The Lantern and the Moth. Song. *See* CHARLES (Harry W.)

— The Lantern Festival. [Part-songs.] *See* BURTCH (Mervyn)

— Lantern-Land. [Song.] *See* SAINT QUENTIN (E.) *pseud.*

— The Lantern Marriage. Operetta. *See* OFFENBACH (J.) [Le Mariage aux lanternes.]

— The Lantern Time of Love. Song. *See* GORDON (W.)

LANTERNE

— La Lanterne Magique. [Song.] *See* GATAYES (J. L.)

— La Lanterne Magique. Folie mélodramatique. *See* MARESCOT (C. de)

— [La Lanterne Véridique.] On blasme à tort nôtre façon. *Vaudeville, etc.* [*Paris,*] 1732. *s. sh.* 4°. *Mercure de France, Sept.,* 1732. **298. a. 25.**

LANTERNLIGHT

— Lanternlight. *See* NOVELLO (Ivor) [Valley of Song.]

LANTIDO

— Lantido dilly. [Part-song.] *See* BRIDGE (F.)

LANTIER (Marcel)

— Idylles romantiques. Quatre Impressions pour Piano. 1. Sous les lilas. 2. Sur l'eau. 3. Dans tes yeux bleux. 4. Un moment capricieux. *E. Ashdown: London, etc.,* 1914. 4°. **g. 272. dd. (8.)**

LANTIER (Pierre)

— Cadences pour le concerto No. 5 en la majeur de W. A. Mozart [K. 219]. Violon. pp. 4. *Gallet et fils: Paris,* [1950.] 4°. **h. 1568. v. (3.)**

— Diptyque pour alto et piano, *etc.* [Score and part.] 2 pt. *Chappell: Paris,* [1971.] 4°. **h. 1785. h. (6.)**

LANTIER (Pierre)

— Quatuor à cordes pour 2 violons, alto et violoncelle ... Partition, *etc.* pp. 86. *Durand & cie: Paris,* [1939.] 8°. **b. 204. r. (4.)**

LANTINIS (Hugo de)

— *See* FICKER (R.) Sieben Trienter Codices ... Fünfte Auswahl: Messen und Messensätze von ... Hugo de Lantinis, *etc.* 1924. fol. [*Denkmäler der Tonkunst in Österreich.* XXXI. Jahrg. *Bd.* 61.] **H. 988.**

LANTY

— Lanty Leary. [Song.] *See* LOVER (S.) [Mac Carthy More.]

LANUSSE ( )

— [La Fête du Diable.] Un Jour la reine de Cythère. Couplets ... Paroles de Mr. Martainville. *Paris,* [1807.] fol. **G. 557. (23.)**

— [La Queue de Lapin.] Le Sylphe fidèle. Romance [begins: "Sylvie à l'âge de quinze ans"] ... Paroles de Mr. Frédéric. *Paris,* [1807.] fol. **G. 557. (22.)**

LA NUX (F. V. de)

— *See* LA NUX (Paul V. de)

LA NUX (Paul Véronge de)

— Chansons. 3 no. *Paris,* [1881.] fol. **H. 1786. e. (13.)**

— Chansons. *Paris,* [1882.] 8°. **F. 607. n. (12.)**

— Farandole. [P. F. With a portrait.] *In:* La Danse. pp. 123–125. [1888.] fol. **H. 2349. b.**

— Judith. Scène lyrique de Mr. ***. [Vocal score.] *Paris,* [1877.] 4°. **F. 1239.**

— Nice Chanson. [Song, begins: "Savez vous les enchanteresses".] Poésie de E. Blement. *Paris,* [1882.] fol. **H. 1793. d. (1.)**

— Trois Pièces pour Piano. *Paris,* [1878.] fol. **h. 1493. n. (11.)**

— Zaïre. Opéra en 2 actes, d'après la tragédie de Voltaire, poème d'E. Blau & L. Besson. Partition pour chant et piano. *Choudens Fils: Paris,* [1890.] 8°. **F. 1239. a.**

LANVAL

— [Lanval et Viviane.] Souvent plus d'une enchanteresse. *Vaudeville de Lanval et Viviane* [words by A. de Murville, music by S. Champein]. Avec Accompagnement de Guittare par M. Chaudet, *etc. Chez Imbault: Paris,* [1788.] 8°. **B. 362. c. (66*.)**

— [Lanval et Viviane.] Souvent une erreur passagère. *Romance de Lanval et Viviane* [words by A. de Murville, music by S. Champein]. Avec Accompagnement de Guittare par M. Chaudet, *etc. Chez Imbault: Paris,* [1788.] 8°. **B. 362. c. (66.)**

LANYCSÚFOLÓ

— Lanycsúfoló. [Part-song.] *See* BARTÓK (B.) [Kórusmüvek.]

LÁNYI (Ernő)

— Adoramus te, Christe. [S.A.T.B.] *Budapest,* [1943.] *s. sh.* 8°. *Magyar kórus. no.* 51. **P. P. 1945. efc.**

LÁNYI (Ernő)

— 84 eredeti magyar dal. bk. 1–11. *Rózsavölgyi és társa:
Budapest*, [1892.] fol.
*A made up set of various issues. Bk. 3, 4, 11 bear the title "85
eredeti magyar dal". Imperfect; wanting bk. 12–15 containing
no. 63–85.*   **H. 1403. m.**

— "Kolozsvári nóták." Hét eredeti magyar dal ... Op. 8, *etc.*
pp. 12. *"Harmonia": Budapest; Leipzig* [printed, c. 1890.] fol.
                                                   H. 1403. c. (1.)

LANYON (F. Beverley)

— Benedicite, omnia opera ... —in shortened form—in ... F.
Weekes & Co.: London, (1910.) 8°.   **C. 799. s. (6.)**

— Benedicite, omnia opera ... in ... G. *Weekes & Co.:
London*, [1914.] 8°.   **C. 799. u. (20.)**

— O God, to whom our Fathers prayed. Hymn in time of war.
Weekes & Co.: London, [1916.] *s. sh.* 8°.   **I. 600. e. (235.)**

— Te Deum. Quadruple Chant, *etc.* [2 settings.] *Weekes & Co.:
London*, [1910.] *cards.*   **I. 600. d. (51.)**

LANYON (W. Herbert)

— Original Compositions for the Pianoforte. 5 no. *Ridgeway &
Co.: London*, [1892.] fol.   **h. 1489. s. (8.)**

— Album Leaflets. Six Sketches for Piano ... No. 1. Simplicity.
No. 2. Barcarolle. No. 3. Tarantella. No. 4. An Album Leaf.
No. 5. A Sketch. No. 6. A Rustic Dance. *A. Hammond &
Co.: London*, [1902.] 4°.
The Academic Edition, No. 179.   **g. 1130. l. (3.)**

— An Album Leaf. [P. F.] *A. Hammond & Co.: London*, [1905.]
fol.
The "Dolly Varden" Series, No. 19.   **h. 3412.**

— Alla Gavotta. Octave Study for the pianoforte. *Weekes &
Co.: London*, [1888.] fol.   **h. 1489. s. (6.)**

— Barcarolle. [P. F.] *A. Hammond & Co.: London*, [1905.] fol.
The "Dolly Varden" Series, No. 7.   **h. 3412.**

— Dance Grazioso. [P. F.] *C. Vincent: London*, 1899. 4°.
No. 202 of the "New Century Series," etc.   **g. 1132.**

— Gavotte-Marche for piano. Op. 15. *Phillips & Page: London*,
[1890.] fol.   **h. 1489. s. (7.)**

— Gavotte marche. Op. 15. [P. F.] *See* Baptiste (A.) Forest
Echoes ... No. 6. [1891.] fol.   **h. 3329. (1.)**

— Impressions for the Piano. 1. Mexican Dance. 2. Slumber
Song. *The Author: St. Ives*, (1908.) 4°.   **g. 442. p. (12.)**

— The Lord is King. Anthem, *etc.* pp. 7. *James Macbeth:
Aberdeen*, [c. 1900.] 8°.   **C. 799. oo.**

— Love's Captive. Song, words by A. J. Warne-Browne.
Ridgeway & Co.: London, [1892.] fol.   **H. 1797. o. (30.)**

— The Password. Patrol March. [P. F.] *Ridgeway & Co.:
London*, [1892.] fol.   **h. 1489. s. (9.)**

— Presto for the pianoforte. *Weekes & Co.: London*, [1888.] fol.
                                                 h. 1489. s. (10.)

— A Rustic Dance. [P. F.] *A. Hammond & Co.: London*, [1905.]
fol.
The "Dolly Varden" Series, No. 29.   **h. 3412.**

— Simplicity. [P. F.] *A. Hammond & Co.: London*, [1905.] fol.
The "Dolly Varden" Series, No. 3.   **h. 3412.**

— Tarantelle. [P. F.] *A. Hammond & Co.: London*, [1905.] fol.
The "Dolly Varden" Series, No. 12.   **h. 3412.**

— True Love. Song, words by C. Oliphant. *Weekes & Co.:
London*, [1887.] fol.   **H. 1788. u. (45.)**

LANYON (W. Herbert)

— A Whimsical Sketch. [P. F.] *A. Hammond & Co.: London*,
[1905.] fol.
The "Dolly Varden" Series, No. 25.   **h. 3412.**

LANZ (Josef)

— *See* Karasek (A.) and Lanz (J.) Das deutsche
Volksschauspiel in Galizien, *etc.* [1960.] 8°. **011879. dd. 12.**

LANZ (Josef) *Composer for the pianoforte*

— Berceuse, mélodie pour le piano. Op. 22. *London*, [1854.] fol.
                                                 h. 723. l. (19.)

LANZA (   )

— *See* Beale (Charles) The Sister Isle ... Piano forte
accompaniment by Sig^r Lanza. [c. 1850.] fol.
                                                 H. 1653. k. (10.)

LANZA (Alcides)

— Acúfenos I (1966–III). For trombone and four instruments.
[Score.] pp. 8. *Boosey & Hawkes: New York, etc.*, [1972.] *obl.*
fol.   **f. 760. jj. (2.)**

— Acúfenos II (1971–IV). For chamber ensemble, electronic
sounds and electronic extensions. [Score.] pp. 10. *Boosey &
Hawkes: New York*, [1975.] *obl.* fol.   **f. 760. aa. (2.)**

— Eidesis II (1967–III). For thirteen instruments. [Score.] pp. 15.
Boosey & Hawkes: New York, [1972.] *obl.* fol. **f. 760. jj. (3.)**

— Eidesis III (1971–II). For one or two orchestras and electronic
sounds. [Score.] pp. 15. *Boosey & Hawkes: New York*, [1975.]
fol.   **h. 1564. r. (7.)**

— Hip'nes I (1973–I). Versions a & b. For one or more
instruments. [Score.] pp. 7. *Boosey & Hawkes: [New York,
1977.] obl.* fol.   **f. 760. aa. (4.)**

— Interferences II (1967–I). For percussion ensemble and
electronic sounds. [Score.] pp. 20. *Boosey & Hawkes: [New
York*, 1969.] *obl.* 4°.   **e. 108. t. (1.)**

— Penetrations V (1970–IV). For a minimum of ten sound
sources, with voices, lights, electronic sounds and electronic
extensions. [Score.] pp. 9. *Boosey & Hawkes: New York*,
[1972.] *obl.* fol.   **E. 600. dd. (2.)**

— Penetrations VI (1972–II). For voice, chamber ensemble, lights,
electronic music and electronic extensions. [Score.] pp. 10.
Boosey & Hawkes: New York, etc., [1976.] *obl.* fol.
                                                 F. 1199. f. (5.)

— Plectros II (1966–I). For piano and electronic sounds. [Score.]
pp. 16. *Boosey & Hawkes: [New York*, 1968.] 4°.
                                                 g. 1138. x. (1.)

LANZA (Francesco)

— The Auricula, theme with variations for the Piano Forte on
Rossini's air "Qual mesto gemito" in Semiramide. pp. 11.
S. Chappell: London, [1827.] fol.   **h. 117. (9.)**

— The Caliph of Bagdad, a grand romantic ballet ... by
Monsieur Vestris ... arranged for the piano-forte with an (ad
libitum) accompaniment for the harp ... Op. 6. pp. 72.
J. Power: London, Dublin, [^WM1808.] fol.
The harp part is printed in score, on pp. 11–17 only.
                                                 g. 833. n.

— [Another copy.]
Imperfect; wanting pp. 71, 72.   **h. 803. a. (3.)**

— The Downshire Quickstep. Arranged as a rondo, for the
piano forte by F. Lanza. pp. 7. *Pearce & Co.: [London*,
^WM1806.] fol.   **h. 60. f. (19.)**

LANZA (Francesco)

— The Exile. ⟨The Siege of St Quintin.—Minuet.⟩ [By Francesco Lanza or Gesualdo Lanza. Dances. P. F.] *In:* La Belle assemblée. vol. 5, between pp. 230, 231. 1808. 8°.

P. P. 5142.

— La Flora, Divertimento per Piano Forte sul tema [from Tancredi] del Sigr. Rossini "Tu che accendi". pp. 11. *Button, Whitaker & Co, for the author: London,* [1818.] fol.

h. 117. (7.)

— A grand military piece for the Piano Forte. Op. 4. pp. 11. *Rt. Birchall: London,* [1808.] fol. **h. 117. (8.)**

— Here awa' there awa', a favorite Scotch air with ... variations ... for the Pianoforte. *London,* [1820?] fol.

h. 1480. m. (13.)

— Honi. soit. qui. mal. y. pense. Valses for the pianoforte ... Work 18. pp. 8. *By J. Ricordi: Mayland,* [c. 1825.] *obl.* fol.

f. 133. pp. (8.)

— Lanza's Hornpipe. ⟨Lady Hodge Podge's Squirril.—Press me again.⟩ [By Francesco Lanza or Gesualdo Lanza. Country Dances. P. F.] *In:* La Belle assemblée, vol. 5, between pp. 282, 283. 1808. 8°. **P. P. 5142.**

— The Lilly. *See infra:* [O cara memoria.]

— The Much admired Castanet Dance ... in the favourite ballet of Don Quichotte, composed by F. Venua, arranged as a rondo. [P. F.] pp. 7. *Printed by Wilkinson & Comp[y].: London,* [[WM]1808.] fol. **g. 272. b. (39.)**

— [A reissue.] The Much admired Castanet Dance, *etc. Preston: London,* [[WM]1809.] fol. **h. 3490. e. (4.)**

— Nice mia bella, a Neapolitan air with variations. [P. F.] *London,* [1820?] fol. **g. 272. p. (2.)**

— O cara memoria ... arranged as a divertimento for the Pianoforte, by F. Lanza. [1822.] fol. *See* CARAFA DI COLOBRANO (M. E. F. V. A. P.) *Prince.* [Adele di Lusignano.]

h. 117. (11.)

— [O cara memoria.] The Lilly, divertimento for the Pianoforte on a favorite Italian air [from the opera of Adele di Lusignano by Carafa di Colobrano]. pp. 9. *S. Chappell: London,* [1827.] fol. **h. 117. (10.)**

— Six Original Italian Canzonets, composed ... for Sig[r] Tramezzani, *etc.* First Set. *Button & Whitaker, for G. Lanza: London,* [1810?] fol. **G. 811. b. (13.)**

— An original Reel and Waltz, composed by Mr. Lanza. [i.e. Francesco Lanza or Gesualdo Lanza. P. F.] *In:* La Belle assemblée. vol. 4, between pp. 188, 189. 1808. *obl.* 4°.

P. P. 5142.

— Sul Margine d'un Rio, a duett for the Flute and Pianoforte. *London,* [1810?] fol. **g. 280. g. (16.)**

— The Villager's Delight. ⟨Dulseanne Park.⟩ Composed by Mr. Lanza. [i.e. Francesco Lanza or Gesualdo Lanza. Country Dances. P. F.] *In:* La Belle assemblée. vol. 4, between pp. 236, 237. 1808. 8°. **P. P. 5142.**

— Three Waltzes with introduction for the harp or Piano Forte. 1st Set. pp. 9. *Chappell & Co.: London,* [1812.] fol.

h. 117. (6.)

— *See* LANZA (G.) The Deserts of Arabia ... Entertainment ... arranged for the Piano Forte by F. Lanza. [1806.] fol.

H. 120. (4.)

LANZA (Francesco Giuseppe)

— Six Canzonettas, two Duetts & one Trio, for the Voice, with an Accompaniment for the Harp or Piano Forte ... Op. 6. *R. Birchall, for the Author: London,* [1794.] *obl.* fol.

E. 532. b. (2.)

LANZA (Francesco Giuseppe)

— Six Canzonettas, two Duetts & one Trio for the Voice with an Accompaniment for the Harp or Piano Forte ... Op. 7. *R. Birchall, for the Author: London,* [1796.] *obl.* fol.

E. 532. b. (3.)

— Six Canzonettas, two Duetts & one Trio, for the Voice with an Accompaniment for the Harp or Piano Forte ... Op. 8. *R. Birchall, for the Author: London,* [1796.] *obl.* fol.

E. 532. b. (4.)

— Twelve Italian Ariettes, for a Single Voice, with an Accompaniment for the Harp or Piano Forte ... Op. 1. *R. Birchall, for the Author: London,* [1794.] *obl.* fol.

E. 532. b. (1.)

— Twelve Italian Ariettes, for a Single Voice with an Accompaniment for the Harp or Piano Forte ... Op. IV. *R. Birchall, for the Author: London,* [1796.] *obl.* fol.

E. 270. (17.)

— Ten Italian Ariettes, for a Single Voice, and a Favorite Duet. With an Accompaniment for the Harp or Piano Forte ... Op. X. *R. Birchall, for the Author: London,* [1800?] *obl.* fol.

E. 532.

— Six Italian Duetts for Two Voices with an Accompaniment for the Piano Forte ... Op. 5. *R. Birchall, for the Author: London,* [1796.] *obl.* fol. **E. 270. (18.)**

— Eight Italian Duets and a Favorite Trio, with an Accompaniment for the Harp or Piano Forte ... Op. XI. *R. Birchall, for the Author: London,* [1800?] *obl.* fol.

E. 532. a.

— The Celebrated Stabat Mater, for two Soprano Voices. Op. 12. [Full score, with P. F. accompaniment.] pp. 61. *R[t] Birchall, for the Author: London,* [[WM]1801.] fol. **G. 908.**

— *See* ARTE. L'Arte antica e moderna. Scelta di composizioni [by F. G. Lanza], *etc.* Vol. 14. [1875.] 8°. **f. 127.**

LANZA (Gesualdo)

— Advice to Mary. [Song.] The words by Peter Pindar Esqr. *In:* La Belle assemblée. vol. 2, between pp. 104, 105. 1807. *obl.* 4°.

P. P. 5142.

— Ah tu sei che stringo al senno [*sic*], a favorite duett ... in the opera of La Vergine del sole [by G. Andreozzi], arranged for the harp or piano forte by Lanza junior. pp. 7. *Chappell & Co: London,* [1820.] fol. **H. 1650. ss. (18.)**

— Alma Virgo ... An offertorium, *etc. London,* [1840?] fol.

G. 517. b. (8.)

— Blow gentle Winds, a Canzonet ... The words by Rannie. *Printed for G. Walker: London,* [[WM]1813.] fol.

G. 808. b. (27.)

— Britannia weeps. A Funeral Monody on ... Lord Viscount Nelson, written by Mr. Orme, arranged with an Accompaniment for the Piano Forte by G. Lanza Jun[r]. pp. 5. *Printed by Goulding, Phipps, D'Almaine & Co.: London, Dublin,* [1805.] fol. **G. 805. h. (26.)**

— [Another copy.] **R. M. 14. b. 1. (31.)**

— [The Castle of Wonders.—Overture.] The Favorite Waltz and Rondo from the Overture to the Dramatic Romance of, "The Castle of Wonders," *etc.* [P. F.] *Chappell & Co., for the Author: London,* [1819?] fol. **h. 141. b. (3.)**

— Lanza's Characteristic Rondoncinos à la militaire for the Piano Forte. *London,* 1850. fol. **h. 715. (25.)**

— The Cinder King. A favorite glee, for two sopranos and a bass. *Rt. Birchall, for the Author: London,* [1802.] *obl.* fol. *P. 1 bears the composer's autograph signature.* **D. 402. (20.)**

LANZA (Gesualdo)

— The Complaint. A new song. *In:* La Belle assemblée. vol. 2, between pp. 328, 329. 1807. *obl.* 4°.   **P. P. 5142.**

— The Deserts of Arabia, a grand Operatical Entertainment, written by F. Reynolds ... arranged for the Piano Forte by F. Lanza. *London*, [1806.] fol.   **H. 120. (4.)**

— "Dreams of love, that shine so brightly," a song, sung by Miss Russell in ... The Marriage of Figaro, written by G. Boyle. pp. 7. *S. Chappell: London*, [1828.] fol.   **H. 1287. (9*.)**

— The Elements of singing familiarly exemplified. Vol. 1. *London*, 1813. *obl.* fol.   **E. 351.**

— Elements of singing in the Italian and English styles. 4 pt. *London*, [1820?] *obl.* fol.   **E. 351. a.**

— Lanza's Elements of singing ... abridged. *London*, [1820?] 8°.   **1042. d. 7.**

— [The Elements of singing.] Lanza's Abridgement of his work on the art of singing, compressed from "The Elements of singing". *London*, [1826.] fol.   **H. 2206.**

— The Exile. ⟨The Siege of S‸ Quintin.—Minuet.⟩ [By Francesco Lanza or Gesualdo Lanza. Dances. P. F.] 1808. 8°. [*La Belle assemblée. vol. 5, between pp.* 230, 231.] *See* LANZA (Francesco)   **P. P. 5142.**

— Fair Ella ... Ballad [begins: "The morn arose"] written by Mrs. G. Adams. *London*, [1815?] fol.   **H. 2832. i. (49.)**

— Fare thee well! Lord Byron's ... poem set to music. *London*, [1820?] fol.   **H. 2832. i. (50.)**

— The free forest's my home, a fairy song, the words by G. Healey. *London*, [1850.] fol.   **H. 1717. (10.)**

— The Friendless Girl, a much admired new ballad written by S. Harding. pp. 4. *Button & Whitaker, for the author: London*, [1815.] fol.   **H. 1287. (4.)**

— [A reissue.] The Friendless Girl ... ballad, *etc. Chappell & Cᵒ: London*, [1820.] fol.   **H. 1601. aa. (21.)**

— [The Friendless Girl.] The Orphan Maid, a favorite ballad ... the words by Wᵐ Ball. pp. 5. *Chappell & Cᵒ: London*, [1824.] fol.   **H. 1287. (8.)**

— God save the King, with additional stanzas composed by a clergyman of the Established Church on the occasion of our ... Monarch entering upon the fiftieth year of his reign. The music arranged for the Piano Forte and Harp, with a vocal score and accompaniments for an orchestra and a Military Band by E. Lanza Jun. *Button & Whitaker: London*, [1809.] fol.   **G. 517. h. (2.)**

— Gran Messa di Gloria ... adattata per Organo o Pianoforte. *London*, [1835?] fol.   **I. 48.**

— Henry ... Ballad [begins: "Sweet weeping willow"] ... written by L. St. G. Skeffington. *London*, 1808. fol.   **H. 2818. b. (20.)**

— Lanza's Hornpipe. ⟨Lady Hodge Podge's Squirril.—Press me again.⟩ [By Francesco Lanza or Gesualdo Lanza. Country Dances. P. F.] 1808. 8°. [*La Belle assemblée. vol. 5, between pp.* 282, 283.] *See* LANZA (Francesco)   **P. P. 5142.**

— I'm a gay and gentle sprite, song, the words written by a lady. pp. 6. *S. Chappell, for the author: London*, [1828.] fol.   **H. 1287. (10.)**

— "If e'er compassion shelter found" — a ballad, the words by W. Earle. pp. 4. *Chappell & Cᵒ: London*, [1821.] fol.   **H. 1287. (7.)**

— Love is like the rose — a ballad. pp. 4. *S. Chappell & Cᵒ.: London*, [1821.] fol.   **H. 1287. (11.)**

LANZA (Gesualdo)

— Love, rage and jealous fear. Song, the words by A. W. Keep. *London*, [1830?] fol.   **H. 2832. i. (52.)**

— Love's Victim. Song [begins: "He loved"] ... The words by H. Downing. *London*, [1830?] fol.   **H. 2832. i. (51.)**

— Lovely Susan, a canzonet, *etc. Printed for G. Walker: London*, [ᵂᴹ1813.] fol.   **G. 808. b. (28.)**

— Mary ... Air [begins: "Dear charming Mary"] ... Words by A. H., Esq. *London*, [1809.] fol.   **H. 2818. b. (21.)**

— Signor Lanza's New Method of teaching Class Singing, *etc.* 4 pt. *Amateur Vocalist Society: London*, [1843.] 4°.   **E. 351. b.**

— Oh! that I were a flower; a ballad, sung by Miss Russell, in ... The Marriage of Figaro. Written by G. Boyle. pp. 5. *S. Chappell: London*, [1828.] fol.   **H. 1287. (9.)**

— The old English Lady, a favorite ballad, the words by Harriet Downing, the music adapted from an old melody by Signor Lanza. pp. 7. *S. Chappell, for the author: London*, [1834.] fol.   **H. 1287. (1.)**

— An original Reel and Waltz, composed by Mr. Lanza. [i.e. Francesco Lanza or Gesualdo Lanza. P. F.] 1808. *obl.* 4°. [*La Belle assemblée. vol.* 4, *between pp.* 188, 189.] *See* LANZA (Francesco)   **P. P. 5142.**

— The Orphan Maid. *See supra:* [The Friendless Girl.]

— Rondo alla Polka for the Piano Forte. *London*, [1845.] fol.   **h. 700. (39.)**

— Rosa Damaschina. The Damask Rose. [Song.] A favorite rondo, with Italian & English words ... The Italian words by Signor Caravita. The English words by I. B. Orme. pp. 6. *Button & Whitaker: [London;] W. Power & Co.: Dublin*, [ᵂᴹ1810.] fol.   **Hirsch M. 1318. (2.)**

— The Rose de Meaux; a favorite ballad, the words by A. H. pp. vii. *Button & Whitaker, for the author: London*, [1813.] fol.   **H. 1287. (3.)**

— Say, where doth love delight to dwell? A Cavatina, *etc.,* ⟨The words by W. Earle.⟩ pp. 9. *Printed for the Proprietor: London*, [1828.] fol.   **H. 1287. (6.)**

— Silently, silently over the sea, a fairy duettino for two sopranos, the words by J. Graham. *London*, [1850.] fol.   **H. 1717. (9.)**

— Spirits of Dew, of Evening, Night & Morning, a musical Masque in three parts ... with an introductory symphony to each part, a Pianoforte & Harp accompaniment ... The Words by Mr. W. Earle, *etc. London*, [1825?] fol. *Imperfect; wanting pt.* 2, 3.   **H. 324.**

— Sunday Evening Recreations, consisting of Sacred Vocal Pieces, with Chorus (ad lib.) the words selected principally from the Psalms of David, composed in a modern style ... No. 1(–3). First Series. 3 pt. *The Author: London*, 1840, 41. fol.   **R. M. 14. e. 8.**

— Tell me, ye little melancholy Tears; a favorite Canzonet, with an accompaniment for the harp or piano forte. pp. 5. *Chappell & Cᵒ: London*, [1819.] fol.   **H. 1287. (2.)**

— La Titania, un morceau à la galop pour le Piano. *London*, [1850.] fol.   **h. 715. (26.)**

— The Villager's Delight. ⟨Dulseanne Park.⟩ Composed by Mr. Lanza. [i.e. Francesco Lanza or Gesualdo Lanza. Country Dances. P. F.] 1808. 8°. [*La Belle assemblée. vol.* 4. *between pp.* 236, 237.] *See* LANZA (Francesco)   **P. P. 5142.**

— Wherefore is my heart opprest. A canzonet. *London*, [1815?] fol.   **G. 809. b. (4.)**

LANZA (Gesualdo)

— *See* Carafa di Colobrano (M. E. F. V. A. P.) *Prince.* Addio Teresa, a favorite romance ... with an accompaniment for the piano forte, by G. Lanza. [1828.] fol.   **G. 426. qq. (29.)**

— *See* Lyric. [The Lyric Novelist.] Fifteen Songs, sung by Mrs Mountain, in the Lyric Novelist ... the music ... by Dr Callcott ... Sig^r Lanza jun^r [and others], *etc.* [1804.] fol.   **H. 1653. l. (28.)**

— *See* Weber (C. M. F. E. von) [*Doubtful and Supposititious Works.*] Weber's farewell ... adapted by G. Lanza. [1829.] fol.   **H. 1287. (5.)**

LANZA (Rosalia)

— Days gone by, ballad, the poetry written by J. L. H., *etc.* pp. 3. *P. Ernst: London,* [c. 1840.] fol.   **G. 296. b. (14.)**

— The Invitation. Come hither at early dawn. Barcarole. *London,* [1865.] fol.   **H. 1772. r. (14.)**

— The Ripplet waltzes. [P. F.] *London,* [1866.] fol.   **h. 1460. u. (35.)**

LANZAVECCHIA (Rinaldo)

— Edvige. Mazurka per pianoforte. *Milano,* [1883.] fol.   **h. 3285. b. (42.)**

— Effetti di Matrimonio. Mazurka per pianoforte. *Milano,* [1884.] fol.   **h. 3285. b. (45.)**

— Reminiscenze di Gavirate. Polka per pianoforte. *Milano,* [1884.] fol.   **h. 3285. b. (44.)**

— Ricordo d'Amicizia. Polka per pianoforte. *Milano,* [1884.] fol.   **h. 3285. b. (46.)**

— Tutta Gioja. Mazurka per pianoforte. *Milano,* [1884.] fol.   **h. 3285. b. (43.)**

LANZELOT

— Lanzelot. Oper. *See* Dessau (P.)

LANZEROTTI (Arturo)

— Life is so short. Song, words by L. Paggi. 2 no. [In F and A flat.] *Leonard & Co.: London,* 1913. fol.   **G. 806. ll. (49.)**

— When. When into your Eyes I gaze. [Song.] Words by E. Teschemacher, *etc. B. Feldman & Co.: London,* 1913. fol.   **H. 1793. s. (11.)**

LANZETTI (Salvatore)

— Allegro vivamente ... Arr. par B. Hambourg et A. Moffat. [Violoncello and P. F.] (1911.) *See* Moffat (A. E.) Klassische Stücke, *etc.* No. 2. (1911, 12.) fol.   **h. 1684. e. (1.)**

— vi. Solos for two Violoncello's with a Thorough Bass for the Harpsichord. *Printed for and Sold by Benjⁿ Cooke: London,* [1740.] fol.
Issued by Walsh as 'Opera Seconda,' with the same contents but in a different order.   **g. 208.**

— Six Solos for two Violoncellos or a German Flute and a Bass ... Opera seconda. [Score.] pp. 34. *Printed for I. Walsh: London,* [1740?] fol.
Containing the same works as Benjamin Cooke's original edition in a different order.   **g. 270. l. (6.)**

— [Another copy.]   **g. 500. (2.)**

— vi. Solos for two Violoncello's with a Thorough Bass for the Harpsichord. *Printed for J. Johnson: London,* [1745?] fol.
A reissue from the plates of the edition published by Benjamin Cooke in 1740, entered above.   **g. 510. (3.)**

LANZETTI (Salvatore)

— Six Solos for two Violoncellos or a German Flute and a Bass, *etc. Printed for I. Walsh: London,* [1745?] fol.
The titlepage of this work is that of Walsh's edition of Op. 2, but the contents are different and are probably some other set by Lanzetti.   **g. 421. v. (2.)**

— Six Solos after an Easy & Elegant Taste for the Violoncello with a Thorough Bass, for the Harpsichord. *Printed for C. Heron:* [*London,* 1760?] fol.   **g. 514. b. (3.)**

— Sonate i. A dur. (ii. G dur.) 2 no. [1897.] *See* Schroeder (C.) Classische Violoncell-Musik, *etc.* Heft xxi. (xxii.) [1894, *etc.*] 4°.   **g. 800.**

— [12 sonate. Op. 1. No. 1.] Sonate G-Dur ... für Violoncello und Basso continuo ... Herausgegeben von Hugo Ruf. [Scores.] 2 pt. *B. Schott's Söhne: Mainz,* [1967.] 4°.
Cello-Bibliothek 103. Two scores, one with and the other without the realisation of the figured bass.   **g. 510. w. (8.)**

LANZI (Maria)

— Three Pieces for the Pianoforte ... 1. Notte stellata—Piccola Serenata—. 2. Ora pensosa. 3. Barcarola. *Weekes & Co.: London,* [1904.] fol.   **h. 3282. ww. (30.)**

LANZKNECHTLIED

— Lanzknechtlied. [Part-song.] *See* Rheinberger (J. G.) Drei Wettgesänge ... Op. 144. No. 2.

LANZONI (Joseph)

— Le Rendezvous. Nocturne pour deux voix [begins: "Γλυκοφεγγει και τἀστρον της Αὐγουλας"] *Paris,* [1875.] fol.   **h. 1777. h. (11.)**

LAO (Chai)

— Hsüan-so shih-san t'ao. [Compositions for stringed instruments, pa-pan, and cheng, based on Mongol folk themes, transcribed from the MS of Lao Chai by Ts'ao An-ho and Wen Yen. Numerical notation.] vol. 1. pp. 127. *Yin-yüeh Ch'u-pan-she: Peking,* 1955. 8°.   **G. 1363. l. (1.)**

LAO (Chih-ch'eng)

— Shepherd's Pastime. Piano-solo. pp. 7. *Alexandre Tcherepnine: Peiping,* [1935.] 4°.
Collection Alexandre Tcherepnine. no. 2.   **g. 819. (3.)**

— [Another copy.]   **g. 819. a. (6.)**

LAODAMIA

— Laodamia. [Song.] *See* Essington (L. F.)

LAOIDE (Eoghan)

— An Cruitire. E. Laoide to ghléas. [Gaelic airs arranged for P. F.] 1903. 4°. *See* Dublin.—*Gaelic Leagne.*   **f. 760. k. (1.)**

LAOIDE (Seosamh)

— *See* Lloyd (Joseph H.)

LAOUREUX (Nicolas)

Practical method for the violin

— A Practical Method for Violin ... Translated from the third French edition by Dr. Th. Baker. 5 pt. *G. Schirmer: New York,* [1917,] 1916, 21. 4°.   **g. 767. a.**

— Método práctico para violín ... Traducido de la tercera edición por J. M. Esparza. 4 pt. *G. Schirmer: New York,* [1916.] 4°.   **g. 767.**

LAOUREUX (Nicolas)

— École pratique du Violon. Gammes et arpèges ... Practical Method for the Violin, *etc.* *G. Schirmer: New York,* 1926. 4°.
g. 498. dd. (7.)

— [Pt. 1.] A Practical Method for the Viola. Transcribed ... by Oscar Raoul Iotti. pp. 60. *G. Schirmer: New York,* [1962.] 4°.
g. 761. qq. (3.)

LAPARRA (Raoul)

— Chants de la Mer et des Villages, pour voix graves et moyennes. Mélodies sur des poésies de P. Fort, *etc.* *Au Menestrel: Paris,* 1926. fol. **H. 1860. g. (30.)**

— Chants des Jardins. 1. C'est un calme qu'on ne peut dire. 2. La Porte d'Espoir. 3. Villanelle. *Éditions Ricordi: Paris,* 1929. fol. **H. 1846. mm. (21.)**

— Gitanerias. Danses pour une Cali ... Piano seul. *Éditions Francis Salabert: Paris,* 1930. fol. **h. 3870. h. (1.)**

— La Habanera. Drame Lyrique en 3 Actes. (Poème et Musique de R. Laparra.) Partition Piano et Chant réduite par l'Auteur, *etc.* *Enoch & Cⁱᵉ: Paris,* 1907. 4°. **F. 1423.**

— La Habanera ... Prélude du deuxième acte. [P. F.] [*Paris,*] 1908. 8°.
Supplement to "L'Illustration," No. 3399. **P. P. 4283. m. (3.)**

— Jeux Printaniers en l'honneur de ma bien-aimée. Suite de Mélodies pour voix graves et moyennes. Rondels de J. Heugel. *Au Menestrel: Paris,* 1926. fol. **H. 1860. g. (31.)**

— La Jota. Conte lyrique en 2 actes. ⟨Poème et musique de R. Laparra.⟩ Partition pour piano et chant réduite par l'auteur. pp. 239. *Enoch & cⁱᵉ.: Paris,* [1911.] 4°.
With press cuttings inserted. **F. 1423. a.**

— Le Joueur de viole. Conte lyrique en quatre actes divisés en cinq tableaux. Poème et musique de Raoul Laparra. La partition chant et piano. pp. 306. *Heugel: Paris,* 1925. 4°. **F. 1423. b.**

— Juergas. Cinq Pièces espagnoles ... Piano seul. *Éditions Francis Salabert: Paris,* 1930. fol. **h. 3870. h. (2.)**

— Lieds de notre amour, *etc.* (Translation by M. Shanafelt.) *Stᵉ. Nouvelle d'Éditions Musicales: Paris,* 1905. fol. **H. 1860. h. (4.)**

— Le Livre de l'Aurore. Suite pour Flûte et Piano, *etc.* *Au Ménestrel: Paris,* 1926. fol. **h. 2140. p. (1.)**

— Livre de l'Aurore. Suite pour Piano, *etc.* *Au Ménestrel: Paris,* 1927. fol. **h. 3870. g. (2.)**

— Seize Mélodies sur des thèmes populaires d'Espagne ... Sixteen Songs on popular themes of Spain. *Span., Fr. & Eng. Au Ménestrel: Paris,* 1920. 4°. **G. 981. j. (6.)**

— Le Messel Chantant. Suite de Mélodies sur de vieilles poésies françaises. 8 vol. *Au Ménestrel: Paris,* 1924–27. 8°. **F. 1763.**

— Pages d'Espagne. Dix Pièces pour Piano, *etc.* *Editions Costallat: Paris,* 1927. fol. **h. 3870. g. (1.)**

— Paseos. Cinq Pièces espagnoles ... Piano seul. *Éditions Francis Salabert: Paris,* 1929. fol. **h. 3870. h. (3.)**

— Pièces Espagnoles à danser, pour Orchestre. No. 1. Zambra. 2. Fandanguillo. 3. Agarena. 4. Jota. Partition d'Orchestre. *Choudens: Paris,* 1929. fol. **h. 1509. ll. (4.)**

— Rythmes espagnols. Suite d'Orchestre ... Partition d'Orchestre. *Enoch & Cie: Paris,* 1932. fol. **h. 1509. uu. (4.)**

— Sueños. Cinq Pièces espagnoles ... Piano seul. *Éditions Francis Salabert: Paris,* 1930. fol. **h. 3870. h. (4.)**

LAPARRA (Raoul)

— Suite Italienne, en forme de Ballet pour petite Orchestre avec Trompette principale. Partition. *G. Ricordi e C.: Milano, etc.,* 1929. 8°. **c. 121. h. (6.)**

LAPCZYNSKI (Henry)

— Mass of Christmas. For S.A.T.B. voices with organ accompaniment. pp. 31. *Gregorian Institute of America: Toledo, Ohio,* [1962.] 8°. **F. 274. ii. (2.)**

LA PEÑA (E. Diaz de)

— *See* Diaz de la Peña (E. E.)

LA PERDIZ (Guillermo de)

— *See* Perdiz.

LAPEYRRE (Maurice)

— Vendanges fleuries. Esquisses pittoresques. [P. F.] [*Paris,*] 1902. 8°.
Supplement to "L'Illustration," No. 3099. **P. P. 4283. m. (3.)**

LAPFUL

— The Lapful of Nuts. Song. *See* Needham (A. A.)

LAPHAM (Claude)

— *See* Broones (Martin) Seeing Stars. Selection. Arranged [for orchestra] by C. Lapham. [1935.] 4°. [*Chappell & Co.'s Orchestral Works. no.* 297.] **f. 424.**

— *See* Foster (S. C.) Oh! Susanna, *etc.* (Edited by C. Lapham.) 1923. 4°. **G. 1275. ss. (28.)**

— *See* Waller (Jack) and Tunbridge (J. A.) Please Teacher! Selection. Arranged [for orchestra] by C. Lapham. [1935.] 8°. [*Chappell & Co.'s Orchestral Works. no.* 295.] **f. 424.**

LAPHINA

— Ἡ λαφινα. [Part-song.] *See* Gallos (A.)

LAPICIDA (Erasmus)

— *See also* Erasmus.

— *See* Nowak (L.) Das deutsche Gesellschaftslied in Österreich von 1480–1550, *etc.* 1930. fol. [*Denkmäler der Tonkunst in Österreich. xxxvii. Jahrgang. 2. Teil. Band* 72.] **H. 988.**

LAPIERRE (Eugene)

— Accompaniment to the Music of Holy Week. Gregorian chant accompaniments. ⟨Psalm-tone accompaniments used with the Music of Holy Week.⟩ 2 pt. *Gregorian Institute of America: Toledo, Ohio,* [1957.] 8°. **E. 460. f. (1.)**

— Ambrosian Gloria and Credo. Organ accompaniment by E. Lapierre. pp. 8. *Gregorian Institute of America: Toledo, Ohio,* [1957.] 8°. **F. 1175. dd. (9.)**

— Chants of the Church. Organ accompaniments by Dr. E. Lapierre. pp. 123. *Gregorian Institute of America: Toledo, Ohio,* [1953.] *obl.* 4°. **D. 835. n.**

— The Gregorian Mass. For congregation and choir. In accordance with the instruction of the Sacred Congregation of Rites (Sept. 3, 1958), including Credo I and Credo III. pp. 20. *Gregorian Institute of America: Toledo, Ohio,* [1959.] 8°. **F. 1175. ff. (15.)**

— Mass viii (de angelis). Credo iii. A simplified modal accompaniment by E. Lapierre. pp. 9. *Gregorian Institute of America: Toledo, Ohio,* [1961.] 8°. **F. 274. ee. (7.)**

LAPIERRE (Eugene)

— Mass XVII (Sundays of Advent and Lent). Mass XVIII (Weekdays of Advent and Lent). Credo III. A simplified modal accompaniment by E. Lapierre. pp. 10. *Gregorian Institute of America: Toledo, Ohio*, [1961.] 8°.

F. 274. ee. (8.)

— Organ Accompaniment to Gregorian Credo VII. ⟨XIII century.⟩ pp. 4. *Gregorian Institute of America: Toledo, Ohio*, [1953.] 4°.

F. 1175. dd. (10.)

— First People's Mass. For congregational use with organ accompaniment. pp. 15. *Gregorian Institute of America: Toledo, Ohio*, [1960.] 8°.

F. 1175. kk. (8.)

— Second People's Mass. For congregational use with organ accompaniment. pp. 15. *Gregorian Institute of America: Toledo, Ohio*, [1960.] 8°.

F. 1175. kk. (9.)

— Propers of the Mass made easy. Organ accompaniment by E. Lapierre. *Gregorian Institute of America: Toledo, Ohio*, [1961.] 8°.

F. 1175. ll. (1.)

— Simple Gregorian Mass. For congregation and choir ... Responses arranged and harmonized by J. Robert Carroll. pp. 20. *Gregorian Institute of America: Toledo, Ohio*, [1960.] 8°.

F. 1175. kk. (10.)

— Simplified Modal Accompaniment to first class and greater Feasts. pp. 113. *Gregorian Institute of America: Toledo, Ohio*, [1953.] *obl.* 4°.

D. 835. p.

— With one Voice. Organ accompaniment. pp. 37. *Gregorian Institute of America: Toledo, Ohio*, [1959.] 8°.

F. 1175. ff. (16.)

— *See* JURGENS (W. A.) Hymns for Morning and Evening Devotions ... Organ accompaniment by E. Lapierre. [1964.] 8°.

E. 497. z. (10.)

— *See* MacKINNON (Kenneth) Mass for the English Liturgy ... Accompaniment by E. Lapierre. [1965.] 8°.

F. 1183. (2.)

LAPIN (Samuel)

— The Jolly Masqueraders. March and Two-Step. [P. F.] *Weber, Fields & Stromberg: New York*, 1899. fol.

h. 3286. g. (9.)

LAPINS

— Les Lapins. [Song.] *See* PIERNÉ (P.) De la mouche à l'éléphant ... IV.

LAPIS (Santo)

— A Libro aperto. Light airs with minuets for the harpsichord and for all sorts of guittars; containing 36 easy lessons ... Opera XVII. ⟨Wm Smith sculp.⟩ pp. 20. *The Author: London*, 1760. *obl.* fol.

e. 5. r. (1.)

— A Favourite Minuet. [Keyboard.] *In:* GREENE (Maurice) [Choice Lessons for the Harpsichord or Spinnet.] A Favourite Lesson, *etc.* pp. 6, 7. [1758.] *obl.* fol.

e. 282. bb. (4.)

— Miss Mayer. A new Guittar Book in 4 Parts, viz. Italian, French, English Airs, and Duets for the Voice accompanied with the Guittar and a Thorough Bass for the Harpsichord ... Opera XVI. *Mr. Liessem, for the Author: London*, 1759. fol. *Engraved by W. Smith.*

G. 809. c. (16.)

— Nouveaux Trios a deux Flutes Traversieres ou a deux Violons avec la Basse Continue ... Dediés a son Excelence Monseigneur Charles Paul Ernest, Comte Regnant de Bentheim, *etc.* [Parts.] *Amsterdam*, 1756. fol. *Engraved by Pieter Mol.*

g. 213. c. (2.)

— x. Solos for the Violoncello with a Thorough Bass ... Opera XV. [*London*, 1760?] fol. *The title-page is mounted.*

g. 801.

LAPIS (Santo)

— [Sonate da camera. Op. 1. No. 3, 4, 8.] Drei leichte Sonaten ... Für ein Melodie-Instrument (Violine, Querflöte, Oboe) und Generalbass (Cembalo, Klavier; Violoncello, Viola da Gamba oder Fagott ad lib.). Herausgegeben von Hugo Ruf. [Score and parts.] 3 pt. *B. Schott's Söhne: Mainz; Schott & Co.: New York*, [1956.] 4°.

g. 500. ee. (4.)

— La Stravaganza per il Cembalo. Of voorstelling van verandering van sleutels voor het Clavier, *etc.* [*Amsterdam*, 1765?] *obl.* fol.

e. 5. i. (5.)

LAPITINO (Francis J.)

— Alice, where art thou? [By J. Ascher.] Transcription [for the harp by] F. J. Lapitino, *etc.* *O. Ditson Co.: Boston*, (1912.) fol.

h. 2605. c. (11.)

— Fedora Gavotte, *etc.* [Harp.] *O. Ditson Co.: Boston*, (1912.) fol.

h. 2605. c. (12.)

— Valse Impromptu in C major. Harp solo. (Op. 4.) *O. Ditson Co.: Boston*, 1914. fol.

h. 2605. e. (7.)

LAPIZBURN (Manolo)

— The Cupids. Valse for Piano Solo. *C. Woolhouse: London*, [1900.] fol.

h. 3286. q. (73.)

LA PLACE (Pierre Antoine de)

— Air d'Hélène de Tournon. Romance historique et tragique. Paroles et musique de M. D. L. P. [i.e. P. A. de la Place.] 1785. 12°. [*P., M. D. L. Pièces intéressantes et peu connues. tom. 3. pp. 485–487.] See* P., M. D. L.

1088. f. 23.

— Air d'Hélène de Tournon. Romance historique & tragique. Paroles et musique de M. D. L. P. [i.e. P. A. de la Place.] 1786. 12°. [*P., M. D. L. Pièces intéressantes et peu connues. tom. 3. pp. 369–371.] See* P., M. D. L.

122. b. 9.

LAPLAND

— The Lapland Swain, who half the year. *The Lapland Swain.* [Song.] Composed by a young Lady seven years old ... The Words by a Lady. *Broderip and Wilkinson: London*, [1799?] fol.

G. 356. (35.)

LAPLANDER

— The Laplander's Song. *See* RELFE (J.)

LAPON (Edmond)

— Romance pour alto avec accompagnement de piano. *E. Lauweryns, Fils: Bruxelles*, [1889.] fol. **h. 1785. b. (2.)**

LAPORTE (   )

— *See* ARLEQUIN. Arlequin-Sentinelle, Comedie-Parade, *etc.* [With the music of a Vaudeville by — Laporte.] [1798.] 8°.

11738. e. 1. (2.)

LAPORTE (André)

— Reflections. (Inner-space music.) ⟨Clarinet solo.⟩ pp. 3. *J. & W. Chester: London*, [1971.] 4°. **g. 1104. pp. (2.)**

LAPORTE (Bernard)

— The Lincolnshire Poacher. Unison Song. (Arr. B. Laporte.) *Leonard, Gould & Bolttler: London*, 1930, [1940?] 8°. *Two issues. [Leonard, Gould & Bolttler's Library of Unison and Part Songs for Schools. No. 18.]* **F. 1843.**

LAPORTE (CHARLES DE)

— Dat Sherman Band ... Song with Chorus. *Laporte & Co.:*
London, [1887.] fol. **H. 1260. f. (21.)**

LAPORTE (CHARLES KROLL)

— The Daisy, transcribed for the Pianoforte. *London*, [1869.]
fol. **h. 1485. s. (20.)**

— Forget-me-not, nocturne. [P. F.] *London*, [1869.] fol.
h. 1485. s. (19.)

— Galop from [J. Offenbach's opera] Orphée aux Enfers,
transcribed for the Pianoforte. *London*, [1868.] fol.
h. 1485. s. (18.)

— Recueil de mélodies bohémiennes (Gipsy-Melodies)
arrangées pour le piano par C. K. Laporte. Op. 7. pp. 19.
Augener & C°: London, [1872?] fol. **h. 721. vv. (9.)**

LA PORTE (JOSEPH DE)

— *See* CHANSONS. [5.] Poësies de M. l'Abbé de l'Attaignant ... &
des Airs notés, *etc.* [Collected and edited by J. de La Porte.]
1757, 56. 12°. **241. h. 17–20.**

LAPPI (PIETRO)

— Basso Principale per l'Organo della Terza, et Litanie si della
B. Vergine come de Santi, Et Hinno Te Deum, a otto voci,
etc. Appresso Alessandro Raverii: Venetia, 1607. fol.
G. 20.

— Canzoni da suonare ... A 4. 5. 6. 7. 8. 9. 10. 11. 12. & 13.
Libro primo. Con partitura ... Opera nona. ⟨Tenore.—
Basso.—Quinto.—Ottavo.⟩ [Parts.] *A stampa del Gardano: In
Venetia*, 1616. 4°.
Imperfect; wanting the other parts. **K. 3. h. 19.**

— [Canzoni da suonare. lib. 1. Op. 9.] La Negrona. Canzone für
acht Instrumente in zwei Chören, *etc.* ⟨Erste praktische
Ausgabe von Paul Winter.⟩ [Score.] pp. 12. *C. F. Peters:*
Frankfurt, etc., [1962.] 8°.
Part of "Canticum". **e. 668. jj. (9.)**

— [Canzoni da suonare. lib. 1. Op. 9.] Canzon 26. La Negrona.
⟨From the collection published in Venice in 1608 by
Alessandro Rauerij.⟩ For 4 trumpets and 4 trombones (3
trumpets, 2 horns, & 3 trombones). ⟨Edited by A. Lumsden.⟩
[Score and parts.] 11 pt. *Musica rara: London*, [1969.] 4°.
[*Venetian Brass Music. 11.*] **g. 1110. s.**

— Canzoni 11 & 12. ⟨From the collection of canzoni published
in 1608 by Alessandro Rauerij.⟩ For 2 trumpets and 2
trombones (2 trumpets, horn & trombone). ⟨[Edited by] Alan
Lumsden.⟩ [Score and parts.] 6 pt. *Musica rara: London*,
[1967.] 4°.
[*Venetian Brass Music. 4.*] **g. 1110. s.**

— Hymni per tutto l'Anno a Quattro Voci con il Basso per
l'Organo ... Nouamente stampati, *etc.* Alto. (Tenore.) (Basso
Continuo.) 3 pt. *Appresso Bartolomeo Magni. Stampa del
Gardano: Venetia*, 1628. 4°. **C. 265. b.**

— Petri Lappi ... Missarum Octonis [Vocibus] Liber Pr[imus],
etc. Ten[or Secundi Chori]. [*Angelo Gardano: Venice*, 1601.]
4°.
The title-page and page 1 are mutilated. **C. 265. a.**

— La Negrona. *See* supra: [Canzoni da suonare. lib. 1. Op. 9.]

— Sacræ Melodiæ Una, Duabus, Tribus, Quatuor, Quinque et
Sex Vocibus. Una cum Symphoniis & Basso ad Organum.
Tenor. (Bassus.) (Bassus ad Organum.) 3 pt. *Ex Officina
Petri Phalesij: Antuerpiæ*, 1622. 4°. **C. 265.**

LAPPLAENDISCHES

— Lappländisches Rennthierlied. [Song.] *See* SALLENEUVE (E.)

LAPRET (LOUIS)

— Duchess' Valse pour le Piano. *Paris*, [1869.] *obl.* fol.
e. 217. b. (26.)

— *See* LABIT (H.) Fleurs et Bruyères, grande valse ... réduite
pour Piano à quatre mains par L. Lapret. [1879.] fol.
h. 1493. n. (1.)

LAPUCHIN (F.)

— Barcarolle pour Piano. *Paris*, [1878.] fol. **h. 1493. n. (12.)**

LARA

— Lara. Opéra-comique. *See* MAILLART (A.)

LARA (ADELINA DE) *pseud.* [i.e. A. PRESTON.]

— The Birds at their Matins. *See* infra: Rose of the World ... 2.

— A Children's Party. A series of easy original pieces for the
pianoforte, *etc.* 6 no. *J. B. Cramer & Co.: London*, 1913. fol.
h. 3284. nn. (13.)

— Six Small Pieces for Christmas. A Children's Party. [P. F.]
J. B. Cramer & Co.: London, 1913. 4°. **g. 442. t. (17.)**

— Fight on, brave Sons. Song, words by F. A. Joseph. *J. B.*
Cramer & Co.: London, 1914. fol. **H. 1793. s. (12.)**

— In the Forest. Suite for strings. 1. Daybreak. 2. The Storm
King rides through the Forest. 3. Glory of the Bluebells
(Noon). 4. As the Sun sets. 5. The March of the Gnomes
(Moonlight) ... Score, *etc.* pp. 25. *Stainer & Bell: London*,
[1949.] 4°. **f. 244. y. (3.)**

— In the Light of your Eyes. Song, words by F. E. Weatherly.
J. B. Cramer & Co.: London, 1913. fol. **H. 1793. s. (13.)**

— Light of my Heart. Song, the words by F. A. Joseph. *Enoch*
& Sons: London, 1911. fol. **H. 1792. r. (21.)**

— Look up from the Darkness. Song, with organ or harm^m.
accp^t. ad lib., the words by E. Lockton. *Enoch & Sons:*
London, 1916. fol. **H. 1846. x. (23.)**

— Love's Dream. [Song.] Words by W. B. Baldry. *J. Ouseley*
Music Co.: London, [1912.] fol. **H. 1793. s. (14.)**

— Love's Waking. Song, the words by E. Clifford, *etc. Enoch &*
Sons: London, 1907. fol. **H. 1794. vv. (2.)**

— Night and Day. Song, words by F. G. Bowles. 3 no. [In B flat,
C and E flat.] *Ascherberg, Hopwood & Crew: London*, 1911.
fol. **H. 1792. r. (22.)**

— Nocturne pour piano. *Stanley Lucas & Co.: London &*
Leipzig, 1896. fol. **g. 605. p. (18.)**

— Nocturne pour Piano. *A. M. Heller & Co.: London*, [1903.]
fol. **h. 3282. ww. (31.)**

— Red Lips, farewell. Song, words by F. E. Weatherly. *J. B.*
Cramer & Co.: London, 1913. fol. **H. 1793. s. (15.)**

— A Red Rose of June. Song, words by W. B. Baldry. 2 no. [In
E flat and G.] *Leonard & Co.: London*, 1912. fol.
G. 806. mm. (1.)

— Rose of the World. Cycle of five Songs, the poems by Mrs. T.
Kelly. 1. Her Garden glows ... 2. The Birds at their Matins ...
3. Love's Elysium ... 4. Now thou art gone ... 5. The
Splendour of Love's Dream, *etc. Enoch & Sons: London*,
1907. 4°. **G. 383. p. (6.)**

— Rose of the World ... 2. The Birds at their Matins, *etc.*
Enoch & Sons: London, 1907. fol. **H. 1794. vv. (1.)**

— Six Small Pieces for Christmas. *See* supra: A Children's
Party.

LARA (ADELINA DE) *pseud.* [i.e. A. PRESTON.]

— Songs of Two Lives, the words by H. Simpson. 1. There was a Song. 2. Into my Life. 3. Through Life there runs a Chain. 4. Across the Void. *Enoch & Sons: London*, 1908. 4°.
G. 383. t. (8.)

— Valse joyeuse. [P. F.] *Chappell & Co.: London*, 1904. fol.
h. 3282. ww. (32.)

LARA (GEORGE DE)

— "Outside Eliza." [Song.] Written & composed by G. de Larga, *etc. B. Feldman: London*, [1894.] fol. **H. 3980. pp. (5.)**

— Outside Show. [Song.] Written & composed by G. de Lara, *etc.* pp. 4. *B. Feldman: London*, [1894.] fol.
H. 3980. pp. (6.)

LARA (ISIDORE DE) [i.e. I. DE L. COHEN.]

— After silent Years. Song, words by the Earl of Lytton. *Enoch & Sons: London*, [1887.] fol. **H. 1562. (1.)**

— After silent Years ... in A. *Enoch & Sons: London*, [1908.] fol. **H. 1794. vv. (3.)**

— All my all ... [Song.] Words by M. Probyn. *Chappell & Co.: London*, [1886.] fol. **H. 1562. (2.)**

— Amy Robsart. Opéra en trois actes de Sir Augustus Harris & P. Milliet. Partition chant & piano. *Choudens Fils: Paris*, 1894. 8°. **F. 1451. a.**

— At Rest. Song, words by H. Deazeley. *Chappell & Co.: London*, [1884.] fol. **H. 1562. (3.)**

— At Shadwell. Song, the lyric by T. Burke. *Enoch & Sons: London*, 1919. fol. **H. 1846. x. (24.)**

— Ave Maria. [Solo.] *London*, [1876.] fol. **H. 1129. a. (27.)**

— Badoura. Serenade, words by H. Hersee. *E. Ascherberg & Co.: London*, [1887.] fol. **H. 1562. (4.)**

— The Bygone Time. Song, words by A. L. *Chappell & Co.: London*, [1884.] fol. **H. 1562. (5.)**

— The Call of the Heart. Song, the words and music by I. de Lara. *Boosey & Co.: London, etc.*, 1919. fol.
H. 1846. x. (25.)

— Come, we'll love. *See infra*: [Messaline.—Viens, aimer.]

— Danse d'une poupée ivre, for violin & piano. *J. Curwen & Sons: London*, 1924. 4°. **g. 500. l. (4.)**

— The Dreamers. Song with violin and pianoforte accompaniment and organ obbligato ad lib. Words & music by I. de Lara. *G. Ricordi & Co.: London, etc.*, 1919. fol.
H. 1846. x. (26.)

— Eldorado. Song, words by E. A. Poe. *B. Mocatta & Co.: London*, [1892.] fol. **H. 1562. (33.)**

— For Love's Sake to love. *See infra*: [Messaline.—Pour aimer d'amour.]

— Forsworn. Song, words by W. B. Kingston. [German translation by H. Strousberg, on a separate sheet.] 2 no. [In D and F.] *Chappell & Co.: London*, [1887.] fol. **H. 1562. (6.)**

— The Garden of Sleep ... Song, the words by C. Scott. 3 no. [In C, A flat, B flat.] *Chappell & Co.: London*, [1887.] fol.
H. 1562. (7.)

— The Garden of Sleep. A summer song. Words by Clement Scott. pp. 7. [c. 1900.] fol.
A pirated edition. **H. 1848. b. (8.)**

— The Garden of Sleep, as a Vocal Duet, arranged by E. R. Terry, *etc. Chappell & Co.: London*, [1889.] fol.
H. 1562. (8.)

LARA (ISIDORE DE) [i.e. I. DE L. COHEN.]

— The Garden of Sleep. [P. F.] *See* SMALLWOOD (W.) Melodious Lays, *etc.* No. 26. [1874, *etc.*] fol. **h. 1412. n.**

— The Garden of Sleep. [P. F.] *See* SMALLWOOD (W.) Pleasing Themes, *etc.* No. 23. [1878, *etc.*] fol. **h. 1412. q.**

— The Garden of Sleep. [P. F.] *See* SMITH (B.) Popular Songs without Words, *etc.* No. 5. [1886–8.] fol. **h. 3025. c. (5.)**

— [The Garden of Sleep.] *See* BUCALOSSI (P.) The Garden of Sleep. Waltz on ... melodies by I. de Lara. [1888.] fol.
h. 3004. b. (6.)

— How will it be? [Song.] ... The words by C. Scott. (With Organ or Harmonium obligato.) *B. Mocatta: London*, [1889.] fol. **H. 1562. (9.)**

— I am thine and thou art mine. [Song, begins: "He came and wooed her".] Words by "Aral". *London*, [1881.] fol.
H. 1787. j. (10.)

— Insomnia. A lyric. [Song, begins: "Thin are the night skirts".] The words by D. G. Rossetti. *Milan*, [1883.] fol.
H. 1794. a. (24.)

— It may be yet! Song, the words by S. K. Cowan, *etc. Enoch & Sons: London*, [1883.] fol. **H. 1562. (10.)**

— The Last Call. Song, words by H. Begbie. *B. Feldman & Co.: London*, 1915. fol. **H. 1846. x. (27.)**

— Last Night. A Lyric, words by C. Scott. 2 no. [In B flat, and G.] *Chappell & Co.: London*, [1883.] fol. **H. 1562. (11.)**

— Leoline. Song, the words by the Earl of Lytton, *etc. B. Mocatta & Co.: London*, [1889.] fol. **H. 1562. (32.)**

— The Light of Asia ... A sacred Legend, adapted from Sir Edwin Arnold's poem by W. B. Kingston, the Italian translation by G. Mazzucato. Vocal Score. *B. Mocatta & Co.: London*, [1891.] 4°. **F. 1451.**

— Lighted Home. Song [begins: "The weary shade of twilight"] written by M. E. Browne. *London*, [1879.] fol.
H. 1783. o. (14.)

— Long Ago. Song [begins: "The rose has faded"]. Words by S. Samuel. *Milan*, [1882.] fol. **H. 1794. a. (23.)**

— Longings. Song, words by A. Austin. *Chappell & Co.: London*, [1887.] fol. **H. 1562. (12.)**

— A love that has sorrowed. Song [begins: "Again I have seen thee"]. The words by M. E. Browne. *London*, [1880.] fol.
H. 1783. o. (17.)

— Marion ... Song, words by Whyte Melville. 2 no. [In C, and E flat.] *Chappell & Co.: London*, [1886.] fol. **H. 1562. (13.)**

Messaline

— Messaline. Tragédie Lyrique en 4 actes et 5 Tableaux, de A. Silvestre & E. Morand. Transcription pour chant et piano de L. Narici. *Choudens: Paris*, 1899. 4°. **G. 1059.**

— [O nuit d'amour.] O Night of Love! Air ... English translation by V. Blackburn. *Chappell & Co.: London, etc.*, 1922. 4°. **G. 1270. f. (9.)**

— [Pour aimer d'amour.] For Love's Sake to love ... Recit and Air ... English translation by V. Blackburn. *Chappell & Co.: London, etc.*, [1922.] 4°. **G. 1270. f. (10.)**

— [Viens, aimer.] Messaline ... Cantilène, *etc.* [*Paris*,] 1900. 8°. *Supplement to "L'Illustration," No.* 2979. **P. P. 4283. m. (3.)**

— [Viens, aimer.] Come, we'll love ... [Song.] English translation by V. Blackburn. *Chappell & Co.: London, etc.*, [1922.] 4°. **G. 1270. f. (11.)**

LARA (ISIDORE DE) [i.e. I. DE L. COHEN.]

— Mine To-Day! Song, words by M. Probyn, *etc.* 3 no. [In E flat, F, and A flat.] *Chappell & Co.: London*, [1885.] fol.
H. 1562. (14.)

— Moïna. Drame lyrique en deux actes de L. Gallet sur un récit dramatique de I. de Lara. Partition chant et piano. 2me édition. *Choudens: Paris*, 1896. 8°.
F. 1451. c.

— My Trust. Song, words by Brunella. 2 no. [In C, and E flat.] *Chappell & Co.: London*, [1884.] fol.
H. 1562. (15.)

— Naïl. Drame lyrique en trois actes. Poème de Jules Bois ... Partition piano et chant. pp. 281. *Choudens: Paris*, [1911.] 4°.
The fly-leaf bears a MS. dedication in the composer's autograph.
G. 1059. d.

— No more! Song, the words by H. Aïdé, *etc.* *Enoch & Sons: London*, [1883.] fol.
H. 1562. (16.)

— O Night of Love. *See supra*: [Messaline.—O nuit d'amour.]

— On the golden sands. Song, words by M. M. Lemon. *London*, [1880.] fol.
H. 1783. o. (16.)

— Once and for ever. Song, the words by G. C. Bingham. 2 no. [In C, and E flat.] *Chappell & Co.: London*, [1885.] fol.
H. 1562. (17.)

— Only a Song. Written by Brunella. 2 no. [In C, and E flat.] *Chappell & Co.: London*, [1888.] fol.
H. 1562. (18.)

— A Passing Soul. Song, words by B. Thomas. *Chappell & Co.: London*, [1885.] fol.
H. 1562. (19.)

— Red and White. Song, words by H. Deazeley. *Chappell & Co.: London*, [1885.] fol.
H. 1562. (20.)

— Ricordi. (Memories.) Romanza [begins: "T'amo dicea"]. Parole del Signor Angiolini. *London*, [1878.] fol.
H. 1783. o. (13.)

— Sanga. Drame Lyrique en Trois Actes de E. Morand et P. de Choudens ... Partition Chant et Piano transcrite par L. Narici. pp. 160. *Choudens: Paris*, 1906. 4°.
G. 1059. a.

— Sanga. Drame lyrique en quatre actes de Eugène Morand et Paul de Choudens ... Partition chant et piano. Transcrite par Louis Narici. ⟨Nouvelle version.⟩ pp. 274. *Choudens: Paris*, [1908?] 4°.
G. 1059. e.

— Sanga ... La Chanson du Grain, *etc.* [Begins: "Sous le ciel bas".] [*Paris*] 1909. 8°.
Supplement to "L'Illustration," Jan. 2nd, 1909.
P. P. 4283. m. (3.)

— Soléa. Drame lyrique en 4 actes et 5 tableaux, musique et poème d'I. de Lara. Mis en vers français par J. Richepin. Partition chant et piano, transcrite par L. Narici. *Choudens: Paris*, 1907. fol.
G. 1059. b.

— Songs from Orval. [Two-part songs.] The words by Lord Lytton. [1887.] *See* CHAPPELL AND CO. Chappell's vocal library of part songs ... No. 101. [1863–1962.] 8°. **G. 440.**

— Sweet Time of May. Song, words by R. Mulholland. *Chappell & Co.: London*, [1887.] fol.
H. 1562. (21.)

— Tattling Tongues. Song [begins: "From tattling tongues"]. Words by C. Bridgman. *London*, [1880.] fol.
H. 1783. o. (18.)

— Ten Years ago. Song, words by M. Kendal. *Enoch & Sons: London*, [1883.] fol.
H. 1562. (22.)

— There, little Girl, don't cry! ... Song. Words by J. W. Riley. *Chappell & Co.: London*, [1894.] fol.
H. 1562. (34.)

— They tell me, my darling. [Song.] Words by Aral. *London*, [1879.] fol.
H. 1783. o. (15.)

— Tired. Song, words by E. Wheeler. *Elkin & Co.: London*, 1919. fol.
H. 1846. x. (28.)

LARA (ISIDORE DE) [i.e. I. DE L. COHEN.]

— To Cordelia. Song, the words written by the Earl of Lytton, *etc.* *B. Mocatta: London*, [1888.] fol.
H. 1562. (23.)

— To Dreamland, song words by Lady Lindsay. pp. 5. *B. Mocatta & C°: London*, [1891?] fol.
H. 1650. nn. (27.)

— To Love. Song, words by Brunella. 3 no. [In G, A flat, and B flat.] *Chappell & Co.: London*, [1888.] fol.
H. 1562. (25.)

— To the Palms. A Cycle of Melodies from Lord Lytton's poem "Lucile". *Chappell & Co.: London*, [1885.] fol.
H. 1562. (26.)

— Told by golden Hours. Song, the words by N. P. Willis. *B. Mocatta: London*, [1889.] fol.
H. 1562. (24.)

— Les Trois masques. Drame lyrique en quatre actes ... Partition d'orchestre. *Ital. & Fr.* pp. 358. *L'Auteur: Paris*, [1912.] fol.
H. 1562. a.

— Les Trois Masques. Drame lyrique en 4 actes, poëme de M. Charles Méré, *etc.* *Choudens: Paris*, [1912.] 4°.
F. 1451. b.

— Les Trois Mousquetaires. Opéra comique en six tableaux, tiré par H. Cain et L. Payen d'après la pièce d'Alexandre Dumas père et d'Auguste Maquet. The English translation by A. Kalisch. *Goodwin & Tabb: London*, 1921. 4°.
G. 1059. c.

— 'Twas Eve and May. Song, words by ... Lord Lytton. 2 no. [In C and E flat.] *Chappell & Co.: London*, [1886.] fol.
H. 1562. (27.)

— Twin Souls. Song, words by H. Deazeley. 2 no. [In D flat, and F.] *Chappell & Co.: London*, [1884.] fol. **H. 1562. (28.)**

— Where Memory dwells. Song, words by G. C. Bingham. 2 no. [In C minor, and D minor.] *Chappell & Co.: London*, [1884.] fol.
H. 1562. (29.)

— With smiling and weeping. Ballad, words by Miss H. Dixon, *etc.* *J. B. Cramer: London*, [1882.] fol. **H. 1562. (30.)**

— You. Song, words by C. Scott. *B. Mocatta: London*, [1888.] fol.
H. 1562. (31.)

LARA (MAURICE DE)

— The Music of your Voice. Song, the words and music by M. de Lara. *Schott & Co.: London*, 1917. fol.
H. 1860. b. (22.)

— The Music of your Voice ... Small orchestra. [Parts.] *Schott & Co.: London*, [1917.] 8°.
f. 760. j. (9.)

LARBALESTIER (J.)

— The Lady Bird Quadrilles, *etc.* [P. F.] pp. 3. *Duncombe & C°: London*, [c. 1845.] fol.
h. 1203. k. (9.)

LARBALESTIER (J. S.)

— The Blue Bells of Scotland [by Mrs. Jordan], arranged for the Pianoforte. *London*, [1864.] fol.
h. 1460. u. (36.)

— Home, sweet home. Air [by Sir H. R. Bishop] and Variations, arranged for the Piano Forte by J. S. Larbalestier. *Newcastle on Tyne*, [1857.] fol.
h. 725. f. (22.)

— Katie Kearney, Irish melody, transcribed for the Pianoforte. *London*, [1866.] fol.
h. 1460. u. (37.)

— Eighteen opera melodies, arranged for the pianoforte, by J. S. Larbalestier. *Newcastle on Tyne*, [1859.] fol. **h. 725. f. (23.)**

— Les premières pensées ... Waltzes. [P. F.] *London*, [1850.] fol.
h. 947. (39.)

LARBALESTIER (J. S.)

— The Rhine Quadrille, composed on popular German Airs by J. S. Larbalestier. [P. F.] *Newcastle*, [1857.] fol.

h. 977. f. (23.)

— Sacred song. The dream (song of Solomon), transcribed from the original by R. Duff. [Begins: "Methinks I hear thy voice, O beloved".] *Newcastle on Tyne*, [1859.] fol.

H. 1187. a. (14.)

— The Snow Queen, polka. [P. F.] *London*, [1858.] fol.

h. 977. f. (24.)

LARBALESTIER (PHILIP GEORGE)

— Alice in Wonderland. A musical play for children based on the famous story by Lewis Carroll. Adaptation, with additional dialogue and lyrics by G. Scott Archer. [Vocal score.] pp. 63. *John Blackburn: Leeds*, [1950.] 8°.

E. 1592. zz. (3.)

— The Banner of Light and Truth. Choral March. [Words by] G. S. Archer and C. Wesley. *J. Blackburn: Leeds*, [1929.] 8°. *The Classic Series, No.* 192. **E. 1624.**

— Calvary. Short Anthem for Passiontide, words by B. Beaudet. *J. Blackburn: Leeds*, [1935.] 8°. *The Classic Series, No.* 265. **E. 1624.**

— The Challenge of Youth. Sacred Choral March, words by B. Beaudet. *John Blackburn: Leeds*, [1938.] 8°. *The Classic Series, No.* 284. **E. 1624.**

— The Climbing Way. Sacred Choral March, [words by] G. S. Archer. *J. Blackburn: Leeds*, [1933.] 8°. *The Classic Series, No.* 250. **E. 1624.**

— Coins in Bible Days. A demonstration service of song and praise ... Words by Beryl Beaudet, *etc.* [Staff and tonic sol-fa notation.] pp. 14. *John Blackburn: Leeds*, [1967.] 8°.

E. 460. ff. (2.)

— Come let us join our cheerful Songs. Anthem, *etc.* *J. Blackburn: Leeds*, [1931.] 8°. *The Classic Series, No.* 234. **E. 1624.**

— Come, let us join our cheerful Songs ... Tonic Sol-fa edition. *J. Blackburn: Leeds*, [1931.] 4°. *"Phlox" Sol-fa Series, No.* 161. **C. 418.**

— Come to the Fair ... A demonstration service of song & praise for young people. pp. 15. *John Blackburn: Leeds*, [1977.] 8°. **E. 1500. j. (6.)**

— A Day in the Car. A demonstration service of song and praise for young people. Words by G. Scott-Archer. pp. 15. *John Blackburn: Leeds*, [1973.] 8°. **E. 460. cc. (3.)**

— The Day Thou gavest, Lord, is ended. Anthem. [Words by] John Ellerton. pp. 7. *J. Blackburn: Leeds*, [1954.] 8°. [*Classic Series. No.* 327.] **E. 1624.**

— The Day Thou gavest Lord, is ended. Anthem, *etc.* 〈Tonic sol-fa edition.〉 pp. 4. *John Blackburn: Leeds*, [1954.] 8°. [*"Phlox" Sol-fa Series. No.* 213.] **C. 418.**

— Emmanuel. A Sacred Cantata. *J. Blackburn: Leeds*, [1928.] 8°. **E. 541. kk. (3.)**

— Eternal Light! Eternal Light! Anthem, *etc. J. Blackburn: Leeds*, [1935.] 8°. *The Classic Series, No.* 269. **E. 1624.**

— Eternal Light! Eternal Light ... Tonic Sol-fa edition. *J. Blackburn: Leeds*, [1935.] 8°. *"Phlox" Sol-fa Series, No.* 184. **C. 418.**

— From the Rising of the Sun. Anthem. *John Blackburn: Leeds*, [1937.] 8°. *The Classic Series, No.* 275. **E. 1624.**

LARBALESTIER (PHILIP GEORGE)

— From the Rising of the Sun ... Tonic Sol-fa edition. *J. Blackburn: Leeds*, [1937.] 8°. *"Phlox" Sol-fa Series, No.* 188. **C. 418.**

— God make my Life a little Light. [Hymn. Words by] M. B. Edwards. [Staff and tonic sol-fa notation.] *John Blackburn: Leeds*, [1967.] *s. sh.* 8°. **E. 497. qq. (5.)**

— Goody Two Shoes. A pantomime for children. Libretto by G. Scott Archer. [Staff and tonic sol-fa notation. Vocal score.] pp. 51. *John Blackburn: Leeds*, [1958.] 8°. **E. 1598. f. (5.)**

— The Heart's Awakening. A song cycle. 1. Reverie. 2. Cameo. 3. Awakening. Words, Lee Tranter. pp. 7. *Regina Music Publishing Co.: Leeds*, [1972.] 4°. **F. 1875. a. (1.)**

— The Host triumphant. Sacred Choral March, words by G. S. Archer and ... E. S. Armitage. *J. Blackburn: Leeds*, [1932.] 8°. *The Classic Series, No.* 240. **E. 1624.**

— I will fill this House with Glory. Festival anthem. 〈S. C. T. B.〉 pp. [8.] *J. Blackburn: Leeds*, [1955.] 8°. [*Classic Series. No.* 328.] **E. 1624.**

— I will fill this House with Glory. Festival anthem. [Tonic sol-fa edition.] pp. 4. *John Blackburn: Leeds*, [1955.] 8°. [*"Phlox" Series. no.* 214.] **C. 418.**

— Journey to the Moon. A demonstration service of song and praise for young people. Words by G. Scott-Archer. pp. 14. *John Blackburn: Leeds*, [1971.] 8°. **E. 353. o. (2.)**

— Joy-bells ringing. [Hymn. Words] anon. [Staff and tonic sol-fa notation.] *John Blackburn: Leeds*, [1967.] *s. sh.* 8°.

E. 497. qq. (6.)

— King's Heath. [Anthem.] Words by G. Scott-Archer. [Staff and tonic sol-fa notation.] pp. 3. *John Blackburn: Leeds*, [1928.] 8°. [*The Festive Choralist. no.* 394.] **F. 989.**

— Let all the World in every Corner sing. Anthem. *J. Blackburn: Leeds*, [1933.] 8°. *The Classic Series, No.* 257. **E. 1624.**

— Let all the World in every Corner sing ... Tonic Sol-fa edition. *J. Blackburn: Leeds*, [1933.] 8°. *"Phlox" Sol-fa Series, No.* 178. **C. 418.**

— Life's Bowling Alley. A demonstration service of song and praise ... Words by Beryl Beaudet, *etc.* [Staff and tonic sol-fa notation.] pp. 15. *John Blackburn: Leeds*, [1967.] 8°.

E. 460. ff. (5.)

— Life's Olympics. A demonstration service of song and praise for young people. Words by G. Scott-Archer. [Staff and tonic sol-fa notation.] pp. 15. *John Blackburn: Leeds*, [1972.] 8°.

E. 353. o. (1.)

— Light of the World. A demonstration service of song and praise ... Words by G. Scott-Archer, *etc.* [Staff and tonic sol-fa notation.] pp. 20. *John Blackburn: Leeds*, [1967.] 8°.

E. 460. ff. (6.)

— The Little Place where I was born. Setting for male voices (T. T. B. B.). Words by Arthur Jones. [Staff and tonic sol-fa notation.] pp. 7. *Cyngor Gwasanaethau Gwirfoddol Clwyd: Rhuthun*, [1979.] 4°. **F. 1128. (1.)**

— Little Red Riding Hood. A children's pantomime in three acts with two prologues. Libretto by G. Scott-Archer. [Staff and tonic sol-fa notation. Vocal score.] pp. 62. *John Blackburn: Leeds*, [1958.] 8°. **E. 1598. f. (6.)**

— Little Snow-white and the seven Dwarfs. Operetta for young people. Book and lyrics by G. Scott-Archer. [Staff and tonic sol-fa notation. Vocal score.] pp. 54. *John Blackburn: Leeds*, [1958.] 8°. **E. 1598. f. (7.)**

LARBALESTIER (PHILIP GEORGE)

— The Lord is my Shepherd. Anthem, *etc. J. Blackburn: Leeds*, [1932.] 8°.
The Classic Series, No. 244.   **E. 1624.**

— The Lord is my Shepherd ... Tonic sol-fa edition.
J. Blackburn: Leeds, [1932.] 8°.
"Phlox" Sol-fa Series, No. 169.   **C. 418.**

— The Lord's Prayer. A demonstration service for Sunday schools. Words by G. Scott Archer, *etc.* [Staff and tonic sol-fa notation.] pp. 22. *John Blackburn: Leeds*, [1967.] 8°.
E. 460. ff. (7.)

— Mine Eyes have seen the Glory. [Anthem, words by] J. W. Howe. *John Blackburn: Leeds*, [1939.] 8°.
The Classic Series, No. 292.   **E. 1624.**

— Mine Eyes have seen the Glory ... Tonic sol-fa edition.
J. Blackburn: Leeds, [1939.] 8°.
"Phlox" Sol-fa Series, No. 197.   **C. 418.**

— O, that I knew where I might find Him. Anthem.
J. Blackburn: Leeds, [1930.] 8°.
The Classic Series, No. 203.   **E. 1624.**

— O, that I knew where I might find Him ... Tonic Sol-fa edition. *J. Blackburn: Leeds*, [1930.] 4°.
"Phlox" Sol-fa Series, No. 153.   **C. 418.**

— Old King Cole. A nursery rhyme operetta for young folk. Book and lyrics by G. Scott-Archer. [Staff and tonic sol-fa notation.] pp. 30. *John Blackburn: Leeds*, [1961.] 8°.
E. 1598. m. (1.)

— On a Nature Trail. A demonstration service of song and praise for young people. Words by G. Scott-Archer. [Staff and tonic sol-fa notation.] pp. 13. *John Blackburn: Leeds*, [1977.] 8°.   **E. 1500. j. (7.)**

— Our Pets. A demonstration service of song and praise ... Words by Beryl Beaudet, *etc.* [Staff and tonic sol-fa notation.] pp. 16. *John Blackburn: Leeds*, [1967.] 8°.   **E. 460. ff. (8.)**

— Perry Barr. [Anthem.] Words by John Milton. [Staff and tonic sol-fa notation.] pp. 3. *John Blackburn: Leeds*, [1931.] 8°.
[*The Festive Choralist. no.* 422.]   **F. 989.**

— Puss in Boots. A pantomime for children. Libretto by G. Scott Archer. [Staff and tonic sol-fa notation. Vocal score.] pp. 56. *John Blackburn: Leeds*, [1959.] 8°.   **E. 1598. f. (8.)**

— Reaching for the Sky. A demonstration service of song and praise for young people. Words by G. Scott-Archer. [Staff and tonic sol-fa notation.] pp. 12. *John Blackburn: Leeds*, [1977.] 8°.   **E. 1500. j. (8.)**

— Robin Hood and his merry Men. A children's operetta in three acts. Book and lyrics by G. Scott Archer. [Staff and tonic sol-fa notation.] pp. 52. *John Blackburn: Leeds*, [1959.] 8°.   **F. 1267. zz. (5.)**

— Rouse ye, brave Army. Choral March, words by G. S. Archer & G. Duffield. *J. Blackburn: Leeds*, [1931.] 8°.
The Classic Series, No. 232.   **E. 1624.**

— St. Helier ... [Anthem.] Words by J. Newton. Words of chorus by G. Scott-Archer. [Staff and tonic sol-fa notation.] pp. 3. *John Blackburn: Leeds*, [1930.] 8°.
[*The Festive Choralist. no.* 411.]   **F. 989.**

— Ships that sail the Seas. A demonstration service of song and praise for young people. Words by G. Scott-Archer. pp. 15.
John Blackburn: Leeds, [1977.] 8°.   **E. 1500. j. (9.)**

— Sing we merrily. Nine songs for young voices. Words by Arthur Jones. pp. 16. [*John Blackburn: Leeds*, 1977.] 8°.
D. 837. n. (6.)

LARBALESTIER (PHILIP GEORGE)

— The Song of the Sink. Humorous action song for ladies. Written by Beryl Beaudet. [Staff and tonic sol-fa notation.] pp. 3. *Linwood Music Publishing Co.: Eastwood, Notts.*, [1966.] 8°.   **E. 270. bb. (10.)**

— Tangled Texts. Words by G. Scott Archer ... A demonstration service for song and praise, *etc.* [Staff and tonic sol-fa notation.] pp. 22. *John Blackburn: Leeds*, [1967.] 8°.   **E. 460. ff. (3.)**

— The Wilderness and the solitary Place. Anthem.
J. Blackburn: Leeds, [1933.] 8°.
The Classic Series, No. 249.   **E. 1624.**

— The Wilderness and the solitary Place ... Tonic Sol-fa edition. *J. Blackburn: Leeds*, [1933.] 8°.
"Phlox" Sol-fa Series, No. 174.   **C. 418.**

— *See* BACH (J. S.) [Herz und Mund und That und Leben.— Wohl mir, dass ich Jesum habe.] As Shadows fall ... Vesper. Arr ... by P. G. Larbalestier. [1954.] *s. sh.* 8°.
D. 835. g. (6.)

— *See* BENNETT (*Sir* William S.) [Six Songs. Op. 35. No. 3. Dawn, gentle Flower.] When we kneel to Pray ... Arr. by P. G. Larbalestier. [1953.] *s. sh.* 8°.   **D. 835. g. (3.)**

— *See* BRAHMS (J.) [Fünf Lieder. Op. 49. No. 4. Wiegenlied.] Sleep softly this Night. Vesper ... Arr. by P. G. Larbalestier. [1951.] *s. sh.* 8°.   **F. 359. l. (9.)**

— *See* CHAIKOVSKY (P. I.) [12 Morceaux. Op. 40. No. 2. Chanson Triste.] Our parting Prayer. Vesper ... Arr. ... by P. G. Larbalestier. [1951.] *s. sh.* 8°.   **D. 835. g. (2.)**

— *See* GLUCK (C. W.) [Orfeo.—Che farò senza Euridice.] O Saviour, bend above us ... Arr. ... by P. G. Larbalestier. [1954.] *s. sh.* 8°.   **C. 799. bb. (6.)**

— *See* HAENDEL (G. F.) [Berenice.—Overture.—Minuet.] Love's Benediction. Vesper ... Arr. by P. G. Larbalestier. [1951.]
s. sh. 8°.   **E. 146. o. (6.)**

— *See* HAENDEL (G. F.) [Rinaldo.—Lascia ch'io pianga.] Through Darkness to Light ... Arr. P. G. Larbalestier. [1948.]
s. sh. 8°.   **E. 146. o. (19.)**

— *See* HAENDEL (G. F.) [Semele.—Where'er you walk.] Once more we meet. *A Hymn for worship* ... Arr. by P. G. Larbalestier. [1953.] *s. sh.* 8°.   **E. 146. r. (18.)**

— *See* HAENDEL (G. F.) [Water Music.—Air.] A Prayer for Blessing ... Arr. P. G. Larbalestier. [1947.] 8°.
E. 146. o. (24.)

— *See* MOZART (W. A.) [Exsultate jubilate. K. 165.] Alleluia! Christ is risen! Introit ... Arr. by P. G. Larbalestier. [1951.]
s. sh. 8°.   **F. 307. d. (11.)**

— *See* MOZART (W. A.) [*Doubtful and Supposititious Works.*] [Wiegenlied. K. Anh. 284f.] Jesus be near us ... Arr. of "Lullaby" by P. G. Larbalestier. [1948.] *s. sh.* 8°.
F. 307. d. (10.)

— *See* SCHUBERT (F. P.) [Die Forelle. Op. 32.] With Joy we come ... Arr. ... by P. G. Larbalestier. [1951.] *s. sh.* 8°.
F. 409. l. (14.)

— *See* SCHUBERT (F. P.) [Vier Gedichte. Op. 59. No. 3. Du bist die Ruh.] Eternal Friend [four-part song.] ... Arr. ... by P. G. Larbalestier. *s. sh.* 8°.   **F. 409. l. (13.)**

— *See* SCHUBERT (F. P.) [Heidenröslein. Op. 3. No. 3.] Loving Saviour, here we meet ... Arr. ... by P. G. Larbalestier. [1951.] *s. sh.* 8°.   **F. 409. l. (15.)**

— *See* SCHUBERT (F. P.) [Rosamunde. Entr'acte No. 3.] Blest Hour of Worship. Introit ... Arr. ... by P. G. Larbalestier. [1951.] *s. sh.* 8°.   **F. 409. l. (17.)**

LARBALESTIER (PHILIP GEORGE)

— *See* SCHUBERT (F. P.) [Schwanengesang. No. 4. Ständchen.]
Evening Benediction. Vesper ... Arr. ... by P. G. Larbalestier.
[1953.] *s. sh.* 8°.   **F. 409. l. (22.)**

— *See* SCHUBERT (F. P.) [Winterreise. Op. 89. No. 5. Der
Lindenbaum.] Our Harvest Praise is ending ... Arr. ... by
P. G. Larbalestier. [1951.] *s. sh.* 8°.   **F. 409. l. (19.)**

— *See* SCHUMANN (R. A.) [Albumblätter. Op. 124. No. 16.
Schlummerlied.] The Divine Invitation ... Arr. P. G.
Larbalestier. [1953.] *s. sh.* 8°.   **D. 835. g. (5.)**

LARBALESTIER (T. S.)

— *See* LARBALESTIER (J. S.)

LARBEY (VICTOR)

— Un Million dans une main d'enfant. Sérénade chantée au 3ᵉ
acte. Paroles de Alfred Machard. *In:* FAURÉ (G. U.) Le
Secret. [1922.] 8°.   **D. 836. g. (8.)**

LARBOARD

— The Larboard Watch. Duet. *See* WILLIAMS (T.) *Songwriter.*

LARCHET (JOHN F.)

— A stoirin ban. Asthoreen Bawn. Sleep Song, the poem by
P. Gregory. *Boosey & Co.: London and New York*, 1922. 4°.
     G. 1270. f. (12.)

— An Ardglass Boat Song. [Song.] Poem by P. Gregory.
Stainer & Bell: London, 1920. fol.   **H. 1846. x. (29.)**

— An Caitín Bán. Sean-amhrán Connachtach ar na ghléas do
ceithre glórtha ban, S. S. A. A. *Piogóid & a Chomhlucht: Baile
Áta Cliath*, [1934.] 8°.   **F. 217. f. (59.)**

— Caoineadh na hÓige; Lament for Youth. Dhá rhéis
Ghaedhlacha. Ar n-a ngléasadh do cheolfhoirinn bheag ag
J. F. Larchet. (Two Irish melodies. Arranged for Small
Orchestra by J. F. Larchet.) [Score and parts.] *Óifig an
tSoláthair: Baile Átha Cliath*, [1939.] 4°.   **g. 1780. h. (6.)**

— Two Characteristic Pieces (based on traditional Irish Airs).
For string orchestra with xylophone. 1. Carlow Tune.
2. Tinker's Wedding. Score, *etc.* pp. 35. *Elkin & Co.: London*,
[1952.] 4°.   **g. 727. v. (8.)**

— The Cormorant. [Song.] Poem by Emily Lawless. pp. 7.
Stainer & Bell: London, [1947.] 4°.   **G. 1270. ww. (44.)**

— De bhárr na gcnoc. (Old Irish Air.) Words by Sean Clárach
Macdomhnaill. Arranged by J. F. Larchet. *Piogóid & a
Chomhlucht: Baile Atha Cliath*, [1953.] 4°.   **G. 1232. a. (31.)**

— In sweet Humility. Song, words by J. Taylor. 2 no. [In E flat
and F.] *Moore, Smith & Co.: London*, [1906.] fol.
     G. 807. jj. (31.)

— Irish Dance No. 1, for Violin & Piano ... Op. 4, *etc. Weekes
& Co.: London*, 1911. fol.   **h. 1612. aa. (13.)**

— The Legend of Lough Rea. The Death Sign. Poem by
Lageniensis ... for mixed voices, unaccompanied. *Stainer &
Bell: London*, 1920. 8°.   **F. 585. gg. (25.)**

— "Love, and a Garden." Song, words by H. Wyles, *etc.
C. Woolhouse: London*, 1906. fol.   **H. 1794. vv. (4.)**

— "Love's Question." Song, words by H. Wyles. *C. Woolhouse:
London*, 1906. fol.   **H. 1794. vv. (5.)**

— Máirseáil, de shórt meidhréiseach. Marcia quazi [*sic*] scherzo.
J. F. Larchet ... do ghléas. Bunuithe ar fhoinn gaelacha.
[Orchestral score.] pp. 16. *Oifig Díolta Foilseacháin Rialtais:
Baile Átha Cliath*, [1955.] 4°.   **g. 727. v. (6.)**

LARCHET (JOHN F.)

— Padraic the Fiddiler. Song, the words by P. Gregory. *Boosey
& Co.: London, etc.*, 1919. fol.   **H. 1846. x. (30.)**

— Peata an mhaoir. Ar "Ceól ár sinsear"—P. Breathnach ...
Arranged by John F. Larchet. [Part-song for S. S. A. A.]
Pigott & Co.: Dublin, [1953.] 8°.   **F. 217. m. (13.)**

— The Philosophy of Love. Song, the words by Shelley, *etc.
Boosey & Co.: London and New York*, 1908. fol.
     H. 1794. vv. (6.)

— Sliabh na Mban. Irish traditional Song ... Arranged as Two
part Song, S. A., with Pianoforte accompaniment ad lib by
J. F. Larchet. *Piogóid & a Chomlucht: Baile Átha Cliath*,
[1934.] 8°.   **F. 1771. b. (10.)**

— An Spailpín Fánach. Irish traditional Song. Arranged as Part
Song for S. S. A. A., or S. S. A. by J. F. Larchet. *Piogóid & a
Co.: Baile Átha Cliath*, 1935. 8°.   **F. 1771. c. (19.)**

— The Stranger. An old Gaelic Rune. Song, words from the
ancient Gaelic (recovered by Kenneth Macleod). *Stainer &
Bell: London*, 1939. 4°.   **G. 1270. qq. (21.)**

— The Thief of the World. Song, words by F. A. Fahy. (Old
Irish Air.) Arranged by J. F. Larchet. *Boosey & Co.: London*,
1939. 4°.   **G. 981. t. (12.)**

— Two Traditional Irish Airs. [No. 1.] The Dirge of Ossian.
[No. 2.] Mac Ananty's Reel. Arranged for String Orchestra,
etc. [Piano conductor and parts.] *Goodwin & Tabb: London*,
1943. 4°.   **g. 822. j. (9.)**

— The Wee Boy in Bed. Song, words by E. Shane. *Boosey &
Co.: London*, 1943. 4°.   **F. 607. vv. (19.)**

— Wee Hughie. [Song.] Poem by Elizabeth Shane. pp. 7.
Stainer & Bell: London, [1947.] 4°.   **G. 1270. ww. (45.)**

— *See* O'LOCHLAINN (Colm) An Claisceadal ... Arranged ... by
J. F. Larchet. [1933, *etc.*] 8°.   **F. 1771. (39.)**

LARCHWOOD

— The Larch Wood. Unison Song. *See* GIBBS (C. A.)

— The Larch Wood. Song. *See* LENNARD (E. B.) *Lady.*

— The Larchwood. Two-part Song. *See* LLOYD (C. H.)

LARD

— Lard how men can Claret drink. *A Dialogue between a Good
Fellow and a Beau*, to the Tune of the old Cibell [attributed
to G. B. Lulli]. The words by Mr. Estcourt. [*London*, 1707?]
s. sh. fol.   **G. 305. (208.)**

— [Another copy.]   **G. 310. (3.)**

— [Another edition.] Lard how men can Claret drink, *etc.*
[*London*, 1720?] *s. sh.* fol.   **H. 1601. (268.)**

LARDEAU ( )

— Lorsque de Jupiter les foudroyantes armes. *Récit de Basse,
etc.* [*Paris*,] 1730. *s. sh.* 4°.
Mercure de France, Dec., 1730.   **298. a. 14.**

LARDELLI (GUGLIELMO)

— Advance and retreat. Humorous song. Written ... by Mel. B.
Spurr. pp. 7. *Reynolds & Co.: London*, [1906.] fol.
     H. 3985. h. (25.)

— Air de Ballet pour Piano. *E. Ashdown: London*, [1900.] fol.
     g. 1181. (10.)

— L'Amour, nocturne pour Piano. *Brighton*, [1878.] fol.
     h. 1494. p. (14.)

LARDELLI (GUGLIELMO)

— Andante in A for the Organ, from 1ˢᵗ Suite for Orchestra. *London*, [1879.] fol.   **h. 2731. f. (27.)**

— Ave Maria [in D minor] pour une voix avec acc. de piano —violon et orgue ad lib.—With English words by A. C. Bunten. *Schott & Co.: London*, [1900.] fol.   **H. 3615. (1.)**

— Ave Maria [in G] for voice and piano with violin part ad lib. *E. Ashdown: London*, [1900.] fol.   **H. 3615. (2.)**

— Bordighera. Valse Caprice pour Piano. *E. Ashdown: London*, [1901.] fol.   **g. 1181. (11.)**

— Bourrée for the piano-forte. *B. Williams: London*, [1886.] fol.   **h. 1484. s. (20.)**

— Bourrée pour Piano. *E. Ashdown: London*, [1900.] fol.   **g. 1181. (12.)**

— Caprice-Gavotte pour Piano. *E. Ashdown: London*, [1901.] fol.   **g. 1181. (13.)**

— Caprice-Mazurka for Piano. *J. Williams: London*, 1899. fol.   **g. 1181. (14.)**

— Chanson d'Amour, pour Piano. *Nicholson & Co.: Perth, etc.*, [1904.] fol.   **g. 1181. a. (3.)**

— Chanson d'Avril. Morceau pour Piano. *E. Ashdown: London*, [1900.] fol.   **g. 1181. (15.)**

— Connemara. Irish Song, words by "Dry Blower". *Bunz & Co.: London*, 1906. fol.   **H. 3615. (16.)**

— The Constant Lover. Song. Words by P. Pinkerton. 2 no. [In B flat and C.] *E. Ashdown: London*, 1900. fol.   **H. 3615. (3.)**

— Danse des Paysans. Mazurka pour Piano. *E. Ashdown: London*, [1902.] fol.   **g. 1181. a. (1.)**

— Danse Espagnole, pour Piano. *E. Ashdown: London*, [1905.] fol.   **g. 1181. a. (4.)**

— Douce Plainte, pour Piano. *Nicholson & Co.: Perth, etc.*, [1904.] fol.   **g. 1181. a. (5.)**

— Eldorado. Song, words by M. Browne. 2 no. [In E flat and F.] *E. Ashdown: London*, 1896. fol.   **G. 805. aa. (2.)**

— The Fair white Rose. [Song.] Words by T. Hood. *E. Ashdown: London*, [1900.] fol.   **H. 3615. (4.)**

— Fleur d'Amour—Valse gracieuse—pour Piano. *E. Ashdown: London*, [1901.] fol.   **g. 1181. (17.)**

— Gavotte in A for the pianoforte. *E. Ashdown: London, etc.*, [1896.] fol.   **g. 1181. (1.)**

— Gavotte in F for the pianoforte. *B. Williams: London*, [1888.] fol.   **h. 1489. s. (11.)**

— The Gay Zingara. Song. Words by A. H. Hyatt. *Phillips & Page: London*, 1897. fol.   **H. 3615. (5.)**

— Good Night. Humorous song. Written ... by Mel. B. Spurr. pp. 5. *Reynolds & Co.: London*, [1901.] fol.   **H. 3985. h. (26.)**

— Good Night! Beloved. Unaccompanied Quartet for male voices. [1886.] *See* GROSVENOR. The Grosvenor Series of Part Songs. No. 4. [1886, *etc.*] 8°.   **F. 1601.**

— Had I an angel's wings. [Song, begins: "O leave me not".] Words by W. Strachan. *Brighton*, [1877.] fol.   **H. 1778. x. (36.)**

— Harbour Boat Song, the words by M. Browne. *Boosey & Co.: London and New York*, 1895. fol.   **H. 1798. u. (18.)**

— Hindoo Love Song. [Song.] Words by A. J. Hyatt. *Reynolds & Co.: London*, 1903. fol.   **H. 3615. (15.)**

LARDELLI (GUGLIELMO)

— Hunting Song for the pianoforte. *E. Ashdown: London, etc.*, [1895.] fol.   **g. 605. f. (5.)**

— Hymn to the Sun. [Song. Words] ... By B. Hamilton. *Novello & Co.: London*, 1898. fol.   **H. 3615. (6.)**

— In Campagna. Morceau pour Piano. *E. Ashdown: London*, [1900.] fol.   **g. 1181. (16.)**

— Joan of Arc. Characteristic Piece for the pianoforte. *E. Ashdown: London*, [1897.] fol.   **g. 1181. (2.)**

— Meditation for the Organ. *Brighton*, [1880.] fol.   **h. 2731. f. (28.)**

— [Meditation.] Slumber Song, arranged for the Pianoforte by H. Latour from G. Lardelli's "Meditation" for the Organ. *Brighton*, [1881.] fol.   **h. 3275. j. (13.)**

— Minuet—Souvenir de Haydn—for the pianoforte. *E. Ashdown: London, etc.*, [1896.] fol.   **g. 1181. (3.)**

— Molly from Galway. Song, words by Teeby. *G. J. Grice: Brisbane*, [1908.] fol.   **H. 3615. (19.)**

— Un morceau du même caractère d'une sonatine. [P. F.] 3 no. *Brighton*, [1879.] fol.   **h. 1494. p. (15.)**

— My Sweetheart of long ago ... Song ... Written ... by M. B. Spurr. *Reynolds & Co.: London*, [1898.] fol.   **H. 3615. (7.)**

— Nicolette. Gavotte pour piano. *E. Ashdown: London*, [1897.] fol.   **g. 1181. (4.)**

— Ninna-Nanna. Hush-a-bye ... for the Pianoforte. *Reynolds & Co.: London*, (1906.) fol.   **h. 3283. p. (12.)**

— Nizza. Morceau de Salon de Piano. *E. Ashdown: London*, [1900.] fol.   **g. 1181. (18.)**

— Nocturne in D flat ... for the Pianoforte. *E. Ashdown: London*, [1900.] fol.   **g. 1181. (19.)**

— Norwegian Boatmen's Song for the Pianoforte. *E. Ashdown: London*, [1897.] fol.   **g. 1181. (5.)**

— Not at 'ome ... Humorous Song. Written by M. B. Spur. *Reynolds & Co.: London*, [1898.] fol.   **H. 3615. (8.)**

— On the Sands. Dance. *Hopwood & Crew: London*, [1897.] fol.   **g. 1181. (6.)**

— On the Sands. A Musical Sketch. Words by J. H. Wood. *Reynolds & Co.: London*, [1899.] fol.   **H. 3615. (9.)**

— Our Girls ... Humorous Song ... Written ... by M. B. Spurr. *Reynolds & Co.: London*, [1898.] fol.   **H. 3615. (10.)**

— Pauline. Minuet for the Pianoforte. *E. Ashdown: London*, [1902.] fol.   **g. 1181. a. (2.)**

— Petites Messes faciles et chantantes ... pour deux voix ou chœur à deux parties et soli avec accomp. d'Orgue ou de piano. 5 no. *Schott & Co.: Londres*, [1896.] 8°.   **F. 1070.**

— Six Pieces for Mandoline and Piano. 6 no. *E. Ashdown: London*, [1898.] fol.   **g. 1181. (8.)**

— Four Pieces for the Organ. 4 no. *E. Ashdown: London, etc.*, [1896.] fol.   **g. 1181. (7.)**

— Recipes. Humorous Song ... Written ... by M. B. Spurr. *Reynolds & Co.: London*, [1898.] fol.   **H. 3615. (13.)**

— Rêve d'Amour. Romance en sol. 1. Piano seul. 2. Violon et Piano. 3. Violoncelle et Piano. 4. Mandoline et Piano. 4 no. *J. & W. Chester: Brighton*, 1897. fol.   **g. 1181. (9.)**

— Rigaudon for the pianoforte. *E. Ashdown: London, etc.*, [1895.] fol.   **g. 605. f. (6.)**

LARDELLI (GUGLIELMO)

— A River Picnic ... Musical Sketch ... written ... by M. B. Spurr. *Reynolds & Co.: London*, [1898.] fol.
H. 1798. u. (19.)

— Romance pour Piano. *Brighton*, [1880.] fol.
h. 1494. p. (16.)

— A Russian Love Song.—Across the Steppes.—Words by A. H. Hyatt. *Reynolds & Co.: London*, [1898.] fol. **H. 3615. (12.)**

— A Russian Village Festival. Characteristic Piece for the Pianoforte. *E. Ashdown: London*, [1900.] fol. **g. 1181. (20.)**

— San Remo. Valse Caprice pour Piano. *E. Ashdown: London*, [1900.] fol. **g. 1181. (21.)**

— The Seville Gipsy Maid. Song. The words by A. H. Hyatt. 3 no. [In D, E and F.] *E. Ashdown: London*, 1899. fol.
H. 3615. (14.)

— Shine silver Moon. A Venetian Song, words by A. H. Hyatt. *Agate & Co.: London*, [1897.] fol. **H. 1798. u. (20.)**

— Slumber Song. *See* also supra: [Meditation.]

— Slumber Song, words by B. E. Damiano. *Reynolds & Co.: London*, (1906.) fol. **H. 3615. (17.)**

— A Song of Parting. [Song.] Written by E. J. Brady. *Frederick Harris Co.: London*, (1906.) fol. **H. 3615. (18.)**

— Suite enfantine. 1. Aubade. 2. Danse des enfants ... 3. Danse des galants ... 4. Danse des filles, *etc. Hawkes & Son: London*, 1919. 4°. **g. 1129. n. (28.)**

— Toccata. Waltz pour le Piano. *Brighton*, [1879.] fol.
h. 1484. c. (24.)

— Toccata in F for the pianoforte. *E. Ashdown: London, etc.*, [1895.] fol. **g. 605. f. (7.)**

— Toccata No. 2, in F, for the pianoforte. *E. Ashdown: London*, [1900.] fol. **g. 1181. (22.)**

— Toccatina in G minor for the Pianoforte. *E. Ashdown: London*, [1900.] fol. **g. 1181. (23.)**

— A Tragedy in five Acts. Musical Monologue ... written ... by M. B. Spurr. *Reynolds & Co.: London*, [1898.] fol. *Musical Monologues. No. 8.* **H. 2087.**

— Under the Minarets ... Song, words by A. H. Hyatt. *Agate & Co.: London*, [1897.] fol. **H. 1798. u. (22.)**

— Valse Andalouse, pour Piano. *E. Ashdown: London*, [1903.] fol. **g. 1181. a. (6.)**

— Valse gracieuse pour Piano. *E. Ashdown: London*, [1901.] fol.
g. 1181. (24.)

— Valse gracieuse. Orchestra by Adolf Schmid. [Orchestral parts.] 12 pt. *Edwin Ashdown: London*, [1901.] 8°. *Orchestral Library. no. 57.* **f. 800. (784.)**

— Valse Tyrolienne, pour Piano. *E. Ashdown: London*, [1904.] fol. **g. 1181. a. (7.)**

— The Way to Woo! Humorous Song ... written ... by M. B. Spurr. *Reynolds & Co.: London*, [1900.] fol. **H. 3615. (11.)**

— When all the World is young. [Song.] Words by C. Kingsley. *J. & J. Hopkinson: London*, [1888.] fol. **H. 1788. u. (46.)**

LARDELLI (MAURIZIO)

— L'Addio a Rubini [begins: "Aimè gia spunta"], poesia di M. Maggioni. *London*, [1842.] fol. **H. 1691. (4.)**

— L'Amante e l'Eco. [Song, begins: "Fra queste rupi".] Parole di C. A. Clericetti. *London*, [1861.] fol. **H. 1775. t. (18.)**

LARDELLI (MAURIZIO)

— Amore e Costanza; Romanza [begins: "So che sperare"], poesia di Metastasio. *London*, [1847.] fol. **H. 1703. (10.)**

— Cerito Polka. [P. F.] Op. 12. *London*, [1846.] fol.
h. 940. (27.)

— Eterno Genitor. Preghiera. pp. 5. *Leader & Cock: London*, [1846.] fol. **H. 1703. (8.)**

— Les folies; grandes Valses pour Piano Forte. *London*, [1846.] fol. **h. 940. (29.)**

— Gorgheggi o Esercizj di canto, *etc. London*, [1852.] fol.
H. 2241. (3.)

— In Girlhood's careless happy hour. Ballad. *London*, [1862.] fol. **H. 1775. t. (19.)**

— L'Innocence, valse pour le Piano Forte. *London*, [1846.] fol.
h. 940. (26.)

— Io non son più giovinetto. Canzone. *London*, [1846.] fol.
H. 1703. (9.)

— The Orange-flower Wreath Waltz. [P. F.] Op. 15. *London*, [1847.] fol. **h. 940. (30.)**

— Queenly Summer. Song [begins: "Summer's like a lovely woman"]. Poetry by W. S. Passmore. *Brighton*, [1868.] fol.
H. 1775. t. (20.)

— La Ranella, pensiero di mazurka per il Pianoforte. *London*, [1862.] fol. **h. 1460. u. (38.)**

— Scheffer Polka. [P. F.] Op. 13. *London*, [1846.] fol.
h. 940. (28.)

— Summer's Serenade. The Song of the Nightingale [begins: "Hark! what enchanting music"]. Poetry by W. S. Passmore. *Brighton*, [1868.] fol. **H. 1775. t. (21.)**

LARDELLI (WILLIAM H.)

— L'Espérance, mélodie variée pour le Piano. *Brighton*, [1877.] fol. **h. 1482. y. (33.)**

— March No. 1 for Pianoforte or Organ. *Brighton*, [1877.] fol.
h. 1482. y. (34.)

LARDENOIS (ANTOINE)

— Paraphrase des Pseaumes de Dauid, en vers françois. Par A. Godeau ... Nouuellement mis en musique ... par A. Lardenois. *Imprimé aux despens de l'Autheur*: [Paris,] 1655. 12°. **843. f. 5.**

— Les Pseaumes de Dauid, mis en rime Françoise, par C. Marot, et T. de Beze. Reduits nouuellement à vne briéue & facile methode pour apprendre le chant ordinaire de l'Eglise, par A. Lardenois. *A. Cellier: Charenton*, 1659. 12°.
C. 46. a. 6. (2.)

LARDI-DOODY-DAY

— Lardi-doody-day. Song. *See* TABRAR (Joseph)

LARDNER (ADOLF)

— Romance, for Violin with Pianoforte accompaniment. *Moore, Smith & Co.: London*, [1911.] fol. **g. 505. ee. (33.)**

LARDNER (EDITH)

— The Gift of Life. Song, words by F. G. Bowles. 2 no. [In D and E flat.] *Moore, Smith & Co.: London*, [1912.] fol
G. 807. yy. (21.)

LARDNER (Edith)

— I would give all. Song, words by A. H. Hyatt. 2 no. [In E flat and F.] *Moore, Smith & Co.: London*, [1911.] fol.
G. 807. yy. (22.)

— The Whitethroat in the Rosebush. Song, words by A. Hyatt. 2 no. [In G and A.] *Moore, Smith & Co.: London*, [1913.] fol.
G. 806. mm. (2.)

LARDNER (T. W.)

— The merciful and gracious Lord. [Anthem.] *Novello & Co.: London*, [1905.] 8°.
E. 442. p. (33.)

LARGE

— A large cold Bottle and a small hot Bird. [Song.] *See* STROMBERG (John A.) [Hurly Burly.]

— A Large Front Room on Broadway. [Song.] *See* DILLON (John) *and* DILLON (H.)

— Large or small? [Song.] *See* MARZO (E.) Songs for Young People. [No. 7.]

LARGE (G. W.)

— Golfhill. Waltz. [P. F.] *St. Cecilia Music Publishing Co.: London*, [1893.] fol.
h. 3285. q. (1.)

LARGE (M.) *Miss*

— The Stanmore galop and valse for the piano forte. *London*, [1855.] fol.
h. 976. d. (23.)

LARGER

— The Larger Prayer. Anthem. *See* BURDETT (G. A.)

LARGESSE

— Largesse, largesse, noble lady. Part song. *See* GLOVER (H.) [Ruy Blas.]

LARGEST

— The Largest Egg's not always laid by the Hen that cackles most. [Song.] *See* DILLON (Harry)

LARGHETTO

— Larghetto. [Part-Song.] *See* STANFORD (*Sir* C. V.) [Sixteen Part-Songs. Book 2. Op. 127. No. 6.]

LARGO

— Largo al factotum della città. Cavatina. *See* ROSSINI (G. A.) [Il Barbiere di Siviglia.]

— Largo al quadrupede. Chorus. *See* VERDI (F. G. F.) [La Traviata.]

LA RICHERIE (DE)

— Sommeil, viens sur mes sens. *Duo, etc.* [*Paris,*] 1746. *s. sh.* 4°. *Mercure de France, Sept.,* 1746.
297. c. 8.

LARIN (*Mde* A. O.)

— Frontenac. Grande Valse. [P. F.] [*A. O. Larin: Montreal?*] 1897. fol.
h. 3286. g. (10.)

LARINDA

— Larinda e Vanesio. Intermezzo. *See* HASSE (J. A.)

LA RIVA (F. DE)

— Hojas de un Album … Dolaras para Piano. *Leipzig,* [1879.] fol.
g. 561.

LARIVIERE (E.)

— A Favorite Andante … [With variations] for the Harp. pp. 7. *J. Duff & Cᵒ: London,* [c. 1835.] fol.
The word "Andante" on the titlepage is followed by four bars of the theme.
h. 2605. aa. (1.)

LA RIVIÈRE (M. DE)

— Pianoforte Lessons, arranged by M. de la Rivière. no. 1, 4–6. *J. Guest: London,* [1874.] fol.
Imperfect; wanting no. 2, 3 and 7.
h. 1489. s. (11*.)

— *See* GOUNOD (C. F.) [Jesus de Nazareth.—Instrumental arrangements.] Nazareth, arranged … by M. de la Rivière. [1874.] fol.
h. 1494. k. (11.)

LARK

— The Lark. Hymn. *See* FROM. From his humble grassy Bed. [ᵂᴹ 1822.] fol.
H. 1601. n. (30.)

— The Lark. Duet. *See* ABT (F. W.)

— The Lark. [Song.] *See* ALLEN (G. B.)

— The Lark. [Duet.] *See* BAYLEY (T. H. R.)

— The Lark. [Musical play.] *See* BERNSTEIN (Leonard)

— The Lark. Song. *See* BOTTERILL (J.)

— The Lark. [Part-song.] *See* EMERY (Walter H. J.)

— The Lark. Part-song. *See* GEIBEL (A.)

— The Lark. Duet. *See* GIBSONE (G. I.)

— The Lark. Song. *See* GILBERT (F.)

— The Lark. Part-song. *See* HATTON (J. L.)

— The Lark. Part-song. *See* HUTCHINSON (T.)

— The Lark. Song. *See* IANSON (E. G.)

— The Lark. Glee. *See* KING (James) *Singing master.*

— The Lark. Song. *See* LAMBERT (W. S.)

— The Lark. [Song.] *See* LAWES (H.)

— The Lark. Song. *See* LEONI (F.)

— The Lark. Gaelic Songs. *See* MACFARLANE (C.) *and* MACILWAINE (H.)

— The Lark, or the Lament of the Exile. [Song.] *See* MARTIN (G. W.)

— The Lark. Song. *See* MEYER (E.)

— The Lark. Unison song. *See* PRITCHARD (Arthur J.)

— The Lark. [Song.] *See* ROHLFFS (J. D.) Juvenile Lyrics. No. 1.

— The Lark. Song. *See* RUBINSTEIN (A. G.) [Sechs Lieder. Op. 33. No. 3. Die Lerche.]

— The Lark. [Trio.] *See* WILLIAMS (William A.) *called* GWILYM GWENT.

— The Lark above the golden corn. [Song.] *See* FISHER (B. M.)

— The Lark and Nightingale. [Song.] *See* METCALFE (W.) Three Songs. No. 3.

— The Lark and the Christian. *See* HOW. How sweet is the song of the lark. [1856.] fol.
H. 1254. (12.)

LARK

— The Lark and the Nightingale. Song. *See* BANISTER (H. C.)

— The Lark and the Nightingale. Song. *See* BISHOP (*Sir* H. R.)

— The Lark and the Nightingale. Duet. *See* DENZA (L.) [The Garden of Flowers.]

— The Lark and the Nightingale. Song. *See* PRATT (E.)

— The Lark and the Nightingale. Part-song. *See* SOMERVILLE (R.)

— The Lark and the Nightingale. [Song.] *See* STUART (F.)

— The Lark his Flight is swiftly winging. Hunting Chorus. *See* JACKMAN (P.)

— The Lark in clear Air. Song. *See* HUGHES (H.)

— A Lark in Ecstasy. [Part-song.] *See* MILKEY (Edward T.)

— The Lark in its nest. Song. *See* GRANT (D.)

— The Lark in the clear Air. [Part-song.] *See* CASHMORE (Donald J.)

— The Lark in the clear Air. [Part-song.] *See* DEALE (Edgar M.)

— The Lark in the clear Air. [Part-song.] *See* DEXTER (Harry)

— The Lark in the clear Air. [Song.] *See* ESPOSITO (M.)

— The Lark in the clear Air. [Part-song.] *See* EVANS (Hal)

— The Lark in the clear Air. [Two-part song.] *See* FISKE (Roger)

— The Lark in the clear Air. [Song.] *See* GEEHL (Henry E.)

— The Lark in the clear Air. [Part-song.] *See* IVES (Grayston) Three Folk Songs. 2.

— The Lark in the clear Air. [Part-song.] *See* JACQUES (Reginald)

— The Lark in the clear Air. [Part-song.] *See* JOHNSTON (Tom) *Arranger.*

— The Lark in the clear Air. Song. *See* MAINE (Basil) [Two Irish Love Songs. No. 1.]

— The Lark in the clear Air. [Part-song.] *See* NELSON (Havelock)

— The Lark in the clear Air. [Unison song.] *See* O'MALLEY (Eileen)

— The Lark in the clear Air. [Part-song.] *See* ROWLEY (Alec)

— The Lark in the clear Air. [Song.] *See* TATE (Phyllis M. D.)

— The Lark in the clear Air. [Part-song.] *See* TRANT (Leonard B.)

— The Lark in the clear Air. [Part-song.] *See* VINE (J.)

— The Lark in the Morn. Folk Song. *See* BEMENT (G. S.)

— The Lark is up. Vocal Gavotte. *See* WILSON (H. J. L.) [Dorothy's Wedding Day.]

— The Lark is warbling to the sky. Song. *See* BETJEMANN (G. S.)

— The Lark may sing. Song. *See* READ (J. F. H.)

— The Lark, my love, is soaring high. A Serenade, the words by G. Walker, adapted to a celebrated Irish air. *London,* [1810?] fol. **H. 2831. a. (10.)**

— The Lark now leaves his watery Nest. Two-part Song. *See* ARKWRIGHT (M. U.)

— The Lark now leaves his watery Nest. Part-Song. *See* CALLCOTT (J. G.)

— The Lark now leaves his watery nest. Choral serenade. *See* HAKING (R.)

LARK

— The Lark now leaves his wat'ry Nest. [Part-song.] *See* HATTON (J. L.)

— The Lark now leaves his watery Nest. [Song.] *See* HORSMAN (E. I.)

— The Lark now leaves his watery nest. Serenade. *See* MASSON (E.)

— The Lark now leaves his watery Nest. [Song.] *See* PARKER (H. W.)

— The Lark now leaves his watery Nest. Three-part song. *See* RICHARDSON (Alfred M.)

— The Lark now leaves his wat'ry Nest. Unison song. *See* ROBERTON (*Sir* Hugh S.)

— The Lark now leaves his watery Nest. [Song.] *See* SMITH (M. S.) Songs, grave and gay. No. 1.

— The Lark now leaves his wat'ry Nest. Song. *See* WATSON (G.)

— The Lark on Portsdown Hill. Song. *See* SWAIN (Freda M.)

— The Lark's aloft. May Carol. *See* WALKER (R. H.)

— The Lark's awake. Unison Song. *See* ELLIOTT (R. B.)

— The Lark sings high in the Cornfield. Song. *See* LINLEY (T.) *the Elder.* [Twelve Ballads. No. 8.]

— The Lark Song. Valse-Ariette. *See* GOUNOD (C. F.) [Voix légère.]

— Lark-Song on Mendip. [Unison song.] *See* SYMONS (T.)

— The Lark that sang when Morning broke. Trio. *See* CHADWICK (G. W.)

— The Lark that shuns on lofty Bough to build. Glee. *See* HAWES (William)

— The Lark to Heaven doth soar. Duet. *See* TULLY (J. H.) [William and Susan.]

— The Lark was up, the Morn was grey. *The Camp Medley.* [Song.] pp. 4. *Longman, Lukey & Cᵒ: London,* [c. 1770.] fol. **H. 1648. e. (7.)**

— The Lark was up, the Morn was grey. *The Camp medley.* [Song.] *Longman and Broderip: London,* [1780?] fol. **G. 312. (211.)**

— The Lark was up the Morning grey. *The Camp Medley* with the original tunes, within compass of the German flute. [Song.] pp. 4. *Printed for S. A. and P. Thompson:* [*London,* 1785?] fol. **H. 1652. z. (17.)**

— The Lark was up the Morn was grey. *The Camp Medley.* [Song.] pp. 4. *Printed for S. A. & P. Thompson: London,* [c. 1790.] fol. **H. 1652. oo. (22.)**

— A Lark went singing. Song. *See* FARLEY (R.)

— The Lark's Carol. Song. *See* NEWTON (E. R.)

— A Lark's Flight. Song. *See* MOIR (F. L.)

— The Lark's Grave. [Two-part song.] *See* STANFORD (*Sir* C. V.)

— A Lark's Lyric. Song. *See* GIBSON (F.)

— The Lark's shril Notes. [Song.] Sung by Mrs. Vincent at Vaux-hall. [*London,* 1765?] fol. **H. 1994. a. (2.)**

— [Another edition.] The Lark's shrill Notes. [Song.] Sung by Mrs. Vincent, *etc.* [*London,* 1770?] fol. **G. 297. (9.)**

— The Larks shrill Notes. [Song.] Sung by Mʳˢ Vincent at Vauxhall. *Sk.* [*T. Skillern: London,* 1780?] fol. **G. 316. l. (21.)**

LARK

— The Lark's shrill Notes. [Song.] Sung at Vaux-hall. [1785?] fol.
A different edition from the preceding.   **G. 316. l. (22.)**

— The Lark's Song. Two-part Song. *See* BAINTON (E. L.)

— The Lark's Song. Unison song. *See* DAVIES (Laurence H.)

— The Lark's Song. [Song.] *See* HARDELOT (G. d') *pseud.*

— The Lark's Song. Song. *See* KOVEN (H. L. R. de)

— The Lark's Song. Canon. *See* MENDELSSOHN-BARTHOLDY
(J. L. F.) [Sechs Lieder. Op. 48. No. 4. Lerchengesang.]

— The Lark's Song. [Song.] *See* SMART (H.)

— The Lark's sweet Song. *The Charms of May.* A new song. *In:*
The New Lady's Magazine. vol. 1. pp. 152, 153. 1786. 8°.
                                                       P.P. 5141. b.

LARKCOM (STANLEY)

— Love's Vision. Song, words by E. Oxenford. *B. Williams:*
London, [1889.] fol.   **H. 1788. u. (47.)**

— Sweet Wedding Bells. Song, words by E. C. Price.
E. Ascherberg & Co.: London, [1888.] fol.   **H. 1788. u. (48.)**

— Upon the Quay. Song, words by E. Oxenford. *E. Ascherberg*
& Co.: London, [1888.] fol.   **H. 1788. u. (49.)**

— Verbum supernum. Motet for the Offertory, *etc.* *Orpheus*
Music Publishing Co.: London, [1911.] 8°.   **F. 274. j. (4.)**

LARKEN (   )

— As Cloe came into the room t'other day. *A Song from Prior,*
etc. [*London*, 1748.] 8°.
Gentleman's Magazine, Vol. XVIII., p. 181.   **249. c. 18.**

— The Incredulous Maid. [Song.] [*London*, 1730?] *s. sh.* fol.
                                                       G. 305. (119.)

— Mutual Love, *etc.* [Song.] [*London*, 1748.] 8°.
Universal Magazine, Vol. II., p. 38.   **P. P. 5439.**

— Stella and Flavia united. [Song.] [*London*, 1750?] *s. sh.* fol.
                                                       G. 316. f. (10.)

— To a young Lady richly drest. [Song.] ... Within Compass of
the German Flute. [*London*, 1740?] *s. sh.* fol.
                                                       G. 316. a. (33.)

LARKIN (MARGARET)

— Singing Cowboy. A Book of Western Songs. Collected and
edited by M. Larkin. Arranged for the Piano by H. Black.
A. A. Knopf: New York, 1931. 8°.   **F. 1836.**

LARKIN (WILLIAM HENRY)

— The Thane March. [P. F.] pp. 7. *Oppenheimer Bros.: London,*
Leipzig printed, [1904.] fol.
The titlepage bears a MS dedication in the composer's
autograph.   **h. 925. k. (13.)**

LARKINS (A.)

— Ten Minutes' Lessons in Sight-singing ... For children ...
Ninth edition (revised and enlarged). pp. 119. *J. Curwen &*
Sons: London; Curwen: Germantown, [1926?] 8°.
                                                       B. 418. xx. (5.)

LARKINS (HELENA BRABAZON)

— Waltz of the Royal Engineers, for Piano. *C. Vincent:*
London, [1899.] fol.   **h. 3286. q. (74.)**

LARKINS (IDA)

— *See* LARKINS (John) and LARKINS (I.) The Trolley Party in the
Sky. Coon song, *etc.* [1898.] fol.   **H. 3980. pp. (8.)**

LARKINS (JOHN)

— Back up, Coons. [Song.] pp. 2–5. *M. Witmark & Sons:* [*New*
York, 1903.] fol.   **H. 3985. h. (27.)**

— Good-bye, Lou. [Song.] Words ... by W. B. Friedlander.
W. Rossiter: [*Chicago,*] 1907. fol.   **H. 1794. vv. (7.)**

— I ain't going to tell you, how I got here. [Song.] Words by
James Burris. *Jos. W. Stern & Co.: New York, etc.*, [1905.]
fol.   **H. 3985. h. (28.)**

— [Another issue.] I ain't going to tell you, how I got here, *etc.*
New York, [1905.] fol.   **H. 3985. h. (29.)**

— Look here, Mr. Yaller Man. [Ballad.] Words by Deas and
Wilson. ⟨Arr. by Wm. H. Tyers.⟩ pp. 5. *Jos. W. Stern: New*
York, [1899.] fol.   **H. 3980. pp. (7.)**

— *See* LEMONIER (Thomas) and LARKINS (J.) De Sun am shinin'
why don't you go? *etc.* [Song.] [1906.] fol.   **H. 3985. s. (64.)**

— *See* SMITH (Chris) and LARKINS (J.) Shame on you. ⟨Song.⟩
[1904.] fol.   **H. 3987. z. (41.)**

LARKINS (JOHN) and EUROPE (JAMES REESE)

— Zola. Jungle song. Words & music by Larkins & Europe.
pp. 5. *G. W. Setchell: Boston*, [1904.] fol.   **H. 3985. h. (30.)**

— [Another copy.]   **H. 3985. h. (31.)**

LARKINS (JOHN) and FRIEDLANDER (WILLIAM B.)

— A Coon of Pedigree. ⟨Song.⟩ Words & music by J. Larkins
and W. B. Friedlander. *Will Rossiter:* [*Chicago*, 1907.] fol.
                                                       H. 3985. h. (32.)

LARKINS (JOHN) and LARKINS (IDA)

— The Trolley Party in the Sky. Coon song. Words & music by
J. & I. Larkins. pp. 5. *Howley, Haviland & Co.: New York,*
[1898.] fol.   **H. 3980. pp. (8.)**

LARKINS (JOHN) and SMITH (CHRIS)

— Dinah dear. [Song.] pp. 5. *Thompson Music Co.: Chicago,*
New York, [1909.] fol.
Followed by the chorus arranged for T. T. Bar. B.
                                                       H. 3985. h. (33.)

— When I want a little Loving ... [Song.] Words by F. E.
Mierisch. *J. W. Stern & Co.: N[ew] Y[ork]*, 1913. 8°.
                                                       F. 637. tt. (19.)

LARKS

— Larks. Part Song. *See* HATHAWAY (J. W. G.)

— Larks. Part-Song. *See* ROOTHAM (C. B.)

— Larks. Part Song. *See* SOMERVELL (*Sir* A.)

— Larks on the Wing. Song. *See* FRIML (R.) [Six Melodious
Pieces. Op. 85. No. 3. Love-Song.]

LARKSPUR

— Larkspur and Lilies tall. Trio. *See* HARRIS (C.)

LARKY

— The Larky little Coon. Song. *See* ELLIS (M. M.)

LARLIE, *pseud.*

— Love's Reward. Song, words by C. Beresford. *Weekes & Co.: London*, [1885.] fol. **H. 1788. u. (50.)**

— Processional March for the organ. *Weekes & Co.: London*, [1884.] fol. **h. 2732. i. (45.)**

LARMANDE (   )

— Allons ma Sœur. Tyrolienne à deux voix. Paroles de A***. *Paris*, [1840?] fol. **G. 544. (39.)**

— Bergerettes d'alentour. Tyrolienne ... Paroles de Mr. A. *Paris*, [1830?] fol. **G. 557. (49.)**

LARMANJAT (JACQUES)

— Valse. [P. F.] *See* DANSES. Treize Danses, *etc.* [No. 5.] 1929. fol. **h. 3865. k. (8.)**

LARME

— Larme! Romance. *See* GELLI (E.)

— Une Larme à Berry. Nocturne à deux voix. *See* PAER (Ferdinando)

— Une Larme d'Enfant.Mélodie. *See* LEDUC (A.)

— Une Larme de tes yeux. Mélodie. *See* LECOCQ (A. C.)

LARMER (OSWALD)

— Carnival Waltz. [P. F.] pp. 5. *Delmar Music Co.: Montreal*, [1909.] fol. **h. 4120. mm. (25.)**

LARMES

— Les Larmes. [Song.] *See* CHAIKOVSKY (P. I.) 6 Mélodies ... Op. 65. No. 5.

— Larmes. [Song.] *See* FAURÉ (G. U.)

— Les Larmes. Romance. *See* REYER (L. E. E.)

— Les Larmes. Song. *See* RIEGO (T. del)

— Larmes d'Amour. Mélodie. *See* LORET (C.)

— Larmes d'Amour. [Song.] *See* MEDAER (L.)

— Larmes de Crocodile. Valse chantée. *See* KLEIN (J.)

— Larmes du Cœur. Mélodie. *See* RENAUD (E.)

— Les Larmes Roses. Valse chantée. *See* QUIDANT (J.)

LARNED (MARY)

— Two Encore Songs ... 1. I dare not ask a Kiss. 2. To Daffodils. Words by R. Herrick. *M. M. Leidt: Buffalo, N. Y.*, 1901. fol. **H. 1799. cc. (47.)**

LA ROCHE (   )

— [MS Rondo expressive pour le forte piano sur une valse de Labitzky.] pp. 9. [MS *R. Cocks & Cº: London*,] [1841.] fol. *The titlepage is in MS.* **h. 850. (32.)**

LAROCHE (A.)

— La Pagode, polka-mazurka pour Piano. *Paris*, [1863.] fol. **h. 1462. r. (8.)**

— Polka du Petit Chat, pour Piano. *Paris*, [1863.] fol. **h. 1462. r. (7.)**

LAROCHE (PIERRE)

— Ballo in Maschera Quadrille [on Verdi's opera. P. F.]. *London*, [1862.] fol. **h. 2925. (1.)**

— Ballo in Maschera Quadrilles, as [P. F.] duets. *London*, [1862.] fol. **h. 2925. (2.)**

— Ballo in Maschera Valses [on Verdi's opera ... P. F.]. *London*, [1862.] fol. **h. 2925. (3.)**

— Un Ballo in Maschera Valses, as [P. F.] duets. *London*, [1862.] fol. **h. 2925. (8.)**

— The Cruiskeen Lawn Polka, on airs from Benedict's opera The Lily of Killarney. [P. F.] *London*, [1862.] fol. **h. 2925. (9.)**

— The Cruiskeen Lawn Quadrille. [Orchestral parts.] *See* CHAPPELL AND CO. Popular Quadrilles, *etc.* No. 3. [1862, *etc.*] 8°. **e. 249.**

— The Cruiskeen Lawn Quadrille on airs from Benedict's opera The Lily of Killarney. [P. F.] *London*, [1862.] fol. **h. 2925. (10.)**

— Cruiskeen Lawn Quadrilles. Duet. [P. F.] *London*, [1862.] fol. **h. 2925. (11.)**

— The Cruiskeen Lawn Waltz. [P. F.] *London*, [1862.] fol. **h. 2925. (12.)**

— The Great Excitement Galop. [Orchestral parts.] *See* CHAPPELL AND CO. Popular Quadrilles, *etc.* No. 4. [1862, *etc.*] 8°. **e. 249.**

— [The Great Excitement Galop.] Galop—The Great Excitement. [Military band parts.] 24 pt. *S. A. Chappell: London*, [1862.] fol. [*Army Journal. no.* 28.] **h. 1562.**

— The Great Excitement Galop. [P. F. with cornet accompaniment.] *London*, [1862.] fol. **h. 2925. (13.)**

— The Hunting Galop. [Orchestral parts.] *See* CHAPPELL AND CO. Popular Quadrilles, *etc.* No. 6. [1862, *etc.*] 8°. **e. 249.**

— The Hunting Galop, from Benedict's opera, the Lily of Killarney, arranged [for P. F.]. *London*, [1862.] fol. **h. 2925. (4.)**

— [A reissue.] The Hunting Galop, *etc. London*, [1862.] fol. **h. 2925. (14.)**

— Hunting Galop. Duet. [P. F.] *London*, [1862.] fol. **h. 2925. (15.)**

— The Juanita Quadrille, on popular airs. [P. F.] *London*, [1862.] fol. **h. 2925. (5.)**

— The Juanita Quadrilles ... as [P. F.] duets. *London*, [1862.] fol. **h. 2925. (16.)**

— The Lily of Killarney, set of waltzes on themes from Benedict's ... opera. [P. F.] *London*, [1862.] fol. **h. 2925. (6.)**

— The Lily of Killarney Waltzes as [P. F.] duets. *London*, [1862.] fol. **h. 2925. (18.)**

— Popular Lancers. [Orchestral parts.] *See* CHAPPELL AND CO. Popular Quadrilles, *etc.* No. 5. [1862, *etc.*] 8°. **e. 249.**

— Laroche's popular Lancers. [P. F.] *London*, [1862.] fol. **h. 2925. (17.)**

— [Rosalie Waltzes.] Valse-Rosalie. [Military band parts.] 24 pt. *S. A. Chappell: London*, [1862.] fol. [*Army Journal. no.* 28.] **h. 1562.**

— Rosalie Waltzes. [P. F.] *London*, [1862.] fol. **h. 2925. (7.)**

— Rosalie Valses as [P. F.] duets. *London*, [1862.] fol. **h. 2925. (19.)**

LA ROCHE (RENÉE)

— See FASCH (Johann F.) Concerto für Fagott, zwei Violinen, Viola, Cello, Bass und Cembalo. (B. c.), *etc.* [Basso continuo realised by R. La Roche.] [1959.] 4°.　　　　**g. 1780. o. (7.)**

— See FASCH (Johann F.) Concerto für Fagott, Streichorchester und Basso continuo, *etc.* [Basso continuo realised by R. La Roche.] [1965.] 8°.　　　　**b. 400. k. (7.)**

— See FASCH (Johann F.) Concerto C-dur für Fagott, Streicher und Basso continuo, *etc.* [Basso continuo realised by R. La Roche.] [1978.] 4°.　　　　**g. 1655. c. (5.)**

LAROCHE-BRUUN (JANINE)

— See BRUUN.

LA ROCHE-JAGU (　　　　PÉAN DE) *Mademoiselle*

— See PÉAN DE LA ROCHE-JAGU (　　　) M*elle*.

LARON

— Laron, laron, velaron! [Song.] See GNYESIN (M. F.)

LA RONDELLE (LOUIS)

— L'Adieu. Chanson sans Paroles pour Violon et Piano. *E. Ascherberg & Co.: London*, 1902. fol.　　**h. 1612. i. (44.)**

— "Aviation." Valse. [P. F.] *Francis, Day & Hunter: London*, 1910. fol.
Two copies, one without the illustrated cover.
　　　　h. 3286. uu. (40.)

— "Le Carillon de St. Martin," *etc.* ⟨Intermezzo. Arr. [for military band] by M. Retford. Conductor [and parts].⟩ *In:* HOWGILL (John S.) "Enchanted Chimes," *etc.* 1909. fol.
[*Boosey & Co.'s new supplemental Journal for military Bands. no.*71.]　　　　**h. 1544. a.**

— Chant du Cygne. Romance pour Violon et Piano. *E. Ascherberg & Co.: London*, 1902. fol.　　**h. 1612. i. (45.)**

— Chant du Cygne ... Piano Solo. *E. Ascherberg & Co.: London*, [1903.] fol.　　**h. 3283. p. (12*.)**

— Dahlia. Intermezzo pour le Piano. *E. Ascherberg & Co.: London*, (1902.) fol.　　**h. 3282. ww. (33.)**

— Feu Follet. Polka de Concert pour Piano. *Leonard & Co.: London*, [1901.] fol.　　**h. 3282. w. (32.)**

— Pensées Fugitives pour Violon et Piano. *Leonard & Co.: London*, [1901.] fol.　　**h. 1612. h. (1.)**

— She walks in Beauty. [Song.] Words by Byron. *St. Clements Music Publishing Co.: London*, [1895.] fol.　**H. 1798. u. (23.)**

— Three Solos for the Violin with Pianoforte Accompaniment. 1. Berceuse. 2. Chanson Hongroise. 3. Barcarolle. 3 no. *Leonard & Co.: London*, [1901.] fol.　　**h. 1612. h. (2.)**

— Three Solos for the Violin with Pianoforte accompaniment. . 1. Tarentelle. 2. Rêverie. 3. Mazurka. 3 no. *Leonard & Co.: London*, [1902.] fol.　　**h. 1612. i. (46.)**

— Suite de ballet. "Hermione," *etc.* [Military band parts.] 26 pt. *Boosey & Co.: London*, 1900. fol.
[*Boosey's military Journal. ser.*109. *no.* 1.]　　**h. 1549.**

LAROSA (GUSTAV)

— See LAROSO.

LA ROSA (JOSEPH)

— It's a Holiday. Four part mixed voices, S. A. T. B. pp. 8. *Remick Music: New York*, [1966.] 8°.　**F. 1744. tt. (6.)**

LA ROSE-FONBRUNNE (G. DE)

— Sappho au Promontoire de Lucate.—Sappho's Complaint on the Rock of Lucate. Romance. See PLEYEL, CORRI AND DUSSEK. Pleyel, Corri and Dussek's Musical Journal, *etc.* [Vocal part.] No. 1. 1797. fol.　　**G. 356. (12.)**

LAROSO (GUSTAV)

— Die Liebenswürdige.—A Nice Girl.—Waltz. Op. 15. *See* infra: Two Salon-Pieces for the Piano. [No. 2.]

— Die Marionetten.—The Puppets.—Polka. Op. 14. *See* infra: Two Salon-Pieces for the Piano. [No. 1.]

— 8 Melodious Sketches for Pianoforte. (Op. 135.) No. 1. Early Morning ... 2. In slow Time ... 3. The Bagpipes ... 4. Ungarisch ... 5. A Lively Dance ... 6. Cradle Song ... 7. Valse lente ... 8. Menuetto giocoso. *A. Hammond & Co.: London*, [1913.] 4°.
The Academic Edition, No. 514.　　**g. 1130. y. (11.)**

— Two Salon-Pieces for the Piano. [No. 1.] Die Marionetten. —The Puppets.—Polka. Op. 14. [No. 2.] Die Liebenswürdige. —A Nice Girl.—Waltz. Op. 15. 2 no. *G. Schirmer: New York*, (1909.) fol.　　**h. 3283. jj. (34.)**

— Scène de Ballet. Morceau Brillante [*sic*] for the Pianoforte. *T. Presser Co.: Philadelphia*, (1913.) fol.　**h. 3284. f. (46.)**

— Serenata, pour Piano. *E. Ashdown: London, etc.* [1907.] fol.
　　　　g. 605. vv. (31.)

LA ROSS (E. D.)

— Berceuse. *See* infra: Three Songs. [No. 1.]

— Softly now the Light of Day. *See* infra: Three Songs. [No. 3.]

— Three Songs. [No. 1.] Berceuse. [Words by C. M. Amelung.] [No. 2.] With broken Heart. [No. 3.] Soft now the Light of Day. 3 no. *T. Presser Co.: Philadelphia*, (1912.) fol.
　　　　H. 1792. r. (23.)

— With broken Heart. *See* supra: Three Songs. [No. 2.]

LAROUSSELLE (　　　　DE)

— Ah! que j'ai de regret. *Chanson*, pour une Basse taille, *etc.* *Récoquilliée:* [*Paris*,] 1770. s. sh. 8°.
Mercure de France, Feb., 1770.　　**297. e. 30.**

L'ARPA (GIOVANNI LEONARDO DI)

— Canzon Napolitane a Tre Voci, Libro Secondo Di L'arpa. Cesaro Todino, Ioan Dominico da Nola. Et di altri Musici, *etc.* Basso. *Appresso Girolamo Scotto: Vinegia*, 1566. 8°.
The composers named in this collection are: Lando, Di Nolla, Ferrello, Todino, Don Fiolo, Zelanno, Roiccerandet, Le Roy, De Nola, Ioan Dominico Fior and Mattee. The dedication is signed "Nicolò Roiccerandet Borgognone".　**A. 247.**

— See PRIMAVERA (G. L.) Il Primo Libro de Canzone ... Con Alcune Napolitane di I. L. di L'arpa, *etc.* 1566. 8°.　**A. 194.**

LARRAD (JENNIFER)

— See HAENDEL (Georg F.) [Suite. G minor. H. G. Vol. 2. pp. 128–130.] Suite in A minor. Arranged for two guitars by J. Larrad. [1979.] fol.　　**g. 61. l. (2.)**

LARRAZABAL (MANUEL)

— Lamentación tercera del Viernes Santo. [Motet. S. A. T. B. and orchestra. Edited by] Claudio García Lazo. [Score.] pp. 34. *Ministerio de Educación:* [*Caracas?*, 1973.] fol.
[*Colección cuadernos de música.* 4.]　　**G. 980. ff.**

LARREA PALACÍN (ARCADIO DE)

— Canciones juglarescas de Ifni, recogidas y transcritas por
A. de Larrea Palacín. pp. 233. *Instituto de Estudios
Africanos: Madrid*, 1956. 8°.
Cancionero del Africa occidental española. 1. **7901. pp. 7.**

— Canciones populares de Ifni, recogidas y transcritas por
A. de Larrea Palacín. pp. 176. *Instituto de Estudios
Africanos: Madrid*, 1957. 8°.
Cancionero del Africa occidental española. 2. **7903. s. 4.**

— Romances de Tetuán ... Recogidos y transcritos por A. de
Larrea Palacín. 2 vol. *Madrid*, 1952. 8°.
[*Cancionero judío del norte de Marruecos. vol.* 1, 2.]
Ac. 132. ia.

LARREGLA (JOAQUIN)

— Coquetuela.—La Coquette.—Mazurka de Salon pour Piano.
Schott & Co.: London, [1905.] fol. **g. 605. vv. (32.)**

— Coquetuela ... pour Piano ... Édition facilitée. *Schott &
Co.: London*, [1906.] fol. **g. 605. vv. (33.)**

— Viva Navarra!! Jota. [P. F.] pp. 10. *Unión músical española:
Madrid, etc.*, [c. 1915.] fol. **h. 60. dd. (5.)**

LARRIEU (ALBERT)

— Aucune ne vaut la Canadienne! Chansonnette ...
Arrangement de L. Duval. *E. L. Turcot: Lowell, Mass.*,
(1911.) fol. **H. 1792. r. (24.)**

LARRIEU (P.) and CANDOLIVES (H.)

— Fleur-de-Marie. Ouverture ... Piano conducteur. pp. 5.
H. Candolives: Bordeaux, [c. 1920.] 8°.
Part of "Répertoire H. Candolives pour cinémas et brasseries,"
sér. 39. **h. 3210. i. (336.)**

LARRODÉ (MIGUEL ARNAUDAS)

— *See* ARNAUDAS LARRODÉ.

LARRUGA (C.)

— De mi España. Canción española, para baritono y
mezzosoprano. Letra de Leonardo del Pozo. pp. 6. *Unión
musical española: Madrid*, [1914.] fol. **H. 1248. z. (11.)**

LARRY

— Larry. [Song.] *See* DOUGHERTY (George B.)

— Larry. [Song.] *See* VAN ALSTYNE (Egbert A.)

— Larry Grogan, or the London Rake's Delight. [Song.] *See*
COME. Come Boys let's be jolly, *etc.* [1750?] *s. sh.* fol.
I. 530. (31.)

— Larry Mick Mc Garry. Song. *See* FRENCH (W. P.)

— Larry Mulligan. Song. *See* REED (David)

— Larry O'Toole. [Song.] *See* CHADWICK (G. W.) 4 Irish Songs,
etc. [No. 1.]

LARSEN (GUSTAV)

— *See* HAENDEL (G. F.) [Dettingen Te Deum.—Vouchsafe, O
Lord.] Aria, "Dignare. Domine" ... Transcription für Violine
und Klavier von G. Larsen. 1934. 4°. **g. 74. aa. (5.)**

— *See* LISZT (F.) [Drei Lieder für eine Tenor- oder
Sopranstimme. No. 3. O lieb', O lieb'.] Liebesträume ...
Transcription für Violine und Klavier von G. Larsen. 1934.
4°. **g. 547. f. (16.)**

LARSEN (GUSTAV)

— *See* MENDELSSOHN-BARTHOLDY (J. L. F.) [6 Gesänge. Op. 34.
No. 2.] Auf Flügeln des Gesanges. On Wings of Song ...
(Transcription von) G. Larsen. 1934. 4°. **g. 635. q. (19.)**

LARSEN (JENS PETER)

— Drei Haydn Kataloge in Faksimile. Mit Einleitung und
ergänzenden Themenverzeichnissen. Herausgegeben von J. P.
Larsen. pp. 138. *Einar Munksgaard: Kopenhagen*, 1941. fol.
L. R. 298. d. 2.

— [Another copy.] **Hirsch 168.**

— *See* HAYDN (F. J.) [*Collected Works.—a.*] Kritische
Gesamtausgabe ... Wissenschaftliche Leitung ... J. P. Larsen.
[1950, 51.] fol. **N. 9.**

— *See* HAYDN (F. J.) [*Collected Works.—a.*] Werke.
Herausgegeben von Joseph Haydn-Institut, Köln, unter der
Leitung von J. P. Larsen. 1958, *etc.* fol. **N. 9. a.**

LARSEN (JENS PETER) and WÖLDIKE (MOGENS)

— Den Danske koralbog. Melodisamling til den danske
salmebog ved Jens Peter Larsen og Mogens Wöldike.
⟨Kildefortegnelse og kommentar ved Jens Peter Larsen og
Henrik Glahn.⟩ 2. reviderede udgave. pp. 330. *Wilhelm
Hansen, Musik-Forlag: København*, 1973. obl. 4°.
D. 835. qq.

LARSEN (NILS)

— Tre klavierstykker ... Op. 3. 1. Gavotte. 2. Pastorale. 3.
Scherzo. pp. 9. *Norsk Musikforlag: Oslo*, [c. 1920.] 4°.
g. 1126. b. (20.)

— Tre norsk danse. ⟨Op. 2. No. 1.⟩ Springdans. ⟨No. 2.⟩ Halling.
⟨No. 3.⟩ Dans paa Laaven. For piano. pp. 13. *Norsk
Musikforlag: Oslo*, [c. 1920.] 4°. **g. 1126. b. (21.)**

LARSEN (WILLIE)

— Larsen's Traditional Scandinavian Songs and Dances.
Compiled by Pietro Deiro, *etc. Accordion Music Publishing
Co.: New York*, 1937. 4°. **G. 981. s. (14.)**

LARSON (DAVID)

— *See* GALUPPI (Baldassare) Kyrie. ⟨1777.⟩ For four-part chorus
of mixed voices with piano accompaniment. Edited by
D. Larson. [1978.] 8°. **E. 460. v. (10.)**

LARSON (EARL ROLAND)

— Children's Voices. (S. A.) [Words by] John Chandler. pp. 4.
J. Fischer & Bro.: Glen Rock, N. J., [1960.] 8°.
E. 263. p. (16.)

— Easter Alleluia. Combined junior and senior choirs.
S. A.—S. A. T. B. ... [Words] anonymous. pp. 8. *J. Fischer
Bro.: Glen Rock*, [1959.] 8°. **E. 335. aa. (15.)**

— A Gladsome Hymn. For treble voices (S. A.) with organ
accompaniment. [Words by] A. N. Blatchford. pp. 5. *B. F.
Wood Music Co.: New York*, [1963.] 8°. **E. 497. z. (8.)**

— God, my King. (S. A. T. B.) [Words by] Richard Mant. pp. 8.
J. Fischer & Bro.: Glen Rock, N. J., [1962.] 8°.
E. 335. ee. (7.)

— God of the Earth. (S. A. T. B.) [Words by] Samuel Longfellow.
pp. 8. *J. Fischer & Bro.: Glen Rock*, [1960.] 8°.
E. 335. aa. (16.)

— Holy Voices. Combined junior and senior choirs S. A.—
S. A. T. B. For Christmas. [Words by] John Cawood. pp. 7.
J. Fischer & Bro.: Glen Rock, [1958.] 8°. **F. 260. m. (21.)**

LARSON (EARL ROLAND)

— Lord God, we worship Thee! Anthem for mixed and treble choirs. [Words by] J. Franck 1618. pp. 8. *J. Fischer & Bro.: Glen Rock*, [1960.] 8°.   **E. 335. aa. (18.)**

— The Lord's own Day. For treble voices (S. A.) with organ accompaniment. Text anonymous. pp. 5. *B. F. Wood Music Co.: New York*, [1960.] 8°.   **E. 335. w. (49.)**

— On Christmas Day. Anthem for combined S. A. T. B. and youth choirs. [Words] traditional. pp. 7. *H. W. Gray Co.: New York*, [1966.] 8°.   **E. 902. (26.)**

— We praise Thee, O God. S. A. T. B. [Anthem, words by] Julia Cady Cory. pp. 6. *J. Fischer & Bro.: Glen Rock, N. J.*, [1959.] 8°.   **E. 335. x. (28.)**

— We praise Thee, O God. (S. A. B.) [Words by] Julia Cady Cory. pp. 7. *J. Fischer & Bro.: Glen Rock*, [1960.] 8°.   **E. 335. aa. (17.)**

— *See* HADLEY (H. K.) October Twilight ... Opus 95. No. 2. Transcribed ... by E. K. Larson. 1937. *obl.* 4°.   **e. 1093. s. (20.)**

LARSON (LEROY)

— Fall. Four part mixed voices. S. A. T. B. a cappella. Words and music by L. Larson. pp. 8. *W-7 Music Corp.: [New York*, 1968.] 8°.   **F. 321. bb. (8.)**

LARSONNEUR (CHARLES)

— *See* LEDUC (A.) En avant, fantaisie alla militaire ... sur une chansonnette de C. Larsonneur. [1855.] fol.   **h. 619. (26.)**

LARSSEN (C. O.)

— *See* MOZART (W. A.) [Eine kleine Nachtmusik. K. 525.] Serenade ... Für Violine und Klavier bearbeitet von C. O. Larssen. [1930.] 4°.   **g. 1018. i. (5.)**

LARSSON (JOHN)

— Glory! A musical. Lyrics John Gowans ... Script John Gowans and John Larsson. Based on The Old Corps by Edward H. Joy. [Vocal score and score of music for the stage band.] pp. v. 117. *Salvationist Publishing and Supplies: London*, [1977.] 4°.   **F. 538. p. (4.)**

— Spirit! A musical. Lyrics, John Gowans ... Script, John Gowans and John Larsson. [Vocal score.] pp. iv. 143. *Salvationist Publishing & Supplies: London*, [1975.] 4°.   **F. 1198. p. (1.)**

LARSSON (LARS ERIK)

— Violinkonsert. Op. 42, *etc.* [Score.] pp. 144. *Carl Gehrmans Musikförlag: Stockholm*, [1956.] 8°.   **b. 276. a. (4.)**

— Förklädd gud. Lyrisk svit, op. 24, för sopran- och barytonsolo, recitation, blandad kör och orkester. Disguised god. Lyrical suite. For soprano and barytone solo, recitation, mixed voices and orchestra. Ord av Hjalmar Gullberg. Translation from the Swedish by Carolyn and Arthur King. Klaverutdrag. Piano score. *Swed. & Eng.* pp. 27. *Carl Gehrmans Musikförlag: Stockholm*, [1946.] 4°.   **G. 1276. mm. (15.)**

— Musik för orkester. Op. 40. Music for Orchestra. Partitur, *etc.* pp. 94. *Carl Gehrmans Musikförlag: Stockholm*, [1951.] 4°. *Part of "Nordiska toner för orkester".*   **g. 474. ee. (4.)**

— [Nattens ljus.] Night Lights. Theme from the Swedish SF film "Nattens ljus" ... Arr. Fred Hartley, *etc.* ⟨Piano conductor [and orchestral parts].⟩ 23 pt. *F. H. P. (Fred Hartley Publications): London*, [1957.] 4°.   **h. 3210. i. (737.)**

LARSSON (LARS ERIK)

— Tre orkesterstycken. Op. 49. Three orchestral pieces. [Score.] pp. 48. *Carl Gehrmans Musikförlag: Stockolm*, [1964.] 4°.   **e. 669. mm. (1.)**

— Orkestervariationer. Op. 50. Orchestral variations. [Score.] pp. 68. *Carl Gehrmans Musikförlag: Stockholm*, [1964.] 8°.   **e. 669. mm. (2.)**

— Pastoralsvit. Op. 19. Pastoral Suite. [Score.] pp. 24. *Carl Gehrmans Musikförlag: Stockholm*, [c. 1970.] 8°. *Part of "Gehrmans studiepartitur".*   **b. 276. d. (3.)**

— Stråkkvartett N: 1. String Quartet No. 1. ⟨Op. 31⟩ ... Score [and parts]. 5 pt. *Stockholm*, 1956 [1957]. 8° & 4°. [*Musikaliska Konstföreningen. Årg. 1956.*]   **H. 700/145.**

— Sonatin No. 3. Op. 41. [With a portrait and facsimile.] *In:* NY. Ny nordisk klavermusik, *etc.* pp. 69–77. [1951.] 4°.   **g. 606. mm. (3.)**

LARTZING (   )

— *See* HUENTEN (F.) Bouquet aux Pianistes, sur des motifs de Lartzing. [1840.] fol.   **h. 670. (17.)**

LA RUE (AL.)

— I dreamed of thee. [Song.] Words by C. Kingston. *M. Witmark & Sons: New York, etc.*, 1899. fol.   **H. 1799. h. (5.)**

— I only ask, remember me. [Song.] Words by Leo Wood. pp. 5. *Chas. K. Harris: New York*, [1905.] fol.   **H. 3985. h. (34.)**

— "If you were like a Rose." [Song.] Words by Leo Wood. pp. 3. *Chas. K. Harris: [Milwaukee*, 1902.] 4°.   **H. 3985. h. (35.)**

— [Another issue.] If you were like a Rose, *etc. Milwaukee*, 1902. fol. *With a cover.*   **H. 3985. h. (36.)**

— Tulips. [Song.] Lyric by Chas H. Brown & Otis F. Wood. *Chas. K. Harris: New York*, [1905.] fol.   **H. 3985. h. (37.)**

— *See* BAUER (A. W.) A Dream of Heaven, *etc.* (Arr. by A. La Rue.) (1903.) fol.   **G. 807. ee. (24.)**

— *See* BRYAN (Frank D.) C-h-i-c-a-g-o spells Chicago ... [Song.] Arr. by A. La Rue. [1904.] fol.   **H. 3982. dd. (1.)**

— *See* BRYAN (Frank D.) I love them all ... [Song.] Arr. by Al. La Rue. [1904.] fol.   **H. 3982. dd. (2.)**

— *See* BRYAN (Frank D.) It makes me think of Home, sweet Home ... [Song.] ⟨Arr. by Al. La Rue.⟩ [1904.] fol.   **H. 3982. dd. (3.)**

— *See* BRYAN (Frank D.) It makes me think of Home, sweet Home ... [Song.] Arr. by A. La Rue. [1914.] fol.   **H. 3989. uu. (32.)**

— *See* BRYAN (Frank D.) You're all, all right. A ... waltz song. ⟨Arr. by Al. La Rue.⟩ [1904.] fol.   **H. 3982. dd. (4.)**

— *See* BURKHARDT (Addison) and HUBBELL (J. R.) Moneyology, *etc.* [Song.] ⟨Arr. by A. La Rue.⟩ [1903.] fol.   **H. 3982. ee. (41.)**

— *See* CANNON (Hughie) Albany, *etc.* [Song.] ⟨Arr. by A. La Rue.⟩ [1904.] fol.   **H. 3982. jj. (1.)**

— *See* CANNON (Hughie) Jim Badger, *etc.* [Song.] ⟨Arr. by A. La Rue.⟩ [1904.] fol.   **H. 3982. jj. (13.)**

— *See* DOUGHERTY (George B.) The Dolly Song ... Arr. by A. La Rue. [1901.] 4°.   **H. 3983. x. (7.)**

— *See* EVANS (George) and SHIELDS (Ren) Waltzing with the Girl you love, *etc.* [Song.] ⟨Arr. by A. La Rue.⟩ [1905.] fol.   **H. 3983. kk. (50.)**

LA RUE (AL.)

— *See* HARRIS (Charles K.) The C. K. Harris Dance Album ...
No. 2 ... Arranged by A. La Rue. (1905.) 4°. **g. 603. n. (3.)**

— *See* HARRIS (Charles K.) For Sale—a Baby. [Song.] ⟨Arr. by
Al La Rue.⟩ [1903.] fol. **H. 3984. l. (51.)**

— *See* HARRIS (Charles K.) The Harris Medley Lancers No. 2.
for Piano. Arranged by A. La Rue. [1905.] fol.
h. 4120. z. (17.)

— *See* HARRIS (Charles K.) Voice of the Night. Arr. [for P. F.] by
A. La Rue. [1904.] fol. **h. 4120. z. (22.)**

— *See* HAWLEY (Walter) and SEARS (R. A.) My little Cuban Sue,
etc. [Song.] ⟨Arr. by A. La Rue.⟩ [1903.] fol. **H. 3984. q. (49.)**

— *See* HOWARD (Joseph E.) Good-bye, my Lady Love, *etc.*
[Song.] ⟨Arr. by A. La Rue.⟩ [1904.] fol. **H. 3984. gg. (4.)**

— *See* JANSEN (B.) After War comes Peace and Love. Arranged
by A. La Rue, *etc.* 1902. 4°. **G. 809. g. (8.)**

— *See* JOLLY (Edward S.) Only a Shop Girl ... [Song.] Arr. by
A. La Rue. [1903.] fol. **H. 3984. ss. (8.)**

— *See* JONES (Irving) I've lost my Appetite for Chicken. [Song.]
⟨Arr. by A. La Rue.⟩ [1904.] fol. **H. 3984. ss. (38.)**

— *See* KENDALL (Edwin F.) A Gay Gossoon ... Arr. [for P. F.]
by A. La Rue. [1905.] fol. **h. 4120. ii. (3.)**

— *See* LOWENTHAL (A.) The Arabian's Dream ... Arr. [for P. F.]
by A. La Rue. [1903.] fol. **h. 4120. ss. (31.)**

— *See* MERRICK (W. N.) Equestrienne March. Piano arr. by
A. La Rue. 1902. 4°. **g. 603. m. (17.)**

— *See* METZ (Theodore A.) Olympia March ... Arr. [for P. F.]
by A. La Rue. [1904.] fol. **h. 4120. vv. (16.)**

— *See* NOLAN (Bob) Cinderella, my Fairy Queen ... [Song.] Arr.
by A. La Rue. [1902.] 4°. **H. 3986. q. (52.)**

— *See* SHIELDS (Ren) Tell me you love me, Barney ... [Song.]
Arr. by A. La Rue. [1904.] fol. **H. 3987. s. (34.)**

— *See* SMITH (Chris) and BOWMAN (E. S.) Ain't dat an awful
Feeling! [Song.] ⟨Arr. by A. La Rue.⟩ [1903.] fol.
H. 3987. z. (2.)

— *See* WOOD (Leo) and NOLAN (B.) The Man up in the Moon
... [Song.] Arr. by A. La Rue. [1903.] fol. **H. 3988. gg. (35.)**

LA RUE (EMILE)

— Mariani. Valse Brillante. [P. F.] *J. E. Belair: Montreal*, 1898.
fol. **h. 3286. g. (11.)**

LA RUE (JAN)

— *See* HAENDEL (G. F.) [Overture. For two clarinets and corno
di caccia.] Sonata in D major for 2 Clarinets and Horn
⟨originally Corno di Caccia⟩, or 3 Clarinets in B♭. Published
for the first time ... Edited ... by J. M. Coopersmith and
J. La Rue. [1950.] 4°. **g. 74. nn. (7.)**

LA RUE (PIERRE DE)

— Thematische catalogus. *In:* ROBYNS (J.) Pierre de la Rue, *etc.*
pp. 177–231. 1954. 8°. [*Académie royale de Belgique. Classe
des beaux-arts. Mémoires. Collection in-8°. Tom. 8. Fasc. 2.*]
Ac. 985/49.

— Requiem und eine Motette zu 4–5 Stimmen. ⟨Missa pro
defunctis. Motette: Delicta juventutis.⟩ Herausgegeben von
Friedrich Blume. 2. unveränderte Auflage. pp. 28. *Möseler
Verlag: Wolfenbüttel*, [c. 1955.] 8°.
[*Das Chorwerk. Hft.* 11.] **E. 1317.**

LA RUE (PIERRE DE)

— Vier Motetten zu 4 Stimmen. ⟨1. Ave regina caelorum. 2.
Considera Israel. 3. Lauda anima mea Dominum. 4. Laudate
Dominum, omnes gentes.⟩ Herausgegeben von Nigel
Davison. *Lat. & Ger.* pp. iv. 28. *Möseler Verlag:
Wolfenbüttel*, [1964.] 8°.
[*Das Chorwerk. no.* 91.] **E. 1317.**

— Motets ... Edited by Nigel Davison. Pater de caelis ... Salve
regina ... Salve mater salvatoris ... Gaude virgo, *etc.* 4 no.
Theodore Presser Co.: Bryn Mawr, [1966.] 8°.
E. 1439. y. (15.)

— Il me fait mal de vous veoir languir, à 3 voix.—S. T. et B. *See*
BORDES (C.) Trois Chansons du XVᵐᵉ Siècle ... II. [1895.] obl.
8°. **C. 738. j. (1.)**

— [Lamentationes Hieremiae prophetae.] The Lamentations of
Jeremiah ... Mixed voices, a cappella. Edited by Nigel
Davison. pp. 61. *Theodore Presser Co.: Bryn Mawr*, [1967.]
8°. **E. 460. z. (6.)**

— Magnificat quinti toni ... Edited by Nigel Davison. pp. 19.
Pennsylvania State University Press: University Park, [1965.]
8°.
[*Penn State Music Series. no.* 8.] **F. 1076.**

— Misse Petri de la Rue. Beate virginis. Puer natus. Sexti. Ut fa.
Lomme arme. Nūqua fue pena major. S[uperius]. (A.) (T.)
(B.) 4 pt. *Per Octauianum Petrutiu[m]: Venetijs*, 1503. obl. 4°.
K. 1. d. 1.

— Liber missarum. Première transcription moderne par le
docteur Tirabassi, *etc.* [Score.] pp. 223. *Dessain: Malines*,
[1945?] 4°. **H. 1125. b.**

— Drie missen. ⟨1. Missa de beata virgine. 2. Missa de
virginibus. "O quam pulchra est." 3. Missa de sancta Anna.
Ediderunt René Bernard Lenaerts et Jozef Robijns.⟩
pp. xiv. 72. *Vereniging voor Muziekgeschiedenis te Antwerpen:
Antwerpen*, 1960. fol.
[*Monumenta musicæ belgicæ.* 8.] **H. 15.**

— Missa Assumpta est Maria. 4 gemischte Stimmen a cappella.
Herausgegeben von Ludwig Finscher. pp. 31. *Verlag
Friedrich Pustet: Regensburg*, 1966. 8°.
[*Musica divina. Hft.* 18.] **F. 1905.**

— Missa Ave sanctissima. pp. 56. *Societas universalis S.
Ceciliæ: Roma*, 1950. 8°.
[*Documenta polyphonicæ liturgicæ. ser.* 1. B. *no.* 1.] **E. 413.**

— Missa Cum iucunditate. For 4 and 5 voices. Transcribed and
edited by Nigel Davison. pp. 29. *Mapa mundi: London*,
[1978.] 4°.
[*Franco-Flemish Church Music. no.* 3.] **G. 1497. a.**

— Missa L'Homme armé I. Zu vier Stimmen. Herausgegeben
von Nigel Davison. pp. iv. 32. *Möseler Verlag: Wolfenbüttel*,
[1972.] 8°.
[*Das Chorwerk. Hft.* 114.] **E. 1317.**

— *See* FEVIN (A. de) Misse ... Quarti toni. Pier zon [i. e. P. de la
Rue]. 1515. obl. 4°. **K. 1. d. 12.**

— *See* MASSES. Missarum diuerso[rum] auctoru[m] Liber primus
... De sancto Antonio Piero de la rue. 1508. obl. 4°.
K. 1. d. 8.

LARUETTE (JEAN LOUIS)

— Le Boulevard. Opéra-Comique Ballet, *etc.* [Words by
Anseaume, music by J. L. Laruette.] 1753. 8°. *See* BOULEVARD.
11738. b. 15. (6.)

— Cendrillon, Opéra-Comique de Mʳ Anseaume ... avec la
Musique [by J. L. Laruette]. 1759. 8°. *See* CENDRILLON.
11738. b. 13. (4.)

LARUETTE (Jean Louis)

— De quel bruit effrayant rententissent ces airs. *Recit de Basse Taille Nouveau.* [*Paris*,] 1755. *s. sh.* 8°.
Mercure de France, Nov., 1755.   **298. c. 26.**

— [Le Diable à quatre.] [For anonymous editions of this work, with music arranged and partly composed by J. L. Laruette and F. A. D. Philidor:] *See* DIABLE.

— Le Docteur Sangrado. Opéra-Comique ... avec la Musique [by E. R. Duni and J. L. Laruette]. 1758. 8°. *See* DOCTEUR.   **11738. b. 13. (2.)**

— La Fausse Aventurière, Opéra-Comique en deux Actes ... Avec la Musique [by J. L. Laruette]. 1757. 8°. *See* FAUSSE.   **11738. b. 13. (1.)**

— Le Guy de Chesne. Comédie en un Acte, *etc.* [Words by J. de Junquières. Full score and parts.] *Chez M* De la Chevardière: Paris*, [1763.] fol.
Engraved by P. L. Charpentier.   **H. 452.**

— Le Guy de Chesne, ou La Feste des Druides. Comédie en un acte ... meslée d'Ariettes, avec un Divertissement; par M. de Junquieres le fils, *etc. Chez Duchesne: Paris*, 1763. 8°.
Part of the 'Supplément aux Parodies du Théatre Italien,' etc.
tom. 2.   **86. b. 15.**

— [Le Guy de Chesne.] Ariettes, *etc.* pp. 20. *Chez Duchesne: Paris*, 1763. 8°.   **B. 362. k. (6.)**

— L'Heureux Déguisement ou la Gouvernante Supposée. Opéra-Comique en deux actes, melée d'Ariettes, [written] Par M. de Marcouville, *etc.* (Recueil des Ariettes de l'Heureux Déguisement, *etc.*) 2 pt. 1758. *See* NOUVEAU. Nouveau Théâtre de la Foire, *etc.* Tom. 4. 1763. 8°.   **11735. d. 2.**

— Le Medecin de l'Amour. Opéra-Comique en un Acte, [words] par M. Anseaume ... avec les petits Airs, *etc. Chez N. B. Duchesne: Paris*, 1758. 8°.   **11738. b. 13. (3.)**

— L'Yvrogne Corrigé, Opéra-Comique en deux Actes, [words] par Mrs. Anseaume **** ... avec les petits Airs. *Chez Duchesne: Paris*, 1759. 8°.   **11738. b. 13. (5.)**

LARUM

— The 'Larum Bell. Chorus. *See* MEHDEN (J. L. von der)

LARUM-LIEBICH (Inga)

— Requiescat in pace. Song, words by W. Meischke-Smith. *West & Co.: London*, 1915. fol.   **H. 1793. s. (16.)**

LARWAY

— Larway Student Series. *See* AUSTIN (E.)

LAS

— Las, ie me plain. [Part-song.] *See* MURET (M. A. de)

— Las! j'étais en si doux servage. [Part-song.] *See* BLANGINI (G. M. M. F.) [Adieu de Raoul de Coucy à la Dame de Fayel.]

— Las je n'yray plus. Chanson. *See* COSTELEY (G.) [Musique.]

— Las! si j'avais pouvoir d'oublier. Chanson. *See* THEOBALD IV., *King of Navarre.*

— Las! voulez-vous q'une personne chante. [Madrigal.] *See* LASSO (O. di) [Les Meslanges.]

LAS (   ) *pseud?*

— The first dear thing that ever I loved, ballad, the words by C. Coxe. *London*, [1856.] fol.   **H. 1758. (4.)**

LASAÏGUES (Jules)

— La Tripière & le tambour-major. Chanson ... Paroles de Camille Soullier. [Melody only.] *Paul Dupont: Paris*, [c. 1895.] 8°.   **E. 270. cc. (12.)**

LASALA (Ángel E.)

— Impresiones de mi tierra ... Para piano. I. Jujeña ... II. Quenas ... III. Amanecer en los cerros nevados ... IV. Bailecito. pp. 19. *Ricordi americana: Buenos Aires*, [1958.] 4°.   **g. 1126. s. (8.)**

LA SALETTE

— "La Salette's holy Mountain". A sacred pastoral. *See* ERRINGTON (   ) *Miss.*

LA SALLE (Dorothy)

— Rhythms and Dances for Elementary Schools ... Compiled by D. La Salle, *etc. A. S. Barnes and Co.: New York*, 1926. 4°.   **7915. f. 30.**

LASALLE D'OFFEMONT (DE) *Marquis*

— Bertholde à la Ville. [For editions of this opera published anonymously:] *See* BERTHOLDE.

LASAR (Sigismond)

— Caecilia; a collection of vocal music, *etc. Boston*, [*Mass.*, 1860.] *obl.* 4°.   **A. 939.**

— The Hymnary, with Tunes. A collection of music for Sunday schools. pp. 176. *Biglow & Main: New York, Chicago*, [1872.] *obl.* 8°.   **A. 1411. f.**

— The New Hymnary: a collection of hymns and tunes for Sunday schools. Edited by S. Lasar. (Supplement especially compiled for the use of Plymouth Sunday School, Brooklyn.) pp. 208. *Biglow & Main: New York, Chicago*, [c. 1885.] *obl.* 8°.   **A. 1236. t.**

— *See* EMMETT (D. D.) [Dixie's Land.] Dixie for the Union ... Quartet arranged by S. Lasar. 1861. fol.   **H. 1780. n. (55.)**

— *See* HALL (C. C.) The Evangelical Hymnal ... Compiled by C. C. Hall and S. Lasar. 1880. 8°.   **D. 910.**

LĂSAŢI

— Lăsaţi-mă să cînt. Operetă. *See* DENDRINO (G.)

LASCA

— Lasca. [Musical monologue.] *See* CLARKE (C.)

— Lasca. Ballad. *See* LEIGHTER (H. C.)

LAS CABANNAS (Emilio Martin)

— *See* CABANNAS.

LASCAR

— The Lascar to the Boy. [Song.] *See* SPOFFORTH (Reginald)

LASCELLES, afterwards BERGER (Annie)

— Dreaming. Ballad [begins: "In the soft, the solemn twilight"]. Words by A. C. Clough. *London*, [1881.] fol.   **H. 1787. j. (11.)**

— I go to thee, love. Song, words by G. J. Whyte Melville. 2 no. [In F and A flat.] *R. Mills & Sons: London*, [1888.] fol.   **H. 1788. u. (51.)**

LASCELLES, afterwards BERGER (ANNIE)

— Listening. Ballad [begins: "I'm listening for footsteps"]. Words by A. Northey. ⟨In C. In E flat.⟩ 2 no. *London*, [1873.] fol.   **H. 1778. x. (37.)**

— Vocal Exercises. (Soprano & contralto.) *London*, [1877.] fol.   **H. 2245. a. (6.)**

LASCELLES (GERALD)

— Barcarolle pour Piano. *London*, [1881.] fol.
h. 2275. j. (15.)

— The Calico Ball, easy polka. [P. F.] *London*, [1878.] fol.
h. 1494. p. (17.)

— Chippendale polka. [P. F.] *London*, [1881.] fol.
h. 3275. j. (14.)

— Fleur d'Innocence. Morceau de salon pour le Piano. *Manchester*, [1876.] fol.   **h. 1482. y. (36.)**

— La Joyeuse, march for Organ. *Manchester*, [1879.] *obl.* fol.   **e. 174. g. (9.)**

— Just as I am. Hymn. Words by Elliott. *London*, [1873.] fol.   **H. 1028. g. (14.)**

— The Loved and the Lost. Song [begins: "She gave me a tress"] written by R. P. Macdonough. *London*, [1871.] fol.   **H. 1775. t. (22.)**

— The Maize Flower waltz for the Pianoforte. *London*, [1878.] fol.   **h. 1494. p. (18.)**

— The Maize Flower. Waltz for the Pianoforte. (Arranged as a ... duet by F. Weekes.) *Weekes & Co.: London*, [1898.] fol.   **h. 3286. g. (12.)**

— Music in the Twilight. Part-song. Words by A. Bealey. *See* WATSON (W. M.) The Choral Society ... No. 47. [1847.] 4°.   **F. 589.**

— A Passing Thought. [P. F.] *London*, [1872.] fol.
h. 1485. s. (24.)

— A Passing Thought. [Song, begins: "Lingering in the misty twilight".] Words by B. Cara. *Manchester*, [1880.] fol.   **H. 1783. o. (19.)**

— The Primrose polka. [P. F.] *London*, [1870.] fol.
h. 1485. s. (22.)

— The Roseland galop. [P. F. duet.] *London*, [1876.] fol.   **h. 1482. y. (38.)**

— Silver Moonlight waltzes. [P. F.] *London*, [1870.] fol.
h. 1485. s. (23.)

— Two Sketches for Piano. *Manchester*, [1876.] fol.
h. 1482. y. (37.)

— Submission. Sacred song [begins: "My Father, thou hast heard the sigh"]. Words by N. Henri. *London*, [1875.] fol.   **H. 1778. x. (39.)**

— Summer Eve. Mazurka. [P. F.] *C. Jefferys: London*, [1886.] fol.   **h. 975. u. (39.)**

— Tell me dearest if you love me. Song, the words by B. Cara. *London*, [1881.] fol.   **H. 1787. j. (12.)**

— Tivoli, easy mazurka. [P. F.] *London*, [1874.] fol.
h. 1482. y. (35.)

— Trusting in Thee, sacred song [begins: "Jesu my Saviour"]. The words by S. A. M. *London*, [1871.] fol.
H. 1775. t. (23.)

— Trusting in Thee, *etc.* *London*, [1872.] fol. **H. 1775. t. (24.)**

— Wake from thy slumbers. Serenade, words by W. J. Pillow. *London*, [1873.] fol.   **H. 1778. x. (38.)**

LASCELLES (GERALD)

— The Water Lily polka. [P. F.] *London*, [1870.] fol.
h. 1485. s. (21.)

LASCELLES (MARIA DONATA) Countess of Harewood, afterwards THORPE (MARIA DONATA)

— *See* GRUBER (Josef) *Czech Composer*. [ABC.] Two at the Piano. 50 duets ... edited by F. Waterman and M. Harewood. 1979. *obl.* 4°.   **d. 161. ee. (9.)**

— *See* WATERMAN (Fanny) and LASCELLES (M. D.) *Countess of Harewood*, afterwards THORPE (M. D.) First Year Piano Lessons with F. Waterman and M. Harewood. 1967. 4°.
g. 338. u. (6.)

— *See* WATERMAN (Fanny) and LASCELLES (M. D.) *Countess of Harewood*, afterwards THORPE (M. D.) Second Year Piano lessons with Fanny Waterman and Marion Harewood. 1969. 4°.   **g. 1138. ll. (8.)**

— *See* WATERMAN (Fanny) and LASCELLES (M. D.) *Countess of Harewood*, afterwards THORPE (M. D.) [Second Year Piano Lessons.] Piano Lessons Book two with Fanny Waterman and Marion Harewood. 1973. 4°.   **g. 352. tt. (10.)**

— *See* WATERMAN (Fanny) and LASCELLES (M. D.) *Countess of Harewood*, afterwards THORPE (M. D.) Piano Lessons Book three with Fanny Waterman and Marion Harewood. 1973. 4°.   **g. 352. tt. (11.)**

— *See* WATERMAN (Fanny) and LASCELLES (M. D.) *Countess of Harewood*, afterwards THORPE (M. D.) Piano Playtime ... selected and edited by F. Waterman and M. Harewood. 1978. 4°.   **g. 354. h. (1.)**

— *See* WATERMAN (Fanny) and LASCELLES (M. D.) *Countess of Harewood*, afterwards THORPE (M. D.) The Young Pianist's Repertoire ... Selected by F. Waterman & M. Harewood. [1969, *etc.*] 4°.   **g. 352. aa. (1.)**

LASCELLES (MARIA DONATA) Countess of Harewood, afterwards THORPE (M. D.) and DUNCAN (RONALD)

— Classical Songs for Children. Edited by the Countess of Harewood and Ronald Duncan. Arrangements by Dr. Percy Young. Illustrations by Milein Cosman. pp. 263. *Anthony Blond: London; Rotterdam* [printed, 1965.] 4°.   **F. 1656. f.**

— Classical Songs for Children. Edited by the Countess of Harewood and Ronald Duncan. Arrangements by Dr. Percy Young. Biographies by David Reid, *etc.* [Voice-parts only.] pp. 126. *Blond Educational: London; Rotterdam* [printed, 1965.] 8°.   **D. 837. i.**

— [Classical Songs for Children.] The Penguin Book of accompanied Songs. Edited by Marion Harewood and R. Duncan. Arrangements by Percy Young. pp. 248. *Penguin Books: Harmondsworth*, 1973. 8°.   **C. 756. qq.**

— The Penguin Book of accompanied Songs. *See* supra: [Classical Songs for Children.]

LASCEUX (GUILLAUME)

— Absence et Retour. Romance [begins: "On est si bien"]. *Paris*, [1820?] fol.   **G. 548. (63.)**

— Nouvelle suite de pieces d'orgue ... Nº 2 contenant les hymnes, prose et répons de l'office de la fête dieu. pp. 22. *Chez Imbault: Paris*, [c. 1810.] *obl.* fol.   **e. 1096. h. (2.)**

LASCIA

— Lascia amor, e siegui Marta và. Aria. *See* HAENDEL (G. F.) [Orlando.]

— Lascia ch'io parta solo. Aria. *See* HAENDEL (G. F.) [Atalanta.]

— Lascia ch'io pianga. Air. *See* HAENDEL (G. F.) [Rinaldo.]

LASCIA

— Lascia che questo labbro. Canzonetta. *See* GALLINARI (A.)

— Lascia O Cara. Sérénade. *See* WALLACE (W. V.)

— Lascia stare il can che dorme. Canto popolare. *See* GORDIGIANI (L.) [Canti popolare toscani. Quarta raccolta. No. 3.]

LASCIALI

— Lasciali dir. Melodia. *See* BARBIERI (G.)

LASCIAMI

— Lasciami. Romanza. *See* PADILLA (M.)

— Lasciami andare. Melodia. *See* PALLONI (G.)

— Lasciami, non t'ascolto. Duett. *See* ROSSINI (G. A.) [Tancredi.]

— Lasciami piangere. [Song.] *See* TROISI (P.)

LASCIATE

— Lasciate mi morire. [Madrigal.] *See* MONTEVERDI (C.) [Arianna.]

LASCO (LEO)

— Little Boy Baby. Song, the lyric by Lady Lindsay. *Enoch & Sons: London*, 1919. 4°. **G. 390. z. (30.)**

LASEKK (CHARLES) *pseud.* [i. e. *Baron* KARL KASKEL.]

— Souvenir de Carlsbad. Fantasie pour le pianoforte. pp. 7. *Au bureau de musique et des beaux arts de Meser: Dresde*, [1825?] *obl.* fol. **Hirsch M. 1311.**

— *See* SPINDLER (F.) Paraphrase über ein Lied von C. Lasekk für Piano. [1854.] fol. **h. 1332. (20.)**

LASERNA (BLAS DE)

— Tonadilla ... Arrang. de G. Cassadó. (Violoncelle et Piano.) *B. Schott's Söhne: Mainz und Leipzig*, 1933. 4°. **g. 514. s. (19.)**

— *See* PEDRELL (F.) Teatro Lirico Español ... Vol. II. ... Varios ... Laserna, *etc.* [1897, *etc.*] 8°. **F. 68.**

LA SERRE (DE)

— Le Temps Fugitif. Air. [*Paris,*] 1732. *s. sh.* 4°. *Mercure de France, Nov.*, 1732. **298. a. 26.**

LASEURIE (ARTHUR DE)

— *See* DELASEURIE.

LASH

— The Lash. [Song.] *See* RUSSELL (H.)

LASH (DE WITT DURGIN)

— Lullaby. Song, with Piano accompaniment, *etc.* (Words & music by De W. D. Lash.) *The Durgin d'Lash Publishers: Chicago*, (1909.) fol. **H. 1792. r. (25.)**

LASHED

— Lash'd to the Helm. Song. *See* HOOK (James)

LASHMAR (ERNEST)

— "My Kingdom." Song, words by P. J. O'Reilly, *etc.* 3 no. [In G, A and C.] *J. B. Cramer & Co.: London*, 1909. fol. **H. 1792. r. (26.)**

LAS HUELGAS

— *See* BURGOS.—*Santa Maria la Real de Las Huelgas.*

LASHWOOD (GEORGE)

— Oh, I wish I was there again! ⟨Song.⟩ Written by Fred. W. Leigh, *etc.* [Staff and tonic sol-fa notation. Voice part.] *Francis, Day & Hunter: London*, [1901.] *s. sh.* fol. **H. 3985. h. (38.)**

— Oh, I wish I was there again! *etc.* ⟨Song.⟩ [With separate voice part.] 2 pt. *Francis, Day & Hunter: London*, [1901.] fol. **H. 3985. h. (39.)**

LAS INFANTAS (FERNANDO DE)

— Sacrarum Varii Styli Cantionum Tituli Spiritus Sancti Liber II. cum Quinque Vocibus. (Tenor.) (Quintus.) 2 pt. *Apud hæredem Hieronymi Scoti: Venetijs*, 1578. 4°. **C. 47.**

— Sequencia de Resurreccion. *See* ESLAVA (M. H.) Lira Sacro-Hispana, *etc.* Sigl. XVI. Ser. 1ª. Tom. 2°. [1869.] fol. **H. 4.**

LASKA (EDWARD)

— Carrie Jones. [Song.] Words and music by E. Laska. pp. 5. *Platt Pub. Co.: New York*, [1906.] fol. *The date has been altered in MS. to* 1907. **H. 3985. h. (40.)**

— "Don't you think I'm pretty?" [Song.] Words & music by E. Laska. *Platt Publishing Co.: [New York*, 1906.] fol. **H. 3985. h. (41.)**

— Eleanor. ⟨Song.⟩ Words & music by E. Laska, *etc.* pp. 5. *Platt Pub. Co.: [New York*, 1907.] fol. **H. 3985. h. (42.)**

— The Girls you loved before. [Song.] Words and music by E. Laska. pp. 5. *Platt Publishing Co.: New York*, [1907.] fol. **H. 3985. h. (43.)**

— "I don't like a Man with a Mustache." [Song.] Words and music by E. Laska. pp. 5. *Trebuhs Publishing Cᵒ: [New York*, 1909.] fol. **H. 3985. h. (44.)**

— "I would like to marry you!" Written by E. Laska & Fred. H. Leigh. [Song. With separate voice part.] 2 pt. *Francis, Day & Hunter: London*, [1905.] fol. **H. 3985. h. (45.)**

— It's better to love a short Man than never to love a tall. [Song.] Words and music by E. Laska, *etc.* pp. 5. *Platt Publishing Co.: New York*, [1907.] fol. **H. 3985. h. (46.)**

— The Moon or Sun? [Song.] Words and music by E. Laska. pp. 5. *Platt Pub. Co.: [New York*, 1907.] fol. **H. 3985. h. (47.)**

— The Wall Street Bear. [Song.] Words and music by E. Laska. pp. 3–5. *Platt Pub. Co.: [New York*, 1907.] fol. **H. 3985. h. (48.)**

— What we want and what we get. [Song.] Words and music by E. Laska. *Platt Publishing Co.: New York*, [1908.] fol. **H. 3985. h. (49.)**

— Why can't Girls propose? [Song.] pp. 5. *Platt Publishing Co.: [New York*, 1906.] fol. *The date has been altered in MS. to* 1907. **H. 3985. h. (50.)**

— "You." [Song.] pp. 5. *Platt Pub. Co.: [New York*, 1906.] fol. **H. 3985. h. (51.)**

LASKA (EDWARD) and **ANATOL** (EDGAR)
— "I never had a Face like that." A photographic complaint.
[Song.] pp. 2–5. *Broadway Music Pub. Co.: [New York*, 1907.]
fol. **H. 3985. h. (52.)**

LASKA (EDWARD) and **BLUMENTHAL** (   )
— I never had a Face like that. A photographic complaint.
[Song.] *Wolf & Co.: Philadelphia*, [1907.] fol.
A different song from the preceding. **H. 3985. h. (53.)**

— Mʳ Watermelon and Miss Canteloupe, *etc.* [Song.] *Wolf &
Co.: Philadelphia*, [1907.] fol. **H. 3985. h. (54.)**

LASKA (EDWARD) and **ELIOTT** (CHARLES)
— Bill Simmon's Waltz Dream. A sin-copated burlesque. [P. F.]
pp. 3–6. *Platt Pub. Co.: [New York*, 1908.] fol.
h. 4120. mm. (26.)

LASKA (EDWARD) and **KEAN** (M. J.)
— It's a Picture of my Sweetheart. [Song.] *Wolf & Co.:
Phildelphia*, [1907.] fol. **H. 3985. h. (55.)**

— Moike's international Serenade. [Song.] Words by Edward
Laska. pp. 5. *Platt Publishing Co.: [New York*, 1906.] fol.
The date has been altered in MS. to 1907. **H. 3985. h. (56.)**

LASKA (EDWARD) and **KELLY** (THOMAS) *Songwriter*
— Daisy Grey. [Song.] Words by Edward Laska. *Wolf & Co.:
Philadelphia*, [1907.] fol. **H. 3985. h. (57.)**

— Give me a good Cigar. [Song.] pp. 5. *Platt Publishing Co.:
[New York*, 1906.] fol.
The date has been altered in MS. to 1907. **H. 3985. h. (58.)**

— "Kiss me good-bye sweet Eileen." [Song.] Lyric by Edward
Laska. pp. 3–5. *Platt Publishing Co.: [New York*, 1908.] fol.
H. 3985. h. (59.)

— O-tan. [Song.] Lyric by Edward Laska. *Wolf & Co.:
Philadelphia*, [1907.] fol. **H. 3985. h. (60.)**

LASKA (EDWARD) and **SCHMITZ** (FREDERICK A.)
— Be mine to-day. Song, *etc.* pp. 5. *Trebuhs Publishing Co.:
New York*, [1909.] fol.
Followed by the chorus arranged for T. T. Bar. B.
H. 3985. h. (61.)

LÁSKA (LAD.)
— *See* DVOŘÁK (A.) Humoreska ... Op. 101, No. 7. Piano facile
(A. Pokorný). ⟨Rev. L. Láska.⟩ [1955.] 4°. **g. 1160. c. (20.)**

— *See* DVOŘÁK (A.) [Symphony. No. 9.] Largo ... Piano, arr.
L. Láska. [1955.] 4°. **g. 1160. c. (19.)**

— *See* MYSLIVEČEK (J.) Concerto per violino con orchestra ...
Edizione per violino & pianoforte rev. K. Moor & L. Láska,
etc. [1948.] 4°. **g. 500. ee. (6.)**

— *See* SMETANA (B.) [Má vlast. No. 4.] Z českých lihů a hájů ...
pro klavír na dvě ruce upravil Albert Pek. ⟨Rev. L. Láska.⟩
[1944.] fol. **h. 3913. j. (2.)**

LASKER (VALLY)
— *See* HOLST (G. T. von) At the Bear's Head ... Op. 42.
Pianoforte arrangement by V. Lasker. 1925. 8°.
F. 1412. (2.)

— *See* HOLST (G. T. von) Brook Green Suite ... Piano
transcription by V. Lasker. 1935. 4°. **g. 1206. b. (1.)**

LASKER (VALLY)
— *See* HOLST (G. T. von) Let all Flesh keep silence ...
Transcribed for piano by V. Lasker. 1921. 8°. [*Festival
Choruses, No.* 5.] **F. 1734. a.**

— *See* HOLST (G. T. von) Let all mortal Flesh keep Silence. For
accompanied treble voices ... Transcribed for piano by
V. Lasker, *etc.* [1963.] 8°. **F. 217. v. (16.)**

— *See* HOLST (G. T. von) The Perfect Fool ... Pianoforte
arrangement by V. Lasker. 1923. 8°. **F. 1412. (1.)**

— *See* HOLST (G. T. von) [The Perfect Fool.] The Ballet ...
Arrangement for pianoforte solo by V. Lasker. 1923. 4°.
g. 1206. (3.)

— *See* HOLST (G. T. von) The Planets ... Arranged for
pianoforte duet by ... V. Lasker. 1923. fol. **h. 3939. b. (5.)**

— *See* HOLST (G. T. von) [The Planets. No. 4.] Jupiter Theme ...
Arranged for piano by V. Lasker. [1964.] 4°. **g. 1138. e. (1.)**

— *See* HOLST (G. T. von) St. Paul's Suite ... Transcribed for
piano solo by V. Lasker. 1923. 4°. **g. 1206. (7.)**

— *See* HOLST (G. T. von) [St. Paul's Suite.] Intermezzo (Jig) ...
Arranged for violin and piano by V. Lasker. 1924. 4°.
g. 1206. (8.)

— *See* WILLIAMS (Ralph V.) Concerto for Pianoforte and
Orchestra. Solo Pianoforte, with Orchestra arranged for
Second Pianoforte. (Arranged by V. Lasker.) 1936. 4°.
g. 1266. a. (1.)

— *See* WILLIAMS (Ralph V.) Job ... Pianoforte arrangement by
V. Lasker. 1931. 4°. **g. 1266. (9.)**

— *See* WILLIAMS (Ralph V.) The Running Set ... Arranged for
Two Pianofortes by V. Lasker, *etc.* 1936. 4°. **g. 1266. a. (2.)**

— *See* WILLIAMS (Ralph V.) A London Symphony ... Arranged
for pianoforte by V. Lasker. 1922. 4°. **g. 1125. f. (27.)**

LASKI (HENRI)
— Bright eyed Nancy. Valse. [P. F.] *Sutton's Proprietary:
Melbourne, etc.*, 1904. fol. **h. 3286. dd. (54.)**

— Maid o' th' Mist. Waltz. [P. F.] *Allan & Co.: Melbourne, etc.*,
(1907.) fol. **h. 3286. ll. (21.)**

— The Scarlet & Blue. March. On Lindsay Lennox [*sic*] famous
song. [P. F.] pp. 6. *W. Paxton: London*, [1905?] fol.
h. 721. n. (23.)

LASKOVSKY (IVAN FEDROVICH)
— [Selected works.] *In:* GINZBURG (S. L.) История русской
музыки в нотных образцах, *etc.* том. 3. pp. 419–439. 1952. 8°.
F. 1594. p.

LASLETT (THOMAS NEWNHAM)
— Carol for Christmas ... Words by W. Pritchard. *Pritchard:
Ramsgate*, 1914. 8°. **E. 602. ee. (40.)**

— Chants for use in churches. [*T. N. Laslett: Old Charlton,*]
(1905.) *obl.* 8°. **A. 487. d. (2.)**

LASNE (PIERRE)
— Pour les anglaises faut que j't'explique. [Song.] Paroles de
Celestin Ganou. *Chappell: Paris*, [1978.] 4°. **F. 606. d. (1.)**

LASOCKI (DAVID)
— *See* BABELL (William) [Concertos in 7 Parts. Op. 3. No. 4.]
Concerto in G ... For descant recorder, strings and basso
continuo. Edited by D. Lasocki. [1979.] 4°. **g. 128. (1.)**

LASOCKI (David)

— *See* BACH (Carl P. E.) Concerto in B♭ major. (Wq. 167.) For flute, strings, *etc.* ⟨Ed. D. Lasocki.⟩ [1975.] 4°.　　**g. 48. t. (4.)**

— *See* BACH (Carl P. E.) Concerto in G major. (Wq. 169.) For flute, strings and basso continuo … Ed. D. Lasocki. [1974.] 4°.　　**g. 48. s. (4.)**

— *See* BACH (Carl P. E.) [2 Trio. Wq. 161. No. 2.] Sonata in B flat. Wq. 161/2. For flute and obligato harpsichord … Edited by D. Lasocki. [1979.] 4°.　　**g. 48. w. (3.)**

— *See* BANG (Betty) and LASOCKI (D.) Preludes [by J. P. Freillon-Poncein and J. Hotterterre le Romain]. For solo treble recorder. Edited by B. Bang and D. Lasocki. [1968.] 4°.　　**g. 109. ee. (3.)**

— *See* BARSANTI (Francesco) [Sonatas or Solos for a Flute. No. 4.] Sonata in c. For treble recorder and basso continuo. Edited by D. Lasocki. [Score and parts.] [1979.] 4°.　　**g. 128. (2.)**

— *See* BELLINZANI (Paolo B.) [Sonate a flauto solo. Op. 3. No. 8, 9.] Two Sonatas in c … and B flat … Edited by D. Lasocki. [1979.] 4°.　　**g. 128. (4.)**

— *See* BELLINZANI (Paolo B.) [Sonate a flauto solo. Op. 3. No. 12.] Sonata in d … (including variations on La Follia). For treble recorder (flute) and basso continuo. Edited by D. Lasocki. [1979.] 4°.　　**g. 128. (3.)**

— *See* BESOZZI (A.) Concerto in G major. For A. Oboe, strings and basso continuo. B. Oboe and piano reduction. ⟨[Edited by] D. Lasocki.⟩ [1972.] 4°.　　**g. 1078. s. (8.)**

— *See* BREVAL (J. B.) Symphonie concertante in F major (opus 31). For flute, bassoon & piano reduction. ⟨[Edited by] D. Lasocki.⟩ [1970.] 4°.　　**g. 934. r. (2.)**

— *See* CORELLI (Arcangelo) [Concerti grossi. Op. 6. No. 3.] Trio Sonata in d … Arr. J. C. Schickhardt. ⟨Edited by D. Lasocki.⟩ [1979.] 4°.　　**g. 45. ff. (3.)**

— *See* CORELLI (Arcangelo) [Sonatas. Op. 5. No. 3.] Sonata in C major … For treble (alto) recorder and basso continuo. ⟨Edited by D. Lasocki.⟩ [1974.] 4°.　　**g. 270. hh. (2.)**

— *See* COUPERIN (F.) *the Younger*. Concerts royaux I–IV. For flute/oboe/violin, viola da gamba & basso continuo. ⟨[Edited by] D. Lasocki.⟩ [1974.] 4°.　　**g. 324. h. (3.)**

— *See* COUPERIN (F.) *the Younger*. [Les Goûts réunis.— 5ᵉ–14ᵉ concert.] Les Goûts-réunis or Nouveaux concerts, *etc.* ⟨Ed. D. Lasocki.⟩ [1975.] 4°.　　**g. 324. i.**

— *See* DANZI (F.) [3 quatuors. Op. 56. No. 1.] Quartet in D major … For flute, violin, viola and cello. ⟨[Edited by] D. Lasocki.⟩ [1972.] 4°.　　**g. 934. v. (11.)**

— *See* DEVIENNE (François) Symphonie concertante in G. For 2 flutes and piano reduction. Op. 76. Edited by D. Lasocki, *etc.* [1974.] 4°.　　**g. 280. qq. (1.)**

— *See* DUSSEK (Jan L.) Grand Sonata in F major, Opus 65 … Ed. D. Lasocki. [1975.] 4°.　　**g. 452. s. (4.)**

— *See* HAENDEL (Georg F.) [Solos.] The Complete Sonatas for treble (alto) Recorder and basso Continuo … edited … by D. Lasocki and W. Bergmann. [Score and parts.] 1979. 4°.　　**g. 1320. i. (6.)**

— *See* HAENDEL (Georg F.) [Solos.] The Three authentic Sonatas … Edited by D. Lasocki. [Score and parts.] [1979.] 4°.　　**g. 61. w. (1.)**

— *See* HOTTETERRE (Jacques M.) called *le Romain*. [Pièces pour la flûte. Liv. 1. Op. 2. No. 1.] Suite in D … For flute/oboe/violin/treble viol and basso continuo … Edited by D. Lasocki. [1979.] 4°.　　**f. 241. k. (3.)**

LASOCKI (David)

— *See* HOTTETERRE (Jacques M.) called *le Romain*. [Sonates en trio.] Trio Sonatas. Opus 3, *etc.* ⟨Edited by D. Lasocki [assisted by] R. P. Block.⟩ [1975.] 4°.　　**g. 1067. ss. (2.)**

— *See* JANITSCH (J. G.) Sonata da camera in C major. Op. 4. For flute, violin, oboe & basso continuo. ⟨[Edited by] D. Lasocki.⟩ [1970.] 4°.　　**g. 1067. gg. (6.)**

— *See* KELLER (Gottfried) Sonata in G. 2 treble recorders (or flutes), 2 oboes/violins (or flutes) & basso continuo. Edited by D. Lasocki. [1979.] 4°.　　**g. 128. (8.)**

— *See* LUSSE (Charles de) [L'Art de la flûte traversière.] 12 Caprices for solo flute. Edited by D. Lasocki. [1979.] 4°.　　**g. 225. o. (6.)**

— *See* MATHER (Betty B.) and LASOCKI (D.) Free Ornamentation in Woodwind Music 1700–1775, *etc.* 1976. 4°.　　**g. 1362. f. (4.)**

— *See* MOLTER (Johann M.) Concerto in G major … For flute, strings & basso continuo, *etc.* ⟨Ed. D. Lasocki.⟩ [1976.] 4°.　　**g. 934. rr. (5.)**

— *See* PEPUSCH (J. C.) [6 concerti. Op. 8. No. 1, 4–6.] 4 Concerti … For 2 treble recorders, 2 flutes/tenor recorders/oboes/ violins & basso continuo, *etc.* ⟨Ed. D. Lasocki.⟩ [1974.] 4°.　　**g. 934. ii. (3.)**

— *See* PEPUSCH (J. C.) [6 concerti. Op. 8. No. 2.] Concerto in G … For 2 flutes, 2 oboes/violins & basso continuo. ⟨Ed. D. Lasocki.⟩ [1974.] 4°.　　**g. 934. ii. (4.)**

— *See* PEPUSCH (J. C.) [6 concerti. Op. 8. No. 3.] Concerto in B flat … For 2 oboes/violins, 2 violins/oboes & basso continuo. ⟨Ed. D. Lasocki.⟩ [1974.] 4°.　　**g. 934. ii. (5.)**

— *See* PLEYEL (I. J.) Quartet in F major. Opus 17. No. 2. For flute, violin, viola and cello. ⟨[Edited by] D. Lasocki.⟩ [1972.] 4°.　　**g. 934. v. (15.)**

— *See* PLEYEL (I. J.) Symphonie concertante No. 5 in F major. For flute, oboe (clarinet), horn, bassoon and orchestra (piano reduction). ⟨Edited by D. Lasocki.⟩ [1974.] 4°.　　**g. 270. hh. (5.)**

— *See* QUANTZ (Johann J.) Concerto in D minor for A. Flute and piano reduction. B. Flute, strings and basso continuo. ⟨Edited by D. Lasocki.⟩ [1974.] 4°.　　**g. 280. oo. (3.)**

— *See* QUANTZ (Johann J.) Trio Sonata in e (K. 28). For 2 flutes … and basso continuo. Edited by D. Lasocki. [1980.] 4°.　　**f. 241. k. (9.)**

— *See* QUANTZ (Johann J.) Trio Sonata in c. (K. 33.) For 2 flutes … and basso continuo. Edited by D. Lasocki. [1980.] 4°.　　**f. 241. k. (10.)**

— *See* QUANTZ (Johann J.) Trio Sonata in C minor. [K. 36.] For flute, oboe & basso continuo. ⟨Edited by D. Lasocki.⟩ [1975.] 4°.　　**g. 934. rr. (7.)**

— *See* QUANTZ (Johann J.) [Sonata a 3 voce.] Trio Sonata in G. K. 46. Oboe … bassoon or violoncello & basso continuo. Edited by D. Lasocki. [Score and parts.] [1979.] 4°.　　**g. 1078. bb. (3.)**

— *See* REICHA (A. J.) Quintet in E major, Opus 106. For horn & string quartet. (Double bass ad lib.) ⟨[Edited by] D. Lasocki, W. Blackwell.⟩ [1971.] 4°.　　**g. 1667. (6.)**

— *See* SCHICKHARD (Johann C.) [Sonatas. Op. 2. No. 5.] Sonata in g … For oboe/violin and basso continuo. Edited by D. Lasocki. [Score and parts.] [1979.] 4°.　　**g. 1078. bb. (7.)**

— *See* SCHICKHARD (Johann C.) [Sonatas. Op. 6. No. 6.] Variations on La Folia … For 2 treble recorders & basso continuo. Edited by D. Lasocki. [Score and parts.] [1979.] 4°.　　**g. 128. (9.)**

LASOCKI (David)

— *See* SCHICKHARD (Johann C.) [6 sonatas. Op. 22.] Sonata in F major ... No. 1 (–6.) For 2 treble recorders (flutes), oboe and basso continuo. ⟨Edited by D. Lasocki.⟩ [1975.] 4°.

g. 934. tt. (7.)

— *See* VIOTTI (G. B.) [Quartets. Op. 22. No. 1.] Flute Quartet in B flat ... For flute, violin, viola & violoncello. ⟨[Edited by] D. Lasocki.⟩ [1969.] 4°.

g. 411. e. (3.)

— *See* VIVALDI (A.) Concerto in D major. (F XII, 43.) [Ryom 84.] For flute, violin and basso continuo. ⟨[Edited by] D. Lasocki.⟩ [1970.] 4°.

g. 33. s. (7.)

— *See* VIVALDI (A.) Concerto ... in D major. [Rinaldi. Op. 44. No. 15. Ryom 90.] For flute, oboe, violin, bassoon and basso continuo. ⟨[Edited by] D. Lasocki.⟩ [1969.] 4°.

g. 33. r. (2.)

— *See* VIVALDI (A.) Concerto in D minor (F. XII, 42). [Ryom 96.] For flute, violin, bassoon and basso continuo. ⟨[Edited by] D. Lasocki.⟩ [1970.] 4°.

g. 33. s. (6.)

— *See* VIVALDI (A.) Concerto in G minor. [Rinaldi. Op. 44. No. 3. Ryom 103.] ... For flute (clarinet), oboe and bassoon, *etc.* ⟨[Edited by] D. Lasocki.⟩ [1971.] 4°.

g. 33. t. (1.)

— *See* VIVALDI (A.) Concerto in G minor ... [Rinaldi. Op. 44. No. 5. Ryom 104.] For flute (violin), bassoon, 2 violins & basso continuo. [Edited by D. Lasocki.] [1969.] 4°.

g. 33. r. (3.)

— *See* VIVALDI (A.) Concerto in G minor ... [Rinaldi. Op. 44. No. 12. Ryom 105.] For treble recorder/flute, oboe, violin, bassoon & basso continuo. ⟨Ed. D. Lasocki.⟩ [1974.] 4°.

g. 33. u. (4.)

— *See* VIVALDI (A.) Concerto in G major ... [Ryom 437.] ⟨Opus 10. No. 6.⟩ For treble recorder/flute, oboe, violin, bassoon & basso continuo. ⟨Ed. D. Lasocki.⟩ [1974.] 4°.

g. 33. u. (3.)

— *See* VIVALDI (A.) Concerto in C minor ... [Rinaldi. Op. 44. No. 19. Ryom 441.] For treble recorder (flute), strings, & basso continuo, *etc.* ⟨[Edited by] D. Lasocki.⟩ [1969.] 4°.

g. 33. r. (4.)

— *See* VIVALDI (A.) Concerto in A minor ... [Rinaldi. Op. 44. No. 26. Ryom 445.] For sopranino recorder (piccolo, treble recorder, flute), strings & basso continuo. ⟨[Edited by] D. Lasocki.⟩ [1969.] 4°.

g. 33. r. (1.)

— *See* VIVALDI (A.) Concerto in D minor ... [Rinaldi. Op. 42. No. 2. Ryom 535.] For 2 oboes, strings and basso continuo, *etc.* ⟨Ed. D. Lasocki.⟩ [1974.] 4°.

g. 33. u. (2.)

— *See* VIVALDI (A.) Concerto in G major. [Ryom 545.] P. 129, *etc.* ⟨[Rinaldi] Opus 42 no. 3. Ed. D. Lasocki.⟩ [1974.] 4°.

g. 33. w. (3.)

— *See* VIVALDI (A.) Concerto in G major. [Ryom 545.] P. 129 ... ⟨[Rinaldi] Opus 42 no. 3. Ed. D. Lasocki.⟩ Oboe, bassoon and piano reduction. [1974.] 4°.

g. 33. w. (2.)

— *See* VIVALDI (A.) Sonata in E minor ... [Ryom 50.] For flute and basso continuo. ⟨Ed. D. Lasocki.⟩ [1974.] 4°.

g. 33. u. (5.)

— *See* VIVALDI (A.) Trio Sonata in G minor ... [Ryom 81.] For 2 oboes and basso continuo. ⟨Ed. D. Lasocki.⟩ [1974.] 4°.

g. 33. u. (6.)

— *See* VIVALDI (A.) [*Doubtful and Supposititious Works.*] Concerto in C minor ... [Ryom Anh. 17.] For oboe, violin and strings, *etc.* ⟨Ed. D. Lasocki.⟩ [1974.] 4°. **g. 33. u. (1.)**

LASS

— Lass ab. Zigeunerlied. *See* DUBUC (A. I.)

— Lass and Lad. [Song.] *See* FOX (J. B.) Two Songs, *etc.* [No. 1.]

LASS

— The Lass and the Highland Plaid. [Song.] *See* NORTHRUP (Theodore H.)

— The Lass and the Looking-glass. Song. *See* DACRE (Harry) *pseud.*

— The Lass at the Brow of yᵉ Hill. [Song.] *See* AT. At the Brow of a Hill, *etc.* [1735?] *s. sh.* fol. **H. 1994. b. (6.)**

— Lass das Fragen. [Song.] *See* SEYFFARDT (E. H.) Sechs Lieder ... Op. 18. No. 6.

— Lass' dein Sichel rauschen. [Part-song.] *See* KLEINMICHEL (R.) Acht Lieder. Op. 32. No. 6.

— Lass dich auf dein Lager nieder. [Song.] *See* HOFFMANN (A.) Zehn Gesänge ... Op. 5. No. 6.

— Lass dich belauschen, du stille Nacht. [Song.] *See* POPPER (D.) Lieder. Op. 40. No. 1.

— Lass dich nur nichts nicht dauren. [Part-song.] *See* BRAHMS (J.) [Geistliches Lied. Op. 30.]

— Lass die Rose schlummern. [Song.] *See* LASSEN (E.) Sechs Lieder. Op. 59. No. 6.

— Lass die Rose schlummern. [Song.] *See* WALLNOEFER (A.) 6 Gedichte ... No. 4.

— Lass die Rosen schlummern. [Song.] *See* RHEINBERGER (J.)

— The Lass for a plain British Tar. Song. *See* NORRIS (Harry B.)

— The Lass for a Sailor. [Song.] *See* ELLIOTT (J. W.)

— The Lass from the Low Country. Folk song. *See* EHRET (Walter)

— The Lass from the low Countree. Chorus. *See* NILES (John J.) [Ballads, Love Songs and tragic Legends from the Southern Appalachian Mountains. No. 3.]

— Lass für ihn den ich geliebet. [Duet.] *See* SPOHR (L.) [Jessonda.]

— Lass gin ye lo'e me, tell me now. Song. *See* I. I ha'e laid a Herring in Sa't, *etc.* [c. 1790.] *s. sh.* fol. **G. 426. kk. (77.)**

— The Lass he left behind. Song. *See* KING (J. L.)

— The Lass I left ashore. Song. *See* SHEPHERD (C. H.)

— The Lass I love. Song. *See* CRAMER (O.)

— The Lass I love. Song. *See* OLCOTT (C.)

— Lass keinen Sonnenstrahl herein. [Song.] *See* BRAMBACH (C. J.) 8 Lieder. No. 3.

— Lass mich allein! [Duet.] *See* GLINKA (M. I.) [Не искуцай.]

— Lass mich dir sagen. [Song.] *See* BECKER (A.) Fünf Lieder, *etc.* Op. 13. No. 1.

— Lass mich in deinen Augen lesen. Song. *See* ABT (F. W.) [3 Lieder ... Op. 543. No. 1.]

— Lass mich in Treue Deine Wege wandeln. [Motet.] *See* SCHWARZ-SCHILLING (R.) Motetten für sechsstimmigen gemischten Chor. 2.

— Lass mich mit Tränen mein Los beklagen. Rezitativ und Arie. *See* HAENDEL (G. F.) [Rinaldo.—Lascia ch'io pianga.]

— Lass mich schlummern, Herzlein schweige. [Song.] *See* WEBER (C. M. F. E. von)

— Lass mir dein Auge leuchten. *See* REINECKE (C. H. C.) [6 Lieder ... Op. 118. No. 6.]

— Lass mir die Thräne. [Song.] *See* AMES (A. P.) Six Romances. No. 1.

LASS

— Lass Nachtigall dein Singen sein. Lied. *See* BECKER (R.)

— Lass, Nachtigall, dein Singen sein. Lied. *See* ROEDER (M.)

— Lass, o Welt, o lass mich sein. [Song.] *See* GOLDSCHMIDT (A. von)

— The Lass of all others, God bless her. [Song.] *See* BOLDEN (T. M. L.) [England's Queen.]

— The Lass of all others; God bless her. [Song.] *See* L., T. M.

— The Lass of all others; God bless her. [Song.] *See also* LITTLE (T. M.) *pseud.*

— The Lass o' Arranteenie. [Part-song.] *See* BELL (J.) *Mus. Doc.*

— The Lass o' Arranteenie. Ballad. *See* ROSS (J.)

— The Lass o' Arranteenie. Song. *See* SMITH (R. A.)

— The Lass of Broomhall Green. [Song.] [*London*, c. 1740.] *s. sh.* fol.
Followed by an arrangement for flute.   **H. 1601. s. (6.)**

— The Lass of Broomhall Green. [Song.] *See* FROUDE (   )

— The Lass of Crayfordness. Song. *See* ANDREWS (M.)

— The Lass o' Eden Side. Song. *See* MATHER (Samuel)

— The Lass o' Gowrie. *See* RANSFORD (E.) The Lass of Gowrie. Glee for four voices, *etc.* [1838?] fol.   **H. 1682. (12.)**

— The Lass of Gowrie. *See* PHILLIPS (W. L.) The favorite Scotch Song ... arranged by W. L. Phillips, *etc.* [1844.] fol.   **H. 1252. (36.)**

— The Lass o' Gowrie. Song. *See* 'TWAS. 'Twas on a simmer's afternoon. [1855.] fol.   **H. 2345.**

— Lass o' Gowrie. Ballad. *See* 'TWAS. 'Twas on a Simmer's Afternoon, *etc.* [c. 1860.] fol.   **G. 426. rr. (33.)**

— Lass o' Gowrie. Ballad. *See* 'TWAS. 'Twas on a Simmer's Afternoon. [c. 1910.] fol.   **H. 1980. zz. (22.)**

— The Lass o' Gowrie. *See* HOPKINSON (J.) The Lass of Gowrie ... arranged ... for pianoforte, *etc.* [1844.] fol.   **h. 708. (10.)**

— The Lass o' Gowrie. [Song.] *See* DEWAR (J. R.) Campbell, Ransford, & Co.'s Edition of Scotch Songs, *etc.* [No. 7.]

— The Lass o' Gowrie. Duet. *See* DIACK (J. M.) Scottish Songs arranged as Duets. No. 2.

— The Lass o' Gowrie. [Part-song.] *See* FINLAY (K. G.)

— The Lass o' Gowrie. Ballad. *See* GOW (Niel) *the Elder.*

— The Lass of Gourie. [Song.] *See* LEE (George A.)

— The Lass o' Gowrie. [Song.] *See* LODER (E. J.)

— The Lass o' Gowrie. Scotch ballad. *See* MACEWEN (J.)

— The Lass of Gowrie. [Song.] *See* NELSON (Sidney)

— The Lass o' Gowrie. Scotch Ballad. *See* SCHUBERT (H.)

— The Lass o' Gowrie. Duet. *See* SMITH (F.) *of Cheltenham.*

— The Lass of Humber-Side. Ballad. *See* BLEWITT (Jonathan)

— The Lass of Humber Side. Ballad. *See* THOMSON (John) *of Edinburgh.*

— The Lass of Isla. Song. *See* AH. Ah Mary sweetest Maid farewell. [c. 1800.] fol.   **G. 295. ee. (26.)**

— The Lass of Kensworth. Ballad. *See* MORE (R.)

— The Lass of Kensworth Dale. Ballad. *See* MOULDS (J.)

LASS

— The Lass o' Killean. Song. *See* STICKLES (W.) Three Songs. [No. 1.]

— The Lass of Limerick Town. Comic Opera. *See* PENN (A. A.)

— The Lass of Liverpool. [Song.] *See* KING (Matthew P.)

— The Lass of Loch Linne. [Song.] *See* SPRAY. The Spray may drive ... [Song.] Music by the author of "The March of the Cameron Men" [i. e. M. M. Campbell]. [1911.] fol.
          H. 1792. kk. (66.)

— The Lass of Loch Lomond. Ballad. *See* PHILLIPS (Henry)

— The Lass of Lockroyan. *See* O. O mirk, mirk is the midnight hour. *Lord Gregory.* Founded upon an old Scotch Ballad, called "The Lass of Lochroyan". [1860.] fol.
          H. 2815. o. (11.)

— The Lass of Lydford Down. [Song.] *See* KAHN (G. F.) [West Country Songs. No. 3.]

— Lass o' mine. Song. *See* BEVAN (F.)

— Lass of mine. Song. *See* PHILLIPS (H. L.)

— The Lass of Norwich-Town. Song. *See* BULLARD (F. F.)

— The Lass of Pattie's Mill. [Song, from A. Ramsay's 'Gentle Shepherd'.] *Cross:* [*London*, 1725?] *s. sh.* fol.
          H. 1601. (471.)

— [Another edition.] The Lass of Patie's Mill. [Song.] [*London*, 1730?] *s. sh.* fol.   **G. 312. (55.)**

— [Another edition.] The Lass of Patie's Mill, *etc.* [*London*, 1735?] *s. sh.* fol.   **G. 316. f. (37.)**

— [Another edition.] The Lass of Peatie's Mill. [Song.] For Two Voices. [*London*, 1765?] *s. sh.* fol.   **H. 1994. a. (223.)**

— The Lass of Peaty's Mill. For two voices [two violins and forte piano. Arranged by P. Urbani.] Words by Ramsay. [Score.] *Urbani & Liston:* [*Edinburgh*, c. 1800.] fol.
A reissue of pp. 43, 44 *of "Urbani's Selection of Scots Songs", bk.* 3.   **G. 424. kk. (29.)**

— The Lass of Peaties Mill. [Song.] *In:* IN. In April when Primroses paint the sweet Plain. *The Yellow haird Laddie.* ⟨The Lass of Peaties Mill.⟩ [Two songs.] [c. 1810.] *s. sh.* fol.
          G. 424. pp. (11.)

— The Lass of Peatie's Mill with Variations for the Harpsichord or Piano Forte also for the German Flute or Violin. *Printed for Straight and Skillern: London,* [1780?] fol.
          g. 271. a. (47.)

— The Lass of Peaties Mill, with Variations for the Harpsichord or Piano Forte also for the German Flute or Violin. *In:* BIRKS. The Birks of Endermay, *etc.* pp. 13–15. [c. 1785.] fol.
          g. 443. s. (19.)

— The Lass of Peatie's Mill, with Variations. [P. F.] pp. 6. [*Harrison, Cluse & Co.: London,* 1801.] 8°.
[*Piano Forte Magazine. vol.* 13. *no.* 6 a.] *Imperfect; wanting the titlepage. The title is taken from the head of p.* 1.   **D. 854.**

— The Lass of Plymouth Town. Song. *See* HERIOT (G.)

— The Lass of Richmond Hill. Part-Song. *See* BREWER (*Sir* A. H.)

— The Lass of Richmond Hill. [Part-song.] *See* COPLEY (Ian A.)

— The Lass of Richmond Hill. Ballad. *See* HOOK (J.)

— The Lass of St. Osyth. [Song.] *See* HOWARD (S.)

— The Lass of the Brook. Song. *See* ON. On a Brook's glassy brink, *etc.* [1750?] *s. sh.* fol.   **G. 316. (106.)**

LASS

— The Lass of the Brook. Song. *See* ON. On a Brook's grassy Brink, *etc.* [1755.] 8°.   **157. l. 17.**

— The Lass of the Brook. Song. *See* ON. On a Brook's grassy Brink, *etc.* [1755.] 8°.   **P. P. 5439.**

— The Lass of the Brook. [Song.] *See* ON. On a Brook's grassy brink, *etc.* [1756.] *s. sh.* 8°.   **P. P. 5439. ab.**

— The Lass of the glad gray Eyes. [Song.] *See* BRANSCOMBE (G.) Songs of the Unafraid. [No. 2.]

— The Lass of the Hatch. [Song.] *See* LET. Let Poets of learning. [1785?] fol.   **G. 310. (48.)**

— The Lass of the Hill. *See* AT. At the Brow of a Hill, *etc.* [1740?] *s. sh.* fol.   **H. 1994. b. (7.)**

— [Another setting.] The Lass of the Hill. [Song, begins: "At the brow of a hill".] *See* HOWARD (S.)

— The Lass of the Mill. [Song, begins: "Who has e'er been at Baldock".] *See* FESTING (M. C.)

— The Lass of the Mill. [Song, begins: "Dan Gay first in vogue".] *See* HOWARD (S.)

— The Lass of the Village. [Song.] *See* As. As Phillis loveliest of the Plain, *etc.* [1775?] *s. sh.* fol.   **H. 1652. w. (15.)**

— The Lass of Watertown. Song. *See* HATTON (J. L.)

— Lass ruh'n die Todten. [Part-song.] *See* WALLNOEFER (A.) Sechs Gesänge. Op. 20. No. 2.

— Lass scharren deiner Rosse Huf. [Song.] *See* PFITZNER (H.) Vier Lieder ... Op. 32. No. 4.

— Lass schlafen mich und träumen. [Song.] *See* HASSE (G.)

— The Lass that loves a Sailor. [Song.] *See* DIBDIN (C.) [The Round Robin.]

— A Lass that was loaden with care. A Scotch Song. [*London*, 1740?] *s. sh.* fol.   **G. 306. (49.)**

— [Another copy.]
With MS. ornaments added in a contemporary hand.
H. 1653. jj. (34.)

— [Another edition.] A Lass that was loaden with Care, *etc. Printed for J. Simpson:* [*London*, 1745?] *s. sh.* fol.
H. 1994. b. (48.)

— A Lass that was loaded with Care. *The Lass that was loaden with Care.* [Song.] Set for ye German flute. [*London*, c. 1750.] *s. sh.* fol.   **G. 809. ww. (24.)**

— A Lass that was leaden'd with Care. *Sae merry as we hae been.* A favorite song sung by Miss R. Ryder. *Hime: Dublin*, [1800?] *s. sh.* fol.   **H. 1601. g. (40.)**

— A Lass there lives upon the Green. Song. *See* COURTIVILLE (R.) [Oroonoko.]

— A Lass there lives upon the green. [Song.] *See* LAMPE (J. F.) [Oroonoko.]

— Lass tief in dir mich lesen. [Song.] *See* SIEBMANN (F.) Sechs Lieder. Op. 63. No. 4.

— The Lass who loved a Sailor. Song. *See* POWELL (Orlando)

— The Lass who takes your Fancy. Song. *See* LUBBOCK (Mark)

— The Lass with golden hair. Ballad. *See* REEVE (W.)

— The Lass with the delicate Air. [Song.] *See* ARNE (M.)

— [Another setting.] The Lass with the delicate Air. [Song.] *See* YOUNG. Young Molly who lives at the Foot of the Hill. [1760?] *s. sh.* fol.   **G. 316. f. (134.)**

LASS

— The Lass with the golden Locks. [Song.] *See* NO. No more of my Harriot, *etc.* [c. 1780.] *s. sh.* fol.   **H. 1860. yy. (18.)**

— The Lass with the Lasso. Song. *See* STUART (L.) *pseud.* [Peggy.]

— The Lass with the Velvet. [Song.] *See* THERE. There was a Buxom Lass. [1710?] *s. sh.* fol.   **G. 305. (26.)**

— The Lass you love, my Laddie. Song. *See* HUSSELL (A. T.)

LASSAILLY (ÉMILE)

— *See* DAREWSKI (H. E.) Carminetta. Selection ... on melodies by E. Lassailly, *etc.* 1917. fol.   **h. 3284. bb. (17.)**

LASSALLE (A. CHIBAS)

— *See* JEANNIN (J.) Mélodies liturgiques syriennes et chaldéennes ... publiées avec la collaboration ... de Dom A. Chibas Lassalle, *etc.* [1925, *etc.*] 8°.   **F. 1060.**

LASSALLE (PIERROT)

— Six Morceaux ... pour piano. 6 no. *R. Cocks & Co.: London*, 1891. fol.   **h. 1489. s. (12.)**

LASSE

— Lasse liten. Sång. *See* SIBELIUS (J.)

LASSEN (EDUARD)
COLLECTIONS, VOCAL

— Songs ... adapted and edited by L. C. Elson. (Paroles françaises de C. Marx.) 14 no. *R. Sulzer: Leipzig*, [1883.] fol.
H. 2614. a. (9.)

— 12 Lieder. *Leipzig*, [1884.] 8°.   **F. 607. r. (9.)**

— Lieder ... Chansons Espagnoles ... Duetti pour soprano et contralto ... Traduction française de V. Wilder. no. 1, 4-22, 26-30. *Paris*, 1885. fol.
Imperfect; wanting no. 2, 3, 23, 24 and 25.   **H. 2614. a. (11.)**

— 12 Songs ... Adapted and edited by Louis C. Elson (Vocal album with German and English words.) pp. 39. *R. Sulzer: Berlin*, [1887?] 8°. *In wrappers bearing the imprint of Pitt & Hatzfeld, London.*   **E. 1501. rr. (2.)**

COLLECTIONS, INSTRUMENTAL

— 2 Lieder ... Für Pianoforte von Franz Liszt. N° 1. Ich weil' in tiefer Einsamkeit. N° 2. Löse Himmel meine Seele. pp. 17. *Gustav Heinze: Leipzig*, [1872.] fol.   **g. 547. o. (8.)**

— Liederstrauss. [Transcriptions of 4 songs for flute and P. F.] *See* GARIBOLDI (G.) Morceaux Favoris pour Flute & Piano, No. 50. [1887.] fol.   **h. 2096. e.**

— Liederstrauss. [Transcriptions of 4 songs for violin and P. F.] *See* HERMANN (F.) Morceaux Favoris pour Violin & Piano, No. 50. [1887.] fol.   **h. 1621. b.**

— Der Abend. *See* infra: Sechs Lieder ... Op. 81. No. 5.

— Abendlied. *See* infra: Sechs Lieder ... Op. 79. No. 3.

— All Souls' Day. *See* infra: [Sechs Lieder. Op. 85. No. 3. Allerseelen.]

— Allerseelen. *See* infra: Sechs Lieder ... Op. 85. No. 3.

LASSEN (Eduard)

— [Als ich dich kaum gesehn.] When first I saw thee ... Im Volkston. [Song. Words by] Storm. English Words by J. Ahrem. *J. Church Co.: [Cincinnati,]* 1899. fol.
H. 1799. h. (6.)

— [Das alte Lied.] Une vieille chanson ... Traduction française de V. Wilder. No. 1. Mezzo-Soprano ... No. 2. Soprano, *etc.* 2 no. *Paris,* 1885. fol. **H. 2614. a. (12.)**

— Among the Flowers. *See* infra: [5 Lieder. No. 1. Ich wandle unter Blumen.]

— An die Nacht. *See* infra: Sechs Lieder ... Op. 85. No. 5.

— Andantino Pastorale für das Pianoforte. *W. Czerny: London,* [1883.] fol. **h. 1484. s. (21.)**

— The Angel of Bethlehem. *See* infra: [5 biblische Bilder. Op. 49. No. 1. Die heilige Nacht.]

— Aus der Frühlingszeit. Ein Liedercyclus von Fräulein O. v. Ahlefeldt-Dehn ... für eine Singstimme mit Pianoforte. Opus 82. *Breslau,* [1885.] fol. **H. 2614. a. (4.)**

— Avril. *See* infra: Trois Duetti ... [Op. 50.] No. 2.

— Ballade. *See* infra: Sechs Lieder ... Op. 85. No. 2.

— Beethoven-Ouverture für grosses Orchester ... Partitur, *etc.* pp. 79. *Julius Hainauer: Breslau,* [c. 1870.] 8°. **f. 222. b.**

— Der Berg des Gebets. *See* infra: [5 Biblische Bilder. Op. 49. No. 4.]

— Fünf biblische Bilder aus den Psalmblättern von R. Gerok ... Op. 49. 1. Die heilige Nacht. Terzett ... 2. "Ich sende Euch." Für Bariton ... 3. Bethania. Quintett ... 4. Der Berg des Gebets. Für Mezzo-Sopran ... 5. Joseph's Garten. Terzett, *etc.* 5 no. *R. Seitz: Leipzig, Weimar,* [1873.] fol.
H. 2614. (1.)

5 biblische Bilder. Op. 49. No. 1. Die heilige Nacht

— The Holy Night. Chorus for three Ladies' Voices with Accompaniment of Violin and Organ or Pianoforte. (English version by M. Knyvet.) *W. Czerny: London,* [1882.] fol.
F. 607. n. (13.)

— The Holy Night in Bethlehem. Part-song for two voices with Pianoforte or Organ Accompaniment, *etc.* (English version by M. Knyvet.) *W. Czerny: London,* [1882.] obl. 4°.
C. 799. c. (2.)

— The Holy Night. [Chorus.] [1895?] *See* SAINT. St. Cecilia. Fourth Series. No. 15. [1890? *etc.*] 4°. **F. 1526.**

— The Holy Night in Bethlehem. [Two-part song.] [1896.] *See* SAINT. St. Cecilia. Sixth Series. No. 17. [1890? *etc.*] 4°.
F. 1526.

— The Angel of Bethlehem. A Biblical Picture for the Voice and Pianoforte or Organ accompaniment. (English version by M. Knyvet.) *W. Czerny: London,* [1882.] fol.
H. 2614. a. (13.)

— The Holy Night in Bethlehem. Pastorale ... Op. 49. (For organ by W. J. Westbrook.) *W. Czerny: London,* [1882.] fol.
h. 2732. i. (46.)

— The Holy Night in Bethlehem. Pastorale for the Pianoforte. *W. Czerny: London,* [1882.] fol. **h. 3275. j. (16.)**

— The Holy Night in Bethlehem. Pastorale ... Op. 49. [Violin and P. F.] *W. Czerny: London,* [1882.] fol. **h. 210. e. (21.)**

—

— [5 biblische Bilder. Op. 49. No. 2. Ich sende Euch.] I send ye forth!—Christ addressing his Apostles. Biblical Picture for voice and pianoforte. (English version by M. Knyvet.) No. 1

LASSEN (Eduard)

in D minor. No. 2 in E minor, with accompaniment of organ or pianoforte, and violoncello. 2 no. *W. Czerny: London,* [1882–4.] fol. **H. 2614. a. (14.)**

— [5 biblische Bilder. Op. 49. No. 3. Bethania.] Fair Bethany. Quintett for Soprano, Alto, Tenor, Baritone & Bass. Words translated from the German of R. Gerok by M. Knyvet. *St. Cecilia Publishing Co.: London,* [1890.] 8°.
E. 442. m. (17.)

— [5 biblische Bilder. Op. 49. No. 4. Der Berg des Gebets.] The Mountain of Prayer. Song, with Organ or Pianoforte accompaniment. (The English version by M. Knyvet.) *W. Czerny: London,* [1882.] fol. **H. 1787. j. (14.)**

— Bitteres Gedenken. *See* infra: Sechs Lieder ... Op. 79. No. 2.

— Le Captif. Opéra en un acte. Paroles de E. Cormon. *Paris,* [1866.] 8°. **F. 442.**

— Chante encore. *See* infra: Trois Duetti ... [Op. 50.] No. 1.

— Cloud and Calm. *See* infra: [5 Lieder. No. 3. Mein Herz ist wie die dunkle Nacht.]

— Concert für die Violine mit Begleitung des Orchesters ... Op. 87 ... Clavierauszug und Solostimme. 2 pt. *Julius Hainauer: Breslau,* [1888.] fol. **h. 1729. i. (2.)**

— Day Dreams. *See* infra: [5 Lieder. No. 5. Mit deinen blauen Augen.]

— Domine salvum fac regem nostrum, für gemischten Chor, Orchester und Orgel. Partitur. *Leipzig,* [1881.] fol.
H. 1028. j. (9.)

— Drei Bitten. *See* infra: Sechs Lieder ... Op. 81. No. 2.

— [Düftet die Lindenblüt.] O fragrant Linden Tree ... Song, words by K. Groth and Mr. J. P. Morgan. Op. 93. 2 no. [In G and B flat.] *Bowerman & Co.: London,* [1902.] fol.
H. 1799. vv. (29.)

— Drei Duette für Sopran und Alt mit Begleitung des Pianoforte. Op. 50. *Leipzig, Weimar,* [1873.] fol.
H. 2614. (5.)

— Trois Duetti pour Soprano & Contralto. [Op. 50.] 1. Chante encore. 2. Avril. 3. Le Vieux Tilleul. Traduction Française de V. Wilder. 3 no. *Paris,* [1884.] fol. **H. 2614. a. (10.)**

— Sechs Duette für Sopran und Alt mit Begleitung des Pianoforte. Op. 55. *Breslau,* [1875.] fol. **H. 2614. (8.)**

— [Das Epheublatt.] The Ivy Leaf ... [Song. Words by] v. Boddien. English Words by J. Ahrem. *J. Church Co.: [Cincinnati,]* 1899. fol. **H. 1799. h. (7.)**

— Ewige Liebe. *See* infra: Sechs Lieder ... Op. 79. No. 4.

— Fair Bethany. *See* supra: [5 biblische Bilder. Op. 49. No. 3. Bethania.]

— Musik zu Goethe's Faust I. und II. Theil nach der O. Devrient'schen Bearbeitung. Op. 57. Klavier-Auszug. *Breslau,* [1876.] 8°. **F. 442. b.**

— Festmarsch für grosses Orchester ... Op. 6. Partitur. pp. 40. *J. Schuberth & Co.: Leipzig, New York,* [1862.] 8°.
e. 666. vv. (2.)

— Festouverturen für grosses Orchester. Op. 51. Partitur. *Breslau,* [1874.] 8°. **f. 222.**

— Flowers that never die. Song, words by J. S. Lyons. *W. Czerny: London,* [1884.] fol. **H. 2614. a. (15.)**

— Frühlingsgedränge. *See* infra: Sechs Lieder ... Op. 83. No. 4.

— Sechs Gedichte von A. Schöll für gemischten Chor. Op. 69. *Breslau,* [1880.] 8°. **E. 308. j. (17.)**

LASSEN (Eduard)

— Ein geistlich Abendlied. *See* infra: Sechs Lieder … Op. 84. No. 2.

— Germanensang—Old German Song—Words by F. Dahn. (English words by A. F. Schmall.) *J. Church Co.: Cincinnati, etc.*, 1901. fol. **H. 1799. cc. (48.)**

— Getrennte Liebe. Ein Lieder Cyclus für Mezzo-Sopran und Baryton mit Begleitung des Pianoforte. [Words by] Richard Pohl. Op. 80. *Breslau*, [1884.] fol. **H. 2614. a. (2.)**

— Grosse Polonaise für Orchester. Partitur. *Breslau*, [1879.] fol. **h. 1509. d. (11.)**

— Gute Nacht. ⟨Gedicht von Robert Baumbach. Männerchor.⟩ [A facsimile of the composer's autograph. With a portrait.] *In*: STRASBURG.—*Strassburger Maenner-Gesangverein.* Strassburger Sängerhaus. pp. 60–63. 1886. fol. **I. 526.**

— Die heilige Nacht. *See* supra: [5 biblische Bilder. Op. 49. No. 1.]

— Herbstlied. *See* infra: Sechs Lieder … Op. 84. No. 3.

— The Holy Night in Bethlehem. *See* supra: [5 biblische Bilder. Op. 49. No. 1. Die heilige Nacht.]

— I send ye forth. *See* supra: [5 biblische Bilder. Op. 49. No. 2. Ich sende Euch.]

— I wander 'mongst the Blossoms. *See* infra: [5 Lieder. No. 1. Ich wandle unter Blumen.]

— Ich hatte einst ein schönes Vaterland. *See* infra: [5 Lieder. No. 2.]

— Ich wandle unter Blumen. *See* infra: [5 Lieder. No. 1.]

— In April. *See* infra: [Fünf Lieder. Op. 46. No. 2. Im April.]

— It was a Dream. *See* infra: [5 Lieder. No. 2. Ich hatte einst ein schönes Vaterland.]

— The Ivy Leaf. *See* supra: [Das Epheublatt.]

— Kleine Lieder. *See* infra: Sechs Lieder … Op. 83. No. 5.

— König Œdipus von Sophocles … Einleitung, Chöre u. Melodramen, nach der Donnerschen Uebersetzung. Partitur. *J. Hainauer: Breslau*, [1875?] 8°. **F. 442. d.**

— König Œdipus … Clavierauszug. *J. Hainauer: Breslau*, [1875?] 4°. **H. 2614. b.**

— Die Künstler. Gedicht von F. v. Schiller für vierstimmigen Männerchor. *Breslau*, [1875.] 8°. **E. 308. b. (14.)**

— Liebespost. *See* infra: Sechs Lieder … Op. 79. No. 5.

— Lied eines Mädchens. *See* infra: Sechs Lieder … Op. 83. No. 1.

— [Lieder.] Two Songs. No. 1. A Resolve.—Vorsatz.—(R. Prutz. Op. 48. No. 4.) No. 2. All souls Day.—Allerseelen.—(H. von Hil … Op. 85. No. 3.) English versions by Mrs. M. Lawson. 3 no. *J. Hainauer: Breslau*, [1894.] fol. **G. 805. aa. (3.)**

5 Lieder

— Five Songs, with German & English words, the latter by J. Goddard. *S. Lucas, Weber & Co.: London*, [1882.] fol. **H. 2614. a. (20.)**

— 5 Favourite Songs with English & German words and pianoforte accompaniment. *Augener & Co.: London*, [1887.] 8°. **F. 636. h. (12.)**

— Five Songs with German and English words, the latter by J. Goddard. No. 1. Ich wandle unter Blumen … [In F sharp and F.] No. 2. Ich hatte einst ein schönes Vaterland … [In F and G.] No. 3. Mein Herz ist wie die dunkle Nacht … No. 4. Vöglein wohin so schnell … No. 5. Mit deinen blauen Augen.

LASSEN (Eduard)

[In A flat.] 6 no. *Stanley Lucas, Weber & Co.: London*, [1890.] fol. *Wanting No. 4.* **H. 1798. u. (24.)**

— [No. 1. Ich wandle unter Blumen.] Among the Flowers. [Song.] *Eng. & Ger.* pp. 3. *Augener & Co.: London*, [1889.] fol. [*Germania. no.* 417.] **H. 2128.**

— [No. 2. Ich hatte einst ein schönes Vaterland.] It was a Dream.—Es war ein Traum.—Song … English translation by J. Goddard. *Stanley Lucas, Weber & Co.: London*, [1876.] fol. **H. 1778. x. (40.)**

— [No. 2. Ich hatte einst ein schönes Vaterland.] Mine no more. Song written by M. X. Hayes. *R. Cocks & Co.: London*, [1882.] fol. **H. 1787. j. (13.)**

— [No. 2. Ich hatte einst ein schönes Vaterland.] 'Twas all a Dream. (Es war ein Traum.) Song … No. 1 in E … No. 2 in F, *etc. Eng. & Ger.* 2 no. *Augener & Co.: London*, [1889.] fol. [*Germania. no.* 421, 422.] **H. 2128.**

— [No. 2.] Ich hatte einst ein schönes Vaterland. *See* MATTHIAS (A.) Lieder-Improvisationen für Pianoforte. No. 4. [1880.] fol. **h. 3280. l. (42.)**

— [No. 2.] Ich hatte einst ein schönes Vaterland. *See* TREHDE (G.) G. Trehde's Transcriptionen beliebter Lieder für Pianoforte. No. 157. [1882.] fol. **h. 3228.**

— [No. 3. Mein Herz ist wie die dunkle Nacht.] Cloud and Calm. [Song.] *Eng. & Ger.* pp. 5. *Augener & Co.: London*, [1889.] fol. [*Germania. no.* 418.] **H. 2128.**

— [No. 4. Vöglein, wohin so schnell?] Spring Song.—Birdling whither away?—(English translation by J. Goddard.) *S. Lucas, Weber & Co.: London*, [1878.] fol. **H. 1783. o. (21.)**

— [No. 4. Vöglein, wohin so schnell?] The Message. [Song.] *Eng. & Ger.* pp. 5. *Augener & Co.: London*, [1889.] fol. [*Germania. no.* 420.] **H. 2128.**

— [No. 5. Mit deinen blauen Augen.] When thy blue Eyes. Song. (English translation by J. Goddard.) [In E flat and F.] 2 no. *S. Lucas, Weber & Co.: London*, [1878.] fol. **H. 1783. o. (20.)**

— [No. 5. Mit deinen blauen Augen.] Day Dreams. [Song.] *Eng. & Ger.* pp. 3. *Augener & Co.: London*, [1889.] fol. [*Germania. no.* 419.] **H. 2128.**

— [No. 5. Mit deinen blauen Augen.] When thy blue Eyes. Arranged for S. A. T. B. with pianoforte accompaniment by Hal Evans. [Words by] Julia Goddard. pp. 7. *Leonard, Gould & Bolttler: London*, [1948.] 8°. [*L. G. B. choral Repertoire. no.* 68.] **F. 1843. a.**

— [No. 5. Mit deinen blauen Augen.] When thy blue Eyes. Two-part song, English translation by Julia Godard. pp. 7. *Leonard, Gould & Bolttler: London*, [1949.] 8°. [*Vocal Duets for Class singing. no.* 2.] **F. 1843. c.**

— [6 Lieder von Peter Cornelius. Op. 5. No. 3.] "Löse, Himmel, meine Seele!" Lied … Für das Pianoforte von Fr. Liszt. pp. 8. *Gustav Heinze: Leipzig*, [1866.] fol. **g. 547. o. (7.)**

— [6 Lieder von Peter Cornelius. Op. 5. No. 3.] "Löse, Himmel, meine Seele." "Sauve, ciel, mon âme" … Für das Pianoforte von F. Liszt. pp. 10. *C. F. Peters: Leipzig*, [1900?] 4°. **g. 547. g. (21.)**

— Sechs Lieder für eine Singstimme mit Begleitung des Pianoforte. Op. 45. *Breslau*, [1873.] fol. **H. 2614. (2.)**

— Fünf Lieder mit Begleitung des Pianoforte. Op. 46. *Breslau*, [1873.] fol. **H. 2614. (3.)**

LASSEN (EDUARD)

— [Fünf Lieder. Op. 46. No. 2. Im April.] In April . . . [Song.] English words by M. Field . . . Edited by A. Howe. *W. Paxton & Co.: London*, 1935. 4°.　　**G. 1270. jj. (35.)**

— Sechs Lieder für eine Singstimme mit Begleitung des Pianoforte. Op. 48. *Breslau*, [1873.] fol.　　**H. 2614. (4.)**

— Sechs Lieder für eine Singstimme mit Begleitung des Pianoforte. Op. 52. *Breslau*, [1875.] fol.　　**H. 2614. (6.)**

— Fünf Lieder für eine Singstimme mit Begleitung des Pianoforte. Op. 54. *London*, [1875.] fol.　　**H. 2614. (7.)**

— Sechs Lieder von P. Cornelius für eine Singstimme mit Begleitung des Pianoforte. Op. 58. *Breslau*, [1877.] fol.　　**H. 2614. (9.)**

— Sechs Lieder, Gedichte von R. Hamerling, für eine Singstimme mit Begleitung des Pianoforte. Op. 59. *Breslau*, [1877.] fol.　　**H. 2614. (10.)**

— Sechs Lieder von F. Bodenstedt für eine Singstimme mit Begleitung des Pianoforte. Op. 60. *Breslau*, [1877.] fol.　　**H. 2614. (11.)**

— Sechs Lieder für eine Singstimme mit Begleitung des Pianoforte. Op. 61. *Breslau*, [1877.] fol.　　**H. 2614. (12.)**

— Sechs Lieder für eine Singstimme mit Begleitung des Pianoforte. Op. 62. *Breslau*, [1878.] fol.　　**H. 2614. (13.)**

— Fünf Lieder für eine Singstimme mit Begleitung des Pianoforte. Op. 65. *Breslau*, [1879.] fol.　　**H. 2614. (14.)**

— Sechs Lieder für eine Singstimme mit Begleitung des Pianoforte. Op. 66. *Breslau*, [1879.] fol.　　**H. 2614. (15.)**

— Sechs Lieder für eine Singstimme mit Begleitung des Pianoforte. Op. 67. *Breslau*, [1879.] fol.　　**H. 2614. (16.)**

— Sechs Lieder für eine Singstimme mit Begleitung des Pianoforte. Op. 68. *Breslau*, [1880.] fol.　　**H. 1786. e. (14.)**

— Sechs Lieder für eine Singstimme mit Begleitung des Pianoforte. Op. 71. *Breslau*, [1881.] fol.　　**H. 1786. e. (15.)**

— Sechs Lieder für eine Singstimme mit Begleitung des Pianoforte. Op. 72. *Breslau*, [1881.] fol.　　**H. 1786. e. (16.)**

— Lieder und Gesänge mit Begleitung des Pianoforte. Op. 74. 3 no. *Breslau*, [1883.] fol.　　**H. 1793. d. (2.)**

— Sechs Lieder für eine Singstimme mit Begleitung des Pianoforte. Op. 75. *Breslau*, [1883.] fol.　　**H. 1793. d. (3.)**

— Sechs Lieder von E. von Wildenbruch für eine Singstimme mit Pianoforte. Op. 79. 1. Nicht weinen. 2. Bitteres Gedenken. 3. Abendlied. 4. Ewige Liebe. 5. Liebespost. 6. Ständchen. *Breslau*, [1884.] fol.　　**H. 2614. a. (1.)**

— Sechs Lieder für eine Singstimme mit Begleitung des Pianoforte. Op. 81. 1. März [begins: "Im Wald der erste Vogel singt"], M. Holm.—2. Drei Bitten.—E. Geibel.—3. Der Morgen [begins: "Fliegt der erste Morgenstrahl"], —Eichendorff.—4. Mittagsruh [begins: "Ueber Bergen, Fluss und Thalen"],—Eichendorff.—5. Der Abend [begins: "Schweigt der Menschen lauter Lust"],—Eichendorff.—6. Die Nacht [begins: "Wie schön, hier zu verträumen"],— Eichendorff. *Breslau*, [1885.] fol.　　**H. 2614. a. (3.)**

— Sechs Lieder für eine Singstimme mit Pianoforte. Op. 83. 1. Lied eines Mädchens [begins: "In meinem Garten die Nelken"],—E. Geibel.—2. Sehnsucht,—J. Grosse.—3. Verschwiegene Liebe [begins: "Ueber Wipfel und Saaten"], —J. v. Eichendorff. 4. Frühlingsgedränge [begins: "Frühlingskinder im bunten Gedränge"],—N. Lenau.—5. Kleine Lieder.—E. Schulze.—6. Vom Strande [begins: "Ich rufe vom Ufer"],—aus dem Spanischen von Eichendorff. *Breslau*, [1886.] fol.　　**H. 2614. a. (5.)**

LASSEN (EDUARD)

— Sechs Lieder für eine Singstimme mit Pianoforte. Opus 84. 1. Mein Lieben [begins: "Wie könnt' ich dein vergessen"], —Hoffmann v. Fallersleben. 2. Ein geistlich Abendlied [begins: "Es ist so still geworden"],—G. Kinkel.—3. Herbstlied [begins: "Feldeinwärts flog ein Vögelein"], —L. Tieck.—4. Trost der Nacht [begins: "Es heilt die Nacht des Tages Wunden"],—G. Kinkel.—5. Ueber Nacht, —J. Sturm.—6. Noch ist die blühende goldene Zeit,— Roquette. *Breslau*, [1886.] fol.　　**H. 2614. a. (6.)**

— Sechs Lieder für eine Singstimme mit Pianoforte. Op. 85. 1. Weisse Rose,—aus "Sind Götter?" von F. Dahn. 2. Ballade [begins: "Und die Sonne macht den weiten Ritt"], —E. M. Arndt.—3. Allerseelen [begins: "Stell auf den Tisch"],—H. v. Hilm.—4. Meeresabend [begins: "Sie hat die ganze Nacht getobt"],—M. Graf Strachwitz.—5. An die Nacht [begins: "Beginne deine heil'ge Feier"], —M. Bernays.—6. Maienlied [begins: "Wie herrlich leuchtet mit die Natur"],—Goethe. *Breslau*, [1886.] fol.　　**H. 2614. a. (7.)**

— [Sechs Lieder. Op. 85. No. 3. Allerseelen.] All Souls Day. As once in May. Song, words by Mrs. Malcolm Lawson. New edition. *Keith Prowse & Co.: London*, 1942. 4°.　　**F. 607. tt. (19.)**

— [Sechs Lieder. Op. 85. No. 3. Allerseelen.] All Souls' Day. Song. (Arranged [for military band] by E. Binding.) [Parts.] *Boosey & Hawkes: London*, 1933. 4°. [*Boosey & Hawkes Military Band Edition. No.* 13 [*b*].]　　**h. 3211. b.**

— Musik zum Festspiel Die Linde am Ettersberg von V. von Scheffel. *Breslau*, [1879.] 4°.　　**G. 808. d. (8.)**

— Little Cissy's dead. Song. Words by M. Foreman. *W. Czerny: London*, [1883.] fol.　　**H. 2614. a. (16.)**

— Löse, Himmel, meine Seele. *See* supra: [6 Lieder von Peter Cornelius. Op. 5. No. 3.]

— März. *See* supra: Sechs Lieder . . . Op. 81. No. 1.

— Maienlied. *See* supra: Sechs Lieder . . . Op. 85. No. 6.

— Meeresabend. *See* supra: Sechs Lieder . . . Op. 85. No. 4.

— Mein Herz ist wie die dunkle Nacht. *See* supra: [5 Lieder. No. 3.]

— Mein Lieben. *See* supra: Sechs Lieder . . . Op. 84. No. 1.

— Douze Mélodies pour chant, *etc.* *Paris*, [1869.] fol.　　**H. 1774. e. (12.)**

— The Message. *See* supra: [5 Lieder. No. 4. Vöglein, wohin so schnell?]

— Mine no more. *See* supra: [5 Lieder. No. 2. Ich hatte einst ein schönes Vaterland.]

— Mit deinen blauen Augen. *See* supra: [5 Lieder. No. 5.]

— Mittagsruh. *See* supra: Drei Lieder . . . Op. 81. No. 4.

— Der Morgen. *See* supra: Drei Lieder . . . Op. 81. No. 3.

— The Mountain of Prayer. *See* supra: [5 biblische Bilder. Op. 49. No. 4. Der Berg des Gebets.]

— My Heart is as the darksome Night. *See* supra: [5 Lieder. No. 3. Mein Herz ist wie die dunkle Nacht.]

— Die Nacht. *See* supra: Sechs Lieder . . . Op. 81. No. 6.

— Musik zu Hebbel's Nibelungen. Elf Characterbilder für Orchester. Op. 47. Partitur. *Breslau*, [1873.] 8°.　　**F. 442. a.**

— Musik zu Hebbel's Nibelungen. 11 Characterbilder für Orchester. Op. 47. Ausgabe für Piano zu 4 Händen. *Breslau*, [1873.] fol.　　**h. 357.**

LASSEN (Eduard)

— Nicht weinen. *See* supra: Sechs Lieder ... Op. 79. No. 1.

— Noch ist die blühende, goldene Zeit. *See* supra: Sechs Lieder ... Op. 84. No. 6.

— O fragrant Linden Tree. *See* supra: [Düftet die Lindenblüt.]

— O loving Heart. Song. *W. Czerny: London*, [1888.] fol.
H. 2614. a. (17.)

— O Woman, lovely Woman! Song. Words by T. Otway. 3 no. [In G, F, and E flat.] *W. Czerny: London*, [1885.] fol.
H. 2614. (18.)

— Musik zu Goethe's Festspiel Pandora. Opus 86. Clavierauszug mit Text. *Breslau*, [1886.] fol. **H. 2614. a. (8.)**

— Zwei Phantasiestücke für Bassposaune, Fagott oder Violoncell mit Orchester- oder Pianofortebegleitung. Partitur. *Leipzig, Weimar*, [1873.] fol. **h. 2270. (7.)**

— Poor Joe, the Marine. Song. (Words by J. Ashley.) 2 no. [In F and E flat.] *W. Czerny: London*, [1883.] fol.
H. 2614. a. (19.)

— Sehnsucht. *See* supra: Sechs Lieder ... Op. 83. No. 2.

— Si mes vers avaient des aîles. [Song, begins: "Mes vers fuiraient".] Poésie de V. Hugo. *Mayence*, [1865?] fol.
H. 2830. d. (67.)

— The Spanish Gipsy Girl, *etc.* [For S. S. C. C.] pp. 7. *J. Curwen & Sons: London*, [1903.] 8°.
[*Choruses for equal Voices. no.* 677.] **E. 861.**

— Spring Song. *See* supra: [5 Lieder. No. 4. Vöglein, wohin so schnell?]

— Ständchen. *See* supra: Sechs Lieder ... Op. 79. No. 6.

— Stars of the Summer Night. Serenade, words by H. W. Longfellow. 3 no. [In E flat, C, and with violin obbligato.] *W. Czerny (Orsborn & Tuckwood): London*, [1883–8.] fol.
H. 2614. a. (21.)

— Stars of the Summer Night. Serenade, with Violin obligato accompaniment (by L. H. d'Egville) ... Edited by A. Randegger. *Hopwood & Crew: London*, [1901.] fol.
H. 1799. cc. (49.)

— Zweite Symphonie in C dur für grosses Orchester. Opus 78. Partitur, *etc.* pp. 182. *Julius Hainauer: Breslau*, [1884.] 8°.
f. 222. a.

— Zweite Symphonie in C dur ... Op. 78. Clavierauszug zu vier Händen von Componisten. *Breslau*, [1884.] fol.
h. 3290. c. (4.)

— Symphonisches Zwischenspiel. *See* infra: Ueber allen Zauber Liebe.

— Te Deum laudamus für Chor und grosses Orchester. Op. 20. Partitur. *Breslau*, [1875.] 8°. **F. 549.**

— Trost der Nacht. *See* supra: Sechs Lieder ... Op. 84. No. 4.

— Trost im Leid. Lied. (E. von Wildenbruch.) *See* SOUVENIR. Souvenir, *etc.* No. 2. [1884.] fol. **h. 3278. (13.)**

— 'Twas all a Dream. *See* supra: [5 Lieder. No. 2. Ich hatte einst ein schönes Vaterland.]

Ueber allen Zauber Liebe

— Musik zu Calderon's fantastischem Schauspiel "Ueber allen Zauber Liebe" (nach der O. Devrient'schen Bearbeitung). Klavierauszug. *Breslau*, [1882.] 8°. **F. 442. c.**

— Symphonisches Zwischenspiel ... zu Calderon's Schauspiel "Ueber allen Zauber Liebe". Opus 77. Partitur. *Breslau*, [1883.] fol. **h. 1509. k. (11.)**

LASSEN (Eduard)

— Symphonisches Zwischenspiel (Intermezzo) zu Calderon's Schauspiel "Ueber allen Zauber Liebe" ... Transcription für Pianoforte von Franz Liszt. *Breslau*, [1883.] fol.
h. 585. f. (19.)

— Ueber Nacht. *See* supra: Sechs Lieder ... Op. 84. No. 5.

— Verschwiegene Liebe. *See* supra: Sechs Lieder ... Op. 83. No. 3.

— Une vieille chanson. *See* supra: [Das alte Lied.]

— Le vieux Tilleul. *See* supra: Trois Duetti ... [Op. 50.] No. 3.

— Vöglein, wohin so schnell. *See* supra: [5 Lieder. No. 4.]

— Vom Strande. *See* supra: Sechs Lieder ... Op. 83. No. 6.

— Weisse Rose. *See* supra: Sechs Lieder ... Op. 85. No. 1.

— When first I saw thee. *See* supra: [Als ich dich kaum gesehn.]

— When thy blue Eyes. *See* supra: [5 Lieder. No. 5. Mit deinen blauen Augen.]

— *See* LANGE (G.) Lieder von E. Lassen für Pianoforte frei übertragen. [1881.] fol. **h. 3101. g. (26.)**

— *See* LISZT (F.) Aus der Musik von E. Lassen zu Hebbel's Nibelungen und Goethe's Faust. Pianofortestücke, *etc.* [1879.] fol. **h. 585. e. (6.)**

— *See* PAGANINI (N.) 24 Capricen für die Violine ... mit hinzugefügten Clavierbegleitung von E. Lassen. Op. 76. [1883.] fol. **h. 1609. y. (17.)**

— *See* SONGS. Album of Sixteen Songs, by ... E. Lassen, *etc.* [1889.] 4°. **F. 636. j. (1.)**

— *See* WAGNER (W. R.) [Tristan und Isolde.] Lyrische Stücke ... eingerichtet von E. Lassen. [1881.] fol. **H. 635. c. (5.)**

LASSEN (Ewald)

— *See* HAYDN (F. J.) Konzert F-dur. Für Klavier oder Cembalo und Streicher, 2 Hörner ad lib. Hoboken XVIII: 3. Herausgegeben von E. Lassen, *etc.* [1958.] 8°.
g. 455. qq. (2.)

— *See* HAYDN (F. J.) Konzert F-dur. Für Klavier oder Cembalo und Streicher, 2 Hörner ad lib. Hoboken XVIII: 3. Herausgegeben von E. Lassen, *etc.* [1958.] 4°.
g. 455. qq. (3.)

— *See* HAYDN (F. J.) Divertimento D dur ... [Hob. II/22.] Für 2 Violinen, Viola, Violoncello (Kontrabass ad lib.), und 2 Hörner. Neue Ausgabe von E. Lassen. [The original version of the work published as the String Quartet, op. 2, no. 5.] [1958.] 4°. **g. 455. qq. (1.)**

— *See* HAYDN (F. J.) [Divertimento. Hob. XIV/13.] Concerto (Divertimento) für konzertierendes Cembalo (Klavier), zwei Violinen und Bass (Violoncello). Herausgegeben von E. Lassen. [1956.] 4°. **g. 455. y. (8.)**

— *See* HAYDN (F. J.) [Symphonies. Hob. I/79.] Sinfonie Nr. 79. F-dur ... Erstmalig in Partitur und Stimmen herausgegeben von E. Lassen, *etc.* [1959.] 4°. **g. 455. qq. (5.)**

— *See* HAYDN (F. J.) [Symphonies. Hob. I/107.] Sinfonia B-dur ... Erstmalig in Partitur und Stimmen herausgegeben von E. Lassen, *etc.* [1958.] 4°. **g. 455. qq. (4.)**

LASSEN (Per)

— *See* LASSON.

LASSENCE (DE)

— Douce Gaîté ... Chansonnette. *Paris*, [1810?] fol.
G. 547. (65.)

— An Original March with Variations for the Harp & Violin or Flute obligato ... arranged for the flute by S. Howship. pp. 8. *J. Platts: London*, [c. 1815.] fol.
g. 661. b. (26.)

LASSER (JOHANN BAPTIST)

— Vollständige Anleitung zur Singkunst, sowohl für den Sopran, als auch für den Alt, *etc. Beym Verfasser: München*, 1798. *obl.* 4°.
C. 365.

— [Another copy.]
Hirsch I. 305.

LASSERRE (CHARLES)

— Alstoria. Valse, *etc.* [P. F.] *Beal & Co.: London*, [1889.] fol.
h. 3285. q. (2.)

— The Bells ... Waltz (with vocal obligato ad lib. Words by E. Oxenford). [P. F.] *Agate & Co.: London*, [1887.] fol.
h. 975. u. (40.)

— The Bells. Valse. Solo B♭ cornet conductor [and military band parts]. 29 pt. *J. R. Lafleur & Son: London*, [1892.] 8°.
Part of the "Alliance Musicale".
f. 800. (785.)

— Holiday-Time. Waltz. [P. F.] (With vocal obbligato ad lib. Written and composed by C. Lasserre.) *Metzler & Co.: London*, [1887.] fol.
h. 975. u. (41.)

— Little Shepherdess. Waltz. [P. F. With vocal obbligato.] *J. B. Cramer & Co.: London*, [1890.] fol. & 8°.
h. 3285. q. (3.)

— Little Shepherdess. Waltz. ⟨1ˢᵗ and 2ⁿᵈ clarinets B♭ (conductor) [and military band parts].⟩ 18 pt. *J. B. Cramer & Co.: London*, [1889.] 8°.
Military Band Parts. no. 15.
f. 800. (786.)

— The Mill-Stream. Waltz (with vocal obligato. Words by H. L. D'A. Jaxone. Orchestrated by J. Rivière). [P. F.] *Metzler & Co.: London*, [1885.] fol.
h. 975. u. (42.)

— The Mill-Stream. Waltz. Arrᵈ. by J. Rivière. [Reed band parts.] *J. R. Lafleur & Son: London*, [1887.] 8°.
Part of the "Alliance Musicale".
f. 401. ee. (15.)

— True Lovers. Valse. [P. F.] *Francis Bros. & Day: London*, [1888.] fol.
h. 975. u. (43.)

LASSERRE (JULES)

— Berceuse pour Violon ou Violoncelle, avec accompagnement de Piano. *Londres*, [1871.] fol.
h. 1609. c. (1.)

— Caprice de Concert pour Violoncello avec accompagnement de Pianoforte. *London*, [1876.] fol.
h. 1849. c. (2.)

— Fantaisie sur le Faust, de C. Gounod, pour Violoncelle avec accompagnement de Piano. *London*, [1871.] fol.
h. 1849. (18.)

— Fantaisie sur Martha, de Flotow, pour Violoncelle avec accompagnement de Piano. *London*, [1871.] fol.
h. 1849. (19.)

— Fileuse pour Violon ou Violoncelle, avec accompagnement de Piano. *London*, [1872.] fol.
h. 1608. e. (2.)

— Rêverie pour Violon ou Violoncelle avec accompagnement de Piano. *London*, [1872.] fol.
h. 1609. m. (6.)

— Romance sans paroles pour Violoncelle (ou Violon) et Piano. *London*, [1874.] fol.
h. 1849. c. (1.)

— Tarentelle pour Violoncelle avec accompagnement de Piano. *London*, [1876.] fol.
h. 1849. c. (3.)

LASSERRE (JULES)

— 2 Transcriptions pour Violoncelle et Piano. 2 no. *Mayence*, [1879.] fol.
h. 1849. h. (10.)

LASSES

— The Lasses. Song. *See* MALCOLM (M.)

— The Lasses at the Tow-Rope. Song. *See* BAINBRIDGE (L.)

— The Lasses left on Shore. Song. *See* DUGGAN (J. F.)

— The Lasses o' Linton. [Part-song.] *See* MILLIGAN (H. V.)

— The Lasses of Dublin. [Song.] *See* POOR. The Poor Soldier.

— The Lasses with a simp'ring air. [Song.] *See* KELLNER (E. A.)

— The Lasses with obliging care. *The White Cockade.* A favorite Air to which is added two fashionable Dances adapted for the Harpsichord, Violin, Ger: Flute and Guitar. *T. Skillern: London*, [1790?] fol.
G. 808. c. (22.)

LASSET

— Lasset die Kindlein zu mir kommen. Cantate. *See* SCHLETTERER (H. M.)

— Lasset eure Lenden umgürtet sein. Motette. *See* STUDER (H.)

— [Lasset uns ablegen die Werke der Finsternis.] Eingangschor aus der Kantate: Lasset uns ablegen die Werke der Finsternis. *See* BACH (W. F.)

— Lasset uns den Herren preisen. Motette. *See* REGER (M.)

— Lasset uns singen. [Part-song.] *See* KLEFISCH (Walter)

LASSIE

— Lassie. Song. *See* COOPER (R. A.)

— Lassie. Musical Comedy. *See* FELIX (H.)

— Lassie. Ballad. *See* LINLEY (George)

— Lassie. Song. *See* TIPTON (L. C.)

— Lassie are you waking. [Song.] *See* LINLEY (George)

— Lassie, dinna sigh for me! Song. *See* GRANT (Hector)

— Lassie, Highland Lassie. Part-Song. *See* STONE (A.)

— The Lassie I love best. [Song.] *See* SPEAKS (O.) Four Songs, *etc.* [No. 4.]

— Lassie mine, whose eyes of grey. *The Bells of Aberdovey* ... Welsh song. The English words by E. Oxenford. *London*, [1879.] fol.
No. 849 of C. Boosey's "Universal" music.
H. 2324.

— Lassie o' mine. Song. *See* TUNBRIDGE (J. A.)

— Lassie o' the Dee. Song. *See* BAYNES (Sydney) and LE CLERQ (G.)

— Lassie o' the witchin E'e. Part Song. *See* FINLAY (K. G.)

— The Lassie of Logan Braes. Song. *See* RITCHIE (J.)

— The Lassie of Lucknow. Ballad. *See* LOVER (S.)

— The Lassie of the Glen. Song. *See* COPE (W. P. R.)

— A Lassie one Day. Song. *See* MONROE (*Mrs* L. B.)

— The Lassie who loved a Soldier. Ballad. *See* GRAHAM (C.)

— Lassie wi' the lint white Locks. [Song.] *See* DIACK (John M.)

— Lassie wi' the yella Coatie. Folk song. *See* HEDGES (Anthony J.)

LASSIE

— Lassie with the Lips sae rosy. Song. *See* RICHARD (R.)

— Lassie with the rosy Lips. [Song.] *See* KREUZ (E.) Songs ... No. 1.

— Lassie would ye love me. Ballad. *See* HOLDER (J. W.)

— Lassie, wad ye lo'e me. [Part-song.] *See* RODDIE (W. S.)

— The Lassie's dream. Ballad. *See* PERRY (E.)

— A Lassie's Love. Song. *See* FRIDAY (W. H.)

LASSIES

— Lassies. Ballad. *See* TRACY (G. L.)

— Lassies, Laddies, come a-maying! Part song. *See* DUTTON (Theodora)

LASSIMONNE (DENISE)

— Les Longs Cheveux de Mélisande, for pianoforte.
Anglo-French Music Co.: London, 1924. fol.   **h. 3865. f. (2.)**

LASSMAN (MARY)

— Madeira Polka. [P. F.]   *F. Pitman: London*, [1899.] fol.
           h. 3286. g. (13.)

LASSO

— Lasso ch'io t'ho perduta. [Song.] *See* VESPASIANO.

LASSO (FERDINANDO DI)

— [Cantiones sacrae.— Macte animo virtute tua.]
Huldigungsmotette an Graf Eitelfriedrich IV von
Hohenzollern, *etc. In:* SCHMID (E. F.) Musik an der
schwäbischen Zollernhöfen der Renaissance. pp. 680–685.
1962. 8°.   **X. 431/107.**

— Huldigungsmotette an Graf Eitelfriedrich IV von
Hohenzollern. *See* supra: [Cantiones sacrae.— Macte animo
virtute tua.]

— [Magnificat.] *See* LASSO (O. di) Liber Primus. Cantiones
Sacræ Magnificat ... His accesserunt quatuor ab ...
Ferdinando de Lasso compositæ, *etc.* 1602. fol.   **K. 2. i. 14.**

— *See* LASSO (O. di) [*Smaller Collections.*] Tertium opus
Musicum, continens Lectiones Hiob et Motetas seu
Cantiones Sacras ... Additæ sunt ... aliquot piæ Ferdinandi
Lassi cantilenæ, *etc.* 1588. *obl.* 4°.   **A. 331. b.**

— *See* LASSO (O. di) [*Smaller Collections.*] Magnum Opus
Musicum Orlandi de Lasso ... A Ferdinando ... & Rudolpho
... Authoris filijs ... collectum, & impensis eorundem Typis
mandatum, *etc.* 1604. fol.   **K. 4. k. 1.**

LASSO (ORLANDO DI)
COMPLETE WORKS

— Sämmtliche Werke. (Magnum Opus Musicum. In Partitur
gebracht von Carl Proske, kritisch durchgesehen und redigirt
von Franz X. Haberl, Adolf Sandberger.) (Madrigale.
Kompositionen mit französischen Text. Kompositionen mit
deutschen Text. Herausgegeben von Adolf Sandberger.)
21 Bd.
    Bd.   1, 3, 5, 7, 9, 11, 13, 15, 17, 19, 21. Magnum Opus
          Musicum.
    Bd.   2, 4, 6, 8, 10. Madrigale.
    Bd.   12, 14, 16. Kompositionen mit französischen Text.
    Bd.   18, 20. Kompositionen mit deutschen Text.
Breitkopf & Härtel: Leipzig, [1894–1927.] fol.   **H. 1047.**

— [Another copy.]   **Hirsch IV. 978.**

LASSO (ORLANDO DI)

— Sämtliche Werke. Neue Reihe. [With facsimiles.]
    Bd. 1.   Lateinische Motetten, französische Chansons
           und italienische Madrigale aus
           wiederaufgefundenen Drucken, 1559–1588.
           pp. xlviii. 188. 1956.
    Bd. 2.   Die vier Passionen. Herausgegeben von Kurt
           von Fischer. pp. xxviii. 60. 1961.
    Bd. 3.   Messen 1–9. Messen der Drucke Venedig 1570
           und München 1574. Herausgegeen von Siegfried
           Hermelink. pp. xxxvi. 279. 1962.
    Bd. 4.   Messen 10–17. Messen des Druckes Paris 1577.
           Herausgegeben von Siegfried Hermelink.
           pp. xxxvii. 213. 1964.
    Bd. 5.   Messen 18–23. Messen der Drucke Paris 1577
           und Nürnberg 1581. Herausgegeben von
           Siegfried Hermelink. pp. xxxii. 216. 1965.
    Bd. 6.   Messen 24–29. Messen des Druckes München
           1589. Herausgegeben von Siegfried Hermelink.
           pp. xxv. 179. 1966.
    Bd. 7.   Messen 30–35. Messen aus Einzel- und
           Sammeldrucken 1570–1588. Herausgegeben von
           Siegfried Hermelink. pp. xxvi. 233. 1967.
    Bd. 8.   Messen 36–41. Messen der Drucke Paris 1607
           und München 1610. Herausgegeben von
           Siegfried Hermelink. pp. xxxviii. 241. 1968.
    Bd. 9.   Messen 42–48. Handschriftlich überlieferte
           Messen I. Herausgegeben von Siegfried
           Hermelink. pp. xxiv. 170. 1969.
    Bd. 10.   Messen 49–55. Handschriftlich überlieferte
           Messen II. Herausgegeben von Siegfried
           Hermelink. pp. xxii. 224. 1970.
    Bd. 11.   Messen 56–63. Herausgegeben von Siegfried
           Hermelink. pp. xxxi. 270. 1971.
    Bd. 12.   Messen 64–70. Handschriftlich überlieferte
           Messen IV, Fragmente, Modelle, Register.
           Herausgegeben von Siegfried Hermelink.
           pp. lix. 352. 1975.
    Bd. 13.   Magnificat 1–24. Magnificat des Druckes
           Nürnberg 1567. Herausgegeben von James Erb.
           pp. xcvi. 308. 1980.
Bärenreiter-Verlag: Kassel, Basel, 1956, *etc.* 8°.   **F. 1071. a.**

SMALLER COLLECTIONS

— Cantiones Orlandi di Lassus: Selectæ in vsum
Argentoratensis Academiæ. Sex vocum. Altus. (Tenor.) (Sexta
Vox.) 3 pt.   *Nicolaus Wyriot: Argentorati*, 1580. *obl.* 8°.
*At the end of each part are MS. Cantiones in a contemporary
hand.*   **K. 1. c. 23.**

— Beatissimae Virginis Mariæ Octo Cantica Modis Tonorum
octo quaternisque vocibus distincta. Adiectis adhæc duplici
Salve Regina. Missa Quinti toni. Veni Creator. Te Deum
laudamus. Adoramus te Christe. Te Deum laudamus.
Adoramus te Christe. 3. & 4. voc. & Tibi Laus, *etc.* Tenor.
*Apud Adrianum le Roy, & Robertum Ballard: Lutetiæ
Parisiorum*, 1586. 4°.   **K. 5. b. 18. (6.)**

— Tertium opus Musicum, continens Lectiones Hiob et
Motectas seu Cantiones Sacras, Quatuor, Quinque et Sex
Vocum, antea quidem tribus fasciculis seorsim excusas, nunc
verò in volumen unum redactas ... Additæ sunt ... aliquot
piæ Ferdinandi Lassi cantilenae, nunc primum in lucem
editæ. Altus. (Bassus.) (Quinta Vox.) (Sexta Vox.) 4 pt.   *In
officina typographica Catharinae Gerlachiæ: Noribergæ*, 1588.
obl. 4°.   **A. 331. b.**

— [Another copy. Quinta Vox.]   **A. 331. c.**

— La Fleur des Chansons d'Orlande de Lassus ... Contenant vn
Recueil de ses Chansons Françoises, & Italiennes, a Quatre,
Cinc, Six & Huit parties, accommodées tant aux Instrumens
comme a la Voix: Toutes mises en ordre conuenable selon
leurs Tons. Superius. (Contratenor.) (Quinta et sexta pars.)
3 pt.   *Chez Pierre Phalese, & chez Jean Bellere: Anuers*, 1592.
obl. 4°.   **A. 337. b.**

LASSO (Orlando di)

— La Fleur des Chansons d'Orlande de Lassus a Quatre, Cinq, Six et Huit Parties, *etc.* Superius. *De l'Imprimerie de Pierre Phalese: Anuers*, 1596. *obl.* 4°.
Imperfect; wanting pp. 45–49. **A. 337. c.**

— Magnum Opus Musicum Orlandi de Lasso ... Complectens Omnes Cantiones quas Motetas vulgo vocant, tam antea editas quam hactenus nondum publicatas II. III. IV. V. VI. VII. IIX. IX. X. XII. vocum. A Ferdinando ... & Rudolpho ... Authoris filijs ... collectum, *etc.* Cantus. (Altus.) (Tenor.) (Bassus.) (Quinta Vox.) (Sexta Vox.) 6 pt. *Ex typographia Nicolai Henrici: Monachii*, 1604. fol. **K. 4. k. 1.**

— [Another copy.] **Hirsch III. 886.**

— Benedictus et Osanna. [A. T. B., unaccompanied. From "Patrocinium Musices". Part II. No. 3.] ⟨Sancta Maria. [S. A. T. B., unaccompanied. Magnum Opus Musicum. No. 146.]⟩ [*Breitkopf und Haertel: Leipzig*, 1842.] 4°. [*Beilage zur Allgemeinen musikalischen Zeitung. Jahrg.* 44. *no.* 5.] **P. P. 1945.**

— Selectio modorum ad Orlando di Lasso compositorum, continens modos quatuor, quinque, sex, septem et octo vocibus concinendos. 8 Bd. [1860–67.] *See* Commer (F.) Musica Sacra, *etc.* Bd. V.–XII. [1839–74.] fol. **G. 6. a.**

— Selectio modorum ad Orlando di Lasso compositorum, continens modos quatuor, quinque, sex, septem et octo vocibus concinendos. Collegit et edi curavit Franciscus Commer. tom. [8]. *T. Trautwein (M. Bahn): Berlin*, [1867.] fol. *Musica Sacra. tom.* 12. **Hirsch M. 938.**

— Sieben Gesänge für gemischten Chor. (Deutsche Textunterlage von A. Sandberger.) [Parts.] *Breitkopf & Härtel: Leipzig*, [1894.] 8°. **F. 607. t. (2.)**

— O temps divers. Sçais tu dir' l'Ave. Quand un cordier. Qui bien se mire. Petite folle. En m'oyant. J'ay de vous voir. [Four-part songs. Score. Edited by H. Expert. With a portrait.] pp. 24. *A la cité des livres: Paris*, 1928. 8°. [*Florilège du concert vocal de la renaissance. no.* 2.] **Hirsch IV. 961.**

— Madrigale und Chansons zu 4–5 Stimmen. Herausgegeben von Heinrich Besseler. 3. unveränderte Auflage. *Ital. & Ger.* pp. 24. *Möseler Verlag: Wolfenbüttel*, [c. 1955.] 8°. [*Das Chorwerk. Hft.* 13.] **E. 1317.**

— Vier Motetten für fünf- und sechsstimmigen gemischten Chor. Four Motets ... Herausgegeben von ... Wolfgang Boetticher. 3. erweiterte Auflage. pp. 20. *Bärenreiter: Kassel, etc.*, [1963.] 8°. **E. 1439. r. (3.)**

— Two early choral Songs. For S. A. T. B. unaccompanied. English version by J. A. P. ... Edited by John A. Parkinson. 1. I know of a Maiden. ⟨Newe teutsche Lieder, 1583.⟩ ⟨2. The Spinning Jenny. Libro de villanelle, *etc.* 1581.⟩ [Staff and tonic sol-fa notation.] 2 no. *J. Curwen & Sons: London; G. Schirmer: New York*, [1970.] 8°. [*Choral Handbook.* 1575, 1576.] **E. 862.**

— Ten Madrigals for mixed Voices. Edited by Denis Arnold. pp. vi. 82. *Oxford University Press: London*, [1977.] 8°. **C. 123. q. (2.)**

— London Lassus Series ... Transcribed and edited by Clive Wearing. *Mapa mundi: London*, [1978, *etc.*] 4°. **G. 1497. e.**

— Adoramus te ... Selected and edited by D. F. Tovey. (Adoramus te.) [Magnum Opus Musicum. No. 43, 44.] *Augener: London*, [1929.] *s. sh.* 8°. **F. 1176. g. (15.)**

— Adoramus te Christe. [Magnum Opus Musicum. No. 43.] (S. S. C. Edited by G. F. Geaussent.) pp. 5. *Stainer & Bell: London*, [1908.] 8°. *Stainer & Bell's Ladies' Choir Library. Sacred, No.* 1. **F. 538. e. (49.)**

LASSO (Orlando di)

— [A reissue.] Adoramus te Christe. (S. S. C. Edited by G. F. Geaussent.) *Stainer & Bell: London*, [1909.] 8°. *Stainer & Bell's Church Choir Library, No.* 27. **F. 1137. b.**

— Adoramus te, Christe ... [Magnum Opus Musicum. No. 44.] Transcribed by Carlo Rossini. *In:* Palestrina (G. P. da) [Lamentations. Bk. 2.—Incipit oratio Jeremiae.] Patres nostri peccaverunt, *etc.* pp. 3, 4. [1931.] 8°. **F. 1175. q. (34.)**

— Adoramus te. (Thee we do adore.) [Magnum Opus Musicum. No. 44.] S. S. A. (T. T. B.) a cappella. English text by Harold Heiberg ... Edited by Castellazzi-Vené. *Lat. & Eng.* pp. 5. *G. Ricordi & Co.: New York*, [1960.] 8°. **F. 1175. ii. (10.)**

— Adoramus te, Christe. [S. S. A.] Magnum Opus Musicum. No. 44.] *In:* Palestrina (G. P. da) [Lamentations. Bk. 2.—Incipit oratio Jeremiae.] Patres nostri peccaverunt, *etc.* pp. 5–7. [1966.] 8°. **E. 1439. u. (21.)**

Adoramus te, Christe. [Magnum Opus Musicum. No. 66.]

— Adoramus te, Christe. [Motet. S. A. T. B.] pp. 3. *W. Sulzbach: Berlin*, [1905.] 8°. [*Auswahl hervorragender Meisterwerke des A Capella-Stils, etc.* Bd. 2. *no.* 8.] **F. 1767.**

— Adoramus te Christe. We adore Thee, O Christ ... Arranged to English words by S. Royle Shore. *Faith Press:* [*London,*] 1920. 8°. *Faith Press Motets. no.* 7. **D. 619. ss. (22.)**

— Adoramus te, Christe ... Edited by Henry Washington. pp. 4. *Church Music Association of the Society of St. Gregory: London*, [1957.] 4°. **F. 1176. aa. (8.)**

— Adoramus te Christe. Motet for Passiontide and feasts of the Holy Cross ... Edited by Henry Washington. pp. 4. *J. & W. Chester: London*, [1957.] 8°. **E. 460. d. (2.)**

— We do adore thee ... [S. A. T. B.] Edited, arranged and with English text by Walter Ehret. *Eng. & Lat.* pp. 6. *Southern Music Publishing Co.: New York; Peer Musikverlag: Hamburg*, [1966.] 8°. [*The Renaissance. no.* 5.] **F. 1744. zz.**

— Adoramus te, Christe. ⟨S. A. T. B. (Unacc.)⟩ Edited by Andrew Parker. pp. 3. *Oxford University Press: London*, [1973.] 8°. [*Oxford Anthems. A* 292.] **F. 1776.**

— [Adoramus te Christe. Magnum Opus Musicum. No. 177.] *See* Krol (B.) Lassus Variationen. ⟨Op. 33.⟩ Viola & Cembalo, *etc.* [1962.] 4°. **g. 762. r. (9.)**

— Agimus tibi gratias. [4 voices. From "Magnum Opus Musicum".] *See* Teschner (G. W.) Mehrstimmige Gesänge, *etc.* Bd. 1. No. 6. [1878, *etc.*] fol. **H. 1965. (1.)**

— Ah, could my Eyes behold thee. *See infra:* [Libro de Villanelle, Moresche, et altre Canzoni.—S'io ti videss'.]

— Alma nemes. *See infra:* [Il Primo Libro dove si contengono madrigali, *etc.* 1555.]

— Alma Venus. *See infra:* [Tiers livre des chansons à quatre, cincq et six parties.]

— Alme deus. *See infra:* [Il Primo Libro dove si contengono madrigali, *etc.* 1555.] Alma nemes.

— Aubade. *See infra:* [Les Meslanges.—Bonjour mon coeur.]

— Audite nova! *See infra:* [Sex Cantiones Latinae.]

— Der Bauer will tanzen. *See infra:* [Newe Teutsche Lieder mit vier Stimmen.—Baur was tregst im Sacke.]

— Blessed art thou, O Lord. *See infra:* [Sacrae Cantiones Quatuor Vocum. 1585.—Bendictus es, Domine.]

— Bonjour, mon cœur. *See infra:* [Les Meslanges.]

LASSO (ORLANDO DI)

— Busstränen des heiligen Petrus. *See* infra: [Lagrime di S. Pietro.]

— Cantica Sacra, recens numeris et modulis musicis ornata, nec ullibi antea typis euulgata. Sex et Octo Vocibus, *etc.* Discantus. (Altus.) (Tenor.) (Bassus.) (Quinta Vox.) (Sexta Vox.) 6 pt. *Adamus Berg: Monachii*, 1585. *obl.* 4°.
A. 334. h.

Cantiones Aliquot Quinque Vocum

— Cantiones Aliquot Quinque Vocum, tum Viua Voce, tum omnis generis instrumentis cantatu commodissimæ. Iam primùm in lucem ... editæ, *etc.* Discantus. (Altus.) (Tenor.) (Bassus.) (Quinta Vox.) 5 pt. *Adamus Berg: Monâci*, 1569. *obl.* 4°.
A. 334.

— [Gratia sola Dei.] Unto Thee, O Lord. Motet for five voices. Edited, and the English words adapted by Sir F. Bridge, *etc. Bosworth & Co.: London, etc.*, (1912.) 8°.
F. 274. m. (14.)

— [Quem ad modum.] Like as the Hart ... Motet for six voices, Canon ad septimam. Edited, and the English words adapted by Sir F. Bridge, *etc. Bosworth & Co.: London, etc.*, (1911.) 8°.
F. 274. m. (12.)

— [Quem vidistis pastores.] Whom saw ye, O Shepherds ... Motet for five voices. Edited, and the English words adapted by Sir F. Bridge, *etc. Bosworth & Co.: London, etc.*, (1911.) 8°.
F. 274. m. (15.)

— Quem vidistis, pastores? Motet for five voices ... Edited by H. B. Collins. *Dinham, Blyth & Co.: London*, [1915.] 4°.
G. 30. (11.)

— [Res neque ab infernis.] Lord, how are they increased. Motet for five voices. Edited, and the English words adapted by Sir F. Bridge, *etc. Bosworth & Co.: London, etc.*, (1912.) 8°.
F. 274. m. (13.)

Cantiones Aliquot Quinque Vocum.—Resonet in laudibus

— Let Zion resound with Praise ... Motet for Christmas. Edited, and the English words adapted by Sir F. Bridge, *etc. Bosworth & Co.: London, etc.*, (1911.) 8°.
F. 274. m. (11.)

— A Christmas Motet. Selected and edited by Donald F. Tovey, *etc.* [S. S. A.] *In:* Monthly Musical Record. vol. 60. p. 368. 1930. 4°.
P. P. 1945. hd.

— Hodie apparuit. [Motet for T. T. B.] *Calcografia Musica Sacra: Milano*, 1890. 8°.
F. 552. (18.)

— Hodie apparuit ... (Dies est laetitiae. XVI Century.) Arranged by C. Rossini. *J. Fischer & Bro.: New York, Birmingham*, 1931. 8°.
F. 1175. q. (32.)

— [Hodie apparuit.] On this Day a Child is born. (Hodie natus est.) (TTB.) Edited and translated by Bernarr Rainbow. *Eng. & Lat.* pp. 4. *Stainer & Bell: London*, [1955.] 8°.
[*Church Choir Library. no.* 578.]
F. 1137. b.

— Hodie apparuit. On this Day it hath appeared. Dyma'r dydd y gwawriodd hyn. Motet for S. S. A. or T. T. B. The translations by ... W. S. Gwynn Williams ... Ed. by W. S. Gwynn Williams. [Staff and tonic sol-fa notation.] *Lat., Eng. & Welsh.* pp. 3. *Gwynn Publishing Co.: Llangollen*, [1960.] 8°.
E. 1439. c. (23.)

— Hodie apparuit. (On this Day the Christ appears.) For three-part chorus of women's or men's voices a cappella. Motet. English text by M. K. ... Edited by Maynard Klein. *Lat. & Eng.* pp. 6. *G. Schirmer: New York*, [1971.] 8°.
E. 1439. ee. (3.)

— Sex Cantiones Latinæ Quatuor, adiuncto Dialogo Octo Vocum. Sechs Teutsche Lieder mit vier, sampt einem Dialogo mit 8. stimmen. Six chansons Francoises nouuelles a quatre voix, auecq vn Dialogue a huict. Sei Madrigali nuoui a

LASSO (ORLANDO DI)

quatro, con vn Dialogo a otto voci. Summa diligentia compositæ ... & nunc primum in lucem æditæ, *etc.* Tenor. *Adamus Berg: Monachij*, 1573. *obl.* 4°.
A. 334. c.

— [Sex Cantiones Latinae.] "Audite nova!" (The Big fat Goose.) For mixed chorus a cappella. English version by Sigmund Spaeth ... Arr. for concert use by Wilhelm Widmann. *Eng. & Ger.* pp. 7. *Chappell & Co.: London*, [1960.] 8°.
F. 1744. ee. (8.)

— Liber Primus. Cantiones Sacræ Magnificat vocant v. et vi. Vocum ... His accesserunt quatuor ab ... Ferdinando de Lasso compositæ, jam primùm in lucem editæ. Discantus. (Altus.) (Tenor.) (Bassus.) (Quinta Vox.) (Sexta Vox.) 6 pt. *Nicolaus Henricus: Monachii*, 1602. fol.
K. 2. i. 14.

— [Liber Primus. Cantiones Sacræ Magnificat vocant.] Magnificant Praeter rerum seriem. Upon the motet by Josquin. For 6 voices. Transcribed and edited by Bruno Turner. ⟨Source: Munich, Bayerische Staatsbibliothek, Mus. Ms. 76, ff. 113-134.⟩ pp. 15. *Mapa mundi: London*, [1978.]. 4°.
[*Franco-Flemish Church Music. no.* 2.]
G. 1497. a

— [Chansons. For collections including works by other composers:] *See* CHANSONS. [2, 4.]

— [Le Premier livre de chansons à quatre parties.] Quand mon mari.—Kommt mein Gespons. Vierstimmiges Lied ... Deutsch von A. Sandberger. [1897.] *See* SQUIRE (W. B.) Ausgewählte Madrigale, *etc.* No. 9. [a.] [1895, *etc.*] 8°.
F. 1604.

— [Le Premier livre de chansons à quatre parties.—Quand mon mari.] When my old Man ... Chanson for S. A. T. B. (unaccompanied) ... Edited, with English words, by John A. Parkinson. *Eng. & Fr.* pp. 6. *Novello & Co.: London*, [1958.] 8°.
[*Musical Times. no.* 1384.]
P. P. 1945. aa.

— [Le Premier livre de chansons à quatre parties.—Quand mon mari.] When my rich Husband is at Home ... For S. A. T. B. mixed chorus. English text by W. E. ... Edited by Walter Ehret. *Eng. & Fr.* pp. 8. *Walton Music Corporation: North Hollywood*, [1963.] 8°.
Part of the "Walton historical choral Series".
F. 1744. nn. (10.)

— Tiers Livre des Chansons a quatre cincq et six parties ... de nouveau plus correctement que cy deuant imprimées & emendèes, conuenables tant aux instrumens comme à la voix. Superius. *Pierre Phalese: Lovain*, 1562. *obl.* 4°.
A. 337. a.

— [Tiers livre des chansons à quatre, cincq et six parties.] Alma Venus or Christe patris verbum. For unaccompanied mixed voices (SATTB). Edited by Laszlo Heltay. With original secular and sacred texts. pp. 14. *Oxford University Press: London*, [1964.] 8°.
E. 1439. j. (29.)

— [Tiers livre des chansons a quatre, cincq et six parties.— Susanne ung iour.] *See* COELHO (M. R.) [Flores de musica.] 4 Susanas oder Tentos über das Chanson "Suzanne un jour," für Tasteninstrumente oder Harfe ... Bearbeitet und herausgegeben von M. S. Kastner. [1955.] 4°.
g. 1128. x. (4.)

— Dixhuictieme liure de chansons à quatre & cinq parties, par Orlande de Lassus. Imprimé en quatre volumes. ⟨Superius.—Tenor.—Bassus.⟩ [Parts.] *Par Adrian le Roy, & Robert Ballard: Paris*, 1567. *obl.* 8°.
Imperfect; wanting the contratenor part.
K. 11. e. 3. (18.)

— Dixhuictieme liure de chansons à quatre & cinq parties, d'Orlande de Lassus. Imprimé en quatre volumes. ⟨Tenor.⟩ [Parts.] *Par Adrian le Roy & Robert Ballard: Paris*, 1570. *obl.* 8°.
Imperfect; wanting ff. 5, 6, *and the superius, contratenor and bassus parts.*
K. 2. b. 4. (17.)

— Dixhuictieme liure de chansons, à quatre & cinq parties, d'Orlande de Lassus. Imprimé en quatre volumes. ⟨Contra.⟩

LASSO (ORLANDO DI)

[Parts.] *Par Adrian le Roy & Robert Ballard: Paris*, 1573. *obl.*
8°.
Imperfect; wanting the superius, tenor and bassus parts.
K. 2. h. 9. (4.)

— Liure de Chansons Nouuelles a Cinc Parties, auec Deux
Dialogues: à Huict, *etc.* Superius. (Contra.) (Tenor.) (Bassus.)
(Quinta Pars.) 5 pt. *Adrian le Roy & Robert Ballard: Paris*,
1571. *obl.* 4°. **A. 337. d. (2.)**

— [Another copy. Bassus.]
Imperfect; wanting the titlepage. **A. 336. b. (8.)**

— Chansons Nouuelles à Cinc Parties, auec Deux Dialogues: a
Huict, *etc.* Superius. (Contratenor.) (Tenor.) (Bassus.) 4 pt.
Adrian le Roy, & Robert Ballard: Paris, 1576. *obl.* 4°.
K. 5. a. 3. (2.)

— Liure de Chansons à Cinc Parties: auec Deux Dialogues: a
Huit. Superius. *Adrian le Roy, & Robert Ballard: Paris*, 1581.
obl. 4°. **A. 337. i.**

— Christ hath arisen. *See* infra: [Newe Teutsche Lieder mit vier
Stimmen.—Christ ist erstanden.]

— [Christe dei soboles.] Lord Christ, Son of God ... For
four-part chorus of mixed voices a cappella. [Magnum Opus
Musicum. No. 139.] Translated by Erminie Huntress ...
Edited by Roy Harris. *Eng. & Lat.* pp. 8. *G. Schirmer: New
York*, [1954.] 8°. **F. 1176. y. (18.)**

— Christe patris verbum. *See* supra: [Tiers livre des chansons à
quatre, cincq et six parties.] Alma Venus.

— A Christmas Motet. *See* supra: [Cantiones Aliquot Quinque
Vocum.—Resonet in laudibus.]

— Christus, resurgens ex mortuis, jam non moritur. *See* infra:
[Sacrae Cantiones Quinque Vocum. 1582.]

— Cognovi Domine. *See* infra: [Modulorum ... modulatorum
secundum volumen. 1565.]

— Cor meum. *See* infra: [Psalmi Davidis pœnitentiales. No. 3.]

— Custodi me. *See* infra: [Sacrae Cantiones Quatuor Vocum.
1585.]

— Day after Day they all say "Sing". *See* infra: [Libro de
Villanelle, Moresche, et altre Canzoni.—Tutto lo di.]

— De ore prudentis procedit mel. *See* infra: [Sacrae Cantiones
... Quinque et Sex Vocum. Liber secundus.]

— Dextera Domini. *See* infra: [Sacrae Cantiones Quatuor
Vocum. 1585.]

— Domine, Domine, in auxilium meum respice. *See* infra:
[Sacrae Cantiones Quatuor Vocum. 1585.]

— Domine exaudi orationem meam. *See* infra: [Sacrae
Cantiones Quatuor Vocum. 1585.]

— L'Eccho. *See* infra: [Libro de Villanelle, Moresche, et altre
Canzoni.—O la, o che buon êco.]

— Echo Song. *See* infra: [Libro de Villanelle, Moresche, et altre
Canzoni.—O la, o che buon êco.]

— Eripe me. [Motet for 3 voices.] *See* PALESTRINA (G. P. da)
[Hymni Totius Anni.] Abor decora, *etc.* 1931. 8°.
F. 1175. q. (33.)

— Expectans expectavi Dominum. *See* infra: [Sacrae Cantiones
Quatuor Vocum. 1585.]

— Factus est Dominus firmamentum meum. *See* infra: [Sacrae
Cantiones Quatuor Vocum. 1585.]

— Farmer, what's that in your Bag? *See* infra: [Newe Teutsche
Lieder mit vier Stimmen.—Baur was tregst im Sacke.]

LASSO (ORLANDO DI)

— Orlandi Lassi ... Fasciculi Aliquot Sacrarum Cantionum cum
quatuor, quinque, sex & octo vocibus, antea quidem
separatim excusi, nunc vero auctoris consensu in unum
corpus reducti. Altus. (Tenor.) (Bassus.) (Quinta Vox.) (Sexta
Vox.) 5 pt. *In Officina Gerlachiana: Noribergae*, 1582. *obl.* 4°.
Wanting the last leaves of the Altus and Tenor parts.
A. 334. e.

— [Orlandi Lassi ... Fasciculi Aliquot Sacrarum Cantionum
cum quatuor, quinque, sex & octo vocibus, *etc.* Bassus.] [*In
Officina Gerlachiana: Noribergae*, 1589.] *obl.* 4°.
Imperfect; wanting the titlepage. **A. 334. f.**

— Fasciculus Aliquot Cantionum Sacrarum, Quinque Vocum.
1572. *See* infra: [Moduli Quinis Vocibus.]

— La Fleur des Chansons. *See* supra: [*Smaller Collections.*]

— Frühlingsmadrigal. *See* infra: [Hor che la nuova e vaga
primavera.]

— Fugger Motetten. *See* infra: [Sacrae Cantiones Quatuor
Vocum. 1585.]

— Gustate et videte. *See* infra: [Il primo libro de mottetti.]

— Hear my Prayer, O Lord. *See* infra: [Sacrae Lectiones Novem
ex Propheta Job. No. 3, Pt. 2. Nonne sicut lac.]

— Hodie apparuit. *See* supra: [Cantiones Aliquot Quinque
Vocum.—Resonet in laudibus.]

— Homo natus de muliere. *See* infra: [Sacrae Lectiones Novem
ex Propheta Job. No. 5, Pt. 1.]

— [Hor che la nuova e vaga primavera.] Frühlingsmadrigal ...
für zehn Stimmen in zwei Chören a cappella (1575). Ins
Deutsche übertragen und herausgegeben von Paul Winter.
Ital. & Ger. pp. 16. *C. F. Peters: Frankfurt, etc.*, [1960.] 8°.
Part of "Canticum".SE. 1563. a. (6.)

— I know a young Maiden. *See* infra: [Newe Teutsche Lieder
mit vier Stimmen.—Ich waiss mir ein Meidlein.]

— I know of a Maiden. *See* supra: [*Smaller Collections.*] Two
early choral Songs. 1.

— Ich waiss mir ein Meidlein. *See* infra: [Newe Teutsche Lieder
mit vier Stimmen.]

— Illumina oculos meos. [Magnum Opus Musicum. No. 63.]
Offertory of 4th Sunday after Pentecost. (Edited by H. B.
Collins.) [*London*, 1921.] 8°.
Lithographed. **F. 995. b. (10.)**

— In hora ultima. [Magnum Opus Musicum. No. 414.] For
Six-part Chorus of Mixed Voices ... English version by
G. Reese ... Edited by J. F. Williamson. *G. Schirmer: New
York*, 1932. 8°. **E. 335. f. (51.)**

— In monte Oliveti. *See* infra: [Selectissimae Cantiones ... Sex
& pluribus vocibus. 1568.]

— Io ti voria. *See* infra: [Libro de Villanelle, Moresche, et altre
Canzoni.]

— Jauchzet Gott alle Lande. (Psalm 100, 1–3.) *See* infra: [Sacrae
Cantiones Quatuor Vocum. 1585.—Jubilate Deo omnis terra.]

— Je l'ayme bien. *See* infra: [Il Primo Libro dove si contengono
madrigali, *etc.* 1555.]

— je l'ayme bien. *See* also infra: [Les Meslanges.]

— Un jour vis un foulon qui foulait. *See* infra: [Les Meslanges.]

— Jubilate Deo. *See* infra: [Sacrae Cantiones Quatuor Vocum.
1585.]

— Justorum animae. *See* infra: [Sacrae Cantiones Quinque
Vocum. 1582.]

LASSO (ORLANDO DI)

— [Lagrime di S. Pietro.] Busstränen des heiligen Petrus zu 7 Stimmen ... herausgegeben von Hans Joachim Therstappen. 2. ⟨3.⟩ unveränderte Auflage. *Ital. & Ger.* 3 Hft. *Moseler Verlag: Wolfenbüttel,* [c. 1955.] 8°. [*Das Chorwerk. Hft.* 34, 37, 41.] **E. 1317.**

— [Lamentations.] Hieremiae Prophetae Lamentationes, et aliæ Piæ Cantiones: nunquam antehac visae. Ab ipso autore ... recens ... compositæ, & in lucem ... editæ. Quinque Vocum. Discantus. (Altus.) (Bassus.) (Quinta Vox.) 4 pt. *Adamus Berg: Monachii,* 1585. *obl.* 4°. **A. 332.**

— [Lamentations.] Ieremiae Prophetæ ... Lamentationes, una cum Passione Domini Dominicæ Palmarum, quinque vocum, *etc.* Tenor. *Apud Adrianum le Roy, & Robertum Ballard: Lutetiæ Parisiorum,* 1586. 4°. *Imperfect; containing* 11 *leaves only, much mutilated.* **K. 5. b. 18. (8.)**

— Las! voulez-vous q'une personne chante. *See* infra: [Les Meslanges.]

— Lauda anima mea Dominum. *See* infra: [Patrocinium Musices. Pars 1.]

— Laudate Dominum. *See* infra: [Moduli sex, septem et duodecim vocum.]

— Laudent deum cithara. [Motet.] [*Munich, c.* 1590.] *s. sh.* fol. *Part of a pictorial engraving by J. Sadeler after Peter Candido.* **K. 9. b. 13.**

— Laughing, singing all the Day long. *See* infra: [Les Meslanges.—Sauter, danser.]

— Lectiones Sacræ Nouem, ex Libris Hiob excerptæ, Musicis Numeris iam recens compositæ, nec non aliæ nonnullæ piæ Cantiones, omnibus qui tam viuæ vocis quàm Instrumentorum Musicorum cantu non imperitè vtuntur, apprimè accommodæ. Quatuor Vocum, *etc.* Discantus. (Altus.) (Bassus.) 3 pt. *Adamus Berg: Monachij,* 1582. *obl.* 4°. **A. 331. a.**

— [Lectiones Sacrae Novem. —Diligis Proximum Tuum.] Quoniam qui talia agunt. Seeing that such Things as these they do. Cans y rhai a wnêl y fath bethau. Mottetto a 2 voci pari ... Edited by W. S. Gwynn Williams. Gal. v. 21. The English adaptation by W. S. Gwynn Williams. Y cyfaddasiad cymraeg gan Robert Davies ... Trascr. L. Castellazzi. *Lat., Eng. & Welsh.* pp. 3. *Gwynn Publishing Co.: Llangollen,* [1950.] 8°. **F. 231. mm. (46.)**

— Let us be gay. *See* infra: [Les Meslanges.—Soyons joyeux.]

— Let us flee this wild Desire. *See* infra: [Les Meslanges.— Fuyons tous d'amour le jeu.]

— Let Zion resound with Praise. *See* supra: [Cantiones Aliquot Quinque Vocum.—Resonet in laudibus.]

— Levavi oculos meos. *See* infra: [Sacrae Cantiones Sex et Octo Vocum.— Liber quartus.]

— Like as the Hart. *See* supra: [Cantiones Aliquot Quinque Vocum.—Quem ad modum.]

— Litaniæ B. M. Virginis Orlandi Lassi quatuor voc. ⟨Cantus.—Cantus secundus.—Altus.—Bassus.⟩ *In:* PALESTRINA (G. P. da) Litaniæ deiparæ Virginis ... Cum quatuor vocibus. 1600. *obl.* 4°. **K. 1. d. 26.**

— Lord Christ, Son of God. *See* supra: [Christe dei soboles.]

— Lord, how are they increased. *See* supra: [Cantiones Aliquot Quinque Vocum.—Res neque ab infernis.]

LASSO (ORLANDO DI)

Madrigals

— [Il Primo Libro dove si contengono madrigali, *etc.* 1555.] Alma nemes or Alme deus. For unaccompanied mixed voices (SATB). Edited by Laszlo Heltay. With original secular and sacred texts. pp. 7. *Oxford University Press: London,* [1964.] 8°. **E. 1439. j. (30.)**

— [Il Primo Libro dove si contengono madrigali, *etc.* 1555.] Je l'ayme bien. Chanson. Deutsche Textunterlage von A. Sandberger. [Parts.] *Breitkopf & Härtel: Leipzig,* [1896.] 8°. **F. 321. j. (25.)**

— Di Orlando di Lassus il Primo Libro di Madrigali a Quatro uoci Nouamente per Antonio Gardano Ristampati, *etc.* Canto. (Alto.) (Tenore.) (Basso.) 4 pt. *Apresso di Antonio Gardano: Venetia,* 1565. *obl.* 4°. *A different work from the book of* 1555. **A. 338. f.**

— Di Orlando di Lassus Il Primo Libro de Madrigali a Quatro Voci Nouamente ... ristampati. Canto. (Alto.) (Tenore.) (Basso.) 4 pt. *Appresso Giacomo Vincenci & Ricciardo Amadino Compagni: Venetia,* 1584. *obl.* 4°. **A. 338. e.**

— Di Orlando di Lassus il Primo Libro di Madrigali a Quattro Voci, Nouamente ... Ristampati. Alto. (Basso.) 2 pt. *Appresso Angelo Gardano: Venetia,* 1592. *obl.* 4°. **A. 338. d.**

— Di Orlando di Lassus il Primo Libro di Madrigali a cinque Voci, nouamente per Antonio Gardano ristampato. Cantus. (Altus.) (Tenor.) (Bassus.) (Quintus.) 5 pt. *Appresso di Antonio Gardano: Venetia,* 1557. *obl.* 4°. **A. 338.**

— Di Orlando di Lassus il Secondo Libro di Madrigali a cinque Voci, Nouamente per Antonio Gardano stampato. Canto. (Alto.) (Tenore.) (Basso.) (Quinto.) 5 pt. *Appresso di Antonio Gardano: Venetia,* 1559. *obl.* 4°. *This work also contains madrigals by A. Barre, Vidue and P. Animuccia.* **A. 338. a.**

— Di Orlando di Lassus il Secondo Libro de Madrigalli a Cinque Voci, Nouamente ristampati. Quinto. *Appresso Girolamo Scotto: Vinegia,* 1573. 4°. **D. 20. b.**

— Di Orlando Lasso ... Libro quarto de Madrigali a Cinque Voci, da lui Nouamente in Germania composti, *etc.* ⟨Canto.—Alto.—Tenore.—Basso.—Quinto.⟩ [Parts.] 5 pt. *Appresso di Antonio Gardano: Venetia,* 1567. *obl.* 4°. *This work contains compositions by Lasso, G. Lochemburgo, G. D. di Nola, F. Rosselli and C. Porta.* **Hirsch III. 885.**

— Di Orlado [*sic*] Lasso ... Il Quarto Libro de Madrigali à Cinque Voci, Nouamente ... ristampati. Canto. (Alto.) (Tenore.) (Basso.) (Quinto.) 5 pt. *Appresso Angelo Gardano: Venetia,* 1593. *obl.* 4°. **A. 338. b.**

— Madrigali nouamente composti a cinque uoci, *etc.* Cantus. (Altus.) (Tenor.) (Bassus.) (Quinta Vox.) 5 pt. *In officina typographica Catharinæ Gerlachiæ: Noribergæ,* 1585. *obl.* 4°. *The Tenor is imperfect, wanting sheet A.* **A. 338. g.**

— Madrigali: a Quattro, Cinque et Sei Voci, novamente composti, *etc.* Tenor. *In officina typographica Catharinæ Gerlachiæ: Noribergae,* 1587. *obl.* 4°. **A. 338. c.**

Magnificat Octo Tonorum, Sex, Quinque et Quatuor Vocum

— Magnificat Octo Tonorum, Sex, Quinque, et Quatuor Vocum, nunc primum excusa, *etc.* Altus. (Tenor.) (Bassus.) (Vagans.) 4 pt. *Apud Theodoricum Gerlatzenum, in officina Ioannis Montani piæ memoriæ: Noribergæ,* 1567. *obl.* 4°. **A. 339.**

— Magnificat Octo Tonorum, Sex, Quinque, et Quatuor Vocum, nunc primum excusa, *etc.* Tenor. *In officina Theodorici Gerlazeni: Noribergæ,* 1573. *obl.* 4°. *With* 28 *pages of manuscript music (Magnificats) at the end of the volume.* **A. 339. b.**

LASSO (ORLANDO DI)

— Magnificat Octo Tonorum, Sex, Quinque et Quatuor Vocum, nunc primum excusa ... Discantus. (Bassus.) 2 pt. *In officina typographica Catharinæ Gerlachiæ & Hæredum Iohannis Montani: Noribergæ,* 1580. obl. 4°.
The Discantus is described as "Cantus" inside the part.
A. 339. c. (2.)

— Magnificat. Tone 1. [For four voices.] (Edited by H. B. Collins.) [*London,* 1916.] 8°. **F. 995. (28.)**

— Magnificat Primi Toni for Four Voices ... Edited by H. B. Collins. *J. & W. Chester: London,* 1938. 8°.
[*Latin Church Music of the Polyphonic Schools. No.* 45.]
F. 995. c.

— Magnificat Quarti Toni for Four Voices ... Edited by H. B. Collins. *J. & W. Chester: London,* 1939. 8°.
[*Latin Church Music of the Polyphonic Schools. No.* 50.]
F. 995. c.

— Magnificat Septimi Toni for Four Voices ... Edited by H. B. Collins. *J. & W. Chester: London,* 1939. 8°.
[*Latin Church Music of the Polyphonic Schools. No.* 51.]
F. 995. c.

— Magnificat Octavi Toni for Four Voices ... Edited by H. B. Collins. *J. & W. Chester: London,* 1938. 8°.
[*Latin Church Music of the Polyphonic Schools. No.* 46.]
F. 995. c.

— Magnificat sex vocum—Primi Toni— ... ex veteri manuscripto in partitionem dispositum curis Henrici de St. Julien. *Ex officina Guilelmi Hasper: Carlsruhe,* [1885?] fol.
H. 879. i. (8.)

— Magnificat septimi toni. For mixed voices [S. S. A. A. T. T. B.] and instruments. Edited by Denis Stevens. [Score.] pp. 16. *Oxford University Press: London,* [1978.] 8°.
E. 1857. a. (12.)

— Magnificat Praeter rerum seriem. *See* supra: [... Cantiones Sacræ Magnificat vocant.]

— Magnificat sex vocum secundi Toni. *See* infra: [Patrocinium Musices. 1587.]

— Magnum Opus Musicum. *See* supra: [*Smaller Collections.*]

— Manus tuas Domine. Motet à 4 voix. Mis en partition ... par E. Delangle, *etc.* [1857.] *See* NIEDERMEYER (L.) La Maîtrise, *etc.* 1ʳᵉ Année. No. 9. [1857–61.] fol.
H. 1237.

Masses.—Collections

— [Quinque missae, *etc.* 1570.] Mass "Quinti Toni," [on Sermisy's chanson "Pilons, pilons lorge,"] *etc. See* TERRY (R. R.) Downside Masses, *etc.* No. 6. 1905. 8°. **F. 1140. a.**

Masses.—Missae variis concentibus ornatae, 1577.—Missa Jäger

— Missa Quatuor Vocum ad Imitationem Moduli, Iager, *etc. Ex Officina Christophori Ballard: Parisiis,* 1687. fol.
K. 10. b. 1. (15.)

— Missa Brevis quatuor vocum inaequalium. *Calcografia Musica Sacra: Milano,* [1895?] 8°. **F. 552. (17.)**

— Missa "Octavi Toni" für 4-stimmigen gemischten Chor ... für den praktischen Gebrauch bearbeitet von C. Thiel. Partitur. *W. Sulzbach: Berlin,* (1903.) 8°. **F. 1175. i. (2.)**

— Agnus Dei à cinq voix. [1859.] *See* NIEDERMEYER (L.) La Maîtrise, *etc.* 2ᵉ Année. No. 12. [1857–61.] fol. **H. 1237.**

— Credo in unum Deum ... à quatre voix. [1858.] *See* NIEDERMEYER (L.) La Maîtrise, *etc.* 2ᵉ Année. No. 9. [1857–61.] fol. **H. 1237.**

LASSO (ORLANDO DI)

— Gloria à quatre voix, *etc.* [1858.] *See* NIEDERMEYER (L.) La Maîtrise, *etc.* 2ᵉ Année. No. 6. [1857–61.] fol. **H. 1237.**

— Kyrie à quatre voix, *etc.* [1858.] *See* NIEDERMEYER (L.) La Maîtrise, *etc.* 2ᵉ Année. No. 5. [1857–61.] fol. **H. 1237.**

— Sanctus, Hosanna et Benedictus ... à quatre voix. [1859.] *See* NIEDERMEYER (L.) La Maîtrise, *etc.* 2ᵉ Année. No. 10. [1857–61.] fol. **H. 1237.**

Masses.—Collections, continued

— [Missae variis concentibus ornatae, 1577.] Missa. "Octavi Toni." Missa ad imitat. Moduli: "Puisque j'ay perdu". Quatuor vocum. *See* PROSKE (C.) Musica divina. Annus 1. Tom. 1. 1853, *etc.* 4°. **F. 357.**

— [Missae variis concentibus ornatae, 1577.] Missa VIII. Toni "Puisque j'ay perdu" quatuor vocum ... Usui practico magis accomodavit L. Mitterer. 1889. *See* HABERL (F. X.) Repertorium Musicæ Sacræ, *etc.* Tom. I. Fasc. VII. 1886, *etc.* 8°. **F. 278.**

— [Missae variis concentibus ornatae, 1577.] Missa VIII. Toni. Puisque j'ay perdu. Transposed and edited by A. J. Silver. *J. Fischer & Bro.: New York, Birmingham,* 1929. 8°.
F. 1176. g. (16.)

— [Liber missarum quatuor et quinque vocum, 1581.] Missa Beschaffens Glück (Il me suffit), 1581, für 4 Stimmen a cappella. Herausgegeben von P. Wilhelm Lueger. pp. 20. *Verlag Friedrich Pustet: Regensburg,* 1953. 8°.
[*Musica divina. Hft.* 9.] **F. 1905.**

— Missæ Orlandi Lassi cum Quinque, et Sex Vocibus canende, nuperrime impresse, *etc.* Cantus. (Altus.) (Tenor.) (Bassus.) (Quintus.) 5 pt. *Apud Angelum Gardanum: Venetijs,* 1591. 4°.
Wanting the sextus part. **R. M. 15. e. 1. (6.)**

— Missæ Orlandi Lassi cum Quinque et Sex Vocibus canende, nuperrime impresse, *etc.* Sextus. *Apud Angelum Gardanum: Venetijs,* 1591. 4°. **D. 20. a.**

— Orlandi de Lasso ... Missae Posthumae, Ritu Veteri Romano Catholico, in Modos qua Senos, qua Octonos temperatæ. Hactenus ineditæ; et omnium, quas edidit, lectissimæ: vulgatæ demum affectu, studio sumtu superstitis filij Rudolphi di Lasso, *etc. Ex typographico musico Nicolai Henrici: Monaci,* 1610. fol. **K. 9. b. 6.**

Masses.—Single masses

— Missa. Ad Imitationem Moduli Beatus qui intelligit ... cum sex vocibus. *Apud Adrianum le Roy, & Robertum Ballard: Lutetiae,* 1587. fol. **K. 9. b. 9. (4.)**

— Missa ad Imitationem Moduli Credidi. *See* infra: [Patrocinium Musices. Pars 2.]

— Missa. Ad Imitationem Moduli Dixit Joseph ... cum sex vocibus. *Ex Officina Petri Ballard: Lutetiæ,* 1607. fol.
K. 9. b. 9. (1.)

— Missa ... (Il me suffit). *See* supra: [Liber missarum quatuor et quinque vocum, 1581.]

— Missa ad Imitationem Moduli In die tribulationis. *See* infra: [Patrocinium Musices. 1589.]

— Missa. Sex Vocum. Ad Imitationem Moduli In Te Domine speraui, *etc. Ex Officina Petri Ballard: Parisiis,* 1613. fol.
K. 9. b. 9. (2.)

— Missa ... ad Imitationem Moduli, Iager [Jäger]. *See* supra: [Missae variis concentibus ornatae, 1577.]

— Missa. Ad Imitationem Moduli Locutus sum ... Cum sex vocibus. *Apud Adrianum le Roy, & Robertum Ballard: Lutetiae,* 1587. fol. **K. 9. b. 9. (3.)**

LASSO (Orlando di)

— Messe, "Or sus à coup," für vier Singstimmen ... nach der heutigen Schreibweise in Partitur gesetzt und mit einer ... Einleitung versehen von J. G. Ferrenberg ... Nebst Einlagen gleizeitiger Meister.—Asola, Pange lingua; Vecchi, Benedictus Dominus Deus Israel; Arcadelt, Ave Maria.
J. M. Heberle: Cöln, Bonn und Brüssel, 1851. *obl.* fol.
D. 20. d.

— Missa super Osculetur me. Für zwei vierstimmige gemischte Chöre. For two four-part mixed choirs. Herausgegeben von ... Siegfried Hermelink. pp. 40. *Bärenreiter: Kassel, etc.*, [1969.] 8°.
Part of "Chor-Archiv". **F. 1183. o. (2.)**

— Missa ... "Puisque j'ay perdu". *See* supra: [Missae variis concentibus ornatae, 1577.]

— Missa "Qual donna". *See* infra: [Patrocinium Musices. 1589.]

— Missa super Scarco di doglia. *See* infra: [Patrocinium musices. Pars 2.]

— Missa ... ad Imitationem Moduli Sydus [Sidus] ex claro. *See* infra: [Patrocinium Musices. Pars 2.]

— Missa super Standomi vn giorno. *See* Baccusi (I.) Hippolyti Baccusii Missarum ... Liber Primus ... Missa (super) Standomi vn giorno (di Orlando). 1570. 4°. **D. 30.**

— Matona, lovely Maiden. *See* infra: [Libro de Villanelle, Moresche, et altre Canzoni.—Matona, mia cara.]

— Matona, mia cara. *See* infra: [Libro de Villanelle, Moresche, et altre Canzoni.]

Les Meslanges

— Mellange d'Orlande de Lassus, contenant plusieurs Chansons, tant en Vers Latins qu'en Ryme Francoyse. A Quatre, Cinq, Six, Huit, Dix Parties. Superius. (Contra.) (Tenor.) (Bassus.) (Quinta et Sexta Pars.) 5 pt. *Adrian le Roy & Robert Ballard: Paris*, 1570. *obl.* 4°. **A. 337. d. (1.)**

— [Another copy. Bassus.]
Wanting the titlepage, which has been supplied in manuscript.
A. 336. b. (7.)

— Mellange d'Orlande de Lassus. Contenant plusieurs chansons, à Quatre parties. Desquelles la lettre profane à esté changée en spirituelle. Contratenor. *P. Haultin: La Rochelle*, 1575. *obl.* 4°. **A. 337. e.**

— Les Meslanges d'Orlande de Lassus. Contenantz plusieurs Chansons a IIII, V, VI, VIII, X, Parties: reueuz par luy, et augmentez. Superius. (Contra.) (Tenor.) (Bassus.) 4 pt. *Adrian le Roy, & Robert Ballard: Paris*, 1576. *obl.* 4°. **K. 5. a. 3. (1.)**

— Melsanges de la Musique d'Orlande de Lassus. A 4. 5. 6. & 10 parties. Superius. *Adrian le Roy & Robert Ballard: Paris*, 1586. *obl.* 4°. **A. 337. j.**

— Les Meslanges. Premier Fascicule. 1894. *See* Expert (H.) Les Maîtres Musiciens de la Renaissance française, *etc.* Livr. I. 1894, *etc.* 8°. **G. 59.**

— Ten Chansons. For four voices or instruments SATB. ([Edited by] Bernard Thomas.) pp. 24. *London Pro Musica Edition: [London*, 1977.] 4°.
[Anthologies of Renaissance Music. vol. 1.] **g. 1784. k.**

— Nine chansons. For four voices or instruments ATTB. ([Edited by] Bernard Thomas.) [Score.] pp. 20. *London Pro Musica Edition: London*, [1979.] 4°.
[Anthologies of Renaissance Music. vol. 2.] **g. 1784. k.**

LASSO (Orlando di)

— Bonjour, mon cœur.—Good-day Sweetheart.— Chanson [for S. A. T. B.], words by Ronsard.—English translation by A. C. Curtis.— ... Edited by L. Benson. [1908.] *See* Oriana. The Oriana, *etc.* No. 49. [1905, *etc.*] 8°. **F. 1685.**

— [Bonjour mon coeur.] Aubade (S. S. A. A.) ... English translation by A. B. C. ... Arranged by Alinda B. Couper. *Fr. & Eng.* pp. 7. *J. Fischer & Bro.: New York*, [1953.] 8°.
F. 217. l. (38.)

— Bonjour, mon coeur. Good-day, dear Heart. Dydd da, fy mherl. Chanson for T. T. B. B. ... The English translation by John A. Parkinson. Y cyfieithiad cymraeg gan John Eilian ... Arr. by John A. Parkinson. [Staff and tonic sol-fa notation.] *Fr., Eng. & Welsh.* pp. 3. *Gwynn Publishing Co.: Llangollen*, [1954.] 8°. **F. 163. nn. (6.)**

— [Fuyons tous d'amour le jeu.] Qui s'y frotte, s'y pique. *Chanson.* (After Maldeghem.) For four-part Chorus of mixed voices ... Edited by F. Damrosch. (English version by Dr. T. Baker.) *G. Schirmer: New York*, 1925. 8°.
F. 585. kk. (38.)

— [Fuyons tous d'amour le jeu.] Out of Range of Cupid's Bow ... Chanson for S. A. T. B. (unaccompanied). Edited with English words by John A. Parkinson. *Eng. & Fr.* pp. 4. *Novello & Co.: London*, [1952.] 8°.
[Musical Times. no. 1313.] **P. P. 1945. aa.**

— [Fuyons tous d'amour le jeu.] Let us flee this wild Desire ... English text by M. K. (Chanson.) For four part chorus of mixed voices, a cappella ... Edited by Maynard Klein. pp. 7. *G. Schirmer: New York*, [1970.] 8°. **F. 1874. m. (15.)**

— Je l'ayme bien. *Chanson.* For four-part chorus of mixed voices ... Edited by F. Damrosch. (English version by Dr. T. Baker.) *G. Schirmer: New York*, 1925. 8°.
F. 585. kk. (39.)

— Un jour vis un foulon qui foulait. Yes, I saw a Fuller who was fulling. (Chanson.) For four-part chorus of mixed voices a cappella. English text by M. K. ... Edited by Maynard Klein. *Fr. & Eng.* pp. 7. *G. Schirmer: New York*, [1970.] 8°.
F. 1874. m. (14.)

— Las! voulez-vous q'une personne chante.—Ah! wouldst thou I should sing a merry Ditty.— Chanson [for S. A. T. B.]. English words by A. C. Curtis ... Edited by L. Benson. [1910.] *See* Oriana. The Oriana, *etc.* No. 58. [1905, *etc.*] 8°.
F. 1685.

— Ne vous soit étrange. *Chanson.* (After Maldeghem.) For four-part Chorus of mixed voices ... Edited by F. Damrosch. (English version by Dr. T. Baker.) *G. Schirmer: New York*, 1925. 8°. **F. 585. kk. (40.)**

— La Nuit froide et sombre. *Chanson.* (After Expert.) For four-part Chorus of mixed voices ... Edited by F. Damrosch. (English version by Dr. T. Baker.) *G. Schirmer: New York*, 1925. 8°. **F. 585. kk. (41.)**

— [Le Rossignol plaisant.] O Nightingale, so pleasant and so gay. Madrigal for mixed voices. (S. A. A. T. B.) Text from Fleur de dame. Translator unknown ... Arr. and ed. by Don Malin. pp. 11. *B. F. Wood Music Co.: New York, London*, [1961.] 8°. **E. 1563. b. (1.)**

— Sauter, danser, O to leap and dance. For Four-Part Chorus of Mixed Voices, a cappella. English version by Willis Wager ... Edited by Roy Harris. pp. 6. *G. Schirmer: New York*, 1944. 8°. **F. 1774. g. (24.)**

— [Sauter, danser.] Laughing, singing all the Day long ... English text by M. K. (Chanson.) For four-part chorus of mixed voices, a cappella ... Edited by Maynard Klein. pp. 7. *G. Schirmer: New York*, [1970.] 8°. **F. 1874. m. (1.)**

LASSO (Orlando di)

— Si vous n'estes en bon point. *Chanson.* (After Expert and Maldeghem.) For four-part chorus of mixed voices ... Edited by F. Damrosch. (English version by Dr. T. Baker.) *G. Schirmer: New York,* 1925. 8°.   **F. 585. kk. (42.)**

— [Si vous n'estes en bon point.] Chanson. After Expert and Maldeghem. Edited by Frank Damrosch. English version by Dr. Th. Baker. For mixed chorus. pp. 4. *Chappell & Co.: London,* [1960.] 8°.   **F. 1744. ee. (7.)**

— [Soyons joyeux.] Let us be gay ... Chanson for S. A. T. B. (unaccompanied) ... Edited with English words, by John A. Parkinson. *Eng. & Fr.* pp. 7. *Novello & Co.: London,* [1959.] 8°.
[*Part-song Book.* 1586.]   **F. 280. b.**

— Continuation du Melange d'Orlande de Lassus. A 3, 4, 5, 6 & 10 parties. Superius. *Adrian le Roy, & la veufue R. Ballard: Paris,* 1596. *obl.* 4°.   **A. 337. k.**

— [Continuation du mellange.—Passan vostri trionfi.] Trionfo del tempo. Madrigal für zehn Stimmen in zwei Chören. (1584.) ⟨Nach Worten von Francesco Petrarca.⟩ Ins Deutsche übertragen und herausgegeben von Paul Winter. *Ital. & Ger.* pp. 11. *C. F. Peters: Frankfurt, etc.,* [1960.] 8°.
Part of "Canticum".   **E. 1563. a. (5.)**

— [Continuation du mellange.—Passan vostri trionfi.] Trionfo del tempo. [Score and parts.] *In:* BAMFORTH (Dennis A.) Two Anthems. Arranged for ten recorders ... by D. A. Bamforth. [1976.] 8°.   **h. 3210. j. (834.)**

— Missa Brevis. *See* supra: [Masses.—Missae variis concentibus ornatae, 1577.—Missa Jäger.]

— Missae. *See* supra: [Masses.]

Moduli

— VII. Moduli ... 3, 4, 5, 6, 8 & 12 voc.—7 Gesänge ... zum Gedächtnis des 300. Todesjahres Lassos ... redigiert von F. X. Haberl. *Sumptibus Friderici Pustet: Ratisbonae, etc.,* 1894. 4°.   **F. 1171. s. (4.)**

— [Modulorum ... modulatorum secundum volumen. 1565.] Cognovi Domine. Motet à 4 voix, mis en partition par E. Delangle, *etc.* [1857.] *See* NIEDERMEYER (L.) La Maîtrise, *etc.* 1ʳᵉ Année. No. 12. [1857–61.] fol.   **H. 1237.**

— Primus (Secundus) Liber Modulorum, Quinis Vocibus constantium, *etc.* Superius. (Contratenor.) (Bassus.) (Quinta Pars.) 8 pt. *Apud Adrianum le Roy, & Robertum Ballard: Lutetiæ Parisiorum,* 1571. *obl.* 4°.
The signatures and foliation are continuous.   **A. 336. a. (1.)**

— [Another copy.]   **A. 336. b. (1.)**

— Moduli Quinis Vocibus Nunquam Hactenus Editi Monachii Boioariæ compositi, *etc.* Superius. (Contratenor.) (Tenor.) (Bassus.) (Quinta Pars.) 5 pt. *Apud Adrianum le Roy, & Robertum Ballard: Lutetiæ Parisiorum,* 1571. *obl.* 4°.
     A. 337. d. (3.)

— [Another copy.] Superius. (Contratenor.) (Bassus.) (Quinta Pars.) 4 pt.   **A. 336. a. (3.)**

— [Another copy. Bassus.]   **A. 336. b. (3.)**

— [Moduli Quinis Vocibus.] Fasciculus Aliquot Cantionum Sacrarum, Quinque Vocum, nunc primum in lucem editus, *etc.* Discantus. (Altus.) (Tenor.) (Bassus.) (Quinta Pars.) 5 pt. *Adamus Berg: Monachij,* 1572. *obl.* 4°.   **A. 336. c.**

— [Moduli Quinis Vocibus.] Venite ad me omnes. (Come unto me all ye who weary.) For full chorus of mixed voices a cappella. Matthew 11 : 28–30. English version by C. B. A. ... Edited by C. Buell Agey. *Lat. & Eng.* pp. 12. *G. Schirmer: New York,* [1966.] 8°.   **E. 1439. f. (23.)**

LASSO (Orlando di)

— [A reissue.] Venite ad me omnes, *etc. G. Schirmer: New York; Chappell & Co.: London,* [1966.] 8°.   **E. 1439. w. (7.)**

— Moduli Quatuor et Octo Vocum, *etc.* Superius. (Contra.) (Bassus.) 3 pt. *Apud Adrianum le Roy, & Robertum Ballard: Lutetiæ Parisiorum,* 1572. *obl.* 4°.   **A. 336. a. (4.)**

— [Another copy. Bassus.]
Imperfect; wanting the titlepage, which has been supplied in manuscript.   **A. 336. b. (4.)**

— Tertius Liber Modulorum, Quinis Vocibus constantium, *etc.* Superius. (Contra.) (Tenor.) (Bassus.) (Quinta Pars.) 5 pt. *Apud Adrianum le Roy & Robertum Ballard: Lutetiæ Parisiorum,* 1573. *obl.* 4°.   **A. 336. a. (2.)**

— [Another copy. Bassus.]
Imperfect; wanting the titlepage, which has been supplied in manuscript.   **A. 336. b. (2.)**

— Moduli Sex Septem et Duodecim Vocum, *etc.* Superius. (Contra.) (Bassus.) (Quinta Pars.) 4 pt. *Apud Adrianum le Roy, & Robertum Ballard: Lutetiæ Parisiorum,* 1573. *obl.* 4°.
     A. 336. a. (5.)

— [Another copy. Bassus.]   **A. 336. b. (5.)**

— [Moduli sex, septem et duodecim vocum.] Laudate Dominum. Motet a 12 Voix ... Transcription pour 12 instruments et étude de René Leibowitz. [Lassus's motet followed by Leibowitz's arrangement. Score.] pp. 10, 13. *Pierre Aelberts: Liège,* [1949.] 4°.   **G. 519. u. (16.)**

— Moduli nondum prius editi Monachii Boioariæ Ternis Vocibus ... Compositi. Superius. (Tenor.) (Bassus.) 3 pt. *Apud Adrianum le Roy, & Robertum Ballard: Lutetiæ Parisiorum,* 1576. *obl.* 4°.   **A. 336. d.**

— Moduli. Quatuor 5. 6. 7. 8. et Nouem Vocum, *etc.* Superius. (Contra.) (Bassus.) (Quinta Pars.) 4 pt. *Apud Adrianum le Roy, & Robertum Ballard: Lutetiæ Parisiorum,* 1577. *obl.* 4°.
     A. 336. a. (6.)

— Sacrarum Cantionum Moduli Quatuor Vocibus Contexti, *etc.* Tenor. *Apud Adrianum le Roy, & Robertum Ballard: Lutetiæ Parisiorum,* 1587. 4°.   **K. 5. b. 18. (1.)**

— Moduli Quatuor et Octo Vocum, *etc.* Tenor. *Apud Adrianum le Roy, & Robertum Ballard: Lutetiæ Parisiorum,* 1588. 4°.
     K. 5. b. 18. (4.)

— Moduli Quinque Vocum, *etc.* Tenor. *Apud Adrianum le Roy, & Robertum Ballard: Lutetiæ Parisiorum,* 1588. 4°.
     K. 5. b. 18. (2.)

— Moduli Sex Vocum, *etc.* Tenor. *Apud Adrianum le Roy, & Robertum Ballard: Lutetiæ Parisiorum,* 1588. 4°.
     K. 5. b. 18. (3.)

— Mon cœur se recommande à vous. *See* infra: [*Doubtful and Supposititious Works.*]

Motets

— Di Orlando di Lassus il primo libro de mottetti a cinque & a sei voci nuouamente posti in luce. Superius. *Per Ioanne Latio: Anuersa,* 1556. *obl.* 4°.   **A. 330.**

— [Il primo libro de mottetti.] Gustate et videte ... Moteta quinque vocum ... edendum curavit S. W. Dehn. *Trautwein et Comp.: Berolini,* [1850?] 8°.   **E. 605. e. (6.)**

— Orlandi de Lasso ... Liber Mottetarum, Trium Vocum, Quæ cum Viuæ Voci, tum omnis generis Instrumentis Musicis ... applicari possunt ... nunc Primum in lucem æditæ. Superius. *Excudebat Petrus Phalesius, sibi & Ioanni Bellero: Louanii,* 1575. *obl.* 4°.   **A. 330. a.**

LASSO (ORLANDO DI)

— Mottetta, Sex Vocum, typis nondum uspiam excusa ...
Quibus tam voces humanæ, quàm cuiusuis generis
Instrumenta Musica concentu ... applicari possunt, *etc.*
Discantus. (Altus.) (Tenor.) (Bassus.) (Quinta (Sexta) Vox.)
6 pt. *Adamus Berg: Monachij*, 1582. *obl.* 4°. **A. 334. l.**

— [Mottetta Sex Vocum.] O altitudo divitiarum, sapientiae, et
scientiae Dei. Motet for six voices ... Edited by H. B. Collins.
Dinham, Blyth & Co.: London, [1917.] 4°. **G. 30. (9.)**

— [Mottetta Sex Vocum.] Salve Regina ... Edited by H. B.
Collins, *etc.* [*London*, 1922.] 8°.
Lithographed. **F. 995. b. (14.)**

— [Mottetta Sex Vocum.] Salve Regina ... Edited by H. B.
Collins. *J. & W. Chester: London,* 1930. 8°.
[*Latin Church Music of the Polyphonic Schools. No.* 18.]
F. 995. c.

— Vier Motetten für fünf- und sechsstimmigen Chor. *See* supra:
[*Smaller Collections.*]

— Mottetti et Ricercari. *See* infra: [Novae ... ad duas voces
cantiones.]

— My Heart commends itself to thee. *See* infra: [*Doubtful and
Supposititious Works.*] [Mon cœur se recommande à vous.]

— My Heart is offered still to you. *See* infra: [*Doubtful and
Supposititious Works.*] [Mon cœur se recommande à vous.]

— My Lonely Heart remembers you. *See* infra: [*Doubtful and
Supposititious Works.*] [Mon cœur se recommande à vous.]

— Ne vous soit étrange. *See* supra: [Les Meslanges.]

— Nonne sicut lac. [*See* infra: Sacrae Lectiones Novem ex
Propheta Job. No. 3, Pt. 2.]

— Nos qui sumus in hoc mundo. *See* infra: [Patrocinium
Musices. Pars. 1.]

— [Novae ... ad duas voces cantiones.] Mottetti et Ricercari ...
a Due Voci, Nouamente ... Ristampati. Libro Primo. Canto.
(Alto.) 2 pt. *Appresso Angelo Gardano: Venetia,* 1585. *obl.* 4°.
Pp. 7, 8 *of the Canto part are wanting.* **A. 330. b.**

— Nouæ aliquot et ante hac non ita usitatæ ad duas voces
Cantiones suavissimæ, omnibus Musicis summè vtiles ...
Summa diligentia correctæ, & nunc primùm in lucem editæ.
Cantus. (Bassus.) 2 pt. *Thomas Este: Londini,* 1598. 4°.
*Imperfect; wanting fol. C. and C II. of the Bassus part, which
have been replaced by the corresponding leaves of the Cantus.*
K. 3. m. 9.

— [Novae ... ad duas voces cantiones.] Oculus non vidit. Eye
hath not perceived ... Motet for S. A. or T. B. The English
translation by W. S. Gwynn Williams. Y cyfieithiad Cymraeg
gan John Eilian ... Ed. by W. S. Gwynn Williams. [Staff and
tonic sol-fa notation.] *Lat., Eng. & Welsh.* pp. 3. *Gwynn
Publishing Co.: Llangollen,* [1961.] 8°. **E. 1439. d. (10.)**

— La Nuit froide et sombre. *See* supra: [Les Meslanges.]

— O altitudo divitiarum, sapientiae, et scientiae Dei. *See* supra:
[Mottetta Sex Vocum.]

— O bella fusa. *See* infra: [Libro de Villanelle, Moresche, et
altre Canzoni.]

— O Eyes of my Beloved. *See* infra: [Libro de Villanelle,
Moresche, et altre Canzoni.—O occhi manza mia.]

— O la, o che buon êco. *See* infra: [Libro de Villanelle,
Moresche, et altre Canzoni.]

— O Lord of Heav'n. *See* infra: [*Doubtful and Supposititious
Works.*] [Mon coeur se recommande à vous.]

LASSO (ORLANDO DI)

— O Nightingale, so pleasant and so gay. *See* supra: [Les
Meslanges.—Le Rossignol plaisant.]

— O occhi manza mia. *See* infra: [Libro de Villanelle,
Moresche, et altre Canzoni.]

— Oculus non vidit. *See* supra: [Novae ... ad duas voces
cantiones.]

— On this Day a Child is born. *See* supra: [Cantiones Aliquot
Quinque Vocum.—Resonet in laudibus.—Hodie apparuit.]

— Tertium opus Musicum. *See* supra: [*Smaller Collections.*]

— Out of Range of Cupid's Bow. *See* supra: [Les Meslanges.—
Fuyons tous d'amour le jeu.]

Patrocinium Musices. Pars 1

— Patrocinium Musices. Orlandi de Lasso ... Cantionum, quas
Mutetas vocant, Opus Novum. Prima Pars ... D. Guilhelmi
... Bavariæ Ducis liberalitate in lucem editum. *Adamus
Berg: Monachij,* 1573. fol. **K. 9. b. 1.**

— [Another copy.] **Hirsch** IV. **1690.**

— Patrocinium Musices. Orlandi de Lasso ... Cantionum
Quatuor, Quinque & Sex Vocum, quas Mutetas vocant, Opus
nouum, *etc.* Superius. (Contratenor.) (Tenor.) (Bassus.)
[Quinta & Sexta Pars.] 5 pt. *Cornelius Phalesius: Louanii,*
1574. *obl.* 4°.
Imperfect; wanting the titlepage and fol. 9–12 *of the Quinta et
Sexta Pars.* **A. 339. a.**

— Lauda anima mea Dominum. (My soul ever shall glorify the
Lord.) Motet for four-part chorus of mixed voices a cappella.
Psalm 146: 1–3. English version by C. B. A. ... Edited by
C. Buell Agey. *Lat. & Eng.* pp. 7. *G. Schirmer: New York,*
[1966.] 8°. **E. 1439. f. (22.)**

— [A reissue.] Lauda anima mea Dominum, *etc. G. Schirmer:
New York; Chappell & Co.: London,* [1966.] 8°.
E. 1439. w. (5.)

— Nos qui sumus in hoc mundo. (We, who Mortals of this
Creation.) For four-part chorus of mixed voices a cappella.
English text by C. B. A ... Edited by C. Buell Agey. *Lat. &
Eng.* pp. 8. *G. Schirmer: New York,* [1965.] 8°.
E. 1439. u. (18.)

— [A reissue.] Nos qui sumus in hoc mundo, *etc. G. Schirmer:
New York; Chappell & Co.: London; London* [printed, 1966.]
8°. **E. 1439. w. (8.)**

— Pauper sum ego. Motet à 4 voix, mis en partition par
E. Delangle. [1858.] *See* NIEDERMEYER (L.) La Maîtrise, *etc.* 2ᵉ
Année. No. 4. [1857–61.] 8°. **H. 1237.**

Patrocinium Musices. Pars 2

— Patrocinium Musices. Orlandi de Lasso ... Missæ aliquot
Quinque Vocum. Secunda Pars ... D. Guilhelmi ... Bavariæ
Ducis liberalitate in lucem editum. *Adamus Berg: Monachij,*
1574. fol. **K. 9. b. 2.**

— [Another copy.] **Hirsch** IV. **1690. a.**

— Missa ad Imitationem Moduli Credidi ... cum quinque
vocibus. *Ex Officina Petri Ballard: Lutetiae,* 1608. fol.
K. 10. b. 1. (16.)

— [Another copy.] **K. 10. b. 2. (2.)**

— Missa super Scarco di doglia. Für fünfstimmigen gemischten
Chor ... Herausgegeben von ... Siegfried Hermelink. pp. 44.
Bärenreiter: Kassel, etc., [1964.] 8°.
Part of "Chor-Archiv". **F. 274. rr. (2.)**

— Missa. Quinque Vocum. Ad Imitationem Moduli Sydus ex
claro, *etc. Ex Officina Petri Ballard: Lutetiæ,* 1614. fol.
K. 10. b. 2. (3.)

LASSO (ORLANDO DI)

— Patrocinium Musices. Orlandi de Lasso ... Officia aliquot, de præcipuis festis anni, 5. vocum. Nunc primùm in lucem editæ. Tertia pars ... D. Guilhelmi ... Bauariæ Ducis, liberalitate in lucem editum. *Adamus Berg: Monachij,* 1576. fol.   **Hirsch IV. 1690. b.**

— Patrocinium Musices. Orlandi de Lasso ... Officia aliquot, de Præcipuis Festis Anni, 5. Vocum, nunc primùm in lucem editæ. Tertia Pars ... D. Guilhelmi ... Bavariæ Ducis, liberalitate in lucem editum. *Adamus Berg: Monachij,* 1580. fol.   **K. 9. b. 3.**

— Patrocinium Musices. Orlandi de Lasso ... Passio quinque vocum: Idem Lectiones Iob, & Lectiones Matutinæ de Natiuitate Christi, quatuor vocum. Quarta Pars ... D. Guilhelmi ... Bavariæ Ducis, liberalitate in lucem editum. *Adamus Berg: Monachij,* 1575. fol.   **K. 9. b. 4.**

— [Another copy.]
Sig. A of the Quarta pars, followed by sig. B-KK of the Quinta pars from the Hirsch copy, misbound.   **Hirsch IV. 1690. c.**

— Patrocinium Musices. Orlandi de Lasso ... Magnificat aliquot, Quatuor, Quinque, Sex, & Octo vocum. Quinta Pars ... D. Guilhelmi ... Bavariæ Ducis, liberalitate in lucem editum. *Adamus Berg: Monachij,* 1576. fol.   **K. 9. b. 5.**

— [Another copy.]
Sig. A of the Quinta pars, followed by sig. B-Rr of the Quarta pars from the Hirsch copy, misbound.   **Hirsch IV. 1690. d.**

— Patrocinium Musices. Beatissimæ, Deiparæq[ue] virginis Mariæ canticum Magnificat. Quattuor, quinq[ue], & sex vocibus, ad imitationem cantilenarum quarundam, singulari concentus hilaritate excellentium, *etc.* *Apud Adamum Berg: Monachij,* 1587. fol.   **K. 9. b. 7.**

— [Patrocinium Musices. 1587.] Magnificat sex vocum secundi Toni [on Striggio's "Ecco chio lasso il core"] ... in partitionem ... dispositum et Henrico de St. Julien dicatum ab amico suo R. L. Pearsall, *etc.* *J. Velten: Carlsruhe,* 1833. fol.   **H. 1187. l. (3.)**

Patrocinium Musices. 1589

— Patrocinium Musices. Missæ aliquot Quinque Vocum, *etc.* *Adamus Berg: Monachii,* 1589. fol.   **K. 9. b. 8.**

— Missa. Ad Imitationem Moduli In die tribulationis ... cum quinque vocibus. *Ex Officina Petri Ballard: Lutetiæ,* 1607. fol.   **K. 10. b. 2. (1.)**

— Missa super: "In die tribulationis". Quinque vocum. [Score and parts.] *See* PROSKE (C.) Selectus Novus Missarum, *etc.* No. XI. 1855, *etc.* 4°.   **F. 350.**

— Fünfstimmige Messe "In die tribulationis". [Edited by Hermann Müller.] pp. 43. *Universal Edition: Wien, Leipzig,* [1929.] 4°.
Part of "Heilige Tonkunst".   **G. 519. kk. (5.)**

— Missa "Qual donna" quinque vocum ... Arrangiert, transponiert und mit Vortragszeichen versehen von M. Filke. Partitur. *L. Schwann: Düsseldorf,* 1900. 8°.   **F. 1175. d. (3.)**

— Missa Quinque Vocum. [Score and parts.] *See* PROSKE (C.) Selectus Novus Missarum, *etc.* No. III. 1855, *etc.* 4°.   **F. 350.**

— Pauper sum ego. *See* supra: [Patrocinium Musices. Pars I.]

— Praise the Lord. *See* infra: [Sacrae Cantiones Quatuor Vocum.—Jubilate Deo omnis terra.]

— Proba me, Deus. *See* infra: [Altera Pars Selectissimarum Cantionum.]

LASSO (ORLANDO DI)

— Prophetiae Sibyllarum zu 4 Stimmen. Herausgegeben von Joachim Therstappen [*sic*]. 3. unveränderte Auflage. *Lat. & Ger.* pp. 26. *Möseler Verlag: Wolfenbüttel,* [c. 1955.] 8°.
[*Das Chorwerk. Hft.* 48.]   **E. 1317.**

— Psalm 36. *See* infra: [Der ander Theil teutscher Lieder. 1572. No. 8. Es sind doch selig alle die.]

Psalmi Dauidis Poenitentiales

— Psalmi Dauidis Pœnitentiales, Modis Musicis redditi, atque antehac nunquam in Lucem æditi. His accessit Psalmus: Laudate Dominum de Cœlis. Quinque Vocum, *etc.* Altus. (Bassus.) (Quinta Vox.) 3 pt. *Adamus Berg: Monachii,* 1584. *obl.* 4°.   **A. 329.**

— [Another copy. Altus.]   **A. 329. a.**

— Psalmos VII. Pœnitentiales ... publici juris fecit ... S. W. Dehn. *Sumtibus Gustavi Crantzii: Berolini,* [1838.] fol.   **G. 121. b.**

— Septem Psalmi poenitentiales, in moderner Partitur, redigiert von H. Bäuerle, *etc.* *Breitkopf & Härtel: Leipzig, etc.,* 1905. 8°.   **F. 1071.**

— [No. 3.] Cor meum. My Heart. Fy nghalon. Motet for 3 equal voices. Psalm xxxviii, 10. The translations by ... W. S. Gwynn Williams ... Ed. and arr. by W. S. Gwynn Williams. [Staff and tonic sol-fa notation.] *Lat., Eng. & Welsh.* pp. 3. *Gwynn Publishing Co.: Llangollen,* [1958.] 8°.   **E. 460. f. (5.)**

— [No. 5. Scribantur haec.] Sedebit dominus. Communion antiphon and psalm for the mass of Christ the King ... Arranged by Peter Peacock. *St. Martins Publications: London,* [1962.] 8°.   **G. 503. d. (8.)**

— [No. 6.] Penitential Psalm No. 6. English version by T. Hamilton ... Edited by N. Cain. *Gamble Hinged Music Co.: Chicago,* 1936. 8°.
Part of "The Musical Research Society Series".   **E. 602. ll. (14.)**

— Cinquante Pseaumes de Dauid, auec la musique a cinq parties d'Orlande de Lassus. Vingt autres Pseaumes à cinq et six parties, par diuers excellents Musiciens de nostre temps. Superius. (Contratenor.) (Tenor.) (Bassus.) (Quinta Pars.) (Sexta Pars.) 6 pt. *De l'imprimerie de Jerosme Commelin:* [*Heidelberg,*] 1597. *obl.* 4°.
In addition to Orlando di Lasso the following composers are named in this collection: Pevernage, Maletty, Alfonse Flores, Goudimel, Faignient, Manenti, Felis, Macque, Sabin and Baccusy.   **K. 2. a. 4.**

— Quand mon mari. *See* supra: [Le Premier livre de chansons à quatre parties.]

— Quem vidistis, pastores? *See* supra: [Cantiones Aliquot Quinque Vocum.]

— Qui s'y frotte, s'y pique. *See* supra: [Les Meslanges.—Fuyons tous d'amour le jeu.]

— Novem Quiritationes Divi Job. *See* also infra: [Sacrae Lectiones Novem ex Propheta Job.]

— Nouem Quiritationes Diui Iob, bis quidem, sed diuersis modis lentiorique concentu quaternis vocibus modulantes ... Adiectis quibusdam ex officio Deffunctorum Responsorijs. Tenor. *Apud Adrianum le Roy, & Robertum Ballard: Lutetiæ Parisiorum,* 1587. 4°.   **K. 5. b. 18. (7.)**

— Quoniam qui talia agunt. *See* supra: [Lectiones Sacrae Novem.— Diligis Proximum Tuum.]

— S'io fusse ciaul. *See* infra: [Libro de Villanelle, Moresche, et altre Canzoni.]

LASSO (ORLANDO DI)

Sacrae Cantiones Quinque Vocum. Libro Primo. 1562

— Sacræ Cantiones Quinque Vocum, tum Viua Voce, tum omnis generis instrumentis cantatu commodissimæ. Discantus. (Altus.) (Tenor.) (Bassus.) (Vagans.) 5 pt. *Impressum in Officina Typographica Ulrici Neuberi: Norinbergæ,* 1569. *obl.* 4°. **A. 334. i.**

— Viginti Quinque Sacræ Cantiones, Quinque Vocum, tum Viua Voce, tum omnis generis instrumentis cantatu commodissimæ, *etc.* Discantus. (Altus.) (Tenor.) (Bassus.) (Quinta Pars.) 5 pt. *Apud Theodoricum Gerlatzenum, in officina Ioannis Montani piæ memoriæ: Noribergæ,* 1570. *obl.* 4°. **A. 334. k.**

— Orlandi Lassi Sacrae Cantiones … Quinque Vocum, Tum viua voce, Tum omnis generis instrumentis cantatu commodissimæ. Liber Primus. Altus. *Apud Angelum Gardanum: Venetijs,* 1586. *obl.* 4°. **A. 334. j. (1.)**

— Surrexit pastor bonus. The Shepherd has arisen. For Five-part Chorus … English version by G. Reese … Edited by C. Deis. *G. Schirmer: New York,* 1933. 8°.

E. 335. g. (17.)

— Taedet animam meam. Motet à quatre voix. Mis en partition par E. Delangle, *etc.* [1858.] *See* NIEDERMEYER (L.) La Maîtrise, *etc.* 2ᵉ Année. No. 8. [1857–61.] fol. **H. 1237.**

Sacrae Cantiones. Books 2–8

— Orlandi Lassi Sacræ Cantiones … Quinque, et Sex Vocum, Tum viua Voce tum omnis generis Instrumentis cantatu commodissimę. Liber Secundus. Altus. *Apud Angelum Gardanum: Venetijs,* 1584. *obl.* 4°. **A. 334. j. (2.)**

— [Sacrae Cantiones … Quinque et Sex Vocum. Liber secundus.] De ore prudentis procedit mel. The Mouth of the Wise Man. For Five-part Chorus of Mixed Voices a cappella. English version by A. Mendel … Edited by J. F. Williamson. *G. Schirmer: New York,* 1933. 8°. **E. 335. g. (49.)**

— Orlandi Lassi Sacræ Cantiones … Quinque, et Sex Vocum, Tum viua voce tum omnis generis Instrumentis cantatu commodissimæ. Liber Tertius. Cantus. (Altus.) (Tenor.) (Bassus.) (Quintus.) 5 pt. *Apud Angelum Gardanum: Venetijs,* 1578. *obl.* 4°. **K. 2. a. 14.**

— Orlandi Lassi Sacræ Cantiones … Quinque, et Sex Vocum, Tum viua voce tum omnis generis Instrumentis cantatu commodissimę. Liber Tertius. Altus. *Apud Angelum Gardanum: Venetijs,* 1587. *obl.* 4°. **A. 334. j. (3.)**

— Orlandi Lassi Sacræ Cantiones … Sex et Octo Vocum, Tum uiua Voce, Tum omnis generis Instrumentis cantatu commodissimæ. Liber Quartus. Altus. *Apud Antonium Gardanum: Venetijs,* 1569. *obl.* 4°. **A. 334. j. (4.)**

— Orlandi Lassi Sacræ Cantiones … Sex et Octo Vocum, Tum Viua Voce, Tum omnis generis Instrumentis cantatu commodissimæ. Liber Quartus. Altus. *Apud Angelum Gardanum: Ventijs,* 1579. *obl.* 4°. **A. 334. n.**

— [Sacrae Cantiones Sex et Octo Vocum. Liber quartus.] Levavi oculos meos. (I will lift up now mine Eyes.) For eight-part chorus of mixed voices (SATB-SATB) a cappella. Psalm 121. English version by C. B. A. … Edited by C. Buell Agey. *Lat. & Eng.* pp. 22. *G. Schirmer: New York,* [1965.] 8°.

E. 1439. u. (19.)

— [A reissue.] Levavi oculos meos, *etc.* *G. Schirmer: New York; Chappell & Co.: London; London* [printed, 1966.] 8°.

E. 1439. w. (4.)

— Orlandi Lassi Sacræ Cantiones … Quinque Sex et Octo Vocum, Tum uiua Voce, tum omnis generis Instrumĕtis cătatu cŏmodissimæ. Liber Quintus. Altus. *Apud Antonium Gardanum: Venetijs,* 1569. *obl.* 4°. **A. 334. j. (5.)**

LASSO (ORLANDO DI)

— Orlandi Lassi Sacræ Cantiones … Quinque Vocum, Tum viua voce tum omnis generis Instrumentis cantatu commodissimæ. Liber Sextus. Altus. *Apud Angelum Gardanum: Venetijs,* 1586. *obl.* 4°. **A. 334. j. (6.)**

— Orlandi Lassi Sacræ Cantiones … Quinque Vocum, Tum viua Voce Tum omnis generis Instrumentis cantatu commodissimæ. Liber Septimus. Altus. *Apud Angelum Gardanum: Venetijs,* 1584. *obl.* 4°. **A. 334. j. (7.)**

— Orlandi Lassi Sacræ Cantiones … Sex Vocum, Tum Viua Voce, Tum omnis generis instrumentis cantatu commodissimæ. Liber Octauus. Altus. *Apud Angelum Gardanum: Venetijs,* 1584. *obl.* 4°. **A. 334. j. (8.)**

Sacrae Cantiones Quinque Vocum. 1582

— Sacræ Cantiones, Quinque Vocum, Quæ cum Viuæ Voci, tum omnis generis instrumentis musicis commodissime applicari possunt. Opus planè nouum, nunquàm alijs Typis excusum, *etc.* Discantus. (Altus.) (Tenor.) (Bassus.) (Quinta Vox.) 5 pt. *Adamus Berg: Monachij,* 1582. *obl.* 4°. **A. 334. d.**

— Christus, resurgens ex mortuis, jam non moritur. Motet for five voices … Edited by H. B. Collins. *Dinham, Blyth & Co.: London,* [1917.] 4°. **G. 30. (12.)**

— Christus resurgens. Motet for Easter for five voices … Edited by H. B. Collins. *J. & W. Chester: London,* 1929. 8°.

F. 995. b. (40.)

— Justorum animae. [Motet for five voices.] [1912.] *See* THIEL (C.) Auswahl hervorragender Meisterwerke, *etc.* Band II. No. 15. [1898, *etc.*] 8°. **F. 1767.**

— Justorum animae. Motet for five voices, *etc.* [Edited by H. B. Collins.] *J. & W. Chester: London,* 1930. 8°. **F. 995. b. (39.)**

— Justorum animae. (The Souls of righteous Men.) Motet for five voices … Edited with an alternative English text by Anthony G. Petti. *Lat. & Eng.* pp. 6. *J. & W. Chester: London,* [1966.] 8°.
Part of "Latin Church Music of the polyphonic schools".

E. 1439. w. (10.)

Sacrae Cantiones Quatuor Vocum. 1585

— Orlandi Lassi … Sacræ Cantiones: antehac nunquam nec visæ nec typis uspiam excusae. Quatuor Vocum. Recens … compositæ, & in lucem … editæ. Discantus. (Altus.) (Tenor.) (Bassus.) 4 pt. *Adamus Berg: Monachii,* 1585. *obl.* 4°.

A. 334. g.

— XV. Offertoria quatuor vocum inaequalium … ad usum hodiernum accomodavit H. B. Collins. Tres partes. *L. Schwann: Düsseldorf,* 1911. 8°. **F. 274. p. (11.)**

— Fugger Motetten. Ausgewählte vierstimmige Motetten … herausgegeben und mit einem deutschen Zweittext versehen von Rudolf Budde. *Lat. & Ger.* pp. 52. *Hänssler-Verlag: Stuttgart,* [1972.] 4°.
Part of "Das Chorwerk alter Meister". **F. 1176. kk. (8.)**

— [Benedictus es, Domine.] Blessed art thou, O Lord … For mixed chorus (SATB). English text by W. E. … Ed. by Walter Ehret. *Eng. & Lat.* pp. 7. *Chappell & Co.: New York,* [1969.] 8°.
Part of "Cathedral choral Series". **E. 1439. x. (17.)**

— Custodi me, Domine. (Guide and keep me, O Lord.) For four-part chorus of mixed voices a cappella. Psalm 140: 4. English version by C. B. A. … Edited by C. Buell Agey. *Lat. & Eng.* pp. 8. *G. Schirmer: New York,* [1966.] 8°.

E. 1439. f. (21.)

— [A reissue.] Custodi me, Domine, *etc.* *G. Schirmer: New York; Chappell & Co.: London; London* [printed, 1966.] 8°.

E. 1439. w. (6.)

LASSO (ORLANDO DI)

— Dextera Domini. (The Right Hand of God.) For S. A. T. B. chorus. English text by M. M. ... Edited by Mason Martens. *Lat. & Eng.* pp. 7. *Walton Music Corporation: North Hollywood,* [1963.] 8°.
Part of the "Walton sacred choral Library".　　**E. 1439. q. (1.)**

— [Domine convertere.] Turn Thee, O Lord, and deliver my Soul. Unaccompanied Anthem. Adapted to English words and edited by I. Atkins. *Bayley & Ferguson: London, Glasgow,* 1925. 8°.
Choral Album, No. 1378.　　**F. 946. c. (67.)**

— Domine, Domine, in auxilium meum respice. Motet for four voices ... Edited by H. B. Collins. *Dinham, Blyth & Co.: London,* [1916.] 8°.　　**F. 995. (24.)**

— Domine exaudi orationem meam. (Lord, hear thou my Prayer) ... Motet for four-part chorus of mixed voices a cappella. [Words] adapted from Psalm 102 [by] C. B. A. ... Edited by C. Buell Agey. *Lat. & Eng.* pp. 7. *G. Schirmer: New York,* [1966.] 8°.　　**E. 1439. f. (34.)**

— Expectans expectavi Dominum. Motet for four voices ... edited by H. B. Collins. [*London,* 1917.] 8°.　　**F. 995. (23.)**

— Exspectans exspectavi. Offertory ... Edited by H. B. Collins. *J. & W. Chester: London,* 1939. 8°.
[*Latin Church Music of the Polyphonic Schools. No.* 54.]
　　F. 995. c.

— Factus est Dominus firmamentum meum. Motet ... for four voices ... Edited by H. B. Collins. [*London,* 1917.] 8°.
　　F. 995. (27.)

— [Jubilate Deo omnis terra.] Praise the Lord. Anthem. Adapted by J. A. Beaumont. 1868. *See* PERIODICAL PUBLICATIONS.— *London.* The Choir, *etc.* No. 127. 1863–78. 4°.
　　P. P. 1945. hc.

— [Jubilate Deo omnis terra.] Jauchzet Gott alle Lande ... Psalm 100, 1–3, nach Luthers Fassung frei übersetzt von Karl Lütge. *In:* PSALMS. [*Polyglot.*] Zwei Psalmen für gemischten Chor, *etc.* pp. 3–5. [1958.] 8°.　　**E. 460. h. (8.)**

— Jubilate Deo. Praise the Lord with Gladness ... Motet for S. A. T. B. Psalm 100. The English version by John A. Parkinson. Y cyfieithiad gan John Eilian. Ed. W. S. Gwynn Williams, *etc.* [Staff and tonic sol-fa notation.] *Lat., Eng. & Welsh.* pp. 4. *Gwynn Publishing Co.: Llangollen,* [1962.] 8°.
　　E. 1439. c. (25.)

— Jubilate Deo. (Make a joyful Noise unto the Lord.) For S. A. T. B. chorus. Text adapted from psalm 100 ... Ed. and arr. by Robert Field. pp. 8. *Boosey & Hawkes:* [*New York,* 1964.] 8°.　　**F. 1176. ss. (4.)**

— Jubilate Deo, omnis terra. Praise thy God, Jehovah, all ye Nations. For four-part Chorus of mixed voices a cappella. Psalm C: 1, 2, 3. English version by C. B. A. ... Edited by C. Buell Agey. *Lat. & Eng.* pp. 9. *G. Schirmer: New York,* [1967.] 8°.　　**E. 1439. x. (8.)**

— Jubilate Deo. (Sing to God.) Motet for four-part chorus of mixed voices a cappella. Psalm 100. English text by M. K. ... Edited by Maynard Klein. *Lat. & Eng.* pp. 8. *G. Schirmer: New York, London,* [1973.] 8°.　　**E. 1439. oo. (11.)**

Sacrae Lectiones Novem ex Propheta Job

— Sacræ Lectiones Nouem ex Propheta Iob, Quatuor Vocum. Discantus. (Altus.) (Tenor.) (Bassus.) 4 pt. *Apud Theodoricum Gerlatzenum in Officina Ioannis Montani piæ memoriæ: Noribergæ,* 1567. *obl.* 4°.　　**A. 331.**

— Nouem Quiritationes Diui Iob. Quaternis Vocibus ... modulatæ, *etc.* Superius. (Tenor.) (Contratenor.) (Bassus.) 4 pt. *Apud Adrianum le Roy, & Robertum Ballard:* [*Paris,*] 1572. *obl.* 4°.　　**A. 336. a. (7.)**

LASSO (ORLANDO DI)

— [Another copy. Bassus.]
Wanting the titlepage.　　**A. 336. b. (6.)**

— [No. 3, Pt. 2. Nonne sicut lac.] Hear my Prayer, O Lord. For four-part chorus of mixed voices a cappella. Text from Psalm 102 ... Edited by C. Buell Agey. pp. 9. *G. Schirmer: New York,* [1966.] 8°.　　**E. 1439. f. (35.)**

— [A reissue.] Hear my Prayer, O Lord ... Edited by C. Buell Agey. *Chappell & Co.: London,* [1967.] 8°.　**E. 1439. w. (21.)**

— [No. 5, Pt. 1.] Homo natus de muliere. Motet for four voices ... edited by H. B. Collins. [*London,* 1918.] 8°.
Lithographed.　　**F. 995. a. (7.)**

— [No. 8, Pt. 3.] Scio enim quod Redemptor meus vivit. [Motet for four voices.] (Edited by H. B. Collins.) [*London,* 1917.] 8°.　　**F. 995. (26.)**

— [No. 8, Pt. 3.] Scio enim quod Redemptor ... Motet for Four Voices ... Edited by H. B. Collins. *J. & W. Chester: London,* 1932. 8°.
[*Latin Church Music of the Polyphonic Schools. No.* 25.]
　　F. 995. c.

— Sacrarum Cantionum Moduli Quatuor Vocibus Contexti. 1587. *See supra:* [Moduli.]

— Salve Regina. Motet à quatre voix. [Magnum Opus Musicum. No. 56.] [1857.] *See* NIEDERMEYER (L.) La Maîtrise, *etc.* 1ʳᵉ Année. No. 3. [1857–61.] fol.　　**H. 1237.**

— Salve Regina for four voices ... [Magnum Opus Musicum. No. 56.] Edited by H. B. Collins. *Dinham, Blyth & Co.: London,* [1916.] 8°.　　**F. 995. (25.)**

— Salve Regina. [Magnum Opus Musicum. No. 56.] Edited by H. B. Collins. *Cary & Co.: London,* 1931. 8°.
　　F. 1175. q. (14.)

— Salve regina. (Hail, Queen of Heaven.) [Magnum Opus Musicum. No. 56.] S. A. T. B. a cappella. English text by Harold Heiberg ... Edited by Zanon-Vené. pp. 9. *G. Ricordi & Co.: New York,* [1957.] 8°.　　**E. 335. r. (50.)**

— Salve Regina. [6 voices.] *See supra:* [Mottetta Sex Vocum.]

— Scio enim quod Redemptor. *See supra:* [Sacrae Lectiones Novem ex Propheta Job. No. 8, Pt. 3.]

— Sedebit Dominus. *See supra:* [Psalmi Davidis Poenitentiales. No. 5. Scribantur haec.]

— Selectiorum Aliquot Cantionum Sacrarum Sex Vocum fasciculus, adiunctus in fine tribus Dialogis octo vocum, Quorum nihil adhuc in lucem est editum, *etc.* Discantus. (Altus.) (Tenor.) (Bassus.) (Quinta Vox.) (Sexta Vox.) 6 pt. *Adamus Berg: Monachij,* 1570. *obl.* 4°.　　**A. 334. a.**

— [Another copy.]　　**A. 334. b.**

Selectissimæ Cantiones ... Sex & pluribus vocibus. 1568

— Selectissimæ Cantiones, quas Vulgo Motettas vocant partim omnino nouæ, partim nusquam in Germania excusae, Sex & pluribus uocibus compositæ, *etc.* Discantus. (Altus.) (Tenor.) (Bassus.) (Quinta [Sexta] Vox.) 6 pt. *Apud Theodoricum Gerlatzenum, in Officina Ioannis Montani piæ memoriæ: Norimbergæ,* 1568. *obl.* 4°.
The Discantus alone has the spelling 'Norimbergæ': the other parts have 'Noribergæ'. The words 'Quatuor, Quinque, Sex & pluribus uocibus' are added incorrectly to the title of the Tenor part.　　**A. 333. b.**

— [Another copy. Bassus.]　　**A. 333. c.**

— Responsorium. In Monte Oliveti. 6 vocum. *See* HABERL (F. X.) Tria Motetta, *etc.* No. 1. 1891. 4°.　　**G. 517. g. (2.)**

LASSO (Orlando di)

— In monte Oliveti. Responsory, etc. [S. A. A. T. B. B. Edited by Bill Tamblyn.] pp. 4. *Chiswick Music: London,* [1975.] 4°.

G. 503. y. (2.)

Selectissimæ Cantiones ... Quinque et Quatuor Vocibus. 1568

— Selectissimæ cantiones, quas vulgo Motetas vocant, partim omnino nouae, partim nusquam in Germania excusae, Quinque et Quatuor Vocibus compositae, etc. Discantus. (Altus.) (Tenor.) (Bassus.) (Vagans.) 5 pt. *Apud Theodoricum Gerlatzenum, in Officina Ioannis Montani piæ memoriæ: Noribergæ,* 1568. *obl.* 4°.

A. 333.

— [Another copy.] Altus. (Bassus.) (Vagans.) 3 pt.

A. 333. a.

— Tristis est anima mea. Motet for five voices ... Edited ... by W. B. Squire. [1894.] *See* BACH. The Bach Choir Magazine, etc. No. 32. [1877–1905.] 8°.

F. 287.

— [Tristis est anima mea.] Sorrowful now is my Soul ... [S. S. A. T. B.] Edited, arranged and with English text by Walter Ehret. *Eng. & Lat.* pp. 10. *Southern Music Publishing Co.: New York; Peer Musikverlag: Hamburg,* [1966.] 8°. [*The Renaissance. no.* 6.]

F. 1744. zz.

— Ubi est Abel, frater tuus? Motet for five voices ... edited by H. B. Collins. *Dinham, Blyth & Co.:* [*London,* 1917.] 4°.

G. 30. (10.)

— Selectissimæ Cantiones, quas uulgo Motetas vocant, partim omnino nouæ, partim nusquam in Germania excusæ, Sex & pluribus vocibus compositæ ... Posteriori huic editioni accessère omnes Orlandi Motetæ, quæ in veteri nostro Thesauro Musico impressæ continebantur, cum ... aliis ... Omnia denuò multò quàm antehac correctius edita. Discantus. (Altus.) (Tenor.) (Bassus.) (Quinta Vox.) (Sexta Vox.) 6 pt. *In officina typographica Catharinæ Gerlachiæ: Noribergæ,* 1587. *obl.* 4°.
The Discantus is imperfect, wanting pp. 4, 5, *which have been supplied in manuscript.*

A. 333. d. (1.)

— Altera Pars Selectissimarum Cantionum, Quas Vulgo Motetas Vocant, Quinque et Quatuor Vocibus ... Aucta & restituta, etc. Discantus. (Altus.) (Tenor.) (Bassus.) (Quinta Vox.) 5 pt. *In officina typographica Catharinæ Gerlachiæ: Noribergæ,* 1587. *obl.* 4°.

A. 333. d. (2.)

— [Another copy.] Altus. (Tenor.) (Bassus.) (Quinta Pars.) 4 pt.

A. 333. e.

— [Altera Pars Selectissimarum Cantionum.] Proba me, Deus. (Search me, O God) ... For four-part chorus of mixed voices a cappella. Psalm 139: 23–24. English version by C. B. A. ... Edited by C. Buell Agey. *Lat. & Eng.* pp. 9. *G. Schirmer: New York; Chappell & Co.: London,* [1966.] 8°.

E. 1439. w. (9.)

— Si vous n'estes en bon point. *See* supra: [Les Meslanges.]

— Sorrowful now is my Soul. *See* supra: [Selectissimae Cantiones.—Tristis est anima mea.]

— The Spinning Jenny. *See* supra: [*Smaller Collections.*] Two early choral Songs. 2.

— Super flumina Babylonis. [Magnum Opus Musicum.] Nonsense-motet for 5 voices (SAATB) ... (ed. Thurston Dart.) pp. 11. *Stainer & Bell: Reigate,* [1967.] 8°. [*Choral Library. no.* 375.]

F. 1137. d.

— Surrexit pastor bonus. *See* supra: [Sacrae Cantiones Quinque Vocum. Libro Primo. 1562.]

— Sweet Maiden. *See* infra: [Libro de Villanelle, Moresche, et altre Canzoni.—O occhi manzo mia.]

— Taedet animam meam. *See* supra: [Sacrae Cantiones Quinque Vocum. Libro Primo. 1562.]

LASSO (Orlando di)

— Take my Heart into your Care. *See* infra: [*Doubtful and Supposititious Works.*] [Mon coeur se recommande à vous.]

— Orlandi Lassi ... Teutsche Lieder mit fünff Stimmen, zuuor vnterschiedlich, jetzund aber ... inn ein Opus zusammen getruckt. Discant. *Durch Katharinam Gerlachin, und Johanns vom Berg Erben: Nürnberg,* 1583. *obl.* 4°.

A. 335. a.

— Orlandi Lassi ... Teutsche Lieder mit fünff Stimmen, zuvor vnterschiedlich, jetzund aber ... in ein Opus zusammen getruckt. Discant. (Altus.) (Tenor.) (Bass.) (v. Stim.) 5 pt. *Gedruckt durch Catharinæ Gerlachin Erben: Nürnberg,* 1593. *obl.* 4°.

A. 335. b.

— Newe Teutsche Liedlein mit fünff stimmen, wölche gantz lieblich zu singen vnnd auff allerley Instrumenten zugebrauchen. Von Orlando di Lassus ... Componiert, vnd von jhm selbst Corrigiert, vnd inn druck verfertiget worden. Discantus. (Altus.) (Tenor.) (Bassus.) (Die fünffte stim.) 5 pt. *Adam Berg: München,* 1569. *obl.* 4°.

A. 335.

— [Der ander Theil teutscher Lieder. 1572. No. 8. Es sind doch selig alle die.] Psalm 36 "Herr, deine Güt und Wahrheit steht" ... Worte: Strophe 1: nach Matthias Jorissen 1793; Strophe 2: nach Strassburg 1545. Weise: Matthäus Greitter 1525, etc. [S. A. T. T. B.] pp. 4. *Bärenreiter-Verlag: Kassel,* [1969.] 8°.

E. 1439. s. (9.)

Newe Teutsche Lieder mit vier Stimmen

— Newe Teutsche Lieder, geistlich vnnd Weltlich, mit vier Stimmen, etc. Tenor. *Gedruckt ... bey Catharina Gerlachin: Nürmberg,* 1589. *obl.* 4°.
Imperfect; wanting all after fol. d 4.

A. 335. c.

— Vier geistliche Lieder—mit deutschem Texte—für gemischten Chor ... Für den Concert-Vortrag eingerichtet von W. Widmann. Partitur. *J. Seiling: München,* [1894.] 8°.

F. 1170. s. (14.)

— [Baur was tregst im Sacke.] Der Bauer will tanzen. [Madrigal.] [1912.] *See* THIEL (C.) Auswahl hervorragender Meisterwerke, etc. Band III. No. 9. [1898, etc.] 8°.

F. 1767.

— [Baur was tregst im Sacke.] "Farmer, what's that in your Bag?" For mixed chorus a cappella. English version by Sigmund Spaeth ... Arr. for concert use by Wilhelm Widmann. *Eng. & Ger.* pp. 5. *Chappell & Co.: London,* [1960.] 8°.

F. 1744. ee. (9.)

— [Christ ist erstanden.] Christ hath arisen ... For four-part chorus of mixed voices a cappella ... Edited by David Pizarro. *Eng. & Ger.* pp. 4. *G. Schirmer: New York,* [1960.] 8°.

E. 1439. c. (22.)

— [Ich waiss mir ein Meidlein.] I know a young Maiden ... [Madrigal for four voices.] Edited by L. S. Benson. English words by A. Watson. *See* ARION. Arion, etc. [Vol. I. No. 25.] [1899.] 8°.

G. 771.

— [Ich waiss mir ein Meidlein.] I know a young Maiden ... For S. A. T. B. chorus. English text by W. E. ... Edited by Walter Ehret. *Eng. & Ger.* pp. 7. *Walton Music Corporation: North Hollywood,* [1963.] 8°.
Part of the "Walton historical choral Series".

F. 1744. nn. (6.)

— Ich waiss mir ein Meidlein. (I know a fair Maiden.) Madrigal. For four-part chorus of mixed voices a cappella. English text by M. K. ... Edited by Maynard Klein. *Ger. & Eng.* pp. 6. *G. Schirmer: New York, London,* [1972.] 8°.

F. 1874. v. (13.)

— 6 teutsche Lieder mit vier, sampt einem Dialogo mit 8 Stimmen. *See* supra: [Sex Cantiones Latinae.]

— Thresor de Musique d'Orlande de Lassus, contenant ses Chansons à quatre, cinq & six parties. Superius. [*Pierre de Saint-André: Paris,*] 1576. *obl.* 4°.

A. 337. h.

LASSO (ORLANDO DI)

— Le Thresor de Musique d'Orlande de Lassus ... Contenant ses chansons Françoises, Italiennes, & Latines, à quatre, cinq & six parties; Reueu & Corrigé ... en ceste troisieme Edition. Contra Tenor. [*Pierre de Saint-André: Paris*,] 1594. *obl. 4°.*
A. 337. g.

— Tibi laus. Praise to Thee. Ti biau'r mawl. Motet for T. T. B. B. [Magnum Opus Musicum. No. 50, 154.] The English translation by W. S. Gwynn Williams. Y cyfieithiad Cymraeg gan John Eilian ... Ed. by W. S. Gwynn Williams. [Staff and tonic sol-fa notation.] *Lat., Eng. & Welsh.* pp. 3. *Gwynn Publishing Co.: Llangollen*, [1956.] 8°. **F. 231. nn. (13.)**

— Tibi laus. [Motet for four voices. Magnum Opus Musicum. No. 50.] [1859.] *See* NIEDERMEYER (L.) La Maîtrise, *etc.* 3ᵉ Année. Grande Maîtrise. No. 5. [1857–61.] fol. **H. 1237.**

— Tibi laus, Tibi gloria. Motet for five voices, unaccompanied ... Edited ... by J. Atkins. 1914. *See* OULD (S. G.) Cantiones Sacrae, *etc.* No. 70. 1899, *etc.* 8°. **F. 1108.**

— Timor et tremor venerunt super me. Motet for six Voices, edited by F. Damrosch. *G. Schirmer: New York*, 1899. 8°.
F. 1179. (20.)

— Trionfo del tempo. *See* supra: [Continuation du mellange.— Passan vostri trionfi.]

— Tristis est anima mea. *See* supra: [Selectissimae Cantiones ... Quinque et Quatuor Vocibus. 1568.]

— Tu exsurgens ... (Vere languores nostros. A. Lotti.) Transcribed by C. Rossini. (S. S. A.) *J. Fischer & Bro.: New York, Birmingham*, 1931. 8°. **F. 1175. q. (43.)**

— Four Tudor Canzonas. *See* infra: [*Unidentified Excerpts.*]

— Turn Thee, O Lord, and deliver my Soul. *See* supra: [Sacrae Cantiones Quatuor Vocum. 1585.—Domine convertere.]

— Tutto lo di mi dici "canta". *See* infra: [Libro de Villanelle, Moresche et altre Canzoni.]

— Ubi est Abel, frater tuus? *See* supra: [Selectissimae Cantiones ... Quinque et Quatuor Vocibus. 1568.]

— Unto Thee, O Lord. *See* supra: [Cantiones Aliquot Quinque Vocum.—Gratia sola Dei.]

— Valle profonda. Deep Valley, Echo song ... Arranged, edited, and English adaptation by Maynard Klein. ⟨Choir I. S. S. A. T. B. Choir II. S. S. A. T. B.⟩ *Ital. & Eng.* pp. 10. *Boosey & Hawkes: [New York*, 1950.] 8°. **F. 1744. j. (21.)**

— Venite ad me omnes. *See* supra: [Moduli Quinis Vocibus.]

— Libro de Villanelle, Moresche, et altre Canzoni, a 4. 5. 6. & 8. voci, *etc.* Alto. *Per Pietro Phalesio & Giovanni Bellero: Anversa*, 1582. *obl. 4°.* **A. 337.**

— [Libro de Villanelle, Moresche, et altre Canzoni.] Io ti voria. (O would that I could tell thee.) Canzonetta. For four-part chorus of mixed voices a capella. English text adapted by M. K. ... Edited by Maynard Klein. *Ital. & Eng.* pp. 4. *G. Schirmer: New York*, [1965.] 8°. **F. 1744. vv. (23.)**

Libro de Villanelle, Moresche, et altre Canzoni.—Matona, mia cara

— Matona, lovely Maiden ... Madrigal for four voices. Words imitated and adapted from the original Italian by W. A. Barrett. 1885. *See* PERIODICAL PUBLICATIONS.— *London*. The Musical Times, *etc.* No. 511. 1844, *etc.* 8°. **P. P. 1945. aa.**

— Matona, dearest Maiden. Arranged for S. S. C. by Geo. Oakey ... Words by A. J. Foxwell. pp. 7. *J. Curwen & Sons: London; Leipzig* [printed, 1896.] 8°. [*Choruses for equal Voices. no.* 373.] **E. 861.**

LASSO (ORLANDO DI)

— Matona, dearest Maiden. Madrigal for four voices. Words by A. J. Foxwell. [1897.] *See* CHORAL. The Choral Handbook. No. 426. [1885, *etc.*] 8°. **E. 862.**

— Matona, dearest Maiden. Madrigal for four voices. [A. T. T. B. Words by] A. J. Foxwell. *J. Curwen & Sons: London*, [1902.] 8°. The Apollo Club, No. 215. **F. 667.**

— Matona, lovely Maiden ... English text by W. A. Barrett ... Edited by G. W. Gore. (Mixed Voices.) *H. Flammer: New York*, 1938. 8°. **F. 585. zz. (27.)**

— Matona, mia cara. Matona, my beloved. Matona, fy anwylyd. Madrigal for T. T. B. B., the English translation by W. S. Gwynn Williams, y Cyfieithiad Cymraeg gan Euros Bowen ... Arr. W. S. Gwynn Williams. *Ital., Eng. & Welsh.* pp. 4. *Gwynn Publishing Co.: Llangollen*, [1949.] 8°.
F. 163. jj. (38.)

— Matona, lovely Maiden ... Madrigal for four mixed voices. Words imitated and adapted from the original Italian by W. A. Barrett. *Eng. & Ital.* pp. 11. *Chappell & Co.: London*, [1960.] 8°. **F. 1744. ee. (10.)**

— Matona, lovely Maiden ... Madrigal for four mixed voices. Words imitated and adapted from the original Italian by W. A. Barrett. *Eng. & Ital.* pp. 11. *Chappell & Co.: London*, [1963.] 8°. **E. 1563. (3.)**

— Matona, lovely Maiden ... Madrigal for four voices. Words imitated from the ... Italian by W. A. Barrett. *See* NOVELLO AND CO. Novello's Tonic Sol-fa Series. No. 346. [1885.] 4°.
B. 885.

— Matona, lovely Maiden ... Transcribed (for Brass or Reed Instruments) by I. Cheyette. (Score.) *Galaxy Music Corporation: New York*, 1938. 8°. The A cappella Wind Choir Series, No. 1. **e. 668. i. (5.)**

— [Libro de Villanelle, Moresche, et altre Canzoni.] O bella fusa. (The Spinning Wheel.) (Canzonetta.) For four-part chorus of mixed voices a cappella ... English text by M. K. Edited by Maynard Klein. *Ital. & Eng.* pp. 7. *G. Schirmer: New York*, [1965.] 8°. **F. 1744. vv. (24.)**

Libro de Villanelle, Moresche, et altre Canzoni.—O la, o che buon êco

— O la, o che buon êco.—Hark, hark! the Echo falling.— Villanella for eight voices, the English words by W. G. Rothery ... Edited by L. Benson. [1908.] *See* ORIANA. The Oriana, *etc.* No. 47. [1905, *etc.*] 8°. **F. 1685.**

— Echo Song. For Double Chorus of Soprano I & II, and Alto, translated by C. F. M. ... Arranged by C. F. Manney. *B. F. Wood Music Co.: Boston, London*, 1935. 8°.
F. 638. f. (39.)

— Echo Song. For Three-part Double Chorus of Women's Voices, English version by A. Marlhom ... Arranged by G. W. Gore. *H. Flammer: New York*, 1937. 8°.
F. 217. h. (12.)

— Echo Song. For Double Chorus of Mixed Voices. English version by F. Bornschein. *J. Fischer & Bro.: New York*, 1939. 8°. **F. 1744. c. (24.)**

— Echo Song. For Double Chorus of Mixed Voices, English version by A. Marlhom ... Arranged by G. W. Gore. *Harold Flammer: New York*, 1940. 8°. **F. 1744. d. (15.)**

— L'Eccho. The Echo. Yr eco. Villanella for double mixed choir (S. A. T. B. & S. A. T. B.) The English translation by W. S. Gwynn Williams. Y cyfieithiad cymraeg gan John Eilian ... Ed. by W. S. Gwynn Williams. [Staff and tonic sol-fa notation.] *Fr., Eng. & Welsh.* pp. 6. *Gwynn Publishing Co.: Llangollen*, [1955.] 8°. **F. 1744. p. (10.)**

LASSO (ORLANDO DI)

— Echo-Song ... For double chorus of mixed voices. English version by Sigmund Spaeth ... Arranged ... by Wilhelm Widmann. *Eng. & Ital.* pp. 12. *Chappell & Co.: London,* [1966.] 8°.   **F. 1874. (19.)**

—- O la, o che buon êco ... Edited by Lionel Benson. [1908.] *See* NOVELLO AND CO. Novello's Tonic Sol-fa Series. No. 1691. [1876, *etc.*] 4°.   **B. 885.**

Libro de Villanelle, Moresche et altre Canzoni. — Other numbers

— [O occhi manza mia.] Sweet Maiden ... English words by P. Newall. Edited and arranged for strings by L. Lebell. Tonic Solfa translation by H. J. Timothy. [P. F. score.] *Stainer & Bell: London,* 1927. 8°.
Stainer & Bell's Choral Library, No. 235.   **F. 1137. d.**

— [O occhi manza mia.] O Eyes of my Beloved ... For S. A. T. B. mixed chorus. English text by W. E. ... Edited by Walter Ehret. *Eng. & Ital.* pp. 6. *Walton Music Corporation: North Hollywood,* [1963.] 8°.
Part of the "Walton historical choral Series".   **F. 1744. nn. (8.)**

— O occhi manza mia. (Thine Eyes, oh, my Beloved.) For four-part chorus of mixed voices a cappella. English text by M. K. ... Edited by Maynard Klein. *Ital. & Eng.* pp. 4. *G. Schirmer:* [*New York, London,* 1979.] 8°.   **F. 1680. r. (2.)**

— S'io fusse ciaul. (Were I a tiny Bird.) Canzonetta for four-part chorus of mixed voices a cappella. English text by M. K. ... Edited by Maynard Klein. *Ital. & Eng.* pp. 7. *G. Schirmer: New York, London,* [1972.] 8°.   **F. 1874. v. (14.)**

— [S'io ti videss'.] Ah, could my Eyes behold thee ... For four-part chorus of mixed voices a cappella. English words by Sidney Maurice ... Edited by Walter Barrie. pp. 4. *Roberton Publications: Wendover,* [1976.] 8°.   **F. 1874. w. (3.)**

— Tutto lo di mi dici "canta". (Day after Day they all say "sing".) Canzonetta for four-part chorus of mixed voices a cappella. English text by M. K. ... Edited by Maynard Klein. *Ital. & Eng.* pp. 8. *G. Schirmer: New York, London,* [1972.] 8°.   **F. 1874. v. (15.)**

— [Tutto lo di.] Day after Day they all say "Sing" ... For eight-part chorus of mixed voices a cappella. English text by M. K. ... Edited by Maynard Klein. *Eng. & Ital.* pp. 16. *G. Schirmer: New York, London,* [1978.] 8°.   **F. 1680. r. (3.)**

— We do adore Thee. *See* supra: [Adoramus te, Christe. Magnum Opus Musicum. No. 66.]

— When my old Man. *See* supra: [Le Premier livre de chansons à quatre parties. — Quand mon mari.]

— When my rich Husband is at Home. *See* supra: [Le Premier livre de chansons à quatre parties. — Quand mon mari.]

— Whom saw ye, O Shepherds. *See* supra: [Cantiones Aliquot Quinque Vocum. — Quem vidistis pastores.]

DOUBTFUL AND SUPPOSITITIOUS WORKS

Mon cœur se recommande à vous

— O let me look on thee. Madrigal. [Attributed to Lasso in J. B. T. Weckerlin's "Échos du Temps passé," vol. 1.] English words by A. Watson. *See* ARION. Arion. [vol. 1. no. 23.] [1899.] 8°.   **G. 771.**

— Take my Heart into your Care ... [Four-part song.] English words by P. Newall. Edited and arranged for Strings by L. Lebell. Tonic Solfa translation by H. J. Timothy. [P. F. score.] *Stainer & Bell: London,* 1927. 8°.
Stainer & Bell's Choral Library, No. 234.   **F. 1137. d.**

LASSO (ORLANDO DI)

— My Heart commends itself to thee. Madrigal for Men's Voices, translation by F. M. Daltry ... Arr. by J. S. Daltry. *B. F. Wood Music: Boston, London,* 1936. 8°.   **F. 638. g. (26.)**

— My Heart is offered still to you. Madrigal for mixed voices. English version by Alice Parker ... Edited by David Randolph. *Eng. & Fr.* pp. 6. *Lawson-Gould Music Publishers: New York,* [1956.] 8°.   **F. 1744. s. (9.)**

— My Heart is offered still to you ... Madrigal for mixed voices S. A. T. B. English version by Alice Parker ... Edited by David Randolph, *etc.* [Staff and tonic sol-fa notation.] *Eng. & Fr.* pp. 4. *J. Curwen: London,* [1961.] 8°.
[*Choral Handbook. no.* 515.]   **E. 862.**

— O Lord of Heav'n. SSA and piano (or organ) ad lib ... English words by Ivan Trusler ... Edited and arr. by John Cramer. pp. 4. *Josef Weinberger: London,* [1961.] 8°.   **F. 1171. uu. (3.)**

— My lonely Heart remembers you ... For S. A. T. B. chorus. English text by W. E. ... Edited by Walter Ehret. *Eng. & Fr.* pp. 7. *Walton Music Corporation: North Hollywood,* [1963.] 8°.
Part of the "Walton historical choral Series".   **F. 1744. nn. (7.)**

— My Heart is offered still to you ... For three-part chorus of equal voices S. S. A. English version by Alice Parker ... Ed. & arr. Jerry Weseley Harris, *etc.* [Staff and tonic sol-fa notation.] *Eng. & Fr.* pp. 4. *Lawson-Gould Music Publishers: New York; J. Curwen & Sons: London; London* [printed, 1965.] 8°.
[*Choruses for equal Voices. no.* 2615.]   **E. 861.**

— Mon cœur se recommande à vous. [Song.] Melody attributed to Orlando di Lasso. Arranged by B. Van Dieren. *Oxford University Press: London,* 1927. fol.   **H. 1846. mm. (8.)**

— *See* ECCARD (J.) Missa a 5 vocibus super Mon coeur se recommende [*sic*] à vous ... Herausgegeben von U. Herrmann. [1964.] 8°.   **F. 1176. kk. (5.)**

UNIDENTIFIED EXCERPTS

— Four Tudor Canzonas. For brass ... Arranged by Neil Butterworth. Score [and parts], *etc.* 8 pt. *Chappell & Co.: London,* [1961.] 4°.   **g. 1110. i. (3.)**

APPENDIX

— *See* BORDES (C.) Chansonnier du XVIᵉ Siècle. Choix des plus excellentes Chansons à 4 voix de ... Roland de Lassus, *etc.* [1905?] *obl.* fol.   **E. 292. (1.)**

— *See* CHANSONS. [2.] Disieme Liure de Chansons à quatre parties, d'Orlande de lassus & autres, *etc.* 1570. *obl.* 16°.   **K. 2. b. 4. (9.)**

— *See* CHANSONS. [2.] Dousieme liure de chansons à quatre & cinq parties, d'Orlande de Lassus & autres autheurs, *etc.* 1569. *obl.* 8°.   **K. 11. e. 3. (12.)**

— *See* CHANSONS. [2.] Dousieme liure de Chansons, *etc.* 1572. *obl.* 16°.   **K. 2. h. 9. (3.)**

— *See* CHANSONS. [2.] Tresieme Liure de Chansons à quatre parties, d'Orlande de lassus & autres, *etc.* 1570. *obl.* 16°.   **K. 2. b. 4. (12.)**

— *See* CHANSONS. [2.] Quatorsieme liure de chansons à quatre & cinq parties, d'Orlande de Lassus & autres autheurs, *etc.* 1567. *obl.* 8°.   **K. 11. e. 3. (14.)**

— *See* CHANSONS. [2.] Quatorsieme Liure de Chansons, à quatre, & cinq parties, d'Orlande de lassus, & autres, *etc.* 1571. *obl.* 16°.   **K. 2. b. 4. (13.)**

LASSO (ORLANDO DI)

— *See* CHANSONS. [2.] Quinzieme liure de chansons à quatre & cinq parties, d'Orlande de Lassus & autres autheurs, *etc.* 1569. *obl.* 8°.　　　　　　　　　　**K. 11. e. 3. (15.)**

— *See* CHANSONS. [2.] Quinzieme Liure de Chansons, à quatre, cinq, & six parties, d'Orlande de lassus, & autres, *etc.* 1571. *obl.* 16°.　　　　　　　　　　　**K. 2. b. 4. (14.)**

— *See* CHANSONS. [2.] Sesieme liure de chansons à quatre & cinq parties, par Orlande de Lassus & autres autheurs, *etc.* 1567. *obl.* 8°.　　　　　　　　　　**K. 11. e. 3. (16.)**

— *See* CHANSONS. [2.] Sesieme Livre de Chansons à quatre & cinq parties d'Orlande de Lassus, & autres, *etc.* 1573. *obl.* 16°.　　　　　　　　　**K. 2. b. 4. (15.)**

— *See* CHANSONS. [2.] Dixsetieme liure de chansons à quatre & cinq parties, par Orlande de Lassus [and others], *etc.* 1567. *obl.* 8°.　　　　　　　　　　**K. 11. e. 3. (17.)**

— *See* CHANSONS. [2.] Dixsetieme Liure de Chansons à quatre & cinq parties, d'Orlande de lassus, *etc.* 1570. *obl.* 16°.　　　　　　　　　　　**K. 2. b. 4. (16.)**

— *See* CHANSONS. [2.] Dixneufieme liure de chansons à quatre & cinq parties, d'Orlande de Lassus & autres, *etc.* 1570. *obl.* 8°.　　　　　　　　**K. 11. e. 3. (19.)**

— *See* CHANSONS. [2.] Dixneufieme liure de Chansons à quatre & cinq parties, d'Orlande de lassus, & autres, *etc.* 1573. *obl.* 16°.　　　　　　　　　　　**K. 2. h. 9. (1.)**

— *See* CHANSONS. [2.] Vingtieme liure de chansons à quatre & cinq parties d'Orlande de Lassus & autres, *etc.* 1569. *obl.* 8°.　　　　　　　　**K. 11. e. 3. (20.)**

— *See* CHANSONS. [2.] Vingtieme Liure de Chansons, à quatre, cinq, & six parties, d'Orlande de lassus, *etc.* 1571. *obl.* 16°.　　　　　　　　　　**K. 2. b. 4. (19.)**

— *See* CHANSONS. [4.] Le Quatoirsiesme Liure a quatre parties contenant Dix Huyet Chansons Italiennes, Six chansons francoises, & Six Motetz, faictz (a la Nouuelle composition d'aucuns d'Italie) par Rolando di Lassus, *etc.* 1555. *obl.* 4°.　　　　　　　　　　**K. 3. a. 13.**

— *See* DOUEN (E. O.) Clément Marot et le Psautier Huguenot ... contenant ... des spécimens d'harmonie de ... Roland de Lattre, *etc.* 1878–9. 8°.　　　　　　**3089. gg. 2.**

— *See* GARDANO (Angelo) Musica di Tredici Autori ... Nella quale si contengono ... Madrigali ... delli infrascritti Autori ... O. di Lassus, *etc.* 1589. 4°.　　　　**K. 3. g. 11.**

— *See* JOLAS (B.) Lassus ricercare. Pour dix instruments. [Based on music by O. di Lasso.] [1972.] 8°.　　**f. 760. u. (3.)**

— *See* PRIMA. Prima Stella. De Madrigali ... Di Orlando Lasso, *etc.* 1570. 4°.　　　　　　　　　**K. 3. g. 12.**

— *See* RENNER (J.) Auswahl deutscher Madrigale ... von O. di Lasso, *etc.* 1875. 8°.　　　　　**F. 585. v. (20.)**

— *See* VALOTTI (F. A.) Responsoria ... Adjectae sunt duae Antiphonae autore Orlando di Lasso. [1830?] *obl.* fol.　　　　　　　　　　**E. 602. h. (4.)**

— *See* VINCENTIUS (C.) In magni illius ... Orlandi de Lasso magnum opus musicum bassus ad organum noua methodo dispositus. 1625. fol.　　　　　**Hirsch III. 887.**

— *See* WILLIAMS (Aaron) *Arranger.* Lassus, Victoria, Palestrina. Three-part vocal compositions arranged for recorders ... by A. Williams. [1975.] 4°.　　　　　**g. 109. y. (4.)**

— *See* WINTERFELD (C. von) Johannes Gabrieli und sein Zeitalter, *etc.* (Dritter Theil, enthaltend ... Tonwerke ... von ... O. Lasso, *etc.*) 1834. 4°.　　　　**7896. h. 6.**

LASSO (ORLANDO DI) and LASSO (RODOLFO DI)

— Cantiones Sacræ, ab Orlando de Lasso et huius Filio, Rudolpho de Lasso, Sex Vocibus Compositæ, Typis iam primo subiectæ & in lucem editæ. Discantus. *Nicolaus Henricus: Monachii,* 1601. 4°.　　　　　　**D. 20. e.**

— Geistliche Psalmen mit dreyen stimmen ... Gedruckt zu München bey Adam Berg—Anno MDLXXXVIII. Neu herausgegeben ... von Walther Lipphardt. pp. 59. *Bärenreiter-Verlag: Kassel, Basel,* [1951.] 8°.　　　　　　　　　　　**F. 1176. v. (14.)**

LASSO (RODOLFO DI)

— *See* LASSO (O. di) [*Smaller Collections.*] Magnum Opus Musicum Orlandi de Lasso ... a Ferdinando ... & Rudolpho ... Authoris filijs ... Collectum, & impensis eorundem Typis mandatum, *etc.* 1604. fol.　　　　**K. 4. k. 1.**

— *See* LASSO (O. di) [*Masses.*] Orlandi de Lasso ... Missae Posthumae ... vulgatæ demum affectu, studio sumtu ... Rodolphi de Lasso, *etc.* 1610. fol.　　　　**K. 9. b. 6.**

— *See* LASSO (O. di) and LASSO (R. di) Cantiones Sacræ, ab Orlando de Lasso et huius Filio, Rudulpho de Lasso ... Compositæ, *etc.* 1601. 4°.　　　　　　**D. 20. e.**

— *See* LASSO (O. di) and LASSO (R. di) Geistliche Psalmen mit dreyen stimmen ... Gedruckt zu München bey Adam Berg—Anno MDLXXXVIII, *etc.* [1951.] 8°.　　**F. 1176. v. (14.)**

LASSON (PER)

— Lasson Album. 15 Sange med Klavier accompagnement. *C. Warmuth: Christiania,* [1890?] fol.　　**F. 636. r. (9.)**

— Crescendo. [P. F.]　*C. Warmuth: Christiania,* [1885?] fol.　　　　　　　　　　**h. 3880. (5.)**

— Crescendo. [P. F.] [1892.] *See* FLEURS. Fleurs et Diamants, *etc.* No. 54. [1882–93.] fol.　　　　　**h. 3294.**

— Crescendo pour piano. *Chappell & Co.: London,* [1899.] fol.　　　　　　　　　　**h. 3282. f. (16.)**

— Crescendo. Morceau pour piano. pp. 4. *Joseph Williams: London,* [c. 1905.] fol.　　　　　**h. 3865. xx. (6.)**

— Crescendo ... Edited by C. Woodhouse. [P. F.]　*J. R. Lafleur & Son: London,* 1923. 4°. *Edition Lafleur, No. 237.*　　　　　**g. 1125. k. (9.)**

— Crescendo ... Arrangiert von L. Artok. [Parts.]　*B. Schott's Söhne: Mainz, Leipzig,* 1926. 4°. [*Schott's Domesticum-Salon-Orchester. No. 203.*]　　**g. 1053. a.**

— Une Demande. [P. F.]　*C. Warmuth: Christiania,* [1890?] 8°.　　　　　　　　　　**f. 133. m. (23.)**

— Fest Marsch ved Ordenskapitlet i Studentersamfundet i Aning H. M. Grisens 5ᵗᵉ Födselsdag, 18ᵈᵉ Martz, 1882. [P. F.] *C. Warmuth: Christiania,* [1882?] fol.　　**h. 3880. (6.)**

LASST

— Lasst die Nacht also vergeh'n. Chor aus Ossian's Gesängen ⟨für Männerstimmen, von *∗∗∗*⟩. [1839.] *See* PERIODICAL PUBLICATIONS.— *Leipzig.*— Neue Zeitschrift für Musik. [Sammlung von Musik-Stücken, *etc.*] Hft. 6. [1838, *etc.*] fol.　　　　　　　　　　**Hirsch M. 1134.**

— Lasst mich euch fragen. *See* FLOTOW (F. F. A. von) *Baron.* [Martha.]

— Lasst mich ruhen. [Song.] *See* JENSEN (A.)

— Lasst mich ruhen, lasst mich träumen. [Song.] *See* KRUG (A.) Fünf Lieder, *etc.* No. 2.

— Lasst mich ruhen. [Song.] *See* LISZT (F.)

LASST

— Lasst mich ruhen. [Song.] *See* MAHLBERG (C.) Fünf Lieder. Op. 16. No. 3.

— Lasst mich ruhen. [Song.] *See* SEYFFARDT (E. H.) Vier Lieder. Op. 4. No. 1.

— Lasst nur die Politicker. *German air* ... with five variations for the piano-forte. *In:* The Harmonicon. vol. 8, pt. 2. pp. 323–327. 1830. 4°. **P. P. 1947.**

— Lasst uns sorgen, lasst uns wachen. Kantate. *See* BACH (J. S.)

— Last [*sic*] uns zur dunkeln Laube gehn. [Three-part song.] *See* SCHIKANEDER (E.)

LASSÙ

— Lassù, lassù, risplendere. *See* VERDI (F. G. F.) [I Masnadieri.]

LASSUS (ROLAND DE)

— *See* LASSO (O. di)

LASSUSIUS

— *See* LASSO.

LAST

— *See also* LASST.

— The Last. Song. *See* DANDRIDGE (M. E.)

— The Last aboard. Song. *See* MARKS (G.)

— Last Act—Finale. Song. *See* REED (Leslie)

— The Last Adieu. Song. *See* DAY (D.)

— The Last Adieu. [Song.] *See* NEULAND (W.)

— The Last Adieu. Ballad. *See* PERRY (E.)

— The Last Advent. Cantata. *See* TOZER (F.)

— The Last Appeal. Song. *See* BLOCKLEY (J.)

— The Last Appeal. Serenade. *See* MACFARREN (*Sir* G. A.)

— The Last Appeal. Ballad. *See* MAJOR (J. S.)

— A Last Appeal. Song. *See* PLUMPTON (A.)

— The Last Autumn Flower. Song. *See* ANCONA (K.)

— The Last Bird. Song. *See* SMART (H.)

— The Last Blessing. [Song.] *See* CROUCH (Frederick N.)

— The Last Blessing. Ballad. *See* WILLIAMS (W. L.)

— Last Blooms. [Part-song.] *See* WAREING (H. W.)

— The Last Boat home. [Song.] *See* SOLOMON (Frederic)

— The Last Bottle. [Musical monologue.] *See* ARPTHORP (H.)

— The last buccaneer. Song. *See* HULLAH (J. P.)

— The Last Bus. [Song.] *See* JONGHMANS (E.)

— The Last 'Bus home at Night. Song. *See* PETHER (Henry E.)

— The Last Call. Song. *See* LARA (I. de)

— The Last Call. Song. *See* SANDERSON (W. E.)

— The Last Cartridge. Song. *See* SERPETTE (G.)

— The Last Chantey. [Song.] *See* COOK (T. A.)

— The Last Chantey. [Two-part song.] *See* PRENDERGAST (W.)

LAST

— The Last Charge. Song. *See* KETTLE (C. E.)

— Last Christmas Day. Song. *See* TABRAR (Joseph)

— A Last Confession. Song. *See* BRUNO (H.)

— The Last Dance. [Song.] *See* WARE (H.)

— The Last Day. Hymn. *See* LEMARE (F.)

— The Last Day of Autumn. Chorus. *See* HICKOX (E. J.)

— The Last Day of Autumn. Song. *See* ROWLAND (A. C.)

— The Last Day of May. Part-Song. *See* MOLIQUE (W. B.)

— The Last Day of Pompeii. [Part-song.] *See* RITZ (J.)

— The last day of the Alabama. Song. *See* THUS. Thus Semmes spoke. [1864.] fol. **H. 1790. c. (18.)**

— The Last Days. [Song.] *See* ROMA (C.)

— Last Days. [Song.] *See* VAN DIEREN (B.)

— The Last dear Thing I was fond to love. [Song.] *See* GREATHEED (Samuel S.) [Hymn of Boyhood.]

— The Last Dream. Song. *See* COTTLE (W.)

— The Last Dream. Song. *See* COWEN (*Sir* F. H.)

— A Last farewell. Song. *See* BARKER (A.)

— A Last Farewell. Song. *See* BLOUNT (E. A. M.)

— A Last Farewell. Song. *See* BOEHR (F.)

— The Last Farewell. Song. *See* HANNA (B.)

— The Last Farewell. [Song.] *See* HARRIS (C. K.)

— The Last Farewell. Ballad. *See* HATTON (J. L.)

— The Last Farewell. Song. *See* LE BRUNN (George)

— A Last Farewell. Song. *See* RUSSELL (R. C. K.)

— A Last Farewell. Song. *See* SOMERVILLE (R.)

— The Last Farewell. Song. *See* VINEN (E. E.)

— The Last Faun seeks. [Song.] *See* ROBBINS (R. C.) Songs, *etc.* 13.

— The Last Faun thinks of Death. [Song.] *See* ROBBINS (R. C.) Songs, *etc.* 14.

— The Last Faun wakes. [Song.] *See* ROBBINS (R. C.) Songs, *etc.* 12.

— The Last Flagon. Song. *See* NEWTON (E. R.)

— The Last Footfall. Song. *See* SMITH (A. M.)

— The Last Furrow. Song. *See* WACHTMEISTER (A. R.)

— The Last Gift. Song. *See* ELLIOTT (L.)

— The Last Glimpse of Erin. Song. *See* COUNSEL (E.)

— The Last Good-bye. Song. *See* BARNES (L.)

— The Last Good-Bye. Song. *See* BRUCE (G.)

— The Last "Good bye". [Part-song.] *See* BURLEIGH (H. T.)

— The Last Good Bye. Song. *See* CARRINGTON (E.)

— The Last Good-bye. Song. *See* MILLARD (H.)

— The Last Good-bye. Song. *See* MURRAY (Fred) and LEIGH (F. W.)

LAST

— The Last Good-bye. Song. *See* SMITH, afterwards WHITE (A. M.)

— The Last Good Night. Serenade. *See* HARGITT (C. J.)

— The Last Good Night. [Song.] *See* ROSSINI (G. A.) [Guillaume Tell.—Quelle sauvage harmonie.]

— The Last Good-Night. [Song.] *See* STANLEY (C.)

— The Last grand Evensong. [Song.] *See* ASHFORDE (I.)

— The Last Green Leaf. Ballad. *See* BAYLY (T. H.)

— Last Greeting. [Song.] *See* SCHUBERT (F. P.) [*Doubtful and Supposititious Works.*] [Adieu.]

— The Last Grip. Song. *See* RODNEY (P.)

— The Last Hope. Hymn. *See* GOTTSCHALK (L. M.) [La Dernière Espérance.]

— The Last Hour. [Song.] *See* KRAMER (A. W.)

— Last Hours. [Song.] *See* JACOBSON (M.)

— The Last Hours. Cantata. *See* WOOD (F. H.)

— The Last Invocation. [Part-song.] *See* BINKERD (Gordon W.)

— The Last Invocation. [Song.] *See* BRIDGE (F.)

— The Last Invocation. [Song.] *See* GARRATT (P.)

— The Last Invocation. [Part-song.] *See* KASTLE (Leonard)

— Last June. Song. *See* JUDGE (E. S.)

— The Last Kiss. Song. *See* BEAUMONT (G.)

— The Last Kiss. [Song.] *See* JACKSON (T. J.)

— The Last Kiss Grandma gave me. Song. *See* DAVIS (G. L.)

— The Last Lay of Chatelard. [Song.] *See* WILSON (John) *Public Singer.*

— The Last Lay of the Forester. [Song.] *See* BARKER (G. A.)

— The Last Leaf. Song. *See* FLETCHER (S.)

— The Last Leaf. [Song.] *See* HOMER (S.) Four Songs, *etc.* [No. 3.]

— The Last Letter. Song. *See* LEE (C.)

— Last Light. [Part-song.] *See* BINKERD (Gordon W.) Choral Strands ... 1.

— The Last Lines in a Letter from Home. [Song.] *See* BOLL (L. H.)

— The last links are broken. Ballad. *See* LODER (E. J.)

— The Last Links are broken. Duet. *See* STEERS (F.)

— The Last little Flower that you gave. Ballad. *See* TOURS (B.)

— The Last Load. Part-Song. *See* CLARKE (J. H. S.)

— The Last Load. Song Service. *See* WITTY (J. S.)

— The Last Loäd Hoäm. Song. *See* FLETCHER (C.)

— The Last Loäd Hoäm. Song. *See* PLUMSTEAD (Mary)

— The Last Loäd Hoäm. Song. *See* YATES (E.)

— The Last Load Home. Solo & Chorus. *See* FRANKS (G. C.)

— The Last long Mile. Song. *See* BREITENFELD (Emil)

— The Last long Trail. [Song.] *See* BENWELL (Archibald H.)

— The Last Look. Song. *See* GUGLIELMO (P. D.)

LAST

— The Last Look. [Service of song.] *See* TIPTON (J.)

— A Last Look. Song. *See* WILSON (*Mrs* W. D.)

— The last look you gave me. Ballad. *See* MORI (F.)

— The Last Lover. Song. *See* CLARKE (R. B.)

— The Last Lullaby. Song. *See* JOSEPHS (T.)

— The Last Lullaby. [Song.] *See* SOMERSET (I. C.) *Lady Henry Somerset.*

— The Last Man. [Song.] *See* CALLCOTT (W. H.)

— The Last Man in Town. Serio-comic Song. *See* VANDERVELL (W.)

— Last May a braw Wooer cam' down the lang Glen. A Favorite Scotch Song, the words ... by R. Burns. [*Dean and Munday: London*, 1824.] 8°.
Ladies' Monthly Museum, etc. Vols. XIX., XX. Musical Appendix, pp. 138–140. **P. P. 5153. i.**

— Last May a braw wooer. Scotch ballad. *London*, [1855.] fol.
No. 315 *of the "Musical Bouquet".* **H. 2345.**

— The Last meeting. Song. *See* LEVI (H.)

— The last meeting, or meet me tonight. Ballad. *See* LINTER (R.)

— The Last Message. Song & chorus. *See* LONG (J. W.)

— The Last Milestone. Song. *See* CARTER (A. L.)

— The Last Milestone. Song. *See* PONTET (Henry T.)

— Last Movement. Opera. *See* WISHART (Trevor)

— The Last Muster. [Song.] *See* PONTET (Henry T.)

— Last New Year's Day. *Dick of Taunton Dean.* Old English Song, [Words] shortened and revised by A. J. Foxwell. [Tonic sol-fa and staff notation.] [1894?] *See* CHORAL. Choral Leaflets. No. 114. [1882, *etc.*] *s. sh.* 4°. **F. 569.**

— Last nicht there were four Maries. *The Four Maries.* [Song.] *Dundee*, [1877.] fol. **H. 1791. b. (34.)**

— Last Night. [Song.] *See* ANSON (H. V.)

— Last Night. Song. *See* ASHTON (A. B. L.)

— Last Night. Ballad. *See* BLAKELEY (W.)

— Last Night. Song. *See* BRAHE (M. H.)

— The Last Night. Part-Song. *See* CLOKEY (J. W.)

— Last Night. [Song.] *See* COX (G. W.) Two Songs ... Op. 13. No. 1.

— Last Night. Song. *See* DANCY (C. E.)

— Last Night. [Song.] *See* FRYER (H.) Five Songs, *etc.* [No. 2.]

— Last Night. Song. *See* JOHNS (C.)

— Last Night. Song. *See* KJERULF (H.) [Længsel.]

— Last Night. Song. *See* KLEIN (B. O.)

— Last Night. [Song.] *See* LARA (I. de) *pseud.*

— Last Night. Song. *See* PARKER (Walter C.)

— Last Night. Song. *See* RAM (N. C.)

— Last Night. [Song.] *See* SHACKFORD (Charles)

— Last Night. [Song.] *See* WALLIS (W. H.)

— Last Night a Dream came into my Head. *The Comical Dreamer.* [Song, written by T. Durfey.] [*London*, 1715?] *s. sh.* fol. **H. 1601. (265.)**

LAST

— Last night all idly dreaming. Song. *See* BARRY (C. A.) Six Songs, *etc.* No. 2.

— Last Night and this. Ballad. *See* CARPENTER (Laura D.)

— Last Night as I lay sleeping. [Song.] *See* KREUZ (E.) Songs ... No. 3.

— Last Night as I lay sleeping. Carol. *See* MARTIN (*Sir* G. C.)

— The Last Night at Bethany. Cantata. *See* WILLIAMS (C. L.)

— Last Night I dreamed. [Song.] *See* CADMAN (Charles W.)

— Last Night I dreamed. Recitative and Aria. *See* MACLENNAN (E. A. F.)

— Last Night I dreamed. [Part-song.] *See* REGER (M.) [8 ausgewählte Volkslieder. No. 4. Ich hab die Nacht geträumet.]

— Last Night I dreamed of you. Ballad. *See* CRUGER (Dox)

— Last Night I dreamed of you. Song. *See* DANMARK (Ribé) and KELLETTE (J. W.)

— Last Night I dreamed of you. Song. *See* SHEETZ (W. L.)

— Last Night I dreamt. Song. *See* LEVI (E.)

— Last Night I had a Vision. Community Song. *See* ATHERTON (P. L.)

— Last Night, I heard the Nightingale. [Song.] *See* SALTER (M. T.) Four Songs ... 3.

— Last night I lay a sleeping. A Christmas carol. *See* GAUNTLETT (H. J.)

— Last Night I lay in Dreamland. [Song.] *See* GROSZ (M. de)

— Last Night I was dreaming of you. [Song.] *See* DISTIN (T.)

— Last Night I woke from dreams of thee. Song. *See* ROMER (F.)

— Last Night in Dreamland. Song. *See* KELLIE (L.)

— Last Night, Love. Song. *See* MOFFAT (A. E.)

— The Last Night of the Year. Four-part song. *See* SULLIVAN (*Sir* A. S.)

— Last night the dogs did bark. *Nobody coming to marry me ...* Ballad. *London,* [1805?] fol.   **G. 796. (23.)**

— Last night the dogs did bark. *Nobody coming to marry me.* Ballad. *London,* [1856.] fol.
No. 465 *of the "Cyclopedia of Music. Miscellaneous Series of Songs".*   **H. 2342.**

— Last Night the Dogs did bark. Two-part Song. *See* BLOWER (M.)

— Last of all. Song. *See* BEHREND (J. A. H.)

— The Last of his race. Song. *See* HIME (E. L.)

— The Last of his Regiment. Song. *See* NELSON (William H.)

— The Last of his Regiment. [Song.] *See* POWELL (W. C.)

— The Last of his Tribe. [Song.] *See* HELLEMANN (Christian)

— The Last of his Tribe. Part-Song. *See* JENKINS (D. C.)

— The Last of the Boys. Song. *See* WATSON (W. M.)

— The Last of the Cabbies. Song. *See* ANDREWS (W. B.)

— The Last of the Crew. Song. *See* KRENKEL (G.)

— The Last of the Crew. Song. *See* MOIR (F. L.)

LAST

— The Last of the Dandies. Song. *See* COLLINS (Charles)

— The Last of the Dandies. Song. *See* LE BRUNN (George)

— The Last of the Fairies. Ballad. *See* LINLEY (G.)

— The Last of the Family. [Comedy.] *See* KELLY (M.)

— The Last of the Leaves on the Bough. Song. *See* BEDFORD (H.) Unaccompanied Songs. [No. 5.]

— The Last of the Sandies. [Song.] *See* LAUDER (*Sir* H. M.)

— Last on the Roll. [Song.] *See* SAINT QUENTIN (E.) *pseud.*

— The Last Oyster. [Song.] *See* FARNIE (H. B.)

— The Last Parade. Song. *See* MOLLOY (J. L.)

— The Last Parade. Song. *See* RODNEY (P.) *pseud.*

— The Last Pilot. [Part-song.] *See* ANDREWS (M.)

— The Last Pilot. Song. *See* BAILEY (F. M.)

— The Last Portage. [Song.] *See* ILLSLEY (P. J.)

— Last Post. [Song.] *See* GARRATT (P.)

— Last Post. Choral Song. *See* STANFORD (*Sir* C. V.)

— The Last Prayer. Song. *See* BUNNETT (E.)

— The Last Prayer. Mélodie religieuse. *See* LOUIS EUGENE NAPOLEON, *Prince Imperial of France.*

— The Last Prayer. Part Song. *See* RHEINBERGER (J. G.) [Jahreszeiten. Op. 186. No. 8. Letztes Gebet.]

— The Last Prayer of Mary, Queen of Scots. Song. *See* RYVES (L. M.)

— The Last Pub. Song. *See* SHAND (Ernest)

— The Last Quarter Moon. [Part-song.] *See* WINSLOW (Richard)

— "The Last Ray of Evening." Duet, for two voices; with an accompaniment for the Piano-Forte.   *London,* [1851.] fol.
                    H. 1253. (45.)

— The Last Ray of evening. Duet.   *London,* [1865.] fol.
                    H. 1790. a. (59.)

— The Last Regret. Song. *See* MOIR (F. L.)

— The Last Repose. Song. *See* NEUKOMM (S. VON)

— The Last Request. Song. *See* CARTER (J. F.)

— A Last Request. Song. *See* GUNNING (M. S. W.)

— The Last Request. Song. *See* HARVEY (R. F.)

— A Last Request. Song. *See* HOMAN (L.)

— A Last Request. Song. *See* LEWIS (G. F.)

— The Last Request. Quartet. *See* MARSCHNER (H. A.)

— The Last Request. Song. *See* PEDE (T. T.)

— The Last Resting Place. [Song.] *See* FAURÉ (G. U.) [Au Cimetière.]

— The Last Revel. [Song.] *See* BANTOCK (*Sir* G.) Songs from the Chinese Poets. 5.

— The Last Rose. Song. *See* GABRIEL, afterwards MARCH (Mary Ann Virginia)

— A Last Rose. Song. *See* PATTINSON (J.)

— The Last Rose. [Song.] *See* SHAPLEIGH (B.) [Two Songs.] Op. 27. No. 1.

LAST

— The Last Rose of Summer. *See* 'TIS. 'Tis the last rose of summer. [1859.] fol. **H. 1392. a. (9.)**

— The Last Rose of Summer. Song. *See* 'TIS. 'Tis the last rose, *etc.* [1872.] fol. **H. 1791. a. (56.)**

— The Last Rose of Summer. Irish Air, *etc.* [1908.] *See* MACNAUGHT (W. G.) Novello's School Songs. No. 896 [b]. 1892, *etc.* 8°. **F. 280. d.**

— The Last Rose of Summer. *See* HERZ (H.) The last Rose of Summer, with variations for the Pianoforte, *etc.* [1848.] fol. **h. 467. (3.)**

— The Last Rose of Summer, and Robin Adair ... arranged with variations. [P. F.] *London*, [1855.] fol. *No. 275 of the "Musical Bouquet".* **H. 2345.**

— The Last Rose of Summer. *See* NAVA (F.) *pseud.* The Exile's Lament. Moments of Leisure, *etc.* No. 21. [1857.] fol. **h. 1363. a. (11.)**

— The Last Rose of Summer, easily arranged ... for the Pianoforte. *London*, [1878.] fol. **h. 526. a. (17.)**

— The Last Rose of Summer. For two voices. *See* ANDREWS (*Mrs* J. H.)

— The Last Rose of Summer. Two-part Song. *See* CHALLINOR (F. A.)

— The Last Rose of Summer. [Song and chorus.] *See* CONGREVE (B.)

— The Last Rose of Summer. [Song.] *See* DEIS (C.)

— The Last Rose of Summer. [Part-song.] *See* DISTIN (T.)

— The Last Rose of Summer. [Part-song.] *See* FLEMING (J.)

— The Last Rose of Summer. [Part-song.] *See* FLETCHER (Percy E.)

— The Last Rose of Summer. Part-Song. *See* HAMMOND (S.)

— The Last Rose of Summer. Unison Song. *See* JACOBSON (M.)

— The Last Rose of Summer. [Part-song.] *See* LEE (J. T.)

— The Last Rose of Summer. Part-Song. *See* LINDÉ (E.)

— The Last Rose of Summer. [Part-song.] *See* MILLIKIN (R. A.)

— The Last Rose of Summer. [Song.] *See* MOORE (Thomas) *the Poet.* [A Selection of Irish Melodies. 5th Number.—'Tis the last Rose of Summer.]

— The Last Rose of Summer. [Part-song.] *See* NELSON (Havelock)

— The Last Rose of Summer. [Two-part song.] *See* PASFIELD (William R.)

— The Last Rose of Summer. [Song.] *See* RANDEGGER (A.)

— The Last Rose of Summer. [Part-song.] *See* ROW (R. D.)

— The Last Rose of Summer. [Song with descant.] *See* SHARPE (Evelyn) Cramer's Descant Series. no. 47.

— The Last Rose of Summer. Song. *See* STUBBS (H.)

— The Last Rose of Summer. [Part-song.] *See* TATE (Phyllis M. D.)

— The Last Rose of Summer is the sweetest Song of all. [Song.] *See* SIDNEY (Harry)

— The Last sad smile of Autumn. Song. *See* HARRIS (J. T.)

— The Last Salute. Song. *See* COBB (G. F.)

LAST

— The Last Serenade. Song. *See* CAMPBELL ( ) *Mrs, of Drimnamuchloch.*

— The Last Serenade. Song. *See* PALADILHE (E.)

— The Last Shilling. [Song.] *See* DIBDIN (C.) [Tom Wilkins.]

— The Last Shot. [Song.] *See* LE BRUNN (G.)

— The Last Sigh of the Moor. Cantata. *See* THANE (C.)

— The Last Song. [Song.] *See* ABT (F. W.)

— The Last Song. [Song.] *See* ROBBINS (R. C.) Songs, *etc.* 115.

— The Last Song. [Song.] *See* ROGERS (J. H.)

— A Last Song. [Song.] *See* STAFFORD (M.)

— The Last Song of Love. Ballad. *See* PACINI (G.) [Le Dernier chant d'amour.]

— Last Spring. Song. *See* ROLT (B.)

— The Last Straw. [Musical monologue.] *See* BARKER (G.) *Songwriter.*

— The Last Straw. [Song.] *See* BRAHAM (Philip E.)

— The Last Supper. [Part-song.] *See* DONATO (Anthony)

— The Last Supper. A Lenten Meditation. *See* FORSYTH (C.)

— The Last Supper. Sacred Cantata. *See* TAYLOR (H. J.)

— The Last Supper. Cantata. *See* THIMAN (E. H.)

— The Last Supper and Gethsemane. [Sacred cantata.] *See* JONES (J. E.)

— The Last Swallow. [Duet.] *See* WAREING (H. W.)

— The Last, Sweet Smile you gave me. Song. *See* HAYS (W. S.)

— The Last, Sweet Words of Mother. Song. *See* PRATT (C. E.)

— The Last Tale. Opera. *See* TOCH (E.)

— The Last Tear. Song. *See* BADDELEY (W. S. C.)

— The Last Time. Song. *See* WATTS (L. M.)

— The Last Time I came o'er the Moor. *Constant Love.* [Song.] Sung by Mr. Vernon ... at Vauxhall. *R. Falkener: London*, [c. 1770.] fol. *Followed by an accompaniment for German flute or guitar. Printed on one side of the leaf only.* **H. 1648. f. (25.)**

— The Last Time I came o'er the Moor. A favorite Scots song set for the voice, piano forte, guitar, &c. *J. McFadyen: Glasgow*, [c. 1800.] fol. *Pp. 106, 107 of an unidentified collection.* **G. 426. kk. (36.)**

— The Last Time I came o'er the Moor. Song. *See* CHERRY (A.)

— The Last Time I came o'er the Moor. [Song.] *See* URBANI (Pietro)

— The Last Time I felt like this. [Part-song.] *See* HAMLISCH (Marvin)

— The Last Time we met. Ballad. *See* PRATT (C. E.)

— The Last Toast. [Musical monologue.] *See* MAYER (K. S.)

— The Last Token. Recitation with Music. *See* ANDREWS (J. C. B.)

— The Last Token or Remember me. Air. *See* BISHOP (*Sir* Henry R.)

— The Last Trail. [Song.] *See* AUSTIN (E.)

— The Last Tree of the Forest. [Song.] *See* RITA.

LAST

— The Last Tryst. Song. *See* Ewald (E.)

— The Last Tryst. Song. *See* Houseley (H.)

— Last Valentine's Day. *Black Sloven.* A New Song. [*London*, 1771.] 8°.
The Universal Magazine, Vol. XLVIII., *p.* 95. **P. P. 5439.**

— The Last Vespers. Song. *See* Vane (C.)

— The Last Vigil. Song. *See* Barri (O.)

— Last Voyage. [Song.] *See* Dacre (H.)

— Last Voyage. Part-song. *See* Enfield (Patrick)

— The Last Waltz. [Song.] *See* Cragg (G. A.)

— The Last Waltz. [Song.] *See* Lambelet (N.)

— The Last Waltz. [Song.] *See* Powell (Orlando)

— The Last Waltz. [Part-song.] *See* Reed (Leslie D.) and Mason (Barry)

— The Last Waltz. Operetta. *See* Straus (O.) [Der letzte Walzer.]

— The Last Waltz of all. Song. *See* Tennant (H. W.)

— The Last Watch. Sea song. *See* Macfarren (*Sir* G. A.)

— The Last Watch. Song. *See* Pinsuti (C. E.)

— The Last Whistle. Song. *See* Shield (W.)

— Last Whitsunday they brought me. Song. *See* Linley (W.) [Vortigern.]

— The Last wild Rose. [Part-song.] *See* Macfarren (*Sir* G. A.)

— The Last Wish. [Song.] *See* Warford (C.)

— The last Woman. Mélange fantastique. *See* Lover (S.)

— The Last Word. [Song.] *See* Bauer (M. E.) Two Songs, *etc.* [No. 2.]

— The Last Word. Song. *See* Parry (John) *Bardd Alaw.*

— A Last Word. Song. *See* Raymond (R.)

— A Last Word. Song. *See* Scott (C. M.)

— The Last Word at the Gate. [Song.] *See* Marriott (C. H. R.)

— The Last Word of a Bluebird. [Song.] *See* Duke (John)

— Last Words. Song. *See* Behrend (J. A. H.)

— Last Words. [Song.] *See* Lawson (M. L.)

— Last Words. [Song.] *See* Rita.

— The Last Words in the Rafters rang. Chorus. *See* Holbrook (J. C.) Apollo and the Seaman. Op. 51.

— The Last Words Mother said. [Song.] *See* Nankivelle (W. E.)

— The Last Words of an Irish Emigrant. [Song.] *See* D., E. J.

— The Last Words of David. [Song.] *See* Freudenthal (J.)

— The last words of Marmion. [Song.] *See* War. The war that for a space did fail. [1810?] fol. **H. 2826. c. (35.)**

— The Last Words of Marmion. [Song.] *See* Clarke, afterwards Clarke Whitfeld (J.)

— The Last Words of Marmion. [Song.] *See* Jansen (Louis)

— Last Year. Song. *See* Dolby, afterwards Sainton (C. H.)

— Last Year. Song. *See* Johns (A.)

LAST

— Last Year. Song. *See* Mora (A. L.)

— Last Year. Song. *See* O'Donoghue (*Mrs* P.)

— Last Year. Song. *See* Strelezki (A.) *pseud.*

— Last Year. [Song.] *See* White (M. V.) Two Songs ... No. 1.

— Last Year, Sweetheart, last Year. Song. *See* Loehr (H.)

— Last Year's Leaves. Song. *See* Barton (C.)

— Last Year's Leaves. Song. *See* Roeckel (J. L.)

— Last Year's Nest. Song. *See* Mott (C. J.)

— A Last Year's Rose. [Song.] *See* Quilter (R.) [Four Songs. Op. 14. No. 3.]

— Last Year's Roses. Song. *See* Troubridge (A.)

LAST (Frederick)

— Sacred Harmony. A selection of Psalm and Hymn Tunes, arranged for the voice, organ, *etc.* London, [1840.] 8°.
E. 427.

LAST (Hans)

— *See* Olias (L.) Alaska ... Arr. by H. Last. [Orchestra.] [1958.] 4°. **h. 3210. i. (549.)**

LAST (Horace)

— Benedicite omnia opera [in E flat]. *Office of "The Organist":* London, [1896.] 8°. **F. 1170. o. (11.)**

— Rejoice in the Lord, O ye Righteous. Harvest Anthem. *Weekes & Co.: London*, 1896. 8°. **F. 231. f. (15.)**

— Te Deum laudamus. [In G.] *Weekes & Co.: London*, 1896. 8°. **F. 1170. q. (4.)**

LAST (Joan)

— Alphabetically yours. 26 short fragments for piano. pp. 14. *Oxford University Press: London*, [1978.] 4°. **g. 1529. s. (10.)**

— At the Zoo. [P. F.] pp. 12. *H. Freeman & Co.: Brighton*, [1968.] 4°.
With my Camera Series. no. 4. **h. 3870. ee. (1.)**

— The Austronaut. Seven pieces for piano. pp. 8. *Augener: London*, [1962.] 4°. **g. 1128. ii. (20.)**

— The Big Top. Eight pieces for piano. pp. 8. *Galliard: London*, [1963.] 4°. **g. 1128. ii. (19.)**

— [A reissue.] The Big Top, *etc. Oxford University Press: London*, [1971.] 4°. **g. 1138. aa. (3.)**

— Black and White. Eight tunes for young pianists. pp. 8. *Oxford University Press: London*, [1973.] 4°. **g. 442. ss. (8.)**

— By Sea and River. [P. F.] pp. 8. *H. Freeman & Co.: Brighton*, [1968.] 4°.
With my Camera Series. no. 5. **h. 3870. ee. (2.)**

— Carnival Procession ... Eight short pieces for piano, *etc.* pp. 8. *Oxford University Press: London*, [1967.] 4°.
g. 1126. qq. (1.)

— Country Outing. Fifteen little piano pieces, *etc.* pp. 11. *Oxford University Press: London*, [1967.] 4°.
g. 1128. zz. (14.)

— Five Dances in Miniature. A piano suite for adult beginners, *etc.* pp. 7. *J. B. Cramer & Co.: London*, [1977.] 4°.
g. 1138. uu. (6.)

LAST (Joan)

— The Day's Play. [P. F.] pp. 11. *Forsyth Bros.: London, Manchester,* [1974.] 4°. **h. 141. aa. (7.)**

— The Day's Play, *etc.* [P. F.] pp. 11. *Forsyth Bros.: London, Manchester,* [1974.] 4°. **g. 606. kk. (11.)**

— Explorers. Eight piano pieces. pp. 8. *Galliard: London,* [1965.] 4°. **g. 1138. j. (10.)**

— The First Concert. Twelve piano pieces, *etc.* pp. 11. *Oxford University Press: London,* [1950.] 4°. **g. 1138. n. (12.)**

— [The First Concert.] Der kleine Virtuose. [P. F.] pp. 11. *Oxford University Press: London,* [1967.] 4°. **g. 1126. qq. (4.)**

— Five formal Dances. A piano suite for older beginners. pp. 5. *Galliard: London,* [1966.] 4°. **g. 1138. j. (11.)**

— The Four Seasons. For piano solo. pp. 4. *Galliard: London,* [1964.] 4°. **g. 1126. ff. (12.)**

— [A reissue.] The Four Seasons, *etc.* *M. S. M. Music Publishers: London,* [1976.] 4°. **g. 1138. uu. (7.)**

— Freedom Technique. ⟨Exercises and studies for piano.⟩ 3 bk. *Oxford University Press: London,* [1971.] 4°. **h. 60. n. (4.)**

— Grave and gay ... Nine easy piano pieces, *etc.* pp. 8. *Bosworth & Co.: London,* [1967.] 4°. **g. 1129. jj. (5.)**

— Gymnastics. Piano pieces for beginners. pp. 8. *Boosey & Hawkes: London,* [1979.] fol. **g. 354. l. (5.)**

— In changing Mood. Nine short easy piano pieces. pp. 11. *Oxford University Press: London,* [1978.] 4°. **g. 1529. s. (11.)**

— Introduction to Pedalling. A guide to the use of the sustaining pedal for students of all ages. pp. 16. *Augener: London,* [1963.] 4°. **g. 338. w. (5.)**

— Der kleine Virtuose. *See* supra: [The First Concert.]

— London today, *etc.* ⟨Eight studies. Piano solo.⟩ pp. 12. *Oxford University Press: London,* [1967.] 4°. **g. 1128. zz. (15.)**

— Lyric Pieces. For piano. ⟨Set 1, 2.⟩ 2 no. *Chappell & Co.: London,* [1978.] 4°. **f. 65. kk. (5.)**

— Magic Circle. Twelve pieces for piano, *etc.* pp. 12. *Oxford University Press: London,* [1967.] 4°. **g. 1128. zz. (13.)**

— Moonlight Fantasies. Nine short descriptive pieces for piano, *etc.* pp. 11. *M. S. M. Music Publishers: London,* [1977.] 4°. **g. 606. vv. (6.)**

— Notes and Notions. Eight short pieces for piano. pp. 8. *Oxford University Press: London,* [1974.] 4°. **g. 442. ss. (9.)**

— Sarabande and Tambourin. Two contrasted pieces for piano. pp. 4. *Galliard: London,* [1964.] 4°. **g. 1138. j. (3.)**

— Three Seascapes. Piano solos, *etc.* pp. 4. *Oxford University Press: London,* [1966.] 4°. **g. 1126. qq. (2.)**

— Singing for Fun. Seven songs for "five-to-sevens". pp. 10. *Galliard: London,* [1963.] 4°. **G. 1487. b. (3.)**

— Studies in Technique and Rhythm. For piano. pp. 12. *Galliard: London; Galaxy Music Corp.: New York,* [1966.] 4°. **g. 1126. qq. (3.)**

— [A reissue.] Studies in Technique and Rhythm, *etc.* *M. S. M. Music Publishers: London,* [1976.] 4°. **g. 606. vv. (7.)**

— Summer is here. 12 little piano sketches for beginners, *etc.* pp. 7. *M. S. M. Music Publishers: London,* [1976.] 4°. **g. 606. vv. (8.)**

— Time Twisters. Five contrapuntal pieces for piano, each with a rhythmic twist. pp. 8. *Oxford University Press: London,* [1972.] 4°. **g. 442. ss. (2.)**

LAST (Joan)

— Tom Tiddler's Tunes. 12 little piano pieces, *etc.* 2 bk. *Bosworth & Co.: London,* [1971.] 8°. **e. 282. kk. (1.)**

— Two Hand Duos. Nine pieces having equal interest for both hands. pp. 12. *Leonard, Gould & Bolttler: London,* [1978.] 4°. **g. 1529. s. (12.)**

— Two of a kind. 8 short inventions introducing contrapuntal style. [P. F.] pp. 8. *Forsyth Bros.: Manchester, London,* [1975.] 4°. **f. 770. pp. (3.)**

— [Another copy.] **g. 338. dd. (12.)**

— Village Pictures. [P. F.] pp. 8. *Forsyth Bros.: London,* [1975.] 4°. **g. 338. dd. (9.)**

— Village Pictures ... Piano pieces. pp. 8. *Forsyth Bros.: London,* [1975.] 4°. **g. 338. dd. (13.)**

— Waltz for Three. One piano, six hands. pp. 7. *Galliard: London,* [1963.] 4°. **h. 3292. b. (6.)**

— *See* CHAIKOVSKY (P. I.) [*Collected Works.—b.*] Piano Album. Edited by J. Last. [1965.] 4°. **g. 557. q. (11.)**

— *See* CORELLI (A.) [*Selections.*] Largo from ... Op. 5. No. 7. Minuetto from ... Op. 6. No. 9 ... Arranged for two pianos by J. Last. [1964.] 4°. **g. 45. w. (5.)**

— *See* CORELLI (A.) [Concerti grossi. Op. 6. No. 11.] Sarabanda and Giga ... Arranged for two pianos by J. Last. [1962.] 4°. **g. 45. bb. (7.)**

— *See* CORELLI (A.) [Sonatas. Op. 4. No. 9.] Tempo di gavotta ... Arranged by J. Last, *etc.* ⟨Two pianos.⟩ [1964.] 4°. **g. 45. w. (4.)**

— *See* GRIEG (E. H.) [*Collections, P. F.*] Piano Album ... Selected and edited by J. Last. [1961.] 4°. **g. 705. t.**

— *See* GRIEG (E. H.) [Lyrische Stücke. Op. 54. No. 3. Troldtag.] March of the Dwarfs ... Arranged by J. Last. ⟨Two pianos.⟩ [1963.] 4°. **g. 705. o. (10.)**

— *See* MOZART (W. A.) [Symphonies. K. 550.] Minuet and Trio ... Arranged for two pianos, eight hands by J. Last. [1962.] 4°. **g. 382. c. (4.)**

— *See* SCHUBERT (F. P.) [Rosamunde.] Ballet Music ... Arranged for two pianos, eight hands by J. Last. [1961.] 4°. **g. 567. z. (5.)**

LASTHÉNIE

— Lasthénie. Opéra. *See* HÉROLD (L. J. F.)

LASTING

— Lasting as th' eternal Sea. *The National Anthem of Japan.* Kimigayo. [For S. A. T. B.] Words adapted by A. Fagge. Author unknown. *Boosey & Co.: London, etc.,* 1914. 8°. **F. 585. bb. (25.)**

— A Lasting Love. Song. *See* CHERIE (P.)

— Lasting Love. Duet. *See* HENSCHEL (*Sir* G.) Drei Duette. Op. 28. No. 1.

— Lasting Love. Ballad. *See* SINGLETON (F. E.)

LASTOVICH-CHULIVS'KY (Semen)

— Збірник українських народних пісень і мелодій для бандури ... A Collection of Ukrainian Folk Songs and Melodies for the Bandura, *etc.* Нью Йорк, 1959, *etc.* 4°. **F. 1594. o.**

LASZKY (Béla)

— Butterflies. Song, the poem by J. Davidson, *etc.* *Enoch & Sons: London,* 1911. fol. **H. 1792. r. (27.)**

LASZKY (BÉLA)

— If any little Word. Song, the words by A. T. *Enoch & Sons: London*, 1911. fol.   **H. 1792. r. (28.)**

— Pierrot. Scène de Ballet. Pour Piano. *Enoch & Sons: London*, 1912. fol.   **h. 3284. f. (47.)**

— When the Snows begin. Song, the words by A. de Courville. *Enoch & Sons: London*, 1911. fol.   **H. 1792. r. (29.)**

LÁSZLÓ (ALEXANDER)

— Präludien für Klavier und Farblicht ... Op. 10. 2. Gelb. [Score.] *In:* MOHOLY-NAGY (L.) Malerei Photographie Film. [1925.] 8°.   **X. 410/1411.**

LATANN (   )

— Light of Foot ... March for one or two Mandolines, with Piano and Guitar Accompaniments. Arranged by O. Allon. *Orpheus Music Publishing Co.: London*, [1900.] fol. *The Orpheus Mandolinist, No. 29.*   **h. 1983.**

LATANN (C.)

— Pizzicato-Gavotte. Herz an Herz. Op. 222. Wiegenlied. Op. 209. [String band parts.] *L. Oertel: Hannover*, [1885.] 8°.   **f. 245. h. (9.)**

— Herz an Herz. Pizzicato-gavotte ... Op. 222. ⟨String quintett.⟩ [Parts.] 5 pt. *Rivière & Hawkes: London*, [1887.] 4°.   **g. 1800. (200.)**

— Komisches Dreigespiel. Op. 180. [Piccolo, trombone and guitar.] *Hannover*, [1885.] fol.   **h. 2851. f. (8.)**

LA TARCHE (ANDRÉ)

— Czárdás. Danse hongroise pour violon avec accompagnement de piano. *Laurier & Laurier: London*, [1896.] fol.   **g. 505. p. (25.)**

— Evette ... Song, words and music by A. La Tarche. *Laurier & Laurier: London*, 1893. fol.   **H. 1798. u. (25.)**

— Evette Valse. [P. F.] *Laurier & Laurier: London*, [1893.] fol.   **h. 3285. q. (4.)**

— First Weeks in Violin Playing. A ... method for beginners, *etc. Laurier & Laurier: London*, 1896. 4°.   **g. 498. c. (1.)**

— Marche Japonaise ... Piano Solo. *Laurier & Laurier: London*, [1894.] fol.   **g. 605. f. (8.)**

— Trois Morceaux de Concert pour violon avec accompagnement de Piano. 1. Danse des Lutins. 2. Méditation.—Violin or 'Cello.—3. Zingaresca. 3 no. *Laurier & Laurier: London*, [1895.] fol.   **g. 505. p. (26.)**

— Trois Morceaux de Salon pour Violon avec accompagnement de Piano. 1. Danse Slave. 2. Rêverie. 3. Scène de Ballet (Danse Tzigane.) 3 no. *Laurier & Laurier: London*, 1894. fol.   **h. 1612. c. (31.)**

— Six Pieces for Violin and Piano. No. 1, 2. *Laurier & Laurier: London*, [1896.] 4°. *No more published.*   **g. 223. c. (8.)**

— Popular new Works specially arranged for the Mandoline with Pianoforte Accompaniment. [Score and part.] no. 3. *John Blockley: London*, [c. 1890.] fol. *Imperfect; wanting all the other numbers.*   **h. 188. o. (1.)**

— Scales and Arpeggi for the Violin ... An Appendix to the Violin Student's Manual. *Laurier & Laurier: London*, 1892. fol.   **h. 1753. (16.)**

— When Jack comes home again. Song, words by L. Lennox. *Laurier and Laurier: London*, [1894.] fol.   **H. 1798. u. (26.)**

LA TARCHE (ANDRÉ)

— *See* ARDITI (L.) Il Bacio ... Arranged for the Violin and Pianoforte by A. La Tarche. [1912.] fol.   **h. 1612. x. (6.)**

— *See* ASCHER (J.) Alice, where art thou ... Arranged ... by A. La Tarche. [1904.] fol.   **h. 1612. k. (3.)**

— *See* BALFE (M. W.) Killarney ... Arranged ... by A. La Tarche. [1904.] fol.   **h. 2831. d. (3.)**

— *See* CHAIKOVSKY (P. I.) [12 Morceaux. Op. 40. No. 2.] Chanson triste ... Arranged ... by A. La Tarche. [1905.] fol.   **h. 2988. d. (24.)**

LATCH

— The Latch-Key. Song. *See* BURGESS (Cyril)

— The Latch String at the Door. [Song.] *See* HARRISON (J.)

— The Latch String is always hanging out for you. [Song.] *See* COHN (Paul)

LATE

— Late. Ballad. *See* ALEXANDER (J.) *of London.*

— Late! Sacred Song. *See* NOWELL (E.)

— Late. [Song.] *See* WASSALL (G.) Ten Songs. [No. 10.]

— Late Afternoon in November. [Part-song.] *See* DICKINSON (Peter)

— The Late and Early Club. [Song.] *See* LE BRUNN (G.)

— Late as by Jesse I did sit. Song. *See* B., G., *Esq.*

— Late have I loved thee. [Part-song.] *See* BUTLER (Eugene S.)

— Late Hours. Comic ballad. *See* GLOVER (C. W.)

— Late Hours. [Song.] *See* WILLIAMS (Bert A.)

— A Late Lark twitters from the quiet Skies. [Part-song.] *See* CLARKE (D. W.)

— A Late Lark. For Tenor Voice with Orchestra. *See* DELIUS (F.)

— A Late Lark. Part-song. *See* HORNE (Jonathan T.)

— A Late Lark twitters from the quiet Skies. Chorus. *See* WEBBE (W. Y.)

— Late, late, so late. Anthem. *See* CASEY (S. W.)

— Late, late, so late. [Song.] *See* GILCHRIST (W. W.) Two Tennyson Songs. [No. 1.]

— Late, late, so late. [Song.] *See* PHILIPPS (H.)

— Late, late, so late. Song. *See* SALAMAN (C. K.)

— Late, Late, so Late. [Song.] *See* STEED (A. O.) Four Songs, *etc.* No. 4.

— Late Leaves. Part-Song. *See* FORSYTH (C.)

— Late Leaves. [Song.] *See* MILFORD (R. H.) Four Seasonable Songs. Op. 40. No. 3.

— Late September. [Part-song.] *See* NELSON (Ron) Four Pieces after the Seasons ... 3.

— Late Summer. [Unison song.] *See* BAYNON (A. J.)

— Late Summer. [Song.] *See* RASCH (H. H.)

— Late Summer. Song. *See* WARLOCK (P.) *pseud.*

LATELY

— Lately. [Song.] *See* WONDER (Stevie) *pseud.*

LATELY

— Lately on yonder swelling Bush. *The Bud.* [Song.] The words by M[r] Waller. Set for y[e] German flute. [*London?* c. 1730.] *s. sh.* fol.
Followed by an accompaniment for flute. **G. 316. n. (11.)**

— Lately on yonder swelling bush. Glee. *See* EVANS (C.)

LATER

— The Later Love. Song. *See* KENDALL (H.)

— Later on. Ballad. *See* BUCALOSSI (P.) [Mia Cara.]

— Later on. [Song.] *See* OSBORNE (C.)

— Later than Spring. [Song.] *See* COWARD (*Sir* Noël P.) [Sail away.]

LATERE (JOANNES DE)

— *See* LATTRE (C. J. de)

LATES (CHARLES)

— Three Sonatas for the Harpsichord or Piano-Forte, *etc.* pp. 21. *Printed for the Author: London,* [[WM] 1794.] fol.
h. 721. x. (4.)

— A favorite Sonata for the Piano-Forte or Harpsichord, *etc.* *Printed for the Author: London,* [1792.] *obl.* fol. **e. 104. (9.)**

LATES (JAMES)

— Six Solos for a Violin and Violoncello, with a Thorough Bass for the Harpsichord ... Opera Terza. *Printed for C. and S. Thompson: London,* [1764.] fol. **g. 422. g. (1.)**

— [Six Solos. Op. 3. No. 3.] Sonata in G major, for Violin and Pianoforte. 1906. *See* MOFFAT (A. E.) Old English Violin Music, *etc.* No. 1. 1906, *etc.* 4°. **G. 778.**

— [Six Solos. Op. 3. No. 5. Allegro assai.] Tempo di Ballo. 1766. [Violin and P. F.] *See* MOFFAT (A. E.) Choice Ayres & Courtly Dances, *etc.* 5. 1919. 4°. **g. 500. d. (25.)**

— Six Sonatas or Duets for two Violins ... Opra [*sic*] Prima. [Parts.] *Printed for Thompson & Son: London,* [1761.] fol. *With MS. notes by Alfred Moffat.* **g. 449. b.**

— Six Sonates or Duets for two German Flutes or Violins ... Opera secondo. [Parts.] 2 pt. *Printed for Thompson & Sons: London,* [1761.] fol. **g. 449. c.**

— Six Sonatas for Two Violins, or a German Flute and Violin, with a Thorough Bass for the Harpsichord. Opera Quarta. *Printed for C. & S. Thompson: London,* [1775?] fol. **g. 449.**

— Tempo di Ballo. *See* supra: [Six Solos. Op. 3. No. 5. Allegro assai.]

— Six Trios for a Violin, Violoncello Obligato, & Bass, with a thorough bass for the Harpsichord ... Opera 5. [Parts.] *C. & S. Thompson, for the Author: London,* [1774.] fol.
g. 449. a.

LA-TESSA (PASQUALE)

— Il Patto di roma. Gran Marcia delle nazioni sorelle, *etc.* [Score.] [*Cremona?* 1916?] fol. **R. M. 26. d. 14. (2.)**

LATEST

— The Latest Chap on Earth. Song. *See* ROGERS (E. W.)

— The Latest Edition. [Song.] *See* ENGLAENDER (L.)

— The Latest Girl in Town. Song. *See* HARGREAVES (William)

— The Latest Light has waned away. Vesper. *See* RICHARDS (A.)

LATEST

— The Latest News. [Song.] *See* HERE. Here you are! [1866.] fol. **H. 1790. (50.)**

— The Latest Sensation in Girls. [Song.] *See* AYER (Nat. D.) and BRATTON (J. W.) The Newlyweds and their Baby.

— The Latest Thing from Paris. [Duet.] *See* FRIML (R.) [The Firefly.]

— The Latest Thing in Dolls. Song. *See* RODDIE (William S.)

— The Latest thing that's out. Duet. *See* CHERRY (J. W.)

LATEU (MAURICE) and CASTELLI (MAX)

— Musette Maurice. Elementary accordion solo. *Charnwood Music Publishing Co.: Leicester,* [1967.] 4°. **g. 657. n. (5.)**

LATEY (JULIA)

— A Lullaby. Song, words and music by J. Latey. *C. Jefferys: London,* [1888.] fol. **H. 1788. u. (52.)**

LATH (H. ELLIOT)

— Caesarea. Gavotte. [P. F.] *F. Pitman: London,* [1887.] fol.
h. 1484. s. (22.)

— Cinderella. Romance for Violin & Piano. *A. M. Heller & Co.: London,* [1904.] fol. **h. 1612. l. (32.)**

— Comrades. Song, words written by G. W. Southey. *H. Klein & Co.: London,* [1889.] fol. **H. 1788. u. (53.)**

— Dado Dance. Entr'acte Caprice. [Orchestral parts.] *A. Hammond & Co.: London,* [1888.] 8°. **e. 1342. a. (11.)**

— Dangerous! Song, words by G. C. Bingham. *R. Cocks & Co.: London,* [1888.] fol. **H. 1788. u. (54.)**

— Fête Normande. Morceau caractéristique pour piano. *Moore, Smith & Co.: London,* [1895.] fol. **h. 1489. s. (13.)**

— The Fortescue Waltz. [P. F.] *F. Pitman: London,* [1887.] fol.
h. 975. u. (44.)

— Happy Days. Polka. [P. F.] *E. Donajowski: London,* [1886.] fol. **h. 975. u. (45.)**

— The Indian Patrol. Descriptive March ... for the pianoforte. *C. Sheard & Co.: London,* 1892. fol. **h. 1489. s. (14.)**

— Joyous Spring ... Polka. [P. F.] *E. Donajowski: London,* [1885.] fol. **h. 975. u. (46.)**

— Lillie. Waltz. [P. F.] *F. Pitman: London,* [1887.] fol.
h. 975. u. (47.)

— Love's Courier. Song, words by C. Franklin. 2 no. [In E flat and D.] *E. Ashdown: London,* [1891.] fol. **G. 807. h. (6.)**

— Moorish Love Song. Words by C. Franklin. 3 no. [In F minor, E minor and D minor.] *E. Ashdown: London,* [1891.] fol.
G. 807. h. (7.)

— Neath the Hawthorns. Song, written & composed by H. E. Lath. *Wilcocks & Co.: London,* [1887.] fol.
H. 1788. u. (55.)

— Ye Ocean Wave. Vocal Waltz. (Lyrics by C. Franklin.) *J. Curwen & Sons: London,* [1894.] fol. **h. 3285. q. (8.)**

— Off for the Holidays ... Vocal Waltz. Lyrics by S. J. A. Fitz-Gerald. *J. Curwen & Sons: London,* [1894.] fol.
h. 3285. q. (5.)

— Old-time Memories. Song, written and composed by H. E. Lath. *Ransford & Son: London,* [1884.] fol.
H. 1788. u. (56.)

LATH (H. ELLIOT)

— Par excellence. Gavotte. [P. F.]   *R. Cocks & Co.: London,*
[1886.] fol.   **h. 1484. s. (23.)**

— La Piquante. Polka. [P. F.]   *A. Hammond & Co.: London,*
[1884.] fol.   **h. 975. u. (48.)**

— Pop-Corn. American Barn Dance. [P. F.]   *Hopwood & Crew:*
London, 1892. fol.   **h. 3285. q. (6.)**

— "Popcorn." ⟨American barn dance. (Shottische [*sic*].)⟩
[Military band parts.] 26 pt. *In:* CARYLL (Ivan) *pseud.* "Ma
mie rosette," *etc.* 1893. fol. [*Boosey's supplemental military
Journal. no.* 380.]   **h. 1544.**

— Prairie Flowers. New American Barn Dance. [P. F.]   *Kay &*
Compy.: London, [1892.] fol.   **h. 3285. q. (7.)**

— Rêve après la Fête. Intermezzo pour le piano.   *Kay &*
Compy.: London, [1892.] fol.   **h. 1489. s. (15.)**

— The Silver Falls. Song, words by C. Franklin.   *Beal & Co.:*
London, [1890.] fol.   **G. 807. h. (8.)**

— Très chic. Morceau à la gavotte. [P. F.]   *J. & J. Hopkinson:*
London, [1886.] fol.   **h. 1484. s. (24.)**

LATHAM (ARLIE W.)

— Modern Bugle Method. pp. 52.   *Chappell & Co.: London;*
Boston Music Co.: Boston, Mass., [1964.] 8°.   **e. 138. d. (3.)**

LATHAM (C. M.)

— Playful she turned. Ballad.   *London,* [1860?] fol.
                                                H. 2835. (21.)

LATHAM (FRANK T.)

— Follow the golden Star. [Song.] Words: E. Lockton.
J. H. Larway: London, 1918. fol.   **H. 1846. x. (31.)**

— The Garden of Forgetting. [Song.] Words by E. Lockton.
J. H. Larway: London, 1920. fol.   **H. 1846. x. (32.)**

LATHAM (GERTRUDE H.)

— Kitchener ... Song, words and music by G. H. Latham.
Reeder & Walsh: London, [1902.] fol.   **G. 807. z. (30.)**

LATHAM (MORTON)

— Dialogo a sette voce by Willaert. Edited by M. Latham.
[1892.] *See* BACH. The Bach Choir Magazine, *etc.* No. 30.
[1877–1905.] 8°.   **F. 287.**

— Jubilee Te Deum, for solo voices, chorus & orchestra, *etc.*
S. Lucas, Weber & Co.: London, [1886.] 4°.   **F. 1171. d. (8.)**

— New Year's Eve. Skating Song. [Part-song.] Words by A. L.
Warner. [1897.] *See* UNION. The Union Choralist, *etc.* No. 49.
[1882, *etc.*] 8°.   **F. 687.**

— O Father, Thou Who hast created all. Baptismal Hymn.
Novello, Ewer and Co.: London & New York, [1890.] 8°.
                                                F. 1171. f. (21.)

— Te Deum laudamus, in F.   *London,* [1881.] 8°.
                                                F. 1170. a. (23.)

LATHAM (RICHARD OSKATEL)

— Come, Sleep. Two-part song ... words by John Fletcher, *etc.*
pp. 4.   *Edward Arnold & Co.: London,* [1950.] 8°.
[*Singing Class Music. no.* 655.]   **E. 802.**

— Communion Service.   *Oxford University Press: London,* 1938.
8°.
[*Oxford Church Music. No.* 482.]   **F. 1777. c.**

LATHAM (RICHARD OSKATEL)

— For all Thy Saints, O Lord. Anthem for Saints Days ...
[Words by] Bishop R. Mant.   *Oxford University Press:*
London, 1934. 8°.
[*The Oxford Series of Easy Anthems. No.* 16.]   **F. 1001.**

— Holy is the true Light. Motet for S. S. A. T. B.
(unaccompanied.) Words from the Salisbury Diurnal by Dr.
G. H. Palmer. pp. 6.   *Novello & Co.: London,* [1951.] 8°.
[*Octavo Anthems. no.* 1281.]   **E. 618. a.**

— The King of China's Daughter. Two-part song ... Words by
Edith Sitwell, *etc.* pp. 4.   *Edward Arnold & Co.: London,*
[1950.] 8°.
[*Singing Class Music. no.* 656.]   **E. 802.**

— Magnificat and Nunc dimittis in E flat.   *Oxford University*
Press: London, 1934. 8°.
[*Oxford Church Music. No.* 460.]   **F. 1777. c.**

— Magnificat and Nunc Dimittis in F major.   *Oxford University*
Press: London, 1933. 8°.
[*Oxford Church Music. No.* 456.]   **F. 1777. c.**

— O glorious Maid. Carol-Anthem ... Translation by
P. Dearmer.   *Oxford University Press: London,* 1937. 8°.
[*The Oxford Series of Easy Anthems. No.* 25.]   **F. 1001.**

— O God of Truth. Motet for Solo Quintet, Chorus and Organ.
Founded on the tune "Martyrs" ... by R. O. Latham. Words
by T. Hughes.   *Novello & Co.: London,* [1932.] 8°.
[*Novello Octavo Anthems. No.* 1183.]   **E. 618. a.**

— Te Deum laudamus ... in ... C, *etc.* [S. A. T. B.] pp. 11.
Novello & Co.: London, [1955.] 8°.
[*Parish Choir Book.* 1343.]   **E. 618.**

— *See* BACH (J. S.) [Christ lag in Todesbanden.—Jesus Christus,
Gottes Sohn.] Now Jesus Christ, the Son of God ... Arranged
for two pianos by R. Latham. [1950.] 4°.   **g. 548. vv. (3.)**

LATHAM (WALTER)

— Jesus is sleeping softly. Carol for Christmastide and
Epiphany. Words by Gordon Walham. [Staff and tonic sol-fa
notation.] pp. 4.   *James Pass & Co.: Birmingham,* [1954.] 8°.
[*Premier Series. no.* 25.]   **E. 1780.**

LA THANGUE (MARION)

— Air de Danse ... pour le piano.   *R. Cocks & Co.: London,*
[1889.] fol.   **h. 1489. s. (16.)**

— Gwendoline. Song [begins: "Oh! Gwendoline"] written by
C. Foster.   *London,* [1881.] fol.   **H. 1787. j. (16.)**

— Old London. Gavotte. [P. F. solo and duet.] *See* SMALLWOOD
(W.) Home Treasures, *etc.* No. 74. [1872, *etc.*] fol.
                                                h. 1412. o.

— Old London. Gavotte. [P. F.]   *C. Seaton: London,* [1887.] fol.
                                                h. 1484. s. (25.)

— Old London. Gavotte. [P. F.] *See* SMALLWOOD (W.) Happy
Thoughts, *etc.* No. 3. [1888.] fol.   **h. 1412. h. (1.)**

— Old London Gavotte. [P. F.] [1895.] *See* SMALLWOOD (W.)
Little Buds, *etc.* No. 84. [1874, *etc.*] fol.   **h. 1412. p.**

— Patrol March. [P. F.]   *C. Seaton: London,* [1883.] fol.
                                                h. 1484. s. (26.)

— Patrol March ... arranged for full orchestra by C. H. R.
Marriott. [Orchestral parts.]   *London,* [1884.] fol.
                                                e. 666. c. (8.)

— Patrol March. For parade ... Arrd. by A. Morelli. Solo
conductor & 1st B♭ cornet [and wind band parts]. 33 pt.
J. R. Lafleur & Son: London, [1892.] 8°.
Part of "Alliance Musicale". The conductor part is in duplicate.
                                                f. 800. (787.)

LA THANGUE (MARION)

— The Trysting. Song [begins: "Somebody's waiting"]. Words by C. Foster. *London*, [1881.] fol.   **H. 1787. j. (15.)**

— The Trysting. Song, words by C. Foster. *C. Seaton: London*, [1882.] fol.   **H. 1788. u. (57.)**

— Wifie. Song, written & composed by M. La Thangue. *R. Cocks & Co.: London*, [1887.] fol.   **H. 1788. u. (58.)**

LA THAUGUE (MARION)

— *See* LA THANGUE.

LATHOM (FRANK T.)

— *See* LATHAM.

LATHOM-SHARP (VERNON)

— *See* SHARP.

LATILLA (GAETANO)

— Crucifixus … (From the Credo.) Edited by Miss Masson. *Leader & Cock: London*, [1855.] fol. [*Songs for the Classical Vocalist. No.* 20.]   **H. 1355. a.**

— Don Calascione. *See* infra: [Gismondo.]

— La Finta cameriera. *See* infra: [Gismondo.]

— [Gismondo.] La Finta cameriera … Introduction by Howard Mayer Brown. (Libretto by G. Barlocci. Score reproduced from Florence, Biblioteca del Conservatorio di musica Luigi Cherubini, MS D. 180.) pp. 124. 100. 80. *Garland Publishing: New York, London*, 1979. *obl.* fol. [*Italian Opera* 1640–1770. 37.]   **F. 1899.**

— [Gismondo.] The Favourite Songs in the Opera call'd Don Calascione. [By G. Latilla. Score.] pp. 20. [1749.] fol. *See* DON.   **G. 809. o. (20.)**

— [Gismondo.] [Songs in Don Calascione. Comic opera.] *See* DELIZIE. Le Delizie dell'Opere, *etc.* Vol. 6. [1776.] fol.   **G. 159.**

— Six Quartettes for two Violins, Tenor, and Violoncello obligato. [Parts.] *Welcker: London*, [1775?] fol.   **R. M. 16. f. 14. (15.)**

LATIN

— Latin American choral Perennials, *etc. See* WILSON (Harry R.)

LATIS ( )

— *See* M., E. de. La Petite marguèrite … Accompagnement de guitarre ou lyre par Mr Latis. [c. 1815.] 8°.   **E. 1717. o. (53.)**

— *See* STRUNZ (J.) Les Adieux … Accompagnement de guitarre ou lyre par Mr Latis. [c. 1815.] 8°.   **E. 1717. o. (70.)**

LA TOMBELLE (FERNAND DE)

— Adoro te Devote. Motet à 3 voix égales pour les offices du T. S. Sacrement. *See* RÉPERTOIRE. Répertoire moderne de Musique vocale, *etc.* No. 6. [1896, *etc.*] fol.   **H. 1048.**

— Ave verum. Motet à 3 voix mixtes pour les offices du T. S. Sacrement. *See* RÉPERTOIRE. Répertoire moderne de Musique vocale, *etc.* No. 9. [1896, *etc.*] fol.   **H. 1048.**

— Ballade. Mélodie. Paroles de A. Theuriet. *T. Michaelis: Paris*, [1883.] fol.   **H. 2836. v. (17.)**

LA TOMBELLE (FERNAND DE)

— Beata viscera. Motet à quatre voix mixtes. *See* RÉPERTOIRE. Répertoire moderne de Musique vocale, *etc.* No. 58. [1896, *etc.*] fol.   **H. 1048.**

— Benedicta es tu. Motet à 3 voix mixtes. *See* RÉPERTOIRE. Répertoire moderne de Musique vocale, *etc.* No. 32. [1896, *etc.*] fol.   **H. 1048.**

— Cantilènes Grégoriennes du XIIIme au XVme siècle tirées des manuscrits de l'Abbaye de Cadouin … Harmonisées par F. de la Tombelle. *Au Bureau d'Édition de la "Schola Cantorum": Paris*, [1905?] fol. *Part of "Concerts Spirituels (Série Ancienne)," etc.*   **G. 872. (8.)**

— Chansons & Rêveries. Recueil de vingt mélodies, deux chœurs et deux pièces à dire, avec accompagnement de piano. Op. 31. *Richault et Cie.: Paris*, [1892.] 8°.   **F. 677.**

— Le Chant du Travail. Pour 4 voix d'hommes ou chœur mixte à l'unisson des ténors avec ou sans accompagnement de musique d'harmonie, ou de fanfare avec sax. Paroles de C. M. Couyba. [Vocal score.] *A. Fougeray: Paris*, 1921. 8°.   **F. 163. t. (27.)**

— Le Chant du Travail, *etc.* [Song. With separate voice part.] *A. Fougeray: Paris*, 1921. fol.   **H. 1846. jj. (5.)**

— Crux. Trilogie Sacrée. Poème de l'Abbé Lecigne … Partition, Piano et Chant. *Édition Mutuelle: Paris*, 1904. 8°.   **F. 1331. (2.)**

— Des Après-Midi sous les Arbres. Pièces pour piano à 2 mains. 1. Chanson de mer. 2. Petite marche. 3. Barcarolle. 4. Vol de libellules. 5. Provençale. 6. Danse lointaine. 7. Crépuscule. 8. Aubade. 9. Voix automnales. 10. Tendresse. 11. Petit canon. 12. Fuguette. 12 no. *Costallat et Cie.: Paris*, 1921. fol.   **h. 3865. c. (3.)**

— Élégie. Paroles de ***. *T. Michaelis: Paris*, [1882.] fol.   **H. 2836. v. (18.)**

— Fileuse. Légende du Val d'Amour. Paroles de J. Delaye. *T. Michaelis: Paris*, [1883.] fol.   **H. 2836. v. (19.)**

— La Fuite. Paroles de M. Fouant. *T. Michaelis: Paris*, [1884.] fol.   **H. 2836. v. (20.)**

— [Le Furet.] The Weasel … Four-Part Song or Quartet, from a poem by P. Gravollet, English version by W. G. Rothery. (1912.) *See* NOVELLO AND CO. Novello's Part-Song Book. Second Series. No. 1242. [1869, *etc.*] 8°.   **F. 280. b.**

— [Le Furet.] The Weasel, *etc.* [1912.] *See* NOVELLO AND CO. Novello's Tonic Sol-fa Series. No. 2026. [1876, *etc.*] 4°.   **B. 885.**

— Interludes dans la tonalité Grégorienne et harmonisation des versets pour la messe: "Dominicis infra annum;" avec Psalmodie ad libitum pendant les Interludes. [Organ.] 4 no. *See* RÉPERTOIRE. Répertoire moderne de Musique … d'Orgue, *etc.* No. 1. [1896, *etc.*] fol.   **H. 1048.**

— Messe de Requiem, à trois voix mixtes. *See* RÉPERTOIRE. Répertoire moderne de Musique vocale, *etc.* No. 48. [1896, *etc.*] fol.   **H. 1048.**

— O gloriosa Virginum. Motet à 2 voix égales, avec Accompagnement d'Orgue ad libitum. *See* RÉPERTOIRE. Répertoire moderne de Musique vocale, *etc.* No. 63. [1896, *etc.*] fol.   **H. 1048.**

— Prélude et Fugue pour deux pianos. *Durand & Schœnewerk: Paris*, [1887.] fol.   **h. 3291. a. (9.)**

— The Promised Land. [Part-song.] Words by A. J. Foxwell. *J. Curwen & Sons: London*, [1899.] 8°. *The Apollo Club, No.* 159.   **F. 667.**

LA TOMBELLE (Fernand de)

— Quatuor en mi majeur pour instruments à cordes. Op. 36. [Parts.] 4 pt. *Vve Richault mère: Paris*, [1897.] fol.
h. 4090. q. (4.)

— Regina cœli. Motet à 3 voix mixtes. *See* Répertoire. Répertoire moderne de Musique vocale, *etc.* No. 76. [1896, *etc.*] fol.
H. 1048.

— Rêverie [for horn and strings. Full score]. *Paris*, [1884?] fol.
h. 1509. m. (8.)

— Sainte-Cécile. Tragédie-Mystère, en 3 actes, en vers, par A. Poizat. Musique de Scène et préface-avertissement sur le chœur antique ... Partition piano et chant d'après l'orchestre. *L'Œuvre Saint-Luc: Lourdes*, 1920. fol.
G. 782. oo. (4.)

— Salve Regina. Motet à 3 voix mixtes. *See* Répertoire. Répertoire moderne de Musique vocale, *etc.* No. 78. [1896, *etc.*] fol.
H. 1048.

— Sancta Maria succure miseris. Motet à 3 voix mixtes. *See* Répertoire. Répertoire moderne de Musique vocale, *etc.* No. 30. [1896, *etc.*] fol.
H. 1048.

— Souvenir. Mélodie. Poésie de ***. *T. Michaelis: Paris*, [1882.] fol.
H. 2836. v. (21.)

— Tantum ergo. Motet à 3 voix mixtes. *See* Répertoire. Répertoire moderne de Musique vocale, *etc.* No. 23. [1896, *etc.*] fol.
H. 1048.

— Vêpres d'un Confesseur Pontife. 5 Antiennes pour les Psaumes 1res et 2es Vêpres, 3 Antiennes pour le Magnificat— 1res 2es Vêpres et ant. des Docteurs, *etc. See* Répertoire. Répertoire moderne de Musique ... d'Orgue, *etc.* No. 12. (VIII.) [1896, *etc.*] fol.
H. 1048.

— The Voice of the Bells. [Part-song. Words by] A. J. Foxwell. *J. Curwen & Sons: London*, [1899.] 8°. The Apollo Club, No. 156.
F. 667.

— Vous êtes le Pardon et la Douceur. *Madrigal Spirituel* à Cinq Voix. Poésie Française de G. Ducos. *Edition Mutuelle: Paris*, [1905?] 4°.
G. 517. t. (5.)

— The Weasel. *See* supra: [Le Furet.]

— *See* Chansons. [5.] Chansons du xvme siècle ... 3. Au jardin de mon père ... Harmonisation et Ritournelle de F. de la Tombelle, *etc.* [1907?] fol.
H. 1208. (3.)

LATONA (Jen.)

— Always true. [Song.] Words by John P. Harrington. pp. 3–5. *M. Witmark & Sons: [New York*, 1902.] fol.
The first letter of the composer's forename has been erased from the head of p. 3 and the letter "J" substituted with a stamp.
H. 3985. i. (1.)

— Can't you love me true? Coon serenade. [Song.] Words by J. P. Harrington. pp. 3–7. *M. Witmark & Sons: [New York*, 1902.] fol.
H. 3985. i. (2.)

— He was thinking! ⟨Song.⟩ Words by John P. Harrington. [Staff and tonic sol-fa notation. Voice part.] *Francis, Day & Hunter: London*, [1902.] *s. sh.* fol.
H. 3985. i. (3.)

— He was thinking! *etc.* ⟨Song.⟩ [Wiith separate voice part.] 2 pt. *Francis, Day & Hunter: London*, [1902.] fol.
H. 3985. i. (4.)

— The Nation's Soldier Sons! ⟨Song.⟩ Written by John P. Harrington. [Staff and tonic sol-fa notation. Voice part.] *Francis, Day & Hunter: London*, [1902.] *s. sh.* fol.
H. 3985. i. (5.)

— The Nation's Soldier Sons! *etc.* ⟨Song.⟩ [With separate voice part.] 2 pt. *Francis, Day & Hunter: London*, [1902.] fol.
H. 3985. i. (6.)

LATORRE (Ricardo Fernandez de)

— *See* Fernandez de Latorre.

LA TOSTIA ( )

— Whither thou goest ... ⟨Song.⟩ Written by Paul Pelham. [Staff and tonic sol-fa notation. Voice part.] *Francis, Day & Hunter: London*, [1903.] *s. sh.* fol.
H. 3985. i. (7.)

— Whither thou goest, *etc.* ⟨Song.⟩ pp. 7. *Francis, Day & Hunter: London*, [1903.] fol.
H. 3985. i. (8.)

LATOSZYŃSKI (B.)

— *See* Lyatoshins'ky (B. M.)

LA TOUCHE (Edmund Digges)

— Back to Sunrise Land and you. Song, words by E. Lockton. *J. B. Cramer & Co.: London*, 1918. 4°.
G. 426. d. (47.)

— Dance of the disappointed Fairies. Air de ballet for the pianoforte. *Cary & Co.: London*, 1914. fol.
h. 3284. nn. (14.)

— Lady mine. Song, words & music by E. D. La Touche, *etc.* *Cary & Co.: London*, (1913.) fol.
H. 1793. s. (17.)

— The Land of Let's pretend. Song, words by U. Bloom. *Cary & Co.: London*, (1914.) fol.
H. 1793. s. (18.)

— The Little Dream Lady. Song, word by U. Bloom. *Cary & Co.: London*, 1916. fol.
H. 1846. x. (33.)

— The Little Irish Maid. [Song.] Words and music by E. D. La Touche. *E. Ascherberg & Co.: London*, 1905. fol.
H. 1794. k. (53.)

— Little red House on the Hill. Song, the words by U. Bloom. *Enoch & Sons: London*, 1913. fol.
G. 806. mm. (3.)

— There are no Roses. Song, words & music by E. D. La Touche. 2 no. [Low and high.] *Cary & Co.: London*, 1911. fol.
H. 1792. r. (30.)

— Yvonne. Song, words by U. Bloom. *Cary & Co.: London*, (1914.) fol.
H. 1793. s. (19.)

LATOUR ( )

— A Collection of Minuets, Rigadoons, & French Dances —Containing 70 in Number—Of two Parts for a Violin & a Bass Being the Newest things Perform'd at Court, the Theatres and Publick Balls Compos'd by Mr Latour Mr Fairbank Mr Hill Mr Essex Mr Vincent Mr Kilburn. 2 pt. *Printed for I. Walsh & I. Hare: London*, [1721.] obl. 8°. *Includes "Mr. L'abee's new Dance for his Majesty's Birth Day 1721".*
a. 26. i. (3.)

LA TOUR (de)

— Ah, que je sens d'inquiétude! *Air Nouveau.* [Words by Madame Des Houlieres.] [*Paris*, 1678.] *s. sh.* obl. 4°. *Nouveau Mercure Galant*, Feb., 1678, *p.* 86.
P. P. 4482.

LATOUR (Alphonse)

— The Amazon's Grand March, for the pianoforte. *C. Sheard: London*, [1879.] fol.
No. 6090–1 of the Musical Bouquet.
H. 2345.

— The Electric Light Galop for the Pianoforte. *C. Sheard: London*, [1879.] fol.
No. 5902–3 of the Musical Bouquet.
H. 2345.

— Fairest of the Fair. Polka Mazurka. [P. F.] *C. Sheard: London*, [1881.] fol.
No. 6476–7 of the Musical Bouquet.
H. 2345.

LATOUR (ALPHONSE)

— Grandmother's chair [by J. Read] for the pianoforte, arranged by A. Latour. (Fantasia.) (Waltz.) (Polka.) 3 no.   *C. Sheard: London*, [1880.] fol.
No. 6159–62 *of the Musical Bouquet.*   **H. 2345.**

— Marche Fantastique ... pour Piano.   *C. Sheard: London*, [1889.] fol.
No. 7433–4 *of the Musical Bouquet.*   **H. 2345.**

— Sounds o' London ... Fantasia on popular Melodies. [P. F.]   *C. Sheard: London*, [1882.] fol.
No. 6679–80 *of the Musical Bouquet.*   **H. 2345.**

— Summer Twilight. Mazurka de Salon ... pour Piano.   *C. Sheard: London*, [1884.] fol.
No. 7094–5 *of the Musical Bouquet.*   **H. 2345.**

— The Waterfall. Galop de Concert pour piano.   *C. Sheard: London*, [1879.] fol.
No. 6092–3 *of the Musical Bouquet.*   **H. 2345.**

— *See* SUPPÉ (F. von) [Boccacio.] Grand March ... Arranged by A. Latour. [1883.] fol.   **H. 2345.**

LA TOUR (AMÉDÉE DE CARAYON)

— *See* CARAYON LA TOUR.

LATOUR (ARISTIDE DE)

— Dors mon ange aux jolis yeux bleus. Romance. Paroles et musique d'A. de Latour.   *Chez Mme A. Guérin: Paris*, [1843?] fol.   **Hirsch M. 1297. (34.)**

— La Fille de la Nuit. Nocturne à deux voix [begins: "Entendez vous"]. Paroles de Madame L. Jourdain.   *Paris*, 1843. fol.   **H. 2830. d. (68.)**

— La Fille de la Vallée. *See* LEDUC (A.) 3 Fantasies élégantes, *etc.* Op. 198. No. 3. [1867.] fol.   **h. 619. e. (54.)**

— I cannot love thee more. Ballad.   *London*, [1848.] fol.   **H. 1702. (31.)**

— J'aime le son du cor. Romance. Paroles de Mme Mélanie Waldor.   *Chez Mme A. Guérin: Paris*, [1843?] fol.   **Hirsch M. 1297. (33.)**

— Je n'ose l'aimer. Romance. Paroles et musique de Latour.   *Chez Colombier: Paris*, [1840?] 8°.   **E. 1771. a. (3.)**

— Loin de France. *See* DELASEURIE (A.) 2 Fantaisies gracieuses pour Piano. [1862.] fol.   **h. 3021. a. (6.)**

— Madona-Maria. [Song, with accompaniment for guitar.] Paroles de Mme Laure Jourdain, *etc.* ⟨Accomp^t par J^h Vimeux.⟩   *Mme A. Guérin: Paris*, [1840?] 8°.   **E. 1771. a. (20.)**

— Non! ⟨Romance.⟩ Paroles de Mme Laure Jourdain, *etc.* ⟨Accomp^t de guitar par Kocken.⟩   *Chez Mme A. Guérin: Paris*, [1840?] 8°.   **E. 1771. a. (14.)**

— Non Monseigneur. Chansonnette [with accompaniment for guitar]. Paroles et musique d'A. de Latour.   *Chez Colombier: Paris*, [1840?] 8°.   **E. 1771. a. (8.)**

— Non Monseigneur. Chansonnette, paroles et musique d'A. de Latour. pp. 3.   *C. Lonsdale: London*, [1845.] fol.   **H. 1698. (3.)**

— Non Monseigneur. Chansonnette. *See* ECHO. L'Echo de la France. No. 62. [1863, *etc.*] fol.   **H. 2402.**

— Picciola pauvre fleur! Romance, *etc.* ⟨Paroles et musique de Mr A. de Latour. Accomp^t de guitare par Kocken.⟩   *Chez Mme A. Guérin: Paris*, [1840?] 8°.   **E. 1771. a. (22.)**

LATOUR (ARISTIDE DE)

— Rêves et soupirs. [Song with accompaniment for guitar.] Paroles de Mme Laure Jourdain. ⟨Accomp^t par J^h Vimeux.⟩   *Chez Mme A. Guérin: [Paris*, 1840?] 8°.
The imprint has been cropped.   **E. 1771. a. (19.)**

— Sans bruit. Nocturne à 2 voix [with accompaniment for guitar]. Paroles de Me Laure Jourdain, *etc.* [*Chez Me A. Guerin: Paris*, 1840.] 8°.
The imprint has been cropped.   **E. 1771. a. (21.)**

— La Visionnaire. Nocturne à deux voix.   *R. Mills: London*, [1845?] fol.   **H. 1652. f. (10.)**

LA TOUR (G. D. C. DE)

— Airs de l'Invention de G. D. C. S^r de La Tour, de Caen, sur plusieurs poemes saints et chretiens, recueillis de diuers auteurs, & diuisez en trois parties ... Liure second, à quatre parties. Superius.   *Chez Iaques Mangeant: Caen*, 1593. obl. 8°.   **K. 8. i. 14.**

LATOUR (GEORGES) *pseud.* [i. e. GEORGE HOWARD CLUTSAM.]

— Déclaration hésitante. Entr'acte pour Piano.   *Enoch & Sons: London*, 1906. fol.   **h. 3283. p. (13.)**

— Melly in the Moonlight. Characteristic piece for the piano.   *Enoch & Sons: London*, 1913. fol.   **h. 3284. nn. (15.)**

— Pourquoi? Entr'acte pour Piano.   *Enoch & Sons: London*, 1906. fol.   **h. 3283. p. (14.)**

— Le Tour du bois. Esquisse Parisienne. Suite de valses pour piano.   *Paris*, [1886.] fol.   **h. 3285. b. (47.)**

LATOUR (GERALD)

— The Wrestling Match. Descriptive fantasia for piano solo. pp. 5.   *W. Paxton; Price & Reynolds: London*, [1906.] fol.
Price & Reynolds' Sixpenny Series. no. 42.
   h. 4120. mm. (27.)

— *See* ATKINSON (R. W.) The Party at Oddfellow's Hall. Song ... Arranged by G. Latour. [1892.] fol.   **H. 3980. a. (27.)**

— *See* WITMARK (I.) He was a Pal of mine ... Song ... arranged by G. Latour. [1892.] fol.   **G. 807. j. (34.)**

LATOUR (HENRI)

— Air de Danse. [Orchestral parts.]   *London*, [1879.] 8°.
Part of the "Alliance Musicale".   **f. 400. u. (10.)**

— Air de Danse. [Reed band parts.]   *London*, [1879.] 8°.
Part of the "Alliance Musicale".   **f. 401. o. (28.)**

— Air de Danse. [Reed band parts.]   *London*, [1883.] 8°.
Part of the "Alliance Musicale".   **f. 401. v. (9.)**

— Air de Danse pour Piano.   *Brighton*, [1879.] fol.   **h. 1494. p. (19.)**

— Air de Danse. [P. F.]   *London*, [1880.] 8°.
No. 584 *of the "Alliance Musicale. Album Bijou".*   **f. 406.**

— Air de Danse ... Arranged by P. Dale. [P. F.]   *E. Ashdown: London*, [1904.] fol.   **g. 605. ll. (15.)**

— Air de Danse pour piano à quatre mains.   *E. Ashdown: London*, [1882.] fol.   **g. 545. a. (13.)**

— Air de Danse. [Violin and P. F.] *See* TAYLOR (W. F.) Popular Pieces, *etc.* No. 9. [1883.] fol.   **h. 3220. b. (21.)**

— Balláre for Pianoforte.   *Brighton*, [1881.] fol.
   h. 3275. j. (17.)

— Coquetterie. Caprice pour Piano.   *E. Ashdown: London*, [1903.] fol.   **g. 605. ee. (28.)**

LATOUR (Henri)

— Danse joyeuse pour Piano. *E. Ashdown: London*, 1901. fol.
g. 605. x. (1.)

— The Elfin Rendezvous. [P. F.] *Brighton*, [1881.] fol.
h. 3275. j. (18.)

— Entente Cordiale Exhibition March, *etc.* [P. F.] *Bunz & Co.: London*, (1908.) fol. **h. 3283. p. (15.)**

— Fête Normande. [P. F.] *Brighton*, [1881.] fol.
h. 3275. j. (19.)

— Fleur de Lys, morceau de salon pour le Piano. *Brighton*, [1878.] fol. **h. 1484. c. (25.)**

— Francesca. Gavotte pour Piano. *E. Ashdown: London*, [1902.] fol. **g. 605. ee. (29.)**

— Gavotte in F for the pianoforte. *E. Ashdown: London*, [1899.] fol. **g. 605. p. (19.)**

— The Kabaro polka. [P. F.] *Brighton*, [1879.] fol.
h. 1494. p. (21.)

— Six Minuettos pour Piano. 6 no. *Brighton*, [1879.] fol.
h. 1494. p. (20.)

— Polkette pour Piano. *E. Ashdown: London*, [1901.] fol.
g. 605. x. (2.)

— Pomponette. [P. F.] *Brighton*, [1881.] fol. **h. 3275. j. (20.)**

— La Reine des Roses. Gavotte pour Piano. *E. Ashdown: London*, [1902.] fol. **g. 605. ee. (30.)**

— Sardonyx. Danse for the Pianoforte. *E. Ashdown: London*, [1900.] fol. **g. 605. x. (3.)**

— Spring Thoughts. Morceau pour Piano. *E. Ashdown: London*, [1900.] fol. **g. 605. x. (4.)**

— Tarantella in F for the Pianoforte. *E. Ashdown: London*, [1900.] fol. **g. 605. x. (5.)**

— *See* Lardelli (G.) Slumber Song, arranged … by H. Latour. [1881.] fol. **h. 3275. j. (13.)**

LATOUR (Pierre)

— Angels of Dawn. Valse angélique … pour piano. *C. Sheard: London*, [1883.] fol.
No. 6902 *of the Musical Bouquet.* **H. 2345.**

— Angels of Dawn. Valse Serenade, *etc.* [P. F.] *C. Sheard: London*, [1883.] fol.
No. 6950 *of the Musical Bouquet.* **H. 2345.**

— Angels of Eve. Reverie pour piano. *C. Sheard: London*, [1883.] fol.
No. 6951 *of the Musical Bouquet.* **H. 2345.**

— The Bee-Hive Waltz. [P. F.] *C. Sheard: London*, [1889.] fol.
No. 7550 *of the Musical Bouquet.* **H. 2345.**

— Calm at Sea. Reverie for the Piano. *C. Sheard: London*, [1882.] fol.
No. 6763 *of the Musical Bouquet.* **H. 2345.**

— Flower Waltz. [P. F.] *See* Bellak (J.) Luddy Polka, *etc.* [1889.] fol. **H. 2345.**

— Home Scenes. Bone of Contention Galop. Delighted to see you Schottische. Live & let live Waltz. Rather too much Polka. "Go slow" mazourka. Not caught yet Quickstep. [*H. N. Hempstead: Milwaukee, Wis.*, 1880?] fol.
The "Not caught yet Quickstep" only. **Hirsch M. 1310. (12.)**

LATOUR (T.)

— "Addio Teresa;" a favorite Italian air, with variations for the Piano Forte. pp. 7. *Chappell & Cᵒ.: London*, [1821.] fol.
h. 315. (46.)

— Admiral Nelson's Glorious Victory obtained over the French Fleet 1ˢᵗ August 1798. Composed for the piano forte, *etc.* pp. 11. *Printed by Longman & Cᵒ: London*, [1798.] fol.
h. 721. bb. (5.)

— Airs à la Malibran, arranged for the Piano Forte by T. Latour. pp. 14. *F. T. Latour: London*, [1829.] fol.
h. 315. (42.)

— Airs à la Pasta arranged for the Piano Forte by T. Latour. pp. 11. *F. T. Latour: London*, [1829.] fol. **h. 315. (43.)**

— Airs à la Sontag arranged for the Piano Forte by T. Latour. pp. 9. *F. T. Latour: London*, [1828.] fol. **h. 315. (44.)**

— The favorite airs in the Ballet of Alfred Le Grand arranged for the Piano Forte with an accompaniment for the flute by T. Latour. Bk. 1–2. *London*, [1823.] fol. **h. 312. (14.)**

— The Favorite Airs from the opera of La Caccia di Enrico IV … Arranged for the harp & piano forte, with an accompaniment for the flute ad libitum, by T. Latour. [1812.] fol. *See* Pucitta (V.) [La Caccia di Enrico IV.] **h. 61. t. (25.) & h. 62. l. (14.)**

— Three airs … from "La Caccia di Enrico IV" arranged as a duett for two performers on the Piano Forte … by T. Latour. [1812.] fol. *See* Pucitta (V.) [La Caccia di Enrico IV.]
h. 317. (5.)

— Three … airs from the opera of La Caccia di Enrico IV … arranged as a divertimento for the pianoforte … by T. Latour. [1812.] fol. *See* Pucitta (V.) [La Caccia di Enrico IV.] **h. 312. (8.)**

— Three favorite airs from the opera of La Caccia di Enrico IV., composed by Pucitta, arranged … for the Pianoforte. *London*, [1816?] fol. **g. 270. j. (19.)**

— Three favorite airs from the opera of La Caccia di Enrico IV … arranged as a duett for … the Pianoforte … by T. Latour. [1816?] fol. *See* Pucitta (V.) [La Caccia di Enrico IV.]
g. 272. e. (19.)

— The Favorite Airs from the Ballet of La Dansomanie … Arranged for the piano forte (with additional movements composed) by T. Latour. pp. 42. *Rᵗ Birchall: London*, [ᵂᴹ 1810.] fol. **h. 3870. ww. (11.)**

— Favorite airs from the opera of Il Don Giovanni [by W. A. Mozart], arranged for two performers on the Piano Forte, with an accompaniment for the harp and flute by T. Latour. *London*, [1817.] fol. **h. 317. (23.)**

— "Alexandre le grand;" a military divertimento for the Piano Forte. pp. 13. *Chappell & Cᵒ.: London*, [1815.] fol.
h. 315. (37.)

— L'Amour et le temps, romance avec accompagnement de piano forte … Nᵒ 24. pp. 3. *Chappell & Cᵒ: London*, [1819.] fol. **G. 809. ww. (7.)**

— Ar hyd y nos, or The Live long Night. With Variations … by T. Latour. [P. F.] [*Chappell & Co.: London*, 1812, 13.] fol. [*National Melodies. No.* 2.] **h. 323.**

— The favorite barcarole in the Opera of Masaniello [composed by D. F. E. Auber] arranged for the Piano Forte by T. Latour. pp. 3. *F. T. Latour: London*, [1829.] fol. **h. 315. (5.)**

— The Battle of Prague, for two performers on one piano forte, adapted by T. Latour. pp. 15. *At Bland & Wellers: London*, [c. 1805.] fol. **h. 3290. gg. (10.)**

— The Battle of Prague [by Franz Kotzwara], for two performers, on one piano forte. Adapted by T. Latour. pp. 15. *Phillips & Mayhew: London*, [ᵂᴹ 1817.] fol. **h. 61. t. (14.)**

LATOUR (T.)

— The Beggar Girl, a favorite air [by H. Piercy] with variations for the piano forte. pp. 4. *At Bland & Wellers: London,* [c. 1805.] fol.   **h. 724. p. (9.)**

— La Belle Catherine, a favorite dance, with variations for the Pianoforte. *London,* [1805?] fol.   **g. 270. j. (13.)**

— "La Biondina in Gondoletta," a favorite air with variations for the Piano Forte with an accompaniment for the flute ad libitum. [Parts.] 2 pt. *Chappell & Cº.: London,* [1817.] fol.   **h. 314. (10.)**

— The Blue Bell of Scotland, a favorite Scotch ballad, sung by Mʳˢ Jordan, with variations for the piano forte, by Mʳ Latour. [The melody attributed to Dorothea Jordan.] pp. 4. *Chappell & Cº: London,* [1819.] fol.   **h. 60. jj. (20.)**

— "Bon jour" premier ("Bon soir" seconde) Divertissement pour le Piano Forte avec accompagnement de flute ad libitum. [Score and parts.] 2 no. 4 pt. *Rᵗ. Birchall: London,* [1808.] fol.   **h. 314. (20.)**

— Bonaparte's New March, with variations, for the piano forte, with or without the additional keys. pp. 4. *At Bland & Weller's Music Warehouse: London,* [ᵂᴹ1815.] fol.   **h. 62. d. (16.)**

— Bonaparte's March, with Variations, for the Piano Forte, *etc.* pp. 4. *Chappell & Cº: London,* [ᵂᴹ1821.] fol.   **h. 3870. aa. (20.)**

— Buonaparte's March, with variations for the piano forte. ⟨New edition.⟩ pp. 4. *S. Chappell: London,* [c. 1830.] fol.   **h. 3870. oo. (18.)**

— The Caledonian Hunt, with variations for the Pianoforte. *London,* [1810?] fol.   **g. 272. b. (41.)**

— The Caledonian Hunt, with variations for the piano forte. pp. 3. *Knapton, White & Knapton: York,* [1820?] fol.   **h. 61. ee. (14.)**

— The Caledonian Laddy. A favorite Scotch air arranged as a rondo for the piano forte. pp. 3. *At Bland & Wellers: London,* [ᵂᴹ1806.] fol.   **h. 60. xx. (18.)**

— "Le carillon du village," a favorite air with variations for the Piano Forte with an accompaniment for the flute ad libitum by T. Latour. *Chappell & Cº.: London,* [1824.] fol. *Without the flute accompaniment.*   **h. 314. (26.)**

— The Chantreuse arranged as a Rondo for the Piano Forte. pp. 4. *Bland & Weller: London,* [c. 1810.] fol.   **h. 3870. s. (4.)**

— The celebrated Chorus [Nel silenzio] in "Il Crociato in Egitto" [composed by G. Meyerbeer] arranged with variations for two performers on the Piano Forte by T. Latour. *London,* [1825.] fol.   **h. 317. (1.)**

— Chorus ⟨"Nel silenzio"⟩ in the opera of "Il Crociato" [by G. Meyerbeer] with variations for the harp and Piano Forte by T. Latour. [Parts.] 2 pt. *E. Dodd: London,* [1836.] fol.   **h. 316. (9.)**

— "La Cocarde blanche," a divertimento for the Piano Forte with an accompaniment for the keyed Harmonica or flute ad libitum. [Score.] pp. 11. *Chappell & Cº.: London,* [1814.] fol.   **h. 314. (12.)**

— Latour's Collection of Rondinos for the Piano Forte by eminent composers. No. 1–8. *F. T. Latour: London,* [1826.] fol.   **h. 315. (13.)**

— A second concerto for the Piano Forte with accompaniments. 7 pt. *Rᵗ Birchall: London,* 1810. fol.   **h. 316. (13.)**

— The Copenhagen Waltz with variations for the Piano Forte by T. Latour. *London,* [1812.] fol.   **h. 315. (38.)**

LATOUR (T.)

— The Copenhagen Waltz, with Variations for the Piano Forte. pp. 5. *Chappell & Co.: London,* [c. 1815.] fol.   **g. 1126. cc. (6.)**

— The Copenhagen waltz with variations for the Pianoforte. pp. 5. *Chappell & Cº.: London,* [1869.] fol.   **h. 1485. s. (25.)**

— "La Coquette" — sonate pour le Piano Forte avec accompagnement de flute ad libitum. [Parts.] 2 pt. *Rᵗ Birchall: London,* [1810.] fol.   **h. 314. (2.)**

— Cory Owen, a favorite Dance ... in the new Pantomine of Harlequin Amulet. Arranged as a rondo for the piano forte or harp. By Mʳ Latour. pp. 4. *Bland & Weller's Music Warehouse: London,* [1801?] fol.   **g. 352. e. (17.)**

— [Cory Owen.] Gary Owen. A favorite dance, performed by Mr. Weippert at the Theatre Royal Drury Lane in the new pantomime of "Harlequin Amulet". Arrang'd as a rondo for the p-forte or harp by Mʳ Latour. pp. 3. *Hime: Dublin,* [1801?] fol.   **g. 443. aa. (11.)**

— Crazy Jane, a favorite Song, the Words by M. Lewis ... with an accompaniment for the Harp or Piano Forte. pp. 4. *Bland & Wellers Music Warehouse: London,* [ᵂᴹ 1799.] fol.   **H. 1652. cc. (6.)**

— Cuckoo! Bagatelle. [Song.] The words by W. B[all?]. pp. 5. *Sold for the author by Chappell: London,* [1835.] fol.   **H. 1287. (17.)**

— Eight Divertimentos, for the Piano Forte, with an accompaniment for the flute, or violin, and tambourine (ad libitum) ... Opera 5. pp. 12. *At Bland & Wellers: London,* [c. 1805.] fol. *Without the accompaniment.*   **h. 724. p. (10.)**

— Eight Divertimentos for the Pianoforte. Op. 5. *London,* [1810?] fol.   **g. 272. b. (40.)**

— A divertimento for the Piano Forte with an accompaniment for the flute ad libitum from the favorite airs in Rossini's opera of "Il Barbiere di Seviglia". *Chappell & Cº.: London,* [1816.] fol. *Without the flute accompaniment.*   **h. 314. (27.)**

— Do not request.—Ballad.—The words by J. A. Wade. pp. 5. *Sold for the author by Chappell: London,* [1835.] fol.   **H. 1287. (14.)**

— Original Duett, for two performers on one piano-forte, as performed by Master Parker & Mʳ Latour ... Op. 6. pp. 11. *At Bland & Wellers: London,* [ᵂᴹ 1797.] fol.   **h. 3388. a. (1.)**

— A Duett for two Performers on one Piano Forte ... Op. 12. pp. 9. *At Bland & Wellers: London,* [ᵂᴹ 1804.] fol.   **h. 3290. gg. (11.)**

— A duett for two performers on the Piano Forte in which are introduced two favorite airs with variations. *London,* [1813.] fol.   **h. 317. (14.)**

— Duo à quatre mains pour le Pianoforte. *Paris,* [1815?] fol.   **g. 270. d. (27.)**

— Duett for two performers on the Piano Forte, on the French air "Au clair de la lune". [Composed by F. A. Boieldieu.] *London,* [1820.] fol.   **h. 317. (11.)**

— A Duett for two performers on one Pianoforte ... in which is introduced ... "Away with melancholy" [i. e. "Das klinget so herrlich" from "Die Zauberflöte" by W. A. Mozart]. Op. 11. *London,* [1803.] fol.   **g. 442. (12.)**

— Two Duetts for two performers on the Pianoforte from the favorite airs in the ballet of La Dansomanie. *London,* [1807.] fol.   **g. 443. e. (13.)**

— A duett for two performers on the Piano Forte in which is introduced the German Hymn [by I. J. Pleyel] with variations by T. Latour. *London,* [1811.] fol.   **h. 317. (20.)**

LATOUR (T.)

— A duett for two performers on the Piano Forte, in which is introduced the air of "In my cot[tage]"; with variations by T. Latour. *London*, [1814.] fol.   **h. 317. (17.)**

— A Duett for two Performers on the Piano Forte in which is introduced the admired Air of "O dolce concento" [i. e. "Das klinget so herrlich" from "Die Zauberflöte" by W. A. Mozart] with Variations. pp. 11. *R¹ Birchall: London*, [c. 1810.] fol. *A different work from the duet Op. 11, entered above.*   **h. 3290. gg. (1.)**

— A Duett for two Performers on the Piano Forte in which is introduced the admired air of "O dolce concento" [by W. A. Mozart] with variations. pp. 11. *R.¹ Birchall: London*, [1811?] fol.   **h. 317. (21.)**

— A Duett, for two performers on the piano forte, in which is introduced the admired air of "O dolce concento" [by W. A. Mozart] with variations. pp. 11. *R¹ Birchall: London*, [ᵂᴹ 1815.] fol.   **h. 1226. e. (6.)**

— A Duett for two performers on the Pianoforte, in which is introduced . . . "O dolce concento" [by W. A. Mozart], *etc. London*, [1815?] fol.   **g. 270. j. (9.)**

— [Another copy.]   **g. 272. k. (28.)**

— A Duett, for two performers on the piano forte, in which is introduced the admired air of "O dolce concento" [by W. A. Mozart] with variations. pp. 11. *R¹ Birchall: London*, [ᵂᴹ 1822.] fol.   **h. 141. gg. (2.)**

— A Duett . . . in which is introduced . . . "O dolce concento". New edition. *London*, [1825?] fol.   **g. 270. j. (10.)**

— Duett (O dolce concento), for two performers on the Piano Forte, with Variations. *London*, [1857.] fol.   **h. 725. f. (24.)**

— Duett for two performers on the Piano Forte in which is introduced the French air "Le petit tambour". *London*, [1819.] fol.   **h. 317. (12.)**

— A duett for two performers on the Piano Forte in which is introduced the air of "Sul margine d'un rio"—with variations by T. Latour. *London*, [1811.] fol.   **h. 317. (22.)**

— A Duett for the Pianoforte and Harp. *London*, [1805?] fol.   **h. 1480. a. (4.)**

— England for me, song, the words by W. Ball. pp. 5. *Sold for the author by Chappell: London*, [1835.] fol.   **H. 1287. (16.)**

— [L'Épouse Persanne.] The Favorite Pas Seul, danced by Madˡᵉ Nora, and performed on the Harp by Madˡᵉ Chery—with an Accompaniment for the Flute, *etc. R. Birchall: London*, [1810.] fol.   **h. 3200. d. (6.)**

— [L'Epouse Persanne.] The favorite Pas Seul . . . for the Harp or Pianoforte. *London*, [1823?] fol.   **h. 1480. i. (18.)**

— Eighteen exercises or variations for the Piano Forte, on the air "Ah! vous dirai-je". pp. 17. *F. T. Latour: London*, [1828.] fol.   **h. 315. (52.)**

— Fal lal la! A favourite Welch air, with variations for the Pianoforte. *London*, [1805?] fol.   **g. 270. j. (11.)**

— Fra tante angoscie, [the music by Prince M. E. F. V. A. P. Carafa di Colobrano, arranged for P. F.] by T. Latour. *See* AIRS. Operatic Airs. No. 3. [1819.] fol.   **h. 300. (2.)**

— A favorite French air, with variations for the Piano Forte, with flute accompaniment ad libitum. [Parts.] 2 pt. *Chappell & Cᵒ.: London*, [1824.] fol.   **h. 314. (18.)**

— French March with variations for the harp & Piano Forte. [Parts.] 2 pt. *E. Dodd: London*, [1836.] fol.   **h. 316. (7.)**

— Brillante galopade for the Piano Forte. pp. 9. *S. Chappell for the author: London*, [1834.] fol.   **h. 315. (47.)**

LATOUR (T.)

— 2ⁿᵈ Galopade, for the Piano Forte, *etc.* pp. 7. *J. Alfred Novello: London*, [c. 1840.] fol.   **h. 3865. rr. (11.)**

— Gary Owen. *See* supra: [Cory Owen.]

— The celebrated Gavotte de Vestris with variations for the Piano Forte with an accompaniment for the flute ad libitum. [Parts.] 2 pt. *Chappell & Cᵒ.: London*, [1813.] fol.   **h. 314. (25.)**

— The favorite Gavot in "Achille et Deidamie," arranged as a Duett for Harp and Piano Forte by T. Latour. [Parts.] 2 pt. *R¹ Birchall: London*, [1808.] fol.   **h. 316. (11.)**

— The favorite gavot with new variations for the harp and Piano Forte. [Parts.] 2 pt. *E. Dodd: London*, [1836.] fol.   **h. 316. (8.)**

— German Hymn. *See also* supra: A Duett . . . in which is introduced the German Hymn, *etc.*

— The German Hymn [composed by I. J. Pleyel] with variations for the harp and Piano Forte with an accompaniment for the flute by T. Latour. [Parts.] 3 pt. *Chappell & Cᵒ.: London*, [1811.] fol.   **h. 316. (4.)**

— The . . . German Hymn [composed by I. J. Pleyel] with variations for the Piano Forte with an accompaniment for the flute ad libitum by T. Latour. [Parts.] 2 pt. *Chappell & Cᵒ.: London*, [1811.] fol.   **h. 314. (8.)**

— Go to the Devil & shake yourself. A favorite Irish air. With variations for the harp or piano forte. pp. 3. *A. Bland & Weller's Music Warehouse: London*, [ᵂᴹ 1798.] fol.   **h. 61. d. (5.)**

— God save the King. With Variations . . . by T. Latour. [P. F.] *Chappell & Co.: London*, [1812, 13.] fol. [*National Melodies. No.* 24.]   **h. 323.**

— The Grand Specific Song. The words by Wᵐ Ball. pp. 7. *Sold for the author by Chappell: London*, [1835.] fol.   **H. 1287. (18.)**

— The favorite "Guaracha dance," in the Ballet of Figaro with variations for the Piano Forte with flute accompaniment ad libitum. [Score.] pp. 8. *Chappell & Cᵒ.: London*, [1811.] fol.   **h. 314. (23.)**

— The Favorite Guitar Dance, introduced . . . in Mr. Didelot's Ballet of Zelis, ou la Forêt aux avantures, with variations for the piano forte with an accompaniment for the flute. [Score.] pp. 7. *Chappell & Co.: London*, [ᵂᴹ 1811.] fol.   **h. 314. (24.)**

— [A reissue.] The Favorite Guitar Dance, with variations for the piano forte with an accompaniment for the flute. [Score.] pp. 7. *Chappell & Co.: London*, [ᵂᴹ 1814.] fol.   **Hirsch M. 1282. (12.)**

— "Hillisborough Castle;" a divertimento for the Piano-forte with an accompaniment for a flute ad libitum. [Parts.] 2 pt. *R. Birchall: London*, [1811.] fol.   **h. 314. (14.)**

— The Favorite Hornpipe, danced by Madame Del Caro . . . in the cantata of La Vittoria, in commemoration of Lord Howe's victory on the 1ˢᵗ of June 1794. With variations for the piano forte, & for the violin & flute. pp. 4. *At A. Bland & Wellers Music Warehouse: London*, [c. 1795.] fol.   **h. 3490. e. (3.)**

— [The Favorite Hornpipe danced by Madame del Caro.] Lord Howe's Hornpipe with Variations, for the piano forte. pp. 4. *Printed by Clementi & Cᵒ: London*, [c. 1815.] fol.   **h. 60. jj. (21.)**

— "Le Hussard et le Tyrolien"—a duett for two performers on the Piano Forte founded on the above two popular airs. *London*, [1817.] fol.   **h. 317. (13.)**

LATOUR (T.)

— The Hussar & Tyrolian, two favorite Airs, with Variations for the Piano Forte, with an accompaniment for the Flute ad libitum, *etc.* [Score.] pp. 13. *Chappell & C⁰: London*, [1817.] fol. **h. 250. i. (13.)**

— If lovely Anna still prove—kind, a new Song, with an accompaniment for the Harp or Piano Forte ... The words by Mʳ J. N. Michell. pp. 3. *Bland & Wellers Music Warehouses: London*, [ᵂᴹ 1799.] fol. **H. 1652. cc. (5.)**

— Imitations of many of the most eminent professors, in twenty-six variations ... for the Pianoforte, with an accompaniment for the Flute (ad libitum), *etc.* [Parts.] 2 pt. *Rᵗ Birchall: London*, [1808.] fol. **g. 280. b. (6.)**

— [Another copy.] **h. 314. (21.)**

— New imitations of eminent composers in twelve variations for the Piano Forte on an air [Non più mesta, from La Cenerentola] by Rossini. pp. 21. *Chappell & C⁰.: London*, [1821.] fol. **h. 315. (32.)**

— Impromptu for the Piano Forte with an accompaniment for the flute. No. 1, 2. [Scores.] 2 no. *Chappell & C⁰.: London*, [1813.] fol. **h. 314. (19.)**

— "In medio tutissimus ibis," aria, ⟨N°. 6⟩ with twelve variations for the Piano Forte and flute accompaniment ad libitum by T. Latour. [Parts.] 2 pt. *Rᵗ. Birchall: London*, [1811.] fol. **h. 314. (9.)**

— In my Cottage near the Wood. *See* also supra: A duett ... in which is introduced the air of "In my cot[tage]," *etc.*

— In my Cottage near the Wood. A favorite Song. The Words ... by Miss Calcraft ... The Variations for the Piano Forte ... by Mr. Latour. *Bland & Weller: London*, [1800?] fol. *Imperfect; wanting pp. 3, 4.* **G. 796. (21.)**

— In my Cottage near the Wood. A favorite song, the words are an imitation of the French poetry by Miss Calcraft. The variations for the piano forte ... by Mʳ Latour. pp. 4. *Bland & Weller's Music Warehouse: London*, [c. 1805.] fol. **H. 1653. l. (27.)**

— In my Cottage near the Wood. A ballad. The words are an imitation of the French poetry by Miss Calcraft. The variations for the piano forte ... by T. Latour. ⟨New edition.⟩ pp. 4. *Chappell & C⁰.: London*, [ᵂᴹ 1821.] fol. **H. 1601. x. (22.)**

— An introduction and the national waltz danced by the Miss Dunnetts, with variations for the Piano Forte. pp. 11. *Chappell & C⁰.: London*, [1819.] fol. **h. 315. (49.)**

— Introduction and Rondo à la Suisse for the Piano Forte. pp. 9. *F. T. Latour: London*, [1829.] fol. **h. 315. (18.)**

— Introduction and variations brillantes pour le Piano Forte avec accompagnement de flute ad libitum sur l'air "Benedetta sia la madre". [Parts.] 2 pt. *D'Almaine & C⁰.: London*, [1837.] fol. **h. 315. (4.)**

— Introduction et rondo sur la polacca de Rossini, *etc. See* infra: [ᴹˢ The favourite Polacca in Rossini's opera of Tancredi.]

— The favorite Scotch air "Kelvin grove" — arranged with an introduction and variations for the Piano Forte. pp. 11. *F. T. Latour: London*, [1828.] fol. **h. 315. (34.)**

— The Knight and the Lady; a ballad the poetry by J. R. Planché. pp. 3. *Chappell & C⁰.: London*, [1821.] fol. **H. 1287. (21.)**

— Ladies' Thorough Bass, *etc.* pp. 35. *F. T. Latour: London*, [1828.] fol. **h. 316. (16.)**

— Lady Caroline Lee's Waltz, arranged as a Rondo, for the Piano Forte, by T. Latour. pp. 3. *Bland & Wellers, Music Warehouse: London*, [c. 1805.] fol. **g. 443. z. (15.)**

LATOUR (T.)

— Lady Shaftsbury's Reel, a favorite air, with variations for the piano forte or harpsichord. pp. 3. *At Bland & Wellers Music Warehouse: London*, [c. 1815.] fol. **h. 62. d. (17.)**

— The Lass of Patie's Mill. Arranged ... by T. Latour. [P. F.] [*Chappell & Co.: London*, 1812, 13.] fol. [*National Melodies. No.* 18.] **h. 323.**

— Lieber Augustine. *See* also infra: Vous et moi.

— Lieber Augustine, with variations originally composed ... by Mr. Latour, *etc.* [1803.] fol. *See* ELOUIS (J.) **h. 184. a. (21.)**

— Lieber Augustine, a favorite Suabian Air with Variations for the Piano Forte, *etc.* pp. 8. *Rt. Birchall: London*, [1807.] fol. **h. 315. (24.)**

— Lieber Augustine, a favorite Suabian air with variations for the piano forte, *etc.* pp. 8. *Rᵗ Birchall: London*, [ᵂᴹ 1811.] fol. **Hirsch M. 1282. (5.)**

— Lieber Augustine, a favorite Suabian Air, with Variations for the Piano Forte, *etc.* pp. 8. *Rᵗ Birchall: London*, [ᵂᴹ 1813.] fol. **g. 443. o. (18.)**

— [A reissue.] Lieber Augustine. A favorite Suabian air, with variations for the piano forte. *London*, [ᵂᴹ 1817.] fol. **H. 3691. v. (4.)**

— Lieber Augustine, a favorite Suabian Air, with Variations for the Piano Forte, *etc.* ⟨New edition.⟩ pp. 9. *F. T. Latour: London*, [1823.] fol. **h. 722. s. (14.)**

— Life let us cherish [first edited by H. G. Nägeli], as a duett with variations for harp & piano forte. [Parts.] 2 pt. *Rᵗ Birchall: London*, [1813.] fol. **h. 316. (10.)**

— Lord Howe's Hornpipe. *See* supra: [The Favorite Hornpipe danced by Madame del Caro.]

— "Mammi mia," a favourite Italian air ⟨N°. 2⟩ with twelve variations for the Piano Forte with an accompaniment for the flute ad libitum by T. Latour. [Score.] pp. 11. *Rᵗ Birchall: London*, [1808.] fol. **h. 314. (4.)**

— The march and chorus in Pietro l'Eremita [composed by G. A. Rossini] arranged for the Piano Forte with an accompᵗ. for the flute by T. Latour. *London*, [1821.] fol. **h. 313. (7.)**

— The march and chorus in Pietro l'Eremita [composed by G. A. Rossini] arranged for two performers on the Piano Forte by T. Latour. *London*, [1822.] fol. **h. 317. (2.)**

— Two favorite new marches, 1ˢᵗ. Marche Britannique, 2ⁿᵈ. General Doyle's new march, for the pianoforte. *London*, [1805?] fol. **g. 272. k. (30.)**

— The Market Chorus, in the opera of Masaniello ... [By D. F. E. Auber.] Arranged for the piano forte by T. Latour. pp. 3. *F. T. Latour: London*, [1829.] fol. **h. 315. (6.)**

— [Another copy.] **h. 61. ee. (15.)**

— T. Latour's new and improved Method of Instruction for the Piano Forte. pp. 58. *F. T. Latour: London*, [1827.] fol. **h. 316. (14.)**

— [Method of Instruction.] Sequel to T. Latour's Instructions for the Piano Forte. pp. 46. *F. T. Latour: London*, [1828.] fol. **h. 316. (15.)**

— "La mia crudel tiranna"—a favourite Italian air ⟨N°. 3⟩ [known also as "The Maid of Lode"]; with twelve variations for the Piano Forte with an accompaniment for the flute ad libitum by T. Latour. [Parts.] 2 pt. *Rᵗ Birchall: London*, [1807.] fol. **h. 314. (5.)**

— A military concerto for the Piano Forte with accompaniments. [Parts.] 16 pt. *Rᵗ Birchall: London*, [1809.] fol. **h. 316. (12.)**

LATOUR (T.)

— A military divertimento for the Pianoforte, in which is introduced the ... air of Lewie Gordon. *London*, [1810?] fol.
g. 272. b. (42.)

— Murphy Delaney, a favorite Dance arranged as Rondo for the Piano Forte. pp. 3. *Bland & Weller: London*, [WM 1804.] fol.
h. 3870. s. (17.)

— Musette for the Piano Forte. pp. 9. *Chappell & Cº.: London*, [1812.] fol.
h. 315. (23.)

— The New rigg'd Ship. A favorite dance with variations for the piano forte. pp. 3. *At Bland & Weller's: London*, [WM 1803.] fol.
h. 3290. gg. (12.)

— The Nightingale, a favourite military Air [by T. Latour] ... Arranged for one or two performers on the piano forte. pp. 3. [1810.] fol. *See* NIGHTINGALE.
g. 443. u. (7.)

— The Nightingale, a favorite Military Rondo with Twelve Variations for the Piano Forte with an Accompaniment for Flute ad libitum, *etc.* pp. 17. 4. *Rt. Birchall: London*, [1811?] fol.
h. 314. (16.)

— [Another issue.] The Nightingale, a favorite Military Rondo, with Twelve Variations for the Piano Forte with an accompaniment for Flute ad libitum, *etc.* pp. 17. *Rt. Birchall: London*, [WM 1812.] fol.
Imperfect; the P. F. part only. Without the "Catalogue of Piano Forte Music" on p. 1.
g. 270. z. (7.)

— The Nightingale, a favorite military rondo. [By T. Latour.] Arranged for the piano forte also as a duet, for two performers. [c. 1815.] fol. *See* NIGHTINGALE.
h. 1226. b. (9.)

— The Nightingale. A celebrated Rondo, for the Piano Forte. [By T. Latour.] ⟨Fall of Paris.⟩ [1815?] fol. *See* NIGHTINGALE.
g. 443. q. (7.)

— The Nightingale, a favorite military Rondo, with twelve Variations for the Piano Forte, with an Accompaniment for the Flute (ad libitum), *etc.* ⟨New edition.⟩ [Parts.] 2 pt. *Chappell & Cº: London*, [1824.] fol.
Variation 4 is in score.
h. 250. l. (6.)

— [The Nightingale.] Britons unite. A favorite military glee. Taken from the much admired air the Nightingale [by T. Latour] ... Arranged for the piano forte by L. Jansen. Written ... by a patriot. pp. 3. [WM 1809.] fol. *See* JANSEN (Louis)
H. 1601. v. (1.)

— O dear what can the Matter be, an air, with variations for the piano forte ... by T. Latour. ⟨New Edition.⟩ pp. 4. *Chappell & Cº: London*, [WM 1823.] fol.
h. 722. p. (5.)

— O dolce concento. *See* also *supra*: A Duett for two Performers on the Piano Forte in which is introduced the admired Air of "O dolce concento" with Variations.

— "O dolce concento," [by W. A. Mozart] a favorite air ⟨Nº. 4⟩ with twelve variations for the Pianoforte and an accompaniment for the Flute (ad libitum). [Parts.] 2 pt. *Rt Birchall: London*, [1809.] fol.
h. 314. (6.)

— O dolce concento, with variations for the Pianoforte. *London*, [1869.] fol.
h. 1485. s. (26.)

— O dolce concento, a favorite Air [by W. A. Mozart], arranged as a Duet for the Harp & Piano Forte by T. Latour. *Rt Birchall: London*, [WM 1812.] fol.
The harp part only.
h. 2605. w. (12.)

— O dolce concento, a favorite air [by W. A. Mozart], arranged as a duet for the harp & piano forte, *etc.* [Parts.] 2 pt. *Rt Birchall: London*, [WM 1820.] fol.
h. 1480. i. (19.)

— "Oh! give me back again;" ballad, the words by J. A. Wade. pp. 5. *Sold for the author by Chappell: London*, [1835.] fol.
H. 1287. (15.)

LATOUR (T.)

— Oh Lady fair! Composed by Thomas Moore ... Arranged with variations for the piano forte, *etc.* pp. 11. *J. Power: London; W. Power: Dublin*, [c. 1810.] fol.
h. 3870. t. (6.)

— Oh Nanny wilt thou fly with me, for the Piano Forte. ⟨Air [by C. T. Carter] with Variations by Mr Latour.⟩ pp. 5. *Printed & Sold at Bland & Weller's: London*, [1810?] fol.
No. 10 of Latour's "Recreations".
g. 443. m. (22.)

— The Favorite Air of "Oh Nanny," [the music by C. T. Carter] with an introduction and variations for the Piano Forte by T. Latour. pp. 7. *Chappell & Co.: London*, [1816.] fol.
h. 315. (19.)

— "O pescator dell'onda;" a favorite Venetian air, with variations for the Piano Forte. pp. 12. *Chappell & Cº.: London*, [1817.] fol.
h. 315. (36.)

— "Oh! wake no more that lay of love & gladness." A ballad ... the poetry by J. R. Planché. pp. 3. *Chappell & Cº.: London*, [1821.] fol.
H. 1287. (19.)

— "L'Orage," Rondo pastorale pour le Piano Forte en imitation du Rondo de Steibelt. pp. 12. *Chappell & Cº.: London*, [1816.] fol.
h. 315. (20.)

— A Favorite Overture, for the piano forte. ⟨Nº. [MS 2.] New edition.⟩ pp. 9. *Chappell & Cº.: London*, [WM 1822.] fol.
h. 1226. m. (15.)

— A Favorite Overture, for the Piano Forte, in which is introduced the favorite Air, of Hope told a flattering Tale [from "La Molinara," by G. Paisiello], *etc.* ⟨Nº 3.⟩ pp. 7. *Bland & Weller's Music Warehouse: London*, [WM 1803.] fol.
g. 443. t. (13.)

— A Favorite Overture ⟨Nº 3⟩, for the piano forte, in which is introduced the favorite air, of Hope told a flattering Tale [from "La Molinara," by G. Paisiello], *etc.* pp. 7. *At Bland & Weller's: London*, [c. 1805.] fol.
h. 724. p. (11.)

— [Another edition.] A Favorite Overture for the Piano Forte, in which is introduced the favorite Air, of Hope told a flattering Tale [from "La Molinara," by G. Paisiello], *etc.* ⟨Nº 3.⟩ pp. 7. *Bland & Weller's Music Warehouse: London*, [WM 1807.] fol.
g. 270. j. (12.)

— A Favorite Overture [No. 3], for the piano forte, in which is introduced the favorite air of Hope told a flattering Tale [from "La Molinara," by G. Paisiello], *etc.* pp. 7. *Halliday's Music Warehouse:* [*London*, WM 1811.] fol.
g. 352. ll. (14.)

— Overture [No. 3] for the Pianoforte, in which is introduced a favorite air, *etc. London*, [1815?] fol.
g. 272. k. (29.)

— A Favorite Overture [No. 4] for the Piano Forte ... in which is introduced the favorite Air of Adeste fideles, with an accompaniment for a Flute, or Violin, and Violoncello ... Op. 7. [P. F. part.] *Bland & Wellers Music Warehouse: London*, [1799.] fol.
Imperfect; wanting the accompaniments.
h. 5. g. (10.)

— A favorite Overture for the Piano Forte ... ⟨Nº. 4⟩ in which is introduced the favorite air of Adeste fideles, with an accompaniment for a flute, or violin, and violoncello ... Op. 7. [Parts.] 3 pt. *London*, [WM 1808.] fol.
g. 232. dd. (2.)

— A Favorite Overture [No. 4] for the Piano Forte, with or without the additional keys, in which is introduced the favorite air of Adeste Fideles, with an accompaniment for a flute, or violin, and violoncello ... Op. 7. [P. F. part.] pp. 9. *Bland & Wellers: London*, [1811.] fol.
g. 1126. cc. (5.)

— A Favorite Overture ⟨Nº 5⟩, for the piano forte. With an accompaniment for a violin ad libitum in which is introduced the favorite air of Life let us cherish [first edited by H. G. Nägeli], *etc.* pp. 7. *At Bland & Wellers: London*, [c. 1805.] fol.
Without the accompaniment.
h. 724. p. (12.)

LATOUR (T.)

— A New Overture for the Piano Forte, with an Accompaniment for a Violin, (ad Libitum) in which is introduced the favorite Air of Whither My Love ... No. 7. *Bland & Wellers: London*, [1800?] fol. *Imperfect; wanting the violin part.*   **g. 270. y. (2.)**

— A New Overture [No. 7] for the Piano Forte, with an accompaniment for a violin, (ad libitum) in which is introduced the favorite air of Whither my Love, *etc.* pp. 9. *Bland & Wellers: London*, [WM 1804.] fol.   **Hirsch M. 1310. (14.)**

— A new Overture for the Pianoforte, *etc.* No. 8. *London*, [1803?] fol.   **g. 272. i. (1.)**

— A New Overture [No. 9] for the Pianoforte, in which is introduced the ... air of "She lives in the valley below" [by J. Hook]. *London*, [1810?] fol.   **g. 270. j. (15.)**

— Overture, N° 16. for the Piano Forte, in which is introduced, the admired Air of Auld Robin Gray, *etc.* pp. 9. *Bland & Weller: London*, [WM 1807.] fol.   **h. 3870. s. (18.)**

— Overture for the Piano Forte and Rondo. pp. 9. *Chappell & C°.: London*, [1811.] fol.   **h. 315. (22.)**

— A Parody on a favorite air for the Piano Forte. pp. 3. *Chappell & C°.: London*, [1811.] fol.   **h. 315. (25.)**

— The parting, a ballad the poetry by J. R. Planché. pp. 3. *Chappell & C°.: London*, [1821.] fol.   **H. 1287. (20.)**

— "Pauvre Jacques" a French air ⟨N°. 5⟩ with variations for the Piano Forte with an accompaniment for the flute ad libitum by T. Latour. [Parts.] 2 pt. *R⁰ Birchall: London*, [1810.] fol.   **h. 314. (7.)**

— Le petit tambour. *See* also supra: A duett ... in which is introduced the French air "Le petit tambour," *etc.*

— "Le petit tambour" a favorite French air with variations for the Piano Forte by T. Latour. pp. 15. *Chappell & C°.: London*, [1819.] fol.   **h. 315. (31.)**

— Petite bagatelle for the Piano Forte. No. 1–5. *Chappell & C°.: London*, [1826.] fol.   **h. 315. (14.)**

— Petite sonate for the Piano Forte. pp. 11. *Chappell & C°.: London*, [1817.] fol.   **h. 315. (35.)**

— The Plough Boy [by W. Shield], arranged as a rondo for the Pianoforte. *London*, [1805?] fol.   **g. 270. j. (16.)**

— [Another copy.]   **h. 1480. b. (26.)**

— [The Plough Boy.] The admired Air of the Plough Boy [by W. Shield], arranged as a rondo, for the piano forte or harp ... by Mʳ Latour. pp. 7. *Printed by Halliday & C°: London*, [WM 1815.] fol.   **h. 1226. e. (7.)**

— [The Plough Boy.] The favorite air of the Plough Boy [by W. Shield] arranged as a rondo for the Pianoforte. *London*, [1825?] fol.   **g. 272. p. (3.)**

— [MS The favorite Polacca in Rossini's opera of Tancredi arranged by T. Latour.] [P. F.] pp. 9. *Chappell & C°: London*, [1822.] fol. [*Operatic Airs. no.* 12.] *The title has been supplied by the publisher, in MS, at the head of p.* 1.   **h. 300. (2.)**

— [MS The favorite Polacca in Rossini's opera of Tancredi.] Introduction et Rondo sur la Polacca de Rossini pour le Pianoforte. pp. 13. *Chez Janet et Cotelle: Paris*, [c. 1825.] fol.   **g. 270. b. (25.)**

— [MS The favorite Polacca in Rossini's opera of Tancredi.] Introduction et rondo sur la polonaise de Rossini pour le piano forte. pp. 11. *Chez tous les marchands de musique: Bruxelles*, [c. 1825.] fol.   **h. 60. hh. (7.)**

LATOUR (T.)

— Polly put the kettle on, a favorite air, arranged as a rondo for the Pianoforte. *London*, [1805?] fol.   **g. 443. e. (14.)**

— Preludes in a progressive style for the Piano Forte. pp. 22. *Chappell & C°.: London*, [1817.] fol.   **h. 316. (17.)**

— Prince Leopold's waltz for the Piano Forte. pp. 3. *Chappell & C°.: London*, [1817.] fol.   **h. 315. (50.)**

— Four progressive sonatinas for the Piano forte. pp. 13. *Chappell & C°.: London*, [1814.] fol.   **h. 315. (41.)**

— [A reissue.] Four progressive Sonatinas, *etc. London*, [WM 1815.] fol.   **h. 61. t. (15.)**

— [4 Progressive Sonatinas.] 1ˢᵗ. Sonatine. Op. 4. *See* LEYBACH (I.) The Progressive Music School ... 1ˢᵗ. Series. No. 1. [1881.] fol.   **h. 1299. h. (1.)**

— [4 Progressive Sonatinas.] 2ⁿᵈ. Sonatine. Op. 4. *See* LEYBACH (I.) The Progressive Music School ... 1ˢᵗ. Series. No. 2. [1881.] fol.   **h. 1299. h. (1.)**

— [4 Progressive Sonatinas.] 3ʳᵈ. Sonatine. Op. 4. *See* LEYBACH (I.) The Progressive Music School ... 1ˢᵗ. Series. No. 5. [1881.] fol.   **h. 1299. h. (1.)**

— [4 Progressive Sonatinas.] 4ᵗʰ. Sonatine. Op. 4. *See* LEYBACH (I.) The Progressive Music School ... 1ˢᵗ. Series. No. 6. [1881.] fol.   **h. 1299. h. (1.)**

— Quadrilles with their proper figures, for the Piano Forte. pp. 9. *Chappell & C°.: London*, [1818.] fol.   **h. 315. (48.)**

— Recreation ⟨N° [MS v]⟩ for the Piano Forte. ⟨Ap Shenkin.⟩ pp. 5. *At Bland & Weller's: London*, [WM 1806.] fol.   **h. 724. p. (19.)**

— Recreation. (No. 7.) Nobody coming to woo, for the piano forte. pp. 5. *Bland & Weller: London*, [1810?] fol.   **g. 270. j. (17.)**

— The Remembrance, or Songs of the Year, for 1832; comprising poetry and music ... edited by T. Latour. *Published for the Editor: London*, [1832.] 4°.   **G. 420.**

— [Another copy.]   **R. M. 14. b. 15.**

— "La replique," a divertimento for the Piano Forte with an accompaniment for the flute ad libitum. [Score.] pp. 11. *Chappell & C°.: London*, [1811.] fol.   **h. 314. (15.)**

— La Réplique. Divertimento pour piano et flûte (ou violon). [Score.] pp. 9. *Chez Pacini: Paris*, [c. 1815.] fol.   **h. 60. jj. (22.)**

— Le Retour d'Espagne; a Divertimento for the Piano Forte. pp. 11. *Chappell & C°.: London*, [1814.] fol.   **h. 315. (21.)**

— Le Retour de Bath, a favorite Rondo, for the Piano Forte. pp. 3. *C. Wheatstone: London*, [WM 1813.] fol.   **h. 3865. ee. (6.)**

— Le Retour de Windsor, a new Sonata, for the Piano Forte with or without the additional keys, with an accompaniment for a violin (ad libitum) ... Op. 9. [Parts.] 2 pt. *Bland & Wellers: London*, [WM 1807.] fol.   **g. 271. e. (1.)**

— Le Retour de Windsor. A new sonata for the piano forte with or without the additional keys. With an accompaniment for a violin (ad libitum) ... Op. 9. pp. 11. *J. McFadyen: Glasgow*, [c. 1810.] fol. *Without the accompaniment.*   **g. 354. b. (11.)**

— Le Retour de Windsor, a new Sonata, for the Piano Forte, with or without the additional keys, with an accompaniment for a violin (ad libitum) ... Op. 9. *Bland & Wellers: London*, [1810?] fol. *Imperfect; wanting the violin part.*   **Hirsch M. 1282. (7.)**

LATOUR (T.)

— Le Retour de Windsor, a new Sonata, for the Piano Forte, with or without the additional keys. With an accompaniment, for a violon (ad libitum) ... Op. 9. *Bland & Weller's: London,* [WM 1811.] fol.
Imperfect; wanting the violin part. **g. 270. j. (14.)**

— Le Retour de Windsor. A new sonata, for the piano forte ... with an accompaniment for a violin (ad libitum) ... Op. 9. [P. F. part.] pp. 11. *Bland & Weller: London,* [WM 1813.] fol.
A reissue of the edition of 1807, entered above. Without the accompaniment. **h. 925. x. (2.)**

— Le Retour de Windsor, a new sonata, for the piano forte ... with an accompaniment for a violin (ad libitum) ... Op. 9. [Violin part.] *Bland & Weller: London,* [WM 1814.] fol.
Imperfect; wanting the P. F. part. **h. 62. l. (15.)**

— Le Retour de Windsor. Sonata for the piano-forte, with an accompaniment for the flute (ad lib.), *etc.* ⟨New edition.⟩ [Parts.] 2 pt. *Phillips & Mayhew: London,* [c. 1820.] fol.
h. 3870. u. (4.)

— The Rising of the Lark, a Welsh air, with variations, for piano forte. pp. 3. *Bland & Wellers' Music Warehouse: London,* [WM 1808.] fol. **g. 443. q. (13.)**

— The Rising of the Sun, a Welsh Air, arranged as a Rondo for the Piano Forte, *etc. Bland & Weller: London,* [1800?] fol.
g. 270. j. (18.)

— Le Romanesque, a divertimento for the Piano Forte with a flute accompaniment ad libitum. [Parts.] 2 pt. *Chappell & Cᵒ.: London,* [1817.] fol. **h. 314. (11.)**

— A New Rondo as Performed by Mademoiselle Parisot, and Danc'd by Madame Laborie ... in the Favorite Ballet [by D'Egville and Bossi] of Renaldo and Leonora, *etc. Bland & Weller: London,* [1800.] fol. **g. 272. u. (8.)**

— Rondo from the Ballet of "Le sultan genereux" arranged for the Piano Forte by T. Latour. pp. 7. *Chappell & Cᵒ.: London,* [1819.] fol. **h. 315. (3.)**

— Twelve Favorite Rondos for the Harpsichord or Piano Forte, *etc. A. Bland & Weller: London,* [1795.] fol. **g. 140. (41.)**

— Rousseau's dream ... with variations for the harp and Piano Forte. [Parts.] 2 pt. *Chappell & Cᵒ.: London,* [1817.] fol.
h. 316. (6.)

— "Rousseau's dream" with variations for two performers on the Piano Forte by T. Latour. *London,* [1817.] fol.
h. 317. (15.)

— Rule Britannia, a favorite air [by T. A. Arne], with variations for the harpsichord or piano forte by T. Latour. pp. 4. *Bland & Wellers: London,* [WM 1813.] fol. **h. 1226. d. (4.)**

— Rule Britannia [by T. A. Arne], with variations for the piano forte. ⟨New edition.⟩ pp. 5. *Chappell & Cᵒ: London,* [WM 1822.] fol. **h. 62. d. (18.)**

— Russian Dance, arranged as a rondo for the Pianoforte. *London,* [1810?] fol. **g. 271. a. (48.)**

— The sacred annual—consisting of six new devotional melodies, for one, or three voices; the words by W. Ball. *The Author: London,* [1836.] fol. **H. 1287. (12.)**

— Select Italian airs arranged and varied for the Piano Forte harp and flute by T. Latour. No. 1, 2. *Chappell & Cᵒ.: London,* [1821.] fol. **h. 316. (3.)**

— Serenade pour le Piano Forte avec accompagnement de harpe ou flute ad libitum. [Parts.] 3 pt. *Rᵗ Birchall: London,* [1807.] fol. **h. 316. (1.)**

— A second serenade for the Piano Forte with an accompaniment for harp or flute ad libitum. [Score and part.] 3 pt. *Rᵗ Birchall: London,* [1814.] fol. **h. 316. (2.)**

LATOUR (T.)

— Short preludes intended as exercises for the Piano Forte. pp. 25. *F. T. Latour: London,* [1828.] fol. **h. 316. (18.)**

— Sir David Hunter Blair, a favorite reel, arranged as a rondo, for the piano forte ... by Mʳ Latour. pp. 3. *At Bland & Wellers Music Warehouse: London,* [c. 1805.] fol.
g. 1138. tt. (13.)

— Sly Cupid—a ballad, written by J. A. Wade. pp. 5. *F. T. Latour: London,* [1830.] fol. **H. 1287. (22.)**

— Somebody. We're [*sic*] I oblig'd to beg my Bread, a favorite air, with variations for the piano forte. pp. 3. *At Bland & Wellers Music Warehouse: London,* [c. 1805.] fol.
h. 724. p. (13.)

— Three Sonatas for the Piano Forte or Harpsichord with an Accompaniment for a Violin and Violoncello ... Op. 1. [Parts.] *A. Bland & Weller: London,* [1795.] fol.
g. 161. b. (9.)

— Two Sonatas for the Piano Forte ... with an Accompaniment for a Flute or Violin ... Op. 2. [Parts.] *A. Bland & Weller: London,* [1796.] fol. **g. 186. (6.)**

— Two Sonatas for the Piano Forte ... with an Accompaniment for a Flute or Violin ... Op. 3. [Parts.] *A. Bland & Weller: London,* [1796.] fol. **g. 186. (7.)**

— A Grand Sonata, for the piano forte, with or without the additional keys, and accompaniments for a violin and bass (ad libitum) in which is introduced, Mozart's favorite air, The Manly Heart ... Op. 8. [Parts.] 3 pt. *At Bland & Wellers: London,* [c. 1800.] fol. **g. 934. dd. (1.)**

— A Grand Sonata, for the Piano Forte, with or without the additional keys. And accompaniments for a violin, and bass, (ad libitum) in which is introduced, Mozarts, favorite air, The manly Heart ... Op. 8. *Bland & Wellers: London,* [1810?] fol.
Imperfect; wanting the accompaniments.
Hirsch M. 1282. (6.)

— A second sonata for the Piano Forte with an accompaniment for the flute or violin ad libitum. [Parts.] 2 pt. *Rᵗ. Birchall: London,* [1808.] fol. **h. 314. (3.)**

— Sonate pour le piano-forte avec accompagnement de violon ad-libitum, *etc.* pp. 16. *Chez Janet et Cotelle: Paris,* [c. 1815.] fol.
Without the violin part. **h. 1728. f. (5.)**

— Songs of the four seasons. *The Author: London,* [1836.] fol.
H. 1287. (13.)

— The favorite Spanish boleros danced by M. Vestris and Madˡˡᵉ Angiolini in the Ballet of Don Quichotte with variations for the Piano Forte with an accompaniment for the flute. [Score.] pp. 9. *Rᵗ Birchall: London,* [1819.] fol.
h. 314. (22.)

— The favorite Spanish dance ... in the Divertissement of Figaro—arranged as a rondo for the Piano Forte by T. Latour. pp. 5. *Chappell & Cᵒ.: London,* [1817.] fol.
h. 315. (51.)

— Stockhausen's swiss air with variations for the Piano Forte by T. Latour. pp. 4. *F. T. Latour: London,* [1828.] fol.
h. 315. (53.)

— Sul margine d'un rio. *See* also supra: A duett ... in which is introduced the air of "Sul margine d'un rio", *etc.*

— Sul margine d'un rio, a favorite Italian air, with 12 variations for the Pianoforte, with an accompaniment for the Flute (ad libitum). [Parts.] 2 pt. *Rt. Birchall: London,* [1810?] fol.
h. 721. c. (1.)

LATOUR (T.)

— Sul margine d'un rio … With 12 variations for the piano forte, with an accompaniment for the flute (ad libitum), *etc.* [P. F. part.] pp. 13.   *R^t Birchall: London,* [^{WM} 1811.] fol.
Without the flute part.   **h. 721. bb. (13.)**

— Sul margine d'un rio. A favorite Italian air, arranged as a duett, for the harp & piano forte … by T. Latour. [P. F. part.] *R^t Birchall: London,* [c. 1810.] fol.
Imperfect; wanting the harp part.   **h. 60. jj. (23.)**

— "They're a'noddin," a Scotch air with variations for the Piano Forte with an accompaniment for the flute by T. Latour. 2 pt.   *Chappell & Co.: London,* [1822.] fol.
h. 314. (1.)

— The Tivoli waltz with variations for the Piano Forte by T. Latour. pp. 6.   *Chappell & Co.: London,* [1817.] fol.
h. 315. (17.)

— "The Troubadour," a divertimento for the Piano Forte with an accompaniment for the flute ad libitum by T. Latour. [Parts.] 2 pt.   *Chappell: London,* [1813.] fol.   **h. 314. (17.)**

— "La [*sic*] Troubadour du Tage," a French air with variations for the Piano Forte. pp. 10.   *F. T. Latour: London,* [1826.] fol.
h. 315. (45.)

— The favorite air "Tu che accendi" [by G. A. Rossini], with variations for the Pianoforte, with an accompaniment for the flute (ad libitum). [Parts.] 2 pt.   *Chappell & Co.: London,* [1817.] fol.
g. 270. i. (31.)

— [Another copy.]   **h. 314. (13.)**

— Tu che accende [*sic*] arranged by T. Latour. [1826.] fol. *See* Rossini (G. A.) [Tancredi.]   **h. 317. (16.)**

— "L'unique,"—Three popular airs with variations for the harp, Piano Forte and Flute by T. Latour. [Parts.] 3 pt.   *Chappell & Co.: London,* [1817.] fol.   **h. 316. (5.)**

— "Vous et moi,"—a duett for two performers on the Piano Forte in which is introduced the air of "Lieber Augustine,"— with new variations by T. Latour.   *London,* [1814.] fol.
h. 317. (10.)

— The favorite waltz in the opera of Der Freischütz [composed by C. M. F. E. von Weber] arranged for the Piano Forte by T. Latour. pp. 3.   *Chappell & Co.: London,* [1824.] fol.
h. 315. (28.)

— The favorite waltz in the Opera of Der Freischütz [composed by C. M. F. E. von Weber] with variations for the Piano Forte by T. Latour.   *Chappell & Co.: London,* [1824.] fol.
h. 315. (7.)

— Two original Waltzes for the Piano Forte. pp. 4.   *Chappell & Co.: London,* [1811.] fol.   **h. 315. (12.)**

— Three waltzes for the Piano Forte. pp. 8.   *Chappell & Co.: London,* [1812.] fol.   **h. 315. (39.)**

— Ye Banks and Braes o' bonny Doon. [By J. Miller.] Arranged … by T. Latour. [P. F.]   *[Chappell & Co.: London,* 1812, 13.] fol.
[*National Melodies.* No. 11.]   **h. 323.**

— *See* Auber (D. F. E.) [Le Dieu et la Bayadère.] Overture … arranged for the Pianoforte … by T. Latour. [1835?] fol.
g. 270. a. (6.)

— *See* Auber (D. F. E.) [La Fiancée.] Overture to "The National Guard," arranged by T. Latour. [1830.] fol.   **h. 315. (1.)**

— *See* Auber (D. F. E.) [Fra Diavolo.] The Favorite Airs in Auber's Opera … arranged … by T. Latour. [1830?] fol.
R. M. 25. i. 4. (13.)

— *See* Auber (D. F. E.) [La Muette de Portici.] The favorite airs … arranged … by T. Latour. [1828.] fol.   **h. 312. (9.)**

LATOUR (T.)

— *See* Auber (D. F. E.) [La Muette de Portici.] The Guaracha … arranged … by T. Latour. [1829.] fol.   **h. 317. (6.)**

— *See* Ball (W.) The shepherd maid … with an accompaniment … by T. Latour. [1828.] fol.   **H. 1281. (4.)**

— *See* Bellini (V.) [Il Pirata.—Del disastro di questi infelici.] Coro … arranged for piano-forte and flute, by T. Latour. 1830. 4°. [*Harmonicon. vol.* 8. *pt.* 2. *pp.* 292–296.]   **P. P. 1947.**

— *See* Bishop (*Sir* H. R.) Thème Anglais … with variations by T. Latour. [1818.] fol.   **h. 315. (29.)**

— *See* Bochsa (R. N. C.) Bochsa's fourth introduction … arranged for the Pianoforte by T. Latour. [1830?] fol.
h. 1480. i. (3.)

— *See* Bochsa (R. N. C.) Bochsa's second (and third) march, arranged by T. Latour. [1821.] fol.   **h. 315. (56.)**

— *See* Boieldieu (F. A.) [Le Calife de Bagdad.] Boïeldieu's celebrated Overture … newly arranged for the piano forte … by T. Latour. [1827.] fol.   **g. 1138. tt. (12.)**

— *See* Boieldieu (F. A.) [La dame blanche.] Select airs … arranged by T. Latour. [1826.] fol.   **h. 315. (11.)**

— *See* Carafa di Colobrano (M. E. F. V. A. P.) *Prince.* Fra tante angoscie … Arranged as a rondo for the Piano forte by T. Latour. [c. 1830.] fol.   **H. 1652. rr. (5.)**

— *See* Cooke (T. S.) [The Brigand.] "Love's Ritornella," with variations by T. Latour. [1829.] fol.   **h. 315. (33.)**

— *See* H***. Thy gentle Beauty's soft Control. *Canzonet* … Composed by H*** [i. e. Henri Herz]; arranged by T. Latour. 1832. 4°. [*Harmonicon. vol.* 10, *pt.* 2. *pp.* 14, 15.]   **P. P. 1947.**

— *See* Hérold (L. J. F.) [La Somnambule.] Select airs … arranged by T. Latour. [1829.] fol.   **h. 315. (2.)**

— *See* Herz (Henri) [Contredanses. Op. 35.] Herz's favorite Set of Quadrilles, arranged as duetts, for the piano forte … by T. Latour. [c. 1833.] fol.   **g. 1563. (5.)**

— *See* Herz (Henri) A second quadrille rondo, arranged by T. Latour. [1829.] fol.   **h. 460. (15.)**

— *See* Kiesewetter (C. G.) Kiesewetter's thema and variations, arranged by T. Latour. [1828.] fol.   **h. 315. (16.)**

— *See* Mayer (J. S.) [Medea.] The favorite airs … arranged by T. Latour. [1826.] fol.   **h. 312. (1.)**

— *See* Meyerbeer (G.) [Il Crociato in Egitto.] The favorite airs … arranged by T. Latour. [1825.] fol.   **h. 313. (6.)**

— *See* Meyerbeer (G.) [Il Crociato in Egitto.] The march and cavatina … arranged for the Piano Forte by F. Latour. [1825.] fol.   **h. 315. (9.)**

— *See* Meyerbeer (G.) [Il Crociato in Egitto.] The March and Chorus "All' armi," arranged by T. Latour. [1825.] fol.
h. 315. (8.)

— *See* Meyerbeer (G.) [Margherita d'Anjou.] The overture (and select airs) … Arranged by T. Latour. [1828.] fol.
h. 312. (4.)

— *See* Mozart (W. A.) [Don Giovanni.] Selection of airs … arranged by T. Latour. [1816.] fol.   **h. 315. (15.)**

— *See* Mozart (W. A.) [Die Zauberflöte.] Selection of airs … arranged by T. Latour. [1817.] fol.   **h. 313. (3.)**

— *See* Musard (F.) Six favorite quadrille airs, arranged by T. Latour. [1819.] fol.   **h. 317. (18.)**

— *See* Quadrille. Quadrille Rondo. No. 6, by T. Latour. [1821.] fol.   **h. 306.**

LATOUR (T.)

— *See* ROSSINI (G. A.) [Il Barbiere di Siviglia.] A duett ... by T. Latour. [1818.] fol.　　　**h. 317. (3.)**

— *See* ROSSINI (G. A.) [Il Barbiere di Siviglia.] The favorite airs ... arranged by T. Latour. [1821.] fol.　　　**h. 313. (8.)**

— *See* ROSSINI (G. A.) "La chasse," arranged by T. Latour. [1827.] fol.　　　**h. 315. (54.)**

— *See* ROSSINI (G. A.) [Le Comte Ory.] Select airs ... arranged by T. Latour. [1828.] fol.　　　**h. 317. (9.)**

— *See* ROSSINI (G. A.) [Le Comte Ory.] The overture and favorite airs ... arranged by T. Latour. [1829.] fol.　　　**h. 312. (12.)**

— *See* ROSSINI (G. A.) [Le Comte Ory.] The favorite airs ... arranged for the Pianoforte ... by T. Latour. [1829.] fol.　　　**h. 312. (13.)**

— *See* ROSSINI (G. A.) [Le Comte Ory.—Buvons, buvons.] Chorus ... arranged for piano-forte and flute, by T. Latour. 1829. 4°. [*Harmonicon. vol.* 7, *pt.* 2. *pp.* 30–32.]　　**P. P. 1947.**

— *See* ROSSINI (G. A.) [La Donna del Lago.] The favorite airs ... arranged by T. Latour. [1823.] fol.　　　**h. 313. (5.)**

— *See* ROSSINI (G. A.) [La Gazza Ladra.] The Favorite Airs in ... La Gazza ladra, arranged for the piano forte ... by T. Latour, *etc.* [1830?] fol.　　　**g. 271. j. (7.)**

— *See* ROSSINI (G. A.) [L'Italiana in Algieri.] Overture, arranged by T. Latour. [1823.] fol.　　　**h. 315. (27.)**

— *See* ROSSINI (G. A.) [Maometto Secondo.] Select airs ... arranged by T. Latour. [1827.] fol.　　　**h. 313. (1.)**

— *See* ROSSINI (G. A.) [Ricciardo e Zoraide.] The favorite airs ... arranged by T. Latour. [1823.] fol.　　　**h. 313. (2.)**

— *See* ROSSINI (G. A.) [Tancredi.] The favorite airs ... arranged by T. Latour. [1826.] fol.　　　**h. 312. (3.)**

— *See* ROSSINI (G. A.) [Il Turco in Italia.] Select airs ... arranged by T. Latour. [1820.] fol.　　　**h. 312. (2.)**

— *See* ROSSINI (G. A.) [Il Turco in Italia.] Overture ... arranged by T. Latour. [1823.] fol.　　　**h. 315. (26.)**

— *See* SPONTINI (G.) [La Vestale.] Select airs ... arranged by T. Latour. [1827.] fol.　　　**h. 313. (4.)**

— *See* STEIBELT (D.) [La Belle Laitière.] Two Duetts ... arranged by T. Latour. [1814.] fol.　　　**h. 317. (19.)**

— *See* TURTLE (S.) The nightingale waltz, arranged by T. Latour. [1828.] fol.　　　**h. 315. (55.)**

— *See* VIOTTI (G. B.) [Concertos. Violin. No. 9.] Viotti's New grand Concerto (in A) as performed at the Opera Concerts, arranged ... by T. Latour. [1798?] fol.　　**Hirsch M. 1282. (2.)**

— *See* WADE (J. A.) "I have fruit" ... arranged by T. Latour. [1827.] fol.　　　**h. 315. (30.)**

— *See* WADE (J. A.) "Love was once" ... arranged by T. Latour. [1827.] fol.　　　**h. 315. (40.)**

— *See* WEBER (C. M. F. E. von) [Der Freischütz.] Overture and airs ... arranged by T. Latour. [1825.] fol.　　　**h. 317. (7.)**

— *See* WEBER (C. M. F. E. von) [Der Freischütz.] The favorite airs arranged for the pianoforte with an accompaniment for the flute by T. Latour. [1825.] fol.　　　**h. 312. (11.)**

— *See* WEBER (C. M. F. E. von) [Der Freischütz.] The favorite airs arranged for two performers on the Piano Forte by T. Latour. [1825.] fol.　　　**h. 317. (8.)**

— *See* WEBER (C. M. F. E. von) [Der Freischütz.] The Favorite Airs in Weber's Opera ... arranged ... by T. Latour. [1830?] fol.　　　**R. M. 25. i. 4. (3.)**

LATOUR (T.)

— *See* WEBER (C. M. F. E. von) [Der Freischütz.] Overture arranged for the piano forte with an accompaniment for the flute by T. Latour. [1825.] fol.　　　**h. 312. (10.)**

— *See* WEBER (C. M. F. E. von) [Der Freischütz.] The ... Jaeger Chorus ... arranged ... by T. Latour. [1827?] fol.　　　**R. M. 25. k. 1. (9.)**

— *See* WEBER (C. M. F. E. von) [Preciosa.] The overture and airs ... arranged by T. Latour. [1825.] fol.　　　**h. 312. (6.)**

— *See* WEBER (C. M. F. E. von) [Preciosa.] The favorite airs arranged for the piano forte with an accompaniment for the flute by T. Latour. [1825.] fol.　　　**h. 312. (7.)**

— *See* WEBER (C. M. F. E. von) [Preciosa.] Overture ... arranged by T. Latour. [1825.] fol.　　　**h. 317. (4.)**

— *See* WINTER (P. von) [Das unterbrochene Opferfest.] Select airs ... arranged by T. Latour. [1826.] fol.　　　**h. 315. (10.)**

LA TOUR D'AUVERGNE (HENRI DE) *Viscount de Turenne*

— Air du Maréchal de Turenne [begins: "Après de penibles combats"]. Accomp^t. par P. P. Blattman. *Paris*, [1830?] fol.　　　**G. 543. (66.)**

LA TOURETTE (CHARLES)

— My sunny southern Babe, *etc.* [Song.] *Hamilton S. Gordon: New York*, [1903.] fol.　　　**H. 3985. i. (9.)**

— My sunny southern Babe ... Words & music by C. H. La Tourette. 1903. 8°. *See* PHILLIPS (W. A.) [4 Choruses for Men's Voices. No. 4.]　　　**F. 163. b. (39.)**

— "My sunny southern Babe" ... Arr. by Al. J. Doyle. [Orchestral parts.] 10 pt. *Hamilton S. Gordon: New York*, [1903.] 8°.　　　**f. 800. (788.)**

LATROBE (CHRISTIAN IGNATIUS)

— Anthem for the Jubilee of the Reign of ... George the Third ... The words taken from the xxth and xxist Psalms ... Adapted for the Piano Forte and Voices. *Printed for the Author: London*, 1809. fol.　　　**H. 879. j. (2.)**

— Anthems for one, two or more voices performed in the Church of the United Brethren, collected, and ... adapted for the organ or piano forte by C. I. Latrobe. Composed by various authors. pp. 8. 199. *Printed for the Editor: London*, [1811] fol.　　　**H. 1132. d.**

— [Anthems for one, two or more Voices. No. 12.] Lord of Life! now sweetly slumber. Anthem ... S. A. T. B. chorus, tenor and bass soli. Text by C. I. Latrobe and John Worthington c. 1790 ... Edited by Ewald V. Nolte. pp. 11. *Boosey & Hawkes: [New York*, 1972.] 8°.
Part of "Moramus Edition".　　　**F. 1744. ww. (8.)**

— The Dawn of Glory, a hymn ... for the Pianoforte & voices. [Vocal score.] *London*, [1803.] fol.　　　**H. 1132. b.**

— The Dawn of Glory. For soli and chorus of mixed voices. ⟨Text by C. I. Latrobe and Ambrose Serle. Edited by Ewald V. Nolte.⟩ [Vocal score.] pp. 102. *Brodt Music Co.: Charlotte, N. C.*, [1968.] 8°.
Part of "Moravian Church Music".　　　**E. 460. ee. (7.)**

— [The Dawn of Glory.] How shall a mortal Song aspire. Soprano or tenor aria. ⟨[Words by] Ambrose Serle (1742–1812) or C. I. Latrobe.⟩ Edited and arranged by Donald M. McCorkle. pp. 9. *Boosey & Hawkes: [New York*, 1963.] 4°.
Part of "The Moramus Edition".　　　**G. 519. bb. (16.)**

LATROBE (CHRISTIAN IGNATIUS)

— Dies Iræ &c., an Ancient Hymn on the Last Judgment, translated ... by ... the Earl of Roscommon ... Adapted for the Piano Forte, and Four Voices. *R. Birchall, for the Author: London,* 1799. fol. **G. 503. (5.)**

— How shall a mortal Song aspire. Aria. *See* supra: [The Dawn of Glory.]

— Hymn-Tunes, sung in the Church of the United Brethren, collected by C. I. La Trobe. pp. 80. *Printed for the Author, by I. Bland: London,* [1790.] obl. 4°. **A. 1231. kk.**

— Hymn-Tunes, sung in the Church of the United Brethren, collected by C. I. La Trobe. pp. xii. 80. *Printed for the Editor by J. Bland: London,* [WM 1803.] obl. 4°. *With MS. notes by Maurice Frost and a typescript letter inserted.* **B. 438. o.**

— Hymn-Tunes, sung in the Church of the United Brethren. Collected by C. I. LaTrobe. pp. xii. 80. *John LeFebvre: London,* [1814?] obl. 8°. *Imperfect; wanting pp.* 5–6. **A. 1236. m.**

— Hymn-tunes, sung in the Church of the United Brethren, collected by C. I. La Trobe. A new edition revised & corrected, with an appendix. pp. 8. 100. *London,* [1826?] obl. 8°. **E. 497. ww.**

— Hymn Tunes sung in the Church of the United Brethren ... With an introduction ... by P. Latrobe. *London,* 1854. obl. 4°. **B. 654.**

— Hymn Tunes sung in the Church of the United Brethren ... arranged in four parts, *etc.* (Moravian Hymn Tunes.) *Society for the Furtherance of the Gospel: London,* 1861. 12°. **A. 735.**

— [Another copy.] **3406. a. 58.**

— Hymn Tunes for the use of the Protestant Church of the United Brethren; or, Unitas fratrum. A revised and enlarged edition [of the collection originally compiled by C. I. Latrobe]. pp. 40. 116. 1887. obl. fol. *See* UNITED BRETHREN. **G. 585. a.**

— [Hymn-Tunes, sung in the Church of the United Brethren.] *See* HYMNS. [*English.*] The Hymn Tunes of the Church of the Brethren, *etc.* (Comprising ... Tunes in Mr. Latrobe's Collection, *etc.*) [*London?*] 1824. obl. fol. **E. 497. l.**

— In Memory of a Beloved Sister ... The words by J. A. La Trobe. *Engraved by E. Lomax: London,* 1826. fol. **G. 424. g. (4.)**

— Lord of Life! now sweetly slumber. *See* supra: [Anthems for one, two or more Voices. no. 12.]

— Miserere mei Deus! Psalm LI ... for the Organ, *etc. London,* 1814. fol. **G. 585.**

— [Miserere mei, Deus.] Psalm 51 ... (Have Mercy upon me, O God) ... Edited by Henry B. Ingram, jr. [Vocal score. With a facsimile.] pp. 96. *Boosey & Hawkes: New York, etc.,* [1972.] 8°. *Part of "Moramus Edition".* **E. 556. w. (5.)**

— Original Anthems, for one, two or more Voices ... the accompaniments arranged for the piano forte or organ. 2 vol. *Printed for the author: London,* [1828.] fol. **H. 1132. a.**

— [Original Anthems.—Make a joyful Noise unto the Lord.] Psalm 100 ... ⟨For SATB soli and chorus with organ or piano.⟩ Edited and arranged by Karl Kroeger. [Vocal score.] pp. 35. *Boosey & Hawkes:* [*New York,* 1978.] 8°. *Part of "The Moramus Edition".* **F. 538. s. (8.)**

— [Original Anthems.] O send out thy Light and thy Truth. For soprano solo, three-part mixed chorus and keyboard. Psalm 43: 3–4 ... Edited by Karl Kroeger. pp. 12. *Boosey & Hawkes:* [*New York,* 1979.] 8°. *Part of "The Moramus Edition".* **E. 1857. d. (6.)**

LATROBE (CHRISTIAN IGNATIUS)

— Psalm 100. *See* supra: [Original Anthems.— Make a joyful Noise unto the Lord.]

— Selection of sacred music from the works of some of the most eminent Composers of Germany and Italy, the vocal parts in score, the instrumental adapted to the Piano Forte. 6 vol. *London,* 1806 [–1826]. fol. **H. 1132.**

— Selection of sacred music, from the most eminent composers of Germany & Italy. No. 2, 5, 6, 10, 15, 24, 27, 31, 37, 43, 51, 52, 58, 59, 62, 66, 70, 77, 85, 147, 172, 198, 199, 208. *London,* [1874.] fol. *No more published.* **H. 1132. c.**

— Three Sonatas for the Piano Forte ... Op. III. *J. Bland, for the Author: London,* [1791.] fol. **g. 148. (5.)**

— Three Sonatas for the Pianoforte. ⟨Op. III.⟩ Edited by Charles E. Stevens. [With a facsimile.] pp. 47. *Boosey & Hawkes:* [*New York,* 1970.] 4°. *Part of "Moramus Edition".* **g. 1129. xx. (12.)**

— [3 Sonatas. Op. 3. No. 1.] Sonata, *etc. In:* LINCOLN (Stoddard) Five eighteenth Century Piano Sonatas. Edited ... by S. Lincoln. pp. 30–41. [1975.] 4°. **g. 270. nn. (4.)**

— Sonatinas, for the piano forte ... inscribed to Dr Burney by C. I. L. T. [i. e. C. I. Latrobe.] pp. 17. *London,* [1787.] fol. *See* T., C. I. L. **h. 62. (3.)**

— [Te Deum laudamus.] We praise Thee, O God! ... ⟨S. A. T. B. chorus and soli. Ancient Latin hymn. Traditional English translation.⟩ Edited by Ewald V. Nolte. pp. 31. *Boosey & Hawkes:* [*New York,* 1972.] 8°. *Part of "Moramus Edition".* **F. 363. n. (4.)**

— We praise Thee, O God. *See* supra: [Te Deum laudamus.]

— *See* GRAUN (C. H.) Te Deum laudamus ... adapted ... by C. I. Latrobe, *etc.* [1830?] fol. **H. 1805. b.**

— *See* SUIDELL (   ) Padre. [Credo.] Crucifixus, *etc.* [P. F. reduction by C. I. Latrobe.] [1978.] 8°. **F. 217. bb. (15.)**

LATROBE (PETER)

— *See* LATROBE (C. I.) Hymn Tunes ... With an introduction ... by P. Latrobe. 1854. obl. 4°. **B. 654.**

LATTER

— A Latter Day Athenian speaks. Secular motet. *See* GARDNER (John L.)

LATTER (RICHARD)

— Back to Moray Land, or A voice from Australia. A song. Words by David Grant, *etc.* pp. 5. *Wood & Cº: Edinburgh, etc.,* [1856?] fol. **H. 1650. nn. (28.)**

LATTER (WALTER)

— Gladys. Song. Words by L. Thompson. *Weekes & Co.: London,* [1900.] fol. **H. 1799. h. (8.)**

— The Love of long ago. Song. Words by C. Hussey. *E. Donajowski: London,* [1900.] fol. **H. 1799. h. (9.)**

LATTER (WILLIAM)

— Caprice in D flat. [P. F.] *London,* [1852.] fol. **h. 723. l. (20.)**

— *See* MOZART (W. A.) [Die Zauberflöte.] Overture ... arranged ... by W. Latter. [1869.] fol. **h. 321. c. (11.)**

LATTÈS (MARCEL)

— La Jeunesse dorée. Opérette en 3 actes de MM. Henri Verne
et Gabriel Faure ... Partition complète pour chant et piano.
pp. 179. *Max Eschig: Paris*, [1913.] 4°. **G. 1274. u.**

— Maggie. A Musical Play in 3 acts by F. Thompson and
H. F. Maltby. The French version by E. Rey and Bousquet,
from the book of F. Thompson. Lyrics by A. Ross. Vocal
Score. *H. Darewski Music Publishing Co.: London*, 1919. 4°.
G. 782. ii. (2.)

— [Maggie.] Nelly. Opérette en trois actes de MM. Jacques
Bousquet et Henri Falk d'après le livret anglais de M. Fred.
Thompson ... Partition chant et piano. Réduite par l'auteur.
pp. 166. *Société Générale Théâtrale et d'Éditions: Paris*,
[1921.] 4°.
With press cuttings inserted. **G. 1274. s.**

— Monsieur l'Amour. Opéra-comique en trois actes de MM.
René Peter et Henri Falk ... Partition complète pour chant et
piano. pp. 216. *Max Eschig: Paris*, [1922.] 4°.
With press cuttings inserted. **G. 1274. t.**

— Nelly. *See supra:* [Maggie.]

LATTRE (CLAUDE JEAN DE)

— Lamentationes aliquot Ieremiæ Musicæ Harmoniæ nouiter
adaptatæ, adiectis aliquot sacris cantionibus, Trium,
Quatuor, Quinque, & Sex vocum ... Acuta Vox.
(Contratenor.) (Tenor.) (Basis.) (Quinta et Sexta Pars.) 5 pt.
Iacobus Bathenius: Traiecti ad Mosam, 1554. *obl.* 4°.
K. 4. g. 5.

— Oh! Gentle Bird. (Philomel.) Madrigal. *See* SONGS. Four-part
Songs, *etc.* No. 1. [1864.] fol. **H. 2826. (5.)**

— *See* CHANSONS. [3. Phalèse's Collections.] Tiers ... Liure des
Chansons, *etc.* (Sixiesme Liure des Chansons ... mises en
musique par Maistre Iehan de Latre, *etc.*) 1555. *obl.* 4°.
K. 3. a. 15.

LATTRE (ROLAND DE)
— *See* LASSO (Orlando di)

LATTUADA (FELICE)

— Caino. Tragedia lirica in un atto di F. Lattuada e
G. Zambianchi dal "Caino" di Byron. Riduzione per canto e
pianoforte. pp. 88. *Casa musicale Sonzogno di Piero Ostali:
Milano*, [1957.] 4°. **G. 1269. f. (1.)**

— Le Preziose ridicole. Commedia lirica in un atto di Arturo
Rossato tratta dall'omonima commedia di Molière.
Riduzione per canto e pianoforte. pp. 153. *Casa musicale
Sonzogno: Milano*, 1929. 4°. **G. 1269. c. (2.)**

— Quartetto in re minore per due violini, viola e violoncello ...
Partitura, *etc.* pp. 40. *G. Ricordi & c.: Milano*, [1919.] 4°.
g. 417. pp. (7.)

LATURE ( )
— *See* LATOUR.

LATVIEŠU

— Latviešu muzikas chrestomatija ... Sastādļjis Latvijas PSR
Valsts Konservatorijas muzikas vēstures pedagogu kolektivs.
Latvijas Valsts Izdevnieciba: Rīgā, 1955, *etc.* 4°. **F. 1771. y.**

LATYMER
— The Latymer School Song. [Unison song.] *See* CUNLIFFE
(Ronald)

LATZKO (ERNST)

— *See* HAYDN (F. J.) [Orlando Paladino.] Ritter Roland ... Für
die deutsche Bühne bearbeitet von Dr. E. Latzko. 1932. 4°.
H. 655. c.

LAU (CHRISTOPH HEINRICH)

— *See* REIMANN (J. B.) J. B. Reimañs ... Choralbuch ...
gestochen und verlegt [with a preface] von C. H. Lau. [1747.]
obl. 4°. **b. 339.**

LAU (HEINZ)

— Tänzerische Musik für drei Instrumente. Dance Melodies.
For three instruments. Blockflötentrio. Recorder trio.
Streichertrio oder jede beliebig gemischte Besetzung. String
trio or mixed instrumentation. [Score.] pp. 15. *Musikverlag
zum Pelikan: Zürich*, [1958.] 8°.
Pelikan-Edition. 765. **f. 502. a. (7.)**

— Zwölf Tanzsätze für vier Instrumente. Twelve Dance-Tunes
for four instruments. Blockflötenquartett, Streichquartett oder
jede beliebig gemischte Besetzung, *etc.* pp. 12. *Musikverlag
zum Pelikan: Zürich*, [1955.] 8°. **f. 502. a. (5.)**

LAU (PAUL)

— Swing along. [Popular songs. Words and chords for guitar
and organ.] ⟨Editor in-chief: Paul Lau.⟩ *Leung Yau Sales
Dept.: Hong Kong*, [1980, *etc.*] 8°. **D. 789. u.**

LAUB (FERDINAND)

— Bonheur perdu. [Violin and P. F.] *See* infra: Quatre morceaux
... Op. 12. No. 2.

— Cadenzen zum Beethoven'schen Violin Concert, Op. 61.
Berlin, [1860.] fol. **h. 1609. c. (2.)**

— Canzonetta. [Violin and P. F.] *See* infra: Quatre morceaux ...
Op. 12. No. 1.

— Impromptu. [Violin and P. F.] *See* infra: Quatre morceaux ...
Op. 12. No. 4.

— Deux Morceaux pour le Violon avec accompagnement de
Piano. 2 no. *Leipzig et Berlin*, [1862.] fol. **h. 1609. c. (4.)**

— Quatre morceaux de violon avec accompagnement de piano.
Op. 12. 4 no. *Hambourg*, [1884.] fol. **h. 1609. u. (13.)**

— Polonaise de Concert pour le Violon avec accompagnement
... de Piano. *Leipzig et Berlin*, [1862.] fol. **h. 1609. c. (5.)**

— Romance sans paroles. [Violin and P. F.] *See* supra: Quatre
morceaux ... Op. 12. No. 3.

— Rondo scherzoso pour le Violon avec accompagnement ...
de Piano. *Berlin*, [1860.] fol. **h. 1609. c. (3.)**

LAUB (MARK)

— All-time Favorites for Christmas. For all organs. Arranged
and edited by M. Laub. pp. 23. *G. Schirmer: New York*,
[1968.] 4°. **g. 1378. ee. (7.)**

— Classics for Organ. Arranged by Mark Laub. pp. 32. *Warner
Bros. Music: London*, [1980.] 4°.
Part of "Warner Bros. All-organ Series". **f. 337. u. (7.)**

— Folk Songs of the World. ⟨For all organ.⟩ Arranged by Mark
Laub. pp. 31. *Warner Bros. Music: London*, [1980.] 4°.
Part of "Warner Bros. All-Organ Series". **F. 1966. hh. (1.)**

— The Great Songs of Christmas. Easy organ, easy piano ...
Arranged by M. Laub. pp. 47. *Richmond Organization: [New
York*, 1969.] 4°. **g. 1378. t. (12.)**

LAUB (Mark)

—— The Home Organist. Classical, standard, popular
compositions. With pitch registrations for all organs ...
⟨Arranged by⟩ M. Laub. pp. 158. *G. Schirmer: New York;
Chappell & Co.: London; London* printed, [1969.] 4°.

g. 1378. cc. (11.)

—— The Hymns of Mary Baker Eddy. ⟨A Family Hymn Book.⟩
With Christmas selections from the Christian Science
Hymnal. Arranged by M. Laub, *etc.* ⟨For all organs and
piano.⟩ pp. 37. *Clem W. Collins: Boston,* [1968.] 4°.

G. 518. l. (10.)

—— Sacred Music. For the Baldwin ⟨Conn—Wurlitzer⟩ spinet
organs. Registrations by M. Laub. 3 vol. *G. Schirmer: New
York,* [1962.] 4°.
Each vol. contains the same works. **g. 1378. h. (8.)**

—— Standard Favorites for all Organs. Arranged by Mark Laub.
pp. 43. *G. Schirmer: New York,* [1969.] 4°. **g. 1378. ee. (13.)**

—— *See* Bernstein (Leonard) West Side Story. Selections for
Conn organ. Arranged by M. Laub, *etc.* [1961.] 4°.

g. 1378. h. (3.)

—— *See* Bernstein (Leonard) West Side Story. Selections for
Baldwin organ. Arranged by M. Laub, *etc.* [1962.] 4°.

g. 1378. d. (6.)

—— *See* Gershwin (George) [*Collections, instrumental.*] George
and Ira Gershwin in Hollywood. For all organs ... Arranged
by M. Laub, *etc.* [1968.] 4°. **g. 1378. a. (9.)**

—— *See* Gershwin (George) Rhapsody in Blue ... Arranged for
organ solo by M. Laub. [1968.] 4°. **g. 1378. a. (11.)**

—— *See* Kander (John) Cabaret ... Selection for all organs.
Arranged by M. Laub, *etc.* [1968.] 4°. **g. 1378. cc. (3.)**

—— *See* Kern (Jerome D.) Show Boat. Selection for all organs ...
Arranged by M. Laub. [1968.] 4°. **g. 1378. a. (12.)**

—— *See* Lane (Burton) Finian's Rainbow. Selection for all organs
... Arranged by M. Laub, *etc.* [1970.] 4°. **g. 1378. kk. (13.)**

—— *See* Loewe (Frederick) My fair Lady. Selection ... Arranged
by M. Laub. For all organs, *etc.* [1967.] 4°. **f. 314. ww. (9.)**

—— *See* Loewe (Frederick) Paint your Wagon. Selection for all
organs ... Arranged by M. Laub. [1970.] 4°. **g. 1378. y. (4.)**

—— *See* Rodgers (Richard) Carousel. Selection for all organs ...
Arranged by M. Laub, *etc.* [1968.] 4°. **g. 1378. cc. (2.)**

—— *See* Rodgers (Richard) The King and I. Selection for all
organs ... Arranged by D. C. Glover and M. Laub, *etc.* [1969.]
4°. **g. 1378. cc. (5.)**

—— *See* Rodgers (Richard) Oklahoma! Selection for all organs
... Arranged by D. C. Glover and M. Laub, *etc.* [1969.] 4°.

g. 1378. cc. (10.)

—— *See* Styne (Jule) Up & down Broadway. For all organs ...
Arranged by M. Laub. [1967.] 4°. **g. 1378. a. (8.)**

LAUB (Thomas)

—— Danske Folkeviser med gamle melodier. Musiken lagt til
Rette ved Thomas Laub. Teksten ved Axel Olrik, *etc.* 2 Hft.
Gyldendalske Boghandels Forlag F. Hegel & Søn:
[*Copenhagen,*] 1899, 1904. 8°.
*Hft. 2 bears the imprint: Gyldendalske Boghandel Nordisk
Forlag.* **F. 1588.**

—— Danske Folkeviser med gamle Melodier ... Tegningerne af
Joakim Skovgaard. pp. 34. x. *Gyldendalske Boghandels
Forlag; Simon Bernsteens Bogtrykkeri: Copenhagen,* 1903. *obl.*
fol. **D. 485. qq.**

LAUB (Thomas)

—— Om Kirkesangen. *C. A. Reitzel: København,* 1887. 8°.

7898. c. 11.

—— 80 Rytmiske Koraler uden Harmonisering, samlede og
indrettede til Menighedsbrug af T. Laub, *etc. C. A. Reitzel:
København,* 1888. 8°. **B. 512. a. (4.)**

—— *See* Nielsen (C. A.) Folkehøjskolens melodibog. Melodier til
sangbog udgivet ... ved C. Nielsen, T. Laub, *etc.* 1940. 8°.

F. 1821. x.

—— *See* Nielsen (C. A.) and Laub (T.) En Snes danske Viser
1915. ⟨2^den Samling. 1917.⟩ [1915, 17.] 4°. **F. 1771. t. (6.)**

LAUB (Váša)

—— Berceuse pour violon et piano. Le même arrangé pour
violoncelle et piano par Popper. Op. 2. 2 no. *Hambourg,*
1884. fol. **h. 1609. u. (14.)**

—— Kvapík.—Galopp. [P. F.] *See* Ceský. Český památník tanecní.
Sešit iv. [1880.] fol. **h. 3913. (13.)**

—— Slavische Lieder für eine Singstimme mit Pianoforte-
Begleitung. *Berlin & Posen,* [1881.] fol. **H. 1786. e. (17.)**

—— *See* Simon (A. Y.) Пѣснь торжествующей любви. Chant de
l'amour triomphant. Arr. par V. Laub. [1905?] fol.

h. 1426. p. (13.)

LAUBACH (Alfred)

—— Complete Scales, Chords and Arpeggios ... compiled by
A. Laubach. (Complete Arpeggi ... separately. English
(Continental) Fingering.) 3 no. *Augener & Co.: London,*
[1897.] fol. **h. 3820. l. (8.)**

—— Fantasia on Scotch Airs for violin & pianoforte.
E. Donajowski: London, [1890.] fol. **h. 1608. x. (36.)**

—— In Cedar Groves. Nocturne for flute or violin, with
pianoforte accompaniment. *A. Phillips & Sons:* [*London,*]
1920. 4°. **g. 70. g. (4.)**

—— Lengnick's Pianoforte Tutor; comprising the Elements of
Music, the Preparatory Finger Exercises ... Written and
compiled by A. Laubach. Newly revised and enlarged edition.
A. Lengnick & Co.: London, [1909.] fol. **h. 3820. v. (3.)**

—— 50 Lessons, Questions & Excercises—the answers ... given
separately—in the Elements of Music, *etc.* 2 pt. *A. Laubach:*
[*London,*] 1919. 4°. **g. 759. a. (2.)**

—— Marche militaire. *See* infra: [Three Pieces. No. 3.]

—— Nocturne. *See* infra: [Three Pieces. No. 2.]

—— [Petit Cours élémentaire de Piano.] Elementary Pianoforte
School, *etc.* Eng. & Fr. *Augener & Co.: London,* [1903.] 4°.

g. 337. h. (13.)

—— [Three Pieces. No. 2.] Nocturne. [Violin and P. F.] *See*
Progressive. The Progressive Violinist, *etc.* Grade 4. No. 2.
[1908, 09.] fol. **g. 791.**

—— [Three Pièces. No. 3.] Marche militaire. [Violin and P. F.] *See*
Progressive. The Progressive Violinist, *etc.* Grade 2. No. 30.
[1908, 09.] fol. **g. 791.**

—— A Practical Method for the Viola, *etc. Augener & Co.:
London,* [1890.] 4°. **g. 762. a. (3.)**

—— Scale and Arpeggio Manual for the Violin, *etc. Augener &
Co.: London,* [1898.] 4°. **g. 498. c. (2.)**

—— Sonatine en Fa majeur pour piano. *Augener & Co.: London,*
[1890.] fol. **g. 605. f. (19.)**

LAUBACH (Alfred)

— Sonatine en Sol majeur pour piano. *Augener & Co.: London,*
[1893.] fol.   **g. 605. f. (20.)**

— Valse Caprice pour piano. *Augener & Co.: London,* [1893.]
fol.   **g. 605. f. (21.)**

— *See* BEETHOVEN (L. van) [*Doubtful and Supposititious Works.*]
[Glaube, Liebe und Hoffnung.] The Adieu ... Revised ... by
A. Laubach. 1927. 4°.   **g. 249. v. (16.)**

— *See* BERTINI (H. J.) Studies for the Pianoforte ... fingered ...
by A. Laubach. [1897.] 4°.   **g. 667. a.**

— *See* CLEMENTI (M.) [Sonatas.—Collections. Op. 36. Op. 4.]
12 Sonatinas ... Revised ... by A. Laubach. [1915.] 4°.
                                                g. 442. u. (3.)

— *See* CLEMENTI (M.) [Sonatas. Op. 4.] 6 Sonatinas for the
Pianoforte ... Op. 37 and 38 ... Revised and fingered [by
A. Laubach], *etc.* [1902.] 4°.   **g. 603. h. (3.)**

— *See* CLEMENTI (M.) 6 Sonatinas. For piano ... Op. 36. (Revised
by A. Laubach.) [1932.] fol.   **g. 323. o. (3.)**

— *See* GADE (N. V.) [Foraarstoner. Op. 2a.] Spring Flowers ...
Revised and fingered by A. Laubach. [P. F.] [1932.] 4°.
                                                g. 494. b. (1.)

— *See* KUHLAU (F. D. R.) Sonatinas. (Op. 20, 55, 59.) Revised ...
by A. Laubach, *etc.* [1915.] 4°.   **g. 442. u. (8.)**

— *See* MOFFAT (A. E.) Album Classique ... Arrangé pour Viola
et Piano par A. Laubach. [1894.] 4°.   **g. 762. a. (4.)**

— *See* PLAIDY (L.) Technische Studien ... English translation by
A. Laubach. [1886.] 4°.   **g. 337. a. (7.)**

LAUBACH (Conrad)

— The Braw Red Lion. [Song, begins: "Wha says that
Caledonia's braves".] Written by N. Taillefer. *London,*
[1869.] fol.   **H. 1775. t. (25.)**

— The Volunteer Fête. [Song.] Written by N. Taillefer. *London,*
[1874.] fol.   **H. 1778. x. (41.)**

LAUBACH (F.)

— Gaberlunzie, an Overture on Scottish Melodies ... for
Pianoforte, Strings & Toy Instruments. [Score and parts.]
Paterson & Sons: London, etc., [1897.] fol.   **h. 1509. p. (2.)**

— Gaberlunzie. An Overture on Scottish Melodies for
Pianoforte, Strings & Toy Instruments ... Parts. (Full Score.)
Paterson & Sons: Edinburgh, London, [1912.] fol.
No. 5 and 6 of "The Scottish Orchestra," etc. **h. 1542.**

LAUBACK (   )

— The Gem Polka. [P. F.] *In:* The Musical Bijou ... for
MDCCCXLIX. pp. 104, 105. [1849.] fol.   **H. 2330.**

LAUBE

— Die Laube. [Song.] *See* HEROUX (F.) Sechs Lieder. No. 6.

LAUBENSTEIN (Paul F.)

— Air from Suite No. 14, by George Frideric Handel, and Kyrie
from the Messe du premier ton, by André Raison.
(Transcribed by P. F. Laubenstein.) [Organ.] pp. 5.
G. Schirmer: New York, [1954.] 4°.   **g. 1380. z. (13.)**

— *See* PALESTRINA (G. P. da) [Motecta Festorum Totius Anni ...
Quaternis Vocibus ... Liber Primus.] Tollite jugum meum ...
Edited by P. F. Laubenstein. [1949.] 8°.   **F. 23. i. (32.)**

LAUBER (J.)

— *See* GODET (A.) Les Chansons de nos Grand' Mères ...
Accompagnements de piano par J. Lauber. 1890–2. *obl.* fol.
                                                D. 779.

LAUBER (Joseph)

— Quartett (G moll) für zwei Violinen, Bratsche und Violoncell
... Op. 5. Partitur, *etc.* pp. 27. *E. W. Fritzsch: Leipzig,* 1899.
fol.   **h. 2785. m. (4.)**

— Quartet for Double Basses. [Score and parts. Edited by
Rodney Slatford.] 5 pt. *Yorke Edition: London,* [1975.] 4°.
                                                g. 867. d. (7.)

LAUBER (Wilhelm)

— Le Crystal, Mazurka pour Piano. *London,* [1863.] fol.
                                                h. 1462. r. (11.)

— La Défiance, pas militaire pour Piano. *London,* [1868.] fol.
                                                h. 1485. s. (29.)

— La Fiorentina. Romanza [begins: "Sono nata in riva"].
London, [1876.] fol.   **H. 1778. x. (42.)**

— Galop brillant pour Piano. *London,* [1868.] fol.
                                                h. 1485. s. (28.)

— Good Night, mélodie by F. Kücken, arranged for the
Pianoforte. *London,* [1866.] fol.   **h. 1485. s. (27.)**

— L'Innominata, mazurka élégante pour Piano. *Londres,*
[1863.] fol.   **h. 1462. r. (12.)**

— Love tints the scene. Recit. & song, the words by E. Maguire.
London, [1874.] fol.   **H. 1778. x. (43.)**

— Le Matin. [Song, begins: "Aux feux de l'aurore".] Paroles de
C. Lebeau. *Londres,* [1868.] fol.   **H. 1774. e. (13.)**

— La Pluie d'Été, morceau brillant pour Piano. *Londres,*
[1861.] fol.   **h. 1462. r. (10.)**

— [The Silver Wedding.] The sun in his glory and splendour.
Ballad ... The words by W. Simms. *London,* [1874.] fol.
                                                H. 1778. x. (44.)

— Un Soir Tranquille, pensée musicale pour Piano. *London,*
[1872.] fol.   **h. 1485. s. (30.)**

— The Woodcutter's song [begins: "Come away"] written by
J. Wilson. *London,* [1874.] fol.   **H. 1778. x. (45.)**

— *See* KUECKEN (F. W.) Gut' Nacht, fahr' wohl ... für das
Piano Forte von W. Lauber. [1856.] fol.   **h. 724. e. (15.)**

LAUBIN (Edward F.)

— Offering. Sacred Song for contralto, poem by B. G. Crozier,
etc. H. W. Gray Co.: [London,] 1915. 4°.   **G. 519. c. (13.)**

LAUBSCHER (Meinie)

— Louis Botha Valse, *etc.* [P. F.] *R. Müller: Kaapstad,* [1910.]
fol.   **h. 3286. uu. (41.)**

LAUCH (C.)

— Deutschlands Wiedergeburt. Schwarz, Roth, Gold. Volkslied,
Gedicht von Schnauffer, für eine Singstimme. *Berlin,* 1848.
fol.   **H. 2138. (22.)**

LAUCHER (Adèle Chazot)

— *See* CHAZOT-LAUCHER.

LAUD

— Laud to the Nativity. [Cantata.] *See* Respighi (O.) [Lauda per la natività del signore.]

— Laud we our God. Arioso. *See* Haendel (G. F.) [*Doutbful and Supposititious Works.*] [Dank sei dir, Herr.]

LAUDA

— Lauda anima. Anthem. *See* Andrews (M.)

— Lauda anima mea Dominum. Motet. *See* Lasso (O. di) [Patrocinium musices. Pars 1.]

— Lauda Hierusalem Dominum. [Motet.] *See* Porta (Constanzo) [Psalmodia vespertina.]

— Lauda Jerusalem. [Motet.] *See* Bartschmid (A.)

— Lauda Jerusalem. *See* Crookall (J.)

— Lauda Jerusalem. [Cantata.] *See* Vivaldi (A.)

— Lauda per la Natività del Signore. [Cantata.] *See* Respighi (O.)

— Lauda Sion. Offertorium. *See* Haydn (Johann M.)

— Lauda Sion. Sacred Cantata. *See* Mendelssohn-Bartholdy (J. L. F.)

— Lauda, Sion, salvatorem. [Motet.] *See* Monteverdi (C.) [Sacrae cantiunculae. Liber primus.]

— Lauda Sion. [Motet.] *See* Ozcoz y Calahorra (R.) [Dos Motetes. No. 1.]

— Lauda, Sion. [Motet.] *See* Palestrina (G. P. da) [Motecta festorum totius anni ... Quaternis vocibus ... Liber primus.]

— Lauda Sion. [Motet.] *See* Rogers (J. H.)

— Lauda Sion. [Motet.] *See* Rubbra (Edmund D.)

— Lauda Sion. [Motet.] *See* Sabino (G. M.) [Secondo Libro delli Motetti.]

— Lauda Sion. [Motet.] *See* Strong (George T.)

— Lauda Sion. [Motet.] *See* Victoria (T. L. de) [Motecta festorum totius anni.]

— Lauda Sion. [Motet.] *See* Webbe (S.) *the Elder*. [A Collection of Motetts or Antiphons.]

LAUDABO

— Laudabo Dominum in vita mea. Anthem. *See* Purcell (H.)

LAUDAMUS

— Laudamus. Anthem. *See* Harris (*Sir* W. H.) *K. C. V. O*.

— Laudamus. Chorale. *See* Owen (William) *of Prysgol.* [Bryn Calfaria.]

LAUDAN (Stanley)

— March of the Champions ... Arranged for military band by Terry Creswick. Solo B♭ clarinet (conductor [and parts]). 30 pt. *Peter Maurice Music Co.; Roberts Music: London,* [1973.] *obl.* 8°.
With several copies of various parts. **a. 340. (13.)**

LAUDATE

— Laudate. A Hymn and Tune Book for use in Secondary Day Schools, *etc.* [Staff and tonic sol-fa notation.] *A. and C. Black: London,* 1900. 8°. **B. 375. pp.**

— Laudate! Song. *See* Piccolomini (M.) *pseud.*

LAUDATE

— Laudate. Chœur. *See* Saint-Saëns (C. C.)

— Laudate. Salmo 112. [Cantata.] *See* Vivaldi (A.)

— Laudate coeli. [Cantata.] *See* Hasse (J. A.)

— Laudate Dominum. Choir and organ. *See* Arnold (Malcolm H.)

— Laudate Dominum. [Motet.] *See* Bartschmid (A.)

— Laudate Dominum. Solo & chorus. *See* Beale (C.)

— Laudate Dominum. Cantata. *See* Benson (J. A.)

— Laudate Dominum. Motett. *See* Beresford (J.)

— Laudate Dominum. Chorus. *See* Bernardi (S.)

— Laudate Dominum. [Motet.] *See* Boëllmann (L.)

— Laudate Dominum. [Anthem.] *See* Brown (Christopher)

— Laudate Dominum. [Anthem.] *See* Burgon (Geoffrey)

— Laudate Dominum. Solokantate. *See* Buxtehude (D.)

— Laudate Dominum. [Motet.] *See* Cavalli (P. F.) [Musiche sacre.]

— Laudate Dominum. Motett. *See* Converse (F. S.)

— Laudate Dominum. [Motet.] *See* Croce (G.) [Motetti a otto voci. lib. 1.]

— Laudate Dominum. [Anthem.] *See* Dalby (Martin)

— Laudáte Dóminum. [Motet.] *See* Dumler (Martin G.)

— Laudate Dominum. Chorus. *See* Edwards (Oliver H.)

— Laudate Dominum. [Anthem.] *See* Ivimey (J. W.)

— Laudate Dominum. Quatuor. *See* J., S. *Brother of the Christian Schools.*

— Laudate Dominum. Chorus. *See* Jacob (Gordon P. S.)

— Laudate Dominum. Motet. *See* Lasso (O. di)

— Laudate Dominum. [Motet.] *See* Mascagni (P.) [Cavalleria rusticana.—Regina cœli.]

— Laudate Dominum. [Cantata.] *See* Monteverdi (C.) [Selva morale e spirituale.]

— Laudate Dominum. [Motet.] *See* Mozart (W. A.) [Vesperae solennes de confessore. K. 339. No. 5.]

— Laudate Dominum. [Motet.] *See* Peloquin (C. A.)

— Laudate Dominum. [Motet.] *See* Pitoni (G. O.)

— Laudate Dominum. [Motet.] *See* Rovetta (G.) [Salmi concertati.]

— Laudate Dominum. [Motet.] *See* Schmitt (F.) Cinq Motets ... Op. 60. v.

— Laudate Dominum! [Hymns.] *See* Schubiger (A.)

— Laudate Dominum. [Motet.] *See* Sweelinck (J. P.) [Cantiones Sacrae.]

— Laudate Dominum. Motet. *See* Tallis (T.)

— Laudate Dominum. Motett for Soprano and Tenor. *See* Terziani (   )

— Laudate Dominum. [Motet.] *See* Weinlig (C. T.)

— Laudate Dominum de caelis. [Motet.] *See* Brumel (Antoine)

LAUDATE

— Laudate Dominum de caelis. [Motet.] *See* GUERRERO (Francisco) [Motecta ... 1597.]

— Laudate Dominum in sanctis ejus. [Motet.] *See* ROVIGO (Francesco)

— Laudate Dominum in sono tubæ. Motet. *See* LENEPVEU (C. F.)

— Laudate Dominum omnes gentes. [Cantata.] *See* CHARPENTIER (M. A.)

— Laudate eum, elementa, Christus natus est. Song. *See* ARBA (E. d')

— Laudate populi. Offertorium. *See* HAYDN (J. M.)

— Laudate Pueri. [Motet.] *See* BARTSCHMID (A.)

— Laudate Pueri. Solo with chorus. *See* CAPOCCI (A.)

— Laudate Pueri. [Psalm.] *See* LOTTI (A.)

— Laudate pueri. [Cantata.] *See* PERGOLESI (Giovanni B.)

— Laudate pueri. [Cantata.] *See* PERTI (G. A.)

— Laudate pueri. [Cantata.] *See* VIVALDI (A.)

— Laudate pueri Dominum. Offertorium. *See* ROSSI (   )

— Laudate, pueri, dominum. Chœur et orgue. *See* SCHMITT (F.)

— Laudate pueri, laudate nomen Domini. [Motet.] *See* PERGOLESI (Giovanni B.) [Psalmus 112.]

— Laudate servi Domini. [Anthem.] *See* MIDDLETON (Hubert S.) A Latin Grace Anthem.

LAUDATIO

— Laudatio Domini. [Cantata.] *See* KOKKONEN (J.)

— Laudatio musicae. [Cantata.] *See* VERESS (S.)

LAUDE

— [For the Italian word of this form:] *See* LAUDI.

— Laude pia Dñm. [Motet.] *See* PEVERNAGE (A.)

LAUDEMUS

— Laudemus tempus actum. [Part-song.] *See* ROREM (Ned)

LAUDENBACH (   )

— Marsch von Problus und Prim, den 3 Juli 1866. [P. F.] *Berlin & Posen*, [1867.] fol.   **h. 1462. r. (13.)**

LAUDENT

— Laudent deum cithara. [Motet.] *See* LASSO (O. di)

LAUDER (*Sir* HARRY MACLENNAN)

— Francis & Day's Album (Francis & Day's 2nd (-5th) Album) of H. Lauder's popular Songs, *etc.* [With a biographical sketch by C. Wilmott.] 5 no. *Francis, Day & Hunter: London*, [1907–30?] 4°.   **F. 1840.**

— Popular Selection, "Harry Lauder's Songs". Selected & arranged [for military band] by J. Ord Hume, *etc.* [Parts.] 33 pt. *Boosey & Co.: London*, [1909.] fol. [*Boosey's military Journal.* ser. 126. no. 2.]   **h. 1549.**

LAUDER (*Sir* HARRY MACLENNAN)

— Harry Lauder's Songs. Selection ... Arranged by C. Greenwood. *Francis, Day & Hunter: London*, 1942. 4°.   **H. 1309. a. (11.)**

— The Best of Harry Lauder. [Songs. Words and music mainly by Harry Lauder. With portraits.] pp. 32. *EMI Music Publishing: London*, [1978.] 4°.   **F. 1966. t. (4.)**

— Always take care of your Nickels. [Song.] Words by S. E. Cleethorpe. *Harms: New York*, 1933. 4°.   **H. 1309. a. (3.)**

— "At the Sign of the Bluebell Inn." [Song.] Written by J. Lindsay, *etc. Francis, Day & Hunter: London, New York*, 1907. fol.   **H. 1309. (1.)**

— [Another copy.] [Voice part only.]   **H. 1309. (2.)**

— The Auld Brig of Ayr. [Song.] Written by J. D. Harper. *Francis, Day & Hunter: London, New York*, 1907. fol.   **H. 1309. (3.)**

— [Another copy.]   **H. 1309. (4.)**

— Aye wakin' O! [Song.] Founded on an old Scotch Song. Written ... by H. Lauder. *Francis, Day & Hunter: London, New York*, 1906. fol. *With a separate voice part.*   **H. 1309. b. (1.)**

— Back, back, to where the Heather grows ... [Song.] Written and composed by H. Lauder. *T. B. Harms and Francis, Day & Hunter: New York*, 1918. fol.   **H. 1309. (43.)**

— [Back, back, to where the Heather grows.] Bella McGraw, *etc. Francis, Day & Hunter: London*, 1919. fol.   **H. 1309. (44.)**

— Bella McGraw. *See* supra: [Back, back, to where the Heather grows.]

— Bella, the Belle o' Dunoon. [Song.] Written by H. Lauder and G. Walker, *etc. Francis, Day & Hunter: London*, 1922. 4°.   **H. 1309. a. (1.)**

— The Blarney Stone. [Song.] Written by M. Hannaway and H. Lauder. *T. B. Harms: New York*, 1913. fol.   **H. 1309. (39.)**

— Bonnie Hielan' Mary. [Song.] Written by A. Melville and H. Lauder. (Arranged by M. Murdoch.) *Francis, Day & Hunter: London*, 1901. fol.   **H. 1309. b. (2.)**

— Bonnie Leezie Lindsay. [Song.] Written by F. Folloy, *etc. Francis, Day & Hunter: London*, 1909. fol.   **H. 1309. (5.)**

— [Another copy.] [Voice part only.]   **H. 1309. (6.)**

— The Boss o' th' Hoose. [Song.] Written and composed by H. Lauder, *etc. Francis, Day & Hunter: London*, 1924. 4°.   **H. 1309. a. (2.)**

— Breakfast in my Bed on Sunday Mornin'. [Song.] Written by G. Grafton and H. Lauder, *etc. Francis, Day & Hunter: London*, 1910. fol.   **H. 1309. (23.)**

— [Another copy.] [Voice part only.]   **H. 1309. (24.)**

— Calligan—call again. [Song.] Written, composed ... by H. Lauder. *Francis, Day & Hunter: London*, 1900. fol. *With a separate voice part.*   **H. 1309. b. (6.)**

— The Camlachie Scout; or, The Man they left behind. [Song.] Written by H. Hunter & H. Lauder. *Francis, Day & Hunter: London*, 1903. fol. *With a separate voice part.*   **H. 1309. b. (7.)**

— Canadian Girls are good enough for me. *See* infra: [Dixie Girls are good enough for me.]

— Charlie Macneil. [Song.] Written by H. Lauder and A. Melville. *Francis, Day & Hunter: London, New York*, 1906. fol. *With a separate voice part.*   **H. 1309. b. (9.)**

LAUDER (*Sir* HARRY MACLENNAN)

— Cronies o' mine; or, Dear old Cronies. [Song.] Written and composed by H. Lauder. *Harms: New York*, 1929. 4°.
      H. 1309. a. (16.)

— Daisy. [Song.] Written by H. Lauder & J. D. Harper. [Voice part only.] *Francis, Day & Hunter: London, New York*, 1905. *s. sh.* fol.
      H. 1309. b. (10.)

— Dixie Girls are good enough for me. [Song.] Written by Sir H. Lauder & W. Mathews, *etc. T. B. Harms & Francis, Day & Hunter: New York*, 1923. fol.
      H. 1309. b. (3.)

— [Dixie Girls are good enough for me.] Canadian Girls are good enough for me, *etc.* [Song.] *Harms: New York*, 1924. fol.
      H. 1309. b. (4.)

— Don't let us sing anymore about War, just let us sing of Love. Peace Song, written and composed by H. Lauder. *T. B. Harms and Francis, Day & Hunter: New York*, 1918. fol.
      H. 1309. (45.)

— [Don't let us sing anymore about War.] Just let us sing of Love. A Peace Song, *etc. Francis, Day & Hunter: London*, 1919. *s. sh.* fol.
      H. 1309. (46.)

— Down in Johnson's. [Song.] Written, composed ... by H. Lauder. *Francis, Day & Hunter: London*, 1900. fol. *With a separate voice part.*
      H. 1309. b. (12.)

— Early in the Morning. [Song.] Written, composed ... by H. Lauder. [Voice part only.] *Francis, Day & Hunter: London*, 1900. *s. sh.* fol.
      H. 1309. b. (13.)

— Early in the morning. [Song.] Written, composed ... by Harry Lauder. pp. 4. [c.1900.] fol. *A pirated edition.*
      H. 1848. b. (9.)

— Fighting for the Empire. [Song.] Written and composed by H. Lauder, *etc. Francis, Day & Hunter: London*, 1941. 4°.
      H. 1309. a. (20.)

— Flower o' the Heather. A Love Song, written and composed by H. Lauder, *etc. Francis, Day & Hunter: London*, 1927. 4°.
      H. 1309. a. (12.)

— From the North, South, East and West. [Song.] Written, composed and sung by H. Lauder. (Arr. by I. Rudisill.) *T. B. Harms and Francis, Day & Hunter: New York*, 1918. fol.
      H. 1309. (47.)

— Gilt-edged Bertie. [Song.] Written by G. Grafton, *etc. Francis, Day & Hunter: London, New York*, 1906. fol.
      H. 1309. (7.)

— [Another copy.] [Voice part only.]
      H. 1309. (8.)

— He was very kind to me! [Song.] Written, composed and sung by H. Lauder. *Francis, Day & Hunter: London, New York*, 1907. fol.
      H. 1309. (9.)

— [Another copy.] [Voice part only.]
      H. 1309. (10.)

— Hey, Donal'! [Song.] Written by H. Lauder and A. Melville. *Francis, Day & Hunter: London*, 1903. fol. *With a separate voice part.*
      H. 1309. b. (14.)

— I like my old Home Town. [Song.] Written, composed ... by Sir H. Lauder. *T. B. Harms & Francis, Day & Hunter: New York*, 1923. fol.
      H. 1309. b. (5.)

— I love a Lassie. Ma Scotch Bluebell. [Song.] Written by H. Lauder and G. Grafton. *Francis, Day & Hunter: London, New York*, 1906. fol.
      H. 1309. b. (15.)

— I love you. Ballad, written and composed by H. Lauder. *Francis, Day & Hunter: London, New York*, 1901. fol. *With a separate voice part.*
      H. 1309. b. (16.)

— I'm looking for a bonnie Lass to love me. [Song.] Written and composed by H. Lauder, *etc. Francis, Day & Hunter: London*, 1924. 4°.
      H. 1309. a. (6.)

LAUDER (*Sir* HARRY MACLENNAN)

— I'm the Man they left behind. *See* supra: The Camlachie Scout.

— I think I'll get wed in the Summer. [Song.] Words and music by H. Lauder. *T.B. Harms and Francis, Day & Hunter: New York*, 1919. fol.
      H. 1309. (48.)

— I think I'll get wed in the Summer-time. [Song.] Written, composed and sung by H. Lauder. *Francis, Day & Hunter: London*, 1921. fol.
      H. 1309. (58.)

— I took him up to take him down. [Song.] Written by J. Malarkey. *Francis, Day & Hunter: London*, 1902. fol. *With a separate voice part.*
      H. 1309. b. (17.)

— "I've loved her ever since she was a Baby" ... [Song.] Written by H. Lauder & B. Beaton, *etc. Francis, Day & Hunter: London*, 1909. fol.
      H. 1309. (11.)

— [Another copy.] [Voice part only.]
      H. 1309. (12.)

— I wish I had someone to love me. [Song.] Written, composed ... by Harry Lauder. pp. 4. *Francis, Day & Hunter: London*, [1905.] fol.
Francis, Day & Hunter's Sixpenny popular Edition. no. 241.
      H. 1601. oo. (21.)

— I wish you were here again. [Song.] *T. B. Harms and Francis, Day & Hunter: New York*, 1919. fol.
      H. 1309. (49.)

— I wonder. [Song.] Written by D. McNeil, *etc. Francis, Day & Hunter: London*, 1932. 4°.
      H. 1309. a. (17.)

— If I were in the L. C. C. [Song.] Written by D. Lipton. *Francis, Day & Hunter: London*, 1903. fol. *With a separate voice part.*
      H. 1309. b. (18.)

— Inverary. [Song.] Written by J. Malarkey & H. Lauder. *Francis, Day & Hunter: London, New York*, 1905. fol. *With a separate voice part.*
      H. 1309. b. (19.)

— The Inverary Harriers. [Song.] Written by B. Beaton. *Francis, Day & Hunter: London, New York*, 1906. fol.
      H. 1309. b. (20.)

— It's a' roon th' Toon. [Song.] Written by J. H. Milligan, *etc. Francis, Day & Hunter: London*, 1932. 4°.   **H. 1309. a. (18.)**

— It's nice to get up in the Mornin' ... [Song.] Written by H. Lauder. *Francis, Day & Hunter: London*, 1913. fol.
      H. 1309. (40.)

— It's nice when you love a wee Lassie. [Song.] Written by H. Lauder & J. D. Harper, *etc. Francis, Day & Hunter: London*, 1912. fol.
      H. 1309. (25.)

— [Another copy.] [Voice part only.]
      H. 1309. (26.)

— Jean M'Neil. [Song.] Written by H. Lauder and A. Melville. *Francis, Day & Hunter: London, New York*, 1906. fol. *With a separate voice part.*
      H. 1309. b. (21.)

— Jerry-co. [Song.] Written by H. Lauder and A. Melville. *Francis, Day & Hunter: London*, 1902. fol. *With a separate voice part.*
      H. 1309. b. (22.)

— Just got off the Chain. Something domestic. [Song.] Written and composed by H. Lauder, *etc. Francis, Day & Hunter: London*, 1927. 4°.
      H. 1309. a. (13.)

— Just let us sing of Love. *See* supra: [Don't let us sing anymore about War.]

— Killiecrankie. [Song.] Written, composed ... by H. Lauder. [Voice part only.] *Francis, Day & Hunter: London*, 1900. *s. sh. fol.*
      H. 1309. b. (23.)

— The Last of the Sandies. [Song.] Written by B. Beaton, and H. Lauder. *Francis, Day & Hunter: London*, 1902. fol. *With a separate voice part.*
      H. 1309. b. (24.)

LAUDER (*Sir* HARRY MACLENNAN)

— Mac Allister. Hame Hame always the same. [Song.] Words by
D. R. McHard and Harry Lauder, *etc. Francis, Day &
Hunter: London*, 1938. 4°.　　　　　　**H. 1309. a. (8.)**

— The Message Boy. [Song.] Written, composed and sung by
H. Lauder. *Francis, Day & Hunter: London*, 1911. fol.
　　　　　　H. 1309. (27.)

— [Another copy.] [Voice part only.]　　　　**H. 1309. (28.)**

— Mr. John Mackie. [Song.] Written, composed ... by
H. Lauder. *Francis, Day & Hunter: London*, 1903. fol.
With a separate voice part.　　　　　**H. 1309. b. (25.)**

— Mrs. Jean MacFarlane. [Song.] Written by H. Lauder and
G. Grafton, *etc. Francis, Day & Hunter: London, New York*,
1907. fol.　　　　　　**H. 1309. (13.)**

— [Another copy.] [Voice part only.]　　　　**H. 1309. (14.)**

— The Night before, *etc.* [Musical comedy, written and
composed by H. Lauder. Four detached vocal numbers.]
T. B. Harms and Francis, Day & Hunter: New York, 1916. fol.
　　　　　　H. 1309. (50.)

— [The Night before.] We a' go Hame the same Way, *etc.
Francis, Day & Hunter: London*, 1919. fol.　　**H. 1309. (51.)**

— O'er the Hill to Ardentinny. [Song.] Written, composed and
sung by H. Lauder. *Francis, Day & Hunter: London*, 1921.
fol.　　　　　　**H. 1309. (59.)**

— Oh! How I wearie, Dearie. [Song.] Written and composed by
H. Lauder, *etc. Francis, Day & Hunter: London*, 1926. 4°.
　　　　　　H. 1309. a. (14.)

— Ohio. [Song.] Written, composed and sung by H. Lauder.
Francis, Day & Hunter: London, 1921. fol.　　**H. 1309. (60.)**

— The Picnic; or, Ev'ry Laddie loves a Lassie. [Song.] Written,
composed and sung by H. Lauder. *Francis, Day & Hunter:
London*, 1910. fol.　　　　　**H. 1309. (29.)**

— [Another copy.] [Voice part only.]　　　　**H. 1309. (30.)**

— Pin your Faith on the Motherland. Song of Empire, written
by J. H. Milligan, *etc. Francis, Day & Hunter: London*, 1931.
4°.　　　　　　**H. 1309. a. (19.)**

— Piper Macfarlane. [Song.] Written by H. Lauder and
G. Grafton. *Francis, Day & Hunter: London, New York*,
1906. fol.
With a separate voice part.　　　　　**H. 1309. b. (26.)**

— The Pirate. [Song.] Written and composed by H. Lauder, *etc.
Francis, Day & Hunter: London*, 1926. 4°.　　**H. 1309. a. (15.)**

— The Portobello Lassie. [Song.] Written by H. Lauder and
G. Wells, *etc. Francis, Day & Hunter: London*, 1913. fol.
　　　　　　H. 1309. (41.)

— Queen amang the Heather. [Song.] Written by H. Lauder and
J. Malarkey, *etc. Francis, Day & Hunter: London*, 1909. fol.
　　　　　　H. 1309. (31.)

— [Another copy.] [Voice part only.]　　　　**H. 1309. (32.)**

— Roamin' in the Gloamin'. [Song.] Written, composed and
sung by H. Lauder. *Francis, Day & Hunter: London*, 1911.
fol.　　　　　　**H. 1309. (33.)**

— [Another copy.] [Voice part only.]　　　　**H. 1309. (34.)**

— Rob Roy Macintosh. [Song.] Written by H. Lauder and
F. Folloy, *etc. Francis, Day & Hunter: London, New York*,
1907. fol.　　　　　　**H. 1309. (15.)**

— [Another copy.] [Voice part only.]　　　　**H. 1309. (16.)**

— Rotary. [Song.] Words & music by H. Lauder. *T. B. Harms
and Francis, Day & Hunter: New York*, 1916. fol.
　　　　　　H. 1309. (52.)

LAUDER (*Sir* HARRY MACLENNAN)

— The Saftest o' the Family. Willie Winks. [Song.] Written by
H. Lauder and B. Beaton. *Francis, Day & Hunter: London*,
1904. fol.
With a separate voice part.　　　　　**H. 1309. b. (27.)**

— The Same as his Faither did before him. [Song.] Written by
W. Terry and G. Wells, *etc. Francis, Day & Hunter: London*,
1912. fol.　　　　　　**H. 1309. (35.)**

— [Another copy.] [Voice part only.]　　　　**H. 1309. (36.)**

— Saturday Night. [Song.] Written by R. C. Tharp and
H. Lauder, *etc. Francis, Day & Hunter: London*, 1922. 4°.
　　　　　　H. 1309. a. (7.)

— Saturday Night, *etc.* [Song.] *T. B. Harms & Francis, Day &
Hunter: New York*, [1923.] fol.　　　**H. 1309. b. (8.)**

— She is ma Daisy. [Song.] Written by H. Lauder and J. D.
Harper. *Francis, Day & Hunter: London, New York*, 1905.
fol.　　　　　　**H. 1309. b. (28.)**

— She is ma Daisy. [Song.] Written by Harry Lauder and J. D.
Harper, *etc.* [1905.] fol.
A pirated edition.　　　　　**H. 1848. b. (10.)**

— Some Folks do and other People don't. [Song.] Written by
W. Hyde and P. Langley. *Francis, Day & Hunter: London*,
1902. fol.
With a separate voice part.　　　　　**H. 1309. b. (29.)**

— Soosie MacLean. [Song.] Written and composed by
H. Lauder, *etc. Francis, Day & Hunter: London*, 1926. 4°.
　　　　　　H. 1309. a. (9.)

— Sound Advice. [Song.] Written by J. D. Harper. *Francis, Day
& Hunter: London, New York*, 1905. fol.
With a separate voice part.　　　　　**H. 1309. b. (30.)**

— The South Pole; or, The Bounding Bounder. [Song.] Written
by R. King & H. Lauder, *etc. Francis, Day & Hunter:
London*, 1909. fol.　　　　　**H. 1309. (37.)**

— [Another copy.] [Voice part only.]　　　　**H. 1309. (38.)**

— Stop yer Tickling Jock! [Song.] Written by H. Lauder and
F. Folloy. *Francis, Day & Hunter: London*, 1904. fol.
With a separate voice part.　　　　　**H. 1309. b. (31.)**

— "Stop yer tickling, Jock!" [Song.] Written by Harry Lauder
and Frank Folloy, *etc.* [*London*, c. 1905.] fol.
　　　　　　H. 1848. b. (11.)

— [Stop yer Tickling Jock.] *See* GODFREY (C.) *the Younger.*
Jock's Patrol ... Founded on H. Lauder's ... Song, *etc.*
1905. fol.　　　　　　**h. 2931. c. (8.)**

— The Sunshine o' a bonnie Lass's Smile. [Song.] Written,
composed and sung by H. Lauder. *Francis, Day & Hunter:
London*, 1921. fol.　　　　　**H. 1309. (61.)**

— Ta-ta, my bonnie Maggie darling! [Song.] Written by
H. Lauder and G. Grafton, *etc. Francis, Day & Hunter:
London*, 1913. fol.　　　　　**H. 1309. (42.)**

— That's the Reason noo I wear a Kilt. [Song.] Written by
H. Lauder and A. B. Kendall. *Francis, Day & Hunter:
London, New York*, 1906. fol.
With a separate voice part.　　　　　**H. 1309. b. (32.)**

— There is Somebody waitin' for me. [Song.] Written, composed
and sung by H. Lauder. *T. B. Harms and Francis, Day &
Hunter: New York*, 1917. fol.　　　**H. 1309. (53.)**

— There is Somebody waiting for me, *etc. Francis, Day &
Hunter: London*, 1919. fol.　　　**H. 1309. (54.)**

— Tobermory. [Song.] Written, composed ... by H. Lauder.
Francis, Day & Hunter: London, 1901. fol.
With a separate voice part.　　　　　**H. 1309. b. (33.)**

LAUDER (*Sir* HARRY MACLENNAN)

— The Waggle o' the Kilt. [Song.] Written and composed by
H. Lauder. *T. B. Harms and Francis, Day & Hunter: New
York*, 1917. fol.   **H. 1309. (55.)**

— We a' go Hame the same Way. *See* supra: [The Night before.]

— We parted on the Shore. [Song.] Written, composed ... by
H. Lauder. *Francis, Day & Hunter: London, New York*, 1906.
fol.
With a separate voice part.   **H. 1309. b. (34.)**

— We parted on the Shore. *See* PETHER (H. E.) Waiting at the
Church. Barn Dance ... introducing ... "We parted on the
Shore." [P. F.] 1906. fol.   **h. 3286. mm. (38.)**

— [We parted on the Shore.] *See* PETHER (H. E.) "Waiting at the
Church" ... Introducing "We parted on the Shore". Harry
Lauder. ⟨Arr. by M. Retford.⟩ [Military band.] 1907. fol.
[*Boosey & Co.'s new supplemental Journal for military Bands.
no. 42.*] [*HUMÉ (James O.) "A Reverie."*]   **h. 1544. a.**

— The Weddin' o' Lauchie M'Graw. [Song.] Written by
H. Lauder & A. Melville. *Francis, Day & Hunter: London,
New York*, 1905. fol.
With a separate voice part.   **H. 1309. b. (35.)**

— The Weddin' o' Sandy MacNab ... [Song.] Written,
composed & sung by H. Lauder. *Francis, Day & Hunter:
London, New York*, 1908. fol.   **H. 1309. (17.)**

— [Another copy.] [Voice part only.]   **H. 1309. (18.)**

— Wee Nelly McKie frae Skye. [Song.] Written by J. D. Harper,
etc. Francis, Day & Hunter: London, New York, 1907. fol.
    H. 1309. (19.)

— [Another copy.] [Voice part only.]   **H. 1309. (20.)**

— When I get back again tae bonnie Scotland. [Song.] Written,
composed & sung by H. Lauder. *Francis, Day & Hunter:
London, New York*, 1908. fol.   **H. 1309. (21.)**

— [Another copy.] [Voice part only.]   **H. 1309. (22.)**

— When I go doon th' Toun. [Song.] Written and composed by
H. Lauder, *etc. Francis, Day & Hunter: London*, 1935. 4°.
    H. 1309. a. (5.)

— When I meet MacKay. [Song.] Written by H. Lauder &
J. Lauder, *etc. Francis, Day & Hunter: London*, 1926. 4°.
    H. 1309. a. (10.)

— When I was twenty one. [Song.] Written and composed by
H. Lauder. *T. B. Harms and Francis, Day & Hunter: New
York*, 1918. fol.   **H. 1309. (56.)**

— When I was twenty-one, *etc. Francis, Day & Hunter:
London*, 1919. fol.   **H. 1309. (57.)**

— *See* DILLON (William) and LAUDER (*Sir* H. M.) The End of
the Road. Written and composed by W. Dillon & H. Lauder.
[1924.] 4°.   **G. 1271. d. (22.)**

— *See* DILLON (William) and LAUDER (*Sir* H. M.) The End of
the Road ... Arranged for mixed voices and pianoforte by
J. Clements. [1949.] 8°. [*F. D. H. choral Library. no. 2.*]
    F. 672. l.

— *See* HUME (James O.) Eight Quick Marches on Harry
Lauder's Songs ... Arr. [for military band] by J. Ord Hume.
1910. *obl.* 8°. [*Boosey's Military Journal. ser. 129. no. 2.*]
    h. 1549.

— *See* JOHSON (W.) Selection. Echoes of Harry Lauder.
Arranged for the Pianoforte, *etc.* 1908. fol.
    h. 3283. n. (26.)

— *See* KAPS (K.) *pseud.* Harry Lauder Quadrilles, founded on
... Lauder Successes, *etc.* 1908. fol.   **h. 681. b. (17.)**

LAUDER (*Sir* HARRY MACLENNAN) and COCHRANE (WILLIE)

— It's a fine Thing to sing. [Song.] Written by H. Lauder and
W. Cochrane. *T. B. Harms & Francis, Day & Hunter: New
York*, 1921. fol.   **H. 1309. (62.)**

LAUDER (*Sir* HARRY MACLENNAN) and HARGREAVES (WILLIAM)

— It's just like bein' at Hame. There's a Piper playing in the
Morning. [Song.] Written and composed by H. Lauder &
W. Hargreaves. *B. Feldman & Co.: London*, [1910.] 4°.
    H. 1309. a. (4.)

— It's just like bein' at Hame, *etc.* [Song.] *J. H. Remick & Co.:
[New York,]* 1911. fol.   **H. 1309. b. (36.)**

LAUDER (*Sir* HARRY MACLENNAN) and PACE (BERNARDO DE)

— Love makes the World a Merry-go-round. Waltz Song, words
by Sir H. Lauder and W. Montagne, *etc. T. B. Harms &
Francis, Day & Hunter: New York*, 1923. fol.
    H. 1309. b. (11.)

LAUDES

— Laudes canamus martyrum. Hymn. *See* L., H. W. R.

— Laudes Domini. A selection of spiritual songs, ancient and
modern. *New-York*, 1884. 8°.   **D. 706.**

— Laudes Hincmari. Emmo. DD. Eugenio Card. Tisserant,
Anselmo M. Albareda Abbatiale munus conferenti, a
Monachis Montisserrati dictae. *See* CHRISTUS. Christus vincit.
[1951.] 8°.   **F. 1196. (2.)**

— Laudes organi. Fantasia for mixed chorus and organ. *See*
KODÁLY (Z.)

LAUDI

— Libro Primo delle Laudi Spirituali da Diuersi ... Autori, *etc.*
1563. 4°. *See* RAZZI (S.)   **K. 8. f. 10.**

— Il Primo Libro delle Laude Spirituali a Tre Voci, stampata ad
instanza delli ... Padri della Congregatione dello Oratorio.
(Il Secondo Libro delle Laude Spirituali, *etc.*) 2 bk. *Per
Alessandro Gardano: Roma*, 1583. 4°.   **D. 33.**

— Il Terzo Libro delle Laudi Spirituali a Tre e a Quattro Voci,
etc. [Edited by F. Soto.] *Per Alessandro Gardano. Ad
instantia d'Iacomo Tornieri: Roma*, 1588. 4°.   **D. 33. a.**

— Libro delle Laudi Spirituali. Doue in vno sono compresi i
Tre Libri gia stampati. E ridutta la Musica à più breuità e
facilità: con l'accrescimento delle parole, e con l'aggiunta de
molte Laudi nuoue, *etc.* [Edited by F. Soto.] *Per Alessandro
Gardano, Ad instantia de Iacomo Tornieri: Roma*, 1589. 4°.
    D. 33. b. (1.)

— [Another copy.]   **D. 33. c. (1.)**

— Lodi deuote per uso della Dottrina Christiana. *Appresso
Girolamo Bartoli: Genoa*, 1589. 12°.   **1354. a. 35. (4.)**

— Il Quarto Libro delle Laudi a Tre et Quatro Voci, *etc.* [Edited
by F. Soto.] *Apud Alexandrum Gardanum. Impensis Ascanij
& Hieronymi Donangeli: Roma*, 1591. 4°.   **D. 33. b. (2.)**

— [Another copy.]   **D. 33. c. (2.)**

— [Another copy.]   **Hirsch III. 1101.**

— Il Quinto Libro delle Laudi Spirituali, a tre, & quattro voci.
Del Reuerendo P. Francesco Soto, *etc. Appresso Vittorio
Baldini: Ferrara*, 1598. 4°.   **D. 33. b. (3.)**

— [Another copy.]   **Hirsch III. 1102.**

LAUDI

— Santuario di Laudi ... Per le feste di ciaschedun santo, *etc.* 1609. 4°. *See* RAZZI (S.) **11427. ee. 25.**

— Laude Spirituali ... per uso delle Congregazioni di S. Filippo Neri, *etc.* 1703. 8°. *See* CORTI (S.) **A. 191.**

— Corona di Sacre Canzoni o Laude Spirituali, *etc.* 1710. 12°. *See* CORONA. **A. 571.**

— Laude di A. Z. per la processione da farsi il dì 2. di luglio da' sacerdoti fiorentini alla Santissima Vergine dell'Impruneta. pp. 15. *Per Michele Nestenus, e Antonmaria Borghigiani: Firenze*, 1711. 8°. **A. 100. (1.)**

— Laudi Spirituali per la Dottrina Cristiana. Raccolte da varij Autori, *etc.* 1722. 12°. *See* SANTINI (P.) **3435. ff. 34.**

— Laudi per la processione da farsi il dì 2. di Iuglio 1730 da' sacerdoti della centuria della Santissima Vergine dell'Impruneta, *etc.* pp. 11. *Nella stamperia di Michele Nestenus, e Francesco Moücke: Firenze*, 1730. 8°. **A. 100. (3.)**

— Laudi da cantarsi da' fratelli della venerabile Confraternità del SS. Nome di Giesu ... nel viaggio da farsi da' medesimi alla Santa Immagine dell'Impruneta l'anno 1731, *etc.* pp. 32. *Nella stamperia di Bernardo Paperini: Firenze*, 1731. 8°. **A. 100. (4.)**

— Laudi da cantarsi dai fratelli della vener. Congregazione di San Gio: Batista de' Cavalieri della Religione Gerosolimitana, in occasione di portarsi alla visita della Santissima Vergine dell'Impruneta il dì 15. maggio 1735, *etc.* pp. 23. *Per Piero Matini: Firenze*, 1735. 8°. **A. 100. (7.)**

— Laude da cantarsi da fratelli della vener. Congregazione del SS. Nome di Maria ... nell'andare a visitare il sagro tempio della SS. Vergine dell'Impruneta il di XIX. maggio MDCCXXXV. pp. 15. *Per i Tartini, e Franchi: Firenze*, 1735. 8°. **A. 100. (8.)**

— Laudi da cantarsi da' fratelli della venerabil Compagnia di S. Antonio di Padova e S. Giorgio detta de' Fanciulli ... nell'andare a visitare la SS. Vergine dell'Impruneta l'anno MDCCXXXV. pp. 16. *Nella stamperia di Francesco Moücke: Firenze*, 1735. 8°. **A. 100. (10.)**

— Laude da cantarsi da' fratelli della venerabil Congregazione del Cuor di Gesù ... in occasione di portarsi a visitare la SS.^ma Vergine dell'Impruneta nella prossima seconda festa di maggio, *etc.* pp. 15. *Nella nuova stamperia di Pietro Gaetano Viviani: Firenze*, 1736. 8°. **A. 100. (11.)**

— Laudi alla vergine Maria. [Motet.] *See* VERDI (Fortunino G. F.) [Quattro pezzi sacri. No. 3.]

— Le Laudi di San Francesco d'Assisi. [Cantata.] *See* SUTER (H.)

LAUDIBUS

— Laudibus in sanctis. [Anthem.] *See* BYRD (W.) [Liber Secundus Sacrarum Cantionum.]

LAUDS

— Lauds. [Part-song.] *See* DYSON (*Sir* G.) [Three Songs of Praise. No. 2.]

— Lauds. [Part-songs.] *See* TUČAPSKÝ (Antonín)

LAUE

— Laue Lüfte, Blumendüfte. [Song.] *See* SCHUBERT (F. P.) [Lob der Tränen. Op. 13. No. 2.]

LAUE (A. CARL)

— Capriccio pour le Piano Forte. Op. 6. *London*, [1853.] fol. **h. 723. l. (21.)**

LAUE (A. CARL)

— Childhood. [Song.] Words by W. Longfellow ... Op. 12. pp. 9. *Augener & Co.: London*, [1889.] fol. [*Germania. no.* 28.] **H. 2128.**

— A Christmas carol [begins: "I hear along our street," words] by H. W. Longfellow, for voice and piano. Op. 13. *London*, [1857.] fol. **H. 1771. l. (13.)**

— Cradle Song. *See* infra: [Wiegenlied. Op. 16.]

— Funeral March composed for the Pianoforte. *London*, [1853.] fol. **h. 723. l. (22.)**

— Vier Lieder (in Oberbayerischer Mundart, Gedicht von Hobell) ... für eine Singstimme mit Piano Forte Begleitung. Op. 7. *London*, [1853.] fol. **H. 2156. (13.)**

— Two marches for the Piano Forte. N°. 1. The Duke of Newcastle's March. N°. 2. The Sherwood Rangers' March. *London*, [1853.] fol **h. 723. l. (23.)**

— [Sängers Trost. Op. 11.] The singer's consolation, song [begins: "Though no mourning lover"]. *London*, [1855.] fol. **H. 1758. (13.)**

— [Sängers Trost. Op. 11.] The Singer's Consolation, *etc.* [Song.] *Eng. & Ger.* pp. 6. *Augener & Co.: London*, [1889.] fol. [*Germania. no.* 423.] **H. 2128.**

— The Singer's Consolation. [Song.] *See* supra: [Sängers Trost. Op. 11.]

— "Souvenir de la Suisse," cinq valses champètres pour le piano-forte. Op. 10. *London*, [1855.] fol. **h. 976. d. (24.)**

— Theoretical and practical Cither-School. *Gustav Scheurmann and Co.: London*, [c. 1855.] 8°. **R. M. 25. e. 18.**

— Theoretical & practical Cither School ... 2nd edition. pp. 64. *Augener & C°.: London*, [1872.] 8°. **e. 328.**

— "Welcome march" for the piano-forte. Op. 14. *London*, [1856.] fol. **h. 724. e. (16.)**

— [Wiegenlied. Op. 16.] Cradle Song, *etc. Eng. & Ger.* pp. 5. *Augener & Co.: London*, [1889.] fol. [*Germania. no.* 30.] **H. 2128.**

LAUE (CARL A.)

— *See* LAUE (A. C.)

LAUÉ (CHARLES)

— *See* LAUE (A. C.)

LAUE (W.)

— Six Waltzes, and six Eccossaises, *etc.* [P. F.] pp. 8. *Printed & publish'd for the Author: London*, [^WM 1811.] **g. 443. z. (16.)**

LAUER (A. B. VON)

— The Fisher Maiden. *See* SONGS. Gems of German Song. Book 11. No. 6. [1843, *etc.*] fol. **H. 2123.**

— The Star of Love. *See* SONGS. Gems of German Song. Book 12. No. 3. [1843, *etc.*] fol. **H. 2123.**

LAUER (ERICH)

— Das völkische Lied. Erstes Buch Lieder des neuen Volkes aus dem ersten Jahrfünft des Dritten Reiches. Ausgewählt von Erich Lauer. pp. 240. *Deutscher Volksverlag: München*, [1939.] 8°. **D. 420. h.**

— *See* MOZART (W. A.) [*Collected Works.—e.*] Mozart wie ihn niemand kennt ... Nach einem fast vergessenen Übungsheft von 1784 dargestellt von E. Lauer. 1958. *obl.* 8°. **b. 201. d.**

LAUER (J. H.)

— Six original Christmas Carols, words by A. Gavin. *R. Cocks & Co.: London*, [1894.] fol. **E. 442. n. (41.)**

LAUF

— Lauf der Welt. [Song.] *See* KARG-ELERT (S.) Stimmungen und Betrachtungen ... Op. 53. No. 2.

— Lauf der Welt. [Song.] *See* KERSTORF (F. von) Zehn Lieder. No. 9.

— Lauf der Welt. [Song.] *See* KUECKEN (F. W.) [Sechs ernste und heitere Lieder. Op. 32. No. 4.]

— Der Lauf der Welt. [Song.] *See* NICOLA (C.)

LAUFFENSTEINER (WOLFF JACOB)

— Zwei Präludien und fünf Partien für Laute. Herausgegeben von Hans Radke. pp. xiii. 36. *Akademische Druck- u. Verlagsanstalt: Graz*, 1973. 4°. [*Musik alter Meister. Hft.* 30.] **G. 920.**

LAUGG (RUDOLF)

— *See* STAMITZ (J. W. A.) Konzert G-dur für Viola, Streichorchester und Cembalo. Zum ersten Mal herausgegeben von R. Laugg. Ausgabe mit Klavier von J. Wojciechowski. [1961.] 4°. **g. 98. b. (2.)**

LAUGH

— Laugh a Bit. Unison Song. *See* ELLIOTT (R. B.)

— Laugh a little Bit. Part-Song. *See* BATCHELDER (J.)

— Laugh and be glad. Song. *See* LINLEY (George)

— Laugh and be merry. Song. *See* GOTTSCHALK (L. F.)

— Laugh and be merry. [Part-song.] *See* HOLBROOK (J. C.)

— Laugh and be merry. Unison Song. *See* SHAW (G. T.)

— Laugh and be merry. Part Song. *See* SWEETING (E. T.)

— Laugh and grow fat. [Part-song.] *See* SEWARD (T. F.)

— Laugh & rejoice. Duett. *See* CLARKE, afterwards CLARKE WHITFELD (John)

— Laugh and sing. Song. *See* DRUMMOND (F.)

— Laugh and sing. Ballad. *See* GLOVER (S.)

— Laugh and the World laughs with you. [Musical monologue.] *See* BARNARD (D.)

— Laugh, and the World laughs with you. Canon. *See* CHALLINOR (F. A.)

— Laugh and the World laughs with you. [Song.] *See* FURNIVAL (H.)

— Laugh and the World laughs with you. *See* GOTTSCHALK (L. F.)

— Laugh and the World laughs with you. Song. *See* LEECHMAN (J.)

— Laugh at Loving if you will. Part-Song. *See* PITT (P.)

— Laugh at old Time. Song. *See* VERDI (Fortunino G. F.) [La Traviata.—Libiamo ne' lieti calici.]

— Laugh at the Times. [Song.] *See* FROM. From the Hill of Parnassus, *etc.* [1763.] *s. sh.* fol. **G. 307. (251.)**

— A Laugh at the World. [Song.] *See* DIBDIN (C.) [The Sphinx.]

LAUGH

— Laugh, Brothers, laugh. Round. *See* RODWELL (George H.) [The Devil's Ring.—Laughing Round.]

— Laugh cough and sneeze. Chorus. *See* OFFENBACH (J.) [Orphée aux Enfers.—Rondeau des Métamorphoses.]

— A Laugh is just like Sunshine. Song. *See* WOOD (N. B.)

— Laugh it by! Song. *See* BINGHAM (C.)

— Laugh, lady, Laugh. Song. *See* GUERNSEY (W.)

— Laugh, little River. Duet. *See* NEWTON (E. R.)

— Laugh, my Friends and Children. [Part-song.] *See* BELLMANN (C. M.) [Five Songs ... II.]

— Laugh not, nor weep. Song. *See* CLAY (F.)

— Laugh not, Youth, at Age. Part-Song. *See* PEARSALL (R. L.)

— The Laugh of a Child. Song. *See* GLOVER (J. H. L.)

— Laugh of a Child. Song. *See* HEINK (F.)

— Laugh or smile. Song. *See* JEFFERSON (E.)

— Laugh, then, laugh. [Part-song.] *See* STORIE (H.)

— Laugh while the sun shines. Song. *See* MATZKA (G.) 3 Songs. No. 3.

— Laugh while you may. Song, *See* GRAZIA (E. N.)

— Laugh with a hearty good will. Song. *See* LEVEY (W. C.)

— The Laugh with a Tear in it. [Song.] *See* OLCOTT (Chauncey) and KLEIN (M.)

— Laugh, yo' little Niggers. [Song.] *See* STARR (Hattie)

LAUGHABET

— The Laughabet. Operetta. *See* MILLIGAN (H. V.)

LAUGHABLE

— Laughable Times. Song. *See* COLLINS (Charles)

LAUGHER (C. CHRIS.)

— International Peace Anthem. Words by J. B. Straith, *etc. J. B. Straith: Owen Sound, Ont.*, 1915. 8°. **F. 281. qq. (24.)**

— Victory be to you. [Song.] Words by J. B. Straith. *J. B. Straith: Owen Sound, Ont.*, [1915.] fol. **G. 806. mm. (5.)**

LAUGHING

— Laughing. Part-Song. *See* ABT (F. W.)

— Laughing. [Song.] *See* TRAHERNE (C.)

— Laughing and Crying. [Song.] *See* SCHUBERT (F. P.) [Vier Gedichte. Op. 59. No. 4. Lachen und Weinen.]

— A Favorite Laughing & Crying Dialogue Duetto. *See* MY. My Spirits alert when good Company by, *etc.* [c. 1790.] fol. **H. 1601. jj. (22.)**

— Laughing and Weeping. [Two-part song.] *See* SCHUBERT (F. P.) [Vier Gedichte. Op. 59. No. 4. Lachen und Weinen.]

— The Laughing Bacchanalian. [Song.] *See also* HOOK (James)

— The Laughing Bacchanalian. [Song. By James Hook.] *See* AS. As the Mind is disturb'd, *etc.* [1770?] *s. sh.* fol. **G. 306. (108*.)**

— The Laughing Bacchanalian, *etc.* [Song. By James Hook.] *See* AS. As the Mind is disturb'd. [1770?] *s. sh.* fol. [*Sadler's Wells Collection. Vol.* 8.] **Crach. 1. Tab. 4. b. 4/8. (122.)**

LAUGHING

— Laughing Beauties. Vocal Waltz. *See* BIENE (A. van)

— Laughing blue Eyes. Song. *See* ASTON (A. F.)

— The Laughing Brook. Song. *See* RASBACH (O.)

— The Laughing Catch. *See* HARINGTON (H.)

— Laughing Cavalier. Song. *See* SANDERSON (W. E.)

— The Laughing Cavalier. Song. *See* TUNBRIDGE (J. A.)

— The Laughing Cavalier. Song. *See* WHITE (F. H.)

— Laughing Chorus. *See* ROOT (G. F.)

— The Laughing Eye is dim. Ballad. *See* EAMES (F.)

— Laughing Eyes. Song. *See* ASHLEIGH (D.)

— Laughing Eyes. Ballad. *See* BLEWITT (J.)

— Laughing Eyes. Song. *See* MAXWELL (Elsa W.)

— Laughing Eyes. [Song.] *See* MELLOR (Tom)

— Laughing Gas, or a Night at the Polytechnic. *See* YOUNG. Young Humphrey Brown, *etc.* [1870.] fol.   **H. 1790. c. (75.)**

— Laughing Gas. Part-Song. *See* GEIBEL (A.)

— The Laughing Husband. Musical Comedy. *See* EYSLER (E.) [Der lachende Ehemann.]

— Laughing Lilian May. Song. *See* AUBER (D. F. E.) [Les Diamants de la Couronne.]

— Laughing little Loo. Comic song. *See* VANDERVELL (W.)

— The Laughing Maiden. Part Song. *See* PEACE (F. W.)

— The Laughing Man. Song. *See* ARMADALE (E. H.)

— The Laughing Man. [Song.] *See* DUNN (J. W.)

— Laughing May. Song. *See* FERRARS (D'A. de)

— Laughing May. Song. *See* MENDELSSOHN-BARTHOLDY (J. L. F.) [12 Gesänge. Op. 8. No. 7. Maienlied.]

— The Laughing Morn. [Song.] *See* MENDELSSOHN-BARTHOLDY (J. L. F.) [Lieder ohne Worte. Op. 62. No. 4.]

— Laughing Pan. Two-part Song. *See* ROWLEY (A.)

— Laughing prohibited. [Song.] *See* DIBDIN (C.) [A Tour to the Land's End.]

— Laughing Rose. [Song.] *See* BAINTON (E. L.)

— Laughing Round. Quartett. *See* RODWELL (G. H.) [The Devil's Ring.]

— Laughing, singing all the Day long. Chanson. *See* LASSO (O. di) [Les Meslanges.—Sauter, danser.]

— The Laughing Song. [Song.] *See* AUBER (D. F. E.) [Manon Lescaut.—C'est l'histoire amoureuse.]

— Laughing Song. Part song. *See* BLOWER (Maurice)

— Laughing Song. Part-Song. *See* BRIAN (H.)

— Laughing Song. [Part-song.] *See* CARR (H.)

— Laughing Song. *See* CROOK (J.)

— Laughing Song. [Song.] *See* DENSMORE (J. H.) Three Songs ... 3.

— Laughing Song. *See* DOW (H. M.)

— Laughing Song. Two-part Song. *See* FLETCHER (P. E.)

— Laughing Song. Part Song. *See* GEIBEL (A.)

LAUGHING

— Laughing Song. Trio. *See* JACKMAN (P.)

— Laughing Song. [Song.] *See* JACOB (Gordon P. S.) Three Songs of Innocence. No. 3.

— A Laughing Song. Unison Song. *See* LONGMIRE (J.)

— The Laughing Song. *See* MASSÉ (F. M. V.) [La Reine Topaze.— Quoi! vraiment vous vous connaissez.]

— Laughing Song. Part Song. *See* MOORE (M.)

— Laughing Song. Part song. *See* NOBLE (Harold)

— A Laughing Song. Duet. *See* PERCEVAL (C.)

— Laughing Song. [S. A. T. B. and orchestra.] *See* RAFTER (Leonard)

— Laughing Song. Part-song. *See* RATCLIFFE (Desmond)

— A Laughing Song. Trio. *See* SELBY (B. L.)

— A Laughing Song. [Two-part song.] *See* STANFORD (*Sir* C. V.)

— The Laughing Song. [Song.] *See* STRAUSS (J.) *the Younger.* [Die Fledermaus.—Mein Herr Marquis.]

— Laughing Song. Two-Part Song. *See* SWEPSTONE (E.)

— Laughing Song. [Unison song.] *See* TATE (Phyllis M. D.)

— Laughing Song. Two-part song. *See* TAYLOR (Henry S.)

— Laughing Song. Trio. *See* TILZER (Harry von)

— Laughing Song. Trio. *See* TREHARNE (B.)

— Laughing Song. [Chorus.] *See* VAN DER STUCKEN (Frank V.) Three Choruses, *etc.* [No. 2.]

— Laughing Song. [Two-part song.] *See* WALKER (E.)

— Laughing Song. Two-part song. *See* WILKINSON (Philip G.)

— Laughing Song. [Two-part song.] *See* WILLEMSEN (Hugo)

— A Laughing Song. *See* YOUNG (D.)

— Laughing Star of Zuni. Operetta. *See* STRICKLAND (Lily T.)

— Laughing Water. Song. *See* HAGER (F. W.)

— Laughing Water. [Song.] *See* LOOMIS (H. W.) Three Indian Songs, *etc.* [No. 1.]

— The Laughing Waves. Two-part Song. *See* RATHBONE (G.)

— The Laughing Waves. Part-Song. *See* SOMERVILLE (R.)

LAUGHINGLY

— Laughingly glitter the Islands. [Song.] *See* AITKEN (R.)

LAUGHLIN (FRANK J.)

— Dead Heat galop. [P. F.]   *London,* [1880.] fol.
                                                    h. 1494. p. (25.)

— Excelsior March. [P. F.] pp. 4.   *Reid Bros.: London,* [c. 1890.] fol.   **h. 1203. h. (17.)**

— Fleurs d'Été valse. [P. F.]   *London,* [1880.] fol.
                                                    h. 1494. p. (28.)

— The Frolic polka. [P. F.]   *London,* [1879.] fol.
                                                    h. 1494. p. (22.)

— Helen's Babies polka. [P. F.]   *London,* [1880.] fol.
                                                    h. 1494. p. (27.)

— In Honor Bound. Song, the words by O. Mitchell.   *Chappell & Co.: London,* [1885.] fol.   **H. 1788. v. (1.)**

LAUGHLIN (Frank J.)

— Love's Message polka. [Orchestral parts.] *London,* [1879.] 8°.
e. 665. a. (4.)

— Love's Message polka. [P. F.] *London,* [1879?] fol.
h. 1494. p. (23.)

— Madcap polka. [P. F.] *London,* [1879.] fol. **h. 1494. p. (24.)**

— Morning's Dawn galop. [P. F.] *London,* [1880.] fol.
h. 1494. p. (26.)

— The Musical Souvenir quadrille. [P. F.] *London,* [1880.] fol
h. 1494. p. (29.)

— Only a Kiss in the Twilight. Song and Chorus. Words and music by F. Laughlin. *Howard & Co.: London,* [1887.] fol.
H. 1795. e. (2.)

— The Orphan. Polka. [P. F.] *Chappell & Co.: London,* [1888.] fol.
h. 3285. q. (9.)

— Pleasure. Waltz. [P. F.] *Chappell & Co.: London,* [1887.] fol.
h. 975. u. (49.)

— Queenie. March ... for piano. *Moore, Smith & Co.: London,* [1895.] fol.
h. 1489. s. (17.)

— Violet polka. [P. F.] *London,* [1880.] fol. **h. 1494. p. (30.)**

— Yachting. Valse. [P. F.] *Francis Bros. & Day: London,* [1887.] fol.
h. 975. u. (50.)

LAUGHTER

— Laughter. [Part-song.] *See* Abt (F. W.) [Vier vierstimmige Männergesänge. Op. 323. No. 4. Lachen.]

— Laughter. [Part-song.] *See* Grayley (A. A.)

— Laughter and Love. Song. *See* Rhodes (T. B.)

— Laughter and Sighs. [Song.] *See* Schubert (F. P.) [Vier Gedichte. Op. 59. No. 4. Lachen und Weinen.]

— Laughter and Tears. [Part-song.] *See* Schubert (F. P.) [Vier Gedichte. Op. 59. No. 4. Lachen und Weinen.]

— Laughter for Kings make I. Song. *See* Fitzgerald (J.)

— Laughter has come. Song. *See* Cox (W. R.)

— Laughter makes a man grow fat. *Slap Bang, here we are again.* Comic Song. *London,* [1866.] fol. **H. 1790. a. (60.)**

— The Laughter of Spring. [Song.] *See* Baumer (C.)

— The Laughter of the Children. [Song.] *See* Wood (Haydn)

— Laughter's dying out. [Part-song.] *See* Harper (F. J.)

— The Laughter Song. [Unison song.] *See* Foster (Arnold)

— Laughter wears a lilied Gown. Duet. *See* Branscombe (G.)

— Laughter's Sunshine. Song. *See* Girardin (C.)

LAUGHTERLAND

— Laughterland. Song. *See* Barthold (L. F.)

— Laughterland. Song. *See* Godfrey (Fred)

— Laughter Land. Part-Song. *See* Marzo (E.)

— Laughter-Land. Song. *See* Newton (E. R.)

— Laughter Land. Song. *See* Saint Quentin (E.) *pseud.*

LAUGHTERTOWN

— Laughtertown. [Part-song.] *See* Buck (D.) Five Three-Part Songs, *etc.* [No. 4.]

LAUGHTON (Wallace)

— Ride on, Moses! S. S. A., arr. by W. Laughton. Negro spiritual. *Waterloo Music Co.: Waterloo, Ont.,* [1950.] 8°.
E. 1850. i. (15.)

LAUGIER (Eugene)

— My pretty Dora Dare ... Ballad, words by T. Scanlan. *National Music Co.: Chicago,* 1896. fol. **H. 1798. u. (27.)**

LAUGIER VILLARS (Henri de)

— Le Muguet valse pour Piano. *Berlin & Posen,* [1879.] fol.
h. 1493. n. (13.)

LAUJON (Pierre)

— *See* L****, M.

LAUKIEN (E.)

— Through Night to Light. March. ⟨Solo B♭ cornet (conductor) [and wind band parts].⟩ 37 pt. *Hawkes & Son: London,* [1904.] 8°.
f. 800. (789.)

LAUKOTSKY (   )

— Hoffnungs Walzer ... für das Pianoforte arrangirt von L. Horwitz. pp. 7. *Bei Gustav Crantz: Berlin,* [c. 1835.] obl. fol.
e. 282. pp. (14.)

LAULUD

— Laulud nelja healega, meeste- ja lega-koorile. Tallinna kirjalaste seltsi wäljaantud. Partitur. I. jagu. pp. 16. *Trükitud Lindworsi pärijate kirjade ja kuluga: Tallinnas,* 1872. obl. 4°. *Imperfect; jag.* 1 *only.* **D. 840. r. (2.)**

LAULUJA

— Lauluja sekaköörille. Kantaatista. *See* Sibelius (J.)

LAUMANN (Cornelia Jean)

— The Extra. Waltz. [P. F.] *Weekes & Co.: London,* [1886.] fol.
h. 975. u. (51.)

— The Malvern quadrilles for the Pianoforte. *London,* [1850?] fol.
h. 1480. e. (15.)

LAUMANN (Maria Caroline)

— Brokenhearted. (Come not when I am dead.) Song, words by A. Tennyson. *London,* [1868.] fol. **H. 1775. t. (26.)**

— Farewell old England, song, words by A. Parsons. *London,* [1858.] fol. **H. 1771. l. (14.)**

— Twilight. Song [begins: "Just above yon sandy bar"]. *London,* [1872.] fol. **H. 1775. t. (27.)**

LAUNAY (Denise)

— Anthologie du motet latin polyphonique en France. (1609–1661.) Transcription et réalisation avec introduction et commentaires par D. Launay. pp. liv. 218. *Heugel et cie.: Paris,* [1963.] 4°.
[*Publications de la société française de musicologie. sér.* 1. *tom.* 17.] **g. 1.**

— Anthologie du psaume français polyphonique (1610–1663). Restitutions de Denise Launay, *etc.* 2 vol. *Les Éditions ouvrières: Paris,* 1974–76. fol.
Part of "Soli Deo gloria". **G. 932. o. (1.)**

LAUNAY (DENISE)

— *See* CHARPENTIER (M. A.) Te Deum pour deux chœurs et deux orchestres. Édition par D. Launay. [1969.] 4°. [*Le Pupitre.* 13.]   **G. 51.**

LAUNAY (E.)

— Coquetterie. Polka pour piano. Op. 3.   *O. Legouix: Paris,* [1886.] fol.   **h. 3281. l. (11.)**

— Dans la Vallée. Historiette pour piano. Op. 6.   *O. Legouix: Paris,* [1886.] fol.   **h. 3281. l. (12.)**

— Gavotte Marie-Stuart pour piano. Op. 1.   *Paris,* [1885.] fol.   **h. 3280. k. (27.)**

— Pavane Henri II. Air de danse du xvime. siècle pour piano. Op. 2.   *Paris,* [1885.] fol.   **h. 3280. k. (28.)**

LAUNAY (PAUL DE)

— Ping Pong. Waltz. [P. F.]   *Donaldson Bros.: Jersey,* [1902.] fol.   **h. 3286. y. (28.)**

LAUNCH

— The Launch. Song. *See* BANDEY (E.)

— The Launch. Song. *See* HAITE (J. J.)

— The Launch of the Fishing Smack. Song. *See* RIDGWAY (J.)

— The Launch of the St. Jean d'Arc. Ballad. *See* BODNAR (C.)

— The Launch of the Trafalgar. Song. *See* NELSON (Sidney)

— Launch the Lifeboat. Song Service. *See* BLACKBURN (John) *of Leeds.*

— Launch the Lifeboat. Song. *See* PLUMPTON (A.)

— Launch thy bark. Hymn. *See* BUSH (*Mrs* J. S.)

— Launch thy Bark, Mariner. [Song.] *See* PARKER (E.)

LAUNDRYMAN

— The Laundryman. [Song.] *See* BAYS (R. E.)

LAUNER (ELISA)

— L'Espagnol. Boléro [begins: "Errant sur ce triste rivage"]. Paroles de C. Ferrette.   *Paris,* [1835?] fol.   **G. 556. (52.)**

LAUNEY (PAUL DE)

— Moment Musical, for the Pianoforte. Op. 19. No. 2.   *T. Presser Co.: Philadelphia,* (1911.) fol.   **h. 3284. f. (48.)**

LAUNIS (ARMAS)

— Aslak Hetta. Kolminäytöksinen ooppera. Kirjoittanut ja säveltänyt Armas Launis. Pianoparttituuri säveltänyt sovittama. 〈Aslak Hetta. Oper in drei Akten. Text und Musik von Armas Launis. Deutsch von Hedwig Attila. Klavier-Auszug mit Text arrangiert vom Komponisten.〉 *Finn. & Ger.* pp. 303.   *Kustannusliike Choudens: Paris,* [1930.] fol.   **G. 190. mm.**

— Eesti runoviisid. Estnische Runenmelodien. Mélodies runiques estoniennes. Korraldanud A. Launis. 1930. 8°. *See* DORPAT.— *Esti Kirjanduse Selts.*   **Ac. 9076/11.**

— Lappische Juoigos-Melodien gesammelt und herausgegeben von A. Launis ... Mémoires de la Société Finno-Ougrienne xxvi. (F. F. Publications. Northern Series. No. 3. A Launis: The Juoigos-Melodies of the Laplanders, *etc.*)   *Helsingfors,* 1908. 8°.   **Ac. 9081/3.**

LAUNIS (ARMAS)

— Seitsemän veljestä. 3-näytöksinen koomillinen ooppera. Hämäläisestä kansanelämästä 1850-luvulla Aleksis Kiven mukaan kirjoittanut ja säveltänyt Armas Launis. 〈Die sieben von Jochenhof. Komische Oper in drei Akten. Aus dem sudfinnischen Volksleben um 1850 nach dem Roman Aleksis Kivis von A. Launis. Deutsche Übersetzung durchgesehen von Gustav Schmidt.〉 *Finn. & Ger.* pp. 168. *Kustannusosakeyhtiö Ahjo: Helsinki,* 1919. 4°.   **F. 1373. y.**

LAUNITZ (ELISE)

— Les Espagnoles — valses brillantes. [P. F.]   *London,* [1844.] fol.   **h. 932. (29.)**

— Fantasia on Ethiopian Melodies. [P. F.]   *London,* [1847.] fol.   **h. 710. (11.)**

— Lonely hours. A song [begins: "Why comes she not"], the words by W. H. Ollivier.   *London,* [1843.] fol.   **H. 1691. (5.)**

LAUNITZ (VLADIMIR)

— The Frog and Toad Dance ... For Piano.   *J. Curwen & Sons: London,* 1927. 4°.   **g. 1127. ii. (10.)**

— The Musical Box. *See* infra: [The Toy Shop.]

— [The Toy Shop.] The Musical Box. (From the Ballet Suite "The Toy Shop".) [P. F.]   *Goodwin & Tabb: London,* 1924. fol.   **h. 3865. f. (3.)**

— [The Toy Shop.] The Wooden Soldiers March, from The Toy Shop, *etc.* [P. F.]   *Goodwin & Tabb: London,* 1924. fol.   **h. 3865. f. (4.)**

— The Wooden Soldiers March. *See* supra: [The Toy Shop.]

LAUNOIS (ACHILLE)

— Les Canards, ou le Crieur des Rues. Scène comique [begins: "Nouvell's du jour"]. Paroles de A. Bouché.   *Paris,* [1835?] fol.   **G. 543. (5.)**

LAUR (FERDINAND)

— Schwarz-Roth-Gold, des deutschen Volkes Freiheitslied von Ferdinand Freiligrath. [Unaccompanied two-part song.] [1840?] 8°.   **F. 638. i. (36.)**

LAURA

— Laura. [Song.] *See* WHEN. When beauteous Laura's gentle Voice. [1778.] *s. sh.* fol.   **G. 313. (196.)**

— Laura, [vocal] valse. *See* BARILI (E.)

— Laura. Part song. *See* BURRINGTON (A. B.)

— Laura. Ballad. *See* GRAY (Thomas B.)

— Laura. Ballad. *See* HALE (Samuel)

— Laura. Song. *Se* HORSLEY (W.)

— Laura. Ballad. *See* JORDAN (W.)

— Laura. [Song.] *See* LANCASTER (Lillian M.)

— Laura. Song. *See* MILES (T.)

— Laura. Ballad [begins: "Ah listen to the plaintive Song"]. *See* PIERCY (H.)

— Laura. Melodia. *See* PINSUTI (C. E.)

— Laura. Sonnet [begins: "Gentle Zephir as you kiss"]. *See* PITMAN (A.)

— Laura. Drame lyrique. *See* PONS (Charles)

LAURA

— Laura. [Song.] *See* RASTRELLI (F.)

— Laura. [Song.] *See* ROCHE (A. D.) [Love's Victory.]

— Laura. Vígopera. *See* TARDOS (B.)

— Laura. [Song, begins: "Lovely are the kindling blushes".] *See* WARE (G.)

— Laura an das Bild ihres Geliebten. [Song.] *See* GABLER (C. A.)

— Laura et Lenza. Ballet. *See* BOSSI (C.)

— Laura forsworn. Ballad. *See* SHIELD (W.)

— Laura from Floradora. [Song.] *See* KUPPER (George)

— Laura Gray. Ballad. *See* HODGSON (C.)

— Laura Lee. [Part-song.] *See* FOSTER (Stephen C.)

— Laura Lee. [Song.] *See* HAYES (W. S.)

— Laura Lee. Song. *See* MORSE (Theodore F.)

— Laura Lee. [Song.] *See* NORTON (F.)

— Laura Lee. [Song.] *See* PETRIE (Henry W.)

— Laura May. [Song.] *See* COX (J. S.)

— Laura May. Ballad. *See* DIEHL (L.)

— Laura soave. [Madrigal.] *See* GABRIELI (A.) [Il Secondo libro de madrigali a cinque voci.]

— Laura, to her Æolian Harp. [Song.] *See* RAWLINGS (Thomas A.)

— Laura's Evening Song. *See* STANDIGL (J.)

LAURANA

— Laurana's Song. [Song.] *See* HART (C.) *Songwriter.*

LAURANCE (FREDERICK)

— Arm! Veterans, arm! [Song.] Words by P. Robson. *The Sanctuary Press: Westminster*, 1915. fol.   **H. 1793. s. (22.)**

LAUREL

— The Laurel. [Songs.] *See* BAILDON (J.)

— The Laurel. Song. *See* ENDERSSOHN (M.)

— The Laurel and the Rose. [Duet.] *See* GRELL (A. E.)

— The Laurel and the Willow. Canzonett. *See* MOZART (W. A.) [Sehnsucht nach dem Frühlinge.]

— The Laurel Crown. [Song.] *See* PARRY (John) *Bardd Alaw.*

— The Laurel Tree. National Song. *See* CARPENTER (J. E.)

— The Laurel Tree. Song. *See* RANSFORD (E.)

LAURELDENE

— Laureldene. [Anthem.] *See* BATE (Horace)

LAURENCE

— Laurence East and his Girl. [Musical sketch.] *See* RICHTER (W.)

LAURENCE (   ) *Mrs*

— The merry month of May, Song the air adapted by M^rs. Laurence. *C. Lonsdale: London*, [1851.] fol.   **H. 1735. (20.)**

LAURENCE (   ) *Mrs*

— [Another copy.]   **R. M. 14. b. 5. (20.)**

LAURENCE (ALBAN)

— The Day is past. Sacred Song, words from the Greek by J. M. Neale. *Shuttleworth's: Bradford*, [1906.] fol.
      H. 1187. ff. (49.)

LAURENCE (E.)

— Antenay over. [Song.] Words by James A. Buchan. pp. 5. *Victor Kremer Co.: Chicago, etc.*, [1909.] fol.
      H. 3985. i. (10.)

LAURENCE (FREDERICK WILLIAM)

— The Go it Polka. [P. F.]   *E. Donajowski: London*, [1900.] fol.
      h. 3286. q. (76.)

— Naïveté. Waltz. [P. F.]   *F. Pitman: London*, [1895.] fol.
      h. 3285. q. (10.)

— Spring Nocturne ... for Violin and Piano, or Harp. *J. Curwen & Sons: London*, 1929. 4°.   **g. 500. o. (9.)**

— Trio for Violin, Violoncello and Pianoforte, *etc.   J. Curwen & Sons: London*, 1925. 4°.   **g. 409. n. (12.)**

— Tristis for string orchestra. Score [and parts]. *Goodwin & Tabb: London*, 1919. 4°.   **g. 420. r. (4.)**

— Tristis ... Arranged for organ by F. G. Sanders, *etc. Goodwin & Tabb: London*, 1919. 4°.   **g. 1380. h. (2.)**

LAURENCE (G. F. H.)

— Mignonette waltz ... for the Pianoforte. *Rome, N. Y.*, 1864. fol.   **h. 1459. g. (6.)**

LAURENCE (J. W.)

— Danse des Sabotiers pour piano. *Weekes & Co.: London*, [1884.] fol.   **h. 1484. s. (27.)**

— Minuet for the pianoforte. *Weekes & Co.: London*, [1891.] fol.   **h. 1489. s. (18.)**

LAURENCE (L. G.)

— Go, lovely rose, song, the words by Waller, *etc. London*, [1853.] fol.   **H. 1735. (21.)**

LAURENCE (S.)

— Dear one I think of thee, [song, begins: "I think of thee when morning light,"] poetry by J. W. Hardwick. *New York*, 1868. fol.   **H. 1780. p. (30.)**

— Duett Vesperi. *New York*, 1863. fol.   **H. 1780. p. (31.)**

— Skating Duett, *etc. New York*, 1863. fol.   **H. 1780. p. (32.)**

LAURENCIE (LIONEL DE LA)

— *See* LA LAURENCIE.

LAURENCINUS, *Romanus*

— *See* BESARDUS (J. B.) Thesaurus Harmonicus diuini Laurencini Romani, *etc.* 1603. fol.   **K. 4. h. 1.**

LAURENDEAU (L. P.)

— "The Chairman." March. ⟨Solo B♭ cornet [and wind band parts].⟩ 20 pt. *Carl Fischer: New York*, [1907.] 8°.
      f. 800. (790.)

LAURENDEAU (L. P.)

— "The Clubman." March. ⟨Solo B♭ cornet [and wind band parts].⟩ 20 pt. *Carl Fischer: New York*, [1909.] 8°.
f. 800. (791.)

— The Dream after the Feast. A Musical Nightmare. [P. F. and orchestra. Parts.] *O. Ditson Co.: Boston*, 1896. fol.
h. 1508. e. (13.)

— A Jolly good Fellow. March. ⟨[With] The Candidate. March. F. P. Atherton. Op. 164.⟩ [Orchestral parts.] 20 pt. *Carl Fischer: New York*, [1908.] 8°.
f. 800. (792.)

— Laurentian March. (Marche laurentienne.) Introducing the Canadian patriotic song: "O Canada". (Lavallée.) [Orchestral parts.] 16 pt. *In:* ROBERTS (Charles J.) Mexican Kisses. [1908.] 8°.
f. 800. a. (199.)

— "The Marksman." March. ⟨Solo B♭ cornet [and wind band parts].⟩ 38 pt. *Carl Fischer: New York*, [1906.] 8°.
Various parts are in duplicate.
f. 800. (793.)

— "Oregonia." March. ⟨Solo B♭ cornet [and wind band parts].⟩ 34 pt. *Carl Fischer: New York*, [1905.] 8°.
Various parts are in duplicate.
f. 800. (794.)

— "The Peacock." Badinette. ⟨Solo, B♭ cornet [and wind band parts].⟩ 20 pt. *Carl Fischer: New York*, [1908.] 8°.
f. 800. (795.)

— "Vive la Canadienne." Arr. par L. P. Laurendeau. [Followed by "Dieu sauve le Roi" (God save the King) and "Chant national" ("O Canada, terre de nos aïeux.") by Calixa Lavallée.] ⟨1er cornet Si♭ [and wind band parts].⟩ 18pt. *Charles Lavallée: Montréal*, [1903.] 4°.
g. 1800. (201.)

— Vive la Canadienne. Orchestration de L. P. Laurendeau. [Followed by "Dieu sauve le Roi," and "Chant national (O Canada, terre de nos aïeux)" by Calixa Lavallée.] [Orchestral parts.] 13 pt. *Charles Lavallée: Montréal*, [1907.] 8°.
Various parts are in duplicate.
f. 800. (796.)

— "Watch dis Chile." Negro dance. ⟨Solo B♭ cornet [and wind band parts].⟩ 20 pt. *Oliver Ditson Co.: Boston, London*, [1896.] 8°.
f. 800. (797.)

— "Way down South." Descriptive fantasia. Solo B♭ cornet [and wind band parts]. 27 pt. *Oliver Ditson Co.: Boston, London*, [1896.] 8°.
Various parts are in duplicate.
f. 800. (798.)

— "Wireless Message." March and two-step. ⟨[With] "Line up." March and two-step. J. C. Heed.⟩ [Orchestral parts.] 36 pt. *Carl Fischer: New York*, [1905.] 8°.
Various parts are in duplicate.
f. 800. (799.)

— *See* ARTHUR (Charles) "The Top Notch" ... Arr. [for orchestra] by L. P. Laurendeau. 1908. 8°. [*CHAMBERS* (*W. Paris*) "Sunshine."]
f. 800. (253.)

— *See* KÉLER (B.) and KRETSCHMER (   ) "Roumanian Festival Overture." Arr. [for wind band] by L. P. Laurendeau. [1904.] 4°.
g. 1800. (158.)

— *See* WAGNER (J. R.) "Woodlark, Cuckoo and Frog" ... Polka di concert ... Arr. [for orchestra] by L. P. Laurendeau. [1906.] 8°.
f. 800. (171.)

LAURENS (EDMOND)

— À travers Champs. 12 Pièces intimes. Op. 36. No. 9. Clair de Lune. [P. F.] [*Paris*,] 1901. 8°.
Supplement to "L'Illustration," No. 3051. **P. P. 4283. m. (3.)**

— Arabesques pour piano. Op. 12. *Paris*, [1884.] fol.
h. 3280. k. (29.)

— Caprice mazurk pour Piano. *Paris*, [1876.] fol.
h. 1487. p. (16.)

— Damoiselle. *See* infra: [Mascarade.]

LAURENS (EDMOND)

— Gigue pour Piano. *Paris*, [1875.] fol. **h. 1487. p. (15.)**

— Lieder-Walzer, No. 2. [P. F.] [*Paris*,] 1904. 8°.
Supplement to "L'Illustration," No. 3197. **P. P. 4283. m. (3.)**

— Madrigal. [Song, begins: "Vous en riez".] Poésie de H. Murger. *Paris*, [1878.] fol. **H. 1781. i. (8.)**

— [Mascarade.] Damoiselle. Mélodie extraite de "Mascarade", Scènes fantaisistes, poésie de G. Guérin. [*Paris*,] 1900. 8°.
Supplement to "L'Illustration," No. 3005. **P. P. 4283. m. (3.)**

— Mascarade. Scènes fantaisistes. Op. 24. No. 3. "Incroyable." [P. F.] [*Paris*,] 1903. 8°.
Supplement to "L'Illustration," No. 3164. **P. P. 4283. m. (3.)**

— La Source. Op. 23. No. 3. [P. F.] [*Paris*,] 1902. 8°.
Supplement to "L'Illustration," No. 3085. **P. P. 4283. m. (3.)**

LAURENS (GERMAIN)

— À moi le pompon. Chansonnette [begins: "Croyez que j'n'aime pas médire"]. Paroles de E. Kuhn. *Paris*, [1880.] fol.
H. 1786. e. (18.)

— La Boutique à un sou. Chansonnette [begins: "Pour une leçon"]. Paroles d'E. Potier. *Paris*, [1874.] fol.
H. 1777. h. (15.)

— L'Hiver. Mélodie [begins: "Dans la campagne"]. Paroles de V. Nadal. *Paris*, [1874.] fol. **H. 1777. h. (16.)**

— Idylle. [Song, begins: "Quand je pris le sentier".] Paroles de V. Nadal. *Paris*, [1874.] fol. **H. 1777. h. (17.)**

— Jeunesse. [Song, begins: "Le mois de Mai commence"]. Paroles de V. Nadal. *Paris*, [1874.] fol. **H. 1777. h. (18.)**

— Le Jour des Rois. [Song, begins: "Un jour fleurs écloses".] Paroles de V. Nadal. *London*, [1874.] fol. **H. 1777. h. (19.)**

— La Maille échappée. Bluette [begins: "Assise à l'ombre"]. Paroles de E. Potier. *Paris*, [1874.] fol. **H. 1777. h. (13.)**

— Le Ménétrier de Meudon. Opéra-Comique en 3 actes, de G. Marot & L. Jonathan. Partition chant et piano. *L. Couderc: Paris*, [1880.] 8°. **F. 797.**

— Noël. [Song, begins: "Quel éclair déchirant".] Paroles de H. Second. *Paris*, [1875.] fol. **H. 1777. h. (22.)**

— Oiseaux envolés. Mélodie [begins: "Le nid était bati"]. Paroles de H. Second. *Paris*, [1874.] fol. **H. 1777. h. (20.)**

— Perle Cachée. Romance [begins: "Madeleine est grande fille"]. Paroles de E. Potier. *Paris*, [1874.] fol.
H. 1777. h. (12.)

— La Première Culotte. Chansonnette [begins: "Monsieur Toto"]. Paroles de E. Potier et H. Second. *Paris*, [1874.] fol.
H. 1777. h. (21.)

— Rose et Papillon. Mélodie [begins: "Dans un jardin"]. Paroles de V. Nadal. *Paris*, [1874.] fol. **H. 1777. h. (14.)**

— Se canto, qué canto! Chant languedocien ... Recueilli, traduit et harmonisé pour solo et chœur à 2, 3 ou 4 voix égales avec accompagnement de piano par G. Laurens. [Score.] pp. 4. *Germain Laurens: Paris*, [1880?] fol.
H. 1248. h. (2.)

— Soleil de Printemps. Mélodie [begins: "J'aime sans le savoir"], paroles de G. Lelio. *Paris*, [1883.] fol.
H. 2836. h. (29.)

LAURENS (H. A.)

— Life in Death. Song, written and composed by H. A. Laurens. *J. Williams: London*, 1898. fol. **H. 1798. u. (30.)**

LAURENT (ADRIEN)

— Nos Intimes quadrille pour le Piano. *Londres*, [1875.] fol.
h. 1482. y. (40.)

LAURENT (ALBERT)

— No. 5 Auxiliary Petrol Company March. [P. F.] *Weekes & Co.: London*, [1917.] fol. **h. 3284. nn. (16.)**

LAURENT (B.)

— Sara la Baigneuse. Berceuse, paroles de V. Hugo. *Paris*, [1876.] fol. **H. 1781. i. (9.)**

LAURENT (G. F.)

— Le Retour du Printemps. Romance [begins: "Dans nos forets"]. *Paris*, [1810?] fol. **G. 548. (46.)**

LAURENT (HENRI)

— H. Laurent's Album of Dance music. *London*, [1858.] fol.
h. 883.

— Egyptian Polka. ([Followed by] The Malakof Galop. By H. Laurent.—Balaclava. Quick step. By W. N. St. Leger.) [Military band parts.] 24 pt. *Boosey & Co.: London*, [1868.] fol.
[*Boosé's military Journal. ser. 20. no. 5.*] **h. 1549.**

— Alexander Romanoff, Valse. [P. F.] pp. 15. *Boosey & Sons: London*, [1857.] fol.
Cropped. **h. 882. (24.)**

— The Amina waltzes, on airs from [V. Bellini's opera] La Sonnambula. [P. F.] *London*, [1853.] fol. **h. 975. e. (22.)**

— The Argyll galop. [P. F.] *London*, [1857.] fol. **h. 882. (15.)**

— The Argyll galop. [P. F.] *London*, [1872.] fol.
h. 1485. s. (31.)

— Beethoven Waltz. [Partly based on a waltz (K.-H. Anh. 14. No. 1) incorrectly ascribed to Beethoven. P. F., with an accompaniment for cornet à piston in B♭. Parts.] 2 pt. *Boosey & Son: London*, [1862.] fol. **h. 882. (30.)**

— Beethoven Valse. [Arranged and adapted by H. Laurent. Partly based on a waltz incorrectly ascribed to Beethoven, K.-H. Anh. 14. No. 1.] ([Followed by] Freikugeln Quadrille. Voss.) [Military band parts.] 23 pt. *Boosey & Co.: London*, [1880.] fol.
[*Boosé's military Journal. ser. 32. no. 3.*] **h. 1549.**

— La Belle Française, valse. [P. F.] *London*, [1854.] fol.
h. 975. e. (26.)

— Beloved Star Valse. ([Followed by] Der Luftschiffer Polka. Kühner.—Nachtwandler Polka. Stasny.) [Military band parts.] 24 pt. *Boosey & Co.: London*, [1871.] fol.
[*Boosé's military Journal. ser. 28. no. 3.*] **h. 1549.**

— Bianca Valse. ([Followed by] Orphée aux enfers Quadrille. [Jules] Strauss.) [Military band parts.] 24 pt. *Boosey & Son: London*, [1871.] fol.
[*Boosé's military Journal. ser. 30. no. 6.*] **h. 1549.**

— The Bridesmaids Valse. *See* BOOSEY AND CO. Boosey's Orchestral Journal, *etc.* No. 52. [1860, *etc.*] 8°. **e. 69.**

— The Bridesmaids valse. [P. F.] *London*, [1856.] fol.
h. 882. (11.)

— Carnaval valse. [P. F.] *London*, [1872.] fol. **h. 1485. s. (33.)**

— Chateau des Fleurs. Schottische. [P. F.] *London*, [1861.] fol.
h. 882. (29.)

— Christmas Annual of dance music, containing ... new compositions by Laurent, *etc. See* BOOSEY AND CO. Boosey's Musical Cabinet. No. 21. [1861, *etc.*] 4°. **F. 160.**

LAURENT (HENRI)

— The Christmas Waits' Quadrille. [P. F.] pp. 5. *Boosey & Sons: London*, [c. 1860.] fol.
Imperfect; wanting the titlepage. **h. 3865. yy. (1.)**

— The Christy Minstrels' Valse. H. Laurent. ([Followed by] Les Grâces. Polka mazurka. Morelly.—Selenen Polka. Herchenröder.) [Military band parts.] 24 pt. *Boosey & Co.: London*, [1858.] fol.
[*Boosé's supplemental military Journal. no. 175.*] *Without titlepage. The title is taken from the head of p. 1 of the first clarinet part.* **h. 1544.**

— Laurent's Christy's Minstrels waltz. [P. F.] *London*, [1859.] fol. **h. 882. (20.)**

— Dinorah Quadrille. [On melodies from G. Meyerbeer's opera "Le Pardon de Ploërmel". Military band parts.] 24 pt. *In:* MOZART (W. A.) [La Clemenza di Tito.—Parto, parto, ma tu ben mio.] Scena ed Aria, *etc.* [1878.] fol. [*Boosé's military Journal. ser. 27. no. 6.*] **h. 1549.**

— Dinorah Quadrille. [P. F.] *London*, [1859.] fol. **h. 882. (17.)**

— Dinorah Valse. H. Laurent. ([Followed by] Feodora Polka Mazurka. [Op. 79.] Neumann.—Maximilian Galopp. Kühner.) [Military band parts.] 24 pt. *Boosey & Co.: London*, [1859.] fol.
[*Boosé's supplemental military Journal. no. 180.*] *Without titlepage. The title is taken from the head of p. 1 of the first clarionet part.* **h. 1544.**

— Dinorah Valse [on G. Meyerbeer's opera. P. F.]. *London*, [1859.] fol. **h. 882. (22.)**

— Laurent's Dinorah Valse as a Pianoforte Duet. *London*, [1859.] fol. **h. 882. (21.)**

— Donna Julia. Valse romantique. [P. F.] *Boston*, [*Mass.*, 1855?] fol. **h. 1459. p. (4.)**

— Egyptian Polka. *See* BOOSEY AND CO. Boosey's Orchestral Journal, *etc.* No. 51. [1860, *etc.*] 8°. **e. 69.**

— The Egyptian polka. [P. F.] *London*, [1856.] fol. **h. 882. (3.)**

— L'Espagnole ou La Mandoline, valse. [P. F. with cornet accompaniment.] *London*, [1851.] fol. **h. 964. (1.)**

— Ethel Newcome Valse. *See* BOOSEY AND CO. Boosey's Orchestral Journal, *etc.* No. 41. [1860, *etc.*] 8°. **e. 69.**

— Ethel Newcome, valse. [P. F.] *London*, [1855.] fol.
h. 882. (12.)

— L'Etoile du Nord polka, from Meyerbeer's opera, and arranged for the piano forte by H. Laurent. *London*, [1855.] fol. **h. 976. d. (22.)**

— Galop des Guides. *See* BOOSEY AND CO. Boosey's Orchestral Journal, *etc.* No. 34. [1860, *etc.*] 8°. **e. 69.**

— Galop des guides. [P. F.] *London*, [1854.] fol.
h. 975. e. (28.)

— The Highlanders Quadrille. *See* BOOSEY AND CO. Boosey's Orchestral Journal, *etc.* No. 36. [1860, *etc.*] 8°. **e. 69.**

— The Highlanders' quadrille. [P. F.] *London*, [1855.] fol.
h. 882. (5.)

— The Highlanders quadrille. [P. F.] *London*, [1872.] fol.
h. 1485. s. (32.)

— Les Huguenots Quadrille. *See* BOOSEY AND CO. Boosey's Orchestral Journal, *etc.* No. 46. [1860, *etc.*] 8°. **e. 69.**

— Les Huguenots, quadrille. [On G. Meyerbeer's opera "Les Huguenots". P. F.] [*London*, 1856.] fol. **h. 882. (6.)**

— The Imperial Guards Galop. *See* BOOSEY AND CO. Orchestral Journal, *etc.* No. 39. [1860, *etc.*] 8°. **e. 69.**

LAURENT (Henri)

— The Imperial guards galop. [P. F.] *London*, [1855.] fol.
h. 882. (1.)

— Killarney. Irish waltz. [P. F.] pp. 9. *Boosey & Sons: London*, [c. 1860.] fol.
h. 61. aa. (25.)

— The Königsberg Polka, arranged by H. Laurent. *See* Boosey and Co. Boosey's Orchestral Journal. No. 7. [1860, *etc.*] 8°.
e. 69.

— Leonora Valse. *See* Boosey and Co. Boosey's Orchestral Journal, *etc.* No. 25. [1860, *etc.*] 8°.
e. 69.

— Leonora valse, founded on a celebrated aria from [D. G. M. Donizetti's opera] La Favorita, *etc.* [P. F.] *Boosey & Sons: London*, [1854.] fol.
h. 975. e. (31.)

— Lord Lovell's Waltz. H. Laurent. ⟨[Followed by] Quadrille—Les Vêpres siciliennes. [Based on melodies from Verdi's opera.] Kühner.—Polka. Sans souci. Strauss.⟩ [Military band parts.] 24 pt. *Boosey & Co.: London*, [1858.] fol.
[*Boosé's supplemental military Journal. no.* 174.] *Without titlepage. The title is taken from the head of p.* 1 *of the first clarinet part.*
h. 1544.

— "Luisa Miller." ⟨Valse.⟩ [On a theme from Verdi's opera.] [Military band parts.] 20 pt. *In:* Bright (M. D.) L'Enfant de France, *etc.* [1858.] fol. [*C. Boosé's supplemental military Journal. no.* 172.]
h. 1544.

— A Maiden's Blush Valse. [P. F.] *London*, [1862.] fol.
h. 882. (31.)

— The Malakoff Galop. *See* Boosey and Co. Boosey's Orchestral Journal, *etc.* No. 48. [1860, *etc.*] 8°.
e. 69.

— The Malakoff galop. [P. F.] [*London*, 1856.] fol.
h. 882. (2.)

— Margaretta Valse ... H. Laurent. ⟨Arranged by C. Boosé.⟩ ⟨[Followed by] Gnomen Quadrille. Fahrbach.⟩ [Military band parts.] 23 pt. *Boosey & Co.: London*, [1860.] fol.
[*Boosé's supplemental military Journal, no.* 186.] *Without titlepage. The title is taken from the head of p.* 1 *of the first clarinet part.*
h. 1544.

— Marguerite polka. [P. F.] *London*, [1857.] fol.
h. 1460. u. (39.)

— The Maud Valse. [Military band parts.] 24 pt. *In:* Pacini (G.) [Gli Arabi nelle Gallie.—Ove alberga amor di gloria.] Cavatina, *etc.* [1879.] fol. [*Boosé's military Journal. ser.* 23. *no.* 4.]
h. 1549.

— Maud, Valse chantante (introducing Balfe's popular song "Come into the garden, Maud"). [P. F.] *London*, [1857.] fol.
h. 882. (23.)

— Old Customs; ballad, written by W. Jones. *London*, [1847.] fol.
H. 1706. (20.)

— Quadrille. Partant pour la Syrie. *See* Boosey and Co. Boosey's Orchestral Journal, *etc.* No. 26. [1860, *etc.*] 8°.
e. 69.

— Partant pour la Syrie, quadrille impérial founded on airs of the empire and melodies composed by Queen Hortense, *etc.* [P. F.] *London*, [1854.] fol.
h. 975. e. (30.)

— Polka du Château rouge pour Piano. *London*, [1846.] fol.
h. 937. (12.)

— The Pretty Eyes Schottisch, *etc.* [P. F.] *New York*, 1853. fol.
h. 1459. p. (5.)

— [Quentin Durward.] "Alone am I in sorrow:" Ballad. ("I come from the land of the mountain:" Ballad. "The halls of my fathers:" Ballad. "The merry dance is not for me:"

LAURENT (Henri)

Ballad. "They call me here:" Song. "Ye skies of azure:" Duet.) The poetry by E. Fitzball. *London*, [1849.] fol.
H. 213.

— [Quentin Durward.] The overture. (Grand March. Favorite Airs.) For the Piano Forte. *London*, [1849.] fol.
H. 213.

— La ravissante, varsoviana. [P. F.] [*London*, 1856.] fol.
h. 882. (9.)

— Regine Valse. [P. F.] *London*, [1857.] fol.
h. 882. (25.)

— Rigoletto Walzer. *See* Boosey and Co. Boosey's Orchestral Journal, *etc.* No. 16. [1860, *etc.*] 8°.
e. 69.

— Rigoletto, valse pour Piano. [On melodies from Verdi's opera.] *London*, [1853.] fol.
h. 975. e. (25.)

— The Rose of England, valse. [P. F.] *London*, [1856.] fol.
h. 882. (13.)

— The Rose waltzes. [P. F.] *London*, [1853.] fol.
h. 975. e. (24.)

— St. Patrick's Quadrille. ⟨[Followed by] Fenella Valse by Tinney.⟩ [Military band parts.] 23 pt. *Boosey & Co.: London*, [1880.] fol.
[*Boosé's military Journal. ser.* 21. *no.* 5.]
h. 1549.

— Satanella, Galop, polka mazurka and polka. [P. F. On airs from Balfe's opera.] *London*, [1859.] fol.
h. 882. (16.)

— Satanella quadrille [on Balfe's opera. P. F.] *etc. London*, [1859.] fol.
h. 882. (18.)

— Satanella Valse. H. Laurent. ⟨[Followed by] Die Enz Flösser Galop. [Op. 159.] Kühner.—Nymphen Polka. Strauss. [Op. 50.]⟩ [Military band parts.] 24 pt. *Boosey & Co.: London*, [1859.] fol.
[*Boosé's supplemental military Journal. no.* 176.] *Without titlepage. The title is taken from the head of p.* 1 *of the first clarionet part.*
h. 1544.

— Satanella valse [P. F. on Balfe's opera]. *London*, [1859.] fol.
h. 882. (26.)

— Second set of Lancers, Quadrille. [P. F.] *London*, [1857.] fol.
h. 882. (19.)

— Second Set of Lancers. [Military band parts.] 27 pt. *In:* Musgrave (Frank) Chère amie, *etc.* [1864.] fol. [*Boosé's supplemental military Journal. no.* 205.]
h. 1544.

— The shamrock waltzes. [P. F.] *London*, [1853.] fol.
h. 975. e. (23.)

— Stradella Quadrilles. [P. F.] *See* Saint. St. James's Album, 1863. [1862.] fol.
H. 1241.

— Valse. The summer bloom. [P. F.] *London*, [1859.] fol.
h. 882. (28.)

— The sweetest Rose is Love. Ballad, written by J. W. Lake. *London*, [1848.] fol.
H. 1706. (21.)

— The Thistle Waltzes. *See* Boosey and Co. Boosey's Orchestral Journal. No. 6. [1860, *etc.*] 8°.
e. 69.

— La Traviata, quadrille on Verdi's opera. [P. F.] *London*, [1856.] fol.
h. 882. (7.)

— Valse de l'hiver des vêpres siciliennes de Verdi. [P. F.] *London*, [1856.] fol.
h. 882. (14.)

— Valse du Carnaval. *See* Boosey and Co. Boosey's Orchestral Journal, *etc.* No. 38. [1860, *etc.*] 8°.
e. 69.

— Valse du Carnaval. [P. F.] *London*, [1854.] fol.
h. 975. e. (29.)

— La Varsoviana. *See* Boosey and Co. Boosey's Orchestral Journal, *etc.* No. 42. [1860, *etc.*] 8°.
e. 69.

LAURENT (HENRI)

— La Varsoviana, new dance, etc. [P. F.] *London*, [1855.] fol.
                                                              h. 882. (8.)

— [Another copy.]   **h. 882. (10.)**

— Les Vêpres Siciliennes Valse. *See* BOOSEY AND CO. Boosey's
Orchestral Journal, etc. No. 49. [1860, etc.] 8°.   **e. 69.**

— Sicilian Vespers. ⟨Valse.⟩ [Based on melodies from Verdi's
opera. Military band parts.] 24 pt. *In:* WADDELL (James)
Fackeltanz, etc. [1859.] fol. [*Boosé's supplemental military
Journal. no.* 179.]   **h. 1544.**

— The Sicilian Vespers (Les Vêpres Siciliennes) Waltz, on
Verdi's opera. *London*, [1859.] fol.   **h. 882. (27.)**

— Vilikins Valse. *See* BOOSEY AND CO. Boosey's Orchestral
Journal, etc. No. 23. [1860, etc.] 8°.   **e. 69.**

— Vilikins waltz, on the song "Vilikins and his Dinah". [P. F.]
London, [1854.] fol.   **h. 975. e. (27.)**

— The Zouaves Polka. *See* BOOSEY AND CO. Boosey's Orchestral
Journal, etc. No. 35. [1860, etc.] 8°.   **e. 69.**

— The Zouaves polka. [P. F.] *London*, [1855.] fol.   **h. 882. (4.)**

— *See* GLOVER (S.) The postman's knock quadrilles, arranged
for an orchestra by H. Laurent. [1856.] 8°.   **e. 79. (4.)**

LAURENT (MAURICE)

— Token of Love. Waltzes. [P. F.] [*W. H. Billing: Ottawa?*]
1897. fol.   **h. 3286. g. (15.)**

LAURENT (MICHEL)

— Fantasia—Hiawatha. Brass Band Score. *Wright & Round:
Liverpool*, [1924.] obl. 4°.   **e. 503. (6.)**

LAURENT (PAUL)

— Britannia for ever. [Song.] Words by J. W. Meredith.
Whaley, Royce & Co.: Toronto, 1903. fol.   **H. 1799. vv. (30.)**

LAURENT (R. S.)

— Trois Danses très faciles pour piano. No. 1. Polka. No. 2.
Valse. No. 3. Galop. *Mayence*, [1886.] fol.   **h. 3280. k. (30.)**

LAURENT (VICTOR)

— Scale Melodies. The Major, Minor, & Chromatic Scales
arranged in a new & progressive order. Each scale being
amplified by two interesting Pieces in the same key. [P. F.]
4 pt. *A. Hammond & Co.: London*, [1904–06.] 4°.
Academic Edition, No. 281, 282, 283 *and* 284.
                                                              g. 1130. m. (2.)

LAURENT DE RILLÉ (FRANÇOIS ANATOLE)

— L'Adieu des Pasteurs Béarnais. Chœur à 4 voix d'hommes.
Paris, [1862.] 8°.   **E. 600. a. (46.)**

— [L'Adieu des Pasteurs Béarnais.] The Swiss Shepherd's
Farewell ... Four-Part Song for men's voices, the English
words ... by P. England. [1910.] *See* ORPHEUS. The Orpheus,
etc. New Series. No. 497. [1879, etc.] 8°.   **E. 1748.**

— [Alerte.] To Arms ... Four-Part Song for men's voices, the
English words by P. England. [1906.] *See* ORPHEUS. The
Orpheus, etc. New Series. No. 411. [1879, etc.] 8°.
                                                              E. 1748.

— [Alerte.] To Arms, etc. [1908.] *See* NOVELLO AND CO.
Novello's Tonic Sol-fa Series. No. 1655. [1876, etc.] 4°.
                                                              B. 885.

LAURENT DE RILLÉ (FRANÇOIS ANATOLE)

— All together rise and sing. [Part-song for men's voices.]
Words by J. Guard. *J. Curwen & Sons: London*, [1885.] 8°.
The Apollo Club, No. 29.   **F. 667.**

— Après la Chasse. Chœur [begins: "Pâle comme l'amour"].
Paris, [1862.] 8°.   **E. 600. a. (42.)**

— L'Assaut, chœur à 4 voix d'hommes [begins: "Hardis
soldats"]. Paroles de L. Durand. *Paris*, [1869.] 8°.
                                                              E. 600. a. (35.)

— L'Assaut. Chœur à 4 voix d'hommes. Paroles de L. Durand.
J. Grandet: Paris, [1889.] 4°.
Part of the Appendix to "L'Œuvre Littéraire de L. Durand".
                                                              12238. k. 1.

— An Autumn Evening. Part-Song for men's voices, the English
words by P. England. [1907.] *See* ORPHEUS. The Orpheus, etc.
New Series. No. 434. [1879, etc.] 8°.   **E. 1748.**

— [Ave Regina.] Jesu, our only Hope of Heaven ... [Four-part
song.] The English words by P. England. [1905.] *See*
ORPHEUS. The Orpheus, etc. New Series. No. 378.
[1879, etc.] 8°.   **E. 1748.**

— [Ave Regina.] Jesu, our only Hope of Heaven ... [Four-part
song.] English words by P. England. [1905.] *See* NOVELLO AND
CO. Novello's Tonic Sol-fa Series. No. 1445. [1876, etc.] 4°.
                                                              B. 885.

Babiole

— Babiole, opérette villageoise en trois actes. Paroles de MM.
Clairville & Gastineau: Partition Chant et Piano arrangée par
L. Roques. *Paris*, [1878.] 8°.   **F. 38. b.**

— Babiole. Opérette villageoise in 3 acts. English version by
R. Reece. *J. Williams: London*, [1880?] 4°.   **F. 38. d.**

— [No. 8, 14, 15.] [1899.] *See* CHORAL. Choral Gems. Secular,
etc. No. 2, 5, 14. [1898–99.] 4°.   **F. 451.**

— *See* ARBAN (J. J. B. L.) Babiole ... quadrille, etc. [1878.] obl.
fol.   **e. 272. h. (8.)**

— *See* GRENVILLE (A.) Babiole. Galop. [1888.] 8°.
                                                              e. 79. f. (11.)

— *See* GRENVILLE (A.) Babiole. Lancers. [1888.] 8°.
                                                              e. 79. f. (12.)

— *See* MÉTRA (J. L. O.) Babiole-polka, etc. [1878.] fol.
                                                              h. 1493. p. (39.)

— *See* RIVIÈRE (J.) Babiole quick march, etc. [1880.] 8°.
                                                              f. 413. f. (12.)

————————

— Les Batteurs de Blé. Chœur à 4 voix [begins: "Battons
d'accord"]. Paroles de P. Lachambeaudie. *Paris*, [1861.] fol.
                                                              E. 600. a. (44.)

— Battle Song. *See* infra: [Le Triomphe du Peuple.]

— Berceuse Corse [for 4 voices. Begins: "Au pays où la sirène"].
Paris, [1863.] 8°.   **E. 600. a. (41.)**

— Bibliothèque des Sociétés Chorales ... Collection de chœurs
d'hommes sans accompagnement. *Paris*, [1861–69.] 8°.
Imperfect; having a few no. only.   **F. 606. (2.)**

— [Les Cavaliers de la Nuit.] The Riders of the Night ...
Four-Part Song for men's voices, the English words ... by
W. G. Rothery. [1912.] *See* ORPHEUS. The Orpheus, etc. New
Series. No. 530. [1879, etc.] 8°.   **E. 1748.**

— [Les Cavaliers de la Nuit.] The Riders of the Night, etc.
[1912.] *See* NOVELLO AND CO. Novello's Tonic Sol-fa Series.
No. 2023. [1876, etc.] 4°.   **B. 885.**

LAURENT DE RILLÉ (François Anatole)

—— Célèbres Valses Viennoises arrangées avec chœurs pour 4
voix d'hommes (avec accompagnement de Piano). 6 no.
Paris, [1883.] 8°.   **F. 607. p. (15.)**

—— Chanson Gasconne. Chœur à 4 voix [begins: "Le long de la
Garonne"]. *Paris*, [1863.] 8°.   **E. 600. a. (37.)**

—— [Le Chant des Travailleurs.] The Workers ... Part-Song for
men's voices, the English words by P. England. [1907.] *See*
ORPHEUS. The Orpheus, *etc*. New Series. No. 418. [1879, *etc*.]
8°.   **E. 1748.**

—— The Chase. *See infra*: [La Saint-Hubert.]

—— [Chœur de Buveurs.] Drinking Song ... Four-Part Song for
men's voices, the English words ... by P. England. [1910.] *See*
ORPHEUS. The Orpheus, *etc*. New Series. No. 499. [1879, *etc*.]
8°.   **E. 1748.**

—— Chœur de chasseurs. [T. T. Bar. B.] Paroles de E. de Chabot,
etc. [With a portrait and a facsimile.] pp. 4. *In:* Album du
Gaulois. vol. 2. [1869.] fol.   **H. 2349. a.**

—— Choeurs classiques ... 3ᵉ Collection ... arrangé par Laurent
de Rillé. 11 no. *Gambogi:* [*Paris*, 1861.] 8°.   **E. 708.**

—— The Christian Martyrs. *See infra*: [Les Martyrs aux Arènes.]

—— Les Cloches du Soir. *See* BATTMANN (J. L.) Les Cloches ...
pour Piano. [1869.] fol.   **h. 3009. (31.)**

—— Come let us march. [Part-song for men's voices.] Words by
J. Guard. *J. Curwen & Sons: London*, [1884.] 8°.
The Apollo Club, No. 31.   **F. 667.**

—— The Dance.—"Come, trip it lightly."— [Four-part song.] The
English words by P. England. [1907.] *See* ORPHEUS. The
Orpheus, *etc*. New Series. No. 432. [1879, *etc*.] 8°.
                                           E. 1748.

—— Dear Land of Beauty. *See infra*: [Patrie absente.]

—— [Le Départ des Compagnons.] The Travellers' Farewell ...
Part-Song for men's voices, the English words by P. England.
[1907.] *See* ORPHEUS. The Orpheus, *etc*. New Series. No. 419.
[1879, *etc*.] 8°.   **E. 1748.**

—— [Le Départ des Compagnons.] The Travellers' Farewell, *etc*.
[1908.] *See* NOVELLO AND CO. Novello's Tonic Sol-fa Series.
No. 1704. [1876, *etc*.] 4°.   **B. 885.**

—— The Departure of the Apostles. Four-Part Song for men's
voices, the English words by W. G. Rothery. [1911.] *See*
ORPHEUS. The Orpheus, *etc*. New Series. No. 520. [1879, *etc*.]
8°.   **E. 1748.**

—— [Des Abymes profonds.] Out of the Deep. [Part-song for
T. T. B. B.] English words by P. England. [1910.] *See* ORPHEUS.
The Orpheus, *etc*. New Series. No. 496. [1879, *etc*.] 8°.
                                           E. 1748.

—— The Destruction of Gaza. *See infra*: [Les Ruines de Gaza.]

—— Drinking Song. *See supra*: [Chœur de Buveurs.]

—— [Les Enfants de Lutèce.] O my City ... Four-Part Song for
men's voices, the English words ... by P. England. [1910.] *See*
ORPHEUS. The Orpheus, *etc*. New Series. No. 500. [1879, *etc*.]
8°.   **E. 1748.**

—— Evening Song. *See infra*: [Le Soir.]

—— The Exiles. Les Exilées. Chorus for S. S. A., the English
version by W. G. Rothery. [1912.] *See* NOVELLO AND CO.
Novello's Collection of Trios, *etc*. No. 434. [1879, *etc*.] 8°.
                                           E. 1746.

—— The Exiles, *etc*. [1912.] *See* NOVELLO AND CO. Novello's Tonic
Sol-fa Series. No. 2028. [1876, *etc*.] 4°.   **B. 885.**

—— Fa La Do. Chœur. *See* MEY (A.) Fa La Do polka, *etc*. [1868.]
fol.   **h. 1462. u. (10.)**

LAURENT DE RILLÉ (François Anatole)

—— The Fame of Britain's Ancient Glory. [Part-song for men's
voices.] Words by J. Guard. *J. Curwen & Sons: London*,
[1884.] 8°.
The Apollo Club, No. 30.   **F. 667.**

—— The Fame of Britain's Ancient Glory, *etc*. [1889.] *See*
CHORAL. The Choral Handbook. No. 180. [1885, *etc*.] 8°.
                                           E. 862.

—— La fauvette du moulin à vent, Chansonnette, [begins:
"Rieuse, un peu folle,"] paroles de A. Vialon. *Paris*, [1857.]
fol.   **H. 1771. p. (13.)**

—— La Fauvette du Moulin à vent. *See* LEVEY (W.) La fauvette du
moulin à vent, nouvelle Polka élégante, sur la chansonnette
de A. Vialon et Laurent de Rillé. [1857.] fol.   **h. 1314. (16.)**

—— [La Fête des Pampres.] Song of the Vineyard ... Four-Part
Song for men's voices, the English words ... by P. England.
[1910.] *See* ORPHEUS. The Orpheus, *etc*. New Series. No. 498.
[1879, *etc*.] 8°.   **E. 1748.**

—— A Fête in Provence. [Part-song for T. T. B. B., words by] M. C.
Gillington. *J. Curwen & Sons: London*, [1905.] 8°.
The Apollo Club, No. 277.   **F. 667.**

—— [Flamme d'Or.] O Flame of Gold ... Invocation. Part-Song
for T. T. B. B., the English words by P. England. [1905.] *See*
ORPHEUS. The Orpheus, *etc*. New Series. No. 373. [1879, *etc*.]
8°.   **E. 1748.**

—— [Flamme d'Or.] O Flame of Gold ... Invocation. Part-Song
for T. T. B. B., words by P. England. [1905.] *See* NOVELLO AND
CO. Novello's Tonic Sol-fa Series. No. 1432. [1876, *etc*.] 4°.
                                           B. 885.

—— Gentle Peace. *See infra*: [Paix charmante.]

—— The Gipsies ... [Cantata.] Translated from the French, and
arranged for mixed voices by J. S. Stallybrass. (Tonic sol-fa
edition.) pp. 22. *Tonic sol-fa Agency: London*, [c. 1880.] 8°.
                                           B. 386. w. (1.)

—— The Golden Calf. [Part-song.] Words by A. J. Foxwell.
J. Curwen & Sons: London, [1899.] 8°.
The Apollo Club. No. 120.   **F. 667.**

—— A Holiday Song. *See infra*: [Joyeux Matin.]

—— Hungarian March. [Part-song for T. T. B. B., words by] M. C.
Gillington. *J. Curwen & Sons: London*, [1905.] 8°.
The Apollo Club, No. 272.   **F. 667.**

—— Hymn to Harmony. Hymne à l'Harmonie. Four-Part Song
for men's voices, the English words ... by P. England. [1911.]
See ORPHEUS. The Orpheus, *etc*. New Series. No. 513.
[1879, *etc*.] 8°.   **E. 1748.**

—— Hymn to the Sun. Part-Song for men's voices, the English
words by W. G. Rothery. 1906. *See* ORPHEUS. The Orpheus,
etc. New Series. No. 410. [1879, *etc*.] 8°.   **E. 1748.**

—— Hymn to the Sun, *etc*. 1906. *See* NOVELLO AND CO. Novello's
Tonic Sol-fa Series. No. 1510. [1876, *etc*.] 4°.   **B. 885.**

—— Hymne du Matin [for 4 voices, begins: "L'aurore brillante"].
Poésie de J. Racine. *Paris*, [1861.] 8°.   **E. 600. a. (36.)**

—— Jesu, our only Hope of Heaven. *See supra*: [Ave Regina.]

—— [Joyeux Matin.] A Holiday Song ... Chorus for men's voices,
the English words by W. G. Rothery. 1905. *See* ORPHEUS. The
Orpheus, *etc*. New Series. No. 391. [1879, *etc*.] 8°.
                                           E. 1748.

—— [Joyeux Matin.] A Holiday Song, *etc*. [1908.] *See* NOVELLO
AND CO. Novello's Tonic Sol-fa Series. No. 1731. [1876, *etc*.]
4°.   **B. 885.**

—— La Leçon de Chant. Opéra comique en un acte. Paroles de
E. Adenis. *Paris*, [1883.] 8°.   **F. 38. c.**

LAURENT DE RILLÉ (François Anatole)

— [La Leçon de Chant.] Ronde Champêtre. *See* RÉCRÉATIONS. Récréations Musicales. Chœurs ... extraits d'opéras-comiques ... par ... L. de Rillé, *etc.* [1888.] 4°.　　　　**C. 457.**

— Like Fairy Elves. Vocal Polka. [Part-song for male voices.] *See* KIDNER (W. J.) The Glee-Men Series ... No. 4. [1888.] 8°.　　　　**F. 585. v. (14.)**

— Like fairy Elves.—Vocal Polka. [Part-song for T. T. B. B.] *J. Curwen & Sons: London*, [1907.] 8°. *The Apollo Club, No.* 327.　　　　**F. 667.**

— The March of the Regiment. [Part-song for men's voices.] Words by J. Guard. *J. Curwen & Sons: London*, [1886.] 8°. *The Apollo Club, No.* 65.　　　　**F. 667.**

— Marche du Roi de Bohème. [Orchestral parts.] *Paris*, [1879.] fol.　　　　**h. 1509. e. (8.)**

— Marche du Roi de Bohème, pour Piano à quatre mains. *Paris*, [1879.] fol.　　　　**h. 1493. t. (4.)**

— Marche républicaine. Chœur d'A. Adam. Arrangé à 3 voix égales par Laurent de Rillé, *etc. See* ORPHÉON. L'Orphéon des Écoles, *etc.* No. 14. [1880, *etc.*] 8°.　　　　**E. 1763.**

— [Marchons ensemble.] The Trumpet sounds ... [Four-part song.] The English words by P. England. [1905.] *See* ORPHEUS. The Orpheus, *etc.* New Series. No. 377. [1879, *etc.*] 8°.　　　　**E. 1748.**

— [Marchons ensemble.] The Trumpet sounds ... [Four-part song.] English words by P. England. [1905.] *See* NOVELLO AND Co. Novello's Tonic Sol-fa Series. No. 1444. [1876, *etc.*] 4°.　　　　**B. 885.**

Les Martyrs aux Arènes

— The Martyrs of the Arena. [Part-song, begins: "Great Cæsar".] Translated by J. S. Stallybrass. *London*, [1872.] 8°. *No.* 10 *of "Plaistow Part-Songs".*　　　　**E. 627.**

— The Martyrs of the Arena. [Chorus for men's voices.] Words by J. S. Stallybrass. *J. Curwen & Sons: London*, [1881.] 8°. *The Apollo Club, No.* 15.　　　　**F. 667.**

— The Martyrs of the Arena, [four-part song. Words] translated and arranged by J. S. Stallybrass, *etc.* [1885.] *See* CHORAL. The Choral Handbook. No. 49. [1885, *etc.*] 8°.　　　　**E. 862.**

— The Christian Martyrs ... [Four-part song.] The English words by P. England. [1905.] *See* ORPHEUS. The Orpheus, *etc.* New Series. No. 376. [1879, *etc.*] 8°.　　　　**E. 1748.**

— The Christian Martyrs ... [Four-part song.] English words by P. England. [1905.] *See* NOVELLO AND Co. Novello's Tonic Sol-fa Series. No. 1443. [1876, *etc.*] 4°.　　　　**B. 885.**

— Messe chorale à quatre voix d'hommes. *Paris*, [1860?] 8°.　　　　**E. 605. e. (11.)**

— Mon porteur d'eau, Ronde aquatique, [begins: "Vous qui voulez qu'on remplisse,"] paroles de A. Vialon. *Paris*, [1857.] fol.　　　　**H. 1771. p. (15.)**

— Montagnarde d'Auvergne. Chœur à 4 voix d'hommes [begins: "Dejà la cime"]. *Paris*, [1863.] 8°.　　　　**E. 600. a. (43.)**

— La Noce de Village. Chœur à 3 voix égales [begins: "Tintez cloches"]. *Paris*, [1870.] 8°.　　　　**E. 600. a. (34.)**

— [La Noce de Village.] A Village Wedding. Words translated ... by J. S. Stallybrass. *J. Curwen & Sons: London*, [1881.] 8°. *The Apollo Club, No.* 7.　　　　**F. 667.**

— [La Noce de Village.] Ring, ye Bells.—A Village Wedding.— Words translated by J. S. Stallybrass, and Music arranged for ... [four voices] by G. Oakey. [1894.] *See* CHORAL. The Choral Handbook. No. 305. [1885, *etc.*] 8°.　　　　**E. 862.**

LAURENT DE RILLÉ (François Anatole)

— La Noce de Village, scène pour le Piano, *etc.* [1868.] fol. *See* CROISEZ (A.)　　　　**h. 1259. a. (27.)**

— La Noce de Village ... pour le Piano, *etc.* [1869.] fol. *See* O'KELLY (J.)　　　　**h. 3155. (8.)**

— Noël. Chant de Baptême [for 4 voices]. *Paris*, [1862.] 8°.　　　　**E. 600. a. (40.)**

— Un nouveau plan de Paris, Chansonnette, [begins: "Par quartiers,"] paroles de A. Vialon. *Paris*, [1857.] fol.　　　　**H. 1771. p. (14.)**

— O Flame of Gold. *See* supra: [Flamme d'Or.]

— O my City! *See* supra: [Les Enfants de Lutèce.]

— The Oath of the Forest. Part-Song for men's voices, the English words by P. England. [1907.] *See* ORPHEUS. The Orpheus, *etc.* New Series. No. 435. [1879, *etc.*] 8°.　　　　**E. 1748.**

— Out of the Deep. *See* supra: [Des Abymes profonds.]

— [Paix charmante.] Gentle Peace ... [Four-part song.] The English words by P. England. [1906.] *See* ORPHEUS. The Orpheus, *etc.* New Series. No. 390. [1879, *etc.*] 8°.　　　　**E. 1748.**

— [Paix charmante.] Gentle Peace, *etc.* [1906.] *See* NOVELLO AND Co. Novello's Tonic Sol-fa Series. No. 1493. [1876, *etc.*] 8°.　　　　**B. 885.**

— Le Pardon d'Auray. Chœur à 4 voix [begins: "Fils du sol Breton"]. *Paris*, [1863.] 8°.　　　　**E. 600. a. (38.)**

— [Patrie absente.] Dear Land of Beauty ... [Four-part song.] The English words by P. England. [1905.] *See* ORPHEUS. The Orpheus, *etc.* New Series. No. 392. [1879, *etc.*] 8°.　　　　**E. 1748.**

— [Patrie absente.] Dear Land of Beauty ... [Four-part song.] English words by P. England. [1905.] *See* NOVELLO AND Co. Novello's Tonic Sol-fa Series. No. 1462. [1876, *etc.*] 4°.　　　　**B. 885.**

— Pattes Blanches, opérette en un acte. Paroles de M. Constantin et Coron. Partition Chant et Piano. *Paris*, [1873.] 8°.　　　　**F. 38. a.**

— [Pattes Blanches.] *See* DUFILS (L.) Bambouli—Valse de l'opérette, *etc.* [1874.] fol.　　　　**h. 3417. (10.)**

— Le Petit Poucet. Opéra bouffe en 3 actes et 4 tableaux, paroles de E. Leterrier et A. Vanloo. Partition Piano et Chant. Réduite ... par I. Legouix. pp. 133. *Colombier: Paris*, [1868.] 8°.　　　　**F. 38.**

— [Another copy.] *Bearing the autograph of Queen Alexandra.*　　　　**R. M. 25. f. 7. (2.)**

— Prière à la Vièrge. Chœur [begins: "Salut Vierge Marie"]. *Paris*, [1863.] 8°.　　　　**E. 600. a. (39.)**

— La Princesse Rose, polka-mazurka. [P. F.] *Paris*, [1878.] fol.　　　　**h. 1493. t. (3.)**

— Rataplan. *See* infra: [La Retraite.]

La Retraite

— The Retreat. [Four-part song, begins: "Hark! the tattoo".] Adapted to English words by G. Linley. *London*, [1860.] fol.　　　　**H. 1299. a. (33.)**

— The Retreat. [Part-song, begins: "Plan, ran-tan-plan".] Adapted to English words by G. Linley. *See* CHAPPELL AND Co. Chappell's Vocal Library, *etc.* No. 31. [1863, *etc.*] 8°.　　　　**G. 440.**

LAURENT DE RILLÉ (FRANÇOIS ANATOLE)

— The Tattoo. [Part-song for men's voices.] Words by A. J. Foxwell. *J. Curwen & Sons: London*, [1884.] 8°.
The Apollo Club, No. 20.　　　　　　　**F. 667.**

— The Tattoo. Arranged for mixed voices by G. Oakey ... Words by A. J. Foxwell. [1885.] *See* CHORAL. The Choral Handbook. No. 98. [1885, *etc.*] 8°.　　　**E. 862.**

— Rataplan ... [Four-part song.] The English words by W. G. Rothery. [1905.] *See* ORPHEUS. The Orpheus, *etc.* New Series. No. 379. [1879, *etc.*] 8°.　　　**E. 1748.**

— The Retreat.—Male Voices. [1898.] *See* CHAPPELL AND CO. Chappell & Co.'s Tonic Sol-fa Series, *etc.* No. 16. [1896, *etc.*] 4°.　　　　　　　　　　**D. 1081.**

— Rataplan! Part-Song for T. T. B. B., English words by W. G. Rothery. [1905.] *See* NOVELLO AND CO. Novello's Tonic Sol-fa Series. No. 1446. [1876, *etc.*] 4°.　　**B. 885.**

— *See* CROISEZ (A.) La Retraite, caprice-militaire ... pour le Piano. [1868.] fol.　　　　**h. 1259. a. (11.)**

— *See* O'KELLY (J.) Le Retraite ... pour Piano. [1868.] fol.　　　　　　　　**h. 3155. a. (4.)**

— [La Révolte à Memphis.] A Revolt at Memphis. Arrival of the Conspirators.—L'Arrivée des Conjurés.— (The Oath.—Le Serment.—) (A Prayer to Isis.—Prière à Isis.—) (War Song.—Chant du Guerre.—) [Four-part songs.] The English words by P. England. 4 no. [1906.] *See* ORPHEUS. The Orpheus, *etc.* New Series. No. 393a–393d. [1879, *etc.*] 8°.　　　　　　　　　　**E. 1748.**

— [La Révolte à Memphis.] A Revolt at Memphis. Arrival of the Conspirators, *etc.* (The Oath.) (A Prayer to Isis.) (War Song.) 4 no. [1906.] *See* NOVELLO AND CO. Novello's Tonic Sol-fa Series. No. 1482a–1482d. [1876, *etc.*] 4°.　　**B. 885.**

— The Riders of the Night. *See* supra: [Les Cavaliers de la Nuit.]

— Ring, ye Bells. *See* supra: [La Noce de Village.]

— Ronde Champêtre. *See* supra: [La Leçon de Chant.]

— [Les Ruines de Gaza.] The Destruction of Gaza. [Part-song for men's voices.] Words [translated] by A. J. Foxwell. *J. Curwen & Sons: London*, [1886.] 8°.
The Apollo Club, No. 66.　　　　　　　**F. 667.**

— [La Saint-Hubert.] The Chase ... [Four-part song.] The English words by P. England. [1905.] *See* ORPHEUS. The Orpheus, *etc.* New Series. No. 380. [1879, *etc.*] 8°.　　　　　　　　　　**E. 1748.**

— [La Saint-Hubert.] The Chase ... [Four-part song.] English words by P. England. [1905.] *See* NOVELLO AND CO. Novello's Tonic Sol-fa Series. No. 1447. [1876, *etc.*] 4°.　　**B. 885.**

— La St. Hubert, chasse pour le Piano, *etc.* [1868.] fol. *See* CROISEZ (A.)　　　　　　　**h. 1259. a. (10.)**

— Sans Souci. Chant populaire [for 4 voices, begins: "Écoutez tous ici"]. *Paris*, [1861.] 8°.　　**E. 600. a. (45.)**

— Serenade. Four-Part Song for men's voices, the English words by P. England. [1910.] *See* ORPHEUS. The Orpheus, *etc.* New Series. No. 495. [1879, *etc.*] 8°.　　**E. 1748.**

— [Le Soir.] Evening Song ... Pastorale [for T. T. B. B.], the English words ... by P. England. [1911.] *See* ORPHEUS. The Orpheus, *etc.* New Series. No. 511. [1879, *etc.*] 8°.　　　　　　　　　　**E. 1748.**

— Soldiers' Song. *See* infra: [Vive la Guerre.]

— Song of the Crusaders. [Part-song for T. T. B. B., words by] M. C. Gillington. *J. Curwen & Sons: London*, [1905.] 8°.
The Apollo Club, No. 271.　　　　　　**F. 667.**

LAURENT DE RILLÉ (FRANÇOIS ANATOLE)

— Song of the Quarrymen. *See* infra: [Les Tailleurs de Pierre.]

— Song of the Vineyard. *See* supra: [La Fête des Pampres.]

— Sous les Bois. Chœur à 4 voix [begins: "C'est une volupté"]. Paroles de E. de Chabot. *Paris*, [1870.] 8°.　**E. 600. a. (33.)**

— Souvenir des Orphéonistes, quadrille pour le Piano. *London*, [1860.] fol.　　　　　　　　**h. 1461. e. (49.)**

— The Swiss Shepherds' Farewell. *See* supra: [L'Adieu des Pasteurs Béarnais.]

— [Les Tailleurs de Pierre.] Song of the Quarrymen ... Four-Part Song for men's voices, the English words ... by P. England. [1911.] *See* ORPHEUS. The Orpheus, *etc.* New Series. No. 512. [1879, *etc.*] 8°.　　**E. 1748.**

— The Tattoo. *See* supra: [La Retraite.]

— Thine is the Glory. *See* infra: [Toi seul es la Gloire.]

— To Arms. *See* supra: [Alerte.]

— [Toi seul es la Gloire.] Thine is the Glory ... [Four-part song.] The English words by P. England. [1905.] *See* ORPHEUS. The Orpheus, *etc.* New Series. No. 389. [1879, *etc.*] 8°.　　　　　　　　　　**E. 1748.**

— The Travellers' Farewell. *See* supra: [Le Départ des Compagnons.]

— [Le Triomphe du Peuple.] Battle Song ... Chant national [for T. T. B. B.], the English words ... by P. England. [1911.] *See* ORPHEUS. The Orpheus, *etc.* New Series. No. 514. [1879, *etc.*] 8°.　　　　　　　　　　**E. 1748.**

— The Trumpet sounds. *See* supra: [Marchons ensemble.]

— The Tziganes.—Hungarian Gipsies.— Chorus for men's voices, the English words ... by W. G. Rothery. [1909.] *See* ORPHEUS. The Orpheus, *etc.* New Series. No. 481. [1879, *etc.*] 8°.　　　　　　　　　　**E. 1748.**

— The Tziganes, *etc.* [1909.] *See* NOVELLO AND CO. Novello's Tonic Sol-fa Series. No. 1819. [1876, *etc.*] 4°.　　**B. 885.**

— A Village Wedding. *See* supra: [La Noce de Village.]

— Vintage Song. Part Song for men's voices, the English words by P. England. [1907.] *See* ORPHEUS. The Orpheus, *etc.* New Series. No. 433. [1879, *etc.*] 8°.　　**E. 1748.**

— [Vive la Guerre.] Soldiers' Song ... [Four-part song.] The English words by W. G. Rothery. [1905.] *See* ORPHEUS. The Orpheus, *etc.* New Series. No. 388. [1879, *etc.*] 8°.　　　　　　　　　　**E. 1748.**

— [Vive la Guerre.] Soldiers' Song ... [Four-part song.] English words by W. G. Rothery. [1905.] *See* NOVELLO AND CO. Novello's Tonic Sol-fa Series. No. 1461. [1876, *etc.*] 4°.　　　　　　　　　　**B. 885.**

— A Waltz of Dreamland. [Part-song for T. T. B. B., words by] M. C. Gillington. *J. Curwen & Sons: London*, [1905.] 8°.
The Apollo Club, No. 276.　　　　　　**F. 667.**

— The Workers. *See* supra: [Le Chant des Travailleurs.]

— *See* BÉRAT (F.) Musique des Chansons de Béranger. Neuvième édition ... augmentée ... d'Airs composés par ... Laurent de Rillé, *etc.* 1868. 8°.　　**E. 294.**

— *See* BOURGET (E.) and LAURENT DE RILLÉ (F. A.) Le Sire de Franc-Boisy, *etc.* [1855?] fol.　　　**G. 561. (2.)**

— *See* CHANTS. Chants poétiques. Musique de ... Laurent de Rillé, *etc.* 1883. 8°.　　　　　**F. 607. o. (17.)**

— *See* LEVEY (W.) Morto insecto! Chansonnette de A. Vialon et Laurent de Rillé ... Polka ... pour piano. [1857.] fol.　　　　　　　　**h. 1314. (15.)**

LAURENTIIS (Carmine de)

— Tutor for Mandoline. *London*, [1882.] 8°.   **f. 181. a. 10.**

LAURENTIUS, *of Schnüffis, a Capuchin* [i. e. Johann Martin.]

— Dess Miranten, eines Welt- und hoch-verwirrten Hirtens nach der Ruhseeligen Einsamkeit Wunderlicher Weeg, *etc. David Hautt: Costantz*, 1690. 8°.   **11517. a. 26. (2.)**

— Mirantische Maul-Trumel, oder Wohlbedenckliche Gegen-Sätze böser, und guter Begirten ... Mit schönen Sinnbilderen, und auff eine neue Art anmüthigen Melodeyen geziehrt, *etc. Leonhard Parcus: Costanz*, 1698. 8°.
11525. df. 16.

— Mirantische Mayen-Pfeiff. Oder Marianische Lob-Verfassung, in welcher Clorus, ein Hirt, der ... Mutter Gottes Mariae ... anmuthig besingt ... Mit schönen Kupffern, und gantz neuen Melodeyen gezihrt, *etc. Bey J. C. Bencard: Dillingen*, 1692. 8°.   **11517. bbb. 48.**

— Mirantische Wald-Schallmey, oder: Schul wahrer Weisheit, welche einem Jungen Herrn und seinem Hof-Meister ... in einem Wald irr-geritten, von zweyen Einsidlern gehalten worden, *etc. David Hautt: Costantz*, 1688. 8°.
11517. a. 26. (1.)

— Mirantisches Flötlein. Oder Geistliche Schäfferey, in welcher Christus, unter dem Namen Daphnis, die in dem Sünden-Schlaff vertiefffte Seel Clorinda zu einem bessern Leben aufferweckt, *etc. In der Fürstl. Bischöffl. Druckerey, Bey D. Hautt: Costantz*, 1682. 8°.   **11517. b. 22.**

— P. F. Laurentii, von Schnüffis ... Mirantisches Flötlein ... Vierte Auflage. Darinnen alle Melodien zu drey Stimmen samt einem Rittornello auffgesetzet, zugleich ein Anhang Neuer Liedern, *etc. Bey E. und J. R. Thurneysen: Franckfurt*, 1739. 8°.   **11517. b. 23.**

— [Another copy.]   **Hirsch III. 916.**

LAURENZI (Carlo)

— Of the glorious body telling. (Pange lingua.) Hymn for Holy Communion. *London*, [1882.] 8°.   **E. 605. n. (22.)**

LAURETTA

— Lauretta's Lied. Ballade. *See* Fischer (D.)

LAURETTE

— Laurette. Opéra-Comique. *See* Haydn (F. J.) [La Vera Costanza.]

— Laurette. Comédie. *See* Le Froid de Méreaux (N. J.)

— Laurette. Ballad. *See* Linley (G.)

LAURI (Edward)

— Ping pong. 〈Song.〉 Words by Chas. H. Taylor. Arranged by J. Neat, *etc.* [With separate voice part.] 2 pt. *Moon & Co.: London*, [1901.] fol.   **H. 3985. i. (11.)**

LAURI (Mabel)

— When Love and I went wooing. Song, words by F. Barron. *Morrice Music Publishing Co.: London*, 1908. fol.
H. 1794. vv. (11.)

— When Love and I went wooing. Madrigal ... Arranged by J. A. Dix. *Morrice Music Publishing Co.: London*, 1908. 4°.
G. 809. h. (8.)

LAURIANE

— Lauriane. Opéra. *See* Machado (A.)

LAURICELLA (Remo)

— African Interlude. Violin and piano. [Score and part.] 2 pt. *Boosey & Hawkes: New York*, [1958.] 4°.   **g. 500. ii. (4.)**

— Echoes from Santiago (de Compostela). Guitar solo. 〈Fingered by Josè Tomás.〉 pp. 6. *Galliard: London*, [1966.] 4°.   **g. 660. bb. (3.)**

LAURIE

— Laurie's Song. [Song.] *See* Copland (Aaron) [The Tender Land.]

LAURIE (Alison Margaret)

— *See* Purcell (Henry) [*Collected Works.—a.*] The Works of Henry Purcell. Volume IX. Dioclesian ... Revised ... by M. Laurie. [1961.] fol.   **I. 466. a.**

— *See* Purcell (Henry) [*Collected Works.—a.*] The Works of Henry Purcell, *etc.* [Second edition.] 〈Vol. 3. Dido and Aeneas. Edited ... by M. Laurie.〉 [1979.] 8°.   **F. 937.**

— *See* Purcell (Henry) Dido and Aeneas ... Edited by M. Laurie and T. Dart. [1961.] 8°.   **F. 659. i. (3.)**

— *See* Purcell (Henry) [King Arthur.] The Music in King Arthur ... Edited by M. Laurie. [1972.] 8°.   **F. 659. p. (2.)**

LAURIE (Fred)

— Happy married Life (or The Kettle on the Hob). Humorous song ... Words by Charles Osborne. Arranged by W. T. Webb. pp. 4. *The London Musical Agency: London*, [1885?] fol.   **H. 1648. p. (28.)**

LAURIE (James Stuart)

— *See* Murby (T.) The Merry-Go-Round ... Edited by J. S. Laurie. [1874.] 8°.   **A. 547. a.**

LAURIE (James Stuart) and **MURBY** (Thomas)

— Rhymes, Jingles, and Songs ... for Voice and Piano, for nurseries and Infant schools. Edited by J. S. Laurie and T. Murby. *London*, [1862.] obl. 8°.   **A. 626. a.**

— Rhymes, Jingles, and Songs. With music for voice and piano, for nurseries & infant schools ... Edited by J. S. Laurie ... and Thomas Murby ... Third edition. pp. 60. *Thomas Murby: London*, [c. 1865.] obl. 8°.   **A. 626. q.**

LAURIE (Malcolm)

— Breathes there the Man. 〈Song for baritone voice.〉 Words by Sir Walter Scott. pp. 7. *J. B. Cramer & Co.: London*, [1953.] 4°.   **G. 1271. (21.)**

LAURIE (Margaret)

— When your Eyes look into mine. Song, words by B. Ford, *etc. L. Wright Music Co.: Leicester*, 1909. fol.   **H. 1792. r. (35.)**

LAURIE (Margaret) *Editor*

— *See* Laurie (Alison Margaret)

LAURIER

— Le Laurier Rose. [Song.] *See* Clapisson (A. L.)

LAURIER (Jay)

— *See* Carlton (Fred) Angel Eyes ... [Song.] Arranged by J. Laurier. [1906.] fol.   **H. 3982. ll. (1.)**

LAURINE

— Laurine. Song. *See* WALKER (J. E.)

LAURO

— Il Lauro Secco. Libro Primo di Madrigali a Cinque Voci di Diuersi Autori. Basso. (Quinto.) 2 pt. *Vittorio Baldini: Ferrara*, 1582. 4°.
*Imperfect; wanting fol. A*21, *A*13 *and pp.* 13–32 *of the Basso part. This collection contains compositions by L. Marenzio, H. Fiorino, C. Porta, L. Bertani, G. d'Wert, G. Eremita, L. Luzzaschi, A. Gabrieli, A. Milleville, R. Giovanelli, P. Isnardi, T. Massaini, C. da Correggio, A. Striggio, A. Zoilo, I. Alberti, P. Virchi, F. Manara, A. dal' Occa, N. Peruve, V. Fronti, B. Spontone, G. B. Mosto, G. Belli, H. Vecchi, M. A. Ingegnieri, A. Stabile, F. Pigna, G. Bardi and G. di Macque.*
D. 156.

— Il Lauro Verde, Madrigali à Sei Voci di diuersi Autori. Quinto. *Vittorio Baldini: Ferrara*, 1583. 4°.
This collection contains madrigals by L. Marenzio, C. Porta, G. B. Lucatelli, G. de Macque, F. di Monte, L. Meldert, L. Bertani, A. Orlandini, G. M. Nanino, G. d'Wert, A. Stabile, F. Rovigo, L. Luzzaschi, S. da Reggio, F. Soriano, N. Peruve, R. Giovanelli, B. Roy, H. Vecchi, A. Trombetti, H. Fiorino, P. Virchi, A. Milleville, G. B. Moscaglia, P. Isnardi, J. Corsini, G. Cavaccio, L. Mira, P. Bellasio, A. Ruotta and F. Nicoletti.
D. 155.

— Il Lauro Verde. Madrigali a Sei Voci Composti di Diuersi Eccellentissimi Musici. Aggiontoui di più doi Madrigali à Otto voci, l'vno d'Alessandro Striggio, & di Gio. Gabrieli. Canto. (Alto.) (Quinto.) (Basso.) 4 pt. *Appresso Pietro Phalesio & Giouanni Bellero: Anuersa*, 1591. obl. 4°.
A reprint of the Ferrara edition, with two additions by A. Striggio and G. Gabrieli. **A. 277. c.**

LAURO (DOMENICO)

— Missæ Tres Octonis Vocibus Decantandæ, Ac omnium instrumentorum generis accomodatę. Addite partes infimæ pro Organo, *etc.* Bassus Primi Chori. *Apud Ricciardum Amadinum: Venetijs*, 1607. 4°. **C. 81.**

LAURUŠAS (VYTAUTAS ANTANO)

— Paklyde paukščiai. Dvieju daliu opera. Libretas A. Kalinausko, E. Matuzeviciaus. Vertimas A. Rolniko. Klaviras. (Заблудившиеся птицы. Перевод с литовского А. Польника. Переложение для пения с фортепиано автора.) *Russ. & Lith.* pp. 287. *Leidykla "Sovietskij kompozitor": Leningrad, Moskva*, 1973. 4°. **F. 1873. e.**

LAUS

— Laus creatorum. [Anthem.] *See* BROWN (Christopher)

— Laus Dei in Ecclesia Sanctorum. [Psalms.] *See* KOBRICH (J. J. A. B.)

— Laus Deo. Hymns of peace and goodwill with tunes, *etc. S. P. C. K.: London*, 1919. 8°. **C. 505. n.**

— Laus Deo. Unison Song. *See* DEMUTH (N. F.)

— Laus Deo. Unison song. *See* JONES (Llifon H.)

— Laus Deo. [Song.] *See* MILFORD (R. H.) Four Songs. Op. 36. 3.

— Laus Deo. [Anthem.] *See* ORREY (L. G.)

— Laus Deo. Unison song. *See* SYKES (Harold H.)

— Laus Deo. [Part-song.] *See* WILLIAMS (Arnold)

— Laus nocturna. [Motets.] *See* WELLESZ (E. J.)

LAUSCH

— Lausch ich am Bach. Song. *See* ABT (F. W.) [4 Lieder für eine Singstimme. Op. 308. No. 3.]

LAUSCHEN

— Lauschen und Küssen. [Song.] *See* NÁPRAVNÍK (E. F.)

LAUSCHMANN (RICHARD)

— *See* MARCELLO (B.) [*Doubtful and Supposititious Works.*] Concerto für Oboe in C moll ... ⟨Benedetto Marcello. [In fact, by Alessandro Marcello.]⟩ Bearbeitet und herausgegeben von R. Lauschmann, *etc.* [1923.] 4°. **h. 2665. h. (3.)**

— *See* PFEIFFER (J.) Sonata für Flöte ... Oboe ... Horn ... und Fagott ... mit Cembalo- ... Begleitung. Bearbeitet und herausgegeben von R. Lauschmann. [1939.] 4°.
g. 420. aa. (5.)

— *See* PROWO (P.) Sonate für Oboe und Cembalo (oder Klavier) ... Urtext-Ausgabe ... herausgegeben von ... R. Lauschmann. [1963.] 4°. **g. 1078. c. (6.)**

— *See* TELEMANN (Georg P.) Konzert c-moll für Oboe, Streicher und B. c ... [Mecklenburgische Landesbibliothek MS. No. 5400. No. 9.] ⟨Herausgegeben von R. Lauschmann.⟩ Partitur, *etc.* [1977.] fol. **g. 401. s. (8.)**

LAUSKA (FRANZ SERAPHINUS)

— Deux grandes Polonaises en forme de Rondeau pour le Pianoforte. Op. 29. *Berlin*, [1820?] obl. fol. **e. 218.**

— Three pleasing and brilliant rondos for the Piano Forte. Op. 44. pp. 17. *T. Boosey & C⁰.: London*, [1820?] fol.
h. 117. (12.)

— Grande Sonate pour le Clavecin ou Piano-Forte ... Oeuvre I. *Chés Günther & Böhme: Hambourg*, [1795.] obl. fol.
c. 58. (1.)

— Grande Sonate pour le Clavecin ou le Piano Forte ... Oeuvre IV. *Chés Günther et Böhme: Hambourg*, [1797.] obl. fol. **c. 58. (2.)**

— Sonate pour le Clavecin ou Piano-Forte ... Oeuvre VI. *Chez Günther et Böhme: Hambourg*, [1797.] obl. fol. **c. 58. (3.)**

— Grande Sonate pour le Forte-Piano. Œuvre 9. *Chés J. A. Böhme: Hambourg*, [1800?] obl. fol. **e. 284. c. (4.)**

— Grande Sonate pour le Forte-Piano ... Œuvre 10. *Chés J. A. Böhme: Hambourg*, [1800?] obl. fol. **e. 284. c. (5.)**

— Sonate pour le Pianoforte avec accompagnement de Violoncelle obligé. Œuvre 28. *Berlin*, [1815?] obl. fol.
e. 277. a. (7.)
& h. 1850. c. (7.)

— VIII. variations pour le forte piano sur l'air: Ich küsse dich o Schleier: aus der Geister Insel von Herrn Kapellmeister Reichard. pp. 9. *Chez M. Falter: Munic*, [1799.] obl. fol.
The music is lithographed throughout. **Hirsch III. 356.**

LAUSSEL (A. ADAM)

— Mary, valse pour Piano. *Paris*, [1880.] fol. **h. 3272. j. (13.)**

LAUT

— Laut und traut. [Song.] *See* SIEBER (F.) Drei Lieder, *etc.* Op. 76. No. 3.

LAUTE

— Die Laute. [Song.] *See* KELLER (C.)

— Die laute Klage. [Song.] *See* BEETHOVEN (L. van)

LAUTE

— Laute Liebe. Song. *See* LACHNER (F.)

LAUTENSCHLAGER (W.)

— The Fairy's Rendezvous. Intermezzo. [Military band parts.] *Boosey & Hawkes: London*, 1933. 4°. [*Boosey & Hawkes Military Band Edition. No.* 19 [*b*].]
h. 3211. b.

LAUTER

— Lauter Wunder. [Duet.] *See* WINTERBERGER (A.) Fünf Slavische Volks-Poesin. No. 2.

LAUTERBACH

— Lauterbach. Folk Song. *See* REUTTER (H.)

LAUTERBACH (   )

— Le Juif Polonais, valse … Instrumentée par O. Métra. *See* RÉPERTOIRE. Répertoire des Bals, *etc.* [1869, *etc.*] 8°.
f. 136.

LAUTERBACH (JOHANN CHRISTOPH)

— Barcarole pour violon avec accompagnement … de piano. Op. 7. *Hamburg*, [1885.] fol.
h. 1609. u. (15.)

— Zwei Concert-Etuden für Violine mit Klavier-begleitung. 2 no. *Hamburg*, [1876.] fol.
h. 1609. h. (6.)

— Legende für Violine mit Pianofortebegleitung. Op. 8. *H. Pohle: Hamburg*, [1889.] fol.
h. 1608. q. (36.)

— *See* BANCK (C.) Sechs Charakterstücke … Die Violinstimme eingerichtet von J. Lauterbach. [1878.] fol.
h. 1751. b. (2.)

— *See* BANCK (C.) Lyrische Stücke für Violine mit Begleitung des Pianoforte … Op. 77. Die Violine bezeichnet von J. Lauterbach. [1883.] fol.
h. 1609. y. (2.)

— *See* HOFMANN (H.) New Hungarian Dances — for Violin and Pianoforte by J. Lauterbach. [1877.] fol.
h. 1609. l. (18.)

— *See* HOFMANN (H.) Drei Stücke in Tanzform … Ausgabe für Violine … von J. Lauterbach. [1881.] fol.
h. 1609. p. (27.)

— *See* MOZART (W. A.) [Il Re Pastore.] L'amerò, sarò costante … Including the cadenza for voice and violin by J. Lauterbach. 1946. 4°.
G. 1276. b. (5.)

— *See* RAFF (J. J.) [Suite. Op. 204. No. 3.] Rigaudon, *etc.* (Bearbeitet von J. Lauterbach.) [1883.] fol.
h. 1297. d. (13.)

— *See* SPOHR (L.) L. Spohr-Album … bearbeitet … von J. Lauterbach. [1878.] fol.
h. 1609. r. (17.)

— *See* SPOHR (L.) Concert No. 8 … Nachgesehen und … bezeichnet von J. Lauterbach. [1890?] fol.
h. 95. a. (8.)

— *See* WERMANN (F. O.) Drei Vortragstücke für Violine … Die Violinstimme bezeichnet … von J. C. Lauterbach. [1886.] fol.
h. 1608. r. (45.)

LAUTH (HENRY)

— *See* ENESCU (G.) Oedipe. Tragedie lirică … Opus 23. Reducţie pentru pian şi voci de H. Lauth, *etc.* 1965. 4°.
G. 1437. a.

LAUTNER (LOIS)

— *See* BACH (J. S.) [Orgel-Büchlein.—Ich ruf' zu Dir, Herr Jesu Christ.] I call to Thee. ⟨Mixed choir SAB and organ.⟩ Arr. by L. Lautner. [1958.] 8°.
F. 956. cc. (24.)

LAUTZ (ELLA M.)

— Rita. Waltz. [P. F.] pp. 5. *M. M. Leidt: Buffalo*, [1905.] fol.
h. 4120. mm. (28.)

— [Another copy.]
h. 4120. mm. (29.)

LAUTZ (HENRY J.)

— Darling with thy Lips so tender. Mädchen mit dem roten Mündchen. (Song.) Poem by H. Heine. English translation by B. Raab. Op. 2. No. 1. 2 no. [In G and E flat.] *E. Schuberth & Co.: New York, London*, 1901. fol.
G. 807. t. (20.)

— Evening Chimes. Abendläuten. [Song.] Poem by H. Stadelmann, English translation by B. Raab. Op. 8. No. 2. 2 no. [In A flat and C.] *E. Schuberth & Co.: New York, London*, 1904. fol.
H. 1799. vv. (31.)

— Gather ye Rosebuds. [Song.]—Herrick.—Pflücket die Rosen.—German version by Mrs. A. Gerber.—For a medium voice. Op. 1. No. 5. *M. M. Leidt: Buffalo, N. Y.*, (1906.) fol.
G. 807. jj. (34.)

— Gather ye Rose-buds. (Pflücket die Rosen.) Song … Op. 1. No. 5, *etc. Orpheus Music Publishing Co.: London*, 1910. fol.
H. 1792. r. (36.)

— Gipsy Music.—Zigeunermusik.—[Song, German words by] M. E. delle Grazie, English by T. Adam. Op. 10. No. 1, *etc. Whaley, Royce & Co.: Winnipeg, Toronto*, (1907.) fol.
G. 805. mm. (15.)

— Heine Lieder. Heine Songs. English version by B. Raab. Op. 3. 1. Im wunderschönen Monat Mai. 2. Aus meinen Tränen sprieszen. 3. Die Rose, die Lilie, die Taube, die Sonne. 4. Wenn ich in deine Augen seh'. 5. Dein Angesicht so lieb und schön. 6. Lehn' deine Wang' an meine Wang', *etc. Eberle Music Co.: Buffalo, N. Y.*, 1909. 4°.
G. 809. h. (9.)

— Heine Lieder … Op. 3. (Low voice.) *Eberle Music Co.: Buffalo, N. Y.*, 1911. 4°.
G. 806. w. (19.)

— In Church.—In der Kirche.—[Song, words by] M. Greif, English version by Mrs. J. W. F. Harrison, *etc. Whaley, Royce & Co.: Winnipeg, Toronto*, (1910.) fol.
G. 807. yy. (23.)

— In the Forest.—Im Walde.—[Song, words by] P. Heyse, English version by R. S. Pigott. Op. 9. No. 1, *etc. Whaley, Royce & Co.: Winnipeg, Toronto*, 1908. fol.
H. 1794. vv. (12.)

— The Kitten. *See infra:* Two Songs. [No. 2.]

— Mädchen mit dem roten Mündchen. *See supra:* Darling with thy Lips so tender.

— Moonlight.—Mond-Nacht.—[Song, words by] Eichendorff … Op. 2. No. 3. *M. M. Leidt: Buffalo, N. Y.*, (1906.) fol.
G. 807. jj. (35.)

— Moonlight.—Mond-Nacht, *etc. Orpheus Music Publishing Co.: London*, 1910. fol.
H. 1792. r. (37.)

— My Luve's like a red, red Rose. Dem rothem Röslein gleicht mein Lieb. [Song.]—R. Burns.—Op. 1. No. 2. *M. M. Leidt: Buffalo, N. Y.*, (1906.) fol.
G. 807. jj. (36.)

— Ne'er-do-weel. Habenichts. [Song.]—J. J. David.—English version by T. Adam. Op. 13. No. 1, *etc. Nordheimer Piano & Music Co.: Toronto, etc.*, (1906.) fol.
H. 1794. vv. (13.)

— Phillis the fair. [Song.] Words by R. Burns. 2 no. [In G and E flat.] *E. Schuberth & Co.: New York, London*, 1900. fol.
G. 807. t. (21.)

— So solemn in their Beauty.—Es stehen unbeweglich.— Song. (Poem by H. Heine, English translation by B. Raab.) Op. 5. No. 2. 2 no. [High and low.] *E. Schuberth & Co.: New York, London*, 1903. fol.
G. 807. z. (31.)

LAUTZ (HENRY J.)

— Two Songs. [No. 1.] Evening. —Der Abend.— Text by Lenau, translation by G. L. Osgood. [No. 2.] The Kitten.—Das Kätzschen.— Text by C. Basse, translation by A. von Szeliski. *Boston Music Co.: Boston, Mass.*, (1912.) fol. *Imperfect; wanting no. 1.* **G. 807. yy. (24.)**

— Thy Presence. Nähe. [Song, words by] L. Uhland, English version by T. Adam ... Op. 5. No. 3. *M. M. Leidt: Buffalo, N. Y.*, (1906.) fol. **G. 807. jj. (37.)**

— Valse Caprice, for Pianoforte. Op. 6. No. 1. *Whaley, Royce & Co.: Winnipeg, Toronto*, (1907.) fol. **g. 605. vv. (34.)**

LAUTZ (S. J.)

— La Somnambule. Romance [begins: "D'Edmond la jeune fiancée"]. Paroles de C. Hannong. *Paris*, [1835?] fol. **G. 551. (19.)**

LAUWERYNS (E.)

— Fanchette polka sur l'opéra Le Cadet de Marine de R. Genée pour Piano. *Bruxelles*, [1880.] fol. **h. 3272. j. (14.)**

— Les Glaneuses ... Polka-mazurka pour Piano. *Bruxelles*, [1882.] fol. **h. 3276. g. (8.)**

— La Muse des Écoles. Recueil de 30 chants à une voix sans accompagnement, paroles de E. Carolus, C. Durant, Comte F. de Gramont, V. Vanneck et J. Wytinck. *R. Bertram: Bruxelles*, [1886.] 8°. **E. 1717. a. (6.)**

— Le National, galop pour Piano. *Bruxelles*, [1883.] fol. **h. 3276. g. (9.)**

— Les Quatre Saisons. Romance [begins: "Quand le printemps à l'haleine embaumée"], paroles de V. Vanneck. *Bruxelles*, 1885. fol. **H. 2836. h. (30.)**

— Reporter polka sur l'opéra Fatinitza de F. de Suppé ... Orchestrée par A. Lagye. *Paris*, [1879.] 8°. **e. 370. b. (10.)**

— Reporter Polka sur l'opéra Fatinitza de F. de Suppé pour Piano. *Bruxelles*, [1879.] fol. **h. 1493. n. (20.)**

LAVAGNE (ANDRÉ)

— Étude baroque. Grande étude de concert pour piano. pp. 17. *Chappell: Paris*, [1971.] 4°. **g. 1138. r. (11.)**

LAVAGNINO (A. F.)

— *See* GRECCO (F.) Sinfonia all'italiana per orchestra da camera. Trascrizione di A. F. Lavagnino, *etc.* [1941.] 4°. **g. 420. qq. (2.)**

LAVAINE (HENRI)

— Nelly's bower [song, begins: "Nelly dear"], words by H. Murry. *London*, [1858.] fol. **H. 1771. l. (12.)**

LAVAINNE (FERDINAND)

— Divertissement oriental ... pour le piano ... Op. 39. pp. 13. *Chez E. Troupenas: Paris*, [c. 1840.] fol. **H. 1838. a. (7.)**

— Fantasie fantastique, pour le piano, avec acc. d'orchestre ... Op: 17. [P. F.] pp. 19. *Chez E. Troupenas et c^{ie}: Paris*, [c. 1840.] fol. **H. 1838. a. (5.)**

— Grande fantaisie militaire pour le piano ... Op: 43. pp. 9. *Chez Mme Lemoine et c^{ie}: Paris*, [c. 1840.] fol. **H. 1838. a. (4.)**

— Feux Follets, caprice ballade pour Piano. *Paris*, [1875.] fol. **h. 1487. p. (1.)**

LAVAINNE (FERDINAND)

— La Fuite d'Egypte. Oratorio en deux parties ... Paroles de A. Couvez. *Paris*, 1835. fol. **H. 1838.**

— Impressions d'un artiste. Grand caprice pour le piano ... Op: 41. pp. 12. *Chez J. Frey: Paris*, [c. 1840.] fol. **H. 1838. a. (6.)**

— Mélancholie. Premier nocturne pour le pianoforte ... Op: 19. pp. 9. *Janet & Cotelle: Paris*, [c. 1835.] fol. **H. 1838. a. (8.)**

— Deux nocturnes pour le piano ... Op: 33. pp. 11. *Chez E. Troupenas & c^o: Paris*, [c. 1840.] fol. **H. 1838. a. (9.)**

— Noël ... pour le Piano. [1865.] fol. *See* KETTERER (E.) **h. 1275. e. (21.)**

— Pantomime et Ballet. Tableau Symphonique. Transcrit par l'auteur pour piano à 4 mains. *Richault et Cie.: Paris*, 1886. fol. **h. 3290. h. (19.)**

— 2ème Quatuor pour piano, violon, alto et violoncello. Op. 98. *Paris*, [1884.] fol. **h. 2831. a. (5.)**

— Grand rondo brillant pour le piano-forte ... Op: 9. pp. 16. *Chez Bohem: Lille*, [c. 1830.] fol. **H. 1838. a. (11.)**

— Rondo élégant, pour piano ... Op: 28. pp. 11. *Chez Prilipp & c^{ie}: Paris*, [c. 1835.] fol. **h. 1203. y. (11.)**

— Sérénade pour Piano, Violon et Violoncelle. *Paris*, [1878.] fol. **h. 2850. a. (7.)**

— Sérénade d'Amour! [begins: "O ma belle, sois fidèle"] paroles de A. Demeunynck. *Paris*, [1883.] fol. **H. 2836. h. (27.)**

— Sonnet [begins: "Mignonne, viens au bois"], paroles de J. Voituriez. *Paris*, [1883.] fol. **H. 2836. h. (28.)**

— Un Soupir. Nocturne ... pour le piano ... Op. 42. pp. 9. *Chez Mme Lemoine et c^{ie}: Paris*, [c. 1840.] fol. **H. 1838. a. (10.)**

— La Veillée bretonne. Grande ballade pour le piano ... Op: 40. pp. 13. *Chez E. Troupenas & c^o: Paris*, [c. 1840.] fol. **H. 1838. a. (3.)**

LAVAL (CLÉMENCE)

— Les Petits Artistes, valse pour Piano. *Paris*, [1869.] fol. **h. 1462. r. (9.)**

— Steeple-Chase quadrille pour Piano. *Paris*, [1870.] *obl.* fol. **e. 217. b. (27.)**

LÁVAL (ÉDOUARD)

— Dans la Vallée. Second set of four tone-poems for the pianoforte, *etc. Weekes & Co.: London*, 1915. 4°. **g. 603. ii. (8.)**

— Dans le Forêt. In the Wood. Four Tone-Poems for the Pianoforte. 1. Dawn. 2. Gambols. 3. Reverie. 4. Content, *etc. Weekes & Co.: London*, 1914. 4°. **g. 1129. (10.)**

— Dans le Salon. Trois morceaux pour piano. *Weekes & Co.: London*, 1917. 4°. **g. 603. pp. (15.)**

— Three Rythmic [*sic*] Pieces for the pianoforte. Op. 43. No. 1. Intermezzo. 2. Swinging. 3. A caprice. *A. Weekes & Co.: London*, 1920. 4°. **g. 1125. c. (25.)**

LAVAL (LOUIS)

— Let's be lazy. A River Song. Words by M. Ambient. 2 no. [In D and F.] *St. Cecilia Music Pub. Co.: London*, 1900. fol. **H. 1799. h. (10.)**

— What care I! A Vagabond's Song. Words by M. Ambient. *Chappell & Co.: London*, 1898. fol. **H. 1799. h. (11.)**

LA VALLA (P.)

— Se m'amassi sempre così. Romanza [begins: "Tuo labbro roseo"]. *Milano*, [1877.] fol.   **H. 1782. a. (8.)**

LA VALLE (Paul)

— Dance of the rubber Dolls, for piano. *S. Pierce: Milwaukee*, 1919. 4°.   **g. 1129. k. (13.)**

LAVALLÉE (Calixa)

— Beautiful Girl of Kildare. Ballad, written by R. A. Warren. *London*, [1874.] fol.
No. 4683 of the "Musical Bouquet".   **H. 2345.**

— The Butterfly. *See* infra: [Le Papillon.]

— Canada, Dominion of the North. *See* infra: [O Canada, terre de nos aïeux.]

— The Ellinger polka de salon. [P. F.] *Troy, N. Y.*, 1863. fol.   **h. 1459. g. (5.)**

— Grande Marche de Concert pour Piano. *Paris*, [1875.] fol.   **h. 1487. p. (2.)**

— Great God of Love! *See* infra: [O Canada, terre de nos aïeux.]

O Canada, terre de nos aïeux

— O Canada, terre de nos aieux! Chant National, words by ... Judge Routhier ... Arranged [for chorus] and edited by Dr. T. B. Richardson. *Whaley, Royce & Co.: Toronto, Winnipeg*, (1906.) 8°.   **F. 321. v. (21.)**

— O Canada, terre de nos aïeux. Chant national, *etc.* (O Canada, beloved Fatherland. Translated by J. Acton.) *Canadian Woman's Magazine Publishing Co.: Toronto*, [1907.] fol.   **I. 600. d. (44.)**

— O Canada, beloved Fatherland ... Harmonized and arranged for mixed voices by E. Broome. Translation by J. Acton. *Nordheimer Piano and Music Co.: [Toronto,]* 1907. fol.   **I. 600. d. (43.)**

— Great God of Love! for this our Land so free. National Song ... Arranged for Chorus by A. Jury. *H. W. Gray Co.: New York*, 1908. 8°.   **F. 321. y. (10.)**

— O Canada! A National Hymn. Melody by C. Lavallée. Arranged for Chorus by W. H. Neidlinger. French Text by ... Judge Routhier, English text by W. H. Neidlinger. *Whaley, Royce & Co.: Winnipeg, Toronto*, (1908.) 8°.   **F. 321. v. (22.)**

— O Canada! A National Song for Canadians. Written by ... Recorder Weir ... Melody by C. Lavallée. Harmonized and arranged for Solo, Quartet or Chorus by G. A. Grant-Schaefer, *etc. Delmar Music Co.: Montreal*, (1908.) fol.   **H. 1794. vv. (8.)**

— O Canada ... Arranged [for S. S. A.] and edited by Dr. T. B. Richardson. *Whaley, Royce & Co.: Toronto, Winnipeg*, (1908.) 8°.   **F. 328. k. (29.)**

— O Canada! our Fathers' Land of Old ... Arranged and edited by Dr. T. B. Richardson ... (T. T. B. B.) *Whaley, Royce & Co.: Toronto, Winnipeg*, (1908.) 8°.   **F. 163. k. (22.)**

— O Canada! our Father's Land of Old ... Chant national ... Arranged and edited by Dr. T. B. Richardson. *Whaley, Royce & Co.: Winnipeg, Toronto*, (1908.) fol.   **G. 805. mm. (14.)**

— O Canada, terre de nos aïeux! Chant National ... Arranged [for S. A. T. B.] and edited by Dr. T. B. Richardson. *Whaley, Royce & Co.: Toronto, Winnipeg*, (1908.) 8°.   **F. 321. x. (21.)**

LAVALLÉE (Calixa)

— O Canada! our dear ancestral Land! A literal English rendering (by G. A. S. Gillespie) of the words of ... Judge Routhier's ... Song ... with the original Vocal Score, *etc. McKechnie Music Co.: Ottawa*, (1909.) fol.   **H. 1794. vv. (10.)**

— O Canada! beloved Country ... Chant national ... English version by W. Campbell ... Arranged and edited by A. L. [i. e. A. L. E. Davies.] *A. H. Goetting: Toronto, etc.*, (1909.) fol.   **H. 1794. vv. (9.)**

— O Canada! [Four-part song.] Words by G. Balfour ... Harmonized by M. M. Stevenson. *Whaley, Royce & Co., for the Author: Winnipeg, Toronto*, (1909.) 8°.   **F. 321. w. (11.)**

— Canada, Dominion of the North. [Four-part song.] Words by G. Balfour ... Harmonized by M. M. Stevenson. *Whaley, Royce & Co., for the Author: Winnipeg, Toronto*, (1909.) 8°.   **F. 321. w. (12.)**

— O Canada ... Written by R. Todd. Melody by C. Lavallée. (Solo, Mixed voices or Unison.) [*A. Cox & Co.: Toronto,*] (1909.) fol.   **H. 1792. r. (31.)**

— O Canada! Canadian National Anthem, words by M. E. P. McCulloch ... Harmonized and arranged by E. Broome. Four-Part arrangement, mixed voices. (Two-Part arrangement for Schools.) 2 no. *Anglo-Canadian Music Publishers' Association: Toronto*, (1910.) 8°.   **F. 585. aa. (25.)**

— O Canada. National Anthem, the words ... by G. C. Holland ... Harmonized by A. Tremblay. [1911.] *See* Novello and Co. Novello's Part-Song Book. Second Series. No. 1213. [1869, *etc.*] 8°.   **F. 280. b.**

— O Canada, beloved Fatherland. A National Song, (words) by L. E. O. Payment. *McKechnie Music Co.: Ottawa*, 1912. fol.   **H. 1792. r. (32.)**

— O Canada. [Four-part song.] Words by ... L. Buchan ... Harmonized and arranged by A. Ham. *Novello & Co.: London*, [1912.] 8°.   **F. 321. z. (27.)**

— O Canada. Canadian National Anthem ... English words by A. Bridle. Arranged by J. C. Marks. *Whaley, Royce & Co.: Winnipeg, Toronto*, (1914.) fol.   **G. 806. mm. (4.)**

— O Canada! ... English words by E. Teschemacher. Arranged (with new accompaniment) by E. James. *F. Harris Co.: London*, (1914.) fol.   **H. 1793. s. (20.)**

— O Canada ... Arranged as a Part Song for male voices ... by E. James. *F. Harris Co.: London*, (1914.) 8°.   **F. 163. q. (18.)**

— O Canada ... Arranged as a Part Song for S. A. T. B. by E. James. *F. Harris Co.: London*, (1914.) 8°.   **F. 585. bb. (13.)**

— O Canada ... Har[monized for four voices and words written] by G. Taggart. [*G. Taggart: Vancouver*, 1914.] *s. sh.* fol.   **H. 1793. s. (21.)**

— The Canadian National Anthems ... O Canada ... by C. Lavallée. 1915. fol. *See* Muir (A.)   **H. 1793. z. (28.)**

— O Canada! [Song, melody by C. Lavallée.] Words by C. N. Merritt. [1915.] *a card. See* O.   **I. 600. e. (168.)**

— O Canada ... English words by E. Teschemacher. Arranged as a vocal duet by E. Newton. (Accompaniment by E. James.) *F. Harris Co.: London, Toronto*, 1917. fol.   **H. 1846. x. (34.)**

— "O Canada, terre de nos aïeux." "Chant national." ⟨1er cornet Si ♭ [and wind band parts].⟩ 18 pt. *In:* Laurendeau (L. P.) "Vive la Canadienne," *etc.* [1903.] 4°.   **g. 1800. (201.)**

— O Canada, terre de nos aïeux. ⟨Chant national.⟩ [Orchestral parts.] 13 pt. *In:* Laurendeau (L. P.) Vive la Canadienne, *etc.* [1907.] 8°.   **f. 800. (796.)**

LAVALLÉE (Calixa)

— O Canada! our Fathers' Land of Old ... Piano Solo ...
Arranged by H. Zoellner. *Whaley, Royce & Co.: Winnipeg,
Toronto,* (1908.) fol.　　　　　　　**g. 606. f. (19.)**

— O Canada ... The Maple Leaf forever. A. Muir. Arr. by
J. Slatter. Solo B♭ Cornet. *R. S. Williams & Sons Co.:
Winnipeg, Toronto,* 1910. *s. sh. obl.* 8°.　**I. 600. d. (214.)**

— *See* Hughes (A. W.) In old Quebec.—Vive la Canadienne &
O Canada! [Composed by C. Lavallée.]—Arr. by A. W.
Hughes. Solo B♭ Cornet. 1908. *s. sh. obl.* 8°.
　　　　　　　　　　　　　　　　　　I. 600. d. (21.)

— *See* Laurendeau (L. P.) Laurentian March. (Marche
laurentienne.) Introducing the Canadian patriotic song: "O
Canada". (Lavallée.) [1908.] 8°. [Roberts (*Charles J.*)
Mexican Kisses, etc.]　　　　　　**f. 800. a. (199.)**

— *See* Perrier (P.) *pseud.* O Canada. Marche nationale, for the
Piano [on the melody by C. Lavallée]. [1908.] fol.
　　　　　　　　　　　　　　　　　　h. 3283. s. (32.)

— *See* Perrier (P.) *pseud.* O Canada. (Fantasia.) A
Transcription for the Piano of O Canada, *etc.* (1908.) fol.
　　　　　　　　　　　　　　　　　　h. 3283. s. (33.)

———————

— Le Papillon, étude de concert pour Piano. *Paris,* [1875.] fol.
　　　　　　　　　　　　　　　　　　h. 1487. p. (4.)

— [Le Papillon.] The Butterfly ... Revised and annotated by
C. von Sternberg. (Piano.) *J. W. Stern & Co.: New York,*
1917. fol.　　　　　　　　　　　　**h. 3284. nn. (17.)**

— The Rocks and Hills. [Chorus.] [1886.] *See* Choral. The
Choral Handbook. No. 122. [1885, *etc.*] 8°.　　**E. 862.**

— Souvenir de Tolède, mazurka de salon pour Piano. *Paris,*
[1875.] fol.　　　　　　　　　　　　**h. 1487. p. (3.)**

— With Pleasure in each Glance. [Chorus.] [1886.] *See* Choral.
The Choral Handbook. No. 121. [1885, *etc.*] 8°.　**E. 862.**

LAVALLIÈRE

— Lavallière aux Carmélites. Scène dramatique. *See* Potharst
(J.)

LAVANDAIA

— La Lavandaia di S. Giovanni. [Song.] *See* Tommasini (V.)

LAVANDIÈRE

— La Lavandière. [Song.] *See* Meyerbeer (G.)

LAVANDIÈRES

— Les Lavandières de Santarem. Opéra comique. *See* Gevaert
(F. A.)

LAVANNARELLA

— La Lavannarella. [Song.] *See* Viscardi (F.)

LAVARNE (A.)

— Quadrille mignonne pour Piano. *London,* [1881.] fol.
　　　　　　　　　　　　　　　　　　h. 3275. j. (21.)

— *See* Jackson (W.) *of Exeter.* Te Deum in F, transcribed ... by
A. Lavarne [1882.] fol.　　　　　　　**h. 3275. i. (9.)**

LAVARNIE (Frank)

— Kissing in the Moonlight ... Ballad, written and composed
by F. Lavarnie. *C. Sheard: London,* [1877.] fol.
No. 5743 *of the Musical Bouquet.*　　　　**H. 2345.**

LAVARNIE (Frank)

— Tender, Loving Eyes of Blue. ... Song & Chorus, written
[and] composed ... by F. Lavarnie. *C. Sheard: London,*
[1884.] fol.
No. 7036 *of the Musical Bouquet.*　　　　**H. 2345.**

LAVASKA (Anna)

— Russian in Song. [Folksongs.] ⟨Arranged by A. Lavaska and
Leonard Olson.⟩ *Russ. & Eng.* pp. 78. *University of
Washington Press: Seattle,* [1949.] 4°.　　**G. 560. j. (1.)**

LAVATER (Hans)

— Streichquartett in g-moll. Partitur, *etc.* pp. 39. *Gebrüder Hug
& Co.: Zürich und Leipzig,* [1931.] 8°.　　**c. 140. ee. (3.)**

— *See* Scarlatti (A.) Exultate Deo ... Für Frauenchor gesetzt
von H. Lavater. [1963?] 8°.　　　　**F. 1176. ss. (5.)**

LAVATER (Louis)

— The Gentle Maiden. (Irish Air.) Two-Part Song. Arrangement
and English words by L. Lavater. pp. 4. *Leonard, Gould &
Bolttler: London,* 1941. 8°.
[*Leonard, Gould & Bolttler's Library of Unison and Part Songs
for Schools. No.* 56.]　　　　　　　　　**F. 1843.**

— Phillis is my only Joy. Canzonet for four voices, words by Sir
Charles Sedley. pp. 4. *Leonard, Gould & Bolttler: London,*
[1947.] 8°.
[*L. G. B. choral Repertoire. no.* 59.]　　　**F. 1843. a.**

— Six Songs by H. Heine. Op. 1. [English translation by E. A.
Bowring and L. Lavater.] *Novello, Ewer and Co.: London &
New York,* [1895.] 8°.　　　　　　**F. 636. z. (8.)**

— When Summer Days grow mild. Ballet for four voices, words
and music by L. Lavater. pp. 4. *Leonard, Gould & Bolttler:
London,* [1947.] 8°.
[*L. G. B. choral Repertoire. no.* 57.]　　　**F. 1843. a.**

— *See* Brahms (J.) [Walzer. Op. 39. No. 15.] Red Rose and dead
Rose ... Music adapted by L. Lavater. [1938?] 8°. [*Leonard,
Gould & Bolttler's Library of Unison and Part Songs for
Schools. No.* 42.]　　　　　　　　　　**F. 1843.**

— *See* Brahms (J.) [Walzer. Op. 39. No. 15.] Red Rose and dead
Rose ... Words written and music adapted by L. Lavater.
[1943?] 8°. [*Leonard, Gould & Bolttler Part-Songs. no.* 38.]
　　　　　　　　　　　　　　　　　　F. 1843. a.

— *See* Leybach (I.) [5ᵉ nocturne. Op. 52.] Soft sighs the Night ...
Vocal score and words by L. Lavater. [1947.] 8°. [*L. G. B.
choral Repertoire. no.* 58.]　　　　　**F. 1843. a.**

— *See* Strauss (J.) *the Younger.* [An der schönen blauen Donau.
Op. 314.] The Blue Danube Waltz ... Vocal Score and words
by L. Lavater. [1938?] 8°. [*Leonard, Gould & Bolttler's
Library of Unison and Part Songs for Schools. No.* 38.]
　　　　　　　　　　　　　　　　　　F. 1843.

— *See* Strauss (J.) *the Younger.* [An der schönen blauen Donau.
Op. 314.] The Blue Danube Waltz ... Vocal score and words
by L. Lavater. [1945?] 8°. [*L. G. B. choral Repertoire. no.* 33.]
　　　　　　　　　　　　　　　　　　F. 1843. a.

— *See* Strauss (J.) *the Younger.* [Geschichten aus dem Wiener
Wald. Op. 325.] Tales from the Vienna Woods ... Score and
words by L. Lavater. [1938?] 8°. [*Leonard, Gould & Bolttler's
Library of Unison and Part Songs for Schools. No.* 41.]
　　　　　　　　　　　　　　　　　　F. 1843.

— *See* Strauss (J.) *the Younger.* [Geschichten aus dem
Wiener-Wald. Op. 325.] Tales from the Vienna Woods ...
Score and words by L. Lavater. [1945?] 8°. [*Leonard, Gould
& Bolttler Part-Songs. no.* 31.]　　　　**F. 1843. a.**

LAVAUX (NICOLAS)

— Six sonates à deux flûtes traversieres, et toutes sortes d'instrumens égaux … Œuvre Iᵉʳ. Gravé par Labassée. [Parts.] 2 pt. *Chez Monsieur Bailleux: Paris*, [c. 1785.] fol. **h. 250. z.**

LAVE (Y. DE)

— Grand Ascension Polka, composed on the tight rope across the Genessee. [P. F.] *Boston*, [1865?] fol. **h. 1459. p. (3.)**

LAVELLO (RODOLPHE)

— Berceuse pour Violon avec accompagnement de Piano. Op. 19. *Paris*, [1883.] fol. **h. 1608. l. (9.)**

— Menuet pour Piano. *Paris*, [1881.] fol. **h. 3272. j. (11.)**

LAVENDER

— Lavender. Song. *See* BONAS (B.)

— Lavender. Song. *See* DAREWSKI (Hermann E.)

— Lavender. Unison song. *See* LEE (Ernest M.)

— Lavender. Song. *See* MOIR (F. L.)

— Lavender. Song. *See* RUSSELL (R. C. K.)

— Lavender. Two-part Song. *See* SARSON (H. M.)

— Lavender. Two-part Song. *See* SWEETING (E. T.)

— Lavender and Thyme. [Part-song.] *See* GODFREY (P.) Second Series of Folk Music … Op. 43. No. 1.

— Lavender Dreams. Song. *See* CLARKE (R. C.) Pot-Pourri. No. 2.

— The Lavender Girl. [Song.] *See* CHERRY (J. W.)

— The Lavender Girl. [Song.] *See* REEVE (W.) [Mirth's Museum.]

— The Lavender Girl. Song. *See* TROTÈRE (H.)

— Lavender Harvest. [Song.] *See* MANN (A.)

— The Lavender Lady. Song. *See* FARJEON (H.)

— The Lavender Lady. [Song.] *See* PADDON (F. A.)

— Lavender Lane. Song. *See* SAMUEL (H.)

— Lavender Leeze. Unison Song. *See* DUNHILL (T. F.)

— Lavender Love of long ago. [Song.] *See* GORDON (W.)

— The Lavender of Life. Song. *See* ETTRICK (H. H.)

— Lavender Pond. [Song.] *See* HEAD (Michael) Six Sea Songs … 5.

— Lavender's blue. [Nursery rhyme.] *See* MACKINLAY (K. S.)

— Lavender's for Ladies. Song. *See* BUSHBY (E. F.)

— The Lavender Seller. Song. *See* SMITH (F. S. B.)

— Lavender, the Howler. [Song.] *See* MACGLENNON (F.)

LAVENDER (PETER)

— *See* SULLIVAN (*Sir* Arthur S.) The Authentic Gilbert & Sullivan Songbook … Collected by M. Binney and P. Lavender, *etc.* 1977. 4°. **H. 1389. p.**

LAVENU (LEWIS)

— Two grand military Marches. Arranged for the pianoforte … by … L. Lavenu. pp. 3. *Printed by Lavenu & Mitchell: London*, [c. 1805.] fol. **h. 61. h. (9.)**

LAVENU (LEWIS)

— L. Lavenu's Musical Journal or Pocket Companion. Containing a great variety of Opera Dances, single Airs, Duets, Waltzs's … arranged for the Flute or Violin. 2 vol. *Printed … by L. Lavenu: London*, [1798.] *obl.* 8°. *Issued in sixty parts, with continuous pagination.* **a. 167.**

LAVENU (LOUIS HENRY)

— Bring me wild Flowers, ballad, the words by E. J. Gill. pp. 5. *Cramer, Beale & Cᵒ: London*, [c. 1860.] fol. **H. 1601. v. (44.)**

— The brooklet. Song. Written by C. Churchill. [Begins: "O'er beds of water lilies".] *London*, [1852.] fol. **H. 1735. (14.)**

— The Clochette Polka. [P. F.] *London*, [1850.] fol. **h. 947. (40.)**

— Come wander with me. Duet written by E. I. Gill. *London*, [1850.] fol. **H. 1717. (15.)**

— The Cottage rose. Ballad written by J. Simmonds. [Begins: "A lovely rose once grac'd a cottage scene".] *London*, [1853.] fol. **H. 1735. (19.)**

— The Deserted. Song [begins: "Lovely, sad"] … written by J. A. Wade. *London*, [1840?] fol. **H. 2832. n. (1.)**

— Flower after flower departs. Duet … the poetry by G. Linley. *London*, [1849.] fol. **H. 1717. (14.)**

— Happy Heart, could thy beating be. *See* infra: [Loretta.]

— The Harvest Queen. Song [begins: "From sunny fields"] … written by E. Fitzball. *London*, [1845?] fol. **H. 2834. (27.)**

— I'm queen of the merry greenwood, Cavatina … written by G. Linley. *Cramer, Beale & Co.: London*, [1850?] fol. **H. 2815. n. (54.)**

— I shall greet thee no more. Song, written by G. Linley. *London*, [1847.] fol. **H. 1717. (11.)**

— I wander o'er moorland and lea. Song of the Zephyr, written by A. W. Hammond. *London*, [1847.] fol. **H. 1717. (12.)**

— "I wandered by the Woodside," ballad … The words by W. H. Ollivier, *etc.* pp. 5. *Mori & Lavenu: London*, [c. 1835.] fol. **G. 425. ff. (17.)**

— If we are not loved again. *See* infra: [Loretta.]

— The joyful summer's come. Song. *London*, [1853.] fol. **H. 1735. (16.)**

— Let some gentle word. Ballad by J. Simmonds. *London*, [1853.] fol. **H. 1735. (17.)**

Loretta

— Happy heart, could thy beating be. Ballad … written by A. Bunn. *London*, [1846?] fol. **H. 1772. r. (16.)**

— "Happy Heart" … Arranged for the piano forte … by Ch. Chaulieu. pp. 9. *Cramer, Beale & Cᵒ: London*, [1846.] fol. **h. 1203. dd. (15.)**

— If we are not loved again. Ballad [begins: "The feeling which exalts the soul"] … written by A. Bunn. *London*, [1846.] fol. **H. 2832. o. (37.)**

— On the banks of Guadalquiver. Ballad … written by A. Bunn. *London*, [1846.] fol. **H. 2832. o. (36.)**

— On the Banks of Guadalquiver. *See* CHAULIEU (C.) The favorite air … arranged for the piano forte. [1846?] fol. **h. 726. j. (21.)**

— On the bosom of ocean. Quartett … written by A. Bunn. *London*, [1846.] fol. **H. 2835. (22.)**

LAVENU (Louis Henry)

— With thee I now will weep. Ballad [begins: "Oh! I can well believe"] ... written by A. Bunn. *London*, [1846.] fol.
H. 2835. c. (32.)

———

— Meet me dearest. Ballad ... The words by E. Howard. *London*, [1845?] fol.
H. 2832. e. (19.)

— Memory's Dream. Ballad [begins: "Oh! tell me not"], the words by J. Augustine Wade. pp. 4. *L. Lavenu: London*, [1840.] fol.
H. 2832. e. (17.)

— [Another copy.]
R. M. 14. b. 3. (9.)

— The minstrel girl. Ballad written by E. Fitzball [begins: "Spring is blooming"]. *London*, [1852.] fol.
H. 1735. (15.)

— The morn wakes in beauty. Cavatina, written by G. Linley. *London*, [1845.] fol.
H. 1698. (4.)

— My dreams are, now, no more of thee, written by G. Linley. *London*, [1851.] fol.
H. 1735. (13.)

— My Molly Asthore. [Song, begins: "As down on Banna's banks".] *London*, [1863.] fol.
H. 1772. r. (15.)

— My own land. Song [begins: "Oh! there's no land"] written by G. Linley. pp. 5. *Addison & Hodson: London*, [1844.] fol.
H. 2832. e. (18.)

— On the banks of Guadalquiver. *See* supra: [Loretta.]

— On the bosom of ocean. *See* supra: [Loretta.]

— Our good ship, [song] written by G. Linley. *London*, [1856.] fol.
H. 1758. (14.)

— The Rose gatherers. Duet ... [begins: "See those blushing roses"] the poetry by G. Linley. *London*, [1849.] fol.
H. 1717. (13.)

— Song of the breeze, written by M. E. Hewitt. [Begins: "Oh call me not idle".] *London*, [1853.] fol.
H. 1735. (18.)

— Those happy Days are gone, Ballad, written by George Linley. pp. 5. *Cramer, Beale & Cᵒ: London*, [1850.] fol.
H. 1980. tt. (17.)

— [A reissue.] Those happy days are gone. Ballad, written by G. Linley. *R. Mills & Sons: London*, [1876.] fol.
H. 1778. x. (46.)

— With thee I now will weep. *See* supra: [Loretta.]

— *See* AUBER (D. F. E.) [Haydée—Glisse, glisse ô ma gondole.] Glide along good Barque ... Barcarole adapted ... by L. Lavenu. [1848?] fol.
G. 426. qq. (7.)

— *See* COSTA (*Sir* M.) [Alma.] The favorite airs ... arranged by L. Lavenu. [1844.] fol.
h. 807.

— *See* COSTA (*Sir* M.) [Alma.] Prologue ... Arranged ... by L. Lavenu, *etc.* [1844?] fol.
g. 545. i. (8.)

— *See* COSTA (*Sir* M.) [Alma.] The favorite Valse et Galop de Fascination ... Arranged ... by L. Lavenu. [1846.] fol.
h. 721. a. (22.)

— *See* RICCI (Luigi) *the Elder.* [Chi dura vince.] Ah! già s'offre al mio pensiero, aria, e Alfin brillar nell'iride, rondo finale ... arranged by L. Lavenu. [1850.] fol.
H. 345. h. (30.)

LAVER (Edith L.)

— Fairies at the Fountain. (Piano.) *C. F. Summy Co.: Chicago*, 1915. fol.
h. 3284. nn. (19.)

— The Sandman. (Piano.) *C. F. Summy Co.: Chicago*, 1915. fol.
h. 3284. nn. (18.)

LAVERGNE (Antoine)

— La Princesse d'Élide. Opéra ... Les paroles sont de Monsieur Roy. *Chez Christophe Ballard: Paris*, 1706. fol.
I. 323.

LAVERGNE (M. Humbert)

— *See* Humbert-Lavergne.

LAVERICK (Arthur)

— When I survey the wondrous Cross. *Rose Street* ... [Hymn, words by] I. Watts. *A. Laverick: Trimdon Station, Durham*, [1943.] *a card.*
I. 600. f. (98.)

LAVERNE (Gabriel)

— Melusine. Valse. [P. F.] *J. Williams: London*, 1896. fol.
h. 3286. g. (14.)

LAVEROCK

— The Laverock. [Song.] *See* PASSAVANT (M. D.) Two Scotch Songs. No. 2.

— The Laverock and the Morn. [Song.] *See* ADLER (F.)

— The Laverock loves the dewy Light. Song. *See* BREWER (*Sir* A. H.)

LAVERTY (E. S.)

— The Boats. Song [begins: "I watched the boats"]. The words by E. Stirling. *London*, [1877.] fol.
H. 1778. x. (47.)

LAVESSIÈRE (Edouard)

— Sous un Berceau de Roses. Mélodie [begins: "Dors doucement"]. Paroles de M. Constantin. *Paris*, [1855?] fol.
H. 2830. d. (69.)

LAVEUSES

— Les Laveuses du Couvent. Romance. *See* GRISAR (A.)

LAVIGNAC (Albert)

— Air de Judas Machabée de Haendel. Transcription. [P. F.] *Paris*, [1875.] fol.
h. 1487. p. (7.)

— Air de Suzanne d'après Haendel. Transcription pour Piano. *Londres*, [1875.] fol.
h. 1482. y. (39.)

— Air extrait de la cantate La Pentecôte de J. S. Bach, transcription symphonique. [P. F.] *London*, [1878.] fol.
h. 1494. p. (31.)

— Barcarolle Vénitienne, pour le Piano. [*Paris*], 1897. 8°. *Supplement to "L'Illustration," No.*2829. **P. P. 4283. m. (3.)**

— Berceuse pour Piano à quatre mains. *Paris*, [1877.] fol.
h. 1493. n. (15.)

— Le Bravo, opéra ... de G. Salvayre, valse de concert pour Piano. *Paris*, [1878.] fol.
h. 1493. n. (19.)

— Cours complet théorique et pratique de dictée musicale. *Paris*, [1882.] 8°.
F. 1639.

— L'École de la pédale. Douze études spéciales pour l'emploi des pédales du piano avec une préface sur leurs effets acoustiques, leur histoire et la façon de s'en servir, *etc.* pp. 137. *Mackar et Noël: Paris*, 1889. fol.
h. 3821. aa.

— Galop-Marche à huit mains sur un seul Piano. *Paris*, [1874.] *obl.* fol.
e. 272. b. (16.)

— Galop-Marche à huit mains sur un seul Piano. *Paris*, [1878.] *obl.* fol.
e. 272. h. (47.)

LAVIGNAC (Albert)

— Galop Marche à 8 mains sur un piano ... Arrangement facile à 6 mains par G. van Calt. *See* Orchestre. L'Orchestre au Salon, *etc.* No. 26. [1874, *etc.*] fol.   **h. 1427.**

— Galop-Marche ... arrangé à quatre mains par L. Lemoine. *Paris*, [1875.] fol.   **h. 1487. p. (10.)**

— Arrangement facile pour Piano du Galop Marche à huit mains de A. Lavignac par J. Rummel. *Paris*, [1876.] fol.   **h. 1487. p. (12.)**

— Galop-Marche pour Piano. *Paris*, [1876.] fol.   **h. 1487. p. (11.)**

— Galop-Marche pour Piano. Arrangement facile par G. van Calt. [Solo and duet.] 2 no. *Paris*, [1877.] fol.   **h. 1487. p. (13.)**

— Harmonies Eoliennes, 2ᵉ. impromptu pour Piano. *Paris*, [1877.] fol.   **h. 1493. n. (16.)**

— Impromptu-Pastoral pour Piano. *Paris*, [1877.] fol.   **h. 1493. n. (14.)**

— Le Jour de Fête. Carillon pour Piano. *Paris*, [1876.] fol.   **h. 1487. p. (14.)**

— 50 Leçons de Solfège à changements de clefs sur cinq clefs. Introduction au Solfège manuscrit. Op. 30. *Paris*, 1885. 4°. *Format Lemoine.*   **G. 833. (2.)**

— Marche Hongroise, extraite des symphonies vocales de Cheland, trancrite pour Piano et Orgue. *Paris*, [1874.] fol.   **h. 1487. p. (5.)**

— O Salutaris, avec accompagnement d'orgue ou piano. No. 1. Baryton. No. 7. Soprano ou Ténor. 2 no. *A. O'Kelly: Paris*, [1887.] fol.   **H. 1187. k. (18.)**

— Pas des Dryades, 2ᵉ. air de ballet pour Piano. *Paris*, [1877.] fol.   **h. 1493. n. (18.)**

— Pas des Naïdes. 1ᵉʳ. air de ballet pour Piano. *Paris*, [1877.] fol.   **h. 1493. n. (17.)**

— 3 Petites pièces caractéristiques dans l'ancien Style. [P. F.] 3 no. *Paris*, [1866.] fol.   **h. 1462. r. (15.)**

— Trois pièces caractéristiques (Feuillets d'Album) pour Piano. 3 no. *Paris*, [1876.] fol.   **h. 1487. p. (9.)**

— 25 Pièces pour piano à quatre mains, extraites de l'École de la Mesure ... Op. 11. *Lemoine & Fils: Paris, Bruxelles*, 1886. fol.   **h. 3290. h. (20.)**

— 10 Préludes pour piano. Op. 31. *A. O'Kelly: Paris*, [1886.] fol.   **h. 3281. l. (8.)**

— Scherzo-Caprice pour Piano. *Paris*, [1883.] fol.   **h. 3276. g. (7.)**

— Sérénade pour flûte avec accompagnement de piano. Op. 32. *Paris*, 1886. fol.   **h. 2050. b. (7.)**

— Solfège Manuscrit. Complément du Solfège des Solfèges. Cent leçons avec accompagnement de piano. Op. 17. 3 pt. *Paris*, [1877–84.] 4°. *Format Lemoine. Imperfect; wanting the 2nd part.*   **G. 833. (1.)**

— Solfège Manuscrit facile. Cent leçons en deux volumes. *Paris, Bruxelles*, 1887. 4°.   **G. 833. a.**

— Six Sonatines pour Piano. 6 no. *Paris*, [1879, 80.] fol.   **h. 3272. j. (12.)**

— Quatre (cinq) Transcriptions pour Piano. No. 2–5. *Paris*, [1872–74.] fol. *Imperfect; wanting no. 1.*   **h. 1458. i. (1.)**

— Valse de concert pour Piano. *Paris*, [1866.] fol.   **h. 1462. r. (14.)**

LAVIGNAC (Albert)

— *See* Beethoven (L. van) [Symphony No. 1. Op. 21.] Première Symphonie ... arrangée ... par A. Lavignac, *etc.* [1877.] fol.   **h. 400. g. (8.)**

— *See* Gounod (C. F.) Marche funèbre d'une Marionette. (Transcription ... par A. Lavignac.) [1877.] fol.   **h. 80. c. (5.)**

— *See* Haendel (G. F.) [Messiah.—Selections, instrumental.] Deux Thêmes du Messie ... Transcription [by] A. Lavignac. [P. F.] [1875.] fol.   **h. 1487. p. (8.)**

— *See* Haendel (G. F.) [Messiah.—For unto us a Child is born.] Chœur du Messie ... Transcription ... à 4 mains par A. Lavignac. [1875.] fol.   **h. 1487. p. (6.)**

— *See* Mendelssohn-Bartholdy (J. L. F.) [Ein Sommernachtstraum.] Marche nuptiale ... transcrite ... par A. Lavignac. [1875.] fol.   **h. 2576. (12.)**

— *See* Renaud de Vilbac (A. Z. C.) Les Beautés dramatiques arrangées ... par R. de Vilbac (A. Lavignac), *etc.* [1873–9.] fol.   **h. 1228. h.**

— *See* Renaud de Vilbac (A. Z. C.) Les Beautés Dramatiques ... par ... A. Lavignac, *etc.* [1875, *etc.*] fol.   **h. 1228. m. (7.)**

— *See* Weber (C. M. F. E. von) Marche posthume ... transcrite ... par A. Lavignac. [1866.] fol.   **h. 1463. d. (26.)**

— *See* Weber (C. M. F. E. von) 4 Pieces de Guitare, Op. 38, transcrites pour le Piano par A. Lavignac. [1868.] fol.   **h. 1463. d. (25.)**

LA VIGNE (DE)

— 1ᵉʳ œuvre ... contenant six suites de pieces à deux musettes qui conviennent aux viéles, flutes-à-bec, flutes traversᵉˢ & haubois. [Score.] pp. 24. *Chez l'auteur: Paris*, [1731.] fol.   **g. 225. d.**

LAVIGNE (Emery)

— Le Retour. Marche. [P. F.] *E. Archambeault: Montreal*, 1900. fol.   **g. 605. x. (6.)**

— Sous les Lilas. Valse. [P. F.] *E. Archambeault: Montreal*, 1900. fol.   **h. 3286. q. (75.)**

LAVIGNE (Ernest)

— 25 Mélodies ... Paroles françaises et anglaises. (English version by S. Byrne.) *S. Park: Montreal*, 1901. 8°.   **G. 1010.**

— Les Oiseaux et les Baisers.—The Birds and the Kisses.— Chant et Piano, paroles de P. Meurice. *P. Sohmer: Montréal*, 1909. fol.   **H. 1792. r. (33.)**

— Que l'heure est donc brève. [Song.] Paroles d'A. Silvestre. *E. Archambeault: Montreal*, 1910. fol.   **H. 1792. r. (34.)**

LAVIGNE (Frederick)

— La Fleurine valses, pour le piano forte, *etc. E. Ransford: London*, [1848.] fol. *Imperfect; the titlepage only. The music consists of the sheets of "Les Valses de la promenade" by A. C. Rowland.*   **h. 939. (36.)**

LA VILLA (Paolo)

— Ave Maria ... con accompᵗᵒ. di Pianoforte. *Milano*, [1880.] fol.   **H. 1028. j. (10.)**

— Collegramole. Duettino [begins: "Tergi ben mio"] ... Parole di C. Martinelli. *Milano*, [1877.] fol.   **H. 1782. a. (9.)**

LA VILLA (PAOLO)

— Dear Life of mine. Song with Violin or Cello obligato, words
by M. S. Harpel. *B. Curtaz and Son: San Francisco*, (1904.)
fol.
*Separate voice part with different words, entitled "Love's holy
Shrine".*   **G. 807. jj. (32.)**

— 3rd Mass, in D, for four voices ... with Latin and English
words. *O. Ditson Co.: Boston, etc.*, 1895. 8°.   **F. 363. l. (2.)**

— O little Zephyr playing.—Al Zeffiretto.—[Song.] With Violin
or 'cello obligato. English version by J. C. M. Parole Italiane
di A. Mancini. *O. Ditson Company: Boston, etc.*, 1894. fol.
H. 1798. u. (29.)

— Sorridimi. Valtz cantabile con accompto. di Pianoforte.
Parole di L. Mancini. *Milano*, [1880.] fol.   **H. 1782. c. (16.)**

— The Splendid Goal ... Notturnino with violin or cello
obligato. English version by J. P. Jackson. Poesia Italiana di
B. Zambrini. *O. Ditson Company: Boston, etc.*, 1894. fol.
H. 1798. u. (28.)

— Tell me, what shall we do? (A cradle song.) [For S. S.] pp. 3.
J. Curwen & Sons: London; Leipzig [printed, 1894.] 8°.
[*Choruses for equal Voices. no.* 136.]   **E. 861.**

— *See* SINDING (C.) [Characterstücke. Op. 34. No. 5.] If Love
were dead. Song, *etc.* (Adapted ... by P. La Villa.) (1904.)
fol.   **G. 807. jj. (33.)**

LAVILLE (SAMUEL)

— The Brookside, [song] for voice, flute & pianoforte. *Rudall,
Carte & Co.: London*, [1882.] fol.   **H. 1788. uu. (35.)**

— Trio, pour deux flûtes et piano. [Parts.] 3 pt. *Rudall, Rose,
Carte & Cᵒ.: London*, [1870?] fol.   **h. 5. t. (2.)**

LA VILLETTE (R.)

— Le Ruisseau. Caprice-étude pour le piano. *Durand &
Schœnewerk: Paris*, [1886.] fol.   **h. 3281. l. (9.)**

— Souvenir d'Antan. Pièce caractéristique pour le piano.
Durand & Schœnewerk: Paris, [1886.] fol.   **h. 3281. l. (10.)**

LAVILLIERS (BERNARD)

— T'es vivant? ⟨Songbook. Paroles & musique de Bernard
Lavilliers [and others].⟩ [With portraits.] pp. 66. *Éditions
Barclay: Paris*, [1980.] 4°.
Part of "Collection rock & folk".   **F. 1966. ff. (7.)**

LAVINGTON (CHARLES WILLIAM)

— An Anthem for Ascension-day (Psalm 24 vers. 7–10).
London, [1851.] fol.   **H. 1183. (16.)**

— Chants as used in Wells cathedral. Edited by C. W.
Lavington. *Wells*, [1855.] 8°.   **F. 167.**

— A Jubilee Hymn by E. H. Plumptre ... also the National
Anthem adapted for the Year of Jubilee. *Novello, Ewer and
Co.: London & New York*, [1886.] 8°.   **E. 442. j. (38.)**

LAVINIA

— Lavinia. Opéra-bouffe. *See* BARRAUD (H.)

— Lavinia. [Cantata.] *See* BILLINGTON (T.)

— Lavinia a Turno. Cantata. *See* GRAUN (C. H.)

— Lavinia's Lament. Comic ballad. *See* LODER (G.) [The Old
House at Home.]

LA VIOLETTE (WESLEY)

— The Broken Vine. An Elegy for tenor solo and chorus with
accompaniment for pipe organ, words from the 80th Psalm.
Gamble Hinged Music Co.: Chicago, 1921. 8°.
F. 1269. ff. (3.)

— Evocation, for Violin and Piano. *De Paul University Press:
Chicago*, 1937. 4°.   **g. 500. q. (35.)**

— Sonata for Violin and Piano. *De Paul University Press:
Chicago*, 1937. 4°.   **g. 500. q. (36.)**

LAVOCAT (   )

— *See* KENDON (   ) A Third Set of Nouvelle Quadrilles
... Finale par Lavocat, *etc.* [c. 1820.] fol.   **h. 925. u. (19.)**

LAVOIR

— Le Lavoir. Chansonnette. *See* CLÉMENT (A.)

LAVOIX (HENRI MARIE)

— *See* LEMAIRE (T.) and LAVOIX (H. M.) Le Chant, *etc.* 1881.
8°.   **7896. ff. 14.**

LAVOTHA

— Lavotha szerelme. Dalmű. *See* HUBAY (J.)

LAVOTTA (JÁNOS)

— Verbunkós Noták, oder aecht ungarische National-Tänze ...
Für das Piano-Forte eingerichtet von ... Abbé Gelinek. pp. 9.
Artaria und Comp.: Wien, [1814.] *obl.* fol.   **e. 284. b. (5.)**

— *See* KÁLDY (G.) Schätze der alten ungarischen Musik ...
Compositionen von ... J. Lavotta, *etc.* [1896.] fol.
g. 605. p. (4.)

LAVRANGA (D.)

— Valse lente. [P. F.] [*Paris*,] 1902. 8°.
Supplement to "L'Illustration," No. 3101.   **P. P. 4283. m. (3.)**

LAVROV (N.)

— *See* LYADOV (A. K.) Polonaise ... Op. 49. Réduction pour
piano à quatre mains par N. Lawrow. 1900. fol.
h. 3581. (25.)

LAVRY (MARC)

— Mizmor shir l'yom hashabat ... For cantor (tenor or
baritone) and mixed voices (S. A. T. B.) with organ
accompaniment. From "Shabbat Mitzion," Israel sabbath
service, *etc.* Heb. pp. 11. *Mills Music: New York*, [1962.] 8°.
E. 1499. k. (29.)

— Song of Songs. Oratorio for soloists, mixed choir &
orchestra. Libretto by Max Brod, based on "Song of Songs".
[Vocal score.] Heb. & Eng. pp. 127. *Israel Music Institute:
Tel-Aviv*, [1962.] 8°.   **E. 1499. w. (1.)**

LAW

— Law. A Comic Song. *See* BLEWITT (J.)

— The Law of Barataria. Song. *See* KERKER (G. A.)

— The Law of Java. [Opera.] *See* BISHOP (*Sir* H. R.)

— The Law of the Lord. Part-Song. *See* CHAFFIN (L. G.)

LAW

— The Law of the Lord. Introit. *See* MATHIAS (William)

— The Law of the Lord is perfect. Hymn. *See* MABON (C. B.)

— The Law of the Lord is perfect. Full anthem. *See* MACFARREN (*Sir* G. A.)

— Law, Phisick & Divinity. [Song.] *See* THREE. Three rosy fac'd Topers as ever was known. [1770?] *s. sh.* fol.
G. 316. (142.)

— Law, Physic and Divinity. Song. *See* THREE. Three rosy fac'd Topers as ever was known. [1772.] 8°.
P. P. 5439.

— The Law won't allow me to do it. [Song.] *See* MACGLENNON (F.)

LAW (A.)

— Litany for Baptisms, written and composed by A. Law. *Novello, Ewer and Co.: London and New York*, [1892.] *s. sh.* 8°.
F. 1171. j. (26.)

LAW (ALICE)

— Annabel Lee. Song, words by E. A. Poe. *Elkin & Co.: London*, [1909.] fol.
H. 1794. vv. (14.)

— Fear no more the Heat o' the Sun. Song, words by Shakespeare, *etc. Elkin & Co.: London*, [1909.] fol.
H. 1794. vv. (15.)

LAW (ANDREW)

— Bunker Hill. For four-part chorus of mixed voices a cappella ... ([Words from] The American Hero a Sapphick ode by Nathaniel Niles.) Edited by Alice Parker and Robert Shaw. pp. 7. *Lawson-Gould Music Publishers: New York*, [1956.] 8°.
F. 1744. s. (10.)

— The Musical Primer; or the First part of the art of singing: containing the rules of psalmody, newly revised and improved; together with a number of practical lessons and plain tunes ... Third edition. pp. 208. [1780?] *obl.* 8°.
A. 1231. ll.

— Select Harmony. Containing ... the Rules of Singing; Together with a Collection of Psalm Tunes, Hymns and Anthems. [*New York*, 1779.] *obl.* 4°.
A. 816.

LAW (CECIL)

— June, and you. Valse Song, words by P. Edgar. *G. Ricordi & Co.: London, etc.*, 1919. 4°.
G. 390. x. (17.)

LAW (FREDERICK)

— Blue Eyed Mary Ann. [Song, begins: "I've reached the age of sixty three".] *London*, [1880.] fol.
H. 1783. o. (22.)

LAW (HAMILTON)

— At last. Song for a high or low voice, words by A. Law. *Leonard & Co.: London*, 1909. fol.
G. 805. mm. (16.)

— Bridal March, for Organ. *Orchestral Publishing Co.: London*, (1910.) *obl.* fol.
f. 314. aa. (17.)

— An Elegy on the Death of a mad Dog. [Song.] Words by O. Goldsmith. *Orchestral Publishing Co.: London*, [1910.] fol.
H. 1792. r. (38.)

— A Farewell. Song, words by A. Tennyson. *J. Williams: London*, (1907.) fol.
H. 1794. vv. (16.)

LAW (HAMILTON)

— Flying Thoughts. [Song.] Words by A. Law. *Stainer & Bell: London*, (1911.) fol.
Stainer & Bell's Modern Songs, No. 50.
H. 1792. r. (39.)

— The Hag. Four-Part Song, words by R. Herrick. *O[rchestral]. P[ublishing]. C[o].: London*, 1909. 8°.
F. 321. w. (13.)

— In Grief and Fear to Thee, O Lord. Motet. S. S. A. T. B. *Opus Music Co.: London*, (1911.) 8°.
F. 231. cc. (17.)

— It was a Lover. Four-Part Song, words by Shakespeare. *O[rchestral]. P[ublishing]. C[o].: London*, 1909. 8°.
F. 321. w. (14.)

— Three Little Songs. 1. The Moon was dim. (Words by Heine.) 2. Break, break, break. (Words by Tennyson.) 3. Love's Philosophy. (Words by Shelley.) *Opus Music Co.: London*, (1911.) fol.
H. 1792. r. (42.)

— Mad Soldier's Song. [Song.] Words by T. Hardy, *etc. Agate & Co.: London*, 1911. fol.
H. 1792. r. (40.)

— The Parting of the Ways. Song, words by A. Law. *Opus Music Co.: London*, [1913.] fol.
H. 1793. s. (23.)

—— The Song of the Veterans. Song —with Chorus ad lib.—, words by A. Law. *Ascherberg, Hopwood & Crew: London*, 1909. fol.
H. 1794. vv. (17.)

— The Top o' the Mornin'. An Irish Song, words by A. Law, *etc. Bach & Co.: London*, 1910. fol.
H. 1792. r. (41.)

LAW (HENRY)

— La Gondola. Valse. [P. F.] *E. Ascherberg & Co.: London*, [1887.] fol.
h. 975. u. (52.)

LAW (ISABELLA)

— Ah! River, golden fated. Song, words by H. O. Boddington. *London*, [1861.] fol.
H. 1772. r. (17.)

— Do you hear the children weeping. [Song.] Words by ... Mrs. E. B. Browning. *London*, [1861.] fol.
H. 1772. r. (18.)

LAW (JAMES)

— Geranium waltz ... arranged for the Pianoforte by R. Law. *Montrose*, [1875.] fol.
h. 1482. y. (42.)

LAW (LEN)

— Little Jesus. A carol for Christmas. Words and music by Len Law ... For unison voices, *etc.* pp. 4. *Basil Ramsey: Eastwood*, [1977.] 8°.
Part of "Choral Music Leaflets".
B. 742. ii. (7.)

LAW (LESLIE GORDON)

— A Little Impromptu & Dance Time. (Two Preparatory accordion solos.) *Charnwood Music Publishing Company: Leicester*, [1974.] 4°.
g. 657. k. (21.)

— A Royal Suite. (Preparatory grade accordion solo.) *Charnwood Music Publishing Company: Leicester*, [1977.] 4°.
g. 657. o. (5.)

— A Space Age Suite. Six easy guitar pieces for the young beginner. pp. 7. *Charnwood Music Publishing Company: Leicester*, [1977.] 4°.
f. 530. n. (7.)

LAW (ROBERT)

— Childhood's Home, song, the poetry written by John Law. pp. 5. *John Blockley: London*, [c. 1870.] fol.
H. 1860. tt. (9.)

LAW (ROBERT)

— O'er the deep a wail of mourning, a song of India, written by J. Law. *London*, [1857.] fol. **H. 1771. l. (15.)**

— *See* LAW (J.) Geranium waltz ... arranged ... by R. Law. [1875.] fol. **h. 1482. y. (42.)**

LAW (RONALD)

— Hodie Christus natus est. [Motet.] *Cathedral Music: London*, [1978.] 8°. **E. 1857. a. (13.)**

— Joy on this Day. [S. A. T. B.] Words and music: Ronald Law. *Cathedral Music: London*, [1978.] 8°. **E. 1857. a. (14.)**

LAWD

— *See* LORD.

LAWES (FRANK)

— On the Way. March. [P. F.] *West & Co.: London*, 1917. fol. **h. 3284. nn. (20.)**

LAWES (HENRY)

— Two Songs, "While I listen to thy Voice" and "Dear, thy Face is Heaven to me" ... edited ... by Miss Wakefield. *Stanley Lucas, Weber & Co.: London*, [1891.] fol. **H. 1797. o. (31.)**

— A Collection of Twenty four Songs by English Composers ... From Lawes to Linley, *etc.* 1908. 4°. *See* ARKWRIGHT (G. E. P.) **G. 295. k. (1.)**

— The Angler's Song. *See* infra: [Man's Life is but vain.]

Ayres and Dialogues

— [Bk. 1–3.] Ten Ayres ... Selected and edited by Thurston Dart. For low voice, *etc.* pp. 14. *Stainer & Bell: London*, [1956.] fol. **H. 1846. uu. (1.)**

Ayres and Dialogues. Book 1

— Ayres and Dialogues, for One, Two and Three Voyces ... The First Booke. FEW MS. NOTES. *T. H., for John Playford: London*, 1653. fol. **K. 3. m. 17. (1.)**

— [The Captive Lover.] If my mistress fix her eye. Trio. *See* HULLAH (J. P.) The Singer's Library of Concerted Music. Secular. No. 64. [1859, *etc.*] 8°. **G. 435.**

— The Captive Lover. [Three-part song.] Arranged by W. Offord. 1891. *See* PERIODICAL PUBLICATIONS.— *London*. The Early English Musical Magazine. No. 7. [a.] 1891. fol. **P. P. 1947. fa.**

— The Captive Lover. Air for three voices, *etc. See* HOLST (G. T. von) Old Airs and Glees. III[a]. 1916. 8°. **F. 1137. a. (88.)**

— I long to sing the siege of Troy. XXIII. Ode of Anacreon. *See* RIMBAULT (E. F.) The Ancient Vocal Music of England ... No. 5. [1847.] fol. **H. 1639. b.**

— I saw fair Chloris ... Three-part Song, [words by] Thomas Carew ... Arr. by E. Rowland. *J. B. Cramer & Co.: London*, 1942. 4°. [*Cramer's Library of School Classics. No.* 12.] **F. 157. f.**

— The Power of Musick. Praise ye the Lord of Hosts. S. A. T. B. a cappella ... Poem by Thomas Randolph, sacred text adapted from Psalm CXLVII by James Woodside ... Transcribed ... by James Woodside. *M. Witmark & Sons: New York*, 1938. 8°. **F. 585. zz. (28.)**

LAWES (HENRY)

Ayres and Dialogues. Book 2

— The Second Book of Ayres, and Dialogues, for One, Two, and Three Voyces. pp. 48. *T. H. for Jo. Playford: London*, 1655. fol. *Imperfect; wanting pp.* 5–8, *supplied in facsimile.* **K. 3. m. 17. (2.)**

— Fear not, dear Love. For Female Voices ... Edited by W. G. Whittaker. *Oxford University Press: London*, 1939. 8°. [*The John Playford Collection of Vocal Part-Music. No.* 15.] **F. 1777. i.**

— A Glee at Christmas ... Arranged for three Voices with Pianoforte Accompaniment by S. O. Lloyd. 1891. *See* PERIODICAL PUBLICATIONS.— *London*. The Early English Musical Magazine. No. 1. [c.] 1891. fol. **P. P. 1947. fa.**

— Hymns to the Holy Trinity. For solo voice and keyboard continuo ... Edited by Gwilym Beechey. ⟨Words by John Crofts (c. 1613–1670).⟩ pp. 8. *Oxford University Press: London*, [1973.] 4°. [*Musica da camera.* 8.] **g. 935.**

Ayres and Dialogues. Book 3

— Ayres and Dialogues, for One, Two, and Three Voyces. The Third Book. *W. Godbid for John Playford: London*, 1658. fol. *The portrait has been cut out of the title-page.* **K. 3. m. 18.**

— A Dialogue on a Kiss. For two solo voices and continuo. Edited by Richard McGrady. [Score.] pp. 8. *Oxford University Press: London*, [1978.] 4°. [*Musica da camera.* 60.] **g. 935.**

— Once Venus' Cheeks. Female voices. (S. S. C.) By H. Lawes ... Sweet Tyraness. (S. S. C.) By Henry Purcell, *etc.* pp. 7. *Oxford University Press: London*, [1937.] 8°. [*The John Playford Collection of Vocal Part-Music. no.* 24, 25.] **F. 1777. i.**

— The Captive Lover. *See* supra: [Ayres and Dialogues. Bk. 1.]

— Chloris, 'twill be. For Female Voices ... Edited by W. G. Whittaker. *Oxford University Press: London*, 1939. 8°. [*The John Playford Collection of Vocal Part-Music. No.* 16.] **F. 1777. i.**

— Come, Cloris, hye we to the Bow'r. [Three-part song. No. 5 of "Six Short Ayrs or Songs" from Playford's "Introduction to the Skill of Musick," 1654. Arranged for Female Voices by E. Rowland.] *J. Williams: London*, [1925.] 8°. [*St. Cecilia. Series* 17. *No.* 19[*b*].] **F. 1526.**

— Come, Chloris. For Mixed Voices. *Oxford University Press: London*, 1937. 8°. [*The John Playford Collection of Vocal Part Music. No.* 31.] **F. 1777. i.**

Comus

— The original music to Milton's Masque of Comus. *See* RIMBAULT (E. F.) The Ancient Vocal Music of England ... No. 8. [1847.] fol. **H. 1639. b.**

— The Original Music ... for the five Songs in Milton's "Comus"; together with incidental music and dances by Matthew Locke. Arranged for the pianoforte by C. W. Smith. pp. 12. *The Mermaid Society: London*, 1904. 4°. **H. 1860. p. (7.)**

— The Masque of Comus, by J. Milton. The original music by H. Lawes together with Incidental Music, Dances, etc., by W. Lawes and other contemporary composers. Selected and arranged by Sir Frederick Bridge, with an Introduction by W. Barclay Squire. *Novello and Co.: London*, 1908. 8°. **E. 1594. v. (3.)**

LAWES (HENRY)

— The Music in 'Comus'. [Selected and arranged from the original music by H. Lawes, *etc.*] [1908.] 8°. *See* DENT (E. J.)
C. 814.

— The Mask of Comus. The poem ... edited by E. H. Visiak. The Airs of the five Songs ... edited by Hubert J. Foss. With a foreword by the Earl of Ellesmere. Ornamented by M. R. H. Farrar. *Nonesuch Press: London*, 1937. fol.
Case 102. l. 21.

— Sweet Echo. Song ... arranged for 3 female voices by H. Heale. *Augener & Co.: London*, [1898.] 8°.
F. 328. h. (17.)

————————

— Cupid detected. [From Bk. 1 of Playford's "Select Ayres and Dialogues".] Four-Part Song ... Arranged by J. F. Bridge. 1901. *See* PERIODICAL PUBLICATIONS.— *London*. The Musical Times, *etc.* no. 703. 1844, *etc.* 8°.
P. P. 1945. aa.

— Cupid detected ... —Arranged by J. F. Bridge.—[1911.] *See* NOVELLO AND CO. Novello's Tonic Sol-fa Series. No. 1968. [1876, *etc.*] 4°.
B. 885.

— A Dialogue on a Kiss. *See* supra: [Ayres and Dialogues. Bk. 3.]

— Farley Castle. *See* infra: [A Paraphrase upon the Psalmes of David. Ps. LXXII.]

— Fear not, dear Love. *See* supra: [Ayres and Dialogues. Bk. 2.]

— A Glee at Christmas. *See* supra: [Ayres and Dialogues. Bk. 2.]

— Hymns to the Holy Trinity. *See* supra: [Ayres and Dialogues. Bk. 2.]

— I long to sing the siege of Troy. *See* supra: [Ayres and Dialogues. Bk. 1.]

— I saw fair Chloris. *See* supra: [Ayres and Dialogues. Bk. 1.]

— If my Mistress fix her Eye. *See* supra: [Ayres and Dialogues. Bk. 1. The Captive Lover.]

— The Lark. [Song, from Bk. II. of Playford's "Select Ayres".] Flute obbligato, Symphonies and Pianoforte Accompaniment by J. H. Young. 1891. *See* PERIODICAL PUBLICATIONS.— *London*. The Early English Musical Magazine. No. 2.[c.] 1891. fol.
P. P. 1947. fa.

— Like to the Damask Rose. Medium voice. From a MS. in Christchurch College, Oxford. Realized and edited by John Edmunds. pp. 3. *Boston Music Co.: Boston*, [1956.] 4°.
G. 1276. q. (7.)

— Lord God of Hosts. *See* infra: [A Paraphrase upon the Psalms of David. Ps. XII.]

Man's Life is but vain

— Man's life is but vain. *The Anglers Song*. For two Voyces, Treble and Basse. *Printed by T. Maxey for Rich. Marriot: London*, 1653. 8°.
Pp. 216 and 217 of I. Walton's 'The Compleat Angler'.
E. Pam. 1488. (1.)

— [Another copy.]
Case 31. a. 3.

— [Another copy.]
G. 2295.

— Man's life is but vain. Angler's song [for three voices]. The words from Walton's "Angler". *See* HULLAH (J.P.) The singer's library of concerted music. Secular. No. 24. [1859, *etc.*] 8°.
G. 435.

— The Angler's Song [from I. Walton's "Compleat Angler"]. With Symphonies and Accompt. ... by J. P. Cole. An additional Verse by O. Mitchell. 1891. *See* PERIODICAL PUBLICATIONS.— *London*. The Early English Musical Magazine. No. 2.[a.] 1891. fol.
P. P. 1947. fa.

LAWES (HENRY)

— Man's Life is but vain. The Angler's Song, words and melody [by H. Lawes] to be found in "The Compleat Angler" by I. Walton. Harmonised and arranged ... by C. L. Williams. 1924. 8°. *See* WILLIAMS (C. L.)
F. 163. v. (20.)

— The Angler's Song. Chorus for S. A. T. B. (T. T. B. B.) unaccompanied ... Arranged by W. G. Whittaker. 2 no. *Oxford University Press: London*, 1929. 8°.
[*The Oxford Choral Songs from the Old Masters. No.* 1464, 1465.]
F. 1777. b.

— The Angler's Song. Chorus for A. T. T. or Bar., B., unaccompanied ... Arranged by W. G. Whittaker. *Oxford University Press: London*, 1929. 8°.
[*The Oxford Choral Songs from the Old Masters. No.* 1466.]
F. 1777. b.

— The Angler's Song ... Descant for boy's voices and accompaniment by W. G. Whittaker. *Oxford University Press: London*, [1929.] 8°.
[*Oxford Descant Series. No.* 14.]
F. 1777. d.

— The Angler's Song. T. T. B. B ... Arranged for Male Voices by T. F. Dunhill. *Joseph Williams: London*, 1936. 8°.
[*St. Cecilia. Series* 20. *No.* 22.]
F. 1526.

— The Angler's Song. Two Part, T. B ... Acc. by C. Loomis. Edited by M. T. Krone. *M. Witmark & Sons: New York*, 1938. 8°.
E. 263. k. (30.)

— The Angler's Song ... Arranged by Harry Robert Wilson. ⟨T.B.B.⟩ pp. 4. *Boosey & Hawkes:* [*New York*, 1945.] 8°.
F. 163. ll. (38.)

————————

— Most glorious Lord of Life. *See* infra: [A Paraphrase upon the Psalmes of David. Ps. LXXII.]

— Not unto us, O Lord. Full Anthem for four voices. Adapted from H. Lawes and R. Farrant by H. Aldrich. The Organ Part added by J. Barnby. 1864. *See* PERIODICAL PUBLICATIONS.— *London*. The Musical Times, *etc.* No. 255. 1844, *etc.* 8°.
P. P. 1945. aa.

— O let me groan. [Song.] Text: William Herbert, Earl of Pembroke. ⟨Quelle: Brit. Mus. (London) [MS. Loan 35.]⟩ *In:* NOSKE (F.) Das ausserdeutsche Sololied 1500–1900. pp. 35–36. [1958.] 4°. [*Das Musikwerk. Hft.* 16.]
G. 16.

— Once Venus' Cheeks. *See* supra: [Ayres and Dialogues. Bk. 3.]

A Paraphrase upon the Psalmes of David

— A Paraphrase upon the Psalmes of David. By G.S. [i.e. George Sandys.] Set to new Tunes for private Devotion: and a thorow Base, for Voice, or Instrument. *Iohn Legatt: London*, 1638. fol.
Forming part of Sandys' "A Paraphrase upon the Divine Poems".
3104. c. 8.

— A Paraphrase upon the Psalmes of David, by G.S. [i.e. George Sandys.] Set to new Tunes, *etc.* [*London?*] 1648. 8°.
Forming part of Sandys' "A Paraphrase upon the Divine Poems".
11623. c. 6.

— A Paraphrase upon the Psalms of David, by G. S. [i.e. George Sandys.] Set to new tunes for private devotion and a thorough base, for voice or instrument. pp. 224. *Printed for O. D.: London*, 1648. 8°.
Forming the second part of Sandys' "A Paraphrase upon the divine Poems".
3054. a. 38.

— [Another copy.]
11634. aa. 2. (2.)

— A Paraphrase upon the Psalms of David. By George Sandys. Set to New Tunes ... And in this Edition ... Revised and Corrected ... by John Playford. *W. Godbid, for Abel Roper: London*, 1676. 8°.
Forming part of Sandys' "A Paraphrase upon the Divine Poems".
1076. m. 7.

LAWES (HENRY)

— Psalmody for a single Voice, being twenty-four Melodies for private devotion, with a Base for Voice or Instrument ... With a variation of each psalm tune on the same page by Matthew Camidge ... To which are prefixed, some introductory reasons for this publication, by W. Mason. pp. viii. 51. MS. ANNOTATIONS [by Arthur H. Mann]. *Printed by W. Blanchard: [York,]* 1789. 8°. **F. 1120. p.**

— [Ps. XII.] Lord God of Hosts. *Hymn*, by L. Housman. Melody by H. Lawes, *etc. H. Milford, for the Church Music Society: London*, 1920. *s. sh.* 8°. **C. 799. w. (28.)**

— [Ps. LXXII.] Most glorious Lord of Life. *Farley Castle.* [Hymn, words by] E. Spenser, *etc.* [*H. Milford, for the Church Music Society: London*, 1919.] *s. sh.* 8°. **C. 799. w. (27.)**

— The Power of Musick. *See* supra: [Ayres and Dialogues. Bk. 1.]

— Psalmody for a single Voice. *See* supra: [A Paraphrase upon the Psalmes of David.]

— Sing, fair Clorinda. S. S. C. *Oxford University Press: London*, 1936. 8°.
[*The John Playford Collection of Vocal Part-Music. No.* 14.] **F. 1777. i.**

— Sweet Echo. *See* supra: [Comus.]

The Treasury of Musick

— The Treasury of Musick: containing Ayres and Dialogues to Sing to the Theorbo-Lute or Basse-Viol. Composed by Mr. Henry Lawes ... and other Excellent Masters. In Three Books. [With prefaces by J. Playford.] *William Godbid for John Playford: London*, 1669. fol.
Wanting pp. 85–86 of Bk. 2. This is a reissue, under a general title, of Playford's First and Second Books of "Select Ayres and Dialogues" and H. Lawes's Third Book of "Ayres and Dialogues". **K. 3. m. 19.**

— [Another copy.] **R. M. 15. c. 7.**

— The Treasury of Musick: containing Ayres and Dialogues to sing to the Theorbo-Lute or Basse-viol ... In three books. [With a frontispiece to bk. 1.] 3 bk. *William Godbid for John Playford: London*, 1669. fol. **Hirsch III. 891.**

— The Treasury of Music. ⟨In three books.⟩ First published by John Playford, London 1669. [A facsimile.] pp. 114. 120. 48. *Gregg Press: Ridgewood, N.J.; printed in Western Germany*, 1966. fol. **G. 1276. ww.**

— Three Songs ... Edited by Anthony Lewis. pp. 24. *Lyrebird Press: Paris*, [1938.] 16°.
[*Lyrebird Books. no.* 7.] **A. 1170.**

— *See* LAWES (William) Dialogues for two Voices and continuo by W. and H. Lawes, *etc.* [1964.] 4°. [*Penn State Music Series. no.* 3.] **F. 1076.**

— View, Lisbia, view. For Female Voices, first verse by an anonymous author ... Second verse by A. G. Latham. *Oxford University Press: London*, 1936. 8°.
[*The John Playford Collection of Vocal Part-Music. No.* 13.] **F. 1777. i.**

— Why shoulds't thou swear I am forsworn? [Song, words by] R. Lovelace ... [From J. Playford's Select Ayres and Dialogues. Bk. 1.] Arranged by A. Howe. *W. Paxton & Co.: London*, 1936. 4°. **G. 1270. nn. (23.)**

— The Willow Garland ... [Song.] Extrait de Select Musicall Ayres and Dialogues ... John Playford, 1653, *etc. F. Alcan: Paris*, 1912. 8°.
Pp. 533 and 534 of "Robert Herrick," etc., by F. Delattre. **011853. dd. 1.**

LAWES (HENRY)

— *See* FRY (A. R.) From Campian to Lawes. Twenty-two selected Songs, *etc.* 1914. 4°. **G. 805. xx. (6.)**

— *See* PLAYFORD (J.) Select Ayres and Dialogues ... Composed by ... H. Lawes, *etc.* 1659. fol. **K. 7. i. 19. (1.)**

— *See* PLAYFORD (J.) Select Ayres and Dialogues to Sing to the Theorbo-Lute or Basse-Viol ... Composed by Mr. Henry Lawes, *etc.* 1669. fol. **K. 7. i. 19. (2.)**

— *See* PLAYFORD (J.) Select Musicall Ayres and Dialogues ... by ... H. Lawes, *etc.* 1652. fol. **K. 7. i. 17. (1.)**

— *See* PLAYFORD (J.) Select Musicall Ayres and Dialogues ... by ... Mr. Henry Lawes, *etc.* 1653. fol. **K. 7. i. 18.**

— *See* ROWLAND (E.) Ayres from Playford by H. Lawes, *etc.* 1935. 8°. **F. 217. g. (7.)**

— *See* STEVENS (R. J. S.) Seven Glees ... and two Glees from Melodies, by H. Lawes, *etc.* [1800?] *obl.* fol. **E. 319. (4.)**

LAWES (HENRY) and LAWES (WILLIAM)

— Choices Psalmes put into Musick, for Three Voices. The most of which may properly enough be sung by any three, with a Thorough Base ... With divers Elegies, set in Musick by sev'rall Friends, upon the death of W. Lawes. And ... nine Canons ... made by William Lawes. (Cantus primus.) (Cantus secundus.) (Bassus.) (Thorow Base.) 4 pt. *James Young, for Humphrey Moseley and for Richard Wodenothe: London*, 1648. 4°.
The composers of the Elegies are: H. Lawes, D' John Wilson, John Taylor, John Cob, Edm. Foster, Simon Ive, John Jinkins and John Hilton. **K. 3. h. 18.**

— [Another copy.]
The Cantus Primus wants fol. E4 (a blank leaf); the Cantus Secundus a similar leaf (P4), and the Bassus fol. Aa. **C. 110.**

— [Another copy.] **R. M. 15. f. 1. (7.)**

LAWES (WILLIAM)

COLLECTIONS, INSTRUMENTAL

— Select Consort Music. Transcribed and edited by Murray Lefkowitz. [With facsimiles. Score.] pp. xxv. 139. *Stainer and Bell: London*, 1963. fol.
[*Musica Britannica.* 21.] **N. 10.**

— Consort Sets in five and six Parts. Edited by David Pinto. [Score and parts.] 8 pt. *Faber Music: London*, 1979. fol. **g. 1655. j.**

COLLECTIONS, VOCAL

— Trois masques à la cour de Charles 1er d'Angleterre. The Triumph of Peace. The Triumphs of the Prince d'amour. Britannia triumphans. Livrets de John Shirley et William Davenant. Dessins d'Inigo Jones ... Introductions, commentaires et transcriptions par Murray Lefkowitz. pp. 355. *Éditions du centre national de la recherche scientifique: Paris*, 1970. 4°.
Part of "Le Choeur des muses". **S. E. 74/156.**

— Two Verse Anthems with Choruses to the common Tune: Have Mercy on us, Lord (Psalm 67) for s (or ba) SATB and organ and The Lamentation for ab SATB (ATB) and organ ... Edited by Gordon Dodd. pp. 11. *Stainer & Bell: London*, [1970.] 8°.
[*Church Choir Library. no.* 675.] **F. 1137. b.**

— Six Songs. Poems by Robert Herrick. Edited by Edward Huws Jones. [With a facsimile.] pp. 14. *Schott & Co.: London*, [1971.] 4°. **G. 809. z. (7.)**

LAWES (WILLIAM)

— Ayres a 3 voc: the first of two sets from the Shirley part books. ⟨Edited by Gordon Dodd.⟩ [Parts.] 3 pt. [*London*, 1966.] fol.
[*Viola da gamba Society, Supplementary Publication. no.* 38.]
g. 1081. a.

— Aire à 4 for two Trebles and two Basses. No. 21 of the 4-part works in B.M. Add. Ms. 40657–61. ⟨Edited by Gordon Dodd.⟩ [Parts.] 4 pt. [*London*, 1964?] *obl.* 8°.
[*Viola da gamba Society, Supplementary Publication. no.* 8.]
g. 1081. a.

— Aire in F. For two trebles and two basses. From the Shirley part books B.M. Add. MSS. 40657–61 ... No. 22 of the 4-part works. ⟨Edited by Gordon Dodd.⟩ [Parts.] 4 pt. [*London*, 1966.] *obl.* 8°.
[*Viola da gamba Society, Supplementary Publication. no.* 34.]
g. 1081. a.

— Aire à 4. No. 25 of the 4-part works in B.M. Addl. Ms. 40657–61, *etc.* ⟨Transcribed by Gordon Dodd.⟩ [Parts.] 4 pt. [*London*, 1964.] fol.
[*Viola da gamba Society, Supplementary Publication. no.* 5.]
g. 1081. a.

— Aire in G. No. 27 of the four-part works, in British Museum Add. mss. 40657–61, *etc.* ⟨[Followed by] Alfonso: Ferabosco: Fantasy No. [24.] Edited by Gordon Dodd.⟩ [Parts.] 4 pt. [*London*, 1971.] fol.
[*Viola da gamba Society, Supplementary Publication. no.* 75.]
g. 1081. a.

— All People that on Earth do dwell. (Psalm 100.) Verse anthem for tenor (or treble) and bass soli, congregation and organ. Edited by Gordon Dodd. pp. 7. *Stainer & Bell: London,* [1966.] 8°.
[*Church Choir Library. no.* 644.]
F. 1137. b.

— Come, lovely Chloris. Female Voices. S.S.C. *Oxford University Press: London,* 1937. 8°.
[*The John Playford Collection of Vocal Part-Music. No.* 12.]
F. 1777. i.

— Consort-Suite C-dur zu sechs Stimmen für 3 Violinen, Bratsche und 2 Violoncelli oder entsprechende andere Instrumente (Gamben, Fideln, Blockflöten, Lauten, Gitarren). ⟨Herausgegeben von Helmut Mönkemeyer.⟩ [Score.] pp. 16. *Heinrichshofen's Verlag: Wilhelmshaven,* [1966.] 4°. *Part of "Consortium".*
g. 934. a. (4.)

— Consort-Suite C-dur zu 5 Stimmen für 2 Violinen, 2 Bratschen und Violoncello oder entsprechende andere Instrumente (Gamben, Fideln, Blockflöten, Lauten, Gitarren). ⟨Herausgegeben von Helmut Mönkemeyer.⟩ [Score.] pp. 12. *Heinrichshofen's Verlag: Wilhelmshaven,* [1966.] 4°. *Part of "Consortium".*
g. 934. a. (3.)

— Four Dances. ⟨Selected from the second part of "A Musicall Banquet," 1651.⟩ Edited and arranged with realization of the continuo by Colin Sterne. [For descant or tenor recorder with P.F. or harpsichord accompaniment. Score and part.] 2 pt. *Schott & Co.: London,* [1961.] 4°.
[*Schott's Recorder Series. no.* 53.]
g. 112.

— Dialogues for two Voices and Continuo by William and H. Lawes. Edited by Roy Jesson. pp. 28. *Pennsylvania State University Press: University Park,* [1964.] 4°.
[*Penn State Music Series. no.* 3.]
F. 1076.

— Fantasy, Almaine and Ayre no. 4 in C. For 2 violins, bass viol and organ. ⟨Edited by Gordon Dodd.⟩ [Parts.] 4 pt. [*London*, 1967.] fol.
[*Viola da gamba Society, Supplementary Publication. no.* 42.]
g. 1081.a.

— Fantasia and Air. ⟨British Museum: Add. Mss. 29412.⟩ Arranged for recorder quintet 2D Tr T B by Ian Lawrence. [Score and parts.] 6 pt. *Faber Music: London,* 1972. 4°.
g. 109. ff. (5.)

LAWES (WILLIAM)

— Fantasy Suite No. 5 in D minor ... For violin, bass viol (or cello), organ (or harpsichord). ⟨Transcribed and edited by Cecily Arnold.⟩ [Score.] pp. 8. *Stainer & Bell: London,* [1957.] 4°.
[*Consort Music. no.* 3.]
g. 420. v. (5.)

— Fantasy Suite No. 5 in D minor ... For two violins, bass viol (or cello), organ (or harpsichord). ⟨Transcribed and edited by Cecily Arnold.⟩ [Score.] pp. 11. *Stainer & Bell: London,* [1957.] 4°.
[*Consort Music. no.* 4.]
g. 420. v. (5.)

— Gather sweet rosebuds. *See infra:* [Gather ye Rosebuds.]

Gather ye Rosebuds

— Gather your Rosebuds while you may. W. Lawes. ⟨A favorite glee. — Ancient Phillis has new Graces. Catch. C: Jenner — The Comical Fellow. Catch. W: Bates.⟩ pp. 3. *Printed for S: Babb:* [*London*, c. 1780.] fol.
G. 383. kk. (29.)

— Gather your rosebuds while you may. *See* GATHER. Gather your Rose-buds, *etc.* [Music by W. Lawes.] [1780?] *s. sh.* fol.
G. 308. (32.)

— Gather sweet rosebuds. *Favourite Glee,* for three voices, *etc.* [*London,*] 1794. *s. sh.* 4°.
The Lady's Magazine, May, 1794.
P. P. 5141.

— Gather your Rosebuds. [Glee for three voices.] Extrait de: The Musical Companion ... John Playford, 1667, *etc.* *F. Alcan: Paris,* 1912. 8°.
Pp. 534 *and* 535 *of "Robert Herrick," etc., by F. Delattre.*
011853. dd. 1.

— Gather ye Rosebuds, *etc.* [No. 1 of "Six Short Ayrs or Songs" from Playford's "Introduction to the Skill of Musick," 1654. Arranged for Female Voices by E. Rowland.] *J. Williams: London,* [1925.] 8°.
[*St. Cecilia. Series* 17. *No.* 18[*a*].]
F. 1526.

— Gather your Rosebuds. Female Voices. S.S.C. *Oxford University Press: London,* 1937. 8°.
[*The John Playford Collection of Vocal Part-Music. No.* 10.]
F. 1777. i.

— Gather ye Rosebuds ... Arranged ... as a Part-Song for Quartet or Chorus of mixed voices by G. Bantock. 1913. *See* PERIODICAL PUBLICATIONS. — *London.* The Musical Times, *etc.* No. 844. 1844, *etc.* 8°.
P. P. 1945. aa.

— O, my Clarissa. Female Voices. *Oxford University Press: London,* 1937. 8°.
[*The John Playford Collection of Vocal Part-Music. No.* 11.]
F. 1777. i.

— Pavan and two Aires a 4 in G minor. *See infra:* [Sett in G minor.]

— [The Royal Consort.] 5 Pieces ... from ... The Royal Consort. 2 descant, treble and tenor recorders, *etc.* ⟨Arranged and edited by Carl Dolmetsch.⟩ pp. 8. *Universal Edition: London,* [1959.] 4°.
[*Dolmetsch Recorder Series. no.* 45.]
g. 125.

— Sarabande from the Temple Masque ... The Tune and Bass from "Court Ayres" published by J. Playford, 1655. [Strings and P. F.] *See* BROWN (J.) *Mus. Bac.* The "Bronze" Album, *etc.* 1925. 4°. [*The Polychordia String Library. No.* 125.]
g. 918.

— [Sett in G minor.] Pavan and two Aires a 4 in G minor. 2 descants, treble (or tenor) and bass recorders, *etc.* ⟨Edited by Layton Ring.⟩ [Score and parts.] 5 pt. *Universal Edition: London,* [1964.] 4°.
[*Dolmetsch Recorder Series. no.* 77.]
g. 125.

LAWES (WILLIAM)

— Suite No. 1 in G minor for two Division Viols and Organ. Edited by Janet Richards. [Parts.] 3 pt. [*London*, 1974.] 4°. [*Viola da gamba Society. Supplementary Publication. no.* 91.]
g. 1081. a.

— [Suite for two Lutes.] Suite for two Guitars. Edited by Julian Bream. [Score.] pp. 4. *Faber Music: London*, 1967. 4°. *Part of "Faber Guitar Series".*
g. 660. ff. (2.)

— *See* BOYCE (W.) Cathedral music: being a collection ... of ... compositions ... by ... [Lawes, *etc.*] 1849. fol.
I. 211.

— *See* LAWES (H.) The Masque of Comus ... with Incidental Music, Dances, etc., by W. Lawes, *etc.* 1908. 8°.
E. 1594. v. (3.)

— *See* LAWES (H.) and LAWES (W.) Choice Psalmes put into Musick, for Three Voices, *etc.* 1648. 4°.
K. 3. h. 18.

— *See* PLAYFORD (J.) Courtly Masquing Ayres ... Composed by ... W. Lawes, *etc.* 1662. obl. 4°.
K. 2. c. 13.

— *See* PLAYFORD (J.) Select Musicall Ayres and Dialogues ... by ... Mr. William Lawes, *etc.* 1653. fol.
K. 7. i. 18.

— *See* PLAYFORD (J.) Select Ayres and Dialogues ... Composed by ... W. Lawes ... and other ... Masters of Musick. 1659. fol.
K. 7. i. 19. (1.)

LAWFELT

— La Lawffelt. Fanfare. *See* DAMPIERRE (de) *Marquis.*

LAWFORD (H. B.)

— In Confidence only ... Song, written and composed by H. B. Lawford. *Francis Bros. & Day: London*, [1889.] fol.
H. 1260. f. (22.)

LAWFUL

— Lawful Love. [Song.] *See* 'TIS. 'Tis true the Law I do profess. [1780?] *s. sh.* fol.
G. 312. (170.)

LAWGIVER

— The Lawgiver's Grave. Trio. *See* HORN (C.E.)

LAWLAND

— *See* LOWLAND.

LAWLANDS

— *See* LOWLANDS.

LAWLER (CHARLES)

— *See* LAWLOR.

LAWLER (DENNIS)

— Bang up in the city. *See* infra: [The Hoax.]

— [The Hoax.] Bang up in the city. A ... comic Song, sung ... in the Burletta of The Hoax, *etc. London*, [1830?] fol.
G. 383. (20.)

— The Soldier's Ditty, or the Death of General Moore ... Song [begins: "Fellow countrymen join me"]. *London*, [1809.] fol.
H. 2830. f. (91.)

LAWLER (THOMAS)

— "The sable flag rebellion rears." Cavatina [begins: "What means this wild and war-like hum"], written by C. Box. *London*, [1857.] fol.
H. 1771. l. (16.)

LAWLISS (LILLIAN)

— Scotia. Schottische. [P. F.] *Weekes & Co.: London*, 1895. fol.
h. 3285. q. (11.)

LAWLOR (CHARLES B.)

— At dear old Coney Isle. Song and chorus. Words and music by C. B. Lawlor. ⟨Arr. by Theo. F. Morse.⟩ pp. 5. *Howley, Haviland & Co.: New York*, [1897.] fol.
H. 3980. pp. (9.)

— The Best in the House is none too good for Reilly. [Song.] Words by James W. Blake. pp. 5. *Hugo V. Schlam: New York*, [1899.] fol.
H. 3980. pp. (10.)

— Daisy McIntyre. [Song.] Words by Jas. W. Blake. pp. 5. *Howley, Haviland & Co.: New York*, [1897.] fol.
H. 3980. pp. (11.)

— Don't be woozy. [Song.] Words by Edgar Selden. pp. 5. *Howley Haviland Co.: New York*, [1897.] fol. *The date has been altered in MS. to 1898.*
H. 3980. pp. (12.)

— How can Things be on the Level when the World is round. [Song.] Words and music by C. B. Lawlor. pp. 5. *Charles B. Lawlor: New York*, [1904.] fol.
H. 3985. i. (12.)

— The Man in the Moon is a Lady. Song and refrain. Words & music by C. B. Lawlor. pp. 5. *M. Witmark & Sons: New York, Chicago*, [1896.] fol.
H. 3980. pp. (13.)

— Pretty Peggy. [Song.] Words and music by C. B. Lawlor. pp. 5. *C. B. Lawlor: New York*, [1906.] fol. *The date has been altered in MS. to 1907.*
H. 3985. i. (13.)

— Songs that take me back to Ireland. [Song.] Words & music by C. B. Lawlor. pp. 5. *M. Witmark & Sons: New York, etc.*, [1905.] fol.
H. 3985. i. (14.)

LAWLOR (CHARLES B.) and **BLAKE** (JAMES W.)

— Doolin and his Bike. [Song.] Words and music by C. B. Lawlor and J. W. Blake. ⟨Piano arrangement by Robert Recker.⟩ pp. 5. *Crescent Publishing Co.: New York*, [1895.] fol.
H. 3980. pp. (14.)

— Every Boy has quarreled with his first Sweetheart. [Song.] ⟨Words & music by C. B. Lawlor & J. W. Blake. Piano arrangement by Robert Recker.⟩ pp. 5. *Crescent Publishing Co.: New York*, [1895.] fol.
H. 3980. pp. (15.)

— Pretty Jennie Slattery. [Song.] Words and music by C. B. Lawlor and J. W. Blake. ⟨Arr. by Frank Banta.⟩ pp. 5. *Crescent Publishing Co.: New York*, [1895.] fol.
H. 3980. pp. (16.)

— She's somebody's Mother. (Song and refrain.) pp. 5. *T. B. Harms & Co.: [New York*, 1897.] fol.
H. 3980. pp. (17.)

— The Sidewalks of New York. [Song.] Words and music by C. B. Lawlor & J. W. Blake. pp. 3–5. *Howley, Haviland & Co.: [New York*, 1894.] fol.
H. 3980. pp. (18.)

— That's when you learn to love them more and more ... Descriptive song and refrain ... Words and music by C. B. Lawlor and J. W. Blake. pp. 5. *M. Witmark & Sons: New York, Chicago*, [1896.] fol.
H. 3980. pp. (19.)

— The Tramp that slept in Astor's Bed. [Song.] pp. 5. *Howley, Haviland & Co.: New York*, [1894.] fol. *The date has been altered by erasure to 1895.*
H. 3980. pp. (20.)

LAWLOR (Charles B.) and **BLAKE** (James W.)

— When you love them more and more. [Song.] Words and music by C. B. Lawlor and J. W. Blake. ⟨Piano arrangement by Robert Recker.⟩ pp. 5. *Crescent Publishing Co.: New York,* [1895.] fol. **H. 3980. pp. (21.)**

LAWN

— Lawn, as white as driven Snow. Song. *See* Linley (W.) [Shakspeare's Dramatic Songs. Vol. II]

— Lawn as white as driven Snow. [Song.] *See* Slater (G. A.)

— Lawn as white as driven Snow. [Song.] *See* Wilson (John) *Mus. Doc.* [Cheerfull Ayres.]

— Lawn Tennis. Song. *See* Carr (H.) and Rolt (B.) [The Girl for the Boy.]

— A Lawn Tennis Song. [Song.] *See* Gallatly (J. M.)

LAWRANCE ( ) Mrs

— Crossing the Bar. [Four-part song.] Words by Lord Tennyson. *Weekes & Co.: London,* [1898.] 8°. **F. 321. n. (22.)**

LAWRANCE (Alfred J.)

— The Blacksmith's Wedding. ⟨Song.⟩ Written and composed by A. J. Lawrence, Tom Mellor and Harry Gifford. [Staff and tonic sol-fa notation. Voice part.] *Francis, Day & Hunter: London,* [1909.] *s. sh.* fol. **H. 3985. i. (15.)**

— The Blacksmith's Wedding. ⟨Song.⟩ Written and composed by A. J. Lawrence, Tom Mellor and Harry Gifford. [With separate voice part.] 2 pt. *Francis, Day & Hunter: London,* [1909.] fol. **H. 3985. i. (16.)**

— Buttercup-Time. Song, words by T. Mellor. *J. Williams: London,* 1909. fol. **H. 1794. vv. (18.)**

— Down at the Country Fair.—A Pastoral Jingle.— Song, words by T. Mellor. *J. Williams: London,* 1909. fol. **H. 1794. vv. (19.)**

— "Every Time the Clock goes tick tock." [Song.] Words by A. E. Sidney Davis. pp. 4. *B. Feldman & Co.: London,* [1909.] fol. **H. 3985. i. (17.)**

— "Farewell, my little Bush-mate!" ⟨Song.⟩ Written by E. Espinosa, *etc.* [Staff and tonic sol-fa notation. Voice part.] *Francis, Day & Hunter: London,* [1906.] *s. sh.* fol. **H. 3985. i. (18.)**

— "Farewell, my little Bush-mate!" *etc.* ⟨Song.⟩ [With separate voice part.] 2 pt. *Francis, Day & Hunter: London,* [1906.] fol. **H. 3985. i. (19.)**

— Like your Apron and your Bonnet (and your little Quaker Gown). [Song.] Written by John P. Harrington. [Staff and tonic sol-fa notation.] pp. 4. *B. Feldman & C⁰: London,* [1911.] fol. *Feldman's Sixpenny Edition. no. 404.* **H. 1860. gg. (22.)**

— My little River Bungalow. ⟨Song.⟩ Written by George Arthurs, *etc.* [Staff and tonic sol-fa notation. Voice part.] *Francis, Day & Hunter: London,* [1909.] *s. sh.* fol. **H. 3985. i. (20.)**

— My little River Bungalow. ⟨Song.⟩ Written by George Arthurs. [With separate voice part.] 2 pt. *Francis, Day & Hunter: London,* [1909.] fol. **H. 3985. i. (21.)**

— "Pretty Pierrette." ⟨Song.⟩ Written by George Arthurs, *etc.* [Staff and tonic sol-fa notation. Voice part.] *Francis, Day & Hunter: London,* [1909.] *s. sh.* fol. **H. 3985. i. (22.)**

— "Pretty Pierrette," *etc.* ⟨Song.⟩ [With separate voice part.] 2 pt. *Francis, Day & Hunter: London,* [1909.] fol. **H. 3985. i. (23.)**

LAWRANCE (Alfred J.)

— "San San Soo," ... ⟨Song.⟩ Written by Percy Edgar. [Staff and tonic sol-fa notation. Voice part.] *Francis, Day & Hunter: London,* [1908.] *s. sh.* fol. **H. 3985. i. (24.)**

— San San Soo, *etc.* ⟨Song.⟩ [With separate voice part.] 2 pt. *Francis, Day & Hunter: London,* [1908.] fol. **H. 3985. i. (25.)**

— *See* Arthurs (George) "I saw Sandy to his front Street-door." ⟨Song.⟩ Written and composed by G. Arthurs ... and A. J. Lawrance. [1910.] *s. sh.* fol. **H. 3988. uu. (29.)**

— *See* Arthurs (George) "I saw Sandy to his front Street-door." ⟨Song.⟩ Written and composed by G. Arthurs ... and A. J. Lawrance. [1910.] fol. **H. 3988. uu. (30.)**

— *See* Arthurs (George) That's when a Fellow feels a Fool! [Song.] Words and music by G. Arthurs, A. J. Lawrance, *etc.* [1910.] fol. **H. 3988. uu. (43.)**

— [For editions and arrangements of songs written and composed by A. J. Lawrance in sole collaboration with George Arthurs:] *See* Arthurs (George) and Lawrance (A. J.)

— *See* Comer (Dave) I want you most of all (while you're away). [Song.] Written by D. Comer ... and A. J. Lawrance. [1917.] fol. **H. 3990. aa. (9.)**

— *See* Cooke (Leonard) The Bull-frogs' Carnival. ⟨Song.⟩ Written and composed by L. Cooke ... and A. J. Lawrance. [1910.] *s. sh.* fol. **H. 3990. cc. (34.)**

— *See* Cooke (Leonard) The Bull-frogs' Carnival, *etc.* ⟨Song.⟩ [1910.] fol. **H. 3990. cc. (35.)**

— *See* David (Worton) and Lawrance (A. J.) In Spooning-Time. ⟨Song.⟩ Written and composed by W. David and A. J. Lawrance. [1911.] fol. **H. 3991. (9.)**

— *See* Edgar (Percy) Moon, Moon, Moon! ... [Song.] Written and composed by P. Edgar, A. J. Lawrance, *etc.* [1909.] 4°. **H. 3983. aa. (16.)**

— *See* Gifford (Harry) My Belle of Bengal. ⟨Song.⟩ Written and composed by Gifford ... & Lawrance. [1908.] 4°. **H. 3984. (15.)**

— *See* Godfrey (Fred) "The Baby's Parade." ⟨Song.⟩ Written and composed by F. Godfrey ... and A. J. Lawrance. [1908.] fol. **H. 3984. c. (3.)**

— *See* Godfrey (Fred) Oh! the Love-birds. ⟨Song.⟩ Written and composed by Godfrey, Lawrance, *etc.* [1908.] *s. sh.* fol. **H. 3984. c. (19.)**

— *See* Godfrey (Fred) Oh! the Love-birds. ⟨Song.⟩ Written and composed by Godfrey, Lawrance and Gifford. [1908.] fol. **H. 3984. c. (20.)**

— *See* Godfrey (Fred) "Underneath your Mushroom Umbrella." ⟨Song.⟩ Written and composed by F. Godfrey, A. J. Lawrance, *etc.* [1909.] *s. sh.* fol. **H. 3984. c. (25.)**

— *See* Godfrey (Fred) "Underneath your Mushroom Umbrella." ⟨Song.⟩ Written and composed by F. Godfrey, A. J. Lawrance, *etc.* [1909.] fol. **H. 3984. c. (26.)**

— *See* Godfrey (Fred) and Lawrance (A. J.) "I love to hear you, Joan" ... ⟨Song.⟩ Written and composed by F. Godfrey and A. J. Lawrance. [1908.] *s. sh.* fol. **H. 3984. c. (37.)**

— *See* Godfrey (Fred) and Lawrance (A. J.) "I love to hear you, Joan" ... ⟨Song.⟩ Written and composed by F. Godfrey and A. J. Lawrance. [1908.] fol. **H. 3984. c. (38.)**

— *See* Letters (Will) Ring up Lucky Boy, London. [Song.] Written and composed by W. Letters, A. J. Lawrance, *etc.* [1909.] 4°. **H. 3985. x. (54.)**

LAWRANCE (Alfred J.)

— [For editions and arrangements of songs written and composed by A. J. Lawrance in collaboration with Tom Mellor and Harry Gifford:] *See* also MELLOR (Tom)

— *See* MELLOR (Tom) "Sloe-eyes." ⟨Song.⟩ Written and composed by T. Mellor ... and A. J. Lawrance. [1909.] *s. sh.* fol. **H. 3985. rr. (7.)**

LAWRANCE (Alfred J.) and ELLIOTT (G. H.)

— "How d'you do, my Baby?" ... ⟨Song.⟩ Written and composed by A. J. Lawrance & G. H. Elliott. [Staff and tonic sol-fa notation. Voice part.] *Francis, Day & Hunter: London,* [1909.] *s. sh.* fol. **H. 3985. i. (26.)**

— "How d'you do, my Baby?" *etc.* ⟨Song.⟩ [With separate voice part.] 2 pt. *Francis, Day & Hunter: London,* [1909.] fol. **H. 3985. i. (27.)**

— "She gets more like the white Gals ev'ry Day" ... ⟨Song.⟩ Written and composed by A. J. Lawrance and G. H. Elliott. [Staff and tonic sol-fa notation. Voice part.] *Francis, Day & Hunter: London,* [1909.] *s. sh.* fol. **H. 3985. i. (28.)**

— "She gets more like the white Gals ev'ry Day," *etc.* ⟨Song.⟩ [With separate voice part.] 2 pt. *Francis, Day & Hunter: London,* [1909.] fol. **H. 3985. i. (29.)**

LAWRANCE (Alfred J.) and GIFFORD (Harry)

— Billy Green. [Song.] Written and composed by Lawrence [*sic*]—Gifford. pp. 5. *Cooper, Kendis & Paley Music Pub. Co.: New York,* [1907.] fol. **H. 3985. i. (30.)**

— Billy Green. ⟨Song.⟩ Written and composed by A. J. Lawrance and H. Gifford, *etc.* [With separate voice part.] 2 pt. *Francis, Day & Hunter: London,* [1907.] fol. **H. 3985. i. (31.)**

— Caroo ... ⟨Song.⟩ Written and composed by A. J. Lawrance & H. Gifford, *etc.* [Staff and tonic sol-fa notation. Voice part.] *Francis, Day & Hunter: London,* [1906.] *s. sh.* fol. **H. 3985. i. (32.)**

— Caroo, *etc.* ⟨Song.⟩ [With separate voice part.] 2 pt. *Francis, Day & Hunter: London,* [1906.] fol. *Followed by a dance and the arrangement of the chorus for S.A.T.B.* **H. 3985. i. (33.)**

— Come with me to Dixie Land. ⟨Song.⟩ Written and composed by A. J. Lawrance and H. Gifford. [Staff and tonic sol-fa notation. Voice part.] *Francis, Day & Hunter: London,* [1909.] *s. sh.* fol. **H. 3985. i. (34.)**

— Come with me to Dixie Land, *etc.* ⟨Song.⟩ [With separate voice part.] 2 pt. *Francis, Day & Hunter: London,* [1909.] fol. **H. 3985. i. (35.)**

— The Daisy and the Sunflower. ⟨Song.⟩ Written and composed by A. J. Lawrance and H. Gifford. [Staff and tonic sol-fa notation. Voice part.] *Francis, Day & Hunter: London,* [1908.] *s. sh.* fol. **H. 3985. i. (36.)**

— The Daisy and the Sunflower, *etc.* ⟨Song.⟩ [With separate voice part.] 2 pt. *Francis, Day & Hunter: London,* [1908.] fol. **H. 3985. i. (37.)**

— "Don't cry, little Girl!" ... ⟨Song.⟩ Written and composed by A. J. Lawrance and H. Gifford, *etc.* [Staff and tonic sol-fa notation. Voice part.] *Francis, Day & Hunter: London,* [1905.] *s. sh.* fol. **H. 3985. i. (38.)**

— "Don't cry, little Girl!" *etc.* ⟨Song.⟩ [With separate voice part.] 2 pt. *Francis, Day & Hunter: London,* [1905.] fol. **H. 3985. i. (39.)**

— "Don't stand there—!" ⟨Song.⟩ Written and composed by A. J. Lawrance and H. Gifford, *etc.* [Staff and tonic sol-fa notation. Voice part.] *Francis, Day & Hunter: London,* [1904.] *s. sh.* fol. **H. 3985. i. (40.)**

LAWRANCE (Alfred J.) and GIFFORD (Harry)

— "Don't stand there—!" *etc.* ⟨Song.⟩ [With separate voice part.] 2 pt. *Francis, Day & Hunter: London,* [1904.] fol. **H. 3985. i. (41.)**

— Don't you know a different Game to that? [Song.] Written and composed by A. J. Lawrance and H. Gifford. pp. 4. *Reeder & Walsh: London,* [1905.] fol. *Reeder & Walsh's Sixpenny Musical Marvels. no. 20.* **H. 3985. i. (42.)**

— "Firefly." ⟨Song.⟩ Written and composed by A. J. Lawrance & H. Gifford. [Staff and tonic sol-fa notation. Voice part.] *Francis, Day & Hunter: London,* [1906.] *s. sh.* fol. **H. 3985. i. (43.)**

— "Firefly," *etc.* ⟨Song.⟩ [With separate voice part.] 2 pt. *Francis, Day & Hunter: London,* [1906.] fol. **H. 3985. i. (44.)**

— The Fireman's Song ... Written and composed by A. J. Lawrance and H. Gifford. [Staff and tonic sol-fa notation. Voice part.] *Francis, Day & Hunter: London,* [1906.] *s. sh.* fol. **H. 3985. i. (45.)**

— The Fireman's Song, *etc.* [With separate voice part.] 2 pt. *Francis, Day & Hunter: London,* [1906.] fol. **H. 3985. i. (46.)**

— "Good-bye, my little London Girl!" Song. Written and composed by A. J. Lawrance and H. Gifford. [With separate voice part.] 2 pt. *Francis, Day & Hunter: London,* [1906.] fol. **H. 3985. j. (1.)**

— I can't Keep my Eyes off the Girls. [Song.] Written and composed by A. J. Lawrance & H. Gifford. pp. 4. *B. Feldman & Co.: London,* [1909.] 4°. **H. 3985. j. (2.)**

— I don't want a Girl for Sunday ... ⟨Song.⟩ Written and composed by A. J. Lawrance & H. Gifford. pp. 3. *Shapiro, von Tilzer Music Co.: London,* [1908.] 4°. **H. 3985. j. (3.)**

— "I want to be a Soldier!" ... ⟨Song.⟩ Written and composed by A. J. Lawrance and H. Gifford. [Staff and tonic sol-fa notation. Voice part.] *Francis, Day & Hunter: London,* [1905.] *s. sh.* fol. **H. 3985. j. (4.)**

— "I want to be a Soldier!" *etc.* ⟨Song.⟩ [With separate voice part.] 2 pt. *Francis, Day & Hunter: London,* [1905.] fol. **H. 3985. j. (5.)**

— Lazy Maisie. ⟨Song.⟩ Written and composed by A. J. Lawrance and H. Gifford, *etc.* [Staff and tonic sol-fa notation. Voice part.] *Francis, Day & Hunter: London,* [1904.] *s. sh.* fol. **H. 3985. j. (6.)**

— Lazy Maisie, *etc.* ⟨Song.⟩ [With separate voice part.] 2 pt. *Francis, Day & Hunter: London,* [1904.] fol. **H. 3985. j. (7.)**

— Ma Havana Queen ... ⟨Song.⟩ Written and composed by A. J. Lawrance and H. Gifford, *etc.* [Staff and tonic sol-fa notation. Voice part.] *Francis, Day & Hunter: London,* [1904.] *s. sh.* fol. **H. 3985. j. (8.)**

— Ma Havana Queen, *etc.* ⟨Song.⟩ [With separate voice part.] 2 pt. *Francis, Day & Hunter: London,* [1904.] fol. **H. 3985. j. (9.)**

— Ma little brown Girl ... Written and composed by A. J. Lawrance & H. Gifford. [Song. With separate voice part in tonic sol-fa.] 2 pt. *Reeder & Walsh: London,* [1904.] fol. **H. 3985. j. (10.)**

— "Maluma." ⟨Song.⟩ Written and composed by A. J. Lawrance & H. Gifford. [Staff and tonic sol-fa notation. Voice part.] *Francis, Day & Hunter: London,* [1906.] *s. sh.* fol. **H. 3985. j. (11.)**

— "Maluma," *etc.* ⟨Song.⟩ [With separate voice part.] 2 pt. *Francis, Day & Hunter: London,* [1906.] fol. **H. 3985. j. (12.)**

LAWRANCE (ALFRED J.) and GIFFORD (HARRY)

— "Moonbeam" ... ⟨Song.⟩ Written and composed by Lawrance and Gifford. [Staff and tonic sol-fa notation. Voice part.] *Francis, Day & Hunter: London*, [1909.] *s. sh.* fol.
H. 3985. j. (13.)

— "Moonbeam," *etc.* ⟨Song.⟩ [With separate voice part.] 2 pt. *Francis, Day & Hunter: London*, [1909.] fol.
H. 3985. j. (14.)

— My Jersey Lily. [Song.] Written and composed by A. J. Lawrance & H. Gifford. [With separate voice part.] 2 pt. *Hopwood & Crew: London*, [1904.] fol. **H. 3985. j. (15.)**

— "My little Redbreast" ... [Song.] Written & composed by A. J. Lawrance & H. Gifford. pp. 4. *Reeder & Walsh: London*, [1904.] fol. **H. 3985. j. (16.)**

— My Orange Girl ... ⟨Song.⟩ Written and composed by A. J. Lawrance & H. Gifford, *etc.* [Staff and tonic sol-fa notation. Voice part.] *Francis, Day & Hunter: London, New York*, [1906.] *s. sh.* fol. **H. 3985. j. (17.)**

— My Orange Girl, *etc.* ⟨Song.⟩ [Followed by the chorus arranged for S.A.T.B. With separate voice part.] 2 pt. *Francis, Day & Hunter: London*, [1906.] fol.
H. 3985. j. (18.)

— The Only Coon without a Gal. ⟨Song.⟩ Written and composed by A. J. Lawrance and H. Gifford, *etc.* [Staff and tonic sol-fa notation. Voice part.] *Francis, Day & Hunter: London*, [1905.] *s. sh.* fol. **H. 3985. j. (19.)**

— The Only Coon without a Gal, *etc.* ⟨Song.⟩ [With separate voice part.] 2 pt. *Francis, Day & Hunter: London*, [1905.] fol.
H. 3985. j. (20.)

— Sweet Eileen. ⟨Song.⟩ Written & composed by A. J. Lawrance and H. Gifford. [With separate voice part.] 2 pt. *Monte Carlo Publishing Co.: London*, [1906.] fol.
M.C.P. Co. Sixpenny Successes. no. 9. **H. 3985. j. (21.)**

— "What is your Name?" ... ⟨Song.⟩ Written and composed by A. J. Lawrance and H. Gifford. [Staff and tonic sol-fa notation. Voice part.] *Francis, Day & Hunter: London*, [1906.] *s. sh.* fol. **H. 3985. j. (22.)**

— "What is your Name?" *etc.* ⟨Song.⟩ [With separate voice part.] 2 pt. *Francis, Day & Hunter: London*, [1906.] fol.
H. 3985. j. (23.)

— "When my Ship is sailing." ⟨Song.⟩ Written and composed by A. J. Lawrance & H. Gifford, *etc.* [Staff and tonic sol-fa notation. Voice part.] *Francis, Day & Hunter: London*, [1905.] *s. sh.* fol. **H. 3985. j. (24.)**

— "When my Ship is sailing," *etc.* ⟨Song.⟩ [With separate voice part.] 2 pt. *Francis, Day & Hunter: London*, [1905.] fol.
H. 3985. j. (25.)

— "Which is the Key to your Heart?" ... ⟨Song.⟩ Written and composed by A. J. Lawrance & H. Gifford. [Staff and tonic sol-fa notation. Voice part.] *Francis, Day & Hunter: London*, [1906.] *s. sh.* fol. **H. 3985. j. (26.)**

— "Which is the Key to your Heart?" *etc.* ⟨Song.⟩ [With separate voice part.] 2 pt. *Francis, Day & Hunter: London*, [1906.] fol.
H. 3985. j. (27.)

— "Which Sailor-boy do you want?" ... ⟨Song.⟩ Written and composed by A. J. Lawrance and H. Gifford. [Staff and tonic sol-fa notation. Voice part.] *Francis, Day & Hunter: London, New York*, [1905.] *s. sh.* fol. **H. 3985. j. (28.)**

— "Which Sailor-boy do you want?" *etc.* ⟨Song.⟩ [With separate voice part.] 2 pt. *Francis, Day & Hunter: London*, [1905.] fol.
H. 3985. j. (29.)

— "Why don't you stick to one Girl?" ⟨Song.⟩ Written and composed by A. J. Lawrance and H. Gifford. [Staff and tonic sol-fa notation. Voice part.] *Francis, Day & Hunter: London, New York*, [1906.] *s. sh.* fol. **H. 3985. j. (30.)**

LAWRANCE (ALFRED J.) and GIFFORD (HARRY)

— "Why don't you stick to one Girl?" *etc.* ⟨Song.⟩ [With separate voice part.] 2 pt. *Francis, Day & Hunter: London*, [1906.] fol.
H. 3985. j. (31.)

LAWRANCE (ALFRED J.) and GODFREY (FRED)

— Ev'rybody calls her Rosa ... ⟨Song.⟩ Written and composed by A. J. Lawrance and F. Godfrey. [Staff and tonic sol-fa notation. Voice part.] *Francis, Day & Hunter: London*, [1908.] *s. sh.* fol. **H. 3985. j. (32.)**

— Ev'rybody calls her Rosa, *etc.* ⟨Song.⟩ [With separate voice part.] 2 pt. *Francis, Day & Hunter: London*, [1908.] fol.
H. 3983. j. (33.)

— Have you got another Girl at home like Mary? ⟨Song.⟩ Written and composed by A. J. Lawrance and F. Godfrey. *Star Music Publishing Co.: London*, [1908.] fol.
H. 3985. j. (34.)

LAWRANCE (ALFRED J.) and MELLOR (TOM)

— I've built a Bamboo Bungalow for you. ⟨Song.⟩ Written and composed by A. J. Lawrance and T. Mellor. [With separate voice part.] 2 pt. *Monte Carlo Publishing Co.: London*, [1905.] fol.
M.C.P. Co. "Sixpenny Successes". no. 7. **H. 3985. j. (35.)**

— I've built a Bamboo Bungalow for you, *etc.* [Song.] [c. 1905.] fol.
A pirated edition. **H. 1848. b. (12.)**

— "In the Blue Alsatian Mountains" ... ⟨Song.⟩ Written and composed by A. J. Lawrance & T. Mellor. pp. 4. *B. Feldman & Co.: London*, [1908.] 4°. **H. 3985. j. (36.)**

— "What's the Use of an old Log-cabin to me?" ⟨Song.⟩ Written and composed by A. J. Lawrance & T. Mellor, *etc.* [Staff and tonic sol-fa notation. Voice part.] *Francis, Day & Hunter: London*, [1905.] *s. sh.* fol. **H. 3985. j. (37.)**

— "Why don't you paddle your own Canoe?" ⟨Song.⟩ Written and composed by A. J. Lawrance & T. Mellor. [Staff and tonic sol-fa notation. Voice part.] *Francis, Day & Hunter: London*, [1906.] *s. sh.* fol. **H. 3985. j. (38.)**

— "Why don't you paddle your own Canoe?" *etc.* ⟨Song.⟩ [With separate voice part.] 2 pt. *Francis, Day & Hunter: London*, [1906.] fol. **H. 3985. j. (39.)**

— "Will you be my Eskimo?" ... ⟨Song.⟩ Written and composed by A. J. Lawrance and T. Mellor. [Staff and tonic sol-fa notation. Voice part.] *Francis, Day & Hunter: London*, [1905.] *s. sh.* fol. **H. 3985. j. (40.)**

LAWRANCE (EDWARD)

— Les agréables, six favorite melodies arranged for the pianoforte by E. Lawrance. 6 no. *London*, [1852.] fol.
h. 964. (2.)

— Album Blätter. Three pieces for the Piano. *London*, [1872.] fol. **h. 3104. (5.)**

— Andante grazioso for the Pianoforte. *London*, [1878.] fol.
h. 1484. c. (26.)

— L'Asphodèle, valse brillante. [P.F.] *London*, [1872.] fol.
h. 3104. (3.)

— Etude de Concert, grand galop for the Pianoforte. *London*, [1872.] fol. **h. 3104. (4.)**

— Fantasia. La Donna è mobile, from Verdi's opera Rigoletto for the piano forte. Op. 6. *London*, [1855.] fol.
h. 724. e. (18.)

— I think of thee, song [begins: "When his sweet note"]. Words by E. W. S. Davis. *London*, [1871.] fol. **H. 1775. t. (28.)**

LAWRANCE (EDWARD)

— Lied ohne Worte. [P.F.] *London*, [1872.] fol. **h. 3104. (1.)**

— Mai-Blümchen. Ein kleines Rondo. [P.F.] *London*, [1872.] fol. **h. 3104. (2.)**

— Deux nocturnes. No. 1. Morning. No. 2. Evening, for the piano forte. Op. 5. 2 no. *London*, [1855.] fol. **h. 724. e. (17.)**

— Souvenir de Donizetti. La Fille du Régiment, fanta[i]sie de salon, for the Piano ... Op. 7. Second edition. *H. White & Son: London*, [1872.] fol. **h. 3104. (6.)**

— A Village Festival (Danse rustique) for the Piano. *London*, [1872.] fol. **h. 3104. (7.)**

LAWRANCE (EDWARD) *Cerddor Tydfil*

— The Evening Hymn.—Abide with me.—[For four voices.] *Novello & Co.: London*, [1900.] 8°. **F. 1171. bb. (39.)**

— Gwarchae Harlech. Cantawd gadeiriol yr Eisteddfod, 1863. The Siege of Harlech: Chair Cantata of yr Eisteddfod, 1863 ... The Libretto by J. C. Hughes. English translation by D. T. Williams (Tydfylyn). *Wrexham*, [1866.] 8°. **E. 636.**

LAWRANCE (HENRY)

— "Would you mind passing the Salt?" ⟨Song.⟩ Written by Lester Reekie, *etc.* [Staff and tonic sol-fa notation. Voice part.] *Francis, Day & Hunter: London*, [1906.] *s. sh.* fol. **H. 3985. j. (41.)**

— "Would you mind passing the Salt?" *etc.* ⟨Song.⟩ [With separate voice part.] 2 pt. *Francis, Day & Hunter: London*, [1906.] fol. **H. 3985. j. (42.)**

LAWRANCE (PETER)

— Three little Suites for Brass Ensemble ... ⟨Score.⟩ Parts, *etc.* 12 pt. *Chester Music: London*, [1979.] 4°. [*Junior Just Brass. no. 2.*] **g. 1110. hh.**

LAWRANCE (WILCOX)

— Méditation. Andante affetuoso pour violon avec accompagnement de piano. Op. 2. *F. W. Chanot: London*, [1892.] fol. **h. 1681. k. (9.)**

— *See* SCHUBERT (F. P.) [Schwanengesang. No. 4. Ständchen.] Serenade ... Transcription ... by W. Lawrance. [1896.] fol. **h. 259. g. (39.)**

LAWREEN (J. B.)

— Who's that calling so sweet, ranch song & chorus newly arranged by Valentine Hemery. ⟨Words [and melody] by J. B. Lawreen [or rather, T. Deveen].⟩ [c. 1915.] fol. *See* HEMERY (Valentine) **H. 1601. mm. (13.)**

— Who's that calling so sweet? Ranch Song. Arranged for Male Voices by Purcell J. Mansfield (Op. 109, No. 2). Words by Terence Deveen. Melody by J. B. Lawreen [or rather, T. Deveen]. pp. 6. *Leonard, Gould & Bolttler: London*, 1946. 8°. [*L.G.B. Choral Repertoire. No. 54.*] **F. 1843. a.**

— Who's that calling so sweet? Ranch song ... Arranged for mixed voices by Purcell J. Mansfield. (Op. 109, No. 5a.) pp. 6. *Leonard, Gould & Bolttler: London*, [1948.] 8°. [*L.G.B. Choral Repertoire. no. 65.*] **F. 1843. a.**

LAWRENCE WRIGHT MUSIC COMPANY

— Lawrence Wright's First [*etc.*] Album of famous novelty Piano Solos by Z. Confrey (Duke Ellington, *etc.*). 5 no. *Lawrence Wright Music Co.: London*, [1933–37.] 4°. **g. 1399. (1.)**

LAWRENCE WRIGHT MUSIC COMPANY

— Lawrence Wright's First Album of world famous Waltzes by H. Nicholls, *etc.* [P. F.] *Lawrence Wright Music Co.: London*, [1934, *etc.*] 4°. **g. 1399. (2.)**

— Lawrence Wright's first Book of Tunes the World plays ... Famous piano pieces, *etc.* pp. 191. *Lawrence Wright Music Co.: London*, [1963.] 4°. *No more published.* **g. 665.**

— Lawrence Wright's Christmas Carols and Choruses, *etc.* [1937.] 4°. *See* NICHOLLS (H.) *pseud.* **F. 1842. d.**

— Lawrence Wright's Christmas Carols and Choruses ... fourth revised edition, *etc.* [1942.] 4°. *See* NICHOLLS (H.) *pseud.* **F. 607. tt. (21.)**

— Lawrence Wright's [1st, 3rd–7th] Dance Annual. *Lawrence Wright Music Co.: London*, [1920–25.] 4°. *Wanting No. 2. Subsequently merged with Lawrence Wright's Song Annual and catalogued accordingly.* **F. 1842. a.**

— Lawrence Wright's International Album. No. 1. Rumba, *etc.* (No. 2. Tango.) (No. 3. Blues.) (No. 4. Swing.) 4 no. *Lawrence Wright Music Co.: London*, [1942–44.] 4°. **F. 1842. e.**

— Lawrence Wright's 1st⟨–6th⟩ Monster Album, *etc.* 6 no. *Lawrence Wright Music Co.: London*, [1934–36.] 4°. **F. 1842. b.**

— Lawrence Wright's [1st] ⟨2nd, 3rd, 5th, 8th⟩ Song Annual, *etc.* ⟨Lawrence Wright's 10th–44th, 51st, 52nd, 55th Song & Dance Album⟩, *etc.* *Lawrence Wright Music Co.: London*, [1919–55.] 4°. *Imperfect; wanting no. 4, 6, 7, 9. With two editions of no. 29, 30. No. 45–50, 53, 54 were not published.* **F. 1842.**

— Lawrence Wright's Songs the World sings. Songs for T.V., radio, film, stage producers. 3 vol. *Lawrence Wright Music Co.: London*, [1956, 63.] 4°. **F. 1842. f.**

— Lawrence Wright's first [*etc.*] supreme Collection of famous Songs. *Lawrence Wright Music Co.: London*, [1963, *etc.*] 4°. **G. 1276. ff.**

— The Wright 1st (–5th) Ukulele ... Album, *etc.* (2nd, 3rd. Arranged by Kel Keech. 4th, 5th. Arranged by Alvin D. Keech.) 5 no. *Lawrence Wright Music Co.: London*, 1925–27. 8°. **F. 1842. c.**

LAWRENCE (   )

— *See* LAWRANCE (Alfred J.)

LAWRENCE (A. M.)

— "Must thou go;" song, the words by Lord Byron, arranged by Mrs. Lawrence. *London*, [1838.] fol. **H. 1675. (9.)**

LAWRENCE (ALAN)

— [The Merchant of Venice.] Incidental Music for Guitar from the Old Vic 1980 Production The Merchant of Venice. A facsimile of the original manuscript. pp. 16. *Fentone Music: London*, [1980.] fol. **g. 1651. e. (7.)**

— Time Pieces. A collection of works for musical clocks by Handel and Haydn. Arranged for guitar by Alan Lawrence. [With a facsimile and illustrations.] pp. 24. *Fentone Music: London*, [1978.] 4°. **g. 1650. t. (5.)**

— Ten traditional English Carols. Arranged for guitar by Alan Lawrence. pp. 8. *Fentone Music: London*, [1978.] 4°. **g. 1650. t. (6.)**

— *See* JESSETT (Michael) and LAWRENCE (A.) Dancing Days. Twelve carols for guitar arranged by M. Jessett and A. Lawrence, *etc.* [1976.] 4°. **F. 1892. n. (8.)**

LAWRENCE (Albert E.)

— All bran' new! Written and composed by A. E. Lawrence, *etc.* [Song. Staff and tonic sol-fa notation. Voice part.] *Francis, Day & Hunter: London*, [1897.] *s. sh.* fol.   **H. 3980. pp. (22.)**

— Keep on the sunny Side. ⟨Song.⟩ Written & composed by A. E. Lawrence, Geo. Lester & Edgar Bateman, *etc.* [Staff and tonic sol-fa notation. Voice part.] *Francis, Day & Hunter: London*, [1900.] *s. sh.* fol.   **H. 3985. k. (1.)**

— Keep on the sunny Side ... ⟨Song.⟩ Written and composed by A. E. Lawrence, Geo. Lester and Edgar Bateman, *etc.* [With separate voice part.] 2 pt. *Francis, Day & Hunter: London*, [1900.] fol.   **H. 3985. k. (2.)**

— "Sweethearts still" ... [Song.] Words by George Lester. pp. 5. *Reeder & Walsh: London*, [1901.] fol.   **H. 3985. k. (3.)**

— *See* BARNES (Fred J.) and LAWRENCE (A. E.) That's another funny Tale he had to tell ... ⟨Song.⟩ Written and composed by F. J. Barnes and A. E. Lawrence, *etc.* [1904.] *s. sh.* fol.   **H. 3982. i. (16.)**

— *See* BARNES (Fred J.) and LAWRENCE (A. E.) That's another funny Tale he had to tell, *etc.* ⟨Song. Written and composed by F. J. Barnes and A. E. Lawrence.⟩ [1904.] fol.   **H. 3982. i. (17.)**

— *See* CARTER (Frank W.) and LAWRENCE (A. E.) Mother went out to find one, *etc.* ⟨Song.⟩ [1900.] *s. sh.* fol.   **H. 3982. mm. (11.)**

— *See* COLE (Herbert) and LAWRENCE (A. E.) Oh, it's homely! very homely! [Song.] Written and composed by H. Cole and A. E. Lawrence. [1899.] *s. sh.* fol.   **H. 3980. k. (39.)**

— *See* SCOTT (Maurice) and LAWRENCE (A. E.) "Though you may leave me now." ⟨Song.⟩ Written and composed by M. Scott and A. E. Lawrence. [1908.] *s. sh.* fol.   **H. 3987. q. (21.)**

— *See* SCOTT (Maurice) and LAWRENCE (A. E.) "Though you may leave me now," *etc.* ⟨Song.⟩ [1908.] fol.   **H. 3987. q. (22.)**

— *See* WESTON (Robert P.) and LAWRENCE (A. E.) A Week and a Day ... ⟨Song.⟩ Written and composed by R. P. Weston and A. E. Lawrence, *etc.* [1906.] *s. sh.* fol.   **H. 3988. w. (50.)**

— *See* WESTON (Robert P.) and LAWRENCE (A. E.) A Week and a Day, *etc.* ⟨Song.⟩ [1906.] fol.   **H. 3988. w. (51.)**

LAWRENCE (Albert E.) and LESTER (George)

— Ain't it all right, eh? ⟨Song.⟩ Written and composed by A. E. Lawrence and G. Lester, *etc.* [Staff and tonic sol-fa notation. Voice part.] *Francis, Day & Hunter: London*, [1901.] *s. sh.* fol.   **H. 3985. k. (4.)**

— Ain't it all right, eh? *etc.* ⟨Song.⟩ [With separate voice part.] 2 pt. *Francis, Day & Hunter: London*, [1901.] fol.   **H. 3985. k. (5.)**

— All wobberlee, *etc.* [Song. Staff and tonic sol-fa notation. Voice part.] *Francis, Day & Hunter: London*, [1899.] *s. sh.* fol.   **H. 3980. pp. (23.)**

— Are you sure you've had enough? ⟨Song.⟩ Written and composed by A. E. Lawrence and G. Lester, *etc.* [Staff and tonic sol-fa notation. Voice part.] *Francis, Day & Hunter: London*, [1900.] *s. sh.* fol.   **H. 3985. k. (6.)**

— A Bit coming in every Week. ⟨Song.⟩ Written and composed by A. E. Lawrence and G. Lester, *etc.* [Staff and tonic sol-fa notation. Voice part.] *Francis, Day & Hunter: London*, [1901.] *s. sh.* fol.   **H. 3985. k. (7.)**

— A Bit coming in every Week, *etc.* ⟨Song.⟩ [With separate voice part.] 2 pt. *Francis, Day & Hunter: London*, [1901.] fol.   **H. 3985. k. (8.)**

LAWRENCE (Albert E.) and LESTER (George)

— He's got it to come. ⟨Song.⟩ Written and composed by A. E. Lawrence and G. Lester, *etc.* [Staff and tonic sol-fa notation. Voice part.] *Francis, Day & Hunter: London*, [1901.] *s. sh.* fol.   **H. 3985. k. (9.)**

— He's got it to come, *etc.* ⟨Song.⟩ [With separate voice part.] 2 pt. *Francis, Day & Hunter: London*, [1901.] fol.   **H. 3985. k. (10.)**

— How are the People at Home? ... ⟨Song.⟩ Written and composed by A. E. Lawrence and G. Lester, *etc.* [Staff and tonic sol-fa notation. Voice part.] *Francis, Day & Hunter: London*, [1900.] *s. sh.* fol.   **H. 3985. k. (11.)**

— How are the People at Home, *etc.* ⟨Song.⟩ [With separate voice part.] 2 pt. *Francis, Day & Hunter: London*, [1900.] fol.   **H. 3985. k. (12.)**

— I'd never noticed it before. Written and composed by A. E. Lawrence and G. Lester, *etc.* [Song. Staff and tonic sol-fa notation. Voice part.] *Francis, Day & Hunter: London*, [1899.] *s. sh.* fol.   **H. 3980. pp. (24.)**

— I diddle-diddle! ⟨Song.⟩ Written and composed by A. E. Lawrence and G. Lester, *etc.* [Staff and tonic sol-fa notation. Voice part.] *Francis, Day & Hunter: London*, [1902.] *s. sh.* fol.   **H. 3985. k. (13.)**

— I diddle-diddle! *etc.* ⟨Song.⟩ [With separate voice part.] 2 pt. *Francis, Day & Hunter: London*, [1902.] fol.   **H. 3985. k. (14.)**

— I'm fond of what I like. Written and composed by A. E. Lawrence & G. Lester, *etc.* [Song. Staff and tonic sol-fa notation. Voice part.] *Francis, Day & Hunter: London*, [1899.] *s. sh.* fol.   **H. 3980. pp. (25.)**

— I thought I'd get out of the Way. ⟨Song.⟩ Written & composed by A. E. Lawrence & G. Lester, *etc.* [Staff and tonic sol-fa notation. Voice part.] *Francis, Day & Hunter: London*, [1903.] *s. sh.* fol.   **H. 3985. k. (15.)**

— I thought I'd get out of the Way, *etc.* ⟨Song.⟩ [With separate voice part.] 2 pt. *Francis, Day & Hunter: London*, [1903.] fol.   **H. 3985. k. (16.)**

— If you've only got a Top-back-room. ⟨Song.⟩ Written and composed by A. E. Lawrence and G. Lester, *etc.* [Staff and tonic sol-fa notation. Voice part.] *Francis, Day & Hunter: London*, [1906.] *s. sh.* fol.   **H. 3985. k. (17.)**

— If you've only got a Top-back-room, *etc.* ⟨Song.⟩ [With separate voice part.] 2 pt. *Francis, Day & Hunter: London*, [1906.] fol.   **H. 3985. k. (18.)**

— It's a "Licker" what Liquor will do. ⟨Song.⟩ Written and composed by A. E. Lawrence & G. Lester, *etc.* [Staff and tonic sol-fa notation. Voice part.] *Francis, Day & Hunter: London*, [1901.] *s. sh.* fol.   **H. 3985. k. (19.)**

— It's a "Licker" what Liquor will do, *etc.* ⟨Song.⟩ [With separate voice part.] 2 pt. *Francis, Day & Hunter: London*, [1901.] fol.   **H. 3985. k. (20.)**

— It's nice to have a Home of your own. ⟨Song.⟩ Written and composed by A. E. Lawrence & G. Lester, *etc.* [Staff and tonic sol-fa notation. Voice part.] *Francis, Day & Hunter: London*, [1900.] *s. sh.* fol.   **H. 3985. k. (21.)**

— "Let me alone, I'm busy." ⟨Song.⟩ Written & composed by A. E. Lawrence & G. Lester, *etc.* [Staff and tonic sol-fa notation. Voice part.] *Francis, Day & Hunter: London*, [1901.] *s. sh.* fol.   **H. 3985. k. (22.)**

— Let me alone, I'm busy, *etc.* ⟨Song.⟩ [With separate voice part.] 2 pt. *Francis, Day & Hunter: London*, [1901.] fol.   **H. 3985. k. (23.)**

LAWRENCE (ALBERT E.) and LESTER (GEORGE)

— Making the Ladies laugh. Written and composed by A. E. Lawrence and G. Lester, *etc.* [Song. Staff and tonic sol-fa notation. Voice part.] *Francis, Day & Hunter: London,* [1899.] *s. sh.* fol.   **H. 3980. pp. (26.)**

— Monday's a lucky Day for me. ⟨Song.⟩ Written and composed by A. E. Lawrence and G. Lester, *etc.* [Staff and tonic sol-fa notation. Voice part.] *Francis, Day & Hunter: London,* [1903.] *s. sh.* fol.   **H. 3985. k. (24.)**

— Monday's a lucky Day for me, *etc.* ⟨Song.⟩ [With separate voice part.] 2 pt. *Francis, Day & Hunter: London,* [1903.] fol.   **H. 3985. k. (25.)**

— Mothers of England. ⟨Song.⟩ Written and composed by A. E. Lawrence & G. Lester, *etc.* [Staff and tonic sol-fa notation. Voice part.] *Francis, Day & Hunter: London,* [1903.] *s. sh.* fol.   **H. 3985. k. (26.)**

— Mothers of England, *etc.* ⟨Song.⟩ [With separate voice part.] 2 pt. *Francis, Day & Hunter: London,* [1903.] fol.   **H. 3985. k. (27.)**

— My best old English Pal. ⟨Song.⟩ Written and composed by A. E. Lawrence & G. Lester, *etc.* [Staff and tonic sol-fa notation. Voice part.] *Francis, Day & Hunter: London,* [1903.] *s. sh.* fol.   **H. 3985. k. (28.)**

— My best old English Pal, *etc.* ⟨Song. Arranged by H. E. Peltrer.⟩ [With separate voice part.] 2 pt. *Francis, Day & Hunter: London,* [1903.] fol.   **H. 3985. k. (29.)**

— Oh my! what can the Matter be? ⟨Song.⟩ Written and composed by A. E. Lawrence and G. Lester, *etc.* [Staff and tonic sol-fa notation. Voice part.] *Francis, Day & Hunter: London,* [1900.] *s. sh.* fol.   **H. 3985. k. (30.)**

— One of my Sunday Pals. ⟨Song.⟩ Written and composed by A. E. Lawrence & G. Lester, *etc.* [Staff and tonic sol-fa notation. Voice part.] *Francis, Day & Hunter: London,* [1900.] *s. sh.* fol.   **H. 3985. k. (31.)**

— One of my Sunday Pals, *etc.* ⟨Song.⟩ [With separate voice part.] 2 pt. *Francis, Day & Hunter: London,* [1900.] fol.   **H. 3985. k. (32.)**

— A Real good Wife. ⟨Song.⟩ Written and composed by A. E. Lawrence and G. Lester, *etc.* [Staff and tonic sol-fa notation. Voice part.] *Francis, Day & Hunter: London,* [1902.] *s. sh.* fol.   **H. 3985. k. (33.)**

— A Real good Wife, *etc.* ⟨Song.⟩ [With separate voice part.] 2 pt. *Francis, Day & Hunter: London,* [1902.] fol.   **H. 3985. k. (34.)**

— She need not have a pretty Face. ⟨Song.⟩ Arranged by John Neat. Written and composed by A. E. Lawrence & G. Lester. pp. 4. *B. Feldman & Co.: London,* [1903.] fol.   **H. 3985. k. (35.)**

— Somebody's Wife. ⟨Song.⟩ Written and composed by A. E. Lawrence and G. Lester, *etc.* [Staff and tonic sol-fa notation. Voice part.] *Francis, Day & Hunter: London,* [1904.] *s. sh.* fol.   **H. 3985. k. (36.)**

— Somebody's Wife, *etc.* ⟨Song. Arranged by William Hargreaves.⟩ [With separate voice part.] 2 pt. *Francis, Day & Hunter: London,* [1904.] fol.   **H. 3985. k. (37.)**

— Sullivan's Birthday Party. ⟨Song.⟩ Written and composed by A. E. Lawrence and G. Lester. [With separate voice part.] 2 pt. *Francis, Day & Hunter: London,* [1901.] fol.   **H. 3985. k. (38.)**

— Sweetheart, come back again. ⟨Song.⟩ Written and composed by A. E. Lawrence and G. Lester, *etc.* [Staff and tonic sol-fa notation. Voice part.] *Francis, Day & Hunter: London,* [1902.] *s. sh.* fol.   **H. 3985. k. (39.)**

LAWRENCE (ALBERT E.) and LESTER (GEORGE)

— Sweetheart, come back again, *etc.* ⟨Song.⟩ [With separate voice part.] 2 pt. *Francis, Day & Hunter: London,* [1902.] fol.   **H. 3985. k. (40.)**

— That is Home! ... ⟨Song.⟩ Written and composed by A. E. Lawrence & G. Lester, *etc.* ⟨Staff and tonic sol-fa notation. Voice part.⟩ *Francis, Day & Hunter: London,* [1904.] *s. sh.* fol.   **H. 3985. k. (41.)**

— That is Home! *etc.* ⟨Song.⟩ [With separate voice part.] 2 pt. *Francis, Day & Hunter: London,* [1904.] fol.   **H. 3985. k. (42.)**

— "There's another one coming out." Written & composed by A. E. Lawrence & G. Lester, *etc.* [Song. Staff and tonic sol-fa notation. Voice part.] *Francis, Day & Hunter: London,* [1899.] *s. sh.* fol.   **H. 3980. pp. (27.)**

— They can all laugh at me. ⟨Song.⟩ Written and composed by A. E. Lawrence & G. Lester, *etc.* [Staff and tonic sol-fa notation. Voice part.] *Francis, Day & Hunter: London,* [1901.] *s. sh.* fol.   **H. 3985. k. (43.)**

— They can all laugh at me, *etc.* ⟨Song.⟩ [With separate voice part.] 2 pt. *Francis, Day & Hunter: London,* [1901.] fol.   **H. 3985. k. (44.)**

— The Village Wedding. Written and composed by A. E. Lawrence and G. Lester, *etc.* [Song. Staff and tonic sol-fa notation. Voice part.] *Francis, Day & Hunter: London,* [1899.] *s. sh.* fol.   **H. 3980. pp. (28.)**

— Wages. ⟨Song.⟩ Written and composed by A. E. Lawrence and G. Lester, *etc.* [Staff and tonic sol-fa notation. Voice part.] *Francis, Day & Hunter: London,* [1901.] *s. sh.* fol.   **H. 3985. k. (45.)**

— Wages, *etc.* ⟨Song.⟩ [With separate voice part.] 2 pt. *Francis, Day & Hunter: London,* [1901.] fol.   **H. 3985. k. (46.)**

— When my little Jack's a Man. ⟨Song.⟩ Written and composed by A. E. Lawrence and G. Lester. [Staff and tonic sol-fa notation. Voice part.] *Francis, Day & Hunter: London,* [1902.] *s. sh.* fol.   **H. 3985. k. (47.)**

— When my little Jack's a Man. ⟨Song.⟩ Written and composed by A. E. Lawrence & G. Lester, *etc.* [Staff and tonic sol-fa notation. Voice part.] *Francis, Day & Hunter: London,* [1903.] *s. sh.* fol.
A different version from the preceding.   **H. 3985. k. (48.)**

— When my little Jack's a Man, *etc.* ⟨Song.⟩ [With separate voice part.] 2 pt. *Francis, Day & Hunter: London,* [1903.] fol.   **H. 3985. k. (49.)**

— When the Children have gone to Bed. ⟨Song.⟩ Written and composed by A. E. Lawrence and G. Lester, *etc.* [Staff and tonic sol-fa notation. Voice part.] *Francis, Day & Hunter: London,* [1901.] *s. sh.* fol.   **H. 3985. k. (50.)**

— When the Children have gone to Bed, *etc.* ⟨Song.⟩ [With separate voice part.] 2 pt. *Francis, Day & Hunter: London,* [1901.] fol.   **H. 3985. k. (51.)**

— When they all go out to Work. ⟨Song.⟩ Written and composed by A. E. Lawrence & G. Lester, *etc.* [Staff and tonic sol-fa notation. Voice part.] *Francis, Day & Hunter: London,* [1901.] *s. sh.* fol.   **H. 3985. k. (52.)**

— When they all go out to Work, *etc.* ⟨Song.⟩ [With separate voice part.] 2 pt. *Francis, Day & Hunter: London,* [1901.] fol.   **H. 3985. k. (53.)**

— A Woman's Work is never done. ⟨Song.⟩ Written and composed by A. E. Lawrence and G. Lester, *etc.* [Staff and tonic sol-fa notation. Voice part.] *Francis, Day & Hunter: London,* [1903.] *s. sh.* fol.   **H. 3985. k. (54.)**

— A Woman's Work is never done, *etc.* ⟨Song.⟩ [With separate voice part.] 2 pt. *Francis, Day & Hunter: London,* [1903.] fol.   **H. 3985. k. (55.)**

LAWRENCE (ALBERT E.) and LESTER (GEORGE)

— "You've got nothing to worry about." ⟨Song.⟩ Written and composed by A. E. Lawrence and G. Lester, *etc.* [Staff and tonic sol-fa notation. Voice part.] *Francis, Day & Hunter: London,* [1901.] *s. sh.* fol.   **H. 3985. k. (56.)**

— You've got nothing to worry about. ⟨Song.⟩ [With separate voice part.] 2 pt. *Francis, Day & Hunter: London,* [1901.] fol.   **H. 3985. k. (57.)**

— You've never seen these before. ⟨Song.⟩ Written and composed by A. E. Lawrence and G. Lester, *etc.* [Staff and tonic sol-fa notation. Voice part.] *Francis, Day & Hunter: London,* [1900.] *s. sh.* fol.   **H. 3985. k. (58.)**

— You've never seen these before, *etc.* ⟨Song.⟩ [With separate voice part.] 2 pt. *Francis, Day & Hunter: London,* [1900.] fol.   **H. 3985. k. (59.)**

LAWRENCE (ALBERT E.) and LINCOLN (FRED)

— That little Home of mine. ⟨Song.⟩ Written and composed by A. E. Lawrence and F. Lincoln, *etc.* [Staff and tonic sol-fa notation. Voice part.] *Francis, Day & Hunter: London,* [1903.] *s. sh.* fol.   **H. 3985. k. (60.)**

— That little Home of mine, *etc.* ⟨Song.⟩ [With separate voice part.] 2 pt. *Francis, Day & Hunter: London,* [1903.] fol.   **H. 3985. k. (61.)**

LAWRENCE (ALFRED J.)

— I often wondered if my Mother knew. [Musical monologue.] Written by A. Matz and F. Elton, *etc. Reynolds & Co.: London,* 1920. fol.
Musical Monologues, No. 214.   **H. 2087.**

LAWRENCE (ARTHUR EVELYN BARNES)

— *See* HYMNS. [*English.*] The Church Mission Hymn Book, *etc.* [Compiled by A. E. Barnes-Lawrence.] [1914.] 8°.   **E. 497. e.**

LAWRENCE (CHARLES)

— Come, fly with me! [Four-part song.] Words by A. Lewis. [1872.] *See* CRAMPTON (T.) The Part-Singer, *etc.* No. 109. [1868–98.] 8°.   **E. 628.**

— Fading away. [Four-part song.] Words by E. Green. [1890.] *See* CRAMPTON (T.) The Part-Singer, *etc.* No. 149. [1868–98.] 8°.   **E. 628.**

— Good Morrow. Four-part song. Words by Miss M. R. Mitford. *London,* [1877.] 8°.   **E. 1708.**

— The Legend of the Crossbill ... Part song [begins: "On the cross"]. Words by Longfellow. *London,* [1883.] 8°.   **F. 585. h. (30.)**

— Music when soft voices die. Four-part song. *London,* [1868.] 8°.
No. 12 *of the Choristers' Album.*   **E. 1708.**

— O Annie, dear Annie. Ballad, written by E. Green. *London,* [1868.] fol.   **H. 1775. t. (29.)**

— Oh! her Smile is like the Summer. [Four-part song.] Words by ... A. Gurney. [1872.] *See* CRAMPTON (T.) The Part-Singer, *etc.* No. 109. [1868–98.] 8°.   **E. 628.**

— Pretty little warbling birds. Song with Flute obbligato. *London,* [1870.] fol.   **H. 1775. t. (30.)**

— The Sentinel, song [begins: "The battle had ceased"]. *London,* [1871.] fol.   **H. 1775. t. (32.)**

— Serenade for four voices and Pianoforte [begins: "Stars of the summer night"]. Words by Longfellow. *London,* [1883.] fol.   **F. 585. h. (31.)**

LAWRENCE (CHARLES)

— The Morning and Evening Service, together with the Office for the Holy Communion, *etc. London,* [1876.] 8°.   **E. 605. c. (6.)**

— Why shouldn't we be jolly. [Song, begins: "I laugh away".] *London,* [1871.] fol.   **H. 1775. t. (31.)**

LAWRENCE (CHARLES WILSON)

— Choral Settings—a cappella—of three ancient Chinese Poems, translated by Arthur Waley. [No. 1.] Reflection ... Lyric by Yang-ti ... [No. 2.] Rejection ... Lyric by the wife of General Liu Hsün ... [No. 3.] Revelation ... Lyric anonymous, *etc.* 3 no. *C. Fischer: New York, etc.,* 1939. 8°.   **F. 1744. c. (25.)**

LAWRENCE (E. S.)

— *See* AVISON (C.) [Sound the loud timbrel.] A Christmas hymn, Zion the marv'lous story be telling, arranged as a duet and chorus ... by E. S. Lawrence. [1858.] fol.   **H. 1187. a. (15.)**

LAWRENCE (ELLIOT)

— *See* LOESSER (Frank) How to succeed in Business without really trying ... Vocal score. Edited by E. Lawrence. [1965.] 4°.   **G. 1282. c. (1.)**

LAWRENCE (EMILY M.)

— All deep things are song ... Four part song for Ladies' voices [begins: "Song should breathe of scents and flowers"] ... Words by Barry Cornwall. *London,* [1884.] 8°.   **F. 585. h. (33.)**

— Andante grave and Rondino in D for Piano. *London,* [1880.] fol.   **h. 1494. p. (32.)**

— At Rest. [Song, begins: "Rest here a little while".] Words by R. B. *London,* [1881.] fol.   **H. 1787. j. (20.)**

— Because. [Song.] Words by A. Procter. *S. Lucas, Weber & Co.: London,* [1883.] fol.   **H. 1788. v. (2.)**

— Second Book of Songs for Girls and Boys. *Weekes & Co.: London,* [1900.] 8°.   **F. 197. d. (9.)**

— Come what may. Song, words by Barry Cornwall. *S. Lucas, Weber & Co.: London,* [1885.] fol.   **H. 1788. v. (3.)**

— Come what may. Song. Words by B. Cornwall. *Weekes & Co.: London,* 1899. fol.   **H. 1799. h. (12.)**

— Do I love thee. Ballad, words by J. G. Saxe. *London,* [1881.] fol.   **H. 1787. j. (17.)**

— Do I love thee? Ballad. Words by J. G. Saxe. *Weekes & Co.: London,* [1899.] fol.   **H. 1799. h. (13.)**

— Evensong for Piano. *London,* [1881.] fol.   **h. 3275. j. (22.)**

— Flow heavenly blessings, on him ... Four-part song for ladies' voices [begins: "Now whilst he dreams"] ... Words by Barry Cornwall. *London,* [1884.] 8°.   **F. 585. h. (33.)**

— In a Garden. Song, words by Swinburne. *Weekes & Co.: London,* 1896. fol.   **H. 1798. u. (31.)**

— In manus tuas, Domine. Sacred song. *London,* [1880.] fol.   **H. 1783. o. (24.)**

— In manus tuas, Domine. Sacred Song. *Weekes & Co.: London,* [1899.] fol.   **H. 879. n. (13.)**

— "Looking out into the Night," song, the words by J. G. Saxe. pp. 5. *Duncan Davison & Cº: London,* [c. 1880.] fol.   **H. 1654. qq. (27.)**

— A Lover's Song. Words by F. W. H. Myers. *S. Lucas, Weber & Co.: London,* [1883.] fol.   **H. 1788. v. (4.)**

LAWRENCE (EMILY M.)

— My Little Doll. Song [begins: "I once had a sweet little doll"] from the "Water Babies," by ... C. Kingsley. *London*, [1881.] fol.   **H. 1787. j. (18.)**

— My Scottish Lassie. [Song.] Words by J. Moultrie. *S. Lucas, Weber & Co.: London*, [1883.] fol.   **H. 1788. v. (5.)**

— My true Love hath my Heart. Song, words by Sir P. Sidney. *S. Lucas, Weber & Co.: London*, [1883.] fol.   **H. 1788. v. (6.)**

— Only one Home. [Song.] Words by G. Macdonald, *etc.* *S. Lucas, Weber & Co.: London*, [1883.] fol.   **H. 1788. v. (7.)**

— Rest, my loved one, rest. Slumber song. *London*, [1881.] fol.   **H. 1787. j. (19.)**

— Romance in E. [P. F.] *London*, [1881.] fol.   **h. 3275. j. (23.)**

— Sarchedon's Love Song. Song, the words ... by W. Melville. *Novello, Ewer & Co.: London & New York*, [1886.] fol.   **G. 806. n. (6.)**

— Singing in the Rain. [Song, begins "Where the elm tree branches".] Words by F. Percy. *London*, [1878.] fol.   **H. 1783. o. (23.)**

— Singing in the Rain. [Song.] Words by F. Percy. *Weekes & Co.: London*, 1899. fol.   **H. 1799. h. (14.)**

— The Sleep. Song, the words by E. B. Browning. *Novello, Ewer and Co.: London and New York*, [1890.] fol.   **G. 807. h. (9.)**

— Sleep beloved, the night has come. Four-part song for ladies' voices. Words by F. Percy. *London*, [1880.] 8°.   **F. 585. d. (34.)**

— Sonata in F♯ minor for violin & piano. Op. 20. *Novello, Ewer & Co.: London & New York*, [1886.] fol.   **g. 505. d. (21.)**

— Four Songs without Words. ⟨Op. 11.⟩ [P.F.] pp. 14. *Stanley Lucas, Weber & Cᵒ: London*, [c. 1880.] fol.   **h. 725. m. (10.)**

— Sowing and Reaping. [Song.] Words by A. Procter. *S. Lucas, Weber & Co.: London*, [1883.] fol.   **H. 1788. v. (8.)**

— Sowing and Reaping. [Song.] Words by A. Procter. *Weekes & Co.: London*, [1899.] fol.   **H. 1187. z. (15.)**

— Time long past, and Sunbeams, two four part songs. *London*, [1879.] 8°.   **F. 585. d. (33.)**

— The Truth of the Spirit. Song, the words by Barry Cornwall. *Boosey & Co.: London*, [1886.] fol.   **H. 1788. v. (9.)**

— A Well of Love. Quartet [begins: "O light of dead and of dying days"] ... Words by G. Macdonald. *London*, [1883.] 8°.   **F. 585. h. (32.)**

LAWRENCE (FANNY)

— The British Tar. Song, words by R. Warmisham. *E. Donajowski: London*, [1905.] fol.   **H. 1794. k. (54.)**

LAWRENCE (FANNY ELIZABETH)

— Songs & Rhythms for the Little Folk. Compiled by F. E. Lawrence, *etc.* *E. J. Arnold & Son: Leeds, etc.*, [1927.] 8°.   **E. 1821.**

LAWRENCE (FRANK W.)

— Bonnie Bell. March Two-Step. [P. F.] *Lawrence Bros.: East Orange, New Jersey*, 1897. fol.   **h. 3286. g. (16.)**

— Columbian World's Fair Grand March. [P. F.] *K. Dehnhof: New York*, 1893. fol.   **h. 1489. s. (19.)**

LAWRENCE (FRANK W.)

— Face to Face. Sacred Solo, words and music by F. W. Lawrence, *etc.* *Whaley, Royce & Co.: [Toronto,]* (1909.) fol.   **H. 1187. ll. (6.)**

— The Happy Dutchman's happy Boarder. Song with waltz chorus, *etc.* pp. 5. *Lawrence Bros.: East Orange, N.J.*, [1905.] fol.   **H. 3985. l. (1.)**

— [Another issue.] The Happy Dutchman's happy Boarder, *etc.* *Wm. Laing: Essex, Ont.*, [1905.] fol.   **H. 3985. l. (2.)**

— Lead, kindly Light. Sacred Quartette ... words by Rev. J. H. Newman. *Lawrence Brothers: East Orange, New Jersey*, (1906.) fol.   **H. 1187. ff. (50.)**

— Lead, kindly Light. Sacred Quartette, *etc.* *W. Laing: Essex, Ont.*, (1906.) fol.   **H. 1187. ff. (51.)**

— Memories of Mother. Song ... words by I. M. Chambers. *Lawrence Brothers: East Orange, N.J.*, 1894. fol.   **H. 1798. u. (32.)**

— One sweetly solemn Thought. Sacred Solo, words by P. Carey. 2 no. [In C and E flat.] *Lawrence Brothers: East Orange, New Jersey*, 1903. fol.   **H. 1187. cc. (38.)**

— One sweetly solemn Thought. Sacred Solo, *etc.* 2 no. [In C and E flat.] *W. Laing: Essex, Ont.*, 1903. fol.   **H. 1187. cc. (39.)**

— Sportman's Dream. Waltzes, *etc.* [P. F.] *Lawrence Brothers: New Jersey*, 1895. fol.   **h. 3285. q. (12.)**

LAWRENCE (FREDERICK LOCKE)

— The Beatitudes. *H. W. Gray Co.: New York*, 1922. 8°. *Church Music Review, No.* 638.   **F. 1171. bb. (69.)**

— God that madest. Closing Sentence. *H. W. Gray Co.: New York*, 1922. 8°. *Church Music Review, No.* 637.   **F. 1171. bb. (70.)**

— He stands at the Helm. [Song.] Poem by W. V. B. Thompson. *Whaley, Royce & Co.: Toronto*, 1899. fol.   **H. 1799. h. (15.)**

— A Joyous March. (Organ.) *H. W. Gray Co.: New York*, 1921. 4°.   **g. 1380. h. (3.)**

— Nightfall. Evening Anthem. *H. W. Gray Co.: New York*, 1922. 8°.   **F. 281. ww. (32.)**

— The Reapers' Song. Poem by W. V. B. Thompson. *Howard & Co.: London*, 1898. fol.   **H. 1799. h. (16.)**

— [Another edition.] The Reapers' Song, *etc.* *Whaley, Royce & Co.: Toronto*, 1898. fol.   **H. 1799. h. (17.)**

LAWRENCE (GEORGE B.)

— Percussion Parade. Score [and parts]. 9 pt. *Boosey & Hawkes: London, etc.*, [1970.] 4°. [*Tonal Perspective Series for tuned Percussion. no.* 7.] *The parts are in duplicate.*   **g. 1609.**

LAWRENCE (GERALD)

— Legende, for Violin and Piano, *etc.* *Elkin & Co.: London*, 1908. fol.   **h. 1612. p. (20.)**

— To Althea from Prison, and Tell me not, Sweet, I am unkind. Two Songs by R. Lovelace, *etc.* *Boosey & Co.: London and New York*, 1925. 4°.   **G. 1270. m. (1.)**

LAWRENCE (IAN)

— An Introduction to Music building Kits, *etc.* pp. 15. *Ginn & Co.: London*, [1970.] obl. 8°.   **e. 108. y. (2.)**

LAWRENCE (IAN)

— Longmans' Song Book. Arranged [for voices, percussion and chordal instruments] by I. Lawrence. pp. 32. *Longmans, Green & Co.: London, Harlow,* 1969. 8°.　**E. 271. a. (7.)**

— Three Madrigals. For recorder quintet. Arranged by I. Lawrence. 1. To shorten Winter's Sadness. Thomas Weelkes. 2. Lullaby, my sweet little Baby. William Byrd. 3. Oft have I vowed. John Wilbye. ⟨Descants 1 & 2, treble, tenor, bass. Score.⟩ pp. 10. *Oxford University Press: London,* [1968.] 8°.　**c. 160. v. (6.)**

— Music building Kits ... Four note phrases. Set 1. Birds. Set 2. Trees. Set 3. Wild Flowers. Five note phrases. Set 4. Insects. Set 5. Snakes. Set 6. Dinosaurs. 6 set. *Ginn & Co.: London,* [1970.] obl. 8°.
Each set contains four copies of ten cards with printed music.　**e. 108. y. (1.)**

— Three Renaissance Pieces. ⟨1. Confitemini Domini. A. Constantini.—2. Hodie apparuit. O. di Lasso.—3. Et resurrexit. G. Croce.⟩ Arranged by I. Lawrence ⟨for three melody instruments⟩. [Score and parts.] 4 pt. *J. & W. Chester: London,* [1971.] 8°.
[*Junior Music. Stage* 2.]　**G. 1487. g.**

— Fifty simple Rounds. For singers, recorders and other instruments. pp. 20. *Novello & Co.: Borough Green, London,* [1971.] obl. 8°.　**D. 837. x.**

— *See* HAYDN (F. J.) [*Collected Works.—b.*] A Haydn Solo Album. Eleven short pieces for trumpet & piano. Arranged & edited by I. Lawrence. [1971.] 4°.　**g. 75. o. (10.)**

— *See* LAWES (William) Fantasia and Air. Arranged for recorder quintet ... by I. Lawrence. 1972. 4°.　**g. 109. ff. (5.)**

— *See* MORLEY (Thomas) [*Madrigalls to foure Voyces.*] Ho! who comes here?, *etc.* ⟨Arranged for recorder quartet by I. Lawrence.⟩ [1972.] 4°. [*Schott's Recorder Bibliothek. no.* 43.]　**g. 112. j.**

LAWRENCE (J. ERNEST)

— The Dreams that never can come true. A Song, words by W. H. Hayne. *Nordheimer Piano and Music Co.: Toronto, etc.,* (1907.) fol.　**H. 1794. vv. (20.)**

— The Happy Mormon Man. ⟨[Song, from a] Western musical comedy "The Westerners".⟩ Words by Ralph Smith. pp. 5. *Westerners Co.: Toronto,* [1909.] fol.　**H. 3985. l. (3.)**

— Molly, my Prairie Girl. ⟨[Song, from a] Western musical comedy "The Westerners".⟩ Words by Ralph Smith. pp. 5. *Westerners Co.: Toronto,* [1909.] fol.　**H. 3985. l. (4.)**

— Nita, my Signiorite. ⟨[Song, from a] Western musical comedy "The Westerners".⟩ Words by Paul Sheard and Ralph Smith. pp. 5. *Westerners Co.: Toronto,* [1909.] fol.　**H. 3985. l. (5.)**

— Twosing. ⟨[Song, from a] Western musical comedy "The Westerners".⟩ Words by Ralph Smith. pp. 3. *Westerners Co.: Toronto,* [1909.] fol.　**H. 3985. l. (6.)**

— The "Westerners". March and two-step. [P.F.] pp. 5. *Westerners Co.: Toronto,* [1909.] fol.　**h. 4120. mm. (30.)**

— The "Westerners". Waltzes. [P.F.] pp. 5. *Westerners Co.: Toronto,* [1909.] fol.　**h. 4120. mm. (31.)**

LAWRENCE (J. H.)

— The King's Colonials. March for the Pianoforte. *E. Ashdown: London,* [1902.] fol.　**g. 605. ee. (31.)**

LAWRENCE (J. PORTER)

— Lord, Thou hast been our Dwelling Place, *etc.* [Anthem.] *A. P. Schmidt: Boston, etc.,* (1909.) 8°.　**F. 281. p. (24.)**

LAWRENCE (JACK) and CHAIKOVSKY (PETR IL'ICH)

— Concerto for two. Love Song. *See* CHAIKOVSKY (P. I.) [Concerto in B flat minor. Op. 23.—Allegro.]

LAWRENCE (LIONEL E.)

— Maudie. [Song.] Words & music by L. Lawrence. pp. 5. *Harry von Tilzer Music Pub. Co.: New York,* [1905.] fol.　**H. 3985. l. (7.)**

— Three little Accidents. [Song.] Written & composed by L. E. Lawrence. pp. 6. *T. B. Harms & Co.:* [*New York,* 1899.] fol.　**H. 3980. pp. (29.)**

LAWRENCE (LUCILE)

— Early English Pieces for the Beginner. For the troubadour and (or) pedal harp. Edited by Lucile Lawrence. pp. 10. *Lyra Music Co.: New York,* [1972.] 4°.　**g. 1098. k. (9.)**

— *See* BACH (C. P. E.) [*Solo für die Harfe. Wq.* 139.] Sonata for Harp. Edited by L. Lawrence, *etc.* [1965.] 4°.　**g. 1098. j. (3.)**

— *See* DUSSEK (J. L.) Six Sonatinas for the Harp. ⟨Edited by L. Lawrence and D. Owens.⟩ [1969.] 4°.　**g. 1098. k. (3.)**

— *See* HAENDEL (G. F.) [*Organ Concertos. Op.* 4. *No.* 6.] Concerto in B♭ for Harp. With piano accompaniment; edited by L. Lawrence. [1972.] 4°.　**g. 61. n. (2.)**

— *See* HARRISON (Lon) Suite ... For violoncello and harp. Edited by S. Barab and L. Lawrence. [1954.] 4°.　**g. 890. (9.)**

LAWRENCE (LUCILE) and SALZEDO (CARLOS)

— Method for the Harp. Fundamental exercises with illustrations and technical explanations, as an introduction and complement to C. Salzedo's "Modern Study of the Harp". Méthode pour la Harpe ... Fifteen Preludes for beginners ... by C. Salzedo. *G. Schirmer: New York,* 1929. 4°.　**g. 1098. (12.)**

— Pathfinder to the Harp. Guide pour la harpe, *etc.* pp. 33. *Southern Music Publishing Co.: New York,* [1954.] 4°.　**g. 1098. a. (17.)**

— Pathfinder Studies for the Troubadour or Irish-type Harp. (Supplement to "Pathfinder to the Harp.") pp. 8. *Southern Music Publishing Co.: New York,* [1962.] 4°.　**g. 1098. i. (2.)**

LAWRENCE (M.)

— [Hyppolita.] My gentle blooming Cashmire Maid. A favorite ballad sung by Mʳ Jones, in the grand equestrian melo-drama called Hyppolita, Queen of the Amazons ... Written by W. Moncrieff. *W. G. Bown: London,* [c. 1820.] fol.
Followed by an arrangement for flute.　**G. 426. dd. (7.)**

— My gentle blooming Cashmire Maid. *See supra:* [Hyppolita.]

— Tho' prim as Saints at Mass we seem. *The much admir'd Friar's Glee.* Sung ... in Manfred, or the Castle of Otranto, written by Mʳ Barret, *etc.* pp. 5. *E. Riley, for the Author: London,* [1803?] fol.　**H. 1653. a. (23.)**

LAWRENCE (MARGRETTA J.)

— Loyalty. Waltz. [P. F.] [1900.] fol.　**h. 3286. q. (77.)**

LAWRENCE (ROY)

— *See* LEWIS (Pete) Sing Life sing Love ... [Songs. Edited by] P. Lewis, R. Lawrence, G. Simpson, *etc.* [1971.] 8°.　**D. 789. m.**

LAWRENCE (Scott)

— I'se been looking for you. [Song.] Words & music by
S. Lawrence. pp. 5.   *F. A. Mills: New York*, [1901.] 4°.
       H. 3985. l. (8.)

LAWRENCE (Thomas Bertie)

— Dashing away with the Smoothing Iron. Folk-Song. Collected
and arranged by C. J. Sharp. Arranged for Mixed Voices by
T. B. Lawrence.   *Boosey & Co.: London*, 1943. 8°.
[*Boosey's Modern Festival Series. No.* 482.]   **F. 160. f.**

— O come you from Newcastle? Arranged [for S.S.A.] by T. B.
Lawrence. ⟨Printed in Playford's English Dancing Master
(1651). The words, from a 17th century manuscript, appear in
Percy's Reliques (1765).⟩ [Staff and tonic sol-fa notation.]
pp. 4.   *Elkin & Co.: London*, [1953.] 8°.
Elkin choral Series. no. 2294.   **F. 217. n. (27.)**

LAWRENCE (Vera Brodsky)

— *See* Joplin (Scott) The Collected Works of Scott Joplin.
Edited by V. B. Lawrence, *etc.* 1971. fol. [*The Americana
Collection Music Series.* 1.]   **H. 1654. t.**

— *See* Joplin (Scott) Treemonisha. Vocal selection. Edited by
V. B. Lawrence. [1957.] 4°.   **H. 654. a. (1.)**

LAWRENCE (Victor J.)

— *See* Rimsky-Korsakov (N. A.) [Сказка о Царе салтане.] The
Flight of the Bumble Bee ... Arranged for guitar ... by V. J.
Lawrence. [1951.] 4°.   **g. 660. f. (20.)**

LAWRENCE (Walter Edward)

— Barcarolle, for the Pianoforte. 1915. *See* Isaacs (E.) Edition
Swift, *etc.* [No. 22.] 1915, *etc.* 4°.   **g. 1134. (21.)**

— June Roses. Song, words by A. Procter.   *Grahame & Black:
London*, 1910. fol.   **H. 1792. r. (43.)**

— Romance sans Paroles, pour Violon avec Accompagnement
de Piano.   *C. Woolhouse: London*, 1905. fol.
       h. 1612. p. (21.)

LAWRENCE (William M.)

— Vowel Songs for Vocal Training in the Kindergarten and
Primary Grades of Schools.   *C. F. Summy Co.: Chicago*,
1909. 4°.   **G. 844. h. (5.)**

LAWRENSON (Leslie Robert)

— O Saviour, ere we part. *Vesper.* Donegal.   *Novello and Co.:
London*, [1934.] *s. sh. obl.* 8°.   **I. 600. f. (68.)**

— Urbs fortitudinis. An Alternative to Te Deum. [S. A. T. B.]
Novello & Co.: London, [1936.] 8°.   **F. 1158. g. (39.)**

LAWRIE (A.)

— Elfrida, mazurka. [P.F.]   *London*, [1859.] fol.
       h. 1460. u. (40.)

LAWRIE (Edith M.) and **LAKE** (Nellie E.)

— Manitoba Nelledi Waltzes. [P.F.] pp. 7.   *Canadian American
Music Co.:* [*Toronto?*, 1903.] fol.   **h. 4120. mm. (32.)**

LAWROW (N.)

— *See* Lavrov.

LAWRY (Eleanor)

— *See* Goudimel (C.) Oeuvres complètes. Publiées par Henri
Gagnebin ... et E. Lawry, *etc.* [1967, *etc.*] [*Gesamtausgaben.
no.* 3.]   **G. 1485. a.**

LAWSON (A. W.)

— We will follow him forever. The Mc.Clellan rally. [Song.]
Boston [*Mass.*], 1864. fol.   **H. 1780. f. (8.)**

LAWSON (Corinne Moore)

— Absence. Song, poem by Pai Ta-Shun.   *J. Church Co.:
Cincinnati, etc.*, 1915. fol.   **H. 1846. x. (35.)**

— The Gray Day. Song, poem by E. J. Appleton.   *J. Church
Co.: Cincinnati, etc.*, 1915. fol.   **H. 1846. x. (36.)**

— Lazy Song. [Song.] Words by P. L. Dunbar.   *Willis Music Co.:
Cincinnati*, 1920. 4°.   **G. 426. n. (26.)**

— My Love in the Garden. Song, poem by E. J. Appleton.
J. Church Co.: Cincinnati, etc., 1915. fol.   **H. 1846. x. (37.)**

— While I have you. Song, poem by E. J. Appleton.   *J. Church
Co.: Cincinnati, etc.*, 1915. fol.   **H. 1846. x. (38.)**

LAWSON (Edward)

— Valse Anglaise. [P.F.]   *London*, [1876.] fol.   **h. 1482. y. (41.)**

LAWSON (Ethel)

— Night has passed. Song, words by M. E. Carr.   *Weekes &
Co.: London*, [1908.] fol.   **H. 1794. vv. (21.)**

LAWSON (F.)

— Once again in God's own Temple. Harvest Hymn ... Words
... by G. B. Doughty.   *Novello and Co.: London*, [1902.] 8°.
       D. 619. s. (3.)

LAWSON (Frank)

— Ruby. Gavotte for piano.   *Patey & Willis: London*, [1886.] fol.
       h. 1484. s. (28.)

LAWSON (G. S.)

— Guess how much the Baby weighs. ... Song & Chorus.
C. Sheard: London, [1889.] fol.
No. 7497 *of the Musical Bouquet.*   **H. 2345.**

LAWSON (Gordon)

— How far is it to Bethlehem. West country carol. Arranged by
G. Lawson. pp. 4.   *Royal School of Church Music: Croydon*,
[1971.] 8°.   **F. 1892. c. (6.)**

— L'il Liza Jane. American Song. [Written and composed by
Countess Ada de Lachau.] Arranged for S.A.T.B.
(unaccompanied) by G. Lawson. pp. 4.   *Novello & Co.:
London*, [1957.] 8°.
[*Musical Times. no.* 1378.]   **P. P. 1945. aa.**

— Magnificat and Nunc dimittis ... in ... F. For congregation
and choir (S.A.T.B.). pp. 12.   *Novello & Co.: London*, [1960.]
8°.
[*Parish Choir Book. no.* 1386.]   **E. 618.**

— O most merciful! Anthem for S.A.T.B. and organ. Words by
Bishop R. Heber. pp. 4.   *Novello & Co.: London*, [1959.] 8°.
[*Short Anthems.* 332.]   **F. 280. f.**

LAWSON (GORDON)

— O Unity of threefold Light. Anthem for S.A.T.B. and organ
... Words by Metrophanes, Bishop of Smyrna, c. 900.
Translated by J. M. Neale. pp. 11. *Novello & Co.: London,*
[1958.] 8°.
[*Octavo Anthems.* 1334.] **E. 618. a.**

— Rejoice To-day with one accord. Anthem for S.A.T.B. and
organ ... Words by Sir H. W. Baker (1821–77). pp. 4. *Novello
& Co.: London,* [1959.] 8°.
[*Short Anthems.* 331.] **F. 280. f.**

LAWSON (H. A.)

— Christ's Heroes. A Service of Sacred Song. *Manchester,
London,* 1886. 8°. **D. 675. i. (8.)**

LAWSON (HARRY)

— Zelia ... (Song.) Words by Moulton G. Farnham. pp. 5.
Harry E. Wolff: [*New York,* 1904.] fol. **H. 3985. l. (9.)**

LAWSON (HENRY)

— Reverie. [Violin and P. F.] *Wickins & Co.: London,* [1896?]
fol.
No. 1 of "Wickins' Violin Literature". **h. 1743. (1.)**

— Royal Horse Artillery Polka, introducing ... regimental calls
... in use by the regiment, *etc.* [P. F.] pp. 4. *Pask & Koenig:*
[*London,* c. 1850.] fol. **g. 271. ww. (7.)**

LAWSON (J.)

— Instructions for the Violin, *etc. London,* [1862.] obl. 8°.
a. 165.

LAWSON (J. ADELBERG)

— Bon Souvenir. Gavotte gracieuse pour le Piano. *Vincent
Music Co.: London,* 1901. fol. **h. 3282. kk. (23.)**

— I hear a Song. Song, words by E. Oxenford. 2 no. [In C and E
flat.] *Bach & Co.: London,* (1912.) fol. **H. 1793. s. (24.)**

— The Mermaid. Song, words by T. H. Wright. *Blyth,* [1895.]
fol. **H. 1798. u. (33.)**

— Polish Dance in F, for the Pianoforte. *Beethoven School of
Music: Harrogate,* (1906.) fol. **h. 3283. p. (16.)**

— Praise the Lord, O Jerusalem. Anthem for Harvest. *The
Composer: Harrogate,* 1897. 8°. **F. 231. g. (37.)**

— Stanley's Rescue. March. [P.F.] pp. 7. *James Brown:
Bradford; Leipzig* printed, [c. 1890.] fol. **h. 61. ss. (13.)**

— 'Tis Joseph! Joey! Joe! Humorous Song, words by E. R.
Baller. *B. Feldman & Co.: London,* 1905. fol.
H. 1794. k. (55.)

— Four Vespers ... words and music by J. A. Lawson.
Beethoven School of Music: Harrogate, [1905.] 8°.
B. 835. f. (1.)

LAWSON (J. M.)

— The Canadian Marching Song. [Song.] Words and music by
J. M. Lawson. *Anglo-Canadian Music Publishers' Association:
Toronto,* (1915.) fol. **H. 1793. s. (25.)**

LAWSON (J. W.)

— A Dream. Song [begins: "All yesterday I was spinning"] ...
written by A. A. Procter. *London,* [1880.] fol.
H. 1785. c. (30.)

LAWSON (JAMES R.)

— *See* HAENDEL (G. F.) [Clock Music.] Ten Tunes for a Music
Clock ... Edited by J. R. Lawson, *etc.* [c. 1955.] fol.
h. 2676. (4.)

LAWSON (JAN L.)

— The Fairies. [Song.] Words by J. L. Lawson. Music adapted
by J. L. Lawson. pp. 3. *Edwin Ashdown: London,* [1939.] 8°.
[*Music for the Singing Class.* 9.] **E. 222.**

— The Fisherman. [Song.] Words by J. L. Lawson. Music
adapted by J. L. Lawson. pp. 3. *Edwin Ashdown: London,*
[1939.] 8°.
[*Music for the Singing Class.* 10.] **E. 222.**

— Learning French. [Song.] Words by J. L. Lawson. Music
adapted by J. L. Lawson. pp. 4. *Edwin Ashdown: London,*
[1939.] 8°.
[*Music for the Singing Class.* 6.] **E. 222.**

— Music Notes. [Song.] Words by J. L. Lawson. Music adapted
by J. L. Lawson. pp. 3. *Edwin Ashdown: London,* [1939.] 8°.
[*Music for the Singing Class.* 7.] **E. 222.**

— Poor Mother Goose. [Song.] Words by J. L. Lawson. Music
adapted by J. L. Lawson. pp. 3. *Edwin Ashdown: London,*
[1939.] 8°.
[*Music for the Singing Class.* 8.] **E. 222.**

— Try, try again. [Song.] Words by J. L. Lawson. Music adapted
by J. L. Lawson. pp. 3. *Edwin Ashdown: London,* [1939.] 8°.
[*Music for the Singing Class.* 11.] **E. 222.**

LAWSON (JOHN) *Composer of sacred music*

— Dismiss me not Thy Service, Lord. Service. [Hymn.] Words
by T. T. Lynch. *Novello and Co.: London,* [1936.] s. sh. 8°.
D. 835. a. (5.)

LAWSON (JOHN) *Singer* and **BESSO** (MOSES)

— Only a Jew. Written and composed by J. Lawson & M. Besso,
etc. [Song. Staff and tonic sol-fa notation. Voice part.]
Francis, Day & Hunter: London, [1896.] s. sh. fol.
H. 3980. pp. (30.)

LAWSON (JOHN) *Songwriter*

— Four Short Songs. 1. My fairest Child.—Kingsley.—2. If thou
art sleeping.—Longfellow.—3. All are sleeping.—Longfellow.
—4. Beware.—Longfellow.—, *etc. A. Lengnick & Co.:
London,* [1910.] 4°. **G. 424. z. (11.)**

LAWSON (JOSEPH)

— Lawson's Selection of the most admired Quadrilles, with
their proper figures ... Arranged for the piano forte, harp, or
violin. set [MS 2.] *J. Lawson: London,* [WM 1822.] fol.
g. 342. ll. (6.)

— 'Twas the last ray of beauty [song] adapted to ... The Last
Rose of Summer. The words by J. B. James. *London,* [1820?]
fol. **G. 808. b. (29.)**

— We're a noddin' ... Scotch Ballad ... arranged with an
Accompaniment for the Piano Forte, by J. Lawson.
J. Lawson: London, [1820?] fol. **G. 383. h. (59.)**

LAWSON (MALCOLM)

— All through the Night. [Song.] Words by Jan L. Lawson.
Music adapted by M. Lawson. pp. 3. *Edwin Ashdown,
London,* [1939.] 8°.
[*Music for the Singing Class.* 1.] **E. 222.**

LAWSON (MALCOLM)

— Early to Bed. [Song.] Words by Jan L. Lawson. Music adapted by M. Lawson. pp. 4. *Edwin Ashdown: London,* [1939.] 8°.
[*Music for the Singing Class.* 2.]   **E. 222.**

— Holidays. [Song.] Words by Jan L. Lawson. Music adapted by M. Lawson. pp. 4. *Edwin Ashdown: London,* [1939.] 8°.
[*Music for the Singing Class.* 3.]   **E. 222.**

— In the Snow. [Song.] Words by Jan L. Lawson. pp. 3. *Edwin Ashdown: London,* [1939.] 8°.
[*Music for the Singing Class.* 4.]   **E. 222.**

— Visitors. [Song.] Words by Jan L. Lawson. pp. 4. *Edwin Ashdown: London,* [1939.] 8°.
[*Music for the Singing Class.* 5.]   **E. 222.**

LAWSON (MALCOLM LEONARD)

— First Album of People's Songs and others. (Second Album of Songs. Words by Marzials.) 2 no. *Stanley, Lucas, Weber & Co.: London,* [1892.] 4°.
No. 214 and 215 of J. Williams's Albums.   **F. 1619.**

— First Album of People's Songs and others. 1. Hereafter. (C. G. Rossetti.) 2. Love's Resolves. (Sir J. Suckling.) 3. The Proud Princess. (C. Kingsley.) 4. The World's Age. (C. Kingsley.) 5. Adieu. (T. Carlyle.) 6. The Passionate Shepherd. (C. Marlowe.) 7. Cavalier Constancy. (Sir J. Suckling.) 8. Love and Debt. (Sir J. Suckling.) 9. Sing Heigh Ho. (C. Kingsley.) 10. Andalusian Moonlight. (A. O'Shaughnessy.) 11. A Jacobite Lament. (Ogilvie.) 12. A Virelay. (E. W. Gosse.) 13. In the Garden. (T. Marzials.) 14. The Angels' Flower. (W. Melville.) 15. Olivia's Song. (O. Goldsmith.) *S. Lucas & Co.: London,* [1893.] 4°.   **F. 636. s. (6.)**

— Second Album of Songs. Words by Marzials. *S. Lucas, Weber & Co.: London,* [1893.] 4°.   **F. 636. s. (7.)**

— Alas! Song ... The words by G. Macdonald. *London,* [1881.] fol.   **H. 2613. (13.)**

— Andalusian Moonlight. [Song, begins: "In a lifted palace".] Words ... by A. O'Shaughnessy. *London,* [1874.] fol.   **H. 2613. (2.)**

— The Angel's Flower. Song [begins: "I knelt by the grave"]. Words by W. Melville. ⟨In E. In G.⟩ 2 no. *London,* [1881.] fol.   **H. 2613. (16.)**

— Banished Love. Song [begins: "For all that we have said"]. The words by P. B. Marston. *London,* [1882.] fol.   **H. 2613. (19.)**

— The Bonnie Banks o' Loch Lomond. *See* infra: The Songs of the North.

— Brother Jack. Song [begins: "Have ye left a little wife"]. The words by R. Henry. *London,* [1882.] fol.   **H. 2613. (20.)**

— Brother Jack. Song, words by R. Henry. *Reid Bros.: London,* [1886.] fol.   **H. 2613. (21.)**

— Choral Music: Glees, Madrigals, Motetts, and other part music ... Edited ... by M. Lawson. no. 1-3, 5. *S. Lucas, Weber & Co.: London,* [1880.] 8°.
No. 1-5 of this Series were announced, but No. 4 was never published.   **E. 308. s. (11.)**

— The Cuckoo in the Orchard. Song, the words by J. Jemmett Browne. *Boosey & Co.: London,* [1883.] fol.   **H. 2613. (22.)**

— Cupid's Curse. Duet [begins: "Faire, faire"] ... written by G. Peele. *London,* [1878.] fol.   **H. 2613. (8.)**

— A Death Song. [Song.] Words by William Morris. *R. Lambert: London,* [1887.] 8°.   **08282. i. 8.**

— The Flowers of the Forest. *See* infra: The Songs of the North.

LAWSON (MALCOLM LEONARD)

— The Happy Wooing Time. Song, the words by A. C. Calmour. *Boosey & Co.: London and New York,* 1892. fol.   **H. 1799. cc. (50.)**

— Hereafter. (When I am dead.) Song, words by C. Rosetti. *London,* [1880.] fol.   **H. 2613. (12.)**

— Kitty's Disaster. A Milk-pail Tragedy. The words by E. Lysaght. *Weekes & Co.: London,* [1888.] fol.   **H. 2613. (23.)**

— Last Words. [Song.] Written by H. Boulton. German words by V. D. H. and H. B[oulton]. *J. B. Cramer & Co.: London,* 1893. fol.   **H. 1799. cc. (52.)**

— Last Words. [Song.] Written by H. Boulton, German words by V. D. H. & H. B. *See* BOULTON (*Sir* H. E.) *Bart.* Seven Songs, etc. [No. 4.] 1893. fol.   **G. 659. a.**

— Leezie Lindsay. *See* infra: The Songs of the North.

— A Love-Dream. Nocturne for the Pianoforte & voice [begins: "The river's mouth is weary wide"]. The words by T. Marzials. *London,* [1881.] fol.   **H. 2613. (17.)**

— Love in Bonds. Song [begins: "When Love with unconfined wings"]. The words by ... R. Lovelace. *London,* [1881.] fol.   **H. 2613. (14.)**

— Love in May. Song [begins: "A lad had wooed a lassie"]. The words by F. Langbridge. *London,* [1882.] fol.   **H. 2613. (18.)**

— The Man o' Airlie. Song, the words by W. G. Wills, *etc. Enoch & Sons: London,* [1882.] fol.   **H. 2613. (24.)**

— Marjory Daw. Song, the words by J. J. Browne. *Boosey & Co.: London and New York,* 1892. fol.   **H. 1799. cc. (51.)**

— May Song. [Four-part song.] Words by K. Somers. [1872.] *See* CRAMPTON (T.) The Part-Singer, *etc.* No. 114. [1868-98.] 8°.   **E. 628.**

— Three Melodies for voice & piano. Words by T. Marzials. 6 no. *London,* [1879, 80.] fol.   **H. 2613. (9.)**

— My Love. [Four-part song.] Words by K. Somers. [1872.] *See* CRAMPTON (T.) The Part-Singer, *etc.* No. 114. [1868-98.] 8°.   **E. 628.**

— O can ye sew Cushions. *See* infra: The Songs of the North.

— Oh! for a peach. *See* supra: Three Melodies, *etc.* No. 1.

— Oh! that my heart. *See* supra: Three Melodies, *etc.* No. 3.

— Olivia's Song [begins: "When lovely woman"]. The words by Goldsmith. ⟨In F. In A.⟩ 2 no. *London,* [1879.] fol.   **H. 2613. (11.)**

— The Passionate Shepherd "Come live with me". A pastoral, the words by Marlowe. *London,* [1879.] fol.   **H. 2613. (10.)**

— People's Songs & Ballads. 17 no. *London,* [1876-78.] fol.   **H. 2613. (5.)**

— Perchance. Song, the words by L. Johnstone. *Boosey & Co.: London,* [1883.] fol.   **H. 2613. (25.)**

— The Pipe of Life. Student's song [begins: "Our life is like the pipe"]. Words by T. Marzials and S. Lever. *London,* [1881.] fol.   **H. 2613. (15.)**

— La Première. Chansonnette [begins: "Ce n'est pas qu'elle fut bien belle"]. Paroles par F. Coppée. *London,* [1876.] fol.   **H. 2613. (6.)**

— Proud Maisie. *See* infra: [Songs of the North. Vol. I.]

— Red as Oleander. *See* supra: Three Melodies ... No. 2.

LAWSON (Malcolm Leonard)

— The Sea Gulls, an episode told in 4 briolets, written by
T. Marzials. *London*, [1878.] fol.　　　**H. 2613. (7.)**

— Sigh no more, ladies. Glee for ladies voices ... Words by
Shakespeare. *London*, [1880.] 8°.　　　**E. 308. i. (31.)**

— Sigh no more Ladies. Glee for Ladies' Voices,
unaccompanied ... Op. 15. No. 1. *Leonard & Co.: London*,
[1903.] 8°.
Leonard & Co.'s Part-Songs, No. 21.　　　**F. 1658.**

— Skye Boat Song. *See* infra: [Songs of the North. Vol. I.]

— Song of the Sirens. Duet for Ladies' Voices from the Tale of
Troy ... the words translated from Homer by G. C. Warr.
Weekes & Co.: London, [1884.] fol.　　　**H. 2613. (27.)**

— Three Songs ... The words by T. Marzials. 3 no. *London*,
[1873.] fol.　　　**H. 2613. (1.)**

Songs of the North

— Songs of the North, gathered together from the Highlands
and Lowlands of Scotland. Edited by A. C. Macleod and
H. Boulton. The music arranged by M. Lawson. (Vol. II.
Edited by H. Boulton. Music arranged by M. Lawson.)
(Vol. III. Edited by H. Boulton. Music arranged by
R. Macleod.) 3 vol. *Field & Tuer (J. B. Cramer & Co.):
London*, [1885–1926.] 4°.　　　**G. 746.**

— Songs of the North ... Vol. I. Second edition. *Field & Tuer:
London*, [1886.] 4°.　　　**G. 746. a.**

— Songs of the North ... Edited by Harold Boulton, music
arranged by Malcolm Lawson. Vol. II. *J. B. Cramer & Co.:
London*, [1895.] 4°.　　　**R. M. 13. f. 9.**

— The Songs of the North ... As Unison Songs ... with Tonic
Sol-fa, *etc.* 6 no. *J. B. Cramer & Co.: London*, [1927.] 8°.
　　　F. 1741.

— Songs of the North. Selected by Sir Harold Boulton and
M. Lawson. Selection No. 1(2). Arranged for Piano by
A. Rowley. 2 no. *J. B. Cramer & Co.: London*, 1927, 29. 4°.
　　　g. 822. c. (22.)

— [Vol. I.] Proud Maisie ... Arranged for S. S. C ... Arranged by
J. Gallie. [Staff notation.] (Tonic Solfa.) 2 no. *J. B. Cramer &
Co.: London*, 1928. 4°.
[Cramer's Library of Unison and Part Songs. No. 49.]
　　　E. 1678. a.

— [Vol. I.] Skye Boat Song ... Chorus part. *J. B. Cramer & Co.:
London*, [1912?] *s. sh.* 8°.
[J. B. Cramer & Co.'s Select Library of Part Songs. No. 78.]
　　　F. 157. a.

— [Vol. I.] Skye Boat Song. Duet, *etc. J. B. Cramer & Co.:
London*, 1927. 4°.　　　**G. 981. e. (15.)**

— [Vol. I.] Skye Boat Song. *See* MACLEOD, afterwards WILSON
(A. C.) *Lady*. Skye Boat Song, for Mixed Voices ... Arr. by
H. Statham. Melody by A. C. Macleod, *etc.* 1928. 4°.
[Cramer's Choral Library. No. 12.]　　　**F. 157. d.**

— Thee only. Song. Words by H. S. Riddell. *Metzler & Co.:
London*, [1883.] fol.　　　**H. 2613. (26.)**

— To Lucasta, on going to the wars. Song [begins: "Tell me not
sweet"] ... the words by R. Lovelace. *London*, [1876.] fol.
　　　H. 2613. (3.)

— Turn ye to me. *See* supra: The Songs of the North.

— A Virelay [song, begins: "Little winged god"] written by
E. W. Gosse. *London*, [1876.] fol.　　　**H. 2613. (4.)**

— *See* ECHOES. Echoes of Hellas. Pianoforte arrangement of the
music, composed by ... M. Lawson, *etc.* 1888. fol.
　　　1876. f. 13.

LAWSON (Mary Comber) *Mrs*

— *See* BENEDICT (M. C.) *Lady*, afterwards LAWSON (M. C.) *Mrs*.

LAWSON (Mary M.)

— Sherwood Rangers. Galop, for the pianoforte, *etc. Weekes &
Co.: London*, [1886.] fol.　　　**h. 975. u. (53.)**

LAWSON (May)

— 5 Characteristic Pieces for Pianoforte. No. 1. Lullaby. No. 2.
A Country Song. 3. A Dance Measure. 4. Valse Caprice.
5. Tarantelle. *A. Hammond & Co.: London*, [1913.] 4°.
The Academic Edition, No. 512.　　　**g. 1130. y. (9.)**

— Two Miniatures for Pianoforte. *Weekes & Co.: London*,
[1907.] fol.　　　**h. 3283. p. (17.)**

LAWSON (Paul)

— Bell Tones. [P.F.] pp. 3. *M. Witmark & Sons: New York, etc.*,
[1908.] fol.　　　**h. 4120. nn. (1.)**

— "Bonnie." *See* infra: Songs of College Days ... 2.

— "Bzt! Bzt!" *See* infra: Songs of College Days ... 9.

— Carnation Pink. Rondo. *See* infra: In Grandma's Garden.
No. 7.

— Clove Pinks. [P.F.] pp. 3. *M. Witmark & Sons: New York,
etc.*, [1908.] fol.　　　**h. 4120. nn. (2.)**

— "The Dutch Company." *See* infra: Songs of College Days ...
4.

— Feather Tips. [P.F.] pp. 3. *M. Witmark & Sons: New York,
etc.*, [1908.] fol.　　　**h. 4120. nn. (3.)**

— Fishey, Fishey in the Brook. *See* infra: Play Time ... [6.]

— "For he's a jolly good Fellow." *See* infra: Songs of College
Days ... 1.

— Fuchsia. March. *See* infra: In Grandma's Garden. No. 1.

— Gay Cavaliers. Mazurka. *See* infra: Youthful Spirits ... 3.

— Georgie Porgie. *See* infra: Play Time ... [9.]

— Girls and Boys come out to play. *See* infra: Play Time ...
[11.]

— Go tell Aunt Sallie. Polka-rondo. *See* infra: Song Games of
Childhood ... [4.]

— "Good-night Ladies!" *See* infra: Songs of College Days ...
10.

— Green Gravel. *See* infra: Play Time ... [10.]

— Happy Elves. *See* infra: Lilliputians ... 3.

— Heliotrope. Reverie. *See* infra: In Grandma's Garden. No. 6.

— Here we go 'round the Mulberry Bush. *See* infra: Play Time
... [2.]

— In Grandma's Garden. [P.F.] No. 1. Fuchsia. March. No. 2.
Rose Geranium. Waltz. No. 3. Verbena. Polka. No. 4.
Marigold. Barn Dance. No. 5. Moss Rose. Two-step. No. 6.
Heliotrope. Reverie. No. 7. Carnation Pink. Rondo. No. 8.
Mignonette. Galop. 8 no. *M. Witmark & Sons: New York,
etc.*, [1909.] fol.　　　**h. 4120. nn. (4.)**

— In Mischief. Polka. *See* infra: Youthful Spirits ... 2.

— "Jingle Bells." *See* infra: Songs of College Days ... 7.

— Jolly Midgets. *See* infra: Lilliputians ... 1.

— Laughing Gnomes. *See* infra: Lilliputians ... 2.

LAWSON (Paul)

— Lilliputians. Three characteristic pieces for the pianoforte. 1. Jolly Midgets. 2. Laughing Gnomes. 3. Happy Elves. 3 no. *Theodore Presser: Philadelphia*, [1908.] fol. **h. 4120. nn. (5.)**

— Lily-Bells. [P.F.] pp. 3. *M. Witmark & Sons: New York, etc.*, [1908.] fol. **h. 4120. nn. (6.)**

— Links of Beauty. Six first-grade Piano Compositions, *etc. M. Witmark & Sons: New York*, 1912. 4°. **g. 232. w. (7.)**

— Little Runaway. [P.F.] pp. 3. *Theodore Presser: Philadelphia*, [1906.] fol. **h. 4120. nn. (7.)**

— Little Sallie Waters. Promenade march. *See* infra: Song Games of Childhood ... [9.]

— London Bridge. Polka. *See* infra: Song Games of Childhood ... [2.]

— Lucy Locket. *See* infra: Play Time ... [7.]

— Marigold. Barn Dance. *See* supra: In Grandma's Garden. No. 4.

— "Merrily we roll along." *See* infra: Songs of College Days ... 3.

— Mignonette. Galop. *See* supra: In Grandma's Garden. No. 8.

— Three Miniatures for the Pianoforte. [1.] Rose Petals. Romance. [2.] Ripples. Valsette. [3.] The Paper Chase. Caprice. 3 no. *Theo. Presser: Philadelphia*, [1908.] fol.

  h. 4120. nn. (8.)

— Miss Jennie O'Jones. Waltz. *See* infra: Song Games of Childhood ... [5.]

— Moss Rose. Two-step. *See* supra: In Grandma's Garden. No. 5.

— Mother may I go out to swim? Barcarolle. *See* infra: Song Games of Childhood ... [7.]

— "Nellie was a Lady." *See* infra: Songs of College Days ... 5.

— Oats, Peas, Beans. Two-step. *See* infra: Song Games of Childhood ... [8.]

— Off to Camp. March. *See* infra: Youthful Spirits ... 1.

— "Oh where is mine little Dog?" *See* infra: Songs of College Days ... 6.

— Old Mʳˢ Dougherty. *See* infra: Song Games of Childhood ... [3.]

— Open the Gates as high as the Sky. *See* infra: Play Time ... [3.]

— Over the Fence is out. *See* infra: Song Games of Childhood ... [6.]

— The Paper Chase. Caprice. *See* supra: Three Miniatures for the Pianoforte. [3.]

— Pine Cones. [P.F.] pp. 3. *M. Witmark & Sons: New York, etc.*, [1908.] fol. **h. 4120. nn. (9.)**

— Play Time. Recreations for the pianoforte, *etc.* [1.] Who was George Washington? [2.] Here we go 'round the Mulberry Bush. [3.] Open the Gates as high as the Sky! [4.] Ten little Injuns. [5.] Pop! goes the Weasel. [6.] Fishey, Fishey in the Brook. [7.] Lucy Locket. [8.] This little Pig went to Market. [9.] Georgie Porgie. [10.] Green Gravel. [11.] Girls and Boys come out to play. 11 no. *Theo. Presser: Philadelphia*, [1907.] fol. **h. 4210. nn. (10.)**

— Playful Kittens. [P.F.] pp. 3. *Theodore Presser: Philadelphia*, [1906.] fol. **h. 4120. nn. (11.)**

— Pop! goes the Weasel. *See* supra: Play Time ... [5.]

LAWSON (Paul)

— Practice and Pleasure. Six easy, progressive Piano Solos ... With appropriate verses by J. Moore, *etc. M. Witmark & Sons: New York, etc.*, (1910.) 4°. **g. 232. m. (8.)**

— Ring around a Rosie. Schottische. *See* infra: Song Games of Childhood ... [1.]

— Ripples. Valsette. *See* supra: Three Miniatures for the Pianoforte. [2.]

— Rose Geranium. Waltz. *See* supra: In Grandma's Garden. No. 2.

— Rose Petals. *See* supra: Three Miniatures for the Pianoforte. [1.]

— Ruby Red. [P.F.] pp. 3. *M. Witmark & Sons: New York, etc.*, [1908.] fol. **h. 4120. nn. (12.)**

— Song Games of Childhood in Dance Form for the Pianoforte. [1.] Ring around a Rosie. Schottische. [2.] London Bridge. Polka. [3.] Old Mʳˢ Dougherty. [4.] Go tell Aunt Sally. Polka Rondo. [5.] Miss Jennie O'Jones. Waltz. [6.] Over the Fence is out. [7.] Mother may I go out to swim? Barcarolle. [8.] Oats, Peas, Beans. Two-step. [9.] Little Sally Waters. Promenade. [10.] Three jolly Sailor Boys. 10 no. *Theodore Presser: Philadelphia*, [1906.] fol. **h. 4120. nn. (13.)**

— Songs of College Days. Ten familiar melodies arranged as pianoforte pieces. 1. "For he's a jolly good Fellow." 2. "Bonnie." 3. "Merrily we roll along." 4. "The Dutch Company." 5. "Nellie was a Lady." 6. "Oh where is mine little Dog?" 7. "Jingle Bells." 8. "Tourelay." 9. "Bzt! Bzt!" 10. "Good-night Ladies!" 10 no. *Theo. Presser: Philadelphia*, [1907.] fol. **h. 4120. nn. (14.)**

— Speed away. Galop. *See* infra: Youthful Spirits ... 5.

— Tally-ho. [P.F.] pp. 3. *Theodore Presser: Philadelphia*, [1906.] fol. **h. 4120. nn. (15.)**

— Ten little Injuns. *See* supra: Play Time ... [4.]

— This little Pig went to Market. *See* supra: Play Time ... [8.]

— Three jolly Sailor Boys. *See* supra: Song Games of Childhood ... [10.]

— "Tourelay." *See* supra: Songs of College Days ... 8.

— Verbena. Polka. *See* supra: In Grandma's Garden. No. 3.

— We two, Waltz. *See* infra: Youthful spirits ... 4.

— Who was George Washington? *See* supra: Play Time ... [1.]

— Youthful spirits. Five dances for the pianoforte. 1. Off to Camp. March. 2. In Mischief. Polka. 3. Gay Cavaliers. Mazurka. 4. We two. Waltz. 5. Speed away. Galop. 5 no. *Theodore Presser: Philadelphia*, [1908.] fol. **h. 4120. nn. (16.)**

LAWSON (Peter)

— Susie and her Motor Bike. A Catastrophe. [Song.] Words by B. Camborne. [With ensemble chorus.] *Ascherberg, Hopwood & Crew: London*, [1911.] fol. **H. 1792. r. (44.)**

LAWSON (Peter W. F.)

— Momenta 94. For solo piano. pp. 14. *Edition Peters: [London*, 1970.] 4°. **g. 1138. z. (11.)**

— Valentia extramaterial. Flute, piano, 2 or 4 percussion. [Score.] pp. 21. *Edition Peters: London, etc.*, [1971.] 4°.

  g. 1780. mm. (4.)

LAWSON (R. E.)

— Fascination. Graceful Dance. [P. F.] *Marshalls: London*, [1891.] fol. **h. 1489. s. (20.)**

LAWSON (R. E.)

— Miss Minnie Palmer's Musical Album No. 2 ... composed
and arranged by R. E. Lawson, *etc. London*, [1886.] 4°.
F. 607. v. (2.)

— The Society Dancing Girl. [Song.] Words and music by R. E.
Lawson, *etc.* pp. 5. *Howard & Co.: London*, [1895.] fol.
H. 3980. pp. (31.)

— Wilt thou forgive? Song, words by E. Oxenford. *Marshalls:
London*, [1889.] fol.
H. 1788. uu. (36.)

LAWSON (REUBEN)

— "Nightingale's Refrain." Ballad. pp. 5. *Jerome H. Remick:
Detroit, New York*, [1908.] fol.
H. 3985. l. (10.)

LAWSON (ROBERT ARCHIBALD)

— The Omdurman March. [P. F.] *R. Rowlands: Liscard*, [1901.]
fol.
g. 605. x. (7.)

— Summer Reverie. [P. F.] *R. A. Lawson:* [*London?*] 1903. fol.
h. 3282. ww. (34.)

LAWSON (W. W.)

— I'll rock you to sleep. [Song.] ... Words by G. W. Croft. (Arr.
by H. S. Woodworth.) *National Music Co.: Chicago*, 1895.
fol.
H. 1798. u. (34.)

LAWSUIT

— A Lawsuit. Song. *See* STEWART (Douglas)

LAWTON (ANNIE)

— Foundations of practical Ear Training. 2 vol. *Oxford
University Press: London*, 1933. 8°.
D. 1085. d. (3.)

— *See* CROWE (E.) The Folk Song Sight Singing Series.
Compiled and edited by E. Crowe, A. Lawton, *etc.* 1933, *etc.*
8°.
B. 978.

— *See* CROWE (E.) The Folk Song Sight Singing Series.
Compiled and edited by E. Crowe, A. Lawton, *etc.* 1934, *etc.*
8°.
E. 365.

LAWTON (D.)

— The Leeds Volunteer's March ... [Full score.] Arranged for
the Organ or Harpsichord, with a Variation. *Longman and
Broderip, for the Author: London*, [1794.] fol.
g. 133. (35.)

LAWTON (DOROTHY G.)

— Constance. Two-Step. [P. F.] *Lawrence Bros.: East Orange,
New Jersey*, 1896. fol.
h. 3286. g. (17.)

LAWTON (F. VAUGHAN)

— Children of the Future ... A Musical Diversion for Children,
written and composed by F. V. Lawton. *J. Curwen & Sons:
London*, 1934. 8°.
F. 1267. m. (7.)

— Matilda, Basil and Jasper. A Musical Farce in four episodes
for one Lady and two Gentlemen. Written & composed by
F. V. Lawton, *etc. Reynolds & Co.: London*, 1938. 4°.
[*Reynolds & Co.'s 2/6 Series of Concert Party Albums. No.* 17.]
G. 821. a.

— *See* BEETHOVEN (L. van) [Sonata. Op. 10. No. 2.] A Summer
Madrigal ... Arranged ... by F. V. Lawton. 1938. 8°.
F. 946. f. (24.)

— *See* ROSAS (J.) [Sobre los olas.] Over the Waves ... Vocal
arrangement for chorus by F. V. Lawton. [1948.] 8°.
F. 1744. h. (7.)

LAWTON (F. VAUGHAN)

— *See* SCHUMANN (R. A.) [Nachtstücke. Op. 23. No. 4.] The
Twilight Hour ... Arranged ... by F. V. Lawton. 1941. 8°.
[*Choral Handbook. No.* 1361.]
E. 862.

LAWTON (FRANK)

— Whistling Polka ... Founded on the ... Scherzo. "Rêve après
le Bal," by Broustet. [P. F.] *Hopwood & Crew: London*,
[1901.] fol.
h. 3286. q. (78.)

LAWTON (LIONEL)

— Magnificat and Nunc Dimittis ... in ... F. *Novello, Ewer &
Co.: London & New York*, [1892.] 8°.
F. 1170. k. (19.)

LAWTON (MITZI)

— *See* HAENDEL (G. F.) [La Resurrezione.—Ho un non so che
nel cor.] Air from The Faithful Shepherd. Arranged by
M. Lawton and D. Peckett. [1960.] 4°.
g. 1320. d. (2.)

— *See* HAENDEL (G. F.) [Rodrigo.—Nasce il sol.] Saltarello ...
Arranged for two pianos by M. Lawton and David Peckett.
[1965.] 4°.
g. 1320. d. (6.)

LAWTON (SIDNEY MAURICE)

— A Book of Clarinet Duets. Four arrangements for two B flat
clarinets and piano by S. M. Lawton. [Score and parts.] 2 pt.
Oxford University Press: London; printed in Holland, [1956.]
4°.
g. 1104. n. (2.)

— A Book of Clarinet Trios [by Purcell, Mendelssohn, Handel,
Haydn, Este and Corelli]. Arranged by S. M. Lawton. [Score
and parts for clarinet II, and clarinet III or bass clarinet.] 3 pt.
Oxford University Press: London, [1968.] 4°.
g. 1104. hh. (11.)

— The Brass Quartet ... Volume I. Twenty short, easy pieces.
⟨Volume II. Eight short pieces by classical composers.⟩
Arranged by S. M. Lawton. For two trumpets in B flat and
two trombones or two trumpets in B flat, horn in F, and
trombone (with optional piano). Piano score [and parts], *etc.*
2 vol. 12 pt. *Oxford University Press: London*, [1960.] 4°.
*Vol. III and IV, edited by Lionel Lethbridge, are entered under
his name.*
g. 1110. h. (5.)

— The Clarinettist's Book of Carols. Arranged by S. M. Lawton.
Twelve well-known carols for B♭ clarinet and piano. [Score
and part.] 2 pt. *Oxford University Press: London*, [1959.] 4°.
g. 1104. n. (6.)

— Fugue on a Nursery Theme. B♭ clarinet and piano. [Score
and part.] 2 pt. *New Wind Music Co.: London*, [1961.] 4°.
g. 1104. bb. (15.)

— The National Anthem. ⟨Arranged for orchestra by S. M.
Lawton.⟩ Score, *etc.* pp. 3. *Novello & Co.: London*, [1965.] 4°.
[*Windscores. no.* 1.]
g. 816.

— Old English Trumpet Tunes. *See infra:* [The Young
Trumpet-player. vol. 2, 3.]

— Windscores. A series of arrangements for school orchestras
by S. M. Lawton. [Scores.] *Novello & Co.: London*, [1965,
etc.] 4°.
g. 816.

— The Young Clarinettist. A series of graded arrangements for
clarinet in B flat and piano, *etc.* [Scores.] 3 vol. *Oxford
University Press: London, etc.*, [1952.] 4°. **g. 1104. f. (9.)**

— The Young Flautist. A series of graded arrangements for flute
and piano, *etc.* [Scores.] 3 vol. *Oxford University Press:
London*, [1957.] 4°.
g. 70. t. (6.)

— The Young Horn-Player. A series of graded arrangements for
horn in F and piano. [Scores and parts.] 3 vol. 6 pt. *Oxford
University Press: London*, [1975.] 4°.
g. 270. nn. (3.)

LAWTON (SIDNEY MAURICE)

— The Young Oboist. A series of graded arrangements for oboe and piano, *etc.* [Scores and parts.] 3 vol. 6 pt.   *Oxford University Press: London*, [1964.] 4°.   **g. 1078. c. (12.)**

— The Young Trombonist. A series of graded arrangements for trombone and piano by S. M. Lawton, *etc.* [Scores and parts for trombone and tenor trombone.] 3 vol. 9 pt.   *Oxford University Press: London*, [1970.] 4°.   **g. 1117. b. (8.)**

— The Young Trumpet-Player. A series of graded arrangements for trumpets in B flat and piano, *etc.* [Scores and parts.] 3 vol. 6 pt.   *Oxford University Press: London*, [1959.] 4°.   **g. 1105. i. (2.)**

— [The Young Trumpet-Player. Vol. 2, 3.] Old English Trumpet Tunes. For trumpet in B flat. Piano accompaniments by Sidney M. Lawton. [Score and part.] 2 pt.   *Oxford University Press: London*, [1971.] 4°.   **g. 1105. t. (1.)**

— *See* BACH (Johann S.) [Herz und Mund und That und Leben.—Wohl mir, dass ich Jesum habe.] Jesu, Joy of Man's Desiring.   [1975.] 4°.   **g. 1700. b. (1.)**

— *See* BACH (Johann S.) [Herz und Mund und That und Leben.—Wohl mir, dass ich Jesum habe.] Jesu, Joy of Man's Desiring. Arranged for clarinet ... and piano by S. Lawton. [1975.] 4°.   **g. 1700. b. (6.)**

— *See* BACH (Johann S.) [Herz und Mund und That und Leben.—Wohl mir, dass ich Jesum habe.] Jesu, Joy of Man's Desiring. Arranged for flute and piano by S. Lawton. [1976.] 4°.   **g. 1700. b. (7.)**

— *See* BACH (Johann S.) [Was mir behagt.—Schafe können sicher weiden.] Sheep may safely graze. Arranged for two flutes or treble recorders and piano by S. Lawton. [1978.] 4°.   **g. 1700. g. (8.)**

— *See* HAENDEL (G. F.) [Overture. For two clarinets and corno di caccia.] Overture in C ... Arranged for three B flat clarinets by S. M. Lawton. [1961.] 4°.   **g. 1320. d. (4.)**

— *See* KEMBER (John) Wind Band Book. Seven pieces arranged by J. Kember, S. Lawton, *etc.* [1974.] 4°.   **g. 270. mm. (2.)**

— *See* TELEMANN (Georg P.) [Musique héroïque.] Heroic Music ... Transcribed for trumpet ... or horn ... or trombone and keyboard by S. Lawton. [1976.] 4°.   **g. 401. dd. (4.)**

LAWYER

— The Lawyer and the Devil. *See* DEVIL. The devil once, *etc.* [1841.] fol.   **H. 1251. (3.)**

— The Lawyer & the Lady's Maid. Duet *See* PLANQUETTE (R.) [Captain Thérèse.]

— Lawyer Brown. Song. *See* FARLEY (R.)

— Lawyer Snare. [Song.] *See* NORMAN (G. P.)

— The Lawyer's Clerk. Comic Song. *See* WILLIE (J.)

— The Lawyer's Duel. [Song and chorus.] *See* AFTER. After a pauze of great Guns loud salute, *etc.* [1655?] fol.   **Harl. 5936. (399.)**

— The Lawyer's Glee. *See* WOMAN. A Woman having a settlement, *etc.* [1799.] fol.   **G. 809. c. (72.)**

— The Lawyer's Invocation to Spring. Part-Song. *See* FORSYTH (C.)

LAX (FREDERIC)

— Buoyant Hearts, quick march for the Pianoforte.   *London*, [1878.] fol.   **h. 1494. p. (35.)**

— Gavotte (La Musette) for the Pianoforte.   *London*, [1878.] fol.   **h. 1494. p. (33.)**

LAX (FREDERIC)

— Live and Hope, waltz for the Pianoforte.   *London*, [1878.] fol.   **h. 1494. p. (34.)**

LAX (W. H.)

— Bravo, British Boys. Song, words by G. Jordison.   *West & Co.: London*, 1915. fol.   **H. 1793. s. (26.)**

LAXDAL (JÓN)

— Tvö sönglög. Zwei Lieder. Fuglar í búri. Vögel im Bauer. Sólskríkjan. Schneeammer. *Icel. & Ger.   Bokverzlun Guðm. Gamalíelssonar: Reykjavik*, 1907. fol.   *With an alternative accompaniment to each song.*   **H. 1860. x. (1.)**

LAXTON (ALWYN)

— Elegy & Le Motif. [Organ.] pp. 8.   *Paxton Music: [Borough Green*, 1973.] 4°.   *Part of "Anthology of Organ Music".*   **f. 337. j. (4.)**

LAY

— The Lay. [A collection of songs.] *See* SEVERN (T. H.)

— Lay a Garland. [Two-part song.] *See* BRIDGE (F.)

— Lay a Garland. [Quartet.] *See* GODFREY (H. G.)

— Lay a Garland on my Hearse. [Song.] *See* AMARASĒKARA (D.)

— Lay a Garland on my Hearse. [Song.] *See* BUSH (Geoffrey) Five Spring Songs ... No. 2.

— Lay a Garland on my Hearse. Song. *See* RAPHAEL (M.)

— Lay aside religion's pleasures. *Dark Times cease for evermore.* [Song.]   *Birmingham*, 1862. fol.   **H. 1790. a. (61.)**

— Lay aside the little Shoes and Stockings. Song. *See* DANKS (H. P.)

— Lay aside the reap-hook. [Song.] *See* LEVERIDGE (R.) [The Mountebank.]

— Lay down your Staffs. [Carol.] *See* PARKER (Alice) and SHAW (R.)

— Lay down your Sword of Thunder. Part Song. *See* WHITE (F. H.)

— Lay his sword by his side. Song and chorus. *See* KIEFFER (J. M.)

— Lay his Sword by his Side. Chorus. *See* STANFORD (*Sir* C. V.)

— Lay me down, lay me down by the stream. Ballad. *See* MACMURDIE (J.)

— Lay me gently near my mother. Song & chorus. *See* FOX (J.)

— Lay me where the sunbeams linger. Ballad. *See* PLUMPTON (A.)

— Lay my Wedding Dress away. [Song.] *See* TILZER (Albert von)

— Lay not up for yourselves. Quartet. *See* BALLARD (L. W.)

— Lay not up for Yourselves. Anthem. *See* DAVIS (F. W.)

— Lay not up for yourselves. [Anthem.] *See* KING (O. A.)

— The Lay of a distant one. [Song.] *See* BEETHOVEN (L. van) [Lied aus der Ferne. K.-H. 137.]

— The Lay of Albert Graeme. Song. *See* LEMARE (W.)

— Lay of an Irish Minstrel. Song. *See* LOVER (S.)

LAY

— A Lay of Ancient Rome. *See* PULLEY (L.)

— The Lay of Gratitude. Melody. *See* ROUSSELOT (S.)

— The Lay of Hope. [Song.] *See* RUSSELL (Henry)

— A Lay of June. [Part-song.] *See* LIDDLE (J. S.)

— The Lay of Love. Song. *See* CLARKE, afterwards CLARKE WHITFELD (J.)

— A Lay of Olde Londonne. Song. *See* ELCUM (C. C.)

— The Lay of Pungstall. [Song.] *See* GRAY (J.) *Songwriter.*

— The Lay of Rosabelle. [Cantata.] *See* COLLINS (A.)

— The Lay of St. Cuthbert. [Cantata.] *See* SPEER (W. H.)

— A Lay of Spring. Song. *See* PATTERSON (A. W.)

— A Lay of the Blackmore Vale. Song. *See* KENNEDY (A. W. M. C.)

— The Lay of the Brown Rosary. Cantata. *See* BOYCE (E. M.)

— The Lay of the Brown Rosary. Cantata. *See* CARSE (A. von A.)

— The Lay of the Chicken. Two-part song. *See* OFFENBACH (J.) [La Créole.—La poularde était de taille.]

— The Lay of the Chimes. Song. *See* ROMER (F.)

— Lay of the Colonists. [Song.] *See* RICKETTS (F. L.)

— Lay of the Cross. Song. *See* GABRIEL, afterwards MARCH (M. A. V.)

— The Lay of the Dandie Dinmont Terrier. Song. *See* HICKS (W. B.)

— A Lay of the early Spring. [Song.] *See* GOUNOD (C. F.)

— The Lay of the Fancy Fair. Part-Song. *See* DAVISON (M.)

— The Lay of the Fountain Pen. [Musical monologue.] *See* JOHNSTON (L.)

— The Lay of the four Winds. [Part-song.] *See* BAUER (Marion E.)

— Lay of the imprisoned Huntsman. [Song.] *See* MAZZINGHI (Joseph)

— Lay of the imprisoned Huntsman. [Song.] *See* SCHUBERT (F. P.) [Sieben Gesänge. Op. 52. No. 7. Lied des gefangenen Jägers.]

— Lay of the imprisoned Huntsman. [Song.] *See* WILSON (John) *Public Singer.*

— The Lay of the Indian Girl. Romance. *See* GUYLOTT (R.)

— The Lay of the Katydid. [Song.] *See* HEINE (L. A.)

— The Lay of the Knight. Song. *See* HOELZEL (G.) Six Songs, *etc.* No. 2.

— The Lay of the Labourer. Song. *See* ALBERT (B.)

— The Lay of the Laborer. [Song.] *See* HOMER (S.) Two Songs ... (Op. 43.) I.

— The Lay of the Last Minstrel. Cantata. *See* MacCUNN (H.)

— The Lay of the Last Minstrel. Cantata. *See* PATTISON (T. M.)

— A Lay of the Lea. [Song.] *See* GOODHART (A. M.)

— The Lay of the Levite. [Song.] *See* MEDHURST (*Mrs* M. A.)

— A Lay of the Links. Song. *See* WHITE (M. V.)

— A Lay of the Links. Song. *See* YORKE (A.)

LAY

— The Lay of the little red Rose. [Song.] *See* OLIVER (H.)

— Lay of the Lost Doll. [Song.] *See* WIGAN (A. C.)

— The Lay of the Merry Jack Tar. Song. *See* BERESFORD (S.)

— The Lay of the Minstrel Knight. Romance. *See* PURDAY (C. H.)

— The Lay of the noble Ten. [Action song.] *See* BONNER (C.)

— The Lay of the Norsemen. Baritone, chorus and orchestra. *See* BRUCH (M. C. F.) [Normannenzug.]

— Lay of the Sailor's Bride. [Song.] *See* THOMSON (John) *of Edinburgh.*

— Lay of the Summer Eve. [Song.] *See* ABT (F. W.) Der Sommerabend.

— Lay of the Troubadour. [Song.] *See* MACIRONE (A.)

— The Lay of the very last Minstrel. Song. *See* KING (J. L.)

— The Lay of the Wanderer. [Song.] *See* KLOSE (F. J.)

— The Lay of the Willow. [Song.] *See* KNIGHT (J. P.)

— A Lay of Venice. [Song.] *See* BIGG (F. S.)

— Lay soft thy Cheek. [Song.] *See* JENSEN (A.) [6 Lieder. Op. 1. No. 1. Lehn' deine Wang'.]

— Lay that sullen garland by thee. [Song.] *See* ATTERBURY (L.)

— Lay the precious body. Hymn. *See* HOLDER (T.)

— Lay thy Hand in mine. Song. *See* BARTON (G.) *of Blackburn.*

— Lay Thy Hand upon me. Hymn-anthem. *See* BONTEMPS (Franklin)

— Lay Thy Hand upon me. [Anthem and sacred song.] *See* THOMSON (S.)

— Lay up for yourselves Treasures in Heaven. [Anthem.] *See* EWENS (R. C.)

— Lay up treasure in Heaven. Song. *See* SKEAF (J.)

— Lay yer Hand upon ma Heart. Song. *See* DACRE (H.) *pseud.*

LAY (GILBERT)
— *See* LAYE.

LAYARD (ARTHUR A. M.)
— How is it you and I. Rondel, words by J. C. Grant. *Leonard & Co.: London,* 1908. fol.   **G. 805. mm. (17.)**

— 5 Love Songs from H. Heine's Lyrisches Intermezzo ... English translations by M. A. C., *etc. C. Woolhouse: London,* 1888. fol.   **H. 1788. v. (10.)**

LAYARD (E. B.)
— In medio bello. [Litany, words by] V. S. S. Coles. *Basil Blackwell: Oxford,* [1939.] *a card.*   **I. 600. f. (82.)**

LAYCOCK (ARTHUR)
— *See* HAWKES AND SON. Hawkes and Son's No. 1. Cornet Solo Album, *etc.* (No. 3. (4.) Arranged and edited by A. Laycock.) 1913–39. 4°.   **g. 1120. d.**

LAYCOCK (GEOFFREY)
— *See* PETTI (Anthony G.) and LAYCOCK (G.) New Catholic Hymnal. Compiled and edited by A. Petti and G. Laycock. Full edition. 1971. 8°.   **D. 561. y.**

LAYCOCK (GEOFFREY)

— *See* PETTI (Anthony G.) and LAYCOCK (G.) New Catholic
Hymnal. Compiled and edited by A. Petti and G. Laycock.
Melody edition. 1971. 8°. **D. 448. d.**

LAYCOCK (HAROLD)

— Hawkes & Son's No. 1 Trombone Solo Album provided with
pianoforte accompaniment. Edited by H. Laycock, *etc.* [Score
and parts.] 3 no. 6 pt. *Hawkes & Son: London, etc.,*
[1925–37.] 4°. **g. 1120. c.**

LAYE (F.)

— Dairy Mary. Written by J. A. Bentham. [Song. With separate
voice part.] 2 pt. *Hopwood & Crew: London,* [1905.] fol.
H. 3985. l. (11.)

LAYE (GILBERT)

— The Bohemian. ⟨Song.⟩ Written by Alec Fairfax. [Staff and
tonic sol-fa notation. Voice part.] *Francis, Day & Hunter:
London,* [1907.] *s. sh.* fol. **H. 3985. l. (12.)**

— The Bohemian, *etc.* ⟨Song.⟩ [With separate voice part.] 2 pt.
Francis, Day & Hunter: London, [1907.] fol.
H. 3985. l. (13.)

— "Cheero!" ⟨Song.⟩ Written by Percy Rhys. [Staff and tonic
sol-fa notation. Voice part.] *Francis, Day & Hunter: London,*
[1907.] *s. sh.* fol. **H. 3985. l. (14.)**

— "Cheero!" *etc.* ⟨Song.⟩ [With separate voice part.] 2 pt.
Francis, Day & Hunter: London, [1907.] fol.
H. 3985. l. (15.)

— In Dreamland's Light. Song, words by C. Bingham. 2 no. [In
F and A flat.] *Ascherberg, Hopwood & Crew: London,* 1911.
fol. **H. 1792. r. (45.)**

— Love, Sunshine and Roses. Song, words by F. G. Bowles.
2 no. [In E flat and C.] *J. B. Cramer & Co.: London,* 1913.
fol. **H. 1793. s. (27.)**

— My Letters ... Song. Written & composed by G. Laye.
⟨Arranged by John Neat.⟩ [With separate voice part.] 2 pt.
Moon & Co.: London, [1901.] fol. **H. 3985. l. (16.)**

— A Seaside Holiday at Home. ⟨Song.⟩ Written by Fred Bowyer,
etc. [Staff and tonic sol-fa notation. Voice part.] *Francis,
Day & Hunter: London,* [1903.] *s. sh.* fol. **H. 3985. l. (17.)**

— A Seaside Holiday at Home, *etc.* ⟨Song.⟩ With separate voice
part.] 2 pt. *Francis, Day & Hunter: London,* [1903.] fol.
H. 3985. l. (18.)

— Star of my Dreams. Song, words by C. Bingham, *etc.*
W. Morley & Co.: London, 1905. fol. **H. 1794. vv. (22.)**

LAYLAND, afterwards BARRATT (FRANCES) *Lady*

— Eyes of tender blue. *See* infra: Four Songs ... No. 1.

— A Little Bunch of Heather. *See* infra: Four Songs ... No. 4.

— A Ring for Remembrance. *See* infra: Four Songs ... No. 2.

— Silently through the dim Ether. *See* infra: Four Songs ...
No. 3.

— Four Songs (words and music) by F. Layland-Barratt ...
No. 1. Eyes of tender blue. No. 2. A Ring for Remembrance.
No. 3. Silently through the dim Ether. No. 4. A Little Bunch
of Heather. 4 no. *Weekes & Co.:* 1914, *etc.* 4°.
G. 390. l. (1.)

LAYLAND (J.)

— A Song of Welcome ... An action song for the opening of
school concerts. Words and music by J. Layland. [Staff and
tonic sol-fa notation.] pp. 5. *J. Curwen & Sons: London;
Curwen: Germantown,* [c. 1930.] fol. **H. 1984. m. (1.)**

LAYLAND (JOHN)

— And suddenly there came a sound. Anthem for Whitsuntide.
London, [1886.] 8°. **E. 605. o. (25.)**

— And suddenly there came a Sound. Anthem ... Tonic sol-fa
edition. *Novello, Ewer & Co.: London & New York,* [1886.]
4°. **B. 559. p. (11.)**

LAYLAND (LAURA)

— I stood in a lovely Garden. Song, words & music by
L. Layland. *Weekes & Co.: London,* 1914. fol.
H. 1793. s. (28.)

— A Song of Spring. [Song.] Words and music by L. Layland.
Weekes & Co.: London, [1914.] 4°. **G. 390. k. (9.)**

LAYLAND (THOMAS)

— Ah Damon, dear Shepherd adieu. A Favorite Elegy, *etc.*
G[eorge] S[mart: London, 1780?] *s. sh.* fol. **G. 306. (93.)**

LAYLAND (WILLIAM)

— As pants the Heart, (Spohr) transcribed for the Pianoforte.
London, [1869.] fol. **h. 3001. (16.)**

— Autumn. Four-part song [begins: "Summer is flying"] written
by S. W. Partridge. *London,* [1861.] fol. **H. 1772. r. (20.)**

— The Bells of Aberdovey, popular Welsh song. The English
words by Edward Oxenford, and new symphonies and
accompaniments by W. Layland. pp. 4. *Cunningham Boosey:
London,* [1881.] fol.
Cunningham Boosey's "Universal" Music. no. 849.
H. 1654. aa. (11.)

— Bishop's Melodies, transcribed for the Pianoforte. 8 no.
London, [1869–72.] fol. **h. 3001. a. (1.)**

— Bishop's melodies transcribed for the Pianoforte. No. 9.
London, [1872.] fol. **h. 1481. j. (9.)**

— Bonnie Prince Charlie, transcribed for the Pianoforte.
London, [1867.] fol. **h. 3001. (5.)**

— Caller Herring. [P. F. fantasia on N. Gow's song.] *London,*
[1867.] fol. **h. 3001. (4.)**

— Caller Herring. [P. F. fantasia on N. Gow's song.] *London,*
[1874.] fol. **h. 3001. a. (8.)**

— Canadian Fête. Sketch for the pianoforte. *Beal & Co.:
London,* [1892.] fol. **h. 1489. s. (21.)**

— La Carità (Rossini) transcribed for the Pianoforte. *London,*
[1878.] fol. **h. 1484. c. (28.)**

— A Carol round the Fireside [song by M. A. V. Gabriel
transcribed for P. F.] by W. Layland. *London,* [1871.] fol.
h. 3001. (23.)

— Chiquita ... Chanson Espagnole transcribed by W. Layland.
[P. F.] *London,* [1876.] fol. **h. 1482. y. (44.)**

— The Class Singer's Guide, a series of progressive exercises
and solfeggi, *etc.* *London,* [1878.] obl. 4°. **B. 512. g. (3.)**

— The Evening Star [Der Wanderer, by A. E. Fesca] ...
transcribed for the Pianoforte. *London,* [1868.] fol.
h. 3001. (16.)

— Les Folies du Carnaval, morceau caractéristique pour Piano.
London, [1864.] fol. **h. 3001. (9.)**

LAYLAND (WILLIAM)

— The Four Jolly Smiths, composed by H. T. Leslie, transcribed for the Pianoforte. *London,* [1873.] fol.   **h. 3001. a. (4.)**

— Gounod's Barcarole ... Où voulez vous aller, transcribed for the Piano. *London,* [1870.] fol.   **h. 3001. (17.)**

— Gounod's Serenade, "Sing on," transcribed for the Piano. *London,* [1870.] fol.   **h. 3001. (18.)**

— Grandfather's Clock ... Song (composed by H. C. Work) transcribed [for P. F.]. *London,* [1879.] fol.   **h. 1484. c. (30.)**

— The Harbour Bay, from J. F. Barnett's cantata, The Ancient Mariner, transcribed for the Pianoforte. *London,* [1868.] fol.   **h. 3001. (19.)**

— Layland's Harmonium School. *London,* [1868.] fol.   **h. 2575. g. (20.)**

— The Hunter's Return, characteristic piece for the Pianoforte. *London,* [1866.] fol.   **h. 3001. (6.)**

— Huntingtower, transcribed for the Pianoforte. *London,* [1868.] fol.   **h. 3001. (11.)**

— I heard the voice of Jesus say. [Hymn, words by H. Bonar.] *London,* [1874.] 8°.   **E. 600. q. (18.)**

— I heard the voice of Jesus say. Sacred song. *London,* [1874.] fol.   **H. 1778. x. (48.)**

— I heard the voice of Jesus say. Sacred song. *London,* [1879.] fol. *No. 675–76 of C. Boosey's "Universal" music.*   **H. 2324.**

— Jenny Jones ... Welsh melody, brilliantly transcribed for Piano. 2 no. *London,* [1876.] fol.   **h. 1482. y. (43.)**

— Joyous Bells. March for the pianoforte. *C. Jefferys: London,* [1891.] fol.   **h. 1489. s. (22.)**

— Just before the battle, descriptive fantasia [on G. F. Root's song. P. F.]. *London,* [1869.] fol.   **h. 3001. (12.)**

— March of the Men of Harlech, transcribed for Piano. *London,* [1865.] fol.   **h. 3001. (8.)**

— March of the Men of Harlech, transcribed for Piano. *London,* [1872.] fol.   **h. 3001. (27.)**

— The Mill Wheel ... popular German melody by Silcher, transcribed for the Pianoforte. *London,* [1879.] fol. *No. 822–23 of C. Boosey's "Universal" music.*   **H. 2324.**

— The modern Pianoforte School. *London,* [1876.] fol.   **h. 3750.**

— Moonlight on the waves is playing. [Part-song.] Poetry by E.W. *London,* [1861.] fol.   **H. 1772. r. (21.)**

— Mrs. Macdonald. [P. F. fantasia on the Scotch melody so called.] *London,* [1867.] fol.   **h. 3001. (3.)**

— The Mulligan Guards march. [P. F.] *London,* [1876.] fol.   **h. 1482. y. (45.)**

— The National Wreath. [P. F. duets.] 6 no. *London,* [1870–72.] fol.   **h. 3001. a. (2.)**

— Ninetta, grand waltz ... for Pianoforte. *London,* [1861.] fol.   **h. 3001. (1.)**

— O Paradise! O Paradise! arranged for the Pianoforte. (Founded upon the ... sacred song composed by H. F. Hemy.) *London,* [1869.] fol.   **h. 3001. (15.)**

— Oft in the stilly night, transcription for Piano. *London,* [1865.] fol.   **h. 3001. (7.)**

— Three Old English melodies ... arranged for the Pianoforte. *London,* [1873.] fol.   **h. 3001. a. (3.)**

LAYLAND (WILLIAM)

— Layland's Pianoforte Trios for three performers on one Pianoforte. 6 no. *London,* [1868–69.] fol.   **h. 3001. (20.)**

— The Pilgrims of the Night. N° 3 of Hemy's Sacred Songs, transcribed for the piano forte by William Layland. pp. 5. *George Emery & C°: London,* [c. 1860.] fol.   **h. 61. pp. (2.)**

— [A reissue.] The Pilgrims of the Night, arranged for the Pianoforte. *London,* [1867.] fol.   **h. 3001. (10.)**

— The polar Star. Song written by A. M. Wicks. [Begins: "Oh what see I".] *London,* [1851.] fol.   **H. 1735. (22.)**

— Popular Melodies, transcribed for the Pianoforte by W. Layland. 96 no. *Hutchings and Romer: London,* [1868–80.] fol.   **h. 3001. (21.)**   **h. 3001. a. (9.)**   **& h. 3001. b.**

— Rossini's Cujus Animam, transcribed for the Pianoforte. *London,* [1871.] fol.   **h. 3001. (24.)**

— Three Sacred Melodies ... transcribed for the Piano. 3 no. *London,* [1863, 64.] fol.   **h. 3001. (2.)**

— Scotch national Melodies. Transcribed for the piano forte by W. Layland, *etc.* no. 1. *Hutchings & Romer: London,* [c. 1880.] fol. *Imperfect; wanting no. 2–6.*   **H. 1980. hh. (22.)**

— Silver Threads among the Gold ... Song [by H. P. Danks] transcribed [for P. F.]. *London,* [1877.] fol.   **h. 1484. c. (27.)**

— Sound the loud Timbrel [by C. Avison], transcribed for the Pianoforte. *London,* [1871.] fol.   **h. 3001. (25.)**

— The Standard on the Braes o' Mar, transcribed [for P. F.], *etc. London,* [1874.] fol.   **h. 3001. a. (6.)**

— Sun of my Soul, transcribed for the Pianoforte. *London,* [1871.] fol.   **h. 3001. (26.)**

— The Sweetest Flower. Ballad [begins: "Sweet flow'rets in my garden bloom"] written by Miss L. E. Hatchard. *London,* [1874.] fol.   **H. 1778. x. (49.)**

— Symphony, andante grazioso for the pianoforte. *London,* [1854.] fol.   **h. 723. l. (24.)**

— There is nae luck, brilliantly transcribed for Piano. *London,* [1879.] fol.   **h. 1484. c. (29.)**

— Layland's universal favorites, arranged for the Pianoforte. *London,* [1879.] fol. *No. 752–75 of C. Boosey's "Universal" music.*   **H. 2324.**

— The Watch on the Rhine ... Prussian national song [by C. Wilhelm] transcribed [for P. F.], *etc. London,* [1870.] fol.   **h. 3001. (22.)**

— When Joan's Ale was new ... transcribed for Piano. *London,* [1879.] fol.   **h. 1484. c. (31.)**

— Where the Bee sucks [by T. A. Arne], brilliant transcription for the Pianoforte. *London,* [1873.] fol.   **h. 3001. a. (5.)**

— Zulee. Song, the words by S. Champion. *Boosey & Co.: London,* [1883.] fol.   **H. 1788. v. (11.)**

— *See* MENDELSSOHN-BARTHOLDY (J. L. F.) [Lieder ohne Worte. Smaller collections.] Two original melodies. (Op. 53 & 85.) Arranged for the harp by W. Layland. [1854.] fol.   **h. 2604. (25.)**

— *See* MOZART (W.A.) [*Doubtful and Supposititious Works.*] [Mass No. 12.] Selections ... transcribed for the Pianoforte, by W. Layland. [1869.] fol.   **h. 3001. (13.)**

— *See* MOZART (W.A.) [*Doubtful and Supposititious Works.*] [Mass No. 12.] Selections ... transcribed ... by W. Layland. [1875.] fol.   **h. 321. e. (13.)**

LAYLAND (William)

— See Rossini (G.A.) [Stabat Mater.] Selections ... transcribed
... by W. Layland. [1874.] fol. **h. 3001. a. (7.)**

— See Wickins and Co. Wickins' Voluntaries for the Organ ...
Book 6. Selected and arranged by W. Layland. [1900? etc.] 4°.
f. 375.

LAYLAND-BARRATT (Frances) Lady

— See Layland, afterwards Barratt (Frances) Lady.

LAYMAN

— Church Psalmody: a collection of tunes, harmonized for four
voices, with an organ accompaniment; expressly adapted for
a selection of "Psalms and Hymns". By a layman [i.e.
Edward B. Frip]. pp. iv. 3. 63. R. Cocks & Co., for the Author:
London, [1829?] obl. 8°.
The titlepage bears a note in the autograph of Samuel Wesley,
attributing the authorship to Edward Frip. **A. 511. dd.**

— A loyal prayer for one, two, three, or four voices, by a
Layman. London, 1831. fol. **H. 1250. (54.)**

— Twelve New Tunes for Catholic Hymns. Composed by a
Layman. The Chiswick Press: London, 1932. obl. 8°.
A. 510.

LAYNG (Judith)

— See Disappointment. The Disappointment: or, The Force of
Credulity ... Edited by J. C. Graue and J. Layng, etc. [1976.]
4°. [Recent Researches in American Music. vol. 3, 4.]
G. 1490. b.

LAYOLLE (Francesco de)

— Collected secular Works for 2, 3, 4 and 5 Voices. ⟨Edited by
Frank A. D'Accone.⟩ [With a portrait.] pp. xix. 86. American
Institute of Musicology: [Dallas, Tex.?,] 1969. fol.
[Corpus mensurabilis musicae. 32. vol. 3.] **H. 3.**

— [50 canzoni a quatro voci.] Collected secular Works for
4 Voices. ⟨Edited by Frank A. d'Accone.⟩ pp. xxi. 113.
American Institute of Musicology: [Dallas, Tex.?,] 1969. fol.
[Corpus mensurabilis musicae. 32. vol. 4.] **H. 3.**

— Masses and penitential Psalms. ⟨Edited by Frank A.
D'Accone.⟩ pp. xiv. 132. American Institute of Musicology:
[Dallas, Tex.?,] 1973. fol.
[Corpus mensurabilis musicae. 32. vol. 6.] **H. 3.**

— Collected Motets for 2, 3, 4, 5 and 6 Voices. ⟨Edited by
Frank A. D'Accone.⟩ pp. xxii. 154. American Institute of
Musicology: [Dallas, Tex.?,] 1973. fol.
[Corpus mensurabilis musicae. 32. vol. 5.] **H. 3.**

— [Motets.] [A book of 12 motets. By F. de Layolle?] Tenor. [c.
1525.] obl. 4°. See Motets. [10.] **K. 8. b. 7. (5.)**

— [3 Motets.] In: Guarnerus (Bernardus) Contrapunctus seu
figurata musica, etc. ff. 77v–80v. 1528. fol. **K. 9. a. 23.**

— [3 Motets.] In: Guarnerus (Bernardus) [Contrapunctus seu
figurata musica.] The Lyons Contrapunctus (1528), etc. pt. 2.
pp. 87–96. [1976.] 4°. [Recent Researches in the Music of the
Renaissance. vol. 2.] **G. 1490. a.**

— See Moderne (J.) Liber decem missarum a praeclaris musicis
contextus, etc. [Edited by F. de Layolle.] [1532.] fol.
K. 2. i. 29.

LAYRIZ (Friedrich)

— CXVII. Geistliche Melodien meist aus dem 16. und 17. Jahrh.
in ihren ursprünglichen Rhythmen zweistimmig gesetzt.
Theodor Bläsing: Erlangen, 1839. 8°.
Lithographed throughout. **A. 951.**

LAYRIZ (Friedrich)

— Geistliche Melodien, meist aus dem 16 und 17 Jahrh. in ihren
ursprünglichen Tonen und Rhythmen ... zweistimmig gesetzt.
2 pt. Erlangen, 1853, 50. 8°. **A. 715.**

— Kern des deutschen Kirchengesangs. Eine Samlung von
CC. Chorälen, meist aus dem XVI und XVII. Jahrhundert, in
ihren ursprünglichen Tönen und Rhythmen mit
altertümlicher Harmonie vierstimmig zum gebrauche für
Kirche und Haus herausgegeben von Dr. F. Layritz.
Nördlingen, 1844. 4°. **F. 346. a.**

— Kern des deutschen Kirchengesangs, zum Gebrauch
evangelisch-lutherischer Gemeinden und Familien ... Dritte
umgearbeitete und sehr vermehrte Auflage. 4 Abth. C. H.
Beck: Noerdlingen, 1854, 55, etc. 4°.
Each Abth. also has a special titlepage. **F. 346.**

— Die Liturgie eines vollständigen Hauptgottesdienstes nach
lutherischem Typus nebst Ratschlägen zu deren
Wiederherstellung ... Mit zwei Musikbeilagen. Nördlingen,
1849. 8°. **3475. dd. 2.**

— 335 Melodien Deutscher Kirchengesänge, meist aus dem 16.
und 17. Jahrhundert, nach Dr. F. Layriz. Revidirte und
vermehrte Ausgabe. pp. [1]–86. Lutherischer Concordia-
Verlag: St. Louis, Mo., 1887. 16°.
Imperfect; wanting all after p. 86, containing melodies
no. 290–335. **A. 1236. d.**

LAYS

— Lays for Little Ones. See Bunning (H.)

— Lays of Erin, selected & arranged as rondos, for the piano
forte, by the most eminent composers. no. 2. J. Power:
London; W. Power: Dublin, [WM1815.] fol.
Imperfect; wanting the other no. **h. 62. gg.**

— Lays of Harmony. Popular Vocal Music with
Accompaniments for the Guitar. 50 no. E. Donajowski:
London, [1894.] fol. **H. 2086.**

— Lays of the Crystal Palace ... written by F. C. Lacy. no. 3, 4.
London, [1851.] fol.
Imperfect; wanting no. 1, 2. **H. 2184. (10 & 11.)**

— Lays of the Forest, etc. no. 1–3. London, [1843.] fol.
H. 1252. (38.)

— Lays of the German Minstrels ... With the original German
words, and a translation, by Wm Ball. 2 bk. J. J. Ewer:
London, [c. 1840.] fol. **G. 809. gg.**

— Lays of the Heart; a series of six ballads by various authors.
London, [1843.] fol. **H. 1432.**

— Lays of the Lower Thames. [Songs.] See Pascal (F.) pseud.

— Lays of Venice and Songs of the Carnival ... Written by
C. Jefferys (H. Stoe Vandyk), composed and arranged by
C. Coote ⟨G. Perry, W. Grossé, S. Nelson, L. Devereaux,
A. Keller⟩. 6 no. For the Proprietor: London, [1843.] fol.
H. 1433.

LAYTON (Mrs A. J.)

— See Thane (C.) Crossing the Bar ... Organ Obligato by
Mrs. A. J. Layton. [1893.] fol. **H. 1797. w. (29.)**

LAYTON (Billy Jim)

— Divertimento. Op. 6. For violin, clarinet, bassoon,
violoncello, trombone, harpsichord and percussion. [Score.]
pp. 32. G. Schirmer: New York, [1963.] 8°.
[G. Schirmer's Edition of study Scores of orchestral Works and
Chamber Music. no. 100.] **f. 687.**

LAYTON (BILLY JIM)

— Three Dylan Thomas Poems. For mixed chorus and brass sextett ... Op. 3. 1. In my Craft or sullen Art ... 2. O make me a Mask ... 3. Twenty-four Years. [Scores.] 3 no. *G. Schirmer: New York*, [1964.] 8°. **F. 1744. qq. (4.)**

— In my Craft or sullen Art. *See* supra: Three Dylan Thomas Poems. 1.

— O make me a Mask. *See* supra: Three Dylan Thomas Poems. 2.

— Three Studies for Piano. Op. 5. pp. 19. *G. Schirmer: New York*, [1966.] 4°. **g. 1126. kk. (6.)**

— Twenty-four Years. *See* supra: Three Dylan Thomas Poems. 3.

LAYTON (CONSTANCE)

— *See* KNOWLES (C.) Dinah's Lament, *etc.* (Arranged for Guitar by C. Layton.) 1898. fol. **H. 1799. g. (32.)**

LAYTON (GILBERT)

— Two Songs. [No. 1.] Love's Passing. (Words by K. D. Morse) ... [No. 2.] Daffodils. (Words by M. Muskett.) *Boosey & Co.: London & New York*, 1912. fol. **H. 1793. s. (29.)**

LAYTON (HARRY U.)

— National Unity. March for piano. *Whaley, Royce & Co.: Toronto*, 1898. fol. **g. 605. p. (20.)**

LAYTON (HENRY C.)

— Lead, Kindly Light. Sacred Song ... with pianoforte and violoncello—obbligato—accompaniment. Words by ... John Henry, Cardinal Newman. *C. Herzog & Co.: London*, [1884.] fol. **H. 879. e. (11.)**

LAYTON (IDA F.)

— Someone's Boy is with the Slain. [Song.] Words and music by I. F. Layton, *etc.* *Layton & Peterson: Brooklyn*, (1915.) fol. **H. 1793. s. (30.)**

LAYTON (J. TURNER)

— Creole Love Songs. A Song Cycle ... Poems by G. Johnstone. *Composers' Music Corporation: New York*, 1923. 4°. **G. 1275. i. (10.)**

— *See* CREAMER (Henry) The Bombo-shay. Song. ⟨By⟩ H. Creamer ... & T. Layton. [1917.] fol. **H. 3990. kk. (1.)**

— *See* CREAMER (Henry) Follow me around. Song. ⟨By⟩ H. Creamer ... & T. Layton. [1917.] fol. **H. 3990. kk. (3.)**

— [For editions and arrangements of songs written and composed by J. T. Layton in sole collaboration with Henry Creamer:] *See* CREAMER (Henry) and LAYTON (J. T.)

LAYTON (JOHN EDWARD)

— Decisive Turning Points. Selection for the piano. *Wickins & Co.: London*, [1896.] fol. **h. 3282. f. (17.)**

— Enthusiastic Moments at the Piano. *Wickins & Co.: London*, [1896.] fol. **h. 3282. f. (18.)**

— The Musician's Friend. Original Exercises for Piano, *etc.* 2 pt. *Wickins & Co.: London*, [1896.] fol. **h. 3820. l. (7.)**

LAYTON (P. E. D.)

— The Norfolk March for the piano. *Weekes & Co.: London*, [1884.] fol. **h. 1484. s. (29.)**

LAYTON (PHILIP E.)

— The Dominion March. [P. F.] *Whaley, Royce & Co.: Toronto*, 1898. fol. **g. 605. p. (21.)**

LAYTON (RICHARD)

— Old Lindum. Polka. [P. F.] *Hutchings & Romer: London*, 1898. fol. **h. 3286. g. (18.)**

— Song of the Snow [begins: "Lightly I come"] written by S. L. Moore. *London*, [1873.] fol. **H. 1778. x. (50.)**

LAYTON (TURNER)

— *See* LAYTON (J. T.)

LAYTON (WALTER)

— My little Sweetheart. [Song.] Written and composed by W. Layton. *Hart & Co.: London*, [1895.] fol. **H. 1798. u. (35.)**

LAZAN (ALBERT)

— *See* VERACINI (F. M.) [12 Solos. Op. 1. No. 1, 4, 8.] 3 Sonatas ... Edited by A. Lazan, *etc.* [1972.] 4°. **g. 422. gg. (6.)**

LAZĂR (FILIP)

— Bagatelle pour Piano. *Paris*, 1927. 8°. *La Revue Musicale*, 8ᵉ année. No. 9. Supplément musical. **P. P. 1948. tda.**

— Two Roumanian Folk Dances. Deux danses populaires roumaines. [Arranged for P. F. by] F. Lazăr. 2 no. *Oxford University Press: London*, 1926. 4°. *[Folk Dances of the World. VIII, IX.]* **g. 824.**

LAZARD (V.)

— Le Corbeau et le Renard. [Song, begins: "Un jour maître corbeau".] Paroles de E. Tréfeu. *Paris*, [1860?] fol. **H. 2831. f. (13.)**

— The Eugénie quadrille. [P. F.] *London*, [1855.] fol. *No. 421 of the "Musical Bouquet".* **H. 2345.**

LAZARE (CARL)

— McClellan's quickstep. [P. F.] *Boston [Mass.]*, 1864. fol. **h. 1459. g. (7.)**

— On Picket Duty. [Song, begins: "O'er the forest".] (Words by R. Torrey.) *Boston [Mass.]*, 1864. fol. **H. 1780. f. (10.)**

— Selections from the ... play of Rosendale ... for Piano, *etc.* *Boston [Mass.]*, 1864. fol. **h. 1459. g. (8.)**

LAZARE (HENRI)

— Chant de Mai. A May Song. Mélodie pour Piano. Op. 16. *B. F. Wood Music Co.: Boston, etc.*, (1913.) fol. **g. 606. n. (35.)**

LAZARE (MARTIN)

— Atalante, galop de concert, pour Piano. *London*, [1862.] fol. **h. 1460. u. (45.)**

— Danse guerrière. [P.F.] *See* infra: Trois Danses ... Op. 40. No. 2.

— Trois Danses caractéristiques pour piano. Op. 40. *Hambourg*, [1885.] fol. **h. 3280. k. (32.)**

— Danse Orientale. [P. F.] *See* supra: Trois Danses ... Op. 40. No. 1.

LAZARE (Martin)

— Six Études de genre pour Piano. *Paris*, [1867.] fol.
h. 1462. r. (20.)

— Introduction et Presto. Étude de Concert pour Piano. Op. 36.
Bruxelles, etc., [1884.] fol. **h. 3280. k. (31.)**

— Io Vivat! morceau de concert sur un air national des
étudiants Hollandais, pour Piano. *London*, [1861.] fol.
h. 1460. u. (41.)

— [Io Vivat.] Grand Duo concertant sur l'air national des
étudiants Hollandais Io Vivat, pour deux Pianos. *London*,
[1862.] fol. **h. 1460. u. (46.)**

— Une Larme! Méditation pour Piano. *Paris*, [1866.] fol.
h. 1462. r. (18.)

— Marche solennelle pour Piano. *Paris*, [1879.] fol.
h. 1493. n. (21.)

— Marguerite au Rouet, caprice pour Piano. *London*, [1862.]
fol. **h. 1460. u. (43.)**

— Paraphrase de Concert pour Piano sur L'Invitation à la Valse
de C. M. de Weber. *Paris*, [1865.] fol. **h. 1462. r. (16.)**

— Pensée Fugitive pour Piano. *London*, [1862.] fol.
h. 1460. u. (44.)

— Sicilienne pour Piano. *Paris*, [1865.] fol. **h. 1462. r. (17.)**

— The Sprite waltz for the Pianoforte. *London*, [1863.] fol.
h. 1460. u. (47.)

— Valse de Salon ... pour Piano. *London*, [1861.] fol.
h. 1460. u. (42.)

— Deuxième Valse de Salon ... pour le Piano. *Paris*, [1867.]
fol. **h. 1462. r. (19.)**

— Valse Styrienne. [P. F.] *See* supra: Trois Danses ... Op. 40.
No. 3.

LAZAREFF (   )

— Song of the Sleigh-Driver. *See* Whishaw (F. J.) Album of
Russian Songs, *etc.* (No. 4.) 1893. 4°. **F. 636. j. (11.)**

LAZARENKO (Andry)

— *See* Maiboroda (P.) and Lazarenko (A.) Хай славиться
наша держава. ⟨Пісні та хори українських радянських
композиторів. Упорядники: П. Майборода, А. Лазаренко.⟩
1967. 4°. **G. 936. jj.**

LAZAREV (Aleksandr Vasil'evich)

— Le Dernier chant des circassiens avant le combat avec les
russes. Послѣдная пѣснь Горцевъ передъ битвой съ Русскими
... Pièce vocale et dramatique avec accompagnement de
piano forté & à grand orchestre. [Score.] *Fr. & Russ.* pp. 36.
[*St. Petersburg?* 1851?] fol. **I. 175.**

— Serenata. Addio del guerriero alla sua amante. Прощанье
воина съ милой. Серенада ... Pezzo di canto con
accompagnamento di pianoforte, due violoncelli ed arpa, *etc.*
[Score.] *Ital. & Russ.* pp. 10. [*St. Petersburg?* 1854?] fol.
I. 175. a.

LAZAREVIĆ (Stojan V.)

— *See* Manojlović (K. P.) Народне мелодије из Источне Србије
... Предговор и редакција С. В. Лазаревића. 1953. 8°.
[*Посебна издања. књ.* 212.] **Ac. 1131.**

LAZAREVICH (Gordana)

— *See* Hasse (Johann A.) [Larinda e Vanesio.] L'Artigiano
gentiluomo ... Edited by G. Lazarevich. [1979.] 4°. [*Recent
Researches in the Music of the Classical Era. vol.*9.]
G. 1490. c.

LAZARI (Alberto)

— Armonie Spirituali Concertate a 1. 2. 3. 4. 5. & 6. voci con le
Lettanie della B. Vergine à 4. & 8. si piace, con il Basso
Continuo ... Libro Secondo. Opera Seconda, *etc.* Canto.
(Alto.) (Tenore.) (Basso.) (Quinto e Sesto.) (Settimo, e
Ottauo.) (Organo.) 7 pt. *Apresso Bartolomeo Magni: Venetia*,
1637. 4°. **D. 50.**

LAZARI (Ferdinando Antonio)

— Sonata à 6. For 2 trumpets, strings and continuo. ⟨[Edited by]
R. P. Block.⟩ A. 2 trumpets and piano reduction. B. Score and
parts. 2 no. 15 pt. *Musica rara: London*, [1978.] 4°.
[*Italian 17th & 18th Century Sinfonias & Sonatas for Trumpets
& Strings.* 33.] *With alternative parts for trumpets in C and B
flat.* **g. 1612.**

LAZARILLA

— Lazarilla. Syngespil. *See* Bay (D. V. R.)

LAZAROF (Henri)

— Asymptotes. For flute and vibraphone. [Score.] pp. 3.
Associated Music Publishers: New York, London, [1972.] fol.
Two copies. **h. 1568. ii. (6.)**

— Cadence I. *See* infra: [Concerto for Cello and Orchestra.]

— Cadence IV. *See* infra: [Textures.]

— [Concerto for Cello and Orchestra.] Cadence I. For solo cello.
pp. 3. *Associated Music Publishers: New York, London*,
[1972?] fol. **h. 1568. ii. (3.)**

— [Concerto for Cello and Orchestra.] [A reissue.] Cadence I.
For solo cello. *New York, London*, [1977?] 4°.
g. 510. ee. (4.)

— Espaces. For chamber ensemble. ⟨Score.⟩ pp. 38. *Associated
Music Publishers: New York, London*, [1972.] 8°.
f. 390. mm. (6.)

— Intonazione. For two pianos. [Score.] pp. 16. *Associated
Music Publishers: New York, London*, [1972.] fol.
Two copies. **h. 1568. ii. (5.)**

— Partita. For brass quintet and tape. ⟨Score.⟩ pp. 19.
Associated Music Publishers: New York, London, [1973.] 8°.
f. 246. r. (4.)

— Three Pieces for Harpsichord. pp. 7. *Associated Music
Publishers: New York, London*, [1972.] fol. **h. 1568. ii. (4.)**

— Rhapsody. For violin and piano. [Score and part.] 2 pt.
Associated Music Publishers: New York, London, [1972.] fol.
h. 1568. ii. (7.)

— Textures. For piano and 5 instrumental groups. ⟨Score.⟩
pp. iv. 52. *Associated Music Publishers: New York, London*,
[1972.] 8°. **f. 246. r. (5.)**

— [Textures.] Cadence IV. For piano. pp. 9. *Associated Music
Publishers: New York, London*, [1977.] 4°. **g. 1529. s. (13.)**

LAZARRE (Paul de)

— The Clank of the Foeman's Steel. Song, words by A. J. Lamb.
T. Presser: Philadelphia, (1907.) fol. **H. 1794. vv. (23.)**

— The Song of the angry Deep. ⟨Song.⟩ Words by Arthur J.
Lamb. *Jos. Morris:* [*Philadelphia*, 1905.] 4°.
H. 3985. l. (19.)

LAZARUS

— Lazarus. [Unison song.] *See* BROADWOOD (L. E.) and MAITLAND (J. A. F.) English County Songs.

— Lazarus. Sacred cantata. *See* DOORLY (M. E.)

— Lazarus. Cantata. *See* EDWARDS (J.)

— Lazarus. [Sacred song.] *See* RAWLINGS (A.)

— Lazarus, oder die Feyer der Aufstehung. Ein musikalisches Drama. *See* ROLLE (J. H.)

— Lazarus. Oster-Cantate. *See* SCHUBERT (F. P.)

LAZARUS (A.)

— La Catherine Varsoviana. [P.F.] *London*, [1857.] fol.
    h. 977. f. (25.)

LAZARUS (DANIEL)

— Hymne juif. *See* infra: [Symphonie avec hymne.]

— Deux Pièces pour piano. *Paris*, 1923. 8°.
La Revue musicale. 4ᵉ année. No. 5. Supplément musical.
    P. P. 1948. tda.

— [Symphonie avec hymne.] Hymne juif. Jewish Hymn ...
Paroles de ... Denise Alphandéry. Traduction anglaise de ...
M. D. Calvocoressi. *Fr. & Eng.* pp. 7. *Éditions Maurice
Senart: Paris*, [1934.] fol.   **H. 1186. o. (2.)**

LAZARUS (DIETER G. U.)

— [Brazilian Suite.] Two Movements ... (Panorama—People of
Rio de Janeiro.) ⟨Conductor [and military band parts].⟩ 37 pt.
Boosey & Hawkes: [*London*, 1970.] 4°.
[*Q.M.B. Edition.* 282.]   **h. 3211. b.**

LAZARUS (GUSTAV)

— At the Dancing-Party. Auf dem Balle. [P. F. duet.] *O. Ditson
Co.: Boston, etc.*, (1912.) fol.   **h. 3290. v. (27.)**

— Canadian Boat-Song. Trio for women's voices with Piano
accompaniment. [Words by] T. Moore. Op. 149. No. 1.
O. Ditson Co.: Boston, (1912.) 8°.   **F. 328. o. (34.)**

— Children's Heaven. Kinder Himmel. Trio or Part Song for
women's voices, English translation by A. S. G. *T. Presser
Co.: Philadelphia*, (1913.) 8°.   **F. 328. g. (26.)**

— The Coming of Spring. Trio for women's voices, translated
from the German by F. H. Martens. Op. 164. No. 1.
O. Ditson Co.: Boston, (1914.) 8°.   **F. 328. s. (20.)**

— Twelve Easy and melodious Pieces in the form of Studies.
Zwölf melodische, leichte Vortragsstücke in Etudenform.
Op. 141. [P. F.] *O. Ditson Co.: Boston*, 1913. 4°.
    g. 232. w. (8.)

— L'Envoi. Trio for women's voices, with Piano
accompaniment. [Words by] H. W. Longfellow. *O. Ditson
Co.: Boston*, (1912.) 8°.   **F. 328. o. (35.)**

— Etudes-Fantaisies, for the pianoforte. *T. Presser Co.:
Philadelphia*, 1916. fol.   **h. 3284. nn. (21.)**

— Far from Home. Op. 136. No. 2. [P. F.] *T. Presser Co.:
Philadelphia*, (1910.) fol.   **h. 3283. jj. (36.)**

— Hakon the strong. (Der starke Hakon.) A Ballad ... for
Tenor Solo and Chorus of mixed voices, with the German
text of F. von Sallet and English translation by I. Martinez.
O. Ditson Co.: Boston, (1912.) 8°.   **F. 1268. g. (8.)**

— Hakon the Strong. A Ballad ... for baritone solo & chorus of
men's voices ... with the German text of F. von Sallet &
English translation by I. Martinez. *O. Ditson Co.: Boston*,
1914. 8°.   **F. 1268. q. (2.)**

LAZARUS (GUSTAV)

— Happiness. Rondo grazioso. Op. 136. No. 3. [P. F.] *T. Presser
Co.: Philadelphia*, (1910.) fol.   **h. 3283. jj. (37.)**

— L'Illustre Magicien. Extrait du Prélude du 2ᵐᵉ Acte. [P. F.]
Paris, 1924. 8°.
La Revue Musicale. 5ᵉ année. No. 11. Supplément musical.
    P. P. 1948. tda.

— Longing for Spring. (Piano.) *O. Ditson Co.: Boston*, 1917.
fol.   **h. 3284. nn. (25.)**

— Melody adapted to the "Little Study" by R. Schumann.
Arranged for Violin and Piano. *G. Schirmer: New York*,
(1909.) fol.   **h. 1612. v. (2.)**

— A Merry Time. Op. 136. No. 1. [P. F.] *T. Presser Co.:
Philadelphia*, (1910.) fol.   **h. 3283. jj. (35.)**

— Midst verdant Woods, in Sunshine bright. Im Wald, im
hellen Sonnenschein. Part Song ... [Words by] E. Geibel,
translated by I. Martinez. Op. 147. *O. Ditson Co.: Boston*,
(1912.) 8°.   **F. 1744. a. (18.)**

— Five Miniatures. Instructive Fantasy Pieces for the Piano.
Op. 120. 1. Frohsinn—Cheeriness— ... 2. Chorlied.—Choral
Song.—3. In der Waldmühle.—The Mill in the Woods.—
4. Waldbächlein.—The Forest Brook.—5. Elfenstückchen.—
The Elves. 5 no. *G. Schirmer: New York*, (1909.) fol.
    g. 606. f. (20.)

— Petite Suite. Five melodious teaching pieces ... Op. 87.
Selected by Mrs. Curwen, *etc.* [P.F.] 5 no. *J. Curwen & Sons:
London*, [1904.] fol.   **h. 141. t. (5.)**

— Piano Solos. Opus 142. No. 1. Little Serenade ... No. 2.
Gavotte of the Sylphs ... No. 3. A Dream of Summer ...
No. 4. At the Spring, *etc.* 4 no. *O. Ditson Co.: Boston*, (1913.)
fol.   **h. 3284. f. (49.)**

— Piano Solos ... Opus 170. No. 1. Rustic minuet. No. 2. Court
minuet. No. 3. Modinha ... No. 4. Pepita ... No. 5.
Grandmother's dance ... No. 6. Round dance ... No. 7.
Dream sprites, *etc.* 4 no. *O. Ditson Co.: Boston*, 1915. fol.
Wanting no. 2, 4, 7.   **h. 3284. nn. (24.)**

— Two Pianoforte Compositions for four hands. [No. 1.] Valse
espagnole. [No. 2.] Serenata d'amore. 2 no. *T. Presser Co.:
Philadelphia*, 1913, 14. fol.   **h. 3284. nn. (22.)**

— 4 Recital Pieces for the Pianoforte. 1. Little Hunting Song.
(Op. 156. No. 1.) 2. Little Darling's Dance. (Op. 156. No. 2.)
3. Mélodie Joyeuse ... 4. The Music Box. 4 no. *E. Schuberth
& Co.: New York, London*, (1912.) fol.   **h. 3284. f. (50.)**

— Souvenir de Naples. Op. 136. No. 4. [P. F.] *T. Presser Co.:
Philadelphia*, (1910.) fol.   **h. 3283. jj. (38.)**

— The Stars move in measure. Slumber Song. Trio for women's
voices, translated from the German by F. H. Martens.
Op. 164. No. 2. *O. Ditson Co.: Boston*, 1914. 8°.
    F. 328. s. (21.)

— Style and Technic. 15 Melodious Studies for the Second and
Third Grades, for the Pianoforte. Op. 129. *T. Presser Co.:
Philadelphia*, (1910.) fol.   **h. 3820. w. (6.)**

— Suite moderne, for the pianoforte. *T. Presser Co.:
Philadelphia*, 1913. fol.   **h. 3284. nn. (23.)**

— Valse lente, for the Pianoforte. *T. Presser Co.: Philadelphia*,
(1909.) fol.   **h. 3283. jj. (39.)**

LAZARUS (HENRY)

— Fantasia on favorite Scotch melodies ... for Clarionet with
accompaniment for Pianoforte. *J. R. Lafleur & Son: London*,
[1887.] fol.
Part of the "Alliance Musicale".   **h. 2915. d. (7.)**

LAZARUS (Henry)

— Ma Normandie, grand fantasia for Clarinet. [Orchestral parts.] *London*, [1881.] 8°.
Part of the "Alliance Musicale". **f. 400. y. (19.)**

— [Ma Normandie.] Fantasia on a favorite French air "Ma Normandie". [Clarinet and P. F.] *J. R. Lafleur & Son: London*, [1883.] fol.
Part of the "Alliance Musicale". **h. 2915. d. (33.)**

— New and modern Method for the Albert and Boehm system, Clarinet, by Berr, Muller and Neerman, approved, revised and corrected with additions by H. Lazarus. pp. 350. *J. R. Lafleur & Son: London*, [1881.] fol.
Part of the "Alliance Musicale". With an appendix of seven unnumbered leaves containing pieces for clarinet composed or arranged by H. Lazarus. **h. 2181.**

— [New and modern Method for the ... Clarinet.] Grand Virtuoso Saxophone Studies. Transcribed by A. Traxler, *etc.* *Belwin: New York*, 1928. 4°. **g. 1112. (12.)**

— Puritani fantaisie for B♭ Clarinet. [Orchestral parts.] *London*, [1883.] 8°.
Part of the "Alliance Musicale". **f. 400. cc. (9.)**

— Fantasia on airs from "I Puritani" [by Bellini]. [Clarinet and P. F.] *J. R. Lafleur & Son: London*, [1883.] fol.
Part of the "Alliance Musicale". **h. 2915. d. (31.)**

— *See* ARNE (T. A.) [As you like it.] When Daisies pied ... arranged with clarionet obligato by H. Lazarus. [1888.] fol. **H. 1788. a. (9.)**

— *See* VERDI (F. G. F.) [Ernani.—Ernani involami.] Cavatina—Ernani for Clarinet & Piano. ([Arranged by] H. Lazarus.) [1881.] fol. **h. 2915. d. (32.)**

LAZELL (Leonard)

— *See* HAENDEL (G. F.) [Alexander's Feast.] Overture ... Arr. L. Lazell. [Organ.] [1961.] 4°. **g. 1320. b. (6.)**

— *See* HAENDEL (G. F.) [Judas Maccabæus.] March ... Arr. L. Lazell. [Organ.] [1961.] 4°. **g. 1320. b. (4.)**

— *See* HAENDEL (G. F.) [Judas Maccabæus.] Sound an Alarm ... Arr. L. Lazell. [Organ.] [1961.] 4°. **g. 1320. b. (5.)**

— *See* HAENDEL (G. F.) [Il Pastor fido. 2nd Version.—Overture.] Bourée ... Arr. L. Lazell. [Organ.] [1961.] 4°. **g. 1320. b. (2.)**

— *See* HAENDEL (G. F.) [Il Pastor fido. 2nd Version.] Minuet ... [C minor. Organ.] Arr. L. Lazell. [1961.] 4°. **g. 1320. b. (1.)**

— *See* HAENDEL (G. F.) [Samson.—Overture.] Minuet ... Arranged by L. Lazell. [Organ.] [1955.] fol. **g. 74. uu. (12.)**

— *See* HAYDN (F. J.) [Symphonies. Hob. I./101.] Minuet ... Arr. L. Lazell. [Organ.] [1961.] 4°. **g. 75. o. (1.)**

— *See* MOZART (W. A.) [Symphonies. K. 543.] Minuet and Trio ... Arranged by L. Lazell. [1954.] 4°. *[Cramer's Library of Organ Music by British & foreign Composers. no. 57.]* **g. 1353. a.**

— *See* PURCELL (Henry) [The Fairy Queen.—Second Music.] Air ... Arr. L. Lazell. [Organ.] [1961.] 4°. **g. 25. l. (1.)**

— *See* PURCELL (Henry) [The Fairy Queen.—Second Music.] Rondeau ... Arranged for the organ by L. Lazell. [1955.] 4°. *[Cramer's Library of Organ Music by British Composers. set 12.1.]* **g. 1353.**

— *See* PURCELL (Henry) [King Arthur.—Second Music.] Overture ... Arr. L. Lazell. [Organ.] [1961.] 4°. **g. 25. l. (2.)**

LAZELLE (L. L.)

— In Violet's Eyes. [Song.] Words and music by L. L. Lazelle. *C. F. Summy Co.: Chicago*, (1905.) fol. **G. 807. jj. (38.)**

LAZELLE (L. L.)

— Sweet Coquette. [Song.] Words and music by L. L. Lazelle. pp. 5. *S. Brainard's Sons Co.: New York, Chicago*, [1899.] fol. **H. 3980. pp. (32.)**

LAZENBY (H. T.)

— Tamil Christian Hymns with Tunes. ⟨H. T. Lazenby, musical edition.⟩ pp. xvi. 336. *Christian Literature Society for India: [Madras*, 1917.] 8°. **F. 1122. k.**

LAZENBY (J.)

— A sonata for the harp or Piano Forte. Op. 1. *London*, [1809.] fol. **h. 117. (13.)**

LAZENBY (William)

— The Wooing. [Part-song.] *J. Curwen & Sons: London*, [1899.] 8°.
The Apollo Club. No. 116. **F. 667.**

LAZILY

— Lazily. Song. *See* AMES (A. P.)

— Lazily, drowsily. [Song.] *See* CARYLL (I.) *pseud.* [Little Christopher Columbus.]

LAZINESS

— Laziness. [Song.] *See* SMITH (D. S.) Four Songs ... Op. 15. No. 3.

LAZING

— Lazing in Lazy-land. Song. *See* ROGERS (E. W.)

LAZO (Claudio García)

— *See* LARRAZÁBAL (Manuel) Lamentación tercera del Viernes Santo. [Motet. S.A.T.B. and orchestra. Edited by] C. G. Lazo. [Score.] [1973.] fol. *[Colección cuadernos de música. 4.]* **G. 980. ff.**

— *See* VELÁSQUEZ (José F.) *the Elder*. Los Cielos destilaban alegría. ⟨Villancico.⟩ [Edited by] C. G. Lazo. [Score.] [1973.] fol. *[Colección cuadernos de música. 3.]* **G. 980. ff.**

LAZULÌ

— Lazulì. [Song.] *See* DUCHÊNES (P.)

LAZY

— Lazy! Song. *See* RUBENS (P. A.) [The Sunshine Girl.]

— Lazy. Song. *See* SCOTT (Maurice)

— Lazy. Song. *See* TILBURY (Walter)

— Lazy Afternoon. [Part-song.] *See* SIEGMEISTER (Elie) [Ozark Set. No. 3.]

— Lazy Andy Ant. [Cantata.] *See* WOLPE (Stefan)

— Lazy Bill. [Song.] *See* SLOANE (Alfred B.)

— Lazy Daisy. [Song.] *See* DARNLEY (Herbert)

— The Lazy Dancing Man. Song. *See* NOVELLO (I.) [Theodore and Co.]

— Lazy June. [Part-song.] *See* WASHBURN (Robert) Spring Cantata. IV.

— Lazy little Maizy Jones. [Song.] *See* TILZER (Harry von)

— Lazy Liza. [Two-part song.] *See* PITFIELD (T. B.)

LAZY

— Lazy Maisie. Song. *See* Lawrance (Alfred J.) and Gifford (H.)

— The Lazy Man. Song. *See* Higgins (E.)

— The Lazy Man. Song. *See* Murphy (Clarence W.) and Lipton (D.)

— The Lazy Man. [Song.] *See* White (F. H.)

— Lazy Moon. [Song.] *See* Johnson (J. R.)

— Lazy Moon, Lazy Moon. Duet. *See* Horn (C. E.)

— Lazy old Moon. [Song.] *See* Myles (B.)

— Lazy River. [Song.] *See* Bond (C. J.)

— Lazy Sam. [Song.] *See* Fredericks (Al.)

— The Lazy Seas of Devon. Song. *See* Clarke (R. C.)

— Lazy Sheep. Unison Song. *See* Poë (M.)

— Lazy Sheep, pray tell me why? Unison Song. *See* Longmire (J.)

— Lazy Song. [Song.] *See* Lawson (C. M.)

— L-a-z-y spells Lazy. [Song.] *See* Wallace (Ramsey)

— The Lazy Twins. Duet. *See* Philp (J. E.)

LAZYLAND

— Lazyland. Song. *See* Rubens (P. A.) and Tours (F. E.) [The Dairymaids.]

— Lazyland. Operetta. *See* Vingoe (A. L.)

LAZZARA

— Lazzara. [Song.] *See* Lacome D'Estalenx (P. J. J.) 3 Mélodies. No. 3.

LAZZARI (Ferdinando Antonio)

— *See* Lazari.

LAZZARI (Joseph Sylvio)

— Armor. Drame lyrique en trois actes ... Poème de E. Jaubert. Dessin de A. Rassenfosse. Version allemande par S. Lazzari. Partition piano et chant réduite par l'auteur. *P. Dupont: Paris*, 1897. 8°. **F. 1438.**

— Chanson des beaux Amants. *See* infra: Trois Chansons de Shéhérazade. [No. 2.]

— Trois Chansons de Shéhérazade, poésies de T. Klingsor. [No. 1.] Demande.—Entreaty.—[No. 2.] Chanson des beaux Amants. [No. 3.] Le Passé.—The Past. 3 no. *G. Schirmer: New York*, (1906.) fol. **G. 807. jj. (40.)**

— Dämmerstunde. *See* infra: Zwei Lieder ... Op. 6. No. 1.

— Demande. *See* supra: Trois Chansons de Shéhérazade. [No. 1.]

— Une Femme. *See* infra: Trois Poésies, *etc.* [No. 2.]

— Drei Gedichte von K. Stieler für eine mittlere Singstimme mit Begleitung des Pianoforte. Op. 9. Mit deutschem und französischem Text. *Breitkopf & Härtel: Leipzig und Brüssel*, [1887.] fol. **H. 2836. v. (22.)**

— Im Sturme. *See* infra: Zwei Lieder ... Op. 6. No. 2.

LAZZARI (Joseph Sylvio)

— La Lépreuse (Die Ausgestossene). Tragédie légendaire en trois actes. Poème de Henry Bataille ... Partition d'orchestre, *etc.* Fr. & Ger. pp. 516. *Max Eschig: Paris*, [1912.] fol. *With a play-bill for the first performance on 7 Feb.* 1912 *inserted.* **H. 1941. a.**

— La Lépreuse.—Die Ausgestossene.— Tragédie légendaire en trois actes, poème de H. Bataille ... Partition Piano et Chant réduite par L. Narici. Version allemande par E. Klingenfeld et S. Lazzari. *M. Eschig: Paris*, [1912.] fol. **H. 1941.**

— Zwei Lieder für eine tiefe Singstimme mit Begleitung des Pianoforte. Op. 6. Mit Deutschem und Französischem Text. (No. 1. Dämmerstunde ... [begins: "Wie wirst du schön zur Dämmerstunde"]—K. Stieler. No. 2. Fur Sturme ... [begins: "Das braust und stöhnt im Waldgehege"]—K. Stieler.) *Leipzig und Brüssel*, [1885.] fol. **H. 2836. h. (32.)**

— Malentendu. *See* infra: Trois Poésies, *etc.* [No. 3.]

— Melænis. Opéra en cinq actes tiré du roman de Louis Bouilhet. Poème de Georges Spitzmuller ... Partition piano et chant réduite par l'auteur. pp. 320. *Max Eschig: Paris; Leipzig printed*, [1913.] fol. *With press cuttings inserted.* **H. 1941. b.**

— Nuit en Mer. *See* infra: Trois Poésies, *etc.* [No. 1.]

— Par les Bois. [Song.] Poésie de L. Bowitsch. [*Paris*,] 1894. 8°. *Supplement to "L'Illustration," No.* 2691. **P. P. 4283. m. (3.)**

— Le Passé. *See* supra: Trois Chansons de Shéhérazade. [No. 3.]

— Trois Poésies d'E. Blémont d'après H. Heine. [Songs.] [No. 1.] Nuit en Mer.—Night at Sea.—[No. 2.] Une Femme.—A Woman.—[No. 3.] Malentendu.—Misunderstanding. 3 no. *G. Schirmer: New York*, (1906.) fol. **G. 807. jj. (39.)**

— Le Sauteriot. Drame lyrique en trois actes et quatre tableaux. Poème de H. P. Roché & Martial Périer d'après la pièce E. de Keyserling ... Partition piano & chant réduite par l'auteur. pp. 291. *Max Eschig & Cᵉ.: Paris*, [c. 1920.] fol. *With a press cutting inserted.* **H. 1941. c.**

— Sonate pour violon et piano ... Op. 24. [Score and part.] 2 pt. *A. Durand & fils: Paris*, [1894.] fol. **h. 210. t. (3.)**

— Symphonie en mi bémol ... Partition d'orchestre, *etc.* pp. 242. *Éditions Max Eschig: Paris*, [1914?] fol. **h. 1540. m.**

— La Tour de feu. Drame lyrique en trois actes, poème et musique de S. Lazzari. Partition chant et piano réduite par l'auteur. pp. 253. *Choudens: Paris*, [1928.] 4°. **G. 1334.**

— Valse brillante pour piano. Op. 4. *Leipzig et Bruxelles*, [1884.] fol. **h. 3280. k. (33.)**

— Vieux motif, [song, begins: "L'Amour est une fleur"] poésie de L. B. *Paris*, [1884.] fol. **H. 2836. h. (31.)**

LAZZARINI (Gustavo)

— Amo ed amar mi duole. *See* infra: [La Discordia conjugale.]

— [La Discordia conjugale.] Amo ed amar di duole, *etc.* [Aria. Score.] pp. 7. *T. Skillern; G. Goulding: London*, [c. 1795.] fol. **H. 1980. qq. (10.)**

LAZZARONE

— Il Lazzarone. Aria Napolitana. *See* Gironci (M. D.)

— Le Lazzarone. Opéra. *See* Halévy (J. F. F. É.)

LAZZARONI

— The Lazzaroni Maid. Song and Chorus. *See* Hawthorne (A.) *pseud.*

LAZZARONNE

— Le Lazzaronne. Romance. *See* ADHÉMAR (A. D') *Count.*

LE

— L'ai-je rêvé? Duettino. *See* ROMAGNESI (A.)

— L'avez vous vû mon bien aimé. Ronde. *See* FÉE. La Fée Urgèle.

— L'on vous dit tous les ans. Air. *See* DUBUISSON (   )

— Le connais-tu, ma chère Éléonore. Ariette Nouvelle. [*Paris,* 1780?] 8°.　　　　　　　　　**B. 362. a. (151.)**

— [Another copy.]　　　　　　　　　**B. 362. e. (32.)**

— Le connais tu, ma chère Éléonore. *Ariette,* avec Accompagne^mt de Guithare, par Mr Comien. *Chez Frère:* [*Paris,* 1785?] 8°.　　　　　**B. 362. e. (18.)**

— Le faccio un inchina. Terzetto. *See* CIMAROSA (D.) [Il Matrimonio Segreto.]

— Le parlate d'amor. Romance. *See* GOUNOD (C. F.) [Faust.]

— Le sais-tu. Mélodie. *See* MASSENET (J.)

— Le sais-tu bien? Mélodie. *See* PIERNÉ (G.)

— Le savez vous. Romance. *See* MUENCK, afterwards CARADORI ALLAN (M. C. R. de)

— Le sentirai cantar le requie e i salmi. Canto popolare. *See* GORDIGIANI (L.) [Canti popolari toscane. Quarta raccolta. No. 8.]

— Le verras-tu jamais. Romance. *See* PANSERON (A. M.)

— Le voici ce beau jour. *Anniversaire de la chûte du dernier Roi des Français* ... [Song, words] Par le Ci. Perrin. *Chez Frère:* [*Paris,* 1794?] 8°.　　　　　**E. 1717. b. (27.)**

LE'

— *See* LET.

LEA

— The Lea-rig. [Song.] *See* ELLIOTT (Kenneth J.)

— The Lea shall have its Lily-bells. Ballad. *See* MAINWARING (   ) *Miss.*

LEA (ANNIE)

— Little blue Jersey. Song, the words by G. Hadath, *etc. Darter & Sons: Cape Town,* 1904. fol.　　　**H. 1792. r. (46.)**

— My little King. Song, the words by ... H. Cossar, *etc. Darter & Sons: Cape Town,* 1904. fol.　　**H. 1792. r. (47.)**

— Tarantella. [Violin and P. F.] *E. Ashdown: London, etc.,* [1908.] fol.
No. 24 of "Modern Violin Music".　　**g. 505. ee. (34.)**

— When we are parted. Song, words by H. Aïdé. *J. Williams: London,* 1902. fol.　　　　**H. 1799. vv. (32.)**

LEA (BARBARA)

— How to sing Jazz, *etc.* pp. 55. *Chappell & Co.:* [*New York,* 1980.] 4°.　　　　　　**F. 1966. vv. (3.)**

LEA (C. M.)

— In nineteen hundred and three. Song. Written and composed by C. M. Lea. pp. 5. *Willis Woodward & Co.: New York,* [1894.] fol.　　　　　　**H. 3980. pp. (33.)**

LEA (FREDERICK W.)

— Lullaby. Song, words and music by F. W. Lea. *Dale, Forty & Co.: Cheltenham,* [1898.] fol.　　　**H. 1798. u. (36.)**

LEA (G.)

— Oh! would I were a Child again. [Song.] Words by John Francis. *In:* PERIODICAL PUBLICATIONS.— *London.* The Album Wreath of Music and Literature. Vol. II. Between pp. 78, 79. [1834.] 4°.　　　　　　　**P. P. 6945.**

— Serenade. [Song.] Words by S. T. Hunt, *etc. In:* PERIODICAL PUBLICATIONS.— *London.* The Album Wreath of Music and Literature. Vol. II. Between pp. 32, 33. [1834.] 4°.
　　　　　　　　　　　　P. P. 6945.

LEA (HENRY)

— The favorite air "Auld Robin Gray" [by W. Leeves] arranged as a solo for the guitar. *London,* [1835?] fol.　**h. 259. (3.)**

— The favorite air Auld Robin Gray [by W. Leeves] (with embellishments), arranged as a solo for the concertina. *London,* [1855.] fol.　　　　**h. 2336. (17.)**

— Choice pieces arranged for the Concertina, with Pianoforte accomp^t. ad lib. 28 no. *London,* [1867.] fol.　**h. 2414. a.**

— A complete scale for the Accordion or Flutina (with 22 or 24 Keys), *etc. London,* [1857.] fol.　　**h. 1066. (11.)**

— A complete scale for the full compassed concertina, *etc. London,* [1855.] fol.　　　　**h. 2326. (4.)**

— A Complete Scale of all the Harmonics on the Guitar, with the frets & strings on which they are produced properly indicated. pp. 3. *T. Prowse: London,* [c. 1850.] fol.
　　　　　　　　　　　h. 259. kk. (4.)

— Concertina Gems ... Arranged ... by H. Lea. 8 no. *H. Lea: London,* [1855–60.] fol.
Imperfect; wanting no. 8.　　　　**h. 2336. (15.)**

— The Concertina shake. Exercises, *etc. London,* [1860.] fol.
　　　　　　　　　　　h. 2414. b. (3.)

— Écoutez moi, romance ... by J. Funke, arranged for the Concertina, *etc. London,* [1861.] fol.　**h. 2414. b. (5.)**

— The evening star is o'er me. Serenade. The words by W. West. The music partly composed and arranged with symphonies and accompaniments by H. Lea. *London,* [1861.] fol.
　　　　　　　　　　　H. 1554. (4.)

— Exercises (fingered throughout) on Thirds, Sixths, Octaves & Tenths, for the full compassed Concertina. (With 48 keys.) *London,* [1855.] fol.　　　　**h. 2326. (6.)**

— Exercises (fingered throughout) for the full compassed concertina (with 48 keys), *etc.* Second edition. *London,* [1855.] fol.　　　　　**h. 2326. (5.)**

— Exercises for the Guitar, on those chords, which are most commonly used for accompanying the voice, with the fingering carefully marked, *etc.* pp. 3. *T. Prowse: London,* [c. 1840.] fol.　　　　**h. 259. kk. (5.)**

— Favorite Airs, Waltzes ... for Accordion or Flutina. bk 1. *London,* [1855.] fol.
Imperfect; wanting bk. 2.　　　　**h. 2414. b. (1.)**

— Six favorite pieces, arranged for the Baritone Concertina. No. 1–5. *London,* [1860.] fol.
Imperfect; wanting no. 6.　　　　**h. 2414. b. (4.)**

— Favorite Songs with Concertina Accompaniments. 12 no. *London,* [1855–1860.] fol.　　　**H. 1554. (1.)**

— Marche militaire with an introduction & variations for the concertina, introducing the Scotch air Roslyn Castle. *London,* [1855.] fol.　　　　**h. 2336. (18.)**

LEA (HENRY)

— Pensez à moi, & love me ever! Ballad, the Words by W. West. The Music arranged with Symphonies & Accompaniments by H. Lea. *London*, [1859.] fol.   **H. 1554. (2.)**

— Pensez à moi and love me ever. Ballad. The words by W. West. The music partly composed and arranged with an accompaniment for the guitar by H. Lea. *London*, [1861.] fol.   **H. 1554. (3.)**

— Popular Songs, arranged with an accompaniment for the Concertina. 24 no. *London*, [1867.] fol.   **H. 1554. a. (1.)**

— Popular Songs sung by Christy's Minstrels, and other celebrated vocalists, arranged with an accompaniment for the Guitar ... by H. Lea, *etc.* 24 no. *London*, [1859.] fol.   **H. 1401. (3.)**

— Popular Songs with Italian and English words, arranged with an accompaniment for the Guitar. no. 25–60, 63. *London*, [1863–65.] fol.
A continuation of the preceding. Imperfect; wanting no. 61, 62.   **H. 1554. b.**

— Select airs, waltzes, quadrilles, polkas ... for the concertina, arranged for amateurs by H. Lea. no. 1–32. *London*, [1855, etc.] fol.   **h. 2414.**

— Select Airs, Waltzes, &c. Arranged for the Spanish guitar. ⟨Lea's select guitar airs.⟩ no. 1. *H. Lea: London*, [c. 1835.] fol. *Imperfect; wanting the other numbers.*   **h. 259. (2.)**

— Select Airs, Waltzes, &c. Arranged for the Spanish guitar. ⟨Lea's select guitar airs.⟩ no. 18. *Prowse: London*, [c. 1840.] fol.
Imperfect; wanting the other numbers.   **h. 2414. c.**

— Select French Songs, arranged with an accompaniment for the Spanish guitar, by Giuliani, Carulli, Diabelli and Henry Lea. no. 7, 10, 13, 15, 18, 20. *George & Manby: London*, [c. 1840.] fol.
The foot of each page bears the series title "Lea's select French Guitar Songs". Imperfect; wanting all the other numbers.   **I. 338.**

— Select Italian Songs, arranged with an accompaniment for the guitar, by F. Carulli, A. Diabelli, M. Giuliani, and Henry Lea. no. 18. *H. Lea: London*, [c. 1835.] fol.
The foot of each page bears the series title "Lea's select Italian Guitar Songs". Imperfect; wanting the other numbers.   **H. 1847. m. (9.)**

— Select Italian Songs, arranged with an accompaniment for the Spanish guitar, by Giuliani, Carulli, Diabelli, and Henry Lea. no. 2–4, 6, 10, 12, 17, 21, 22, 25. *George & Manby: London*, [c. 1840.] fol.
The foot of each page bears the series title "Lea's select Italian Guitar Songs". Imperfect; wanting all the other numbers.   **I. 338. a.**

— Sweetly blooms the opening rose. [Song.] *London*, [1845?] fol.   **H. 2832. o. (38.)**

— Thy name is ever in my mind. Ballad. The words by W. West. The music partly composed and arranged with symphonies and accompaniments by H. Lea. *London*, [1861.] fol.   **H. 1554. (7.)**

— 'Tis lovely summer day. Song. The words by W. West. *London*, [1863.] fol.   **H. 1554. (8.)**

— 'Tis Lovely ... for the Pianoforte. [1863.] fol. *See* HENNEN (H. J. A.)   **h. 638. a. (6.)**

— Toujours le même, a motto true. Ballad, the words by W. West. *London*, [1863.] fol.   **H. 1554. (9.)**

— Toujours le même ... for the Pianoforte. [1863.] fol. *See* HENNEN (H. J. A.)   **h. 638. a. (7.)**

LEA (HENRY)

— True love never seeks to change. Ballad. The words by W. West. The music partly composed and arranged with symphonies and accompaniments by H. Lea. *London*, [1861.] fol.   **H. 1554. (5.)**

— Untrue to thee, no never. Ballad, the words by W. West, the music partly composed and arranged with symphonies and accompaniments by H. Lea. *London*, [1861.] fol.   **H. 1554. (6.)**

— La Varsoviana ... arranged for the Concertina. *London*, [1860.] fol.   **h. 2337. (6.)**

— The vocal shake, three exercises for a bass or contralto voice, *etc.* *London*, [1854.] fol.   **H. 2243. (9.)**

— The vocal shake. Exercises for a soprano or tenor voice. *London*, [1854.] fol.   **H. 2243. (8.)**

— *See* BELLINI (V.) [Norma.] Deh! con te li prendi, arranged for the concertina by H. Lea. [1855.] fol.   **h. 2336. (19.)**

— *See* BOIELDIEU (F.A.) [Le Calife de Bagdad.] Boieldieu's overture to the Caliph of Bagdad, arranged for the concertina by H. Lea. [1855.] fol.   **h. 2336. (20.)**

— *See* MAEDER (J.G.) The Unwilling Bride ... Arranged by H. Lea. [1858.] fol.   **H. 2348.**

— *See* MOZART (W.A.) [Le Nozze di Figaro.] Overture ... arranged ... by H. Lea. [1825?] fol.   **h. 117. (14.)**

— *See* RODE (P.) Rode's celebrated airs with variations for the concertina, arranged by H. Lea. [1855.] fol.   **h. 2336. (21.)**

— *See* SONGS. Select Italian Songs, arranged ... by ... H. Lea. [1835?] fol.   **H. 2401. (5.)**

— *See* TULLY (J.H.) Topsy's polka; arranged for the concertina by H. Lea. [1855.] fol.   **h. 2336. (16.)**

LEACH (A.)

— The Methodist Band of Hope Hymnal. Edited by ... A. Leach. *London*, 1876. 8°.   **D. 620. k. (14.)**

— The Methodist Band of Hope Hymnal. Edited by ... A. Leach. Enlarged edition. *London*, [1881.] 8°.   **C. 679.**

LEACH (AUGUSTUS)

— Ding Dong. [Song, begins: "Last summer time".] *London*, [1879.] fol.   **H. 1783. o. (25.)**

— I'd tell you if I were a little Fly ... Comic Song, written and composed by Gus Leach. *C. Sheard: London*, [1877.] fol. *No. 5707–8 of the Musical Bouquet.*   **H. 2345.**

— Nancy fancied a soldier. [Song.] *London*, [1881.] fol.   **H. 1787. j. (21.)**

— You're getting it up for me ... Comic Song, written and composed by Gus. Leach. *C. Sheard: London*, [1878.] fol. *No. 5763–4 of the Musical Bouquet.*   **H. 2345.**

LEACH (CLARISSA)

— [The Poacher and his Dog.] The Day is done. Ballad ... The words by A. W. Arnold. *London*, [1835?] fol.   **H. 2832. o. (39.)**

LEACH (FLORENCE LILLIAN)

— *See* SHIELDS (L. G.) and LEACH (F. L.) Colby Junior College Song Book, *etc.* 1935. 8°.   **F. 1773.**

LEACH (GEORGE)

— Church and Home, a collection of sacred music ... selected and adapted by G. Leach. *Boston* [*Mass.*], 1857. *obl.* fol.
E. 1419.

— Laus Domino: a new collection of Anthems, Mottets, and Canticles, *etc. New York*, [1865.] *obl.* fol. **D. 581.**

— There lives a voice within me. Song. *New York*, 1869. fol.
H. 1780. p. (33.)

— *See* THOMAS (J. R.) Shining Lights ... from ... Leach, *etc.*
1870. 4°. **G. 444.**

LEACH (J.)

— Neptune's Holiday. Hornpipe. Seemannstanz. [Parts.] *Schott & Co.: London*, 1938. 8°.
[*Schott & Co.'s Domesticum Salon Orchestra. No.* 486.]
g. 1053. a.

LEACH (JAMES)

— Canaan. *See* infra: [A Second Sett of Hymns and Psalm Tunes.]

— A Collection of Hymn Tunes and Anthems. Composed and adapted for a full choir. pp. 265. MS. ANNOTATIONS [by J. S. Bumpus]. *T. Preston: London*, [c. 1800.] *obl.* fol.
Published in separate numbers, with continous pagination.
D. 596. aa.

— Psalmody ... harmonised in compressed score by J. Butterworth. *London*, [1884.] 4°. **F. 1072.**

— A New Sett of Hymns and Psalm Tunes ... with Accompaniments & a Thoro' Bass, the whole figured for the Organ, Harpsichord or Piano-Forte. *Preston & Son, for the Author: London*, [1789.] *obl.* 4°. **B. 844. (1.)**

— A New Sett of Hymns and Psalm Tunes, *etc. J. A. Novello: London*, [1835?] *obl.* 4°.
This is a reprint from the original plates. **B. 844. a.**

— A Second Sett of Hymns and Psalm Tunes, *etc. Preston & Son, for the Author: London*, [1794.] *obl.* 4°. **B. 844. (2.)**

— [A Second Sett of Hymns and Psalm Tunes.] Canaan. A Favorite Anthem. *M. McCalley: Dublin*, [1803?] fol.
H. 1173. (11.)

— [A Second Sett of Hymns and Psalm Tunes.] Canaan. [Chorus.] [1870.] *See* TONIC. The Tonic Sol-fa Times, *etc.*
No. 75. [a.] [1864–73.] 4°. **B. 559. f.**

— *See* WALKDEN (N.) Psalm & hymn tunes. Arranged ... by J. Leach. 1841. *obl.* 4°. **B. 467.**

LEACH (JOEL)

— *See* RODGERS (Richard) [Love me tonight.] Mimi ... Arranged [for military band] by J. Leach. [1978.] 8°. **e. 1330. (7.)**

LEACH (JOHN H.)

— Exercises in tongueing for the Flute. pp. 2. *Joseph S. Saikali: Beyrouth*, [1959.] *obl.* 4°. **e. 340. j.**

— Suite for unaccompanied Double Bass. pp. 5. *Yorke Edition: London*, [1974.] 4°. **g. 867. d. (8.)**

— *See* BUSH (Alan D.) Két tánc cimbalomra ... Op. 64.
⟨Közreadja J. Leach.⟩ 1966. 4°. **g. 1780. w. (5.)**

— *See* HOFFMEISTER (F. A.) [Six sonates. Oeuvre 1.] Premier sonate concertante. Pour deux flûtes ... editée par J. Leach.
[1959.] fol. **h. 2140. t. (1.)**

— *See* WISEMAN (Charles) Trio for 2 Flutes and Cello or Bassoon ... Edited by J. Leach. [1974.] 4°. **g. 934. jj. (11.)**

LEACH (JOSEPH W.)

— A Memory. [Song.] Poem by F. T. Greenhalge. *Washington Music Co.: Lowell, Mass.*, 1898. fol. **H. 1799. h. (18.)**

— O praise the Lord all ye Nations. [Anthem.] *O. Ditson Co.:* [*Boston, etc.*,] 1899. 8°. **F. 1529. b. (34.)**

— The Poet's Song ... Poem by A. Tennyson. *C. W. Thompson & Co.: Boston* [*Mass.*], 1900. fol. **H. 1799. h. (19.)**

— The Sabbath in the Mountains. [Song.] Words by W. Thayer. *C. W. Thompson & Co.: Boston* [*Mass.*], 1900. fol.
H. 1799. h. (20.)

— Why? [Song.] Words by W. Thayer. *Washington Music Co.: Lowell, Mass.*, 1899. fol. **H. 1799. h. (21.)**

LEACH (MACEDWARD)

— Folk Ballads and Songs of the lower Labrador Coast. [With the melodies.] pp. viii. 332. *Ottawa*, 1965. 8°.
National Museum of Canada. Bulletin. no. 201.
Anthropological Series. no. 68. **Ac. 1883. c.**

— *See* RAVENSCROFT (Thomas) Pammelia, Deutromelia [*sic*], Melismata ... Edited by M. Leach, *etc.* 1961. 8°. **C. 112. a.**

LEACH (RICHARD)

— Long, long ago in his Lady's Bower ... Song ... in the drama of 'Faith's Reward,' words & music by R. Leach. *The Author: Lowestoft*, [1887.] fol. **H. 1788. v. (12.)**

— *See* MORA (A. L.) and LEACH (R.) Faith's Reward ... Drama. [Incidental music. P. F.] [1887.] fol. **h. 1484. w. (3.)**

LEACH (ROWLAND EDGAR)

— Good Night, dear Heart, *etc.* [Song.] *C. F. Summy Co.: Chicago*, (1912.) fol. **G. 807. yy. (25.)**

— Great and marvellous. A short Festival Cantata, *etc. H. W. Gray Co.: New York*, 1927. 8°. **E. 541. jj. (5.)**

— I remember. [Song, words by] L. Colcord. *C. F. Summy Co.: Chicago*, (1912.) fol. **G. 807. yy. (26.)**

— Out of the dusky Midnight. [Song, words by] L. V. Ledoux.
C. F. Summy Co.: Chicago, (1912.) fol. **G. 807. yy. (27.)**

— The Token. [Song.] Words and music by R. E. Leach. *C. F. Summy Co.: Chicago*, (1912.) fol. **G. 807. yy. (28.)**

LEACH (S.)

— Damon. A cantata. [With string accompaniment in short score.] [1780?] fol. **H. 1652. w. (7.)**

— Go gentle Breezes to yon verdant Grove. Glee. *See* HERSCHEL (F. W.) The favorite Eccho Catch, and the preceeding Glee [by S. Leach], *etc.* [1780.] *obl.* fol. **F. 607. y. (8.)**

LEACH (THOMAS) *Organist of Cheshunt*

— The Hatfield Royal Review, full military piece, *etc.* [For trumpet in E flat, horns in E flat, clarinets, bassoon and P.F. or harp. Score.] pp. 14. *Printed for the Author: London*, [WM1801.] fol. **h. 61. h. (10.)**

— The Hertfordshire Yeomanry Cavalry. A New Song, *etc.*
pp. 3. *Longman and Broderip, for the Author: London*, [1796.] fol. **G. 376. (23.)**

— The Hertfordshire Yeomanry Cavalry. A new song. pp. 3.
Longman & Broderip, for the Author: London, [c. 1797.] fol.
G. 296. a. (28.)

— Rouse, Britons rouse, humble the plund'ring Crew, a favorite song. pp. 2. *Printed by W. Rolfe: London*, [c. 1805.] fol.
G. 296. a. (30.)

LEACH (V. M.)

— *See* JAMES (Caradog V.) Russian Song-Book ... Music arranged by V. M. Leach and N. Dannatt. 1962, *etc.* 8°. [*Pergamon Oxford Russian Series. Teaching Aids. no. 2, etc.*] **12994. w. 5a/2.**

LEAD

— Lead (and we will follow). [Song.] *See* GORDON (Harry) and CLIFTON (E.)

— Lead, kindly Light. Duet. *See* ADLAM (F.)

— Lead, kindly Light. [Hymn.] *See* AIKIN (W. A.)

— Lead, kindly Light. Sacred Song. *See* AITKEN (George B. J.)

— Lead, kindly Light. [Sacred song.] *See* ANDREWS (M.)

— Lead, kindly Light. [Anthem.] *See* ARCHER (J.)

— Lead, kindly Light. Sacred Song. *See* ASHLEY (C. W.)

— Lead, kindly Light. Hymn. *See* BARBER (C.)

— Lead, kindly Light. Sacred Song. *See* BARNARD (D.)

— Lead, kindly Light. Quartet. *See* BARTLETT (H. N.)

— Lead, kindly Light. [Sacred song.] *See* BASS (H. E.)

— Lead, kindly Light. [Sacred song.] *See* BASSFORD (W. K.)

— Lead, kindly Light. [Hymn.] *See* BEECROFT (G. A. B.)

— Lead, kindly Light. [Hymn.] *See* BENTHAM (C.)

— Lead, kindly Light. Anthem. *See* BERWALD (William H.)

— Lead, kindly Light. Anthem. *See* BIBBY (E. H.)

— Lead, kindly Light. Sacred Song. *See* BOEHR (F.)

— Lead, kindly Light. [Hymn.] *See* BOWDLER (C.)

— Lead, kindly Light. Quartet. *See* BOWLES (E. R.)

— Lead, kindly Light. Hymn-Anthem. *See* BRIDGE (S.)

— Lead, kindly Light. [Anthem.] *See* BRIGGS (C. S.)

— Lead, kindly Light. Quartet. *See* BROOME (E.)

— Lead, kindly Light. Song. *See* BROWN (William H.)

— Lead, kindly Light. Anthem. *See* BRUESCHWEILER (F.)

— Lead, kindly Light. Hymn. *See* BUCK (D.)

— Lead, kindly Light. Sacred Song. *See* BUTTON (H. E.)

— Lead, kindly Light. Anthem. *See* CHALLINOR (F. A.)

— Lead, kindly Light. [Sacred song.] *See* CLARK (James) *of Manchester.*

— Lead, kindly Light. Sacred Song. *See* CLEGG (J. A.)

— Lead, kindly Light. [Anthem.] *See* COLEMAN (J.)

— Lead, kindly Light. Anthem. *See* CRASTON (E. S.)

— Lead kindly light. Duet. *See* DAVIS (Eliza)

— Lead, kindly Light. [Anthem.] *See* DEANE (W.)

— Lead, kindly Light. Sacred Song. *See* DICKS (E. A.)

— Lead, kindly Light. Hymn-Anthem. *See* DUNSTAN (R.)

— Lead, kindly Light. Hymn. *See* DYKES (J. B.)

— Lead, kindly Light. [Anthem.] *See* EDWARDS (C.) *Organist.*

— Lead, kindly Light. [Hymn.] *See* EDWARDS (E.) *of Halifax.*

LEAD

—— Lead, kindly Light. Anthem. *See* ELLIS (S.) *pseud.* [Lead Thou me on!]

— Lead, kindly Light. Anthem. *See* ELY (T.)

— Lead, kindly Light. [Hymn.] *See* EVANS (D.)

— Lead, kindly Light. Sacred Song. *See* EVANS (D. P.)

— Lead, kindly Light. Chorus. *See* EVANS (H.)

— Lead, kindly Light. Sacred Song. *See* FAIRLIE (M. B.)

— Lead, kindly Light. Anthem. *See* FINLAY (K. G.)

— Lead, kindly Light. Chorus. *See* FRICKER (H. A.) [Song of Thanksgiving.]

— Lead, kindly Light. Sacred Song. *See* GALBRAITH (J. L.)

— Lead, kindly Light. Duet. *See* GEIBEL (A.)

— Lead, kindly Light. [Hymn.] *See* GERHARD (F.)

— Lead, kindly Light. Sacred Song. *See* GILLETTE (P.)

— Lead, kindly Light. Sacred Song. *See* GOODACRE (E. R.)

— Lead, kindly Light! [Sacred song.] *See* GRATTANN (W. H.)

— Lead, kindly Light. Sacred Song. *See* HALWARD (E.)

— Lead, kindly Light. Sacred Song. *See* HANDLEY (B. R.)

— Lead, kindly Light. Sacred Song. *See* HARRIS (C.)

— Lead, kindly Light. Hymn. *See* HARRIS (*Sir* W. H.) *K.C.V.O.*

— Lead, kindly Light. Sacred Song. *See* HARRISON (W.)

— Lead, kindly Light. Anthem. *See* HARRISS (C. A. E.)

— Lead, kindly Light. Hymn. *See* HARWOOD (B.)

— Lead, Kindly Light. Anthem. *See* HATHAWAY (J. W. G.)

— Lead, kindly Light. [Sacred song.] *See* HAWLEY (C. B.)

— Lead, kindly light. Sacred song. *See* HEAP (C.S.)

— Lead, kindly Light. Sacred Song. *See* HICKLEY (A. C.)

— Lead, kindly Light. [Sacred song.] *See* HIDEN (T. D.)

— Lead, kindly Light. Sacred Song. *See* HOPE (E.)

— Lead, kindly Light. Sacred Song. *See* HOSKEN (R. S.)

— Lead kindly Light. Anthem. *See* HULLETT (C. H.)

— Lead, kindly Light. Hymn-Anthem. *See* HUNT (N. A. B.)

— Lead, kindly Light. Chorus. *See* JONES (T. H.) *Mus. Bac.*

— Lead, kindly Light. [Anthem.] *See* JONES (William B.)

— Lead, kindly Light. Sacred Song. *See* KAYE (A. D.)

— Lead, kindly Light. Sacred Song. *See* KNAPP (J.)

— Lead, kindly Light. Anthem. *See* LAER (C. E. van)

— Lead, kindly Light. Quartette. *See* LAWRENCE (F. W.)

— Lead, kindly Light. Sacred Song. *See* LAYTON (H. C.)

— Lead, kindly Light. Anthem. *See* LEE (Ernest M.)

— Lead, kindly Light. Solo and Chorus. *See* LEHMANN, afterwards BEDFORD (L.)

— Lead, kindly Light. [Anthem.] *See* LEY (H. G.)

— Lead, kindly Light. Sacred Song. *See* LIDDLE (S.)

— Lead, kindly Light. Hymn-Anthem. *See* LITTLE (A. E.)

LEAD

— Lead, kindly Light. [Hymn.] *See* M., H. B.

— Lead, kindly Light. Sacred Song. *See* MACFARREN (*Sir* G. A.)

— Lead, kindly Light. Sacred Song. *See* MANN (A.)

— Lead kindly Light. Anthem. *See* MANN (F. G.)

— Lead, kindly Light. Anthem. *See* MARK (H. R.)

— Lead, kindly Light. Sacred Song. *See* MAUNDER (J. H.)

— Lead, kindly light. Sacred song. *See* MEACHAM (C. J. B.)

— Lead kindly light. Song. *See* MENDELSSOHN-BARTHOLDY (J. L. F.) [Lieder ohne Worte. Op. 30. No. 3.]

— Lead, kindly Light. Anthem. *See* MERRIN (J.)

— Lead, kindly Light. Hymn-Anthem. *See* MIDDLETON (James R.)

— Lead, kindly Light. Song. *See* MORGAN (F.)

— Lead, kindly Light. Song. *See* MORRIS (W. B.)

— Lead, kindly Light. Anthem. *See* MUELLER (F. W.)

— Lead, kindly Light. Anthem. *See* NAYLOR (C. L.)

— Lead, kindly Light. Sacred Song. *See* O'HARA (G. de V.)

— Lead, kindly Light. Solo and Chorus. *See* PARCELL (A. E.)

— Lead, kindly Light. [Sacred song.] *See* PARTRIDGE (W. H.)

— Lead, kindly Light. Sacred song. *See* PINCOTT (F. G.)

— Lead, kindly Light. Sacred Song. *See* PINSUTI (C. E.)

— Lead, kindly Light. [Anthem.] *See* PROTHEROE (D.)

— Lead, kindly light. Sacred song. *See* PURDAY (C. H.)

— Lead, kindly Light. Sacred Song. *See* RAKHMANINOV (S. V.) [Romanzen. Op. 4. No. 3.]

— Lead, kindly Light. [Anthem.] *See* RAMSDEN (A. R.)

— Lead, kindly Light. [Hymn.] *See* RANDLE (C. W.)

— Lead, kindly Light. Sacred Song. *See* RIEGO (T. del)

— Lead, kindly Light. Sacred Song. *See* ROBERTS (O.)

— Lead, kindly Light. Sacred Song. *See* ROGERS (R.)

— Lead, kindly Light. [Sacred song.] *See* RUMSEY (J. W.)

— Lead, kindly Light. Sacred Song. *See* SANDERSON (W. E.)

— Lead, kindly Light. Solo and Quartett. *See* SCHNECKER (P. A.)

— Lead, kindly Light. Anthem. *See* SHAPCOTT (F. J.)

— Lead, kindly Light. Anthem. *See* SHELLEY (H. R.)

— Lead, kindly Light. [Cantata.] *See* SHERWOOD (E.)

— Lead, kindly Light. Anthem. *See* SMITH (B.)

— Lead, kindly Light. Quartette. *See* SPROSS (C. G.)

— Lead, kindly Light. Anthem. *See* STAINER (*Sir* J.)

— Lead, kindly Light. Anthem. *See* STATHER (H.)

— Lead, kindly Light. Hymn Anthem. *See* STORER (H. J.)

— Lead, kindly Light. Anthem. *See* STULTS (R. M.)

— Lead, kindly Light. [Part-song.] *See* THOMPSON (R. G.)

— Lead, kindly Light. Hymn. *See* TILLEARD (James)

— Lead, kindly Light. [Hymn.] *See* TOVEY (*Sir* D. F.)

LEAD

— Lead, kindly Light. [Sacred] Song. *See* TOZER (F.)

— Lead, kindly Light. Sacred Song. *See* TRUMAN (E.)

— Lead, kindly Light. [Sacred song.] *See* WHITE (E. J.)

— Lead, kindly Light. Sacred Song. *See* WHITE (M. V.)

— Lead kindly Light. Chorus. *See* WHITEHEAD (A. E.)

— Lead, kindly Light. Hymn. *See* WHYTE (R.)

— Lead, kindly Light. [Sacred] Song. *See* WILLING (Christopher E.)

— Lead, kindly Light. [Hymn.] *See* WOOD (A. R.)

— Lead me. Sacred song. *See* COSTA (*Sir* M.)

— Lead me all the Way. Sacred Song. *See* BRIGGS (C. S.)

— Lead me aright. Anthem. *See* ASHFORD (E. L.)

— Lead me Father by the Hand. Sacred Song. *See* WICHER (A.)

— Lead me gently home, Father. Anthem. *See* BERWALD (William H.)

— Lead me gently Home, Father. Solo or Duet. *See* THOMPSON (W. L.)

— Lead me in the Way. Response. *See* BARTLETT (H. N.)

— Lead me in Thy Truth. Anthem. *See* BUNNETT (E.)

— Lead me, Lord. Anthem. *See* CHRISTOPHER (Cyril S.)

— Lead me, Lord. Chorus. *See* HARKER (F. F.)

— Lead me, Lord. Anthem. *See* WESLEY (S. S.) [Praise the Lord, O my Soul.]

— Lead me, O Lord. Anthem. *See* DOCKSEY (A.)

— Lead me, O Lord. Anthem. *See* LLOYD (C. F.)

— Lead me, O Lord. [Song.] *See* LUDEBUEHL (J. P.)

— Lead me, O Lord. [Anthem.] *See* WILSON (H.)

— Lead me, O my Redeemer. Anthem. *See* BLOUNT (C. B.)

— Lead me sometimes where she's sleeping. Song. *See* SHATTUCK (C. F.)

— Lead me to the Rock. [Anthem.] *See* SCOTT (C. H.)

— Lead me to Thee. [Song.] *See* BIRD (P. D.)

— Lead me to Thee. Sacred Song. *See* WEST (J. E.)

— Lead on brave Nimphs. [Song.] *See* LEVERIDGE (R.)

— Lead on, Ebenezer. [Duet.] *See* KERKER (G. A.)

— Lead on, lead on. Chorus. *See* HAENDEL (G. F.) [Judas Maccabæus.]

— Lead on, O King eternal. Anthem. *See* BURDETT (G. A.)

— Lead on, O King eternal. Anthem. *See* LEWIS (John L.)

— Lead on, O King eternal. [Sacred song.] *See* MARZO (E.)

— Lead on, O King eternal. [Anthem.] *See* SMART (Henry) [Lancashire.]

— Lead on, O King eternal. [Chorus.] *See* TERRY (R. H.)

— Lead on, we'll follow thee. Patriotic song. *See* MACKWELL (D.)

— The Lead strikes English Ground. Song. *See* GILHOLY (B. M.)

— Lead the way and I will follow. Song. *See* BENDIXEN (L.)

LEAD

— Lead them straight. Song. *See* SMALLWOOD (W.)

— Lead Thou and guide me. Motet. *See* PALESTRINA (G. P. da) [Offertoria Totius Anni . . . Pars Prima.—Perfice gressus meos.]

— Lead Thou me on. Sacred Song. *See* BARTH (T. W.)

— Lead Thou me on. [Sacred] Duett. *See* BLOCKLEY (John J.) *the Younger.*

— Lead Thou me on! Sacred Song. *See* ELLIS (S.) *pseud.*

— Lead Thou me on. [Sacred song.] *See* HALL (W. J.) *Songwriter.*

— Lead Thou me on. Sacred ballad. *See* JOSEPHINE.

— Lead Thou me on. [Anthem.] *See* NEVIN (G. B.)

— Lead Thou me on. Sacred Song. *See* ROYLE (F.)

— Lead Thou me on. Sacred Song. *See* WOOD (W. McC.)

— Lead Thou me on. Sacred Song. *See* YATES (E.)

— Lead Thou, O kindly Light. [Sacred song.] *See* FABER (J.)

— Lead us gently Home. [Anthem.] *See* BRIGGS (C. S.)

— Lead us, heavenly Father. Duet. *See* ADAM (F.)

— Lead us, heavenly Father, lead us. Anthem. *See* AKERMAN (R. F. M.)

— Lead us, heavenly Father. Anthem. *See* BERWALD (W. H.)

— Lead us, heavenly Father. Duet. *See* COLBURN (A. G.)

— Lead us, heavenly Father. Anthem. *See* COWLES (E.)

— Lead us, heavenly Father. Song. *See* DAVIES (T. V.)

— Lead us, heavenly Father. [Anthem.] *See* GRAY (A.)

— Lead us heavenly Father. Anthem. *See* LITTLE (H. W.)

— Lead us, Heavenly Father, lead us. Anthem. *See* POWELL (C. T.)

— Lead us, Heavenly Father. Motet. *See* POWELL (J. B.)

— Lead us, Heavenly Father. [Anthem.] *See* QUILTER (R.)

— Lead us, heavenly Father. Anthem. *See* REED (W.)

— Lead us, heavenly Father. Anthem. *See* ROBERTS (Herbert A.)

— Lead us, heavenly Father. Anthem. *See* ROSSINI (G. A.) [Stabat Mater.—Pro peccatis.]

— Lead us, heavenly Father. Hymn-Anthem. *See* SCHNECKER (P. A.)

— Lead us, heavenly Father. Sacred Song. *See* STEANE (B. H. D.)

— Lead us, heavenly Father. Sacred Song. *See* STULTS (R. M.)

— Lead us, heavenly Father. Anthem. *See* WADELY (F. W.)

— Lead us, Heavenly Father. Anthem. *See* WRIGHT (J.)

— Lead us Home to Thee. Song. *See* BARRI (O.)

— Lead us in the Paths of Peace. Anthem. *See* BROOME (E.)

— Lead us not into Temptation. Sacred Song. *See* PARKER (Henry T.)

— Lead us not into temptation. Song and chorus. *See* WHITE (C. A.)

— Lead us, O Father. [Anthem.] *See* ATKINSON (R. H.)

— Lead us, O Father. Anthem. *See* BIRD (P. D.)

LEAD

— Lead us, O Father. Anthem. *See* BRACKETT (F. H.)

— Lead us, O Father. Trio. *See* COERNE (Louis A.)

— Lead us, O Father. Anthem. *See* DOSWELL (Michael)

— Lead us, O Father. Duet. *See* GALBRAITH (J. L.)

— Lead us, O Father. Anthem. *See* PROTHEROE (D.)

— Lead us, O Father. [Hymn.] *See* TAYLOR (C. V.)

— Lead us, O Father. Anthem. *See* WHITBY (E.)

— Lead us, O Father. Sacred Song. *See* WOOLER (A.)

— Lead us, O Father, in the Paths of Peace. Hymn-anthem. *See* BERWALD (William H.)

— Lead us, O Lord. Response. *See* GREENE (C. W.)

— Lead us, O Lord. [Sacred song.] *See* HESS (H.)

— Lead us to Rest. [Sacred song.] *See* MOIR (F. L.)

LEADBELLY

— *See* LEDBETTER (H.)

LEADBETTER (MARTIN)

— Soliloquy. Op. 26. For flute (or violin) and piano. [Score and part.] 2 pt. *Fentone Music: London*, [1980.] 4°.

g. 225. i. (6.)

LEADEN

— The Leaden Echo and the golden Echo. Cantata. *See* WELLESZ (E. J.)

LEADER

— De Leader of de Co. B. Song. *See* REED (David)

— Leader of faithful Souls. Sacred Song. *See* BARNES (T.)

— The Leader of Frocks and Frills. Song. *See* ELLIS (M. M.)

— A Leader of Society. Song. *See* PETHER (Henry E.)

— The Leader of the Ball. [Song.] *See* LEMONIER (Thomas)

— Leader of the colored Aristocracy. [Song.] *See* COOK (Will M.)

— The Leader of the German Band. Song. *See* MORSE (T. F.)

— The Leader of Vanity Fair. [Song.] *See* FRANCIS (William T.)

LEADERS

— The Leaders of the Church of Christ. [Hymn.] *See* FETHERSTON (*Sir* G. R.) *Bart.*

LEADGATE

— Leadgate. [Anthem.] *See* WITTY (Robert)

LEAF

— The Leaf. Ballad. *See* KING (M. P.)

— The Leaf. Song. *See* SMITHURST (E.)

— The Leaf. Song. *See* SPEER (C. T.) Six Songs. No. 2.

— Leaf by Leaf. Song. *See* LEIGH (L.)

— Leaf by leaf the roses die. Ballad. *See* HERVÉ (F.) *pseud.*

— Leaf by Leaf the Roses fade. Ballad. *See* VANE (A.)

LEAF

— Leaf by Leaf the Roses fall. [Song.] *See* BISHOP (T. B.)

— Leaf by Leaf the roses fall. [Song.] *See* BUCKLEY (F.)

— Leaf by Leaf the Roses fall. Ballad. *See* HARRISON (James)

— A Leaf from the Spray. Song-waltz. *See* MEY (A.)

— A Leaf of Shamrock. Song. *See* ARTHURS (George)

— A Leaf on the Water. Unison Song. *See* DAYMOND (E. R.)

— A Leaf that reminds of thee. [Song.] *See* LOVER (Samuel) [Songs of Handy Andy. No. 3.]

LEAF (ANN)

— *See* MOLLOY (J. L.) The Kerry Dance ... Organ arrangement by A. Leaf. 1937. 4°. **g. 1380. q. (8.)**

— *See* SCHUMANN (R. A.) [Kinderscenen. Op. 15. No. 7.] Traumerei ... Organ arrangement by A. Leaf. 1937. 4°. **g. 715. l. (16.)**

LEAF (J. ALBERT)

— Ave Maria. Song. *London*, [1866.] fol. **H. 1772. r. (23.)**

— The Heathery Moor. Song [begins: "Before the golden sun"]. Words by R. M. M. *London*, [1867.] fol. **H. 1772. r. (24.)**

— Memories of Bygone Days. Songs without words for the Piano. 4 no. *London*, [1864.] fol. **h. 1460. v. (1.)**

LEAF (ROBERT)

— I hear a Song. For full chorus of mixed voices a cappella. [Words by] R. Leaf. pp. 7. *G. Schirmer: New York*, [1971.] 8°. **F. 1874. p. (6.)**

LEAFLAND

— A Leafland Lullaby. [Song.] *See* WOOD (H.)

LEAFLESS

— The Leafless Sycamore. [Song.] *See* DONIZETTI (D. G. M.) [*Doubtful and Supposititious Works.*]

— The Leafless Tree. Ballad. *See* NELSON (S.)

LEAFY

— The Leafy Dell. Song. *See* BROCKMAN (L.)

— Leafy June. Song. *See* WAKEFIELD (A. M.)

— A Leafy Lane. [Two-part song.] *See* FOSTER (M. B.) [Six Landscapes. No. 4.]

— The Leafy Lanes of England. [Song.] *See* HARDING (Phyllis B.)

— The Leafy Trees. [Two-part song.] *See* PETERKIN (N.)

— The Leafy Way. Serenade. *See* COLE (J. P.)

— A Leafy Wood. Song. *See* BRAHE (May H.)

LEAGUE

— The League Invitation. [Hymn.] *See* W., F. G.

— League of Nations. Song. *See* BARLOW (George S.)

— The League of Nations. Song Book. *See* SHAW (M. F.)

— League of Notions. [Revue.] *See* BARRATT (W. A.)

LEAGUE

— League of the Arts for National and Civic Ceremony. *See* LONDON.

LEAH

— Leah's Song. *See* RICHARDS (H. B.)

LEAH (JOHN E.)

— Dedication. [Hymn, begins: "Standing forth"]. *Novello and Co.: London*, [1903.] *a card*. **I. 600. b. (125.)**

LEAHY (C. F. N.)

— Um-ti-um. Song, words & music by C. F. N. Leahy. *Cary & Co.: London*, 1918. 4°. **G. 426. c. (35.)**

LEAKE (FRANCIS AUBREY EYTON)

— Service of Holy Communion. *Abbey Music Co.: London*, 1926. 8°. **E. 605. u. (14.)**

LEAKE (GEORGE)

— Military Postlude. Organ. *Weekes & Co.: London*, 1919. obl. 4°.
No. 46 of "The Western Organist". **e. 1203.**

— Two Vesper Hymns. No. 1. Words by A. Cooper. Music by G. Leake. (No. 2. Words & music by A. Cooper.) *Vincent Music Co.: London*, [1908.] *a card*. **I. 600. c. (197.)**

— A Vesper Verse. Words by A. Cooper. [*A. Cooper: Southampton*, 1907.] *obl.* 8°.
Subsequently published as No. 1 of Two Vesper Hymns, entered above. **A. 868. j. (2.)**

— *See* COOPER (A.) A Vesper Verse ... Arranged ... by G. Leake. [1907.] *s. sh.* 4°. **I. 600. c. (166.)**

LEAKY

— A Leaky Boat. Chantey. *See* DÉGUIRE (William W.)

LEAL (LUÍS PEREIRA)

— *See* PEREIRA LEAL.

LEALI (LUIGIA)

— In the Woodlands. Ballad. (Words by Miss S.) *London*, [1870.] fol. **H. 1775. u. (1.)**

LEAL-TRUE

— The Leal-true hearted Mason. [Song.] *See* YOUNG (W.) *Freemason*.

LEAMAN (ISABELLE)

— One little angry Word. [Song.] Words and Music by I. Leaman. *M. Witmark & Sons: New York & Chicago*, 1898. fol. **H. 1799. h. (22.)**

LEAMAN (LOU)

— *See* LAI (Francis) Love Story. ⟨Where do I begin⟩ ... Arranged by L. Leaman. [For 3 voices.] [1971.] 8°.
F. 1874. p. (3.)

LEAMAN (LOU)

— *See* SHERMAN (Richard M.) and SHERMAN (R. B.) [Mary Poppins.] Songs ... Arranged by L. Leaman. [1964.] 8°.
F. 217. z. (2.)

— *See* SHERMAN (Richard M.) and SHERMAN (R. B.) [Mary Poppins.] Songs, *etc.* [With organ.] Arranged by L. Leaman. [1964.] 4°.
F. 314. ww. (4.)

— *See* SHERMAN (Richard M.) and SHERMAN (R. B.) [Mary Poppins.] Chim chim cher-ee. S. A. Arranged by L. Leaman. [1964.] 8°.
F. 217. y. (40.)

— *See* SHERMAN (Richard M.) and SHERMAN (R. B.) [Mary Poppins.] Feed the Birds ... S. A. Arranged by L. Leaman. [1964.] 8°.
F. 217. bb. (10.)

— *See* SHERMAN (Richard M.) and SHERMAN (R. B.) [Mary Poppins.] Jolly Holiday. S. A. Arranged by L. Leaman. [1964.] 8°.
F. 217. y. (34.)

— *See* SHERMAN (Richard M.) and SHERMAN (R. B.) [Mary Poppins.] A Spoonful of Sugar. S. A. Arranged by L. Leaman. [1964.] 8°.
F. 217. y. (35.)

— *See* SHERMAN (Richard M.) and SHERMAN (R. B.) [Mary Poppins.] Supercalifragilisticexpialidocious ... S. A. Arranged by L. Leaman. [1964.] 8°.
F. 217. y. (37.)

LEAMINGTON SPA. — *School of English Church Music*
— *See* CROYDON. — *Royal School of Church Music.*

LEAMORE (TOM E.)

— Good-bye, Mother, I must leave you. ⟨Song.⟩ Written, composed ... by T. Leamore. [Staff and tonic sol-fa notation. Voice part.] *Francis, Day & Hunter: London*, [1909.] *s. sh.* fol.
H. 3985. l. (20.)

— Good-bye, Mother, I must leave you, *etc.* ⟨Song.⟩ [With separate voice part.] 2 pt. *Francis, Day & Hunter: London*, [1909.] fol.
H. 3985. l. (21.)

— I'll never leave Home any more. ⟨Song.⟩ Written, composed ... by T. Leamore. [With separate voice part.] 2 pt. *Hopwood & Crew: London*, [1902.] fol.
H. 3985. l. (22.)

— The Lifeboat-man's Story. ⟨Song.⟩ Written by Mark Lorne and T. Leamore, *etc.* [Staff and tonic sol-fa notation. Voice part.] *Francis, Day & Hunter: London*, [1901.] *s. sh.* fol.
H. 3985. l. (23.)

— The Lifeboat-man's Story, *etc.* ⟨Song.⟩ [With separate voice part.] 2 pt. *Francis, Day & Hunter: London*, [1901.] fol.
H. 3985. l. (24.)

— My Son! my Son!! my Son of a Gun. Written, composed ... by T. E. Leamore. [Song. Staff and tonic sol-fa notation. Voice part.] *Francis, Day & Hunter: London*, [1899.] *s. sh.* fol.
H. 3980. pp. (34.)

— The Park Keeper. ⟨Song.⟩ Written by Mark Lorne, *etc.* *East London Printing Co.: London*, [1906.] fol. H. 3985. l. (25.)

— Percy from Pimlico. [Song. With separate voice part.] Written, composed ... by T. Leamore. 2 pt. *Howard & Co.: London*, [1898.] fol.
H. 3980. pp. (35.)

— *See* TIZARD (Wilfrid) and LEAMORE (T. E.) Those Days when I was young. Written & composed by W. Tizard & T. Leamore, *etc.* [Song.] [1906.] fol.
H. 3988. e. (14.)

— *See* WILLMOTT (Charles) and LEAMORE (T. E.) Out for a fair old Beano. ⟨Song.⟩ Written and composed by C. Willmott & T. Leamore, *etc.* [1894.] *s. sh.* fol. H. 3981. ss. (52.)

LEAMORE (TOM E.) and **COLLINS** (CHARLES)

— I'm going to Sea (see). ⟨Song.⟩ Written by C. Collins, *etc.* [Staff and tonic sol-fa notation. Voice part.] *Francis, Day & Hunter: London*, [1904.] *s. sh.* fol.
H. 3985. l. (26.)

LEAMORE (TOM E.) and **COLLINS** (CHARLES)

— I'm going to Sea (see), *etc.* ⟨Song.⟩ [With separate voice part.] 2 pt. *Francis, Day & Hunter: London*, [1904.] fol.
H. 3985. l. (27.)

LEA-MORGAN (JOHN)
— *See* MORGAN.

LEAN

— Lean out of the Window. [Song.] *See* HEAD (Michael)

— Lean thy Cheek. [Song.] *See* JENSEN (A.) [Sechs Lieder. Op. 1 No. 1. Lehn' deine Wang'.]

LEAN (ALASDAIR)

— Eight easy Pieces for Beginners' String Orchestras (in traditional style). [Score.] pp. 10. *A. Lean: London*, 1976. 8°. *Blue Cow Publications. no.* 1. c. 160. bb. (4.)

LEANBHAÍ

— Na leanbhaí i mBeithil. Amhrán. Trí pháirt. *See* NORAIDH (L. de)

LEANDER (HENRY)

— By those Eyes. A Favorite Duett for Two Voices ... with an Accompaniment for a Pedal Harp, or Piano Forte, *etc.* *London*, [1800?] fol. G. 805. h. (27.)

— By those Eyes. A Favorite Duett ... with an Accompaniment for Pedal Harp or Piano Forte. pp. 3. *Printed for the Author by R{t} Birchall: London*, [1815?] fol. H. 1652. o. (35.)

— By those Eyes ... Duet. *London*, [1867.] fol.
H. 1772. r. (22.)

— *See* DUFRESNOY ( ) *Madame.* A Favorite Sonata ... for the Harp ... arranged with Accompaniments for Two French Horns ... by H. Leander. [1800?] fol. h. 1480. h. (7.)

LÉANDRE

— [Léandre Candide.] En fixant notre planette. *Vaudeville de Léandre Candide* ... Sur l'Air de Figaro. [*Paris*, 1784.] 8°.
B. 362. c. (27.)

— Léandre chez Colinette un jour. *Suite de la Lanterne Magique.* Air, Philis de[mande] son portrait [by É. J. I. A. Albanese]. [*Paris*, 1780?] 8°. B. 362. a. (160.)

— Léandre et Héro. Tragédie [words by Lefranc de Pompignan], mise en Musique par l'Auteur du Ballet de l'Empire de l'Amour [i. e. the Marquis René de Bearn Brassac], *etc.* Partition ... Gravée par Labassée. *Chés Mme Boivin, etc.: Paris*, 1750. fol. I. 322.

— Léandre et Héro. Cantate à voix seule. *See* CLÉRAMBAULT (L. N.) [Cantates Françoises. Liv. II.]

— Léandre Nanette, ou le Double Qui-pro-quo. Parade en un acte, en vers et en Vaudevilles, *etc.* [By C. F. Ragot de Grandval. With the music of an Air and a Vaudeville.] *Clignancourt*, 1756. 8°. 11738. f. 39. (9.)

LEANED

— Leaned on Jesus' Breast. [Trio.] *See* MOLIQUE (B.) Six Songs. Op. 51. No. 2.

LEANING

— Leanin'. Song. *See* BENNETT (T. C. S.)

— Leaning on a Balcony. Song. *See* LEE (A.)

LEANING

— Leaning on Jesus. Song. *See* GLOVER (C. W.)

— Leaning on the Garden Gate. Song. *See* CONVERSE (F. B.)

— Leaning on Thee. Sacred Song. *See* BLOCKLEY (T.)

— Leaning on Thee. Anthem. *See* BRACKETT (F. H.)

LEAP

— Leap into a Dance. [Song.] *See* WHITE (F. H.)

— The Leap of Kurroglou. [Cantata.] *See* DEAR (J. R.)

— The Leap of Roushan Beg. Ballad for Chorus. *See* PARKER (H. W.)

— Leap-year, a Valentine Ballad. *See* BLEWITT (J.)

— Leap Year. Song. *See* BLOXSOM (S.)

— Leap Year. [Song.] *See* BONHEUR (I.) *pseud.*

— Leap Year. Song. *See* BURTON (H. S.)

— The Leap Year. Song. *See* CALDWELL (David)

— Leap Year. [Song, begins: "Come round me ye lasses".] *See* DIBDIN (C.) [Christmas Gambols.]

— Leap Year. [Song, begins: "Won't you hail the leap year".] *See* DIBDIN (C.) [Private Theatricals.]

— Leap Year. Song. *See* DIEHL (L.)

— Leap Year. [Song.] *See* LOWITZ (William W.)

— Leap Year. Air. *See* MACFARREN (*Sir* G. A.)

— Leap Year. Ballad. *See* PEMBROKE (E. L.)

— Leap Year. [Song, begins: "A Shepherdess one Morning fair".] *See* T., J.

— A Leap-Year Appeal. Song. *See* CARR (E.)

— Leap Year in Midnight Town. [Song.] *See* HAMMERSTEIN (Oscar)

LEAPER (KENNETH)

— Mister Crummles's Infant Phenomena. A variety bill for performance by schools with speech and mime, voices and piano, instrumentalists. [Score.] pp. 40. *EMI Music Publishing: London*, [1980.] 4°. **F. 1272. m. (5.)**

— Rites of Spring ... ⟨Cantata.⟩ For two speakers, children's voices, games players, piano, with occasional recorders, tuned and untuned percussion, *etc.* [Score.] pp. 31. *Chappell Music: London*, 1979. 4°. **F. 1272. m. (7.)**

— Three Victorian Scenes ... 1. Market Street. 2. Seaside. 3. Paradise Row. For children's voices, piano, with occasional recorders, melodicas, tuned and untuned percussion, *etc.* [Score.] pp. 63. *Chappell & Company: London*, 1978. 4°. **G. 809. z. (8.)**

— Yule. ⟨A Christmas cantata for junior school celebrating the winter solstice.⟩ For two speakers, children's voices, games players, piano, with occasional recorders: melodicas, tuned and untuned percussion, *etc.* [Score.] pp. 36. *Chappell: London*, 1979. 4°. **F. 1272. m. (1.)**

LEAP-FROG

— The Leap-frog Game. [Unison song.] *See* WILKINSON (Philip G.)

LEAP-YEAR

— *See* LEAP.

LEAR

— Lear. Oper. *See* REIMANN (Aribert)

LEAR (EDWARD)

— Laughable Lyrics: a Fourth Book of Nonsense Poems, Songs, Botany, Music, *etc.* *R. J. Bush: London*, 1877 [1876]. 4°. **Case 116. e. 23.**

— Poems and songs by A. Tennyson, set to music ... by E. Lear. 9 no. *London*, [1859.] fol. **H. 1560.**

LEAR (JUDITH)

— For England, Queen, and Empire. [Song.] Words by J. B. Bryant. *Novello & Co.: London*, [1900.] fol. **H. 1799. h. (23.)**

LEAR (THOMAS)

— Shylock. B♭ Cornet Solo with Pianoforte accompaniment. *Boosey & Co.: London and New York*, 1927. 4°. **g. 1110. (14.)**

LEAR (W. HOGARTH)

— Barney's Tune. For brass band, *etc.* ⟨Piano-conductor in B♭ [and parts].⟩ 34 pt. *Chester Music: London*, [1976.] 4°. [*Just Brass. no. 2BB.*] *With several copies of various parts.* **g. 1110. cc.**

— Chinese Take away. For cornet trio and brass band. ⟨Piano conductor in B♭ [and parts].⟩ 26 pt. *Chester Music: London*, [1976.] 4°. [*Just Brass. no. 4BB.*] *With several copies of various parts.* **g. 1110. cc.**

— Cops and Robbers. For brass band ... Conductor (in B♭) [and parts]. 27 pt. *Paxton Music: Borough Green*, [1978.] 8°. *With several copies of various parts.* **h. 3210. j. (952.)**

— Hogarth's Hoe-down. For brass band, *etc.* ⟨Piano-conductor in B♭ [and parts].⟩ 26 pt. *Chester Music: London*, [1976.] 4°. [*Just Brass. no. 1BB.*] *With several copies of various parts.* **g. 1110. cc.**

— Mr. Lear's Carnival. For brass band ... [Score.] Parts, *etc.* 26 pt. *Chester Music: London*, [1979.] 4°. [*Just Brass. no. 14BB.*] *With several copies of various parts.* **g. 1110. cc.**

— Paris le soir. For brass band, *etc.* ⟨Piano conductor in B♭ [and parts].⟩ 26 pt. *Chester Music: London*, [1976.] 4°. [*Just Brass. no. 3BB.*] *With several copies of various parts.* **g. 1110. cc.**

— Pel Mel. For Brass band. ⟨Conductor [and parts].⟩ 25 pt. *Paxton Music: Borough Green*, [1975.] 8°. *With several copies of various parts.* **e. 1330. (74.)**

— Pop goes the Posthorn. For brass band. ⟨Conductor [and parts].⟩ 29 pt. *Paxton Music: Borough Green*, [1975.] 8°. *With several copies of various parts.* **e. 1330. (73.)**

— Red Sky at Night. For brass band. ⟨Piano-conductor in B♭ [and parts].⟩ 26 pt. *Chester Music: London*, [1976.] 4°. [*Just Brass. no. 7BB.*] *With several copies of various parts.* **g. 1110. cc.**

— *See* HOWARTH (Elgar) Fireworks. For brass band. (Variations on a theme of W. H. Lear.) [1975.] *obl.* 4°. **e. 501. e. (12.)**

LEARN

— Learn how to lose. [Song.] *See* KREISLER (F.) [The King steps out.]

— Learn to do well. Anthem. *See* WAGNER (O.)

— Learn to forbear. Song. *See* WADE (J. A.)

LEARN

— Learn to say yes. [Sacred song.] *See* GAINES (S. R.) Three Devotional Songs. 3.

— Learn to take your Troubles lightly. Song. *See* SAMUEL (H.)

— Learn to wait. Cavatina. *See* CELLIER (A.) [Doris.]

LEARNED

— The Learned Leviathan. Comic Song. *See* BUCALOSSI (P.)

— The Learned of Rome's antient grandeur. *Peace, or Old England Triumphant*, a song written on the preliminaries of peace being sign'd ... 1801. The words by a Gentleman of Salisbury and set to music by an Eminent Master. *J. & H. Banks: Salisbury*, [1801.] fol. **G. 423. (2.)**

— The Learned Owl. Song. *See* STANHOPE (E. M.)

— The Learned Pig. Comic Song. *See* SINCE. Since London's the place, *etc.* [1780?] fol. **H. 1994. (59.)**

— Learned Women. Part-Song. *See* EDWARDS (F.)

LEARNED (CHARLES)

— Communion Service ... in ... A flat, *etc.* *H. W. Gray Co.: New York*, 1912. 8°. *Church Music Review, No.* 323. **F. 1169. u. (13.)**

— Communion Service ... in ... E, *etc.* *H. W. Gray Co.: New York*, 1901. 8°. **F. 1169. o. (19.)**

— A Morning and Evening Service in ... A flat. Te Deum. (Opus 3.) Jubilate Deo. (Opus 4.) Magnificat and Nunc dimittis. (Opus 5.) 3 no. *H. W. Gray & Co.: New York*, 1912. 8°. **F. 1169. u. (14.)**

LEARNING

— Learning French. Action Song. *See* KEENE (F. A.)

— Learning French. [Song.] *See* LAWSON (Jan L.)

— Learning Geography. [Song.] *See* SAGESSE (L. A.)

— Learning her Lessons. [Song.] *See* PENN (Arthur A.)

— Learning to be Soldiers. Action Song. *See* READ (E.)

— Learning to love. Ballad. *See* GRIFFITHS (E. H.)

— Learning to ride the Byke. Song. *See* MONTAGUE (Harold)

— Learning to walk. Song. *See* CORNABÉ (W. E.)

— Learning's Sway. Glee. *See* HARGREAVES (G.)

LEARY (A. HAYDN)

— Barcarolle. [Organ.] *Gould & Co.: London*, 1915. 4°. *The Organist Recital Series, No.* 10. **g. 1380. a. (7.)**

— The Battle Song of the Free. [Song.] Written by R. F. Drury. 2 no. [In C and D.] *J. B. Cramer & Co.: London*, 1915. fol. **H. 1793. s. (31.)**

— Two Pieces for Violin & Piano. No. 1. Lullaby. No. 2. Chant d'Amour. 2 no. *Augener: London*, (1912.) fol. **g. 505. ee. (35.)**

LEARY (ARTHUR O')

— *See* O'LEARY.

LEARY (PATRICK O')

— *See* O'LEARY.

LEARY-VINNING (ROSETTA O')

— *See* O'LEARY-VINNING.

LEASK (HOWARD)

— Nature's Praise. Sacred song. Words by the Rev⁴ William Leask. pp. 7. *Metzler & Cᵒ: London*, [1881.] fol. **G. 424. nn. (9.)**

LEASK (LEONARD)

— Girl of my Dreams. Song. Words by Harold Peacock. *Allday: Birmingham*, [c. 1915.] 4°. **G. 425. ll. (14.)**

— Sunshine on the Sea. Song, *etc.* *Leonard & Co.: London*, 1909. fol. **G. 807. yy. (29.)**

— Vesper Hymn. For war-time ... Words by Captain H. D. Peacock, *etc.* *Midland Educational Co.: Birmingham*, [c. 1915.] *obl.* 8°. **I. 600. g. (48.)**

LEASOWE

— Leasowe. Song. *See* SCOTT (C. H. H.)

LEAST

— The Least of these. Sacred Song. *See* BARRETT (R.)

LEATH (VAUGHN DE)

— The Lilac-Flower. A Song of early Spring, *etc.* (Words by C. A. M. Dolson. Op. 29. No. 1.) *G. Schirmer: New York*, 1926. 4°. **G. 1275. w. (13.)**

— Wild Geese. A Song ... Words by G. Johnstone. (Op. 107. No. 1.) *G. Schirmer: New York*, 1926. 4°. **G. 1275. w. (14.)**

LEATHER

— Leather away the Wattle O! [Part-song.] *See* REGGE (Earnán de)

— The Leather Bottèl. [Song.] *See* 'TWAS. 'Twas God above that made all Things, *etc.* [1860.] fol. [*B. Williams' Collection of old English Songs. No.* 1.] **H. 2828. d. (12.)**

— The Leather Bottèl. Song. *See* 'TWAS. 'Twas God above, who made all things, *etc.* [1878.] fol. **H. 2345.**

— The Leather Bottel. Song. *See* WHEN. When I survey, *etc.* [1878.] fol. **H. 1791. b. (85.)**

— The Leather Bottel. [Part-song.] *See* COPLEY (Ian A.)

— The Leather Bottèl. Ballad. *See* HATTON (J. L.)

— The Leather Bottel. Ballad. *See* MACFARREN (*Sir* G. A.)

— The Leather Bottelle. Song. *See* STRATTON (H. W.)

LEATHER (E. M.) and WILLIAMS (RALPH VAUGHAN)

— Twelve Traditional Carols from Herefordshire. Collected, edited and arranged by E. M. Leather and R. V. Williams. *Stainer & Bell: London*, 1920. 8°. **F. 538. h. (17.)**

LEATHER-WINGED

— The Leather-winged Bat. Folk song. *See* WILLIAMS (Ronald R.)

LEATHES (CARTERET DE MUSSENDEN)

— Battle March, for piano. *E. Donajowski: London*, 1914. fol. **h. 3284. nn. (26.)**

— March, for piano. *E. Donajowski: London*, [1914.] fol. **h. 3284. nn. (27.)**

LEAVE

— Leave a Girl or two for the Boys in blue. [Song.] *See* RUSSELL (R. C. K.)

— Leave a little Bit for your Tutor. [Song.] *See* LE BRUNN (G.)

— Leave her alone with them. Song. *See* OSBORNE (Charles)

— Leave her Picture on the Wall. [Song.] *See* MAYWOOD (George)

— Leave him alone. Song. *See* GRAHAM (C.)

— Leave it all to Tommy. Song. *See* HOWARD (L.)

— Leave it alone. [Song.] *See* LLOYD (M.)

— Leave it to Bill. Song. *See* COLE (Robert A.)

— Leave it to Father. Song. *See* BENNETT (T. C. S.)

— Leave it to me. [Song.] *See* DILLEA (Herbert)

— Leave it to me. Comic Song. *See* HAZELDINE (P.)

— Leave it to the Navy. [Song.] *See* DEWEY (Hale E.)

— Leave leave for a while thy own sunny isle. Cavatina. *See* GOODBAN (C.)

— Leave me. Air. *See* HAENDEL (G. F.) [Rinaldo.—Lascia ch'io pianga.]

— Leave me and save the glorious flag. [Song.] *See* MOON (C. R.)

— Leave me, Comrades. [Song.] *See* MACGLENNON (F.)

— Leave me, Damon, cease to woo me. *The Repulse*. A new song. Set to music by an eminent master [i. e. William Shield]. *In:* The New Lady's Magazine. vol. 5. pp. 424–426. 1790. 8°.
P. P. 5141. b.

— Leave me, deceiver. Recitative and air. *See* HAENDEL (G. F.) [Rinaldo.—Lascia ch'io pianga.]

— Leave me ere it be too late. [Song.] *See* THOMAS (A. G.)

— Leave me, for ever leave me. Duetto. *See* MOZART (W. A.) [Don Giovanni.—Ma quel mai s'offre.]

— Leave me free to die. [Song.] *See* SCARLATTI (A.) [O cessate di piegarmi.]

— Leave me, I pray. Duettino. *See* LODER (E. J.) [Never judge by appearances.]

— Leave me in this sweet enchantment. [Song.] *See* SIMPSON (M. M.)

— Leave me, loathsome Light. Air. *See* HAENDEL (G. F.) [Semele.]

— Leave me no more. [Song.] *See* DENZA (L.)

— Leave me not. Song. *See* DENZA (L.)

— Leave me not. Song. *See* MATTEI (T.)

— Leave me not. Air. *See* VERDI (F. G. F.) [Luisa Miller.—Tu puniscimi.]

— Leave me not, Douglas! Song. *See* STANLEY (E.)

— Leave me not in Anger. Song. *See* PERSLEY (G. W.)

— Leave me not yet! Chorus. *See* NEIDLINGER (W. H.)

— Leave me, O Love. [Song.] *See* ARUNDELL (D. D.)

— Leave me shephard. Song. *See* STANLEY (J.)

— Leave me to mourn. Duet. *See* WEBER (C. M. F. E. von) [Tre Duetti. Op. 31. No. 2.]

LEAVE

— Leave me to sorrow awhile. Ballad. *See* LINWOOD (M.) [The White Wreath.]

— Leave me where you met me. Song. *See* TABBAR (Joseph)

— Leave me with my mother. [Song.] *See* FOSTER (S. C.)

— Leave me your Heart. Song. *See* WAKEFIELD (M.)

— Leave no Stone unturned. [Part-song.] *See* MILLET (K.)

— Leave prolonging thy Distress. [Madrigal.] *See* RUBBRA (E. D.) Madrigals, 2nd Set ... Opus 52. No. 1.

— Leave the Clouds behind. Song. *See* COSTIN (Harold)

— Leave the Door ajar. Ballad. *See* BRATTON (John W.)

— Leave the old one. Song. *See* RUDD (Austin)

— Leave the rest to me. Song. *See* DAVID (Worton) and ARTHURS (G.)

— Leave the World awhile. Hymn. *See* VINNING (W. S.)

— Leave them alone, Boys. [Song.] *See* LEO (Frank)

— Leave us nevermore. [Sacred song.] *See* BLUMENSCHEIN (W. L.)

— Leave us not. Song. *See* COYNE (A.) Two Songs. No. 1.

— Leave us not. Anthem. *See* JAMOUNEAU (A. J.)

— Leave us not! Song. *See* OGDEN (Jonathan R.)

— Leave us not. Song. *See* PINSUTI (C. E.) Six Songs. No. 1.

— Leave us not. [Song.] *See* ZETA, *pseud.*

— Leave us not, neither forsake us. Anthem. *See* STAINER (Sir J.)

— Leave your Burden at de Bottom ob de Hill. Song. *See* BRISTOW (F. L.)

— Leave your Flock. [Unison song.] *See* BROOK (Harry)

— Leave yor Folded Flocks in Peace. *A new Song* by an Eminent Master [i. e. H. Carey]. [*London*, 1720?] *s. sh.* fol.
H. 1601. (294.)

— Leave your folded Flocks in Peace to sleep. *Pastoral*. [By H. Carey.] [*London*, 1740?] *s. sh.* fol.
A leaf from Vol. 1. of Carey's "Musical Century".
G. 316. a. (34.)

LEAVENS (B. F.)

— The Service of Song, a new collection of Church music, *etc. Philadelphia*, 1849. fol.
G. 910.

LEAVER (W. J.)

— Féodora. Songs, words by F. E. Weatherly. *Scott & Co.: London*, 1892. fol.
H. 1797. o. (32.)

— I lov'd a lass, a fair one. Part-Song. Words by G. Wither. *Novello, Ewer and Co.: London and New York*, [1887.] 8°.
F. 321. c. (19.)

— Impromptu for the Pianoforte. *London*, [1877.] fol.
h. 1494. p. (36.)

— Laddie's Love. Song, words by F. E. Weatherly. *Scott & Co.: London*, 1893. fol.
H. 1797. o. (33.)

LEAVES

— The Leaves. [Unison song.] *See* LEE (Ernest M.)

— Leaves. Song. *See* PARROTT (Horace I.)

— Leaves. Two-part Song. *See* RATHBONE (G.)

LEAVES

— Leaves. [Song.] *See* WHITLEY (A.)

— Leaves. [Song.] *See* ZUCCA (M.) *pseud.* Two Songs, *etc.* [No. 2.]

— Leaves a-dancing. Song. *See* LEY (H. G.)

— Leaves and Flowers. Song. *See* GOEDBÉ (Samuel)

— The Leaves and the friends. Ballad. *See* WILLIAMS (W. L.)

— The Leaves and the Wind. [Song.] *See* LEONI (F.)

— The Leaves are falling. Part-Song. *See* CELLIER (A.)

— The Leaves are falling. [Song.] *See* VAN DIEREN (B.)

— The Leaves are turning red. Song. *See* WALLACE (William V.)

— Leaves around are falling. Ballad. *See* PORTER (J. S.)

— The Leaves be greene. "Browning" for string orchestra. *See* BYRD (W.)

— Leaves from the human Heart. Song. *See* ANDINO (J. E.)

— The Leaves have fallen to the Ground. Ballad. *See* COENIAL (C. F. de)

— Leaves have their time to fall. Cavatina. *See* COWARD (J.)

— Leaves of Autumn. Song. *See* BADIA (L.)

— Leaves of Autumn. Song. *See* HOWELL (H.)

— Leaves of autumn. Song. *See* SHATTUCK (C. F.)

— Three Leaves of Grass. Song cycle. *See* SEGERSTAM (Leif)

— Leaves of Life. Ballad-cantata. *See* JOUBERT (John)

— The Leaves of Life. [Part-song.] *See* ROWLEY (A.)

— Leaves of Memory. Song. *See* PINSUTI (C. E.)

— The Leaves of Terpsichore. *See* PERIODICAL PUBLICATIONS.— *London.*

— The Leaves of Yesterday. [Part-song.] *See* GRAY (A.)

— Leaves on the River. Song. *See* LEONI (F.)

— The Leaves so green. [Song.] *See* ARNOLD (S.) [The Castle of Andalusia.]

— Leaves that are fairest. Song. *See* DAWBER (J.)

— Leaves that fall in May. Ballad. *See* PROUT (T. J.)

— The Leaves that fall in Spring. Ballad. *See* THOMAS (J. R.)

— The Leaves to one another say. Part-song. *See* DOERING (C. H.)

— Leaves upon the Stream. Song. *See* CRAMER (W. O.)

LEAVE-TAKING

— The Leave-Taking. Song. *See* EARNSHAW (A. H.)

— A Leave Taking. [Song.] *See* KELLIE (L.) Two Songs ... No. 2.

— A Leave-Taking. [Song.] *See* MANNEY (C. F.)

— A Leave-Taking. Song. *See* SALAMAN (C. K.)

— A Leave-Taking. Song. *See* VOLONNINO (A.)

— Leavetaking. Song. *See* WHITE (M. V.)

— A Leave-Taking. Part-song. *See* WILSON (A. W.)

LEAVING

— Leaving. [Song.] *See* MEYER (George W.)

— Leaving all to Jesus. Sacred Song. *See* LANCELOTT (W. F.)

— Leaving by the Transport. Song. *See* HENRY (J. H.)

— Leaving Home. [Song.] *See* GERMANIA. Germania, *etc.* No. 51. [1861, *etc.*] fol.   **H. 2128.**

— Leaving Home. [Song.] *See* OUR. Our dear delightful hills forsaking. [1864.] fol.   **H. 2345.**

— The Leaving of the old Home. Song. *See* GLOVER (Charles W.)

— Leaving on a Jet Plane. [Part-song.] *See* DENVER (John)

— Leaving School. Unison Song. *See* SHAW (M. F.) [Thursday's Child. No. 2.]

— Leaving yet loving. Song. *See* MARZIALS (T. J. H.)

LEAVIS (RALPH)

— *See* MENDELSSOHN-BARTHOLDY (J. L. F.) Kyrie. Edited, with reduction for organ, by R. Leavis. For S. S. A. T. B., *etc.* [1964.] 8°.   **F. 274. ff. (12.)**

LEAVITT (BURTON E.)

— Tea Tephi. A Romantic and Historic Opera in Three Acts, words by N. W. and B. E. Leavitt. Piano and Vocal Score. *R. Banks & Son: London,* 1912. 4°.   **H. 326.**

LEAVITT (H. Y.)

— Bye, bye, Belinda. Song and chorus. Words and music by H. Y. Leavitt. pp. 5. *M. Witmark & Sons: New York, Chicago,* [1897.] fol.   **H. 3980. pp. (36.)**

— Debonair Waltz. [P. F.] *Brooks & Denton: New York,* 1900. fol.   **h. 3286. r. (1.)**

— "Hannah Lou." (Song and chorus.) Words and music by H. Y. Leavitt. pp. 3–5. *F. A. Mills:* [*New York,* 1898.] 4°.   **H. 3980. pp. (37.)**

— "Here's a Toast." Drinking song. Words and music by H. Y. Leavitt. pp. 5. *Brooks & Denton: New York,* [1899.] fol.   **H. 3980. pp. (38.)**

— Here they come—March ... Arr. by W. C. O'Hare. ⟨1st B♭ cornet (solo) [and wind band parts].⟩ 26 pt. *Brooks & Denton: New York,* [1901.] 8°.
Various parts are in duplicate.   **f. 800. (800.)**

— If you'se gwine to love anybody, please love me. [Song.] Words & music by H. Y. Leavitt. pp. 5. *M. Witmark & Sons: New York, Chicago,* [1898.] fol.   **H. 3980. pp. (39.)**

— Little Baby Bunny. Darky song. ⟨Words and music by H. Y. Leavitt.⟩ *F. A. Mills: New York,* [1898.] fol.   **H. 3980. pp. (40.)**

— Ma Gum-Elastic Girl!—A Cake Walk.—[P. F.] *Brooks & Denton: New York,* 1900. fol.   **h. 3286. r. (2.)**

— My Billee. A song of the sea. Words and music by H. Y. Leavitt. pp. 5. *Brooks & Denton: New York,* [1899.] fol.   **H. 3980. pp. (41.)**

— The Slipshod Squad. March and Two-Step. [P. F.] *Willis, Woodward & Co.: New York,* 1899. fol.   **h. 3286. g. (19.)**

— So 'long, ma Honey! Two step ... Arr. by Herbert L. Clarke. [Orchestral parts.] 16 pt. *Brooks & Denton: New York,* [1899.] 8°.   **f. 800. (801.)**

— The Stars all shine to-night. Song, words and music by H. Y. Leavitt. *F. A. Mills: New York,* 1898. 4°.   **G. 424. j. (5.)**

LEAVITT (H. Y.)

— The Stars simper slyly. Song and chorus. Words and music by H. Y. Leavitt. pp. 5. *George L. Spaulding: New York,* [1897.] fol.   **H. 3980. pp. (42.)**

— The Stuttering Coon. [Song.] Words and music by H. Y. Leavitt. pp. 5. *M. Witmark & Sons: New York, Chicago,* [1898.] fol.   **H. 3980. pp. (43.)**

— You can't win me from my Man. [Song.] Words & music by H. Y. Leavitt. pp. 5. *Brooks & Denton: New York,* [1899.] fol.   **H. 3980. pp. (44.)**

— *See* SILBERBERG (J. A.) and LEAVITT (N. Y.) "Lookin' for a little Recreation." [Song.] [1898.] fol.   **H. 3981. x. (17.)**

LEAVITT (J.)

— Fünf Lieder für eine Singstimme mit Begleitung des Pianoforte. Op. 4. 1. "Ich stand in dunklen Träumen."— H. Heine.—2. "Es fällt ein Stern herunter."—H. Heine.— 3. "Mein Engel hüte dein."—W. Hertz.—4. Veilchen.— H. Seidl.—5. "Es hat die Nachtigall."—L. v. Plönnies. *Breitkopf & Härtel: Leipzig, etc.,* 1894. fol.   **G. 805. aa. (4.)**

LEAVITT (JOSHUA)

— The Christian Lyre, adapted for use in families, prayer meetings, and revivals of religion. The music printed in patent notes. [Edited] by J. Leavitt. ⟨Vol. I.⟩ *J. Leavitt: New York,* 1832. 12°.   **A. 820.**

— The Christian Lyre; a collection of hymns and tunes ... The work complete, two volumes in one, with a supplement ... Eighteenth edition, revised. ⟨Supplement ... containing more than one hundred psalm tunes.⟩ 3 pt. *Jonathan Leavitt: New-York,* 1833. 12°.
The supplement bears the date 1831.   **A. 1236. z.**

LEAVY ( )

— *See* RENAUD (A.) Marche solennelle, from Leavy. [Organ.] 1888. *obl.* fol.   **e. 1091.**

LEAVY (ARTHUR JAMES)

— A Farewell-Melody [begins: "Flow down cold rivulet"]. Words by A. Tennyson. *London,* [1872.] fol.   **H. 1775. u. (2.)**

— Salut à Marie. Mélodie religieuse [begins: "Quand Dieu daignant enfin"]. Poésie de A. Appay. *Paris,* [1883.] fol.   **H. 1793. d. (4.)**

LEAYCRAFT (AGNES)

— Across the Sea. [Song.] Words and music by A. Leaycraft. *T. Presser: Philadelphia,* (1906.) fol.   **G. 805. mm. (18.)**

— The Garden fair. [Song.] Words and music by A. Leaycraft, *etc. T. Presser: Philadelphia,* (1908.) fol.   **G. 805. mm. (19.)**

— He leads the Way. [Sacred song.] Words and music by A. Leaycraft, *etc. T. Presser: Philadelphia,* (1905.) fol.   **H. 1187. ff. (52.)**

— Her Crown. [Song.] Words and music by A. Leaycraft. *M. Witmark & Sons:* [*New York,*] 1902. fol.   **H. 1199. cc. (53.)**

— What the Daisies saw ... [Song.] Words and music by A. Leaycraft. *T. Presser: Philadelphia,* (1905.) fol.   **G. 807. jj. (41.)**

LEBA (FRANZ)

— Fünf Clavierstücke. No. 1. Valsette. No. 2. Mazurka. No. 3. Capriccietto. No. 4. Romance. No. 5. Air de Ballet. [P. F.] 5 no. *Paterson & Sons: Edinburgh, London,* [1901.] fol.   **h. 3282. w. (33.)**

LEBANO (FELICE)

— Compositions pour Harpe. 5 no. *Milan,* [1881.] fol.   **h. 3212. e. (11.)**

— Pensée poétique. Morceau pour la harpe. *Ricordi: Milan,* [1886.] fol.   **h. 3200. b. (8.)**

— Tristesse. Romance sans paroles pour Harpe. *Milan,* [1881.] fol.   **h. 3212. e. (12.)**

LEBANO (PIETRO)

— Primo Notturno per Pianoforte. *See* infra: Prima Romanza, *etc.*

— Prima Romanza senza parole. Primo Notturno per Pianoforte. 2 no. *Milano,* [1882.] fol.   **h. 3280. k. (34.)**

— Tristezza! ... Melodia per canto ... con accomp[o]. di pianoforte. *F. Lucca: Milano,* [1887.] fol.   **H. 2836. v. (23.)**

LE BARGE (J. A.)

— Amorita. Waltz. Arranged ... by W. Loraine. [P. F.] *H. V. Schlam: New York,* 1901. fol.   **h. 3286. r. (3.)**

— Bonita. Waltzes. [Mandolines, guitar and P. F.] *H. V. Schlam: New York,* 1901. fol.   **h. 188. h. (1.)**

— A complete Method for the Mandolin. *Wulschner & Son: Indianapolis, Ind.,* [1899.] 4°.   **g. 1102. (3.)**

— Dat Man's all mine ... [Song.] Words and music by J. A. Le Barge. *Draper Music Pub. Co.: Toronto; Hugo V. Schlam: New York,* [1899.] fol.   **H. 3985. l. (28.)**

— Marionetta. Waltzes. [Mandolines, guitar and P. F.] *H. V. Schlam: New York,* 1900. fol.   **h. 188. h. (2.)**

— Tally-Ho. Two-Step. Piano Arrangement [by] J. Monk. *Vessall & Draper: Toronto,* 1897. fol.   **h. 3286. g. (20.)**

LE BARGY (ARMAND)

— Sylphes Parisiennes. Valse lente. [P. F.] *J. H. Larway: London,* 1908. fol.   **h. 3286. ll. (22.)**

LE BARON (ELLA)

— The Cotillion. March (two-step). [P. F.] pp. 5. *Jos. W. Stern & Co.: New York,* [1909.] fol.   **h. 4120. oo. (1.)**

LEBARRE (THÉODORE)

— [La Révolte du Sérail.] *See* TOLBECQUE (J. B.) Trois Quadrilles sur les motifs de La Révolte du Sérail, de T. Lebarre, *etc.* [1830.] *obl.* 4°.   **e. 41. (3.)**

LEBÂS ( )

— Six Album Leaves for violin and pianoforte, *etc. Oliver Ditson Company: Boston, etc.,* 1893. 4°.   **g. 505. i. (7.)**

— Six Album Leaves for violin and pianoforte, *etc.* 6 no. *O. Ditson Company: Boston, etc.,* 1893. fol.   **h. 3095. (1.)**

— A Fiddler's Fancies. Six Pieces for Violin and Piano. 6 no. *C. Sheard & Co.: London,* 1892. fol.   **h. 3095. (2.)**

— In the Days of my Youth. Six duets for two violins with piano accompaniment, *etc.* [Score and parts.] no. 2. *C. Sheard & Co.: London; Leipzig* printed, [1892.] fol. *Imperfect: wanting no.* 1, 3–6.   **g. 218. dd. (1.)**

LEBÂS (   )

— Just one Day. Six Scenes of Childhood for violin ... with pianoforte accompaniment. 6 no. *O. Ditson Company: Boston, etc.*, 1893. fol. **h. 3095. (3.)**

— Romanzetta for violin and pianoforte. 2 no. [Violin and P. F. and P. F. solo.] *O. Ditson Company: Boston, etc.*, 1893. fol. **h. 3095. (4.)**

— Terpsichorean. Six Movements for two violins with piano accompaniment. 3 no. *C. Sheard & Co.: London*, 1892. fol. **h. 3095. (5.)**

LE BAS (GERTRUDE)

— The Gates of Paradise. Song, words by M. Hamilton-Fellows, *etc. Weekes & Co.: London*, [1915.] fol. **H. 1793. s. (32.)**

— Love's Dawn. Song, words by F. G. Bowles, *etc. Weekes & Co.: London*, [1913.] fol. **H. 1793. s. (33.)**

— Roses in my Garden Way. Song, words by J. Gade. *J. Church Co.: Cincinnati, etc.*, 1911. fol. **H. 1792. r. (48.)**

— True Love is blind. Song, words by M. E. Farr, *etc. Weekes & Co.: London*, [1909.] fol. **H. 1792. r. (49.)**

— You, Love and June. Song, words by M. Fellows. *Weekes & Co.: London*, [1913.] fol. **H. 1793. s. (34.)**

LE BAS (JEAN)

— L'Extase d'amour. Valse lente, *etc.* [P. F.] *Hawkes & Son: London*, 1910. fol. **h. 3286. uu. (42.)**

LEBAS DE COURMONT (CHARLES CL.)

— Cavatine suivie d'une Contredanse ... arrangées pour la Harpe ou Piano par F. Petrini. *Paris*, [1815?] fol. **G. 557. (1.)**

LEBEAU (ALFRED)

— A la Chapelle, prière pour Orgue-Harmonium. Op. 81. *Paris*, [1865.] fol. **h. 2550. (2.)**

— À la Chapelle. Prière pour Orgue avec Accompagnement de double Quatuor. Op. 81 bis. [Score and parts.] *Lebeau aîné: Paris*, [1870.] fol. [*La Musique Populaire. No. 47.*] **H. 2349. (2.)**

— L'Abandon. Romance sans paroles. *See* infra: Six Morceaux, *etc.* No. 1.

— L'Abbaye de Montiers. Pensée religieuse. *See* infra: Souvenirs de la Puisaye. No. 4.

— Les Adieux. Romance sans paroles. *See* infra: Souvenirs de la Puisaye. No. 6.

— Aida, opéra de G. Verdi. Duo de concert pour Piano et Orgue. *Milano*, [1874.] fol. **h. 3105. (31.)**

— All' Usignuolo. *See* infra: [Au Rossignol.]

— L'Allée Mystérieuse. Idylle. *See* also infra: Souvenirs de la Puisaye. No. 1.

— L'Allée Mystérieuse. Idylle pour Piano. *Paris*, [1874.] fol. **h. 3105. (30.)**

— L'Angelus au Couvent, impromptu pour le Piano. Op. 69. *Paris*, [1864.] fol. **h. 3105. (2.)**

— [Another copy.] *Issued as music supplement to "La Musique populaire," année 2. no. 8.* **P. P. 1948. s/2. (32.)**

— L'Appel des Pâtres, pastorale pour Piano et Orgue. Op. 34 ter. *Paris*, [1869.] fol. **h. 3105. (13.)**

LEBEAU (ALFRED)

— L'Appel des Pâtres, pastorale pour Piano. Op. 34 bis. *Paris*, [1869.] fol. **h. 3105. (14.)**

— L'Arlésienne de G. Bizet. Menuet transcrit pour Piano. *Paris*, [1874.] fol. **h. 3105. (29.)**

— L'Attente. Romance [begins: "Au pays où se fait la guerre"]. Poésie de T. Gautier. *Paris*, [1874.] fol. **H. 1777. h. (23.)**

— Au printemps. Mélodie de Ch. Gounod. Transcription-rêverie pour piano ... Op: 107. pp. 5. *Choudens: Paris*, [c. 1865.] fol. *Issued as music supplement to "La Musique populaire".* **P. P. 1948. s/2. (151.)**

— Au Printemps, mélodie de C. Gounod. Transcription-rêverie pour Piano. *London*, [1879.] fol. **h. 1494. p. (37.)**

— Au Rossignol. Mélodie [begins: "Quand ta voix céleste"]. Poésie de Lamartine. *Paris*, [1875.] fol. **H. 1777. h. (27.)**

— [Au Rossignol.] All' Usignuolo. (To the Nightingale.) Melodia [begins: "Quando vola".—"How it charms"] ... Poesia di A. de Lamartine. Versione italiana di S. Farina. English version by H. Stevens. *Milano*, [1876.] fol. **H. 1777. h. (29.)**

— Aubade [for harmonium]. Op. 35. *Paris*, [1869.] fol. **h. 2550. (7.)**

— Ballet de la Reine, scherzo-menuet, transcription pour Piano. *Paris*, [1876.] fol. **h. 3105. (39.)**

— Ballet de la Reine. Scherzo-menuet, transcription pour Piano. *London*, [1876.] fol. **h. 1482. y. (48.)**

— [Ballet de la reine.] *See* BANGER (G.) Das Königsballet. Kindersymphonie nach dem Werk "Ballet de la reine" von A. Lebeau. [1880.] fol. **h. 3210. a. (3.)**

— Beaux Jours passés! (Long, long ago.) Mélodie Américaine transcrite pour le Piano. *London*, [1873.] fol. **h. 1482. y. (46.)**

— Deux Bergeries. Paroles de E. Boysse. 2 no. *Paris*, [1877.] fol. **H. 1781. i. (10.)**

— Brises du Soir, rêverie-nocturne. Trio, Violon ou Violoncello, Orgue et Piano. Op. 68. *Paris*, [1863.] fol. **h. 3105. (1.)**

— Caprice Ecossais. Morceau de genre pour le Piano. *Paris*, [1875.] fol. **h. 3105. (36.)**

— Caprice Ecossais, morceau de genre pour Piano. *London*, [1876.] fol. **h. 1482. y. (51.)**

— Caprice-étude sur l'air J'ai du bon tabac. Pour piano. ⟨Op. 36.⟩ *Lebeau aîné: Paris*, [c. 1860.] fol. *Issued as music supplement to "La Musique populaire," année 2, no. 14.* **P. P. 1948. s/2. (38.)**

— Célèbre Menuet de Boccherini. Transcription pour Piano. *Londres*, [1872.] fol. **h. 3105. (24.)**

— Les Champs. Mélodie [begins: "Rose, partons"]. Poésie de Béranger. *Paris*, [1874.] fol. **H. 1777. h. (24.)**

— Chanson Béarnaise de J. Offenbach. Transcription pour Piano. *Paris*, [1874.] fol. **h. 3105. (28.)**

— Chanson moldave. *See* infra: [Impressions de voyage. Op. 98.]

— Chanson Provençale pour le Piano. *London*, [1876.] fol. **h. 1482. y. (49.)**

— Chant de Nazareth, mélodie de C. Gounod ... illustration poétique pour le Piano. *Paris*, [1875.] fol. **h. 3105. (33.)**

— Chant Indien. [P. F.] *See* infra: Cinq petites pièces ... No. 4.

— Chants Éoliens, rêverie-nocturne pour Piano. Op. 78. *Paris*, [1868.] fol. **h. 3105. (5.)**

LEBEAU (ALFRED)

— Comme à Vingt Ans, mélodie d'E. Durand, transcrite pour le Piano. *Londres*, [1873.] fol. **h. 3105. (25.)**

— Confidence. Méditation poetique [begins: "Viens, chercher cette ombre"] de A. de Lamartine. *Paris*, [1869.] fol. **H. 1774. e. (18.)**

— Confidenza. Meditazione poetica di A. Lamartine. [Song, begins: "Vien, cerchiam quest'ombra"]. (Parole di S. Farina.) *London*, [1874.] fol. **H. 1778. x. (52.)**

— Confidenza. Meditazione poetica di A. Lamartine. (Parole italiane di S. Farina.) *Milano*, [1874.] fol. **H. 1777. h. (26.)**

— Danse aux Flambeaux ... pour Piano. *London*, [1871.] fol. **h. 1485. s. (34.)**

— Danse aux Flambeaux ... pour Piano. *Paris*, [1872.] fol. **h. 3105. (21.)**

— Danse bretonne, Villanelle. *See* infra: Six Morceaux ... No. 2.

— Danse des Korigans, legende bretonne pour Orgue Harmonium. Op. 80. *Paris*, [1865.] fol. **h. 2550. (3.)**

— Danse Silesienne. *See* infra: Impressions de Voyage. No. 2.

— Dernier Rayon, contemplation maritime pour Piano. *Paris*, [1877.] fol. **h. 1493. n. (22.)**

— Derniers Rayons. Contemplation-Maritime pour piano. Op. 150. *J. B. Cramer & Co.: London*, [1892.] fol. **h. 1489. s. (23.)**

— En Mer. Chant maritime. *See* infra: Six Morceaux ... No. 5.

— En ronde, scène maritime pour Orgue harmonium. *Paris*, [1872.] fol. **h. 2550. (8.)**

— En Traineau. *See* infra: Impressions de Voyage. No. 1.

— L'Étoile des Amours. Mélodie [begins: "J'aime une étoile"]. Poésie du Vicomte O. de Poli. *Bruxelles*, [1880.] fol. **H. 1786. e. (19.)**

— L'Excentrique. Polka pour piano. pp. 5. *Lebeau aîné: Paris*, [c. 1860.] fol.
Issued as music supplement to "La Musique populaire," année 1. *no.* 6. **P. P. 1948. s/2. (12.)**

— Farandole. Impression de Voyage. (Op. 151.) [Harmonium.] *Paris*, [1883.] fol. **h. 2575. a. (9.)**

— Farandole. Op. 151. Piano Solo. *Metzler & Co.: London*, [1892.] fol. **h. 1489. s. (24.)**

— Fête Champêtre. Paysannerie. *See* infra: Souvenirs de la Puisaye. No. 5.

— Fête des Patineurs ... Caprice caractéristique pour Piano. *Paris*, [1875.] fol. **h. 3105. (34.)**

— Fête des Patineurs ... Caprice caractéristique pour Piano. *Milano*, [1876.] fol. **h. 3105. (43.)**

— La Fille de Mme. Angot, de C. Lecocq. Transcription pour Orgue-Harmonium. *Paris*, [1875.] fol. **h. 3105. (32.)**

— Historiette. [P. F.] *See* infra: Cinq petites pièces ... No. 5.

— Hymne à Sainte Cécile, de C. Gounod, transcription pour Piano et Orgue Harmonium. Op. 91. *Paris*, [1866.] fol. **h. 3105. (8.)**

Impressions de voyage

— Impressions de Voyage, deux morceaux pour Piano. [1.] Danse silésienne. ⟨Op. 83.⟩ [2.] En traineau. ⟨Op. 87.⟩ 2 no. *Paris*, [1867.] fol. **h. 3105. (10.)**

LEBEAU (ALFRED)

— [Another copy.]
Issued as music supplement to "La Musique populaire", année 4. *no.* 24. **P. P. 1948. s/2. (91, 108.)**

— Impressions de voyage. Deux morceaux. Pour piano. [1.] Refrain du berger. ⟨Op. 97.⟩ [2.] Chanson moldave. ⟨Op. 98.⟩ *H. L. d'Aubel: Paris*, [c. 1865.] fol.
Imperfect; wanting no. 2. *Issued as music supplement to "La Musique populaire," année* 6. *no.* 10. **P. P. 1948. s/2. (124.)**

— [Op. 97.] Refrain du Berger, caprice rêverie pour Piano. *Londres*, [1872.] fol. **h. 3105. (23.)**

— Chanson moldave ... Pour le piano ... Op. 98. *H. L. d'Aubel: Paris*, [c. 1865.] fol.
Issued as music supplement to "La Musique populaire," année 5. *no.* 24. **P. P. 1948. s/2. (114.)**

— [Op. 98.] Chanson Moldave, caprice caractéristique pour le Piano. *Londres*, [1872.] fol. **h. 3105. (22.)**

— Impromptu. *See* infra: Six Morceaux, *etc.* No. 6.

— Interlaken, souvenir de Suisse, valse brillante pour Piano. Op. 41. *Paris*, [1866.] fol. **h. 3105. (4.)**

— Ma Mie Annette. Chanson rustique [begins: "Rêveillez vous"]. Poésie de H. Murger. *Paris*, [1869.] fol. **H. 1774. e. (17.)**

— [Ma Mie Annette.] La Mia Buona Annetta. Canzone. Parole francesi di H. Murger, versione italiana di S. Farina. *Paris*, [1871.] fol. **H. 1775. u. (3.)**

— [Ma Mie Annette.] My sweet Annette, song [begins: "Awake! awake!"]. Words by M. Hayes. *London*, [1871.] fol. **H. 1775. u. (4.)**

— Le Mal du Pays. Mélodie de A. Jungmann [begins: "Partir, partir"]. Poésie du Vᵗᵉ. O. de Poli, arrangée pour chant par A. Le Beau. *Paris*, [1875.] fol. **H. 1777. h. (28.)**

— Marche Persane, chant national pour Piano. *Paris*, [1873.] fol. **h. 3105. (27.)**

— Marche tunisienne pour le piano ... Op. 70. pp. 5. *Lebeau aîné: Paris*, [c. 1860.] fol.
Issued as music supplement to "La Musique populaire," année 2. *no.* 20. **P. P. 1948. s/2. (44.)**

— Marche Tunisienne pour le Piano. Op. 70. *Paris*, [1864.] fol. **h. 3105. (3.)**

— Méditation religieuse sur un Ave Maria de P. Bensit, arrangée en Trio pour Piano, Orgue, Violon ou Violoncelle. *Bruxelles*, [1878.] fol. **h. 2851. c. (8.)**

— Medjé, chanson arabe de C. Gounod, transcrit pour piano. *London*, [1879.] fol. **h. 1494. p. (38.)**

— Mélodie Danoise (air populaire) transcription pour Piano. *Paris*, [1876.] fol. **h. 3105. (41.)**

— Mélodie Danoise. (Air populaire.) Transcription pour Piano. *London*, [1877.] fol. **h. 1482. y. (54.)**

— La Mia Buona Annetta. *See* supra: [Ma mie Annette.]

— Trois morceaux de salon pour piano. ⟨Nº 1. Caprice-étude (sur un air ancien.)—Nº 2. Le Repos (Berceuse). Op. 76.—No. 3. Sur le Nil (Orientale). Op. 77.⟩ no. 2, 3. *Lebeau aîné: Paris*, [c. 1865.] fol.
Imperfect; wanting no. 1. *Issued as music supplement to "La Musique populaire," année* 4. *no.* 2, 4. **P. P. 1948. s/2. (70, 72.)**

— Six Morceaux originaux pour Harmonium. 6 no. *Paris*, [1862.] fol. **h. 2550. (1.)**

LEBEAU (ALFRED)

— Cinq Morceaux, Rentrée de Procession, Offertoire, Élévation, Communion, et Sortie. [Organ.] *Paris*, [1866.] *obl. fol.*
Liv. 13 *of "Répertoire de Musique d'Eglise".* **e. 174. b. (6.)**

— Musette, de C. Gounod. Transcription pour Orgue Harmonium. *Paris*, [1867.] fol. **h. 2550. (5.)**

— My sweet Annette. *See* supra: [Ma mie Annette.]

— Nel veron della vicina. (The Window Curtain.) Canzone [begins: "In the room"] ... Poesia di A. de Musset. Versione italiana di S. Farina. English version di H. Stevens. *Milano*, [1877.] fol. **H. 1782. a. (11.)**

— Occitanie, idylle-sérénade pour Piano. *Paris*, [1870.] fol. **h. 3105. (18.)**

— L'Ombre, opéra comique de Flotow, duo de salon pour Orgue Harmonium et Piano. *Paris*, [1876.] fol. **h. 3105. (40.)**

— La Paix. [Song, begins: "Que notre âme soit fière".] Paroles de Mᵐᵉ. Baïlen. *Paris*, [1870.] fol. **H. 1774. e. (19.)**

— Passa bel viator. *See* infra: [Sur ma barque légère.]

— La Patrouille, ronde nocturne. [P. F.] *Paris*, [1875.] fol. **h. 3105. (35.)**

— La Patrouille, ronde nocturne pour Piano. *London*, [1876.] fol. **h. 1482. y. (50.)**

— Petit Carillon. [P. F.] *See* infra: Cinq petites pièces ... No. 3.

— Petite Valse. [P. F.] *See* infra: Cinq petites pièces ... No. 1.

— Cinq petites pièces pour piano, *etc.* 5 no. *Paris*, [1885.] fol. **h. 3280. k. (35.)**

— Les Pifferari, de C. Gounod, fantaisie-tarentelle pour Piano. Op. 85. *Paris*, [1866.] fol. **h. 3105. (6.)**

— [Les Pifferari.] Fantaisie-Tarentelle sur les Pifferari de C. Gounod pour Piano. *Paris*, [1879.] fol. **h. 1493. n. (23.)**

— Les Pifferari, de C. Gounod, transcription pour Orgue Harmonium. *Paris*, [1867.] fol.
Different from the preceding. **h. 2550. (4.)**

— Polyeucte, opera ... de C. Gounod, fantaisie pour Orgue. *Paris*, [1879.] fol. **h. 2575. f.(9.)**

— Le Pré aux Clercs. Opéra Comique de F. Hérold. Duo brillant pour piano et orgue. *Paris*, [1880.] fol.
No. 13 *of Duos de salon pour orgue et piano.* **h. 2576. a. (9.)**

— La Prière des Anges, transcription-nocturne pour le Piano. Op. 74. *Paris*, [1867.] fol. **h. 3105. (12.)**

— [Another copy.]
Issued as music supplement to "La Musique populaire," année 6. *no.* 20. **P. P. 1948 s/2. (134.)**

— Recueil de douze morceaux pour Orgue-Américain, *etc.* no. 1–4. *London*, [1872.] fol.
No more published. **h. 2731. i. (6.)**

— Refrain du berger. *See* supra: [Impressions de voyage. Op. 97.]

— Les Reliques. Mélodies [begins: "J'ouvre d'une main"]. Poésie de C. Reynaud. *Paris*, [1869.] fol. **H. 1774. e. (16.)**

— Renovare. Mélodie [begins: "Avez vous oublié"]. Poésie de H. Murger. *Paris*, [1867.] fol. **H. 1774. e. (14.)**

— Renovare. Melodia [begins: "Di l'aiola"]. Imitazione da Murger di S. Farina. *Milano*, [1877.] fol. **H. 1782. a. (10.)**

— Le Repos (Berceuse). Op. 76. *See* supra: Trois morceaux de salon pour piano. Nº 2.

LEBEAU (ALFRED)

— Le Réveil. Aubade. Avec accompᵗ de piano & orgue ad lib. Poésie de Eug. Tourneux. [Song. With parts for voice and organ.] 3 pt. *Lebeau aîné: Paris*, [c. 1860.] fol.
Issued as music supplement to "La Musique populaire," année 1. *no.* 6. **P. P. 1948. s/2. (7.)**

— Ronde Militaire. [P. F.] *See* supra: Cinq petites pièces ... No. 2.

— La Rosée du Matin. Caprice. *See* supra: Six Morceaux, *etc.* No. 3.

— Roxane. Polka pour piano. pp. 5. *Lebeau aîné: Paris*, [c. 1860.] fol.
Issued as music supplement to "La Musique populaire," année 1. *no.* 9. **P. P. 1948. s/2. (18.)**

— Royale Chacone pour Piano. *Paris*, [1875.] fol. **h. 3105. (38.)**

— Royale Chacone pour Piano. *London*, [1877.] fol. **h. 1482. y. (53.)**

— Scène pastorale, fantaisie de concert pour Orgue. *Paris*, [1881.] fol. **h. 2575. h. (7.)**

— Sérénade, de C. Gounod. Transcription pour Orgue Harmonium. *Paris*, [1867.] fol. **h. 2550. (6.)**

— Sérénade, de C. Gounod, fantaisie-caprice pour Piano. Op. 56. *Paris*, [1863?] fol. **h. 3105. (9.)**

— [Another copy.]
Issued as music supplement to "La Musique populaire," année 1. *no.* 11. **P. P. 1948. s/2. (22.)**

— Sérénade de C. Gounod, fantaisie-caprice pour Piano. *Milano*, [1876.] fol. **h. 3105. (42.)**

— Sérénade, de C. Gounod, fantaisie-caprice pour le Piano à quatre mains. Op. 56. bis. *Paris*, [1866.] fol. **h. 3105. (7.)**

— Soleil Couchant. Rêverie pastorale pour piano. *Paris*, [1875.] fol. **h. 3105. (37.)**

— Soleil Couchant, rêverie pastorale pour Piano. *London*, [1876.] fol. **h. 1489. a. (25.)**

— Il Sospiro valse pour le Piano. *London*, [1871.] fol. **h. 1485. s. (36.)**

— Il Sospiro, valse pour le Piano. *Paris*, [1872.] fol. **h. 3105. (20.)**

— La Source du Loing. Rêverie. *See* infra: Souvenirs de la Puisaye. No. 3.

— Souvenir de Aida, de G. Verdi, fantasie pour Orgue Harmonium. *Milano*, [1874.] fol. **h. 2550. (10.)**

— Souvenir Pompadour, air favori du roi Louis XV. [P. F.] *London*, [1873.] fol. **h. 1482. y. (47.)**

— Souvenirs de la Puisaye. Six morceaux originaux pour Orgue Harmonium. 6 no. *Paris*, [1873.] fol. **h. 2550. (9.)**

— Stella Maris, prière à la Vierge, de C. Gounod, fantaisie transcription pour Piano. Op. 106. *Paris*, [1869.] fol. **h. 3105. (16.)**

— [Another copy.]
Issued as music supplement to "La Musique populaire". **P. P. 1948. s/2. (142.)**

— Stella Maris, prière à la Vierge de C. Gounod. Fantaisie transcription pour Piano. *Paris*, [1870.] fol. **h. 3105. (19.)**

— Sur le Nil (Orientale). Op. 77. *See* supra: Trois morceaux de salon pour piano. Nº 3.

— Sur les Flots, étude maritime pour Piano. *London*, [1877.] fol. **h. 1482. y. (52.)**

LEBEAU (ALFRED)

— [Sur ma barque légère.] Passa bel viator. Barcarola. (Parole italiane di S. Farina. Parole francesi di L. B. de Villars.) *Milano*, [1874.] fol.   **H. 1777. h. (25.)**

— [Sur ma barque légère.] Passa bel viator. Barcarola. (Parole di S. Farina.) *London*, [1874.] fol.   **H. 1778. x. (51.)**

— Sylvie. Souvenir d'autrefois. *See* supra: Six Morceaux, *etc.* No. 4.

— Le Tocsin, caprice galop pour le Piano. Op. 109. *Paris*, [1870.] fol.   **h. 3105. (17.)**

— Le Tocsin, caprice galop pour le Piano. *London*, [1871.] fol.   **h. 1485. s. (35.)**

— La Tour abandonnée. Légende. *See* supra: Souvenirs de la Puisaye. No. 2.

— Tzigane-Marsch, ronde Bohême pour Piano. Duet. *London*, [1872.] fol.   **h. 1485. s. (37.)**

— Les Vagues Bleues ... Suite de valses pour Piano. *Paris*, [1873.] fol.   **h. 3105. (26.)**

— Valse des Rêves pour Piano. Op. 84. *Paris*, [1867.] fol.   **h. 3105. (11.)**

— Vieille Chanson du Jeune Temps, transcription rêverie de la mélodie de J. O'Kelly pour Orgue. *Paris*, [1875.] fol.   **h. 2550. (11.)**

— Viens, partons! [Song, begins: "Lève toi".] Poésie de L. Bouilhet. *Paris*, [1868.] fol.   **h. 1774. e. (15.)**

— Le Voeu à la Madonne. 2me. Nocturne pour Piano. Op. 104. *Paris*, [1869.] fol.   **h. 3105. (15.)**

— La Vœu à la Madone. 2de. nocturne pour Piano. *London*, [1872.] fol.   **h. 1485. s. (38.)**

— *See* BEETHOVEN (L. van) [Piano concerto No. 4.] Grand Concerto ... Op. 58. Andante. Arrangé pour Orgue-Harmonium avec Accompagnement de Quatuor par A. Le Beau. [1870.] fol. [*La Musique Populaire*.]
                    H. 2349. (2.)

— *See* BIZET (A. C. L.) L'Arlésienne ... Menuet, transcrit (par) A. Le Beau. [1890.] fol.   **h. 3281. w. (38.)**

— *See* BOCCHERINI (L.) [Quintetts. Op. 13. No. 5.] Menuetto ... Duo pour Orgue et Piano par A. Lebeau. [1875.] fol.
                    h. 2575. g. (6.)

— *See* CONCONE (G.) Vade Mecum des Chapelles Versets ... extraits des œuvres de J. Concone ... par A. Le Beau. [1873.] 8°.   **f. 117.**

— *See* GOUNOD (C. F.) Le Bal d'Enfants ... (Transcription à 4 mains par A. Le Beau.) [1886.] fol.   **h. 80. f. (3.)**

— *See* GOUNOD (C. F.) Chant national ... Transcription ... par A. Lebeau. [1878.] fol.   **h. 80. c. (11.)**

— *See* GOUNOD (C. F.) Chant National ... Transcription ... par A. Le Beau. [1881.] fol.   **h. 3275. g. (26.)**

— *See* GOUNOD (C. F.) Menuet pour piano. (Transcription ... par A. Le Beau.) [1886.] fol.   **h. 80. f. (1.)**

— *See* GOUNOD (C. F.) Musette ... (Transcription à 4 mains par A. Le Beau.) [1886.] fol.   **h. 80. f. (7.)**

— *See* GOUNOD (C. F.) Royal-Menuet ... (Transcription à 4 mains par A. Le Beau.) [1886.] fol.   **h. 80. f. (9.)**

— *See* HERMAN (A.) and LEBEAU (A.) Lucie de Lammermoor. Grand trio, *etc.* [1881.] fol.   **h. 2850. m. (4.)**

— *See* VERDI (F. G. F.) Messa da Requiem ... Riduzione ... di A. Lebeau. [1878.] 8°.   **F. 369. c.**

LEBEAU (ALFRED)

— *See* VERDI (F. G. F.) Messe de Requiem ... Réduction pour Orgue par A. Lebeau. [1874.] fol.   **h. 1492. a.**

— *See* VERDI (F. G. F.) [Messa da Requiem.] Requiem ... Transcription for Orgue-Harmonium ... by A. Lebeau. [1875.] fol.   **h. 1492. e.**

— *See* VERDI (F. G. F.) [Messa da Requiem.] Requiem. Transcriptions pour Orgue seul par A. Lebeau. [1875.] fol.
                    h. 1492. h. (7.)

LEBEAU (AUGUSTE)

— Trois Mélodies enfantines. Paroles de M. Spenner. 3 no. *Paris*, [1866.] fol.   **H. 1774. e. (20.)**

— *See* GOUNOD (C. F.) La Cigale et la Fourmi ... Reduction à 3 voix par A. Lebeau. [1868.] 8°.   **E. 600. a. (22.)**

— *See* HYMNS. [*French*.] 80 Cantiques anciens ... avec accompagnement d'orgue ... par ... A. Lebeau, *etc.* [1886.] 8°.   **F. 322. a. (2.)**

LEBEAU (FRÉDÉRIC)

— La Cloche du Matin, morceau de salon pour Piano. *Offenbach s. M.*, [1866.] fol.   **h. 1462. r. (23.)**

— Ne m'oubliez pas! Mélodie pour le Piano. *Offenbach s. M.*, [1865.] fol.   **h. 1462. r. (21.)**

— La Pluie d'Or, mazurka de Salon pour Piano. *Offenbach s. M.*, [1866.] fol.   **h. 1462. r. (22.)**

LEBEAU (H.)

— La Charmante, polka-mazurka. *See* ETINCELLES. Les Etincelles, *etc.* No. 3. [1854.] fol.   **h. 526. (4.)**

— La Gentille, polka. *See* ETINCELLES. Les Etincelles, *etc.* No. 2. [1854.] fol.   **h. 526. (4.)**

LE BEAU (LUISE ADOLPHA)

— Even-Song. *See* TRIOS. Popular Trios for Ladies' Voices. No. 11. [1882.] 8°.   **F. 1623. a. (7.)**

— Gavotte für Clavier. Op. 32. *Hamburg*, [1885.] fol.
                    h. 3280. k. (37.)

— Gavotte. [Violoncello and P. F.] *See* infra: Vier Stücke ... Op. 24. No. 2.

— Improvisata. Clavierstudie für die linke Hand allein. Op. 30. *Hamburg*, [1885.] fol.   **h. 3280. k. (36.)**

— Drei Lieder für eine Sopranstimme mit Klavierbegleitung. *Berlin*, [1880.] fol.   **H. 1786. e. (20.)**

— Mazurka. [Violoncello and P. F.] *See* infra: Vier Stücke ... Op. 24. No. 4.

— Quartett für Klavier, Violine, Viola und Violoncell ... Op. 28. *Leipzig und Brüssel*, [1884.] fol.   **h. 2831. b. (4.)**

— Romanze. [Violoncello and P. F.] *See* infra: Vier Stücke ... Op. 24. No. 1.

— Ruth. Biblische Scenen, gedichtet von R. Músiol, für Soli, Chor und Orchester.—Bible Scenes, words ... translated by E. Brock ... Op. 27. Clavierauszug mit Text. *Leipzig*, [1885.] 8°.   **F. 1284.**

— Drei Stücke für Viola mit Clavierbegleitung zum Concertgebrauch. Op. 26. 3 no. *Leipzig*, [1884.] fol.
                    h. 1785. a. (8.)

— Vier Stücke für Violoncell mit Clavierbegleitung. Op. 24. *Leipzig u. Winterthur*, 1882. fol.   **h. 1847. d. (18.)**

LE BEAU (LUISE ADOLPHA)

— Wiegenlied. [Violoncello and P. F.] *See supra*: Vier Stücke ...
Op. 24. No. 3.

LEBEDEV (A.)

— Konzert für Tuba und Klavier. [Score and part.] 2 pt.
Friedrich Hofmeister: Leipzig, [1954.] 4°. **g. 1110. d. (10.)**

LEBEDEV (K.)

— *See* RAKHMANINOV (Sergei V.) Колокола ... Переложение для
пения с фортепиано в четыре руки К. Лебедева. 1973. 4°.
G. 1433. b.

LEBEDINETS (ANTON DMITRIEVICH)

— Державний гімн Української Радянської Соціалістичної
Республіки. Музика групи композиторів під керівництвом
А. Д. Лебединця. Партитура. Для симфонічного оркестру.
pp. 7. *Державне видавництво "Мистецтво": Київ*, 1954.
4°. **g. 822. p. (10.)**

LEBEDINSKY (LEV NIKOLAEVICH)

— Башкирские народные песни и наигрыши. Под общей
редакцией С. В. Аксюка. pp. 249. *Советский композитор:
Москва*, 1962. 8°. **E. 878. b.**

LEBEDJEW (A.)

— *See* LEBEDEV.

LE BÈGUE (NICOLAS ANTOINE)

— Œuvres complètes d'orgue. ⟨[Edited by] Alexandre Guilmant
avec la collaboration de André Pirro.⟩ [With a facsimile.]
pp. xxi. 295. *A. Durand et fils: Paris*, 1909. fol.
[*Archives des maîtres de l'orgue. vol. 9.*] **h. 2699.**

— Chacone grave. *See infra*: [Pièces de clavessin. Liv. 2.—Suite
in G major.]

— Fugue. [Organ.] *See* AUSWAHL. Auswahl vorzüglicher
Musik-Werke ... No. 48. 1841. 8°. **E. 1691.**

— Premier Liure des Pieces d'Orgues ... avec les Varietez, les
agréements, et la maniere de toucher l'Orgue aprésant Sur
tous les Jeux, *etc. Chez le Sieur Lesclop:* [*Paris*, 1676?] *obl.*
fol. **K. 10. a. 13.**

— Second liure d'orgue ... Contenant des pieces courtes et
faciles sur les huit tons de l'eglise et la messe des festes
solemnelles. Gravées ... par feu P. Baillon, et reueues
exactement par l'auteur. pp. 89. *Se vend ... chez la veufue
Baillon: Paris*, [c. 1680.] *obl.* 4°.
Imperfect; wanting pp. 3, 4, supplied in photographic facsimile.
K. 11. e. 5.

— [Second livre d'orgue.] Messe pour orgue. ⟨Transcription et
registration par N. Pierront.⟩ *In*: MASSES. Deux grand' messes.
N. Le Bègue. G. Litaize. pp. 3–15. [1956.] 4°. **h. 2733. n. (1.)**

— [Troisieme liure d'orgue ... Contenant des grandes offertoires
et des eleuations; et tous les noëls les plus connus, des
symphonies et les cloches que l'on peut joüer sur l'orgue et le
clauecin, grauez par le Sieur de Baussen.] pp. 120. *Paris*,
[c. 1685.] *obl.* 4°.
*Imperfect; wanting the titlepage, supplied in photographic
facsimile.* **K. 11. e. 6.**

Pièces de clavessin

— Pieces pour le Clavecin ... par ... A. Le Bègue, *etc. See*
FARRENC (J. H. A.) Le Trésor du Pianiste, *etc.* Livr. xx.
1861–72. fol. **h. 26.**

LE BÈGUE (NICOLAS ANTOINE)

— [Liv. 1, 2.] Œuvres de clavecin. Publiées par Norbert
Dufourcq. pp. 91. *Éditions de l'oiseau-lyre: Monaco*, [1956.]
4°. **g. 1126. r. (6.)**

— Les Pièces de Clauessin composées par Mr. le Begue, *etc.
Chez le S*ʳ *Baillon: Paris*, 1677. *obl.* fol. **K. 10. a. 14.**

— Second Livre de Clavessin, *etc. Chez le Sieur Lesclop: Paris*,
[1680?] *obl.* fol. **K. 10. a. 15.**

— [Liv. 2.—Suite in G major.] Chacone grave. Mise au jour par
Paul Brunold. [P. F.] pp. 4. *Éditions Maurice Senart: Paris*,
[1921.] fol.
Part of "Les Maîtres français du clavecin des XVII*ᵐᵉ et* XVIII*ᵐᵉ
siecles".* **h. 722. ww. (7.)**

— Deux Préludes pour orgue. [1857.] *See* NIEDERMEYER (L.) La
Maîtrise, *etc.* 1ᵉ Année. No. 12. [1857–61.] fol. **H. 1237.**

LE BEL ( )

— Les Récréations d'Apollon, ou les quatuors concertants à
deux violons, alto et basse. Contenant les airs des opéra
comique de Tomjones [*sic*], Lucile, Rose et Colas. Avec
l'ouverture de chaque piece ... Œuvre ɪ. [Parts.] 4 pt. *Chez
M. De la Chevardière: Paris*, [c. 1775.] fol. **h. 2801. k. (1.)**

— ɪɪᵉ recueil d'airs en quatuor choisis dans les opéra comiques
du Huron, l'Isle sonante, et l'Amant déguisé. Avec
l'ouverture de chaque piece ... Œuvre ɪɪᵉ. Gravé par le Sʳ
Huguet. [Parts.] 4 pt. *Ches M. De la Chevardière: Paris*,
[c. 1775.] fol. **h. 2801. k. (2.)**

— ɪɪɪᵉ recueil d'airs en quatuor choisis dans les opéra
d'Ernelinde, du Déserteur, et du Roi et le fermier. Avec
l'ouverture de chaque piece ... Œuvre ɪɪɪᵉ ... Gravé par le Sʳ
Huguet. [Parts.] 4 pt. *Chés M. De la Chevardière: Paris*,
[c. 1775.] fol. **h. 2801. k. (3.)**

— ɪvᵉ recueil d'airs en quatuor choisis dans les opéra de Silvain,
du Sorcier, et du Tableau parlant. Avec l'ouverture de
chaque piece ... Œuvre ɪv. [Parts.] 4 pt. *Chés M. De la
Chevardière: Paris*, [c. 1775.] fol. **h. 2801. k. (4.)**

— v.ᵗ [*sic*] recueil d'airs en quatuor choisis dans les opéra
comiques de Zémire et Azor et de l'Ami de la maison. Avec
l'ouverture de chaque piece ... Œuvre v. [Parts.] 4 pt. *Chés
M. De la Chevardière: Paris*, [c. 1775.] fol. **h. 2801. k. (5.)**

LEBEL (LOUIS BON)

— Lœtitia, caprice original pour Piano. *Paris*, [1870.] fol.
h. 1462. r. (24.)

— Marche triomphale pour Piano. *Paris*, [1870.] fol.
h. 1462. r. (25.)

LEBELL (LUDWIG)

— Aria, for violoncello & piano. Op. 20. No. 1. *Augener:
London*, 1922. 4°. **g. 510. g. (16.)**

— Arias and Songs from the 17th and 18th Centuries. Edited
and set [with accompaniment] for Strings [and P. F.] by
L. Lebell, *etc.* [Score and parts.] 20 no. 100 pt. *Stainer & Bell:
London*, [1925–28.] 4° & 8°. **G. 1190.**

— Caprice, for violoncello & piano. Op. 19. *Augener: London*,
1922. 4°. **g. 510. g. (17.)**

— Kol Nidrei, for Violin and Piano. *E. Ashdown: London*,
1912. fol. **g. 505. ee. (36.)**

— 4 Miniatures in the first position for violoncello and piano
... Op. 10. No. 1. Méditation ... No. 2. Gavotte gracieuse ...
No. 3. Menuet ... No. 4. Legende, *etc.* 4 no. *Augener:
London*, 1914. fol. **h. 1851. i. (44.)**

LEBELL (LUDWIG)

— Notturno, for violoncello & piano. Op. 20. No. 2. *Augener: London*, 1922. 4°.   **g. 510. g. (18.)**

— Papillons, pour Violon et Piano, *etc.* (Op. 9.) *E. Ashdown: London, etc.* 1912. fol.   **g. 505. ee. (37.)**

— 3 Pièces pour Violoncelle et Piano. Op. 7. No. 1. Mélodie. No. 2. Marche Miniature. No. 3. Menuet Rococo. 3 no. *Laudy & Co.: London*, (1910.) fol.   **h. 1851. f. (1.)**

— 4 Pieces ... for violoncello and piano. Op. 12. No. 1. Chant ... No. 2. Capriccio ... No. 3. Humoresque ... No. 4. Intermezzo. 4 no. *Augener: London*, 1919. 4°.   **g. 514. o. (12.)**

— Four Pieces ... for Violoncello & Piano. Op. 28. 1. Capriccio. 2. Saltarello. 3. Humoresque. 4. Soiree de Vienne. 4 no. *Augener: London*, 1925. 4°.   **g. 514. q. (10.)**

— Cinq Pièces mélodiques pour violon avec accomp. de piano. Op. 17. No. 1. Idylle. 2. Menuet. 3. Sérénade. 4. Gavotte. 5. Humoresque. 5 no. *Schott & Co.: London*, 1922. fol.   **h. 1613. e. (11.)**

— Polonaise in D minor, for violoncello & piano. Op. 11. *Augener: London*, 1922. 4°.   **g. 510. g. (20.)**

— Preparatory Bowing and Finger Exercises for the Violoncello. Op. 23a. *J. Williams: London*, 1925. 4°.   **g. 514. q. (1.)**

— Shockheaded Peter. [P. F.] *Oxford University Press: London*, 1928. 4°.
[*The Oxford Piano Series. No.* 113.]   **g. 1231.**

— Three Short and easy Pieces for Violoncello ... and Piano. Op. 21. No. 1. Idyll. 2. Humoresque. 3. Menuet. *Schott & Co.: London*, 1923. fol.   **h. 1851. k. (13.)**

— Four Short Pieces for Violoncello & Piano. Op. 24. 1. Couplet. 2. Saltarello. 3. Serenata. 4. Buccolica. 4 no. *Augener: London*, 1925. 4°.   **g. 510. i. (33.)**

— Three Short Pieces ... for Violoncello & Piano. Op. 29, *etc. Augener: London*, 1925. 4°.   **g. 154. q. (11.)**

— Spanish Serenade, Op. 30, for Violoncello & Piano. *Augener: London*, 1928. 4°.   **g. 514. r. (13.)**

— 42 Studies and Exercises for the Violoncello. Op. 23, *etc.* 2 bk. *J. Williams: London*, 1925, 26. 4°.   **g. 514. q. (2.)**

— Suite miniature pour violoncello et piano. Op. 8. 2 bk. *Laudy & Co.: London*, 1914. fol.   **h. 1851. i. (43.)**

— The Technique of the Lower Positions for Violoncello. Op. 22. 2 bk. *Schott & Co.: London*, 1923, 25. 4°.   **g. 514. p. (8.)**

— Eight Very easy Pieces for violoncello ... and pianoforte. Op. 16. *Schott & Co.: London*, 1921. 4°.   **g. 510. g. (19.)**

— *See* ALBERT (H.) [Dritter Theil der Arien.—Junges Volck man ruffet euch.] Come and join our merry Throng ... Edited ... by L. Lebell, *etc.* 1927. 8°. [*Choral Library. No.* 232.]   **F. 1137. d.**

— *See* ARNE (T. A.) [*Collections, Instrumental.*] A Suite of three Pieces from the Works of T. A. Arne. Arranged for String Orchestra by L. Lebell, *etc.* 1944. 4°. [*Oxford Orchestral Series. No.* 132.]   **g. 1263.**

— *See* ARNE (T. A.) [Artaxerxes.] Water parted from the Sea ... Edited by L. Lebell, *etc.* [1931.] 8°. [*Unison Songs. No.* 90.]   **F. 1137. e.**

— *See* BACH (J. S.) [Ich habe genug.—Schlummert ein, ihr matten Augen.] In thy Love I find Content ... Arranged by L. Lebell. 1942. 4°.   **g. 548. pp. (14.)**

LEBELL (LUDWIG)

— *See* BACH (J. S.) Sonata in G major [B. G. Jahrg. 9. p. 260] for Two Flutes and Pianoforte ... Transcribed and edited by H. Geehl and L. Lebell. 1946. 4°.   **g. 548. ss. (20.)**

— *See* DUNKLER (E.) Ballade, *etc.* (Revue ... par L. Lebell.) (1910.) fol.   **h. 1869. (1.)**

— *See* DUNKLER (E.) Berceuse, *etc.* (Revue ... par L. Lebell.) (1910.) fol.   **h. 1869. (3.)**

— *See* DUNKLER (E.) Caprice Hongroise, *etc.* (Revue ... par L. Lebell.) (1910.) fol.   **h. 1869. (6.)**

— *See* DUNKLER (E.) Chanson à boire, *etc.* (Revue ... par L. Lebell.) (1910.) fol.   **h. 1869. (7.)**

— *See* DUNKLER (E.) Danse Hollandaise, *etc.* (Revue ... par L. Lebell.) (1910.) fol.   **h. 1869. (2.)**

— *See* DUNKLER (E.) La Fileuse, *etc.* (Revue ... par L. Lebell.) (1910.) fol.   **h. 1869. (4.)**

— *See* DUNKLER (E.) Une Larme, *etc.* (Revue ... par L. Lebell.) (1910.) fol.   **h. 1869. (9.)**

— *See* DUNKLER (E.) Rêverie, *etc.* (Revue ... par L. Lebell.) (1910.) fol.   **h. 1869. (8.)**

— *See* DUNKLER (E.) Tarantelle, *etc.* (Revue ... par L. Lebell.) (1910.) fol.   **h. 1869. (5.)**

— *See* HAENDEL (G. F.) [Susanna.] Ask if yon Damask Rose ... Edited by L. Lebell. 1925. 8°. [*Unison Songs. No.* 89.]   **F. 1137. e.**

— *See* HUMPHRIES (J.) [XII Concertos. Op. 2. No. 9.] Concerto for Strings ... Edited by L. Lebell. 1927. 4°. [*Oxford Orchestral Series. No.* 33.]   **g. 1263.**

— *See* LASSO (O. di) [Libro de Villanelle.—O occhi, manza mia.] Sweet Maiden ... Edited by L. Lebell, *etc.* 1927. 8°. [*Stainer & Bell's Choral Library, No.* 235.]   **F. 1137. d.**

— *See* LASSO (O. di) [*Doubtful and Supposititious Works.*] [Mon cœur se recommande à vous.] Take my Heart into your Care ... Edited ... by L. Lebell. 1927. 8°. [*Stainer & Bell's Choral Library. No.* 234.]   **F. 1137. d.**

— *See* LEE (S.) First Steps in Violoncello Playing ... Op. 101. (Revised by L. Lebell.) 1920. 4°.   **g. 514. p. (1.)**

— *See* LEE (S.) Twenty Studies. Op. 92, 76 & 105. (Edited by L. Lebell.) 1917. 4°.   **g. 510. f. (8*.)**

— *See* PURCELL (H.) [The Libertine.] In these delightful, pleasant Groves. Edited ... by L. Lebell, *etc.* 1927. 8°. [*Choral Library. No.* 233.]   **F. 1137. d.**

— *See* ROMBERG (B. H.) Concertino ... Op. 51. Edited by L. Lebell. 1920. 4°.   **g. 514. o. (22.)**

— *See* SCARLATTI (D.) [*Collections.*] Four Arias ... Edited by L. Lebell, *etc.* 1927. 8°.   **E. 1830. (36.)**

— *See* SCHUMANN (R. A.) [Phantasiestücke. Op. 88. No. 3.] Duett ... Arranged by L. Lebell. 1941. 4°.   **g. 715. m. (7.)**

LEBEN

— Das Leben. Symphonisches Chorwerk. *See* MESSNER (J.)

— Das Leben am Rhein. [Song.] *See* ZWING (M.)

— Leben des Orest. Grosse Oper. *See* KŘENEK (E.)

— Leben in dieser Zeit. Lyrische Suite. *See* NICK (E.)

— Das Leben ist der schwule Tag. [Song.] *See* HEIDINGSFELD (L.) Zwei Lieder. Op. 4. No. 1.

— Das Leben ist ein Possenspiel. Aria. *See* BIEREY (G. B.) [Das Donauweibchen.]

LEBEN

— Leben ohne Liebe. Lied. *See* Varlamov (A. E.)

— Leben und Bestehen. Kantate. *See* Schroeder (H.) *Professor at the Musikhochschule, Cologne.*

— Leben wir so leben wir dem Herrn. Motette. *See* Schurig (V.)

LEBENDIG

— Lebendig begraben. Gesänge. *See* Schoeck (O.)

LEBENDORF (Nicolaus Schmall von)

— Skladby z tabulaturového sborníku pro loutnu z r. 1613. Kompositionen aus der Tabulaturensammlung für Laute aus d. J. 1613. *In:* Jirmal (J.) Česká a slovenská kytarová a loutnová hudba, *etc.* pp. 6–19. 1971. 4°.   **g. 660. uu. (14.)**

LEBENS

— Des Lebens Frühling ist dahin. [Song.] *See* Erseev (   )

— Des Lebens Mai. Lied. *See* Uschmann (C.)

— Des Lebens Sonnenschein. [Part-song.] *See* Haas (J.) Hymnen an den Frohsinn. Opus 73. No. 1.

LEBENSANSICHT

— Lebensansicht. [Song.] *See* Weber (C. M. F. E. von)

LEBENSBUCH

— Das Lebensbuch Gottes. Oratorium. *See* Haas (J.)

LEBENSFESTE

— Lebensfeste. Zyklus von vier Gesängen. *See* Vycpálek (L.) Slavnosti života.

LEBENS-GENUSS

— Lebens-Genuss. [Song.] *See* Beethoven (L. van) [Vier Arietten und ein Duett. Op. 82. No. 5. Lebens-Genuss.]

LEBENSGLUECK

— Lebensglück. [Song.] *See* Beethoven (L. van) [Das Glück der Freundschaft. Op. 88.]

LEBENSLICHT

— Das Lebenslicht. [Opera.] *See* Knab (A.)

LEBENSLIED

— Lebenslied. [Song.] *See* Lassen (E.) Sechs Lieder. Op. 67. No. 5.

— Lebenslied. Eine Frühlings-Cantate. *See* Scholz (B.)

— Lebenslied am Geburtstage. [Four-part song.] *See* Weber (C. M.F. E. von)

LEBENSLUST

— Lebenslust. [Part-song.] *See* Lachner (F.) Vier Gesänge, *etc.* Op. 186. No. 3.

LEBENSMUEDE

— Der Lebensmüde an den Tod. [Song.] *See* Schmelz (Philipp)

LEBENSUEBERFLUSS

— Lebensüberfluss. [Song.] *See* Taubert (E. E.) 6 Gesänge. Op. 19. No. 5.

LEBENSWEG

— Lebensweg. [Song.] *See* Jarnach (Philipp) Zwei Lieder ... Op. 7. N° 2.

LEBER (Auguste)

— Alsace, élégie pour Piano. *Paris,* [1878.] fol.
    h. 1493. n. (24.)

LEBERMANN (Walter)

— Flöten-Konzerte der Mannheimer Schule. Herausgegeben von W. Lebermann. pp. 124. *Breitkopf & Härtel: Wiesbaden,* fol.
[*Das Erbe deutscher Musik. Bd.* 51.]   **H. 995. b.**

— *See* Bach (C. P. E.) Sinfonie A-dur ... für Streichorchester. Wotquenne 184,4. Herausgegeben von W. Lebermann, *etc.* [1970.] 4°.   **g. 48. q. (6.)**

— *See* Bach (C. P. E.) Sinfonie G-Dur ... für Streichorchester. Wotquenne 182, 1 (1773). Herausgegeben von W. Lebermann, *etc.* [1970.] 4°.   **g. 48. q. (5.)**

— *See* Bach (Johann C.) Sinfonie D-Dur ... [Terry p. 283.] Herausgegeben von W. Lebermann, *etc.* [1976.] 4°.
    g. 435. d. (1.)

— *See* Bach (W. F.) Adagio und Fuge d-Moll ... für 2 Querflöten und Streicher ... Herausgegeben von W. Lebermann, *etc.* [1971.] 4°.   **g. 934. r. (4.)**

— *See* Bach (W. F.) Sinfonie D-Dur ... Falck 64 ... Herausgegeben von W. Lebermann, *etc.* [1971.] 4°.
    g. 860. z. (6.)

— *See* Bach (W. F.) Sinfonie D-Dur (Falck 67). Herausgegeben von W. Lebermann, *etc.* [1973.] 4°.   **g. 934. hh. (1.)**

— *See* Benda (Franz) Konzert e-Moll ... für Flöte und Streichorchester ... Erstmals herausgegeben und mit Kadenzen versehen von W. Lebermann, *etc.* [1969.] 4°.
    g. 1067. u. (2.)

— *See* Benda (Franz) Konzert e-Moll ... für Flöte und Streichorchester. Generalbass ad lib. Erstmals herausgegeben und mit Kadenzen versehen von W. Lebermann. Klavierauszug, *etc.* [1969.] 4°.   **g. 70. pp. (4.)**

— *See* Benda (G.) Konzert F-Dur ... für Viola und Streicher mit Cembalo ... Erstmals herausgegeben und mit Kadenzen versehen von W. Lebermann. Partitur, *etc.* [1968.] 4°.
    g. 934. (11.)

— *See* Benda (G.) Konzert F-Dur ... für Viola und Streicher mit Cembalo ... Erstmals herausgegeben und mit Kadenzen versehen von W. Lebermann. Klavierauszug, *etc.* [1968.] 4°.
    g. 762. ẇ. (6.)

— *See* Biber (Heinrich I. F.) Passacaglia C-moll für Viola. Herausgegeben von W. Lebermann. [1975.] 4°.
    g. 762. dd. (4.)

— *See* Boccherini (L.) [Concertos. Violoncello. G. 477.] Konzert No. 1 C-Dur ... für Violoncello und Streichorchester ... Herausgegeben und mit Kadenzen versehen von W. Lebermann. Partitur, *etc.* [1968.] 4°.   **h. 42. z. (9.)**

— *See* Boccherini (L.) [Concertos. Violoncello. G. 477.] Konzert No. 1 C-Dur ... für Violoncello und Streichorchester ... Herausgegeben und mit Kadenzen versehen von W. Lebermann. Klavierauszug, *etc.* [1968.] 4°.   **h. 42. z. (7.)**

LEBERMANN (Walter)

— *See* BOCCHERINI (L.) [Concertos. Violoncello. G. 479.] Konzert No. 2 D-Dur ... für Violoncello und Streichorchester. Herausgegeben und mit Kadenzen versehen von W. Lebermann. Partitur, *etc.* [1973.] 4°. **h. 42. ii. (3.)**

— *See* BOCCHERINI (L.) [Concertos. Violoncello. G. 479.] Konzert No. 2 D-Dur ... für Violoncello und Streichorchester. Herausgegeben und mit Kadenzen versehen von W. Lebermann. Klavierauszug, *etc.* [1973.] 4°. **h. 42. ii. (2.)**

— *See* BOCCHERINI (L.) [Concertos. Violoncello. G. 480.] Konzert No. 3. G-Dur ... WV 480. Für Violoncello und Streichorchester. Herausgegeben und mit Kadenzen versehen von W. Lebermann, *etc.* [1970.] 4°. **h. 42. gg. (3.)**

— *See* BOCCHERINI (L.) [Concertos. Violoncello. G. 481.] Konzert No. 4 für Violoncello und Klavier C-Dur. Klavierauszug mit Kadenzen versehen von W. Lebermann. [1974.] 4°. **h. 42. ii. (4.)**

— *See* BOCCHERINI (L.) [Quintets. Op. 45. No. 1–3.] Quintette für Oboe, zwei Violinen, Viola und Violoncello ... Herausgegeben von W. Lebermann, *etc.* [1967.] 4°. **h. 42. z. (4.)**

— *See* BOCCHERINI (L.) [Quintets. Op. 45. No. 1–3.] Quintette für Oboe, zwei Violinen, Viola und Violoncello ... Herausgegeben von W. Lebermann. Studienpartitur. [1968.] 8°. **c. 160. dd. (15.)**

— *See* BOCCHERINI (L.) Quintette für Oboe, zwei Violinen, Viola und Violoncello. Opus 45. Nr. 1–3. Herausgegeben von W. Lebermann, *etc.* [1968.] 8°. [*Edition Eulenburg. no.* 209.] **b. 212.**

— *See* BOCCHERINI (L.) [Première symphonie à quatre parties obligés. G. 500.] Sinfonie D-Dur ... für Streichorchester und zwei Hörner in D ad lib. Herausgegeben von W. Lebermann, *etc.* [1968.] 4°. **h. 42. z. (6.)**

— *See* BRIXI (F. X.) Konzert C-Dur ... für Viola und Orchester. Erstmals herausgegeben und mit Kadenzen versehen von W. Lebermann. Klavierauszug, *etc.* [1970.] 4°. **g. 762. v. (7.)**

— *See* BURGMUELLER (N.) Duo Es-dur ... für Klarinette und Klavier. Opus 15. Herausgegeben von W. Lebermann. [1970.] 4°. **g. 421. nn. (2.)**

— *See* CAMBINI (G. M. G.) Duo A-Dur ⟨G-Dur⟩ ... für zwei Querflöten. Opus 11. No. 5 ⟨6⟩. Herausgegeben von W. Lebermann. [1968.] 4°. **g. 70. ll. (1.)**

— *See* CAMBINI (G. M. G.) Duo e-Moll ... für zwei Querflöten. Opus 11. Nr. 4. Herausgegeben von W. Lebermann. [1967.] 4°. **g. 70. ll. (2.)**

— *See* DANZI (I.) Konzert für Violoncello und Orchester G-Dur ... Herausgegeben von W. Lebermann ... Ausgabe für Violoncello und Klavier von Hans Feldigl. [1969.] 4°. **g. 512. i. (4.)**

— *See* DEVIENNE (F.) [3 duos concertants. Op. 67.] Duos für zwei Klarinetten. Opus 69. Herausgegeben von W. Lebermann, *etc.* [1968.] 4°. **g. 421. mm. (8.)**

— *See* DITTERS VON DITTERSDORF (C.) Konzert in F-dur für Viola und Orchester. Erstmals herausgegeben von W. Lebermann, *etc.* [1959.] 4°. **g. 762. p. (6.)**

— *See* DITTERS VON DITTERSDORF (C.) Konzert in F-Dur für Viola und Orchester ... herausgegeben von W. Lebermann. Orchester-Partitur, *etc.* [1966.] 4°. **g. 1620. vv. (3.)**

— *See* DITTERS VON DITTERSDORF (C.) Konzert in C-dur. Krebs, Them. Verz. 157 ... für Violine und Streichorchester. Erstmals herausgegeben von W. Lebermann, *etc.* [1961.] 4°. **g. 500. pp. (10.)**

LEBERMANN (Walter)

— *See* DITTERS VON DITTERSDORF (C.) Konzert C-dur ... für Violine und Streichorchester. (Krebs, Them. Verz. 158.) Erstmalig veröffentlicht und mit Kadenzen versehen von W. Lebermann. Ausgabe für Violine und Klavier. (Viktor Kreiner.) [1963.] 4°. **g. 223. nn. (9.)**

— *See* DITTERS VON DITTERSDORF (C.) Konzert C-Dur ... für Violine und Streichorchester ... Erstmals herausgegeben und mit Kadenzen versehen von W. Lebermann, *etc.* [1970.] 4°. **g. 1067. ee. (6.)**

— *See* DITTERS VON DITTERSDORF (C.) Violinkonzert G-dur. Herausgegeben von W. Lebermann. [1963.] 4°. **g. 420. vv. (4.)**

— *See* DITTERS VON DITTERSDORF (C.) Divertimento für Violine, Viola und Violoncello. Krebs 131. Herausgegeben von W. Lebermann. [1969.] 4°. **g. 1067. x. (5.)**

— *See* DITTERS VON DITTERSDORF (C.) Duo Es-Dur ... für Viola und Violoncello. Krebs 218. Erstmals herausgegeben von W. Lebermann. [1968.] 4°. **g. 1780. ff. (6.)**

— *See* DITTERS VON DITTERSDORF (C.) Sinfonie D-Dur ... Herausgegeben von W. Lebermann, *etc.* [1970.] 4°. **g. 860. z. (3.)**

— *See* GABRIELI (A.) [Madrigali et ricercari a quattro voci.] Ricercari a quattro Nos. II, III e V ... Herausgegeben von W. Lebermann, *etc.* [1977.] 4°. **g. 1655. c. (6.)**

— *See* GABRIELI (A.) [Madrigali et ricercari a quattro voci.] Ricercari a quattro Nos. VI e VII. Für Sopran-, Alt-, Tenor- und Bassblockflöte ... Herausgegeben von W. Lebermann, *etc.* [1972.] 4°. **g. 109. oo. (6.)**

— *See* GABRIELI (A.) [Madrigali et ricercari a quattro voci.] Ricercari a quattro Nos. VI e VII. Für zwei Violinen, Viola und Violoncello ... Herausgegeben von W. Lebermann, *etc.* [1973.] 4°. **g. 410. ii. (7.)**

— *See* GEMINIANI (Francesco) Adagio e fuga Es-dur für Viola ... herausgegeben von W. Lebermann. [1974.] 4°. **g. 38. g. (2.)**

— *See* GIORNOVICHI (G. M.) Konzert Nr. 1 in A-dur für Violine und Orchester (1773). Herausgegeben von W. Lebermann. Dirigier-Klavierauszug von B. Weigart, *etc.* [1962.] 4°. **g. 223. hh. (7.)**

— *See* GIORNOVICHI (G. M.) Konzert für Violine und Orchester Nr. 4 A-Dur ... Herausgegeben von W. Lebermann. [1968.] 4°. **g. 1620. yy. (7.)**

— *See* GIORNOVICHI (G. M.) Konzert für Violine und Orchester Nr. 4 A-Dur. Herausgegeben von W. Lebermann. Ausgabe für Violine und Klavier von H. Feldigl. [1968.] 4°. **g. 500. uu. (8.)**

— *See* GRAUN (Johann G.) Konzert Es-dur für Viola und Streicher ... ⟨Herausgegeben und bearbeitet von W. Lebermann.⟩ Klavierauszug, *etc.* [1976.] 4°. **g. 420. ss. (12.)**

— *See* HAYDN (F. J.) [6 Sonatas for violin and viola. Hob. VI.] Sechs Sonaten für Violine und Viola ... Herausgegeben und mit Kadenzen versehen von W. Lebermann. [1970.] 4°. **g. 75. o. (9.)**

— *See* HOFFSTETTER (R.) Konzert C-Dur ... für Viola, Streicher, 2 Oboen und 2 Hörner. Erstmals herausgegeben und mit Kadenzen versehen von W. Lebermann. Klavierauszug, *etc.* [1971.] 4°. **g. 762. v. (9.)**

— *See* HOFFSTETTER (R.) Konzert C-Dur ... für Viola, Streicher, 2 Oboen und 2 Hörner. Erstmals herausgegeben und mit Kadenzen versehen von W. Lebermann, *etc.* [1972.] 4°. **g. 474. nn. (3.)**

— *See* HOLZBAUER (I.) Konzert d-moll für Oboe und Streicher ... herausgegeben von W. Lebermann. Kadenzen vom Herausgeber. [1974.] 4°. **g. 934. oo. (5.)**

LEBERMANN (Walter)

— *See* Holzbauer (I.) Konzert d-moll für Oboe und Streicher zum ersten Mal herausgegeben von W. Lebermann, *etc.* [1975.] 4°.　　　　　　　　　　　　　**g. 934. oo. (4.)**

— *See* Hummel (J. N.) [Sonatas. Op. 5. No. 3.] Sonate Es-Dur ... für Viola und Klavier ... Herausgegeben von W. Lebermann. [1969.] 4°.　　　　　　　　　　　　　**g. 403. h. (7.)**

— *See* Kraus (J. M.) Konzert für Violine und Orchester ... Revidiert und mit Kadenzen versehen von W. Lebermann, *etc.* [1958.] 4°.　　　　**g. 500. pp. (11.)**

— *See* Kraus (J. M.) Quintett D-dur, *etc.* ⟨Herausgegeben von W. Lebermann.⟩ [1959.] 4°.　　　　**g. 420. ee. (2.)**

— *See* Kraus (J. M.) Trio D-dur, *etc.* ⟨Erstveröffentlichung herausgegeben von W. Lebermann.⟩ [1959.] 4°.　　　　　　　　　　　　　**g. 1000. b. (1.)**

— *See* Lebrun (Ludwig A.) Concerto No. 4. C-dur ... ⟨Herausgegeben von W. Lebermann.⟩ [1964.] 4°.　　　　　　　　　　　　　**g. 1620. nn. (3.)**

— *See* Lebrun (Ludwig A.) Concerto No. 4 C-dur ... für Oboe und Orchester ... Klavierauszug und Solostimme ⟨Kadenzen⟩ ... ⟨⟨Herausgegeben und bearbeitet von⟩ W. Lebermann). [1978.] 4°.　　　**g. 1078. dd. (5.)**

— *See* Nardini (P.) [Concertos. Op. 1. No. 3.] Concerto F-Dur ... für Violine und Streichorchester, zwei Hörner in F ad lib. ... Herausgegeben und mit Kadenzen versehen von W. Lebermann, *etc.* [1968.] 4°.　　　**g. 934. i. (10.)**

— *See* Nardini (P.) [Concertos. Op. 1. No. 3.] Concerto F-Dur ... für Violine und Streichorchester, zwei Hörner in F ad lib ... Herausgegeben und mit Kadenzen versehen von W. Lebermann. Klavierauszug, *etc.* [1968.] 4°.　　　　　　　　　　　　　**g. 223. tt. (6.)**

— *See* Nardini (P.) [Six Duets for two Tenors.] Sechs Duette für Violen. Herausgegeben von W. Lebermann. [1969.] 4°.　　　　　　　　　**g. 218. q. (9.)**

— *See* Offenbach (J.) [6 duos faciles. Op. 50.] Sechs Duos für Violoncelli ... Herausgegeben von W. Lebermann. [1969.] 4°.　　　**g. 512. c. (15.)**

— *See* Offenbach (J.) [3 duos. Op. 51.] Drei Duette für Violoncelli ... Herausgegeben von W. Lebermann. [1970.] 4°.　　　**g. 512. l. (2.)**

— *See* Pergolesi (G. B.) [Sonata per violino "in stile di concerto".] Konzert B-Dur ... für Violine, Streicher und Basso continuo. Herausgegeben von W. Lebermann, *etc.* [1968.] 4°.　　　　　　　　　　　　　**g. 934. i. (7.)**

— *See* Pergolesi (G. B.) [Sonata per violino "in stile di concerto".] Konzert B-Dur ... für Violine, Streicher und Basso continuo. Herausgegeben von W. Lebermann. Klavierauszug von H. May, *etc.* [1968.] 4°.　　**g. 934. i. (4.)**

— *See* Plà (J.) [Six Sonatas. Bk. 1.] Sechs Sonaten für zwei Oboen (Flöten) ... Herausgegeben von W. Lebermann. [1969.] 4°.　　　　　　　　　　　　　**g. 1078. q. (5.)**

— *See* Platti (G. B.) Konzert G-Dur ... für Oboe oder Flöte und Streichorchester ... Herausgegeben von W. Lebermann, *etc.* [1966.] 4°.　　　**h. 1620. tt. (1.)**

— *See* Platti (G. B.) Konzert G-Dur ... für Oboe oder Flöte und Streichorchester. Erstmals herausgegeben von W. Lebermann. Klavierauszug von W. May, *etc.* [1966.] 4°.　　　　　　　　　　　　　**g. 1078. k. (4.)**

— *See* Reicha (A. J.) [Duo. Op. 103.] Sonate D-Dur ... für Flöte und Klavier. Herausgegeben von W. Lebermann. [1968.] 4°.　　　**g. 70. mm. (12.)**

— *See* Reicha (A. J.) Sonate B-Dur ... für Fagott und Klavier. Opus posthumum ... Herausgegeben von W. Lebermann. [1968.] 4°.　　　**g. 1667. (4.)**

LEBERMANN (Walter)

— *See* Richter (F. X.) Sinfonia a quattro C-moll für Streicher. Zum ersten Mal herausgegeben von W. Lebermann, *etc.* [1972.] 4°.　　　**g. 1067. kk. (8.)**

— *See* Ries (F.) Sonate g-Moll ... für Klarinette in B und Klavier. Opus 29. Herausgegeben von W. Lebermann. [1967.] 4°.　　　　**g. 1104. nn. (2.)**

— *See* Ries (F.) [Sonatas. Op. 34.] Sonate F-Dur ... für Horn und Klavier ... Herausgegeben von W. Lebermann. [1969.] 4°.　　　**g. 1094. l. (8.)**

— *See* Rossini (G. A.) [6 Sonatas. No. 1.] Sonata per archi ... G-Dur ... 2 Violinen, Violoncello und Kontrabass ... Herausgegeben von W. Lebermann, *etc.* [1970.] 4°.　　　　　　　　　　　　　**g. 637. c. (8.)**

— *See* Rossini (G. A.) [6 Sonatas. No. 2.] Sonata per archi ... A-Dur ... Herausgegeben von W. Lebermann, *etc.* [1974.] 4°.　　　**g. 637. k. (2.)**

— *See* San Martini (G. B.) Sinfonie A-Dur. [Jenkins. 62A.] ... Erstmals herausgegeben von W. Lebermann, *etc.* [1970.] 4°.　　　**g. 934. p. (4.)**

— *See* Stamitz (A.) 8 Capricen für Flöte. Herausgegeben von W. Lebermann. [1974.] 4°.　　　**g. 280. mm. (10.)**

— *See* Stamitz (A.) Konzert für 2 Flöten in G-Dur und Streichorchester, 2 Oboen und 2 Hörner ad lib. Herausgegeben von W. Lebermann, *etc.* [1967.] 4°.　　　　　　　　　　　　　**g. 934. j. (8.)**

— *See* Stamitz (A.) Konzert für zwei Flöten in G-Dur und Streichorchester ... Herausgegeben von W. Lebermann. Klavierauszug, *etc.* [1967.] 4°.　　　**g. 70. ii. (1.)**

— *See* Stamitz (A.) Konzert für Viola B-dur ... Erstmals herausgegeben und mit Kadenzen versehen von W. Lebermann, *etc.* [1972.] 4°.　　　**g. 1780. vv. (6.)**

— *See* Stamitz (A.) Konzert No. 2. F-dur ... für Viola und Streichorchester (1779). Herausgegeben und mit Kadenzen versehen von W. Lebermann. Partitur, *etc.* [1970.] 4°.　　　　　　　　　　　　　**g. 1620. xx. (3.)**

— *See* Stamitz (A.) Konzert No. 2 F-Dur ... für Viola und Streichorchester (1779). Herausgegeben und mit Kadenzen versehen von W. Lebermann. Klavierauszug (Helmut May), *etc.* [1970.] 4°.　　　**g. 762. x. (12.)**

— *See* Stamitz (A.) Konzert Nr. 4 D-dur für Viola und Streicher ... Herausgegeben mit Kadenzen von ... W. Lebermann, *etc.* [1973.] 4°.　　　**g. 934. hh. (9.)**

— *See* Stamitz (A.) Konzert Nr. 4 D-dur für Viola und Streicher ... Herausgegeben mit Kadenzen von ... W. Lebermann. [1973.] 4°.　　　**g. 934. s. (6.)**

— *See* Stamitz (C.) Konzert für Flöte in G dur mit Streichorchester, 2 Oboen, 2 Hörner ad lib. Opus 29. Herausgegeben von W. Lebermann, *etc.* [1965.] 4°.　　　　　　　　　　　　　**g. 280. w. (11.)**

— *See* Stamitz (C.) Konzert für Flöte in G-Dur ... Opus 29. Herausgegeben von W. Lebermann. Klavierauszug von Helmut May, *etc.* [1966.] 4°.　　**g. 1065. l. (1.)**

— *See* Stamitz (C.) Konzert No. 1 F-Dur ... für Klarinette und Streicher, zwei Oboen und zwei Hörner ad lib. Herausgegeben und mit Kadenzen versehen von W. Lebermann, *etc.* [1972.] 4°.　　**g. 474. nn. (4.)**

— *See* Stamitz (C.) Konzert No. 1 F-Dur ... für Klarinette (B) und Streicher ... Herausgegeben und mit Kadenzen versehen von W. Lebermann. Klavierauszug, *etc.* [1971.] 4°.　　　　　　　　　　　　　**g. 1065. o. (2.)**

— *See* Stamitz (C.) Konzert für zwei Klarinetten und Orchester. B-dur. Herausgegeben von W. Lebermann, *etc.* [1968.] 4°.　　　**g. 1065. n. (6.)**

LEBERMANN (Walter)

— *See* Stamitz (C.) Konzert für zwei Klarinetten und Orchester B-dur. Herausgegeben von W. Lebermann. Ausgabe für zwei Klarinetten und Klavier von Theo Mölich. [1968.] 4°.
g. 1065. n. (5.)

— *See* Stamitz (C.) Drei Duette für zwei Violen ... Herausgegeben und für den Praktischen Gebrauch bearbeitet von W. Lebermann, *etc.* [1955.] 4°.
g. 762. l. (6.)

— *See* Stamitz (C.) Sechs Duette für zwei Violen ... Heft II (4–6). ⟨Erstmals herausgegeben von W. Lebermann.⟩ [1968.] 4°.
g. 1065. n. (2.)

— *See* Stamitz (C.) [2 Duette. Op. 10. No. 1.] Duo C-Dur ... für Violine und Viola. Herausgegeben von W. Lebermann. [1969.] 4°.
g. 1065. n. (4.)

— *See* Stamitz (C.) Sonate B-Dur ... für Viola und Klavier. Herausgegeben von W. Lebermann. [1969.] 4°.
g. 1065. n. (3.)

— *See* Stamitz (C.) [*Doubtful and Supposititious Works.*] Konzert Es-Dur ... für Horn und Streichorchester, zwei Flöten und zwei Hörner. Erstmals herausgegeben von W. Lebermann, *etc.* [1968.] 4°.
g. 1065. l. (5.)

— *See* Stamitz (J. W. A.) Concerto B♭ major. For clarinet and orchestra ... Edited by W. Lebermann, *etc.* [1972.] 8°. [*Edition Eulenburg. no.* 1297.]
b. 212.

— *See* Stamitz (J. W. A.) Konzert für Klarinette B-Dur ... mit Streichorchester und zwei Hörnern. Herausgegeben von W. Lebermann, *etc.* [1967.] 4°.
g. 98. b. (6.)

— *See* Stamitz (J. W. A.) Konzert für Klarinette B-Dur ... mit Streichorchester und zwei Hörnern. Herausgegeben von W. Lebermann, *etc.* ⟨Klavierauszug von H. May.⟩ [1967.] 4°.
g. 98. b. (5.)

— *See* Stamitz (J. W. A.) Concerto D major. For flute and string orchestra ... Edited by W. Lebermann. [1962?] 8°. [*Edition Eulenburg. no.* 1240.]
b. 212.

— *See* Stamitz (J. W. A.) Konzert C-dur ... für Violine und Streichorchester ... veröffentlicht von W. Lebermann, *etc.* [1965.] 4°.
g. 1620. nn. (7.)

— *See* Stamitz (J. W. A.) Konzert für Violine in G-dur mit Streichorchester und 2 Hörnern ad lib. Erstmals herausgegeben von W. Lebermann, *etc.* [1964.] 4°.
g. 1620. r. (8.)

— *See* Sterkel (J. F. X.) [6 duos. Op. 8.] Sechs Duette für Violine und Viola ... Herausgegeben von W. Lebermann. [1969.] 4°.
g. 421. mm. (11.)

— *See* Telemann (G. P.) Konzert G-Dur ... für 2 Violen, Streicher und Basso continuo. Herausgegeben von W. Lebermann, *etc.* [1970.] 4°.
g. 401. w. (2.)

— *See* Telemann (G. P.) Konzert G-Dur ... für 2 Violen, Streicher und Basso continuo. Herausgegeben von W. Lebermann. Klavierauszug, *etc.* [1970.] 4°.
g. 401. w. (1.)

— *See* Telemann (G. P.) [Der getreue Musik Meister.] Suite in G moll für Violine (Oboe) und Basso continuo ... Herausgegeben von ... W. Lebermann, *etc.* [1961.] 4°.
g. 401. i. (1.)

— *See* Toeschi (C. G.) [Duos. Op. 11.] Sechs Duette für Fagotte. Herausgegeben von W. Lebermann, *etc.* [1969.] 4°.
g. 1083. j. (9.)

— *See* Toeschi (C. G.) [Duos. Op. 11.] Sechs Duette für Querflöten. Herausgegeben von W. Lebermann, *etc.* [1969.] 4°.
g. 70. mm. (9.)

— *See* Tromlitz (Johann G.) Sechs Partiten für Flöte. Zum ersten Mal herausgegeben von W. Lebermann. [1976.] 4°.
g. 280. pp. (10.)

LEBERMANN (Walter)

— *See* Viotti (G. B.) Konzert No. 2. E-Dur ... für Violine und Streichorchester ... Herausgegeben von W. Lebermann, *etc.* [1968.] 4°.
g. 1067. t. (5.)

— *See* Viotti (G. B.) Konzert No. 2 E-Dur ... für Violine und Streichorchester; zwei Oboen und zwei Hörner ad lib. Herausgegeben und mit Kadenz versehen von W. Lebermann, *etc.* [1974.] 4°.
g. 422. gg. (7.)

— *See* Vivaldi (A.) [Il Cimentia dell'armonia e dell' inventione. Op. 8. No. 12.] Konzert C-Dur ... für Oboe, Streichorchester und Generalbass ... Herausgegeben von W. Lebermann, *etc.* [1971.] 4°.
g. 33. s. (4.)

— *See* Vivaldi (A.) Concerto ripieno C-Dur ... für Streichorchester und Basso continuo ... [Ryom 114.] Herausgegeben von W. Lebermann, *etc.* [1973.] 4°.
g. 33. t. (2.)

— *See* Vivaldi (A.) Concerto per archi E-Moll ... für Streichorchester und Basso continuo. P-V. 113. [Ryom 133.] Erstmals herausgegeben von W. Lebermann, *etc.* [1970.] 4°.
g. 33. s. (5.)

— *See* Vivaldi (A.) Concerto F-Dur ... für drei Violinen, Streichorchester und Basso continuo ... [Rinaldi Op. 23. No. 1. Ryom 551.] Herausgegeben von W. Lebermann, *etc.* [1969.] 4°.
g. 33. q. (2.)

— *See* Vivaldi (A.) Concerto F-dur ... RV 551. [Rinaldi. Op. 23. No. 1.] Herausgegeben von W. Lebermann. Klavierauszug, *etc.* [1975.] 4°.
g. 33. x. (3.)

LEBERT (Sigmund)

— Instructive Ausgabe Klassischer Klavierwerke. Unter Mitwirkung von H. von Bülow, I. Faisst, I. Lachner, F. Liszt bearbeitet und herausgegeben von S. Lebert, *etc.* 7 Abtheilungen. *J. G. Cotta: Stuttgart,* 1875, *etc.* fol.
h. 1063. a.

— Polka-caprice pour le Piano. *Mayence,* [1863.] fol.
h. 1462. r. (26.)

— Souvenir des Alpes. Morceau caractéristique pour Piano. *Mayence,* [1863.] fol.
h. 1462. r. (27.)

— *See* Beethoven (L. van) [*Collected Works.—c.*] Easy compositions ... Edited and fingered by S. Lebert and H. von Bülow. [1950.] 4°.
g. 249. pp. (2.)

— *See* Beethoven (L. van) Sonatas. [Complete collections.] For the piano. Revised and fingered by Dr. H. von Bülow and Dr. S. Lebert, *etc.* [1950.] 4°.
g. 249. ll.

— *See* Beethoven (L. van) [Variations. P. F.—Collections.] Variations for the Piano. Edited and fingered by H. von Bülow, S. Lebert and others, *etc.* [1950.] 4°.
g. 249. ss. (3.)

— *See* Haydn (F. J.) [Sonatas. Hob. XVI. Large Collections.] Twenty Sonatas for the Piano. Edited and fingered by L. Klee and Dr. S. Lebert, *etc.* [1950.] 4°.
g. 455. s. (3.)

— *See* Mozart (Wolfgang A.) [Concertos. P. F. K. 413.] Concerto Nº 5 (12), *etc.* ⟨Bearbeitet von S. Lebert. Piano solo.⟩ 1881. fol.
h. 405. jj. (2.)

— *See* Mozart (Wolfgang A.) [Concertos. P. F. K. 415.] Concerto Nº 7 (5), *etc.* ⟨Bearbeitet von S. Lebert. Piano solo.⟩ 1881. fol.
h. 405. jj. (3.)

— *See* Mozart (Wolfgang A.) Sonate No. 1. C dur. [K. 545.] ⟨No. 2. G dur. [K. 283.]—No. 3. C dur. [K. 330.]⟩ ... unter Mitwirkung von I. von Faisst ... bearbeitet von S. Lebert. [c. 1900.] fol.
h. 321. rr. (5.)

— *See* Stark (L.) Deutsche Liederschule ... Unter S. Lebert's Mitwirkung ... herausgegeben. 1861. 4°.
H. 1809.

LEBERT (SIGMUND) and **STARK** (LUDWIG)

— Grosse theoretisch-praktische Klavierschule ... mit Beiträgen von Benedikt, Faisst, Herzog, F. Hiller, Krüger, F. Lachner, I. Lachner, Moscheles & Speidel. 3 Tl. (Supplement zum ersten Theil ... Uebungsstücke, *etc.*) *Stuttgart*, 1858. 4°.
h. 1063.

LE BERTON (   )

— *See* MAHONI (   ) called LE BERTON.

LEBESGUE (PHILÉAS)

— Les Chants féminins serbes. Poèmes populaires, traduits en français ... avec un commentaire comparatif, des airs traditionnels et diverses études critiques, *etc.* (Mélodies populaires serbes pour piano à deux mains, arrangées par M. Miloïevitch.) *E. Sansot: Paris*, 1920. 8°.
011586. b. 83.

LEBEWOHL

— Lebewohl. [Song.] *See* GERMAN. German Volkslieder, *etc.* No. 6. [1864.] fol.
H. 2827. a. (3.)

— Lebewohl! [Song.] *See* ABT (F. W.) Vier Lieder ... Op. 308. No. 2.

— Ein Lebewohl. Song. *See* ATKINSON (F. C.) A Farewell.

— Lebewohl. Song. *See* BARRY (C. A.) Six Songs, *etc.* No. 5.

— Lebewohl. [Song.] *See* BUNGERT (A.) Junge Lieder. Op. 5. No. 1.

— Lebewohl. Song. *See* GILBERT (R. S.)

— Lebewohl. Song. *See* GOLDBERG (J. P.)

— Lebewohl. [Song.] *See* GOLLMICK (A.)

— Lebe wohl. [Song.] *See* JENSEN (A.)

— Lebewohl. Song. *See* KLENGEL (P.) Six Songs. No. 4.

— Lebewohl. [Song.] *See* KRILL (C.) Fünf Lieder, *etc.* No. 1.

— Lebewohl. [Song.] *See* KRUG (A.) Fünf Lieder, *etc.* No. 4.

— Lebewohl. [Song.] *See* LECHNER (J.) Wanderlieder ... Op. 5. No. 1.

— Lebe wohl! [Song.] *See* LISZT (F.) [*Collected Works.—d.*] F. Liszt's gesammelte Lieder, *etc.* No. 44. [c. 1880.] fol.
H. 1878. e.

— Lebewohl. Romanze. *See* PAUFLER (K.)

— Lebewohl! [Song.] *See* PRESSEL (G.)

— Lebewohl! [Song.] *See* PROCH (Heinrich)

— Lebewohl. [Part-song.] *See* REGER (M.) Neun ausgewählte Volkslieder für Männerchor. No. 2.

— Lebe wohl. [Part-song.] *See* SENFF (R.) Wanderlieder ... Op. 9. No. 1.

— Lebewohl. [Song.] *See* WHITE (M. V.) Six Volkslieder. No. 1.

— Lebewohl. [Song.] *See* WÜERST (R.) Vier Lieder, *etc.* No. 2.

— Lebewohl du hohe Bergeswand. [Part-song.] *See* RHEINBERGER (J. G.)

— Leb' wohl du warmes Sonnenlicht. [Chorus.] *See* BEETHOVEN (L. van) [Leonore.]

— Leb wohl, Frau Welt. Liederzyklus. *See* EINEM (G. von)

— Lebewohl, lebewohl mein Lieb. [Song.] *See* RITTER (C.) Zwölf Lieder ... Op. 4. No. 9.

LEBEWOHL

— Leb' wohl, liebes Gretchen. [Song.] *See* GADE (N. V.) [Lieder und Gesänge. Heft IV. No. 2.]

— Lebewohl, mein Ayr. [Song.] *See* JENSEN (A.) 7 Lieder ... Op. 49. No. 7.

— Leb' wohl! wenn je ein heisses Flehen. [Song.] *See* GOLDSCHMIDT (A. von)

LEBIERRE (OLIVIER)

— Adieu à Lucerne. Scheidegruss an Luzern. Valse pour piano. Op. 40. *A. Cranz: Hambourg*, [1886.] fol.
h. 3098. (16.)

— Les Adieux. Mélancolie pour piano. Op. 61. *B. Schott's Söhne: Mayence*, [1887.] fol.
h. 3098. (24.)

— L'Alsacienne. Morceau lyrique pour piano. Op. 23. *Hambourg*, 1885. fol.
h. 3098. (5.)

— L'Arc de Triomphe. Marche pour piano. Op. 22. *Hambourg*, 1885. fol.
h. 3098. (4.)

— L'Argonnaise. Danse caractéristique pour piano. Op. 50. *A. Cranz: Hambourg*, [1886.] fol.
h. 3098. (21.)

— La Belle Hollandaise. Mazurka ... pour piano. Op. 18. *Mayence*, [1884.] fol.
h. 3098. (1.)

— Les Bouquetières de Reims. Scherzo brillant pour Piano. Op. 148. *Schott & Co.: London*, [1900.] fol.
g. 605. x. (8.)

— Caprice bohémien. Morceau de Salon pour piano. Op. 20. *Mayence*, [1884.] fol.
h. 3098. (3.)

— Les Dentellières de Bruges. Bluette pour piano. Op. 31. *Hambourg*, [1885.] fol.
h. 3098. (10.)

— Fête Champenoise. Mazurka ... pour piano. Op. 59. *B. Schott's Söhne: Mayence*, [1887.] fol.
h. 3098. (23.)

— Fidélia. Danse Espagnole pour piano. Op. 33. *Mayence*, [1885.] fol.
h. 3098. (12.)

— Fidelia. Danse Espagnole. Op. 33. [Violin and P. F.] *See* RITTER (E. W.) Les Succès du Salon, *etc.* No. 50. [1891, *etc.*] fol.
h. 3665. a.

— Fleurs printanières. Bluette pour piano. Op. 45. *A. Cranz: Hambourg*, [1886.] fol.
h. 3098. (18.)

— La Grecque à Hambourg. Polka ... pour piano. Op. 35. *Hambourg*, [1885.] fol.
h. 3098. (14.)

— Katinka. Polonaise brillante pour piano. Op. 47. *A. Cranz: Hambourg*, [1886.] fol.
h. 3098. (19.)

— Les Lessiveuses de Champigneul. Polka brillante pour piano. Op. 49. *A. Cranz: Hambourg*, [1886.] fol.
h. 3098. (20.)

— La Montagnarde. Tyrolienne pour piano. Op. 32. *Hambourg*, [1885.] fol.
h. 3098. (11.)

— La Petite Méchante. Polka pour piano. Op. 24. *Hambourg*, [1885.] fol.
h. 3098. (6.)

— Les Pompiers de Fluelen. Marche Militaire pour piano. Op. 34. *Mayence*, [1885.] fol.
h. 3098. (13.)

— Les Précieuses Ridicules. Menuet élégant pour piano. Op. 43. *A. Cranz: Hambourg*, [1886.] fol.
h. 3098. (17.)

— Des Sennen Abschied. Idylle für das Pianoforte. Op. 39. *Berlin & Posen*, [1885.] fol.
h. 3098. (15.)

— Soleil de Mai. Bluette pour piano. Op. 72. *B. Schott's Söhne: Mayence*, [1888.] fol.
h. 3098. (26.)

— Les Sons du Cœur. Morceau de Salon pour piano. Op. 71. *B. Schott's Söhne: Mayence*, [1888.] fol.
h. 3098. (25.)

LEBIERRE (OLIVIER)

— Sous les châtaigniers. Rêverie pour piano. Op. 30. *Mayence*, [1885.] fol.   **h. 3098. (9.)**

— Souvenir de Badenweiler. Valse pour piano. Op. 26. *Hambourg*, [1885.] fol.   **h. 3098. (7.)**

— Souvenir de Blankenberghe. Redowa ... pour piano. Op. 29. *Mayence*, [1885.] fol.   **h. 3098. (8.)**

— Souvenirs d'autrefois. Valse ... pour piano. Op. 19. *Mayence*, [1884.] fol.   **h. 3098. (2.)**

— La Sucrée de Saverne. Mazurke élégante pour piano. Op. 51. *A. Cranz: Hambourg*, [1886.] fol.   **h. 3098. (22.)**

— Tarentelle pour Piano. Op. 62 ... à 4 mains, arrangée par A. Kaiser. Op. 62. *B. Schott's Söhne: Mayence*, (1910.) fol.   **g. 545. p. (11.)**

LEBLAN (PIERRE JOSEPH)

— La Badine. *See* infra: [Livre de clavecin.—Suite. No. 2.]

— [Livre de clavecin.—Suite No. 2.] La Badine. [Carillon.] [*Office of The Carillonneur, Rockefeller Memorial Chapel, University of Chicago: Chicago*, c. 1955.] fol. *With a sheet of "biographical notes" inserted.*   **h. 2676. (2.)**

LEBLANC (   )

— La Folle Gageure, Comédie, en un Acte et en prose, mêlée d'Ariettes ... Paroles de M. Leger, *etc. Chez Cailleau & Fils: Paris*, 1790. 8°. *Containing the voice part of a few songs only.*   **11738. h. 13. (3.)**

— Gabrielle et Paulin. [For songs, etc., published anonymously:] *See* GABRIELLE.

— Nicodème dans la Lune. [Folie in prose, with songs, etc. Words and music by Cousin Jacques, accompaniments by Leblanc. For songs, etc. published anonymously:] *See* NICODÈME.

— [La Noce Béarnaise.] Rôder, veiller, sans cesse être aux aguets. *Ariette, etc.* [1787.] 8°. *See* NOCE.   **B. 362. c. (72.)**

LEBLANC (DIDIER)

— Airs de Plusieurs Musiciens. Sur les Poësies de Ph. Desportes & autres de plus excellans Poetes de nostre tems. Reduiz à 4. parties, Par M. D. Le Blanc. Superius. (Tenor.) 2 pt. *Adrian le Roy, & Robert Ballard: Paris*, 1582. obl. 16°.   **K. 2. b. 7.**

— Airs de plusieurs musiciens réduits à quatre parties. *Éditions Maurice Senart: Paris*, 1925. 4°. [*Monuments de la musique française au temps de la Renaissance. Vol.* III.]   **G. 59. a.**

— [Airs de plusieurs musiciens.] Chansons. [Words by] Philippe Des Portes. *Leiter-Nypels: Maastricht*, 1926. obl. 8°. *A selection of four chansons, one without music, issued in a limited edition "Pour les amis de René-Louis Doyon & Charles Nypels".*   **K. 10. a. 34.**

— Second Livre d'Airs des plus excelants Musiciens de nostre tems. Reduiz à quatre parties. Par M. Di. Le Blanc. Superius. *Adrian le Roy, & Robert Ballard: Paris*, 1579. obl. 16°.   **K. 2. b. 6.**

LEBLANC (EDOUARD)

— Le National. Nouveau Quadrille valsant ... inventé et composé par E. Leblanc, *etc. H. Klein: London*, [1883.] fol.   **h. 975. u. (54.)**

— La Nationale. Nouveau quadrille-valsant, *etc.* [P. F.] pp. 12. *E. George & Cº: London*, [c. 1890.] fol.   **h. 3865. ss. (14.)**

LE BLOND (ALFRED)

— À ma chère Amie. Valse. [P. F.] *Hutchings & Co.: London*, [1885.] fol.   **h. 975. u. (55.)**

LEBLOND (*Mdme* ALPHONSE)

— Valse Minto. [P. F.] *Mercier & Co.: Levis, P. Q.*, 1900. fol.   **h. 3266. r. (4.)**

LEBLOND (F.)

— Souvenir de Terpsichore. Recueil de contre-danses. ⟨Premier—troisieme quadrille.⟩ [With plates.] *Chez Alp. Giroux: Paris*, [1820?] obl. 8°.   **K. 1. b. (14.)**

LE BŒUF (FRANÇOIS HENRY)

— Le Berger timide. Cantatille à voix seule avec Simphonie ... Gravée par J[h] Renou. [Score.] pp. 9. *Chez l'auteur, etc.: Paris*, [1756.] fol.   **H. 346. e. (23.)**

— Traité d'Harmonie et Règles d'Accompagnement servans à la Composition, suivant le Sistème de M. Rameau, *etc.* pp. 59. *Au Bureau Musical: Paris*, [1768.] obl. fol.   **e. 358.**

LEBOFFE (ENRICO)

— At Sunset. Il Tramonto. [Song, Italian words by] P. Thouar, translated by Dr. T. Baker, *etc. Boston Music Co.: Boston, Mass.*, (1906.) fol.   **G. 805. mm. (20.)**

— Aubade. Mattinata. [Song, Italian words by] P. E. Bosi, translated by Dr. T. Baker, *etc. Boston Music Co.: Boston, Mass.*, (1906.) fol.   **G. 805. mm. (21.)**

— Ave Maria, per soprano o Tenore, Piano e Violino obbligato. *B. F. Wood Music Co.: Boston, New York*, (1905.) fol.   **G. 807. jj. (49.)**

— Awakening, Risveglio. [Song, Italian words by] E. Panzacchi, translated by Dr. T. Baker, *etc. Boston Music Co.: Boston, Mass.*, (1906.) fol.   **G. 805. mm. (22.)**

— Bluette, pour Pianoforte. (Op. 16.) *B. F. Wood Music Co.: Boston, etc.*, (1909.) fol.   **g. 606. f. (21.)**

— Chiostro. [Song.] Versi di G. Prati. *B. F. Wood Music Co.: Boston, New York*, (1905.) fol.   **G. 807. jj. (44.)**

— [Another edition.] Chiostro. The Novice. [Song.] Versi di G. Prati, translation by A. Mathewson. *B. F. Wood Music Co.: Boston, etc.*, (1905.) fol.   **G. 807. jj.(47.)**

— Echi Campestri.—Woodland Echoes.—Piano Solo. *B. F. Wood Music Co.: Boston, New York*, (1905.) fol.   **g. 605. ll. (16.)**

— Madrigali d'Aprile ... Four songs with piano. [Words by E. Pedio.] *Boston Music Co.: Boston*, 1916. 4°.   **G. 295. n. (11.)**

— Il mio caro segreto. [Song.] Versi della Sig[na] Vanyna de Vellis. *B. F. Wood Music Co.: Boston, New York*, (1905.) fol.   **G. 807. jj. (42.)**

— [Another edition.] Il Mio caro segreto. My Secret. [Song.] Versi della Sig[na] Vanyna de Vellis, translation by A. Mathewson. *B. F. Wood Music Co.: Boston, etc.*, (1905.) fol.   **G. 807. jj. (45.)**

— Nocturne. Notturno. [Song, Italian words by] A. Rossato, English translation by Dr. T. Baker, *etc.. Boston Music Co.: Boston, Mass.*, (1906.) fol.   **G. 805. mm. (23.)**

— O salutaris Hostia.—O saving Victim.—[Anthem.] *B. F. Wood Music Co.: Boston, Mass.*, (1905.) 8°. *Choir Jornal*, No. 151.   **F. 986.**

— Quaggiù. [Song.] Versi di P. E. Bosi. *B. F. Wood Music Co.: Boston, New York*, (1905.) fol.   **G. 807. jj. (43.)**

LEBOFFE (Enrico)

— [Another edition.] Quaggiù. Below. [Song.] Versi di P. E. Bosi, translation by A. Mathewson. *B. F. Wood Music Co.: Boston, etc.*, (1905.) fol.　　　　　**G. 807. jj. (46.)**

— Smiles in Tears. Sorriso in pianto. [Song, Italian words by] G. S. Pini, translated by Dr. T. Baker, *etc. Boston Music Co.: Boston, Mass.*, (1906.) fol.　　　**G. 805. mm. (24.)**

— Snow-Storm. Nevicata. [Song, Italian words by] G. Pascoli, English translation by Dr. T. Baker, *etc. Boston Music Co.: Boston, Mass.*, (1906.) fol.　　**G. 805. mm. (25.)**

— Sognando. Dreaming. Melodia. (Violin and Piano.) *B. F. Wood Music Co.: Boston, New York*, (1905.) fol.
　　　　　　　　　　　　　　　g. 505. t. (31.)

— Te sola. Thee only. [Song.] Versi di E. I. Giuffre, translation by A. Mathewson. *B. F. Wood Music Co.: Boston, etc.*, (1905.) fol.　　　　**G. 807. jj. (48.)**

— To Maria. A Maria.—Acrostico.—[Song, Italian words by] E. Gamberini, translated by Dr. T. Baker, *etc. Boston Music Co.: Boston, Mass.*, 1906. fol.　　**G. 805. mm. (26.)**

— A Voice at Evening. Voce vespertina. Song, *etc.* (From the Italian of S. Vitale by N. H. Dole.) *Boston Music Co.: Boston*, 1916. fol.　　　**H. 1846. x. (39.)**

LEBORNE (Aimé Ambroise Simon)

— La Contredanse. Chansonnette [begins: "Vous voyez bien"] de Mr. A. de la Villette. *Paris*, [1830?] fol.　**G. 559. (54.)**

LE BORNE (Fernand)

— A une passante. *See* infra: Six Mélodies ... Op. 12. No. 1.

— L'Amour de Myrto. Poëme de P. Berlier. Deutsche Übersetzung von Th. Hauptner. *Berlin & Posen*, [1885.] 8°.
　　　　　　　　　　　　　　　F. 607. r. (11.)

— Angelus pour piano. Op. 11. *L. Grus: Paris*, [1886.] fol.
　　　　　　　　　　　　　　　h. 3281. l. (13.)

— Garde toujours ces fleurs. *See* infra: Six Mélodies ... Op. 12. No. 4.

— Les Girondins. Drame lyrique en 4 actes et 6 tableaux de Delormeil et Paul Bérel ... ⟨Op. 52.⟩ Partition chant et piano. pp. 309. *Choudens: Paris*, [1905.] 4°.
With press cuttings inserted.　　　　**F. 1373. rr.**

— Les Girondins. Drame lyrique ... paroles de Delormeil et P. Berel. O mon Jean. [Song.] [*Paris*.] 1906. 8°.
Supplement to "L'Illustration," No. 3290.　**P. P. 4283. m. (3.)**

— Ici-bas. *See* infra: Six Mélodies ... Op. 12. No. 2.

— Cinq Lieder [words by P. Berlier, F. Le Borne, C. Ferbonne and V. Hugo]. Chant et piano. Op. 7. *Leipzig et Bruxelles*, [1884.] 8°.　　　　**F. 607. r. (10.)**

— Matutina. *See* infra: Six Mélodies ... Op. 12. No. 6.

— Méditation religieuse. *See* infra: Six Mélodies ... Op. 12. No. 5.

— Six Mélodies pour chant et piano. Op. 12. No. 1. A une passante. A. Silvestre. No. 2. Ici-bas. Sully Prudhomme. No. 3. Notre amour à fui! P. Berlier. No. 4. Garde toujours ces fleurs. A. Silvestre. No. 5. Méditation religieuse—avec violoncelle—paroles françaises et latines. No. 6. Matutina. A. Silvestre. 6 no. *Schott Frères: Bruxelles*, [1887.] fol.
　　　　　　　　　　　　　　　H. 2836. v. (24.)

— Notre Amour à fui! *See* supra: Six Mélodies ... Op. 12. No. 3.

— Poëme pour orchestre. 2ème Suite. Scènes de Ballet. (Op. 9.) Partition d'orch. *Bruxelles*, 1886. 8°.　**e. 666. h. (7.)**

LEBORNE (J. F.)

— During the Gavotte. Small Piece for the Pianoforte. *Chappell & Co.: London*, [1890.] fol.　　**h. 1489. s. (25.)**

LEBOSSÉ (Albert)

— Les Élégantes. 12 petites récréations mélodiques. [P. F.] 12 no. *Paris*, [1882.] fol.　　　**h. 3276. g. (10.)**

— Mascarade Louis XIII pour le Piano. *Paris*, [1878.] fol.
　　　　　　　　　　　　　　　h. 1493. n. (25.)

LEBOUC (Charles)

— Recréations de l'enfance. Recueil de rondes avec jeux et de petites chansons pour faire jouer, danser et chanter les enfants avec un accompagnement de piano très-facile par C. Lebouc. Troisième édition, revue et corrigée. pp. 36. *E. Heu: Paris*, [1885?] 8°.　　　**F. 1838.**

— Rondes avec Jeux et de petites Chansons traditionelles. Rounds for Singing and Dancing ... with the original French words, an English translation by E. M. Traquair, and pianoforte accompaniment by C. Lebouc. *Augener & Co.: London*, [1890.] 8°.　　　**F. 636. n. (4.)**

LEBOUC (Charles Joseph)

— Praise to the Lord. Hymne au Seigneur. *See* Concerts. Les concerts de Société ... for Voice ... and Violin. No. 55. [1845, *etc.*] fol.　　　　　**H. 2085. a.**

— Praise to the Lord, (Hymne au Seigneur) for voice, piano & violoncello obligato. The English version [beginning: "God of harmony"] by D. Ryan. Op. 4. *London*, [1853.] fol.
　　　　　　　　　　　　　　　H. 1185. (4.)

— *See* Renaud de Vilbac (A. Z. C.) Les Beautés Dramatiques arrangés pour piano et violoncelle par ... C. Lebouc d'après A. Blanc. [1873–9.] fol.　　　**h. 1228. h.**

LE BOUCHER (Maurice)

— La Duchesse de Padoue. Action dramatique en 2 actes d'après le drame de Oscar Wilde. Livret de Paul Grosfils ... Partition piano et chant. pp. 176. *Éditions Salabert: Paris*, [1931.] 4°.　　　　　**G. 1129. a.**

— *See* Chabrier (E. A.) Capriccio pour piano. ⟨Terminé par M. Le Boucher.⟩ [1914.] fol.　　　**h. 3685. m. (7.)**

LEBOUC-NOURRIT (Jeannette)

— Petit Manuel de mesure et d'intonation à l'usage des jeunes enfants. 60 Tableaux-Calques, *etc.* 5 cah. *Paris*, [1879.] *obl.* fol.　　　　　**E. 779.**

LEBOURNE (S. M.)

— A Trip to London. Action Song ... words & music by S. M. Lebourne. *Weekes & Co.: London*, [1918.] 8°.
　　　　　　　　　　　　　　　E. 1766. v. (9.)

LE BOUTILLIER (Arthur)

— *See* Sullivan (*Sir* A. S.) The Lost Chord. Arranged ... by A. Le Boutillier. 1938. 4°.　　　**g. 657. b. (27.)**

LEBOWSKY (Stanley)

— The Children's Crusade. A morality play for the young. For four-part chorus of mixed voices, three soloists, narrator, piano and guitar accompaniment. Lyrics and text by Fred Tobias. [Vocal score.] pp. 88. *G. Schirmer: New York, London*, [1978.] 4°.　　　**G. 1282. zz. (4.)**

LEBOWSKY (STANLEY)

— [The Children's Crusade.] Deus vult ... For four-part chorus of mixed voices with piano and optional drums and guitar accompaniment. Text by Fred Tobias. [Score.] pp. 4.
G. Schirmer: [*New York*, 1978.] 8°.　　　　**E. 1857. d. (7.)**

— Deus vult. *See* supra: [The Children's Crusade.]

LEBOY (GRACE)

— Are you lonesome. [Song.] Words by Gus Kahn. pp. 4.
Thompson Music Co.: Chicago, New York, [1909.] fol.
　　　　　　　　　　　　　　H. 3985. l. (29.)

— I wish I had a Girl. [Song.] Words by Gus Kahn.　*Jerome H. Remick & Co.: Detroit, New York*, [1909.] fol.
　　　　　　　　　　　　　　H. 3985. l. (30.)

— June, July and August. [Song.] Words by Gus Kahn. pp. 4.
[1909.] fol.　　　　　　　　　　**H. 3985. l. (31.)**

— Liking's not a Bit like Loving. [Song.] Words by Gus Kahn.
Victor Kremer Co.: Chicago, etc., [1908.] fol.
　　　　　　　　　　　　　　H. 3985. l. (32.)

— Pretty soft for me. [Song.] Words by Gus Kahn. pp. 5.
Maurice Shapiro: New York, [1909.] fol.　　**H. 3985. l. (33.)**

— Say Boys! I've found a Girl. [Song.] Words by Gus Kahn.
pp. 5.　*Maurice Shapiro: New York*, [1908.] fol.
　　　　　　　　　　　　　　H. 3985. l. (34.)

— What's the Use of Moonlight? ... Song with quartet chorus [for T. T. Bar. B. Words by] Gus Kahn. ⟨Arr. by Gus. La Forest.⟩ pp. 6.　*Will Rossiter: Chicago*, [1909.] fol.
　　　　　　　　　　　　　　H. 3985. l. (35.)

LEBRA (ANTON)

— Tra-la-la. Polka. [P. F.]　*C. Howes: Morecambe*, [1897.] fol.
Lithographed throughout.　　　　**h. 3286. g. (21.)**

LE BRETON (LUCIEN)

— Je suis poivreau. Chanson typique.　*Paris*, [1881.] fol.
　　　　　　　　　　　　　　H. 1786. e. (21.)

LE BRUM (GEORGE)

— *See* GILBERT (Walter) The Night I played Richard the Third, *etc.* [Song.] ⟨Arranged by G. Le Brum.⟩ [1890.] fol.
　　　　　　　　　　　　　　H. 3980. y. (37.)

LE BRUN (D. R.)

— Four pieces for the Pianoforte. 1. Adagio. 2. Clavierstück. 3. Petite Romance. 4. Tonal Procedures, No. 7.　*J. & W. Chester: London*, 1937. fol.　　　**h. 3870. i. (39.)**

LEBRUN (E.)

— Inspiration. Valse. [P. F.]　*W. Paxton: London*, [1905.] fol.
　　　　　　　　　　　　　　h. 3286. dd. (55.)

LE BRUN (FRANZISKA)

— Six Sonatas, for the Harpsichord or Piano Forte with an Accompaniment for a Violin, *etc.* [Op. 1.]　*Printed for the Author: London*, [1780.] fol.　　　**h. 1689. (1.)**

— Six Sonatas ... Op. 1. [Parts.]　*J. Bland: London*, [1785?] fol.
　　　　　　　　　　　　　　h. 1480. c. (13.)

— Six Sonatas for the Piano Forte or Harpsichord with an Accompanyment for a Violin ... Op. II. [Parts.] 2 pt.　*The Author: London*, [1778?] fol.　　　**h. 1689. (2.)**

LE BRUN (GEORGE)

— *See* LE BRUNN.

LEBRUN (GUSTAVE)

— Ma pauvre petite Belgique. Poème patriotique, paroles de A. Bourboux, *etc.* (English version by A. Bourboux and F. W. Leigh.)　*Francis, Day & Hunter: London*, 1915. fol.
　　　　　　　　　　　　　　H. 1793. s. (35.)

LE BRUN (JEANNE)

— Love in idleness, polka, pour le piano forte, *etc.　London*, [1859.] fol.　　　　　　　**h. 977. f. (26.)**

— Love in Idleness waltzes, for the Pianoforte.　*London*, [1859.] fol.　　　　　　　　**h. 1460. v. (2.)**

— A Tale of Love. Song [begins: "The spring time is blooming"]. Words by H. D. B.　*London*, [1873.] fol.
　　　　　　　　　　　　　　H. 1778. x. (53.)

LEBRUN (LOUIS)

— Badinage. Idylle pour Piano—sans Octaves—.　*A. M. Heller & Co.: London*, [1902.] fol.　　**h. 3282. kk. (24.)**

— Caprice Breton pour piano.　*Rossini & Co.: London*, [1899.] fol.　　　　　　　　**h. 3282. f. (19.)**

— Valsette, pour Piano—sans Octaves—.　*H. M. Heller & Co.: London*, [1902.] fol.　　**h. 3282. kk. (25.)**

LEBRUN (LOUIS SÉBASTIEN)

— Marcelin. Opéra en un acte et en prose, paroles de Bernard Valville, *etc.* [Score.] pp. 88.　*Les frères Gaveaux: Paris*, [1800?] fol.
A slip bearing the imprint of Henri Lemoine et c^{ie}., Paris, has been pasted over the original imprint.　　**G. 289. a.**

— [Marcelin.—Auprès de ce qu'on aime.] Couplets. Paroles de Bernard Valville ... Arrangé [*sic*] pour guitarre par Lintant.
Les frères Gaveaux: [*Paris*, 1805?] 8°.　　**E. 1717. g. (30.)**

— [Marcelin.—Ce jeune homme depuis huit jours.] Romance ... Paroles de C. Bernard Valville ... Arrangée pour la guitare ou lyre par Lintant.　*Chez les frères Gaveaux: Paris*, [1805?] 8°.　　　　　　　　**E. 1717. g. (29.)**

— Le Rossignol. Opéra comique en un acte ... Paroles de Mr Étienne, *etc.* [Score.] pp. 147.　*Chez l'auteur: Paris*, [1816?] fol.　　　　　　　**G. 289.**

— [Another copy.]　　　　　　**Hirsch II. 506.**

— [Le Rossignol.—Arbres que vous êtes heureux.] Air ... Arrangé pour guitare par Meissonnier. pp. 7.　*Chez Terry: Bruxelles*, [1816?] 8°.　　　**E. 1717. n. (15.)**

— [Le Rossignol.—Dieu quel bruyant ramage.] Duo ... Arrangé pour guitare par Meissonnier. pp. 11. [*Chez Terry: Bruxelles*, 1816?] 8°.　　　　　　**E. 1717. n. (16.)**

— [Le Rossignol.—Ma chère enfant.] Trio ... Arrangé pour la guitare par Meissonnier. pp. 11.　*Chez Terry: Bruxelles*, [1816?] 8°.　　　　　　　　**E. 1717. n. (17.)**

LE BRUN (LUDWIG AUGUST)

— The Favorite Airs, in the grand Ballet of Adel de Ponthiew ... Book I. pp. 27.　*Printed for Wm Forster: London*, [1782.] obl. 4°.
Plate number 21.　　　　　　**b. 53. g.**

— Konzert No. 1 d-Moll für Oboe und Orchester. Herausgegeben von Hermann Töttcher. Partitur, *etc.* pp. 55.
B. Schott's Söhne: Mainz, [1977.] 4°.
Concertino. 90.　　　　　　**g. 1078. u. (11.)**

LE BRUN (LUDWIG AUGUST)

— Konzert No. 1 d-Moll für Oboe und Orchester.
Herausgegeben von Hermann Töttcher. Kadenz von Lothar
Koch. Klavierauszug von Helmut May, *etc.* [Score and part.]
2 pt. *B. Schott's Söhne: Mainz*, [1977.] 4°.
*Oboe Bibliothek. 13. With a separate leaf, containing the
cadenzas, inserted.* **g. 1078. u. (10.)**

— Concerto No. 4. C-dur ... Solo-Oboe, 2 Hörner ad lib. &
Streicher. Partitur, *etc.* ⟨Herausgegeben von Walter
Lebermann.⟩ pp. 43. *N. Simrock: Hamburg, London*, [1964.]
4°. **g. 1620. nn. (3.)**

— Concerto No. 4 C-dur ... für Oboe und Orchester ...
Klavierauszug und Solostimme ⟨Kadenzen⟩ ...
(⟨Herausgegeben und bearbeitet von⟩ Walter Lebermann).
3 pt. *N. Simrock: Hamburg, London*, [1978.] 4°.
The cadenzas are printed in a separate part. **g. 1078. dd. (5.)**

— The Favorite Dances for the Year 1782 called Armida.
J. Blundell: London, [1782.] *obl.* 4°. **b. 51. d. (3.)**

— [A reissue.] The Favorite Dances in the Opera of Armida.
[Score.] *London*, [1782.] *obl.* 8°. **b. 51. i.**

— [Dances in the Opera of Armida.—Gavotta in B flat.] *See*
GIORDANI (T.) The much admired Dance [by L. A. Le Brun]
as performed by Sig^ra Theodore in Armida. Adapted to
English words by Sig^r Giordani. [1782.] fol.
H. 1980. jj. (21.)

— Six Trios pour Deux Violons et Violoncelle ... Œuvre 1er.
[Parts.] *Chez M: Goetz: Mannheim*, [1780?] fol.
g. 420. d. (7.)

— Six Trios a deux violons ou une flûte, violon et basse ...
Œuvre 2. [Parts.] 2 pt. *Chez le Sr Sieber: Paris*, [1775?] fol.
Imperfect; wanting the bass part. **Hirsch M. 1466. (2.)**

LEBRUN (PAUL)

— *See* CLESSE (A.) Nouvelles Chansons ... (Airs notés.) [By ...
P. Lebrun, *etc.*] 1888. 8°. **11482. l. 20.**

— *See* GHENT.— *Willems-Fonds.* Nederlandsche zangstukken met
klavierbegeleiding, *etc.* [Songs by P. Lebrun and others.]
[1880, *etc.*] fol. **H. 1660. i.**

LEBRUN (PAUL HENRY JOSEPH)

— A toi. [Song.] Idylle de Charles Fuster. pp. 3. *A. Durand &
fils: Paris*, [c. 1920.] fol. **H. 1654. u. (10.)**

LE BRUNN ( ) Monsieur

— *See* LE BRUN (L. A.)

LE BRUNN (ALBERT)

— The Waverley Gavotte, for Pianoforte. *A. M. Heller & Co.:
London*, [1905.] fol. **h. 3282. ww. (35.)**

LE BRUNN (GEORGE)

— A, B, ab. [Song.] Written by H. Hunter. *Francis, Day &
Hunter: London*, 1896. *s. sh.* fol. **H. 3602. (30.)**

— 'Ackney with the 'Ouses took away. [Song.] Written by
E. Bateman. *Francis, Day & Hunter: London*, 1900. *s. sh.* fol.
H. 3602. b. (1.)

— Across the Bridge. [Song.] Written by F. Bowyer, *etc. Francis
Bros. & Day: London*, [1888.] fol. **H. 1260. f. (23.)**

— Advance, Australia! England Number Two. [Song.] Written
by W. Pink. *Francis, Day & Hunter: London*, 1897. *s. sh.* fol.
H. 3602. (31.)

LE BRUNN (GEORGE)

— All except the last. [Song.] Written by E. Bateman, *etc.
Francis, Day & Hunter: London*, 1899. *s. sh.* fol.
H. 3602. b. (2.)

— All Girls are Angels. [Song.] Written by John P. Harrington,
etc. [Staff and tonic sol-fa notation. Voice part.] *Francis,
Day & Hunter: London*, [1904.] *s. sh.* fol. **H. 3985. l. (36.)**

— All Girls are Angels, *etc.* ⟨Song.⟩ [With separate voice part.]
2 pt. *Francis, Day & Hunter: London*, [1904.] fol.
H. 3985. l. (37.)

— All that glitters is not Gold. [Song.] Written by A. J. Morris.
Howard & Co.: London, [1896.] fol. **H. 3602. a. (1.)**

— Among my Knick-knacks. [Song.] Written by Mon Tresor.
Francis, Day & Hunter: London, 1896. *s. sh.* fol.
H. 3602. (32.)

— And Lots of other Things. [Song.] Written by A. Atkins.
Francis, Day & Hunter: London, 1893. fol. **H. 3602. a. (2.)**

— And the Leaves began to fall. ⟨Song.⟩ Written by J. P.
Harrington, *etc.* [Staff and tonic sol-fa notation. Voice part.]
Francis, Day & Hunter: London, [1904.] *s. sh.* fol.
H. 3985. l. (38.)

— And the Leaves began to fall, *etc.* ⟨Song.⟩ [With separate
voice part.] 2 pt. *Francis, Day & Hunter: London*, [1904.] fol.
H. 3985. l. (39.)

— 'Appy 'Ampstead. Barn Dance. [P. F.] *Francis, Day &
Hunter: London*, 1903. fol. **h. 3286. y. (29.)**

— [Another copy.]
With a different titlepage. **h. 3286. dd. (56.)**

— As in a Looking-Glass. [Song.] Written by J. P. Harrington,
etc. Francis Bros. & Day: London, [1889.] fol.
H. 1260. f. (25.)

— As long as she's Irish she'll do. ⟨Song.⟩ Written by John
P. Harrington, *etc.* [Staff and tonic sol-fa notation. Voice
part.] *Francis, Day & Hunter: London*, [1902.] *s. sh.* fol.
H. 3985. l. (40.)

— As long as she's Irish she'll do, *etc.* ⟨Song.⟩ [With separate
voice part.] 2 pt. *Francis, Day & Hunter: London*, [1902.] fol.
H. 3985. l. (41.)

— At Constantinople. [Song.] Written by J. P. Harrington.
Francis, Day & Hunter: London, 1894. *s. sh.* fol.
H. 3602. (33.)

— At our Outing ... ⟨Song.⟩ Written by John P. Harrington.
[Staff and tonic sol-fa notation. Voice part.] *Francis, Day &
Hunter: London*, [1905.] *s. sh.* fol. **H. 3985. l. (42.)**

— At our Outing, *etc.* ⟨Song.⟩ [With separate voice part.] 2 pt.
Francis, Day & Hunter: London, [1905.] fol.
H. 3985. l. (43.)

— Baby and I! [Song.] Written by J. P. Harrington. *Francis,
Day & Hunter: London*, 1895. *s. sh.* fol. **H. 3602. (34.)**

— The Ballad-Monger. [Song.] Written by A. Hall. *Francis, Day
& Hunter: London*, 1898. *s. sh.* fol. **H. 3602. b. (3.)**

— Ballooning ... [Song.] Written by J. P. Harrington, *etc.
Francis Bros. & Day: London*, [1889.] fol. **H. 1260. f. (26.)**

— Bathing. [Song.] Written by J. P. Harrington. *Francis, Day &
Hunter: London*, 1898. *s. sh.* fol. **H. 3602. b. (4.)**

— The Bazaar Maids. [Song.] Written by J. P. Harrington.
Francis, Day & Hunter: London, 1896. *s. sh.* fol.
H. 3602. (35.)

— Be mine own again. [Song.] Written by A. Williams. *Francis,
Day & Hunter: London*, 1896. *s. sh.* fol. **H. 3602. (36.)**

LE BRUNN (George)

— A Beautiful Man like me! ⟨Song.⟩ Written by John P. Harrington, *etc.* [Staff and tonic sol-fa notation. Voice part.] *Francis, Day & Hunter: London*, [1901.] *s. sh.* fol.
H. 3985. l. (44.)

— A Beautiful Man like me! *etc.* ⟨Song.⟩ [With separate voice part.] 2 pt. *Francis, Day & Hunter: London*, [1901.] fol.
H. 3985. l. (45.)

— Because it was made in London … Song. Written by J. P. Harrington. *Francis, Day & Hunter: London*, 1900. fol.
H. 3602. b. (5.)

— Bella was a Barmaid. ⟨Song.⟩ Written by John P. Harrington. [Staff and tonic sol-fa notation. Voice part.] *Francis, Day & Hunter: London*, [1902.] *s. sh.* fol.
H. 3985. l. (46.)

— Bella was a Barmaid, *etc.* ⟨Song.⟩ [With separate voice part.] 2 pt. *Francis, Day & Hunter: London*, [1902.] fol.
H. 3985. l. (47.)

— The Belles of London. [Song.] Written by J. P. Harrington, *etc. Francis Bros. & Day: London*, [1888.] fol.
H. 1260. f. (27.)

— Below! [Song.] Written by A. Hall. *Howard & Co.: London*, 1897. fol.
H. 3602. a. (3.)

— The Best little Woman in the World. [Song.] Written by Murray & Leigh. *Francis, Day & Hunter: London*, 1898. *s. sh.* fol.
H. 3602. b. (6.)

— The Bicycle Barn-Dance. [P. F.] *Francis, Day & Hunter: London*, 1895. fol.
h. 3285. q. (13.)

— Bid me not forget the Past. Ballad. Written by A. Atkins. *Howard & Co.: London*, [1897.] fol.
H. 3602. a. (4.)

— A Big Ship is waiting! … ⟨Song.⟩ Written by J. P. Harrington. [Staff and tonic sol-fa notation. Voice part.] *Francis, Day & Hunter: London*, [1905.] *s. sh.* fol.
H. 3985. l. (48.)

— A Big Ship is waiting! *etc.* ⟨Song.⟩ [With separate voice part.] 2 pt. *Francis, Day & Hunter: London*, [1905.] fol.
H. 3985. l. (49.)

— The Bond Street Tea Walk. Written by J. P. Harrington. [With separate voice part.] 2 pt. *Francis, Day & Hunter: London*, [1902.] fol.
H. 3985. l. (50.)

— The Bond Street Tea Walk, *etc.* ⟨Song.⟩ [Staff and tonic sol-fa notation. Voice part.] *Francis, Day & Hunter: London*, [1902.] *s. sh.* fol.
H. 3985. l. (51.)

— Boys of London Town. [Song.] Written by J. P. Harrington. *Moon & Co.: London*, 1900. fol.
H. 3602. b. (7.)

— The Boys of the brave Reserve. ⟨Song.⟩ Written by John P. Harrington, *etc.* [Staff and tonic sol-fa notation. Voice part.] *Francis, Day & Hunter: London*, [1902.] *s. sh.* fol.
H. 3985. l. (52.)

— The Boys of the brave Reserve, *etc.* ⟨Song.⟩ [With separate voice part.] 2 pt. *Francis, Day & Hunter: London*, [1902.] fol.
H. 3985. l. (53.)

— The Boys of the Racketty Club. [Song.] Words by C. Wilmot. *T. B. Harms & Co.: New York*, 1894. fol.
H. 3602. (5.)

— Boys of the Rank and File. [Song.] Written by J. P. Harrington. *Francis, Day & Hunter: London*, 1896. *s. sh.* fol.
H. 3602. (37.)

— By their Language. [Song.] Written by J. P. Harrington. *Francis, Day & Hunter: London*, 1897. *s. sh.* fol.
H. 3602. (38.)

— The Cabbies' Lament; or crawl, crawl, crawl. [Song.] Written by W. Pink. *Francis, Day & Hunter: London*, 1899. *s. sh.* fol.
H. 3602. b. (8.)

LE BRUNN (George)

— Cabby knows his Fare! [Song.] Written by F. Bowyer, *etc. Francis Bros. & Day: London*, [1889.] fol.
H. 1260. f. (28.)

— Callaghan does it for me. [Song.] Written by A. Hall. *Francis, Day & Hunter: London*, 1899. *s. sh.* fol.
H. 3602. b. (9.)

— Captain Piffity Puff. [Song.] Written by A. J. Morris. *Francis, Day & Hunter: London*, 1895. *s. sh.* fol.
H. 3602. (39.)

— Captain Sparrowstarver. ⟨Song.⟩ Written by Edgar Bateman, *etc.* [Staff and tonic sol-fa notation. Voice part.] *Francis, Day & Hunter: London*, [1901.] *s. sh.* fol.
H. 3985. m. (1.)

— Captain Sparrowstarver, *etc.* ⟨Song.⟩ [With separate voice part.] 2 pt. *Francis, Day & Hunter: London*, [1901.] fol.
H. 3985. m. (2.)

— Chance your Luck! [Song.] Words by W. Pink. *Francis, Day & Hunter: London*, 1896. *s. sh.* fol.
H. 3602. (40.)

— Charley was a good, good Boy. ⟨Song.⟩ Written by J. P. Harrington. [Staff and tonic sol-fa notation. Voice part.] *Francis, Day & Hunter: London*, [1902.] *s. sh.* fol.
H. 3985. m. (3.)

— Charley was a good, good Boy, *etc.* ⟨Song.⟩ [With separate voice part.] 2 pt. *Francis, Day & Hunter: London*, [1902.] fol.
H. 3985. m. (4.)

— The Children's Circus. ⟨Song.⟩ Written by John P. Harrington. [Staff and tonic sol-fa notation. Voice part.] *Francis, Day & Hunter: London*, [1904.] *s. sh.* fol.
H. 3985. m. (5.)

— The Children's Circus, *etc.* ⟨Song.⟩ [With separate voice part.] 2 pt. *Francis, Day & Hunter: London*, [1904.] fol.
H. 3985. m. (6.)

— The Chili Widow. [Song.] Written by W. T. Lytton. *Howard & Co.: London*, [1896.] fol.
H. 3602. a. (6.)

— Chloe. [Song.] Written by J. P. Harrington. *Francis, Day & Hunter: London*, 1895. *s. sh.* fol.
H. 3602. (41.)

— The City Waif … Song, written by J. P. Harrington, *etc. Francis Bros. & Day: London*, [1889.] fol.
H. 1260. f. (29.)

— Clamber closer Clara. [Song.] Written by J. P. Harrington. *Francis, Day & Hunter: London*, 1894. fol.
H. 3602. a. (7.)

— Claudie. [Song.] Words by John P. Harrington. *M. Witmark & Sons: New York*, *etc.*, [1904.] fol.
H. 3985. m. (7.)

— Clever, ain't you? … Song. Written by J. P. Harrington. *Francis, Day & Hunter: London*, 1896. *s. sh.* fol.
H. 3602. (42.)

— The Club Raid upside down. ⟨Song.⟩ Written by Edgar Bateman, *etc.* [Staff and tonic sol-fa notation. Voice part.] *Francis, Day & Hunter: London*, [1901.] fol.
H. 3985. m. (8.)

— The Club Raid upside down, *etc.* ⟨Song.⟩ [With separate voice part.] 2 pt. *Francis, Day & Hunter: London*, [1901.] fol.
H. 3985. m. (9.)

— The Cockney Sportsman. ⟨Song.⟩ Written by J. P. Harrington, *etc.* [Staff and tonic sol-fa notation. Voice part.] *Francis, Day & Hunter: London*, [1901.] *s. sh.* fol.
H. 3985. m. (10.)

— The Cockney Sportsman, *etc.* [With separate voice part.] 2 pt. *Francis, Day & Hunter: London*, [1901.] fol.
H. 3985. m. (11.)

— The Cockney's Travels. [Song.] Words by E. Bateman. *Francis, Day & Hunter: London*, 1896. *s. sh.* fol.
H. 3602. (43.)

— Cock-o'-the-Walk. [Song.] Written by J. P. Harrington & C. Bignell. *Francis, Day & Hunter: London*, 1898. *s. sh.* fol.
H. 3602. b. (10.)

LE BRUNN (George)

— The Colleen Dhu. [Song.] Written by H. Boden and
W. Munroe, *etc. Francis Bros. & Day: London,* [1886.] fol.
H. 1260. f. (30.)

— Come along, let's make it up. ⟨Song.⟩ Written by Thos. Le
Brunn, *etc.* [Staff and tonic sol-fa notation. Voice part.]
Francis, Day & Hunter: London, [1901.] fol.
H. 3985. m. (12.)

— Come along, let's make it up, *etc.* ⟨Song.⟩ [With separate
voice part.] 2 pt. *Francis, Day & Hunter: London,* [1901.] fol.
H. 3985. m. (13.)

— Come and kiss your Honey on the Lip! [Song.] Written by
R. Morton. *Francis, Day & Hunter: London,* 1895. *s. sh.* fol.
H. 3602. (44.)

— Come, come to me, Darling. [Song.] Written by Alfred
J. Morris. pp. 4. *Francis, Day & Hunter: London,* [1892.] 4°.
H. 3980. pp. (45.)

— "Come in!" said Widdy Malone. ⟨Song.⟩ Written by J. P.
Harrington, *etc.* [Staff and tonic sol-fa notation. Voice part.]
Francis, Day & Hunter: London, [1904.] *s. sh.* fol.
H. 3985. m. (14.)

— "Come in!" said Widdy Malone, *etc.* ⟨Song.⟩ [With separate
voice part.] 2 pt. *Francis, Day & Hunter: London,* [1904.] fol.
H. 3985. m. (15.)

— The Consequential Coon. [Song.] Written by F. W. Leigh.
Francis, Day & Hunter: London, 1897. *s. sh.* fol.
H. 3602. (45.)

— Cooey, cooey, coo! ... Song. Written by W. Burnot. [With
banjo accompaniment by N. Greenop.] *J. A. Turner:
London,* [1898.] fol.
H. 3602. b. (11.)

— A Cook's Excursion Trip. [Song.] Written by R. Morton.
Francis, Day & Hunter: London, 1897. *s. sh.* fol.
H. 3602. (46.)

— Cool! [Song.] Written by W. Pink. *Francis, Day & Hunter:
London,* 1898. *s. sh.* fol. **H. 3602. b. (12.)**

— The Coon Ambassador. ⟨Song.⟩ Written by J. P. Harrington,
etc. [Staff and tonic sol-fa notation. Voice part.] *Francis,
Day & Hunter: London,* [1903.] *s. sh.* fol. **H. 3985. m. (16.)**

— The Coon Ambassador, *etc.* ⟨Song.⟩ [With separate voice
part.] 2 pt. *Francis, Day & Hunter: London,* [1903.] fol.
H. 3985. m. (17.)

— The Coon that never told a Lie. ⟨Song.⟩ Written by Richard
Morton, *etc.* [Staff and tonic sol-fa notation. Voice part.]
Francis, Day & Hunter: London, [1903.] *s. sh.* fol.
H. 3985. m. (18.)

— The Coon that never told a Lie, *etc.* ⟨Song.⟩ pp. 7. *Francis,
Day & Hunter: London,* [1904.] fol. **H. 3985. m. (19.)**

— The Coon's Playmate. ⟨Song.⟩ Written by Edgar Bateman, *etc.*
[Staff and tonic sol-fa notation. Voice part.] *Francis, Day &
Hunter: London,* [1902.] *s. sh.* fol. **H. 3985. m. (20.)**

— The Coon's Playmate, *etc.* ⟨Song.⟩ [With separate voice part.]
2 pt. *Francis, Day & Hunter: London,* [1902.] fol.
H. 3985. m. (21.)

— The Coon's Serenade. [Song.] Words by J. P. Harrington.
B. Mocatta: London, 1894. fol. **H. 3602. a. (8.)**

— The Coster's Ban-quee-et ... Song. Written by J. P.
Harrington. *Francis, Day & Hunter: London,* 1898. *s. sh.* fol.
H. 3602. (47.)

— The Coster's Christening. ⟨Song.⟩ Written by J. P. Harrington,
etc. [Staff and tonic sol-fa notation. Voice part.] *Francis,
Day & Hunter: London,* [1904.] *s. sh.* fol. **H. 3985. m. (22.)**

LE BRUNN (George)

— The Coster's Christening, *etc.* ⟨Song.⟩ [With separate voice
part.] 2 pt. *Francis, Day & Hunter: London,* [1904.] fol.
H. 3985. m. (23.)

— The Coster's Daughter. [Song.] Written by P. Pelham.
Francis, Day & Hunter: London, 1897. *s. sh.* fol.
H. 3602. (48.)

— The Coster's Family Tree. [Song.] Written by J. P. Harrington.
Francis, Day & Hunter: London, 1901. fol. **H. 3602. b. (13.)**

— The Coster's Mansion; or You've only got to stop just where
you is! [Song.] Written by W. Fieldhouse. *Francis, Day &
Hunter: London,* 1899. *s. sh.* fol. **H. 3602. b. (14.)**

— The Coster's Muvver. [Song.] Written by M. Arnold. *Francis,
Day & Hunter: London,* 1894. *s. sh.* fol. **H. 3602. (49.)**

— The D. T. Fund. [Song.] Written by E. Bateman. *Francis, Day
& Hunter: London,* 1896. *s. sh.* fol. **H. 3602. (56.)**

— Daddy's gone to Glory. [Song.] Written by F. E. D'Albert.
Howard & Co.: London, [1896.] fol. **H. 3602. a. (9.)**

— Daisy don't want you. ⟨Song.⟩ Written by J. P. Harrington,
etc. [Staff and tonic sol-fa notation. Voice part.] *Francis,
Day & Hunter: London,* [1901.] *s. sh.* fol. **H. 3985. m. (24.)**

— Daisy don't want you, *etc.* [With separate voice part.] 2 pt.
Francis, Day & Hunter: London, [1901.] fol.
H. 3985. m. (25.)

— Dancin' for de Cake! [Song.] Written by J. P. Harrington.
Francis, Day & Hunter: London, 1896. *s. sh.* fol.
H. 3602. (50.)

— Dancing in the Moonbeams. Vocal Gavotte. Written by T. Le
Brunn. *Francis, Day & Hunter: London,* 1893. fol.
H. 3602. a. (10.)

— The Dandy Coloured Coon. [Song.] Words by R. Morton.
Francis, Day & Hunter: London, 1893. fol. **H. 3602. (51.)**

— The Dandy coloured Coon. [Song.] Written by Richard
Morton, *etc.* pp. 4. *Francis, Day & Hunter: London,* [1893.]
fol.
*The song with banjo accompaniment is printed on the verso of
the front cover.* **I. 525. v. (2.)**

— The Dandy Coloured Coon's Barn Dance. [P. F.] *Francis,
Day & Hunter: London,* 1894. fol. **h. 3285. q. (14.)**

— The Dandy Coon's Sweetheart. [Song.] Written ... by
N. Christie. *Francis, Day & Hunter: London,* 1894. *s. sh.* fol.
H. 3602. (52.)

— The Darkey Aristocrat ... Song. Written by J. P. Harrington.
Francis, Day & Hunter: London, 1895. *s. sh* fol.
H. 3602. (53.)

— The Darkie's Wedding. [Song.] Written by J. P. Harrington.
B. Mocatta & Co.: London, 1895. fol. **H. 3602. a. (11.)**

— The Days of the Ruffle and the Patch. ⟨Song.⟩ Written by
John P. Harrington, *etc.* [Staff and tonic sol-fa notation.
Voice part.] *Francis, Day & Hunter: London,* [1903.] *s. sh.* fol.
H. 3985. m. (26.)

— The Days of the Ruffle and the Patch, *etc.* ⟨Song.⟩ [With
separate voice part.] 2 pt. *Francis, Day & Hunter: London,*
[1903.] fol. **H. 3985. m. (27.)**

— The Days of Tom and Jerry. ⟨Song.⟩ Written by John
P. Harrington, *etc.* [Staff and tonic sol-fa notation. Voice
part.] *Francis, Day & Hunter: London,* [1905.] *s. sh.* fol.
H. 3985. m. (28.)

— The Days of Tom and Jerry, *etc.* ⟨Song.⟩ [With separate voice
part.] 2 pt. *Francis, Day & Hunter: London,* [1905.] fol.
H. 3985. m. (29.)

LE BRUNN (George)

— Dear Marguerite, good-bye! ⟨Song.⟩ Written by Fred. W. Leigh, *etc.* [Staff and tonic sol-fa notation. Voice part.] *Francis, Day & Hunter: London*, [1903.] *s. sh.* fol.
H. 3985. m. (30.)

— Dear Marguerite, good-bye! *etc.* ⟨Song.⟩ pp. 9. *Francis, Day & Hunter: London*, [1903.] fol.
H. 3985. m. (31.)

— Dear old Chums ... [Song.] Written by Alfred J. Morris, *etc.* pp. 5. *Hopwood & Crew: London*, [1892.] fol.
H. 3980. pp. (46.)

— Detective Camera. [Song.] Words by J. Newland, *etc. C. Sheard & Co.: London*, 1892. fol.
H. 3602. (2.)

— Dey loved each other all de while, original coon song, written by Charles Wilmott. pp. 4. *Francis, Day & Hunter: London*, [1896.] fol.
H. 1654. qq. (29.)

— Dey loved each other all de while ... Song. Written by C. Wilmott. *Francis, Day & Hunter: London*, 1896. *s. sh.* fol.
H. 3602. (57.)

— Dinner-time! ... Song. Written by J. P. Harrington. *Francis, Day & Hunter: London*, 1896. *s. sh.* fol.
H. 3602. (54.)

— Do not nurse your Anger. [Song.] Written by H. Hunter. *Francis, Day & Hunter: London*, 1898. fol.
H. 3602. a. (12.)

— "Doesn't anybody want the Curate?" ⟨Song.⟩ Written by J. P. Harrington, *etc.* [With separate voice part.] 2 pt. *Francis, Day & Hunter: London*, [1905.] fol.
H. 3985. m. (32.)

— "Doesn't anybody want the Curate?" *etc.* ⟨Song.⟩ [Staff and tonic sol-fa notation. Voice part.] *Francis, Day & Hunter: London*, [1905.] *s. sh.* fol.
H. 3985. m. (33.)

— The Donah's Wedding. ⟨Song.⟩ Written by Edgar Bateman, *etc.* [Staff and tonic sol-fa notation. Voice part.] *Francis, Day & Hunter: London*, [1901.] *s. sh.* fol.
H. 3985. m. (34.)

— The Donah's Wedding, *etc.* ⟨Song.⟩ [With separate voice part.] 2 pt. *Francis, Day & Hunter: London*, [1901.] fol.
H. 3985. m. (35.)

— Don't laugh. [Song.] Written by R. Morton, *etc. Francis, Day & Hunter: London*, [1891.] fol.
H. 3602. (3.)

— Don't rob the Children of the Sunshine. ⟨Song.⟩ Written by Edgar Bateman, *etc.* [Staff and tonic sol-fa notation. Voice part.] *Francis, Day & Hunter: London*, [1902.] *s. sh.* fol.
H. 3985. m. (36.)

— Don't rob the Children of the Sunshine, *etc.* ⟨Song.⟩ [With separate voice part.] 2 pt. *Francis, Day & Hunter: London*, [1902.] fol.
H. 3985. m. (37.)

— Dreaming ... [Song.] Written by J. P. Harrington, *etc. Francis Bros. & Day: London*, [1888.] fol.
H. 1260. f. (31.)

— The Drummer's Letter. [Song.] Written by J. P. Harrington. *Francis, Day & Hunter: London*, 1894. *s. sh.* fol.
H. 3602. (55.)

— 'E talks like a Picture-book. [Song.] Written by A. R. Marshall. *Francis, Day & Hunter: London*, 1893. fol.
H. 3602. a. (13.)

— England in Danger? [Song.] Written by J. P. Harrington, *etc. Francis Bros. & Day: London*, [1888.] fol.
H. 1260. f. (32.)

— The English Rose. [Song.] ... Written by A. R. Marshall. *R. Maynard: London*, [1893.] fol.
H. 3602. (5.)

— Ere the Lamps are lit. [Song.] Written by J. P. Harrington, *etc. Francis, Day & Hunter: London*, [1890.] fol.
H. 3602. (6.)

— Every Hour and every Day. ⟨Song.⟩ Written by J. P. Harrington. [Staff and tonic sol-fa notation. Voice part.] *Francis, Day & Hunter: London*, [1904.] *s. sh.* fol.
H. 3985. m. (38.)

LE BRUNN (George)

— Every Hour and every Day, *etc.* ⟨Song.⟩ [With separate voice part.] 2 pt. *Francis, Day & Hunter: London*, [1904.] fol.
H. 3985. m. (39.)

— Every Time the Bell goes. [Song.] Written by A. Hall. *Francis, Day & Hunter: London*, 1897. *s. sh.* fol.
H. 3602. (59.)

— Everything in the Garden's lovely! [Song.] Written by J. P. Harrington. *Francis, Day & Hunter: London*, 1898. *s. sh.* fol.
H. 3602. (58.)

— A Faithful Woman. [Song.] Written by J. P. Harrington, *etc. Francis, Day & Hunter: London*, 1898. *s. sh.* fol.
H. 3602. b. (15.)

— Falling in and falling out. ⟨Song.⟩ Written by John P. Harrington, *etc.* [Staff and tonic sol-fa notation. Voice part.] *Francis, Day & Hunter: London*, [1901.] *s. sh.* fol.
H. 3985. m. (40.)

— Falling in and falling out, *etc.* ⟨Song.⟩ [With separate voice part.] 2 pt. *Francis, Day & Hunter: London*, [1901.] fol.
H. 3985. m. (41.)

— The Family Scapegrace. [Song.] Written by A. Hall. *Francis, Day & Hunter: London*, 1896. *s. sh.* fol.
H. 3602. (60.)

— The Fashionable Coon. [Song.] Written by C. Wilmott. *Francis, Day & Hunter: London*, 1896. *s. sh.* fol.
H. 3602. (61.)

— Feminine Moods and Tenses. Song. Written by J. P. Harrington. *Francis, Day & Hunter: London*, 1901. fol.
H. 3602. b. (16.)

— Fighting for the Flag they love. [Song.] Written by N. Atkins. *Francis, Day & Hunter: London*, 1896. *s. sh.* fol.
H. 3602. (62.)

— The Fighting Ships of England ... [Song.] Written by E. Bateman. *Francis, Day & Hunter: London*, 1898. *s. sh.* fol.
H. 3602. (63.)

— Flo, the Waterman's Daughter. Song. Written by J. P. Harrington. *Francis, Day & Hunter: London*, 1899. *s. sh.* fol.
H. 3602. b. (17.)

— Flyaway. Post-Dance. [P. F.] *Francis, Day & Hunter: London*, [1898.] fol.
h. 3282. f. (20.)

— Folkestone for the Day. [Song.] Written by E. Bateman. *Francis, Day & Hunter: London*, 1901. fol.
H. 3602. b. (18.)

— "Forget—forgive!" ⟨Song.⟩ Written by John P. Harrington. [Staff and tonic sol-fa notation. Voice part.] *Francis, Day & Hunter: London*, [1903.] *s. sh.* fol.
H. 3985. m. (42.)

— Forget—forgive, *etc.* ⟨Song.⟩ [With separate voice part.] 2 pt. *Francis, Day & Hunter: London*, [1903.] fol.
H. 3985. m. (43.)

— Gallant Gordon Highlanders. [Song.] Written by J. P. Harrington. *Francis, Day & Hunter: London*, 1897. *s. sh.* fol.
H. 3602. (64.)

— The Game of Life. Duet. Written by W. Pink. *Francis, Day & Hunter: London*, 1899. *s. sh.* fol.
H. 3602. b. (19.)

— The Geisha. [Song.] Written by C. Wilmott. *Francis, Day Hunter: London*, 1896. *s. sh.* fol.
H. 3602. (65.)

— George, Dear! [Song.] Written by J. P. Harrington. *Francis, Day & Hunter: London*, 1897. *s. sh.* fol.
H. 3602. (66.)

— The Girl in the Khaki Dress. [Song.] Written by J. P. Harrington, *etc. Francis, Day & Hunter: London*, 1900. *s. sh.* fol.
H. 3602. b. (20.)

LE BRUNN (George)

— The Girl you leave behind you. [Song.] Written by J. P. Harrington, *etc. Francis, Day & Hunter: London*, 1899. *s. sh.* fol.　　　　　　　　　　　　　　**H. 3602. b. (21.)**

— The Girls from Bryants and May. ⟨Song.⟩ Written by Edgar Bateman, *etc.* [Staff and tonic sol-fa notation. Voice part.] *Francis, Day & Hunter: London*, [1901.] *s. sh.* fol.　　　　　　　　　　　**H. 3985. m. (44.)**

— The Girls of to-day. [Song.] Written by J. P. Harrington, *etc. Francis, Day & Hunter: London*, [1888.] fol.　　　　　　　　　　　　　　**H. 1260. f. (33.)**

— Girls wouldn't be wanted at all. ⟨Song.⟩ Written by John P. Harrington, *etc.* [Staff and tonic sol-fa notation. Voice part.] *Francis, Day & Hunter: London*, [1904.] *s. sh.* fol.　　　　　　　　　　　**H. 3985. m. (45.)**

— Girls wouldn't be wanted at all, *etc.* ⟨Song.⟩ [With separate voice part.] 2 pt. *Francis, Day & Hunter: London*, [1904.] fol.　　　　　　　　　**H. 3985. m. (46.)**

— The Glorious Days of my Youth. [Song.] Written by R. Morton. *Francis, Day & Hunter: London*, 1898. *s. sh.* fol.　　　　　　　　　　　　　　**H. 3602. (67.)**

— Go easy! ⟨Song.⟩ Written by John P. Harrington, *etc.* [Staff and tonic sol-fa notation. Voice part.] *Francis, Day & Hunter: London*, [1902.] *s. sh.* fol.　　**H. 3985. m. (47.)**

— Go easy! *etc.* ⟨Song.⟩ [With separate voice part.] 2 pt. *Francis, Day & Hunter: London*, [1902.] fol.　　**H. 3985. m. (48.)**

— Going Home! [Song.] Written by J. P. Harrington. *Francis, Day & Hunter: London*, 1895. *s. sh.* fol.　　**H. 3602. (68.)**

— The Golden Dustman ... [Song.] Written by E. Graham. *Francis, Day & Hunter: London*, 1897. *s. sh.* fol.　　　　　　　　　　　　　　**H. 3602. (69.)**

— Good-for-nothing Nan. [Song.] Written by Thos. Le Brunn. pp. 4. *Francis, Day & Hunter: London*, [1893.] 4°.　　　　　　　　　　　　　**H. 3980. pp. (47.)**

— Good old Santa Claus. [Song.] Written by P. Heathcote-Snape. *Francis, Day & Hunter: London*, 1896. *s. sh.* fol.　　　　　　　　　　　　　**H. 3602. (70.)**

— Grandad's Birthday ... [Song.] Written by J. P. Harrington. *Francis, Day & Hunter: London*, 1894. *s. sh.* fol.　　　　　　　　　　　　　**H. 3602. (71.)**

— Half-past Nine. [Song.] Words by W. Pink. *Francis, Day & Hunter: London*, 1893. fol.　　　　**H. 3602. (7.)**

— Half-past Nine. [Song.] Words by W. Pink. (Om half tien. Vrij naar het Engelsch door George.) *J. J. Eggers: Leiden*, [1896.] fol.　　　　　　　　　**H. 3602. a. (14.)**

— Half-past Nine. March. [P. F.] *Francis, Day & Hunter: London*, 1894. fol.　　　　　　　**h. 1489. s. (26.)**

— The Handkerchief marked with "M". ⟨Song.⟩ Written by Edgar Bateman, *etc.* [Staff und tonic sol-fa notation. Voice part.] *Francis, Day & Hunter: London*, [1903.] *s. sh.* fol.　　　　　　　　　**H. 3985. n. (1.)**

— The Handkerchief marked with "M," *etc.* ⟨Song.⟩ [With separate voice part.] 2 pt. *Francis, Day & Hunter: London*, [1903.] fol.　　　　　　　　**H. 3985. n. (2.)**

— Happy 'cos dey foun' dis coon. [Song.] Written by J. P. Harrington. *Francis, Day & Hunter: London*, 1897. *s. sh.* fol.　　　　　　　　　　**H. 3602. (72.)**

— Hard to say! [Song.] Written by J. P. Harrington. *Francis, Day & Hunter: London*, 1898. *s. sh.* fol.　　**H. 3602. (73.)**

— Has anybody here seen Casey? ⟨Song.⟩ Written by John P. Harrington, *etc.* [Staff and tonic sol-fa notation. Voice part.] *Francis, Day & Hunter: London*, [1902.] *s. sh.* fol.　　　　　　　　　　**H. 3985. n. (3.)**

LE BRUNN (George)

— Has anybody here seen Casey? ⟨Song.⟩ [With separate voice part.] 2 pt. *Francis, Day & Hunter: London*, [1902.] fol.　　　　　　　　　**H. 3985. n. (4.)**

— He is ignorant ... Song. Words by J. P. Harrington. *B. Mocatta & Co.: London*, [1896.] fol.　　**H. 3602. a. (15.)**

— He kissed I once ... ⟨Song.⟩ Written by J. P. Harrington, *etc.* [Staff and tonic sol-fa notation. Voice part.] *Francis, Day & Hunter: London*, [1904.] *s. sh.* fol.　　**H. 3985. n. (5.)**

— He kissed I once, *etc.* ⟨Song.⟩ [With separate voice part.] 2 pt. *Francis, Day & Hunter: London*, [1904.] fol.　　**H. 3985. n. (6.)**

— He knows a good Thing when he sees it. [Song.] Written by J. P. Harrington. *Francis, Day & Hunter: London*, 1895. *s. sh.* fol.　　　　　　　　　　　**H. 3602. (75.)**

— He's going there every Night. [Song.] Written by Murray and Leigh, *etc. Francis, Day & Hunter: London*, 1898. *s. sh.* fol.　　　　　　　　**H. 3602. b. (22.)**

— He's off to the Land of Nod. ⟨Song.⟩ Written by John P. Harrington. [Staff and tonic sol-fa notation. Voice part.] *Francis, Day & Hunter: London*, [1901.] *s. sh.* fol.　　　　　　　　　　**H. 3985. n. (7.)**

— He's off to the Land of Nod, *etc.* ⟨Song.⟩ [With separate voice part.] 2 pt. *Francis, Day & Hunter: London*, [1902.] fol.　　　　　　　　**H. 3985. n. (8.)**

— He was Whistling this Tune all Day. [Song.] Written by J. P. Harrington. *Francis, Day & Hunter: London*, [1891.] fol.　　　　　　　　　　**H. 3602. (8.)**

— Heigho! It might have been! [Song.] Written by J. P. Harrington. *Francis, Day & Hunter: London*, 1896. *s. sh.* fol.　　　　　　　　**H. 3602. (74.)**

— A Henley Romance ... [Song.] Written by J. P. Harrington. *Francis, Day & Hunter: London*, 1896. *s. sh.* fol.　　　　　　　　　　**H. 3602. (76.)**

— Hi! Boys, Hi! Boys. *See* infra: [Uncle Joe's Spree.]

— Hide yer pretty Face behind yer Fan. [Song.] Written by F. Leo. *Howard & Co.: London*, [1896.] fol.　　　　　　　　　　　　**H. 3602. a. (16.)**

— Hippity Hip Hooray ... [Song.] Written by T. Le Brunn. *Francis, Day & Hunter: London*, 1893. fol.　　**H. 3602. a. (17.)**

— Hi-tiddley-hi-ti ... [Song.] ... Written by E. W. Rogers. *Francis, Day & Hunter: London*, [1890.] fol.　　**H. 3602. (11.)**

— Hi-tiddley-hi-ti. *See* WILLIAMS (W.) Hi-ti-hi. Polka, *etc.* [On G. Le Brunn's song.] [1890.] fol.　　**h. 3806. (16.)**

— Hi-tiddley-hi-ti. *See* WILLIAMS (W.) Hi-tiddley-hi-ti. Quadrilles [on G. Le Brunn's song]. [1891.] fol.　　　　　　　　　　　**h. 3806. (15.)**

— The Hoodoo. [Song.] Written by R. Morton. *Francis, Day & Hunter: London*, 1897. *s. sh.* fol.　　**H. 3602. (77.)**

— How India kept her Word. [Song.] Written by J. P. Harrington. *Francis, Day & Hunter: London*, 1898. *s. sh.* fol.　　　　　　　　　**H. 3602. (78.)**

— How will the Voyage end? ... [Song.] Words by W. Pink. *Francis, Day & Hunter: London*, 1894. *s. sh.* fol.　　　　　　　　　　**H. 3602. (79.)**

— Hullo! I've been looking for you. [Song.] Written by J. P. Harrington. *Francis, Day & Hunter: London*, 1901. fol.　　　　　　　　　　　**H. 3602. b. (24.)**

— Hulloa! hulloa!! hulloa!!! [Song.] Written by G. Rollit, *etc. Francis, Day & Hunter: London*, 1899. *s. sh.* fol.　　　　　　　　　　　**H. 3602. b. (23.)**

LE BRUNN (George)

— I 'aven't told 'im. [Song.] Written by Murray & Leigh, *etc.*
Francis, Day & Hunter: London, 1898. *s. sh.* fol.
H. 3602. b. (25.)

— I can tell it by your Bumps. [Song.] Written by J. P.
Harrington, *etc. Hopwood & Crew: London,* [1888.] fol.
H. 1260. f. (35.)

— I can't resist you, Sir. [Song.] Words by T. Le Brunn.
M. Witmark & Sons: New York, 1893. fol. H. 3602. a. (19.)

— I'd like one like Pa had yesterday ... Song. Written by J. P.
Harrington. *Francis, Day & Hunter: London,* 1895. *s. sh.* fol.
H. 3602. (83.)

— I didn't know what to say. [Song.] Written by H. Castling.
Francis, Day & Hunter: London, 1897. *s. sh.* fol.
H. 3602. (81.)

— I do know! [Song.] Written by J. P. Harrington, *etc. Francis,
Day & Hunter: London,* 1900. fol. H. 3602. b. (26.)

— I know now. [Song.] Written by W. T. Lytton. *Francis, Day
& Hunter: London,* 1895. *s. sh.* fol. H. 3602. (87.)

— I like you, and you like me. [Song.] Written by T. Le Brunn.
Francis, Day & Hunter: London, 1895. *s. sh.* fol.
H. 3602. (88.)

— I love one Girl—she loves me! [Song.] Written by J. P.
Harrington. *Francis, Day & Hunter: London,* 1896. *s. sh.* fol.
H. 3602. (89.)

— I love you both the best! ⟨Song.⟩ Written by John P.
Harrington. [Staff and tonic sol-fa notation. Voice part.]
Francis, Day & Hunter: London, [1901.] *s. sh.* fol.
H. 3985. n. (11.)

— I love you both the best! *etc.* ⟨Song.⟩ [With separate voice
part.] 2 pt. *Francis, Day & Hunter: London,* [1901.] fol.
H. 3985. n. (12.)

— I'm looking for the Owner. [Song.] Written by J. P.
Harrington, *etc. Francis & Day: London,* [1889.] fol.
H. 1260. f. (34.)

— I'm looking for Trilby! [Song.] Solo Version. Written by J. P.
Harrington. *Francis, Day & Hunter: London,* 1895. *s. sh.* fol.
H. 3602. (90.)

— "I'm sorry, but I can't come out!" ... ⟨Song.⟩ Words by John
P. Harrington. [Staff and tonic sol-fa notation. Voice part.]
Francis, Day & Hunter: London, [1906.] *s. sh.* fol.
H. 3985. n. (13.)

— "I'm sorry, but I can't come out," *etc.* ⟨Song.⟩ [With separate
voice part.] 2 pt. *Francis, Day & Hunter: London,* [1906.] fol.
H. 3985. n. (14.)

— I shall always love you. ⟨Song.⟩ Written by Harry Castling.
[Staff and tonic sol-fa notation. Voice part.] *Francis, Day &
Hunter: London,* [1901.] *s. sh.* fol. H. 3985. n. (15.)

— I shall always love you, *etc.* ⟨Song.⟩ [With separate voice
part.] 2 pt. *Francis, Day & Hunter: London,* [1901.] fol.
H. 3985. n. (16.)

— I shall always love you. [Song.] Written by Harry Castling.
[c. 1905.] fol.
A pirated edition. H. 1848. b. (13.)

— I should drive it in the Lord Mayor's Show. [Song.] Written
by F. W. Leigh. *Francis, Day & Hunter: London,* 1897.
s. sh. fol. H. 3602. (95.)

— I still love you, my Lou! ... ⟨Song.⟩ Written by J. P.
Harrington, *etc.* [Staff and tonic sol-fa notation. Voice part.]
Francis, Day & Hunter: London, [1903.] *s. sh.* fol.
H. 3985. n. (17.)

LE BRUNN (George)

— I still love you, my Lou, *etc.* [With separate voice part.] 2 pt.
Francis, Day & Hunter: London, [1903.] fol.
H. 3985. n. (18.)

— I thought her as sweet as a Plum. [Song.] Written by A. Hall.
Francis, Day & Hunter: London, 1896. *s. sh.* fol.
H. 3602. (96.)

— "I want to have a Chinese Honeymoon." ⟨Song.⟩ Written by
J. P. Harrington, *etc.* [Staff and tonic sol-fa notation. Voice
part.] *Francis, Day & Hunter: London,* [1904.] *s. sh.* fol.
H. 3985. n. (19.)

— "I want to have a Chinese Honeymoon," *etc.* ⟨Song.⟩ [With
separate voice part.] 2 pt. *Francis, Day & Hunter: London,*
[1904.] fol. H. 3985. n. (20.)

— I was one of 'em. [Song.] Written by J. P. Harrington, *etc.*
Francis Bros. & Day: London, [1889.] fol. H. 1260. f. (38.)

— I wouldn't care to change you for a new Wife now. ⟨Song.⟩
Written by Walter P. Keen, *etc.* [Staff and tonic sol-fa
notation. Voice part.] *Francis, Day & Hunter: London,*
[1903.] *s. sh.* fol. H. 3985. n. (21.)

— I wouldn't care to change you for a new Wife now, *etc.*
⟨Song.⟩ [With separate voice part.] 2 pt. *Francis, Day &
Hunter: London,* [1903.] fol. H. 3985. n. (22.)

— The Idler. [Song.] Written by J. P. Harrington. *Francis, Day
& Hunter: London,* 1896. fol. H. 3602. (82.)

— If I was King of England. ⟨Song.⟩ Written by Jay Bee, *etc.*
[Staff and tonic sol-fa notation. Voice part.] *Francis, Day &
Hunter: London,* [1902.] *s. sh.* fol. H. 3985. n. (23.)

— If I was King of England, *etc.* ⟨Song.⟩ [With separate voice
part.] 2 pt. *Francis, Day & Hunter: London,* [1902.] fol.
H. 3985. n. (24.)

— If it wasn't for the 'Ouses in between ... [Song.] Written by
E. Bateman. *Francis, Day & Hunter: London,* 1894. *s. sh.* fol.
H. 3602. (84.)

— If only your Heart could speak. ⟨Song.⟩ Written by Fred. W.
Leigh, *etc.* [Staff and tonic sol-fa notation. Voice part.]
Francis, Day & Hunter: London, [1901.] *s. sh.* fol.
H. 3985. n. (25.)

— If only your Heart could speak, *etc.* ⟨Song.⟩ [With separate
voice part.] 2 pt. *Francis, Day & Hunter: London,* [1901.] fol.
H. 3985. n. (26.)

— If she'd only been a poor Girl. ⟨Song.⟩ Written by J. P.
Harrington, *etc.* [Staff and tonic sol-fa notation. Voice part.]
Francis, Day & Hunter: London, [1903.] *s. sh.* fol.
H. 3985. n. (27.)

— If she'd only been a poor Girl, *etc.* ⟨Song.⟩ [With separate
voice part.] 2 pt. *Francis, Day & Hunter: London,* [1903.] fol.
H. 3985. n. (28.)

— If that's your Game, I'm going. [Song.] Written by A. Hall.
Francis, Day & Hunter: London, 1896. *s. sh.* fol.
H. 3602. (85.)

— If the Thames could only speak. [Song.] Written by J. P.
Harrington. *Francis, Day & Hunter: London,* 1897. *s. sh.* fol.
H. 3602. (86.)

— If you go, then this will bring you back. ⟨Song.⟩ Written by
John P. Harrington, *etc.* [Staff and tonic sol-fa notation.
Voice part.] *Francis, Day & Hunter: London,* [1901.] *s. sh.* fol.
H. 3985. n. (29.)

— If you want to come in, come in. [Song.] Written by J. P.
Harrington, *etc. Francis, Day & Hunter: London,* 1899. *s. sh.*
fol. H. 3602. b. (27.)

— In England. [Song.] Written by J. P. Harrington, *etc.*
Hopwood & Crew: London, [1888.] fol. H. 1260. f. (36.)

LE BRUNN (GEORGE)

— In old England o'er the Sea. [Song.] Written by J. P. Harrington. *Francis, Day & Hunter: London*, 1894. *s. sh.* fol.
H. 3602. (93.)

— In the Royal Artillery ... ⟨Song.⟩ Written by J. P. Harrington. [Staff and tonic sol-fa notation. Voice part.] *Francis, Day & Hunter: London*, [1905.] *s. sh.* fol.
H. 3985. n. (30.)

— In the Royal Artillery, *etc.* ⟨Song.⟩ [With separate voice part.] 2 pt. *Francis, Day & Hunter: London*, [1905.] fol.
H. 3985. n. (31.)

— India's Reply. [Song.] Written by J. P. Harrington. *Francis, Day & Hunter: London*, 1895. *s. sh.* fol.
H. 3602. (92.)

— India's Reply. Grand March. [P. F.] *Francis, Day & Hunter: London*, [1895.] fol.
h. 3282. f. (21.)

— The Indian Prince. [Song.] Written by A. Hall. *Francis, Day & Hunter: London*, 1898. *s. sh.* fol.
H. 3602. (91.)

— The Irish are always in front. A National Song. Words by J. F. Lambe, *etc.* (Arranged by G. F. Hayward.) *Houghton & Co.: London*, [1900.] fol.
H. 3602. b. (28.)

— It didn't come off after all! ⟨Song.⟩ Written by J. P. Harrington, *etc.* [Staff and tonic sol-fa notation. Voice part.] *Francis, Day & Hunter: London*, [1902.] *s. sh.* fol.
H. 3985. n. (32.)

— It didn't come off after all! *etc.* ⟨Song.⟩ [With separate voice part.] 2 pt. *Francis, Day & Hunter: London*, [1902.] fol.
H. 3985. n. (33.)

— It's a bright Look out! ⟨Song.⟩ Written by Edgar Bateman, *etc.* [Staff and tonic sol-fa notation. Voice part.] *Francis, Day & Hunter: London*, [1902.] *s. sh.* fol. **H. 3985. n. (34.)**

— It's a bright Look out! *etc.* ⟨Song.⟩ [With separate voice part.] 2 pt. *Francis, Day & Hunter: London*, [1902.] fol.
H. 3985. n. (35.)

— It's a great big Shame! or I'm blowed if 'e can call 'isself 'is own. ⟨Song.⟩ Written by Edgar Bateman. pp. 4. *Francis, Day & Hunter: London*, [1896.] fol.
H. 1654. tt. (6.)

— It's a jolly fine Game, played slow! [Song.] Written by J. P. Harrington. *Francis, Day & Hunter: London*, 1895. *s. sh.* fol.
H. 3602. (97.)

— It's just like Money frown away. ⟨Song.⟩ Written by Worton David, *etc.* [Staff and tonic sol-fa notation. Voice part.] *Francis, Day & Hunter: London*, [1901.] *s. sh.* fol.
H. 3985. n. (36.)

— It's just like Money frown away, *etc.* ⟨Song.⟩ [With separate voice part.] 2 pt. *Francis, Day & Hunter: London*, [1901.] fol.
H. 3985. n. (37.)

— It's Money well laid out. [Song.] Written by H. Castling. *Francis, Day & Hunter: London*, 1898. *s. sh.* fol.
H. 3602. (98.)

— It's not the one who's richest who has got the biggest Heart. ⟨Song.⟩ Written by J. P. Harrington, *etc.* [Staff and tonic sol-fa notation. Voice part.] *Francis, Day & Hunter: London*, [1903.] *s. sh.* fol. **H. 3985. n. (38.)**

— It's not the one who's richest who has got the biggest Heart, *etc.* ⟨Song.⟩ [With separate voice part.] 2 pt. *Francis, Day & Hunter: London*, [1903.] fol. **H. 3985. n. (39.)**

— It's the strangest Co-in-ci-dence I 'ave seen. [Song.] Written by E. Bateman, *etc. Francis, Day & Hunter: London*, 1900. *s. sh.* fol.
H. 3602. b. (29.)

— It's very much warmer there. [Song.] Written by J. P. Harrington, *etc. Francis Bros. & Day: London*, [1887.] fol.
H. 1260. f. (37.)

LE BRUNN (GEORGE)

— It went—went quick! [Song.] Written by R. Morton. *Francis, Day & Hunter: London*, 1897. *s. sh.* fol. **H. 3602. (99.)**

— Jack Sheppard. [Song.] The Words by R. Morton. *Francis, Day & Hunter: London*, 1894. *s. sh.* fol. **H. 3602. (80.)**

— Jacob Strauss. [Song.] Written by W. Pink. *Francis, Day & Hunter: London*, 1893. fol. **H. 3602. a. (18.)**

— Josephine. [Song.] Written by G. D. Wheeler. *Francis, Day & Hunter: London*, 1897. *s. sh.* fol. **H. 3602. (94.)**

— Josephine. [Song.] Written by G. D. Wheeler. [c. 1900.] fol. *A pirated edition.* **H. 1848. b. (14.)**

— Just as I was getting into Bed. ⟨Song.⟩ Written by John P. Harrington, *etc.* [Staff and tonic sol-fa notation. Voice part.] *Francis, Day & Hunter: London*, [1901.] *s. sh.* fol.
H. 3985. n. (40.)

— Just as I was getting into Bed, *etc.* ⟨Song.⟩ [With separate voice part.] 2 pt. *Francis, Day & Hunter: London*, [1901.] fol.
H. 3985. n. (41.)

— Keep away. [Song.] Written by W. T. Lytton, *etc. Francis, Day & Hunter: London*, [1891.] fol. **H. 3602. (12.)**

— Keep yer 'air on. [Song.] Written by H. M. Watkins, *etc. Francis, Day & Hunter: London*, 1900. fol. **H. 3602. b. (30.)**

— Kruger's Dinner Party; or we'll be there. Song. Words by F. C. Smale. *Keith, Prowse & Co.: London*, 1899. fol.
H. 3602. b. (31.)

— De Lamb from Alabam'. [Song.] Written by J. P. Harrington. *Francis, Day & Hunter: London*, 1896. *s. sh.* fol.
H. 3602. (100.)

— The Last Farewell. ⟨Song.⟩ Written by J. P. Harrington, *etc.* [Staff and tonic sol-fa notation. Voice part.] *Francis, Day & Hunter: London*, [1902.] *s. sh.* fol. **H. 3985. n. (42.)**

— The Last Farewell, *etc.* ⟨Song.⟩ [With separate voice part.] 2 pt. *Francis, Day & Hunter: London*, [1902.] fol.
H. 3985. n. (43.)

— The Last of the Dandies. ⟨Song.⟩ Written by J. P. Harrington. [With separate voice part.] 2 pt. *Francis, Day & Hunter: London*, [1902.] fol. **H. 3985. n. (44.)**

— The Last Shot. [Song.] Written by C. Wilmott. *Francis, Day & Hunter: London*, 1894. fol. **H. 3602. a. (20.)**

— The Late and Early Club ... [Song.] Words by J. P. Harrington. *M. Witmark & Sons: New York*, 1893. fol.
H. 3602. a. (21.)

— Leave a little Bit for your Tutor. [Song.] Written by J. P. Harrington, *etc. Francis, Day & Hunter: London*, 1901. fol.
H. 3602. b. (32.)

— Let us have a Song we can all sing. ⟨Song.⟩ Written by John P. Harrington, *etc.* [Staff and tonic sol-fa notation. Voice part.] *Francis, Day & Hunter: London*, [1902.] *s. sh.* fol.
H. 3985. n. (45.)

— Let us have a Song we can all sing, *etc.* ⟨Song.⟩ [With separate voice part.] 2 pt. *Francis, Day & Hunter: London*, [1902.] fol.
H. 3985. n. (46.)

— Like a Lady. [Song.] Written by J. P. Harrington. *Francis, Day & Hunter: London*, 1893. fol. **H. 3602. a. (22.)**

— Little Miss Black and Mr. White. ⟨Song.⟩ Written by John P. Harrington. [Staff and tonic sol-fa notation. Voice part.] *Francis, Day & Hunter: London*, [1904.] *s. sh.* fol.
H. 3985. n. (47.)

— Little Miss Black and Mr. White, *etc.* ⟨Song.⟩ [With separate voice part.] 2 pt. *Francis, Day & Hunter: London*, [1904.] fol.
H. 3985. n. (48.)

LE BRUNN (George)

— The Little Mother. [Song.] Written by W. T. Lytton, *etc.*
Francis, Day & Hunter: London, 1901. fol.　　**H. 3602. b. (33.)**

— Lizer 'Awkins ... [Song.] Written by A. J. Morris, *etc.*
Reynolds & Co.: London, [1892.] fol.　　**H. 3602. (1.)**

— 'Liza Johnson ... ⟨Song.⟩ Written by Edgar Bateman, *etc.*
[Staff and tonic sol-fa notation. Voice part.] *Francis, Day &
Hunter: London*, [1901.] *s. sh.* fol.　　**H. 3985. n. (49.)**

— 'Liza Johnson, *etc.* [With separate voice part.] 2 pt. *Francis,
Day & Hunter: London*, [1901.] fol.　　**H. 3985. n. (50.)**

— 'Liza Johnson or the Rag-time coster. ⟨Song.⟩ Written by
Edgar Bateman. [c. 1905.] fol.
A pirated edition.　　**H. 1848. b. (15.)**

— Looking for a Coon like me! [Song.] Written by J. P.
Harrington. *Francis, Day & Hunter: London*, 1894. *s. sh.* fol.
　　H. 3602. (101.)

— Louie didn't know! ⟨Song.⟩ Written by J. P. Harrington, *etc.*
[Staff and tonic sol-fa notation. Voice part.] *Francis, Day &
Hunter: London*, [1901.] *s. sh.* fol.　　**H. 3985. n. (51.)**

— Louie didn't know!, *etc.* ⟨Song.⟩ [With separate voice part.]
2 pt. *Francis, Day & Hunter: London*, [1901.] fol.
　　H. 3985. n. (52.)

— Love keeps dem always young. [Song.] Written by J. P.
Harrington. *Howard & Co.: London*, [1896.] fol.
　　H. 3602. a. (23.)

— Love steals in. (A song of Harlequin and Columbine.)
Written by Wal Pink, *etc.* [Staff and tonic sol-fa notation.
Voice part.] *Francis, Day & Hunter: London*, [1901.] *s. sh.* fol.
　　H. 3985. n. (53.)

— Love steals in. (A song of Harlequin and Columbine), *etc.*
[With separate voice part.] 2 pt. *Francis, Day & Hunter:
London*, [1901.] fol.　　**H. 3985. n. (54.)**

— The Lovers' Walk. ⟨Song.⟩ Written by J. P. Harrington, *etc.*
[Staff and tonic sol-fa notation. Voice part.] *Francis, Day &
Hunter: London*, [1902.] *s. sh.* fol.　　**H. 3985. n. (55.)**

— The Lovers' Walk, *etc.* ⟨Song.⟩ [With separate voice part.] 2 pt.
Francis, Day & Hunter: London, [1902.] fol.
　　H. 3985. n. (56.)

— Ma Coon am a Millionaire. ⟨Song.⟩ Written by J. P.
Harrington, *etc.* [Staff and tonic sol-fa notation. Voice part.]
Francis, Day & Hunter: London, [1904.] *s. sh.* fol.
　　H. 3985. o. (1.)

— Ma Coon am a Millionaire, *etc.* ⟨Song.⟩ [With separate voice
part.] *Francis, Day & Hunter: London*, [1904.] fol.
　　H. 3985. o. (2.)

— Ma dusky Rose. ⟨Song.⟩ Written by J. P. Harrington, *etc.*
[Staff and tonic sol-fa notation. Voice part.] *Francis, Day &
Hunter: London*, [1904.] *s. sh.* fol.　　**H. 3985. o. (3.)**

— Ma dusky Rose, *etc.* ⟨Song.⟩ [With separate voice part.] 2 pt.
Francis, Day & Hunter: London, [1904.] fol.　　**H. 3985. o. (4.)**

— Ma Jeannette and Marguerite. [Duet.] Written by J. P.
Harrington. *Francis, Day & Hunter: London*, 1893. fol.
　　H. 3602. a. (24.)

— Ma Little Darkey Fairy. Plantation Song. Written by
W. Burnot. [With] Banjo accompaniment arranged by
N. Greenop. *J. A. Turner: London*, [1898.] fol.
　　H. 3602. b. (35.)

— Ma Starlight Queen. ⟨Song.⟩ Written by J. P. Harrington.
pp. 4. *E. Ascherberg & Co.: London*, [1902.] fol.
　　H. 3985. o. (5.)

— Maisey! my Maisey! ... [Song.] Written by F. W. Leigh.
Francis, Day & Hunter: London, 1901. fol.　　**H. 3602. b. (34.)**

LE BRUNN (George)

— The Man in the dirty Coat. ⟨Song.⟩ Written by J. P.
Harrington, *etc.* [Staff and tonic sol-fa notation. Voice part.]
Francis, Day & Hunter: London, [1901.] *s. sh.* fol.
　　H. 3985. o. (6.)

— The Man in the dirty Coat, *etc.* ⟨Song.⟩ [With separate voice
part.] 2 pt. *Francis, Day & Hunter: London*, [1901.] fol.
　　H. 3985. o. (7.)

— Many can help one, where one can't help many. ⟨Song.⟩
Written by J. P. Harrington, *etc.* [Staff and tonic sol-fa
notation. Voice part.] *Francis, Day & Hunter: London*,
[1904.] *s. sh.* fol.　　**H. 3985. o. (8.)**

— Many can help one, where one can't help many, *etc.* ⟨Song.⟩
[With separate voice part.] 2 pt. *Francis, Day & Hunter:
London*, [1904.] fol.　　**H. 3985. o. (9.)**

— Maria of Turnham Green. ⟨Song.⟩ Written by John P.
Harrington, *etc.* [Staff and tonic sol-fa notation. Voice part.]
Francis, Day & Hunter: London, [1903.] *s. sh.* fol.
　　H. 3985. o. (10.)

— Maria of Turnham Green, *etc.* ⟨Song.⟩ [With separate voice
part.] 2 pt. *Francis, Day & Hunter: London*, [1903.] fol.
　　H. 3985. o. (11.)

— Selection of Marie Lloyd's Popular Songs. Arranged for the
Pianoforte by G. Le Brunn. *Francis, Day & Hunter: London*,
1901. fol.　　**h. 3282. w. (34.)**

— [Another edition.] Marie Lloyd's Songs. Selection, *etc.*
Francis, Day & Hunter: London, 1901. fol.　　**h. 3282. w. (35.)**

— Mary kissed the Captain. ⟨Song.⟩ Written by J. P. Harrington,
etc. [Staff and tonic sol-fa notation. Voice part.] *Francis,
Day & Hunter: London*, [1904.] *s. sh.* fol.　　**H. 3985. o. (12.)**

— Mary kissed the Captain, *etc.* ⟨Song.⟩ [With separate voice
part.] 2 pt. *Francis, Day & Hunter: London*, [1904.] fol.
　　H. 3985. o. (13.)

— Mary's Cheeks are rosy. [Song.] Written by T. Le Brunn, *etc.*
Francis, Day & Hunter: London, [1891.] fol.　　**H. 3602. (13.)**

— Masks and Faces. [Song.] Written by J. P. Harrington, *etc.*
Francis Bros. & Day: London, [1888.] fol.　　**H. 1260. f. (39.)**

— "May cannot mate with December." ⟨Song.⟩ Written by John
P. Harrington. [Staff and tonic sol-fa notation. Voice part.]
Francis, Day & Hunter: London, [1904.] *s. sh.* fol.
　　H. 3985. o. (14.)

— "May cannot mate with December," *etc.* ⟨Song.⟩ [With
separate voice part.] 2 pt. *Francis, Day & Hunter: London*,
[1904.] fol.　　**H. 3985. o. (15.)**

— Me and 'Er. [Song.] Written by W. Hastings. *Francis, Day &
Hunter: London* 1894. *s. sh.* fol.　　**H. 3602. (102.)**

— Merrie, merrie England. [Song.] Written by W. Pink. *Francis,
Day & Hunter: London*, 1893. fol.　　**H. 3602. a. (25.)**

— Mickey's visiting Cards. ⟨Song.⟩ Written by J. P. Harrington,
etc. [Staff and tonic sol-fa notation. Voice part.] *Francis,
Day & Hunter: London*, [1903.] *s. sh.* fol.　　**H. 3985. o. (16.)**

— Mickey's visiting Cards, *etc.* ⟨Song.⟩ [With separate voice
part.] 2 pt. *Francis, Day & Hunter: London*, [1903.] fol.
　　H. 3985. o. (17.)

— Milk O! or, the Up-to-date Yodeller. [Song.] Written by J. P.
Harrington, *etc. Francis, Day & Hunter: London*, 1898.
s. sh. fol.　　**H. 3602. b. (36.)**

— A Millionaire. [Song.] Written by A. Hall. *Francis, Day &
Hunter: London*, 1897. *s. sh.* fol.　　**H. 3602. (103.)**

— Minding it for Uncle. [Song.] Written by J. P. Harrington, *etc.*
H. Beresford: London, [1890.] fol.　　**H. 3602. (14.)**

LE BRUNN (GEORGE)

— Mine did. [Song.] Written by H. Leighton, *etc. Francis, Day & Hunter: London*, [1891.] fol.   **H. 3602. (15.)**

— Mister Brown and the Venetian Blind. [Song.] Written by J. P. Harrington. *Francis, Day & Hunter: London*, 1895. *s. sh.* fol.   **H. 3602. (104.)**

— 'Mongst the Poppies and the Corn. ⟨Song.⟩ Written by John P. Harrington, *etc.* [Staff and tonic sol-fa notation. Voice part.] *Francis, Day & Hunter: London*, [1902.] *s. sh.* fol.   **H. 3985. o. (18.)**

— 'Mongst the Poppies and the Corn, *etc.* ⟨Song.⟩ [With separate voice part.] 2 pt. *Francis, Day & Hunter: London*, [1902.] fol.   **H. 3985. o. (19.)**

— The Moocher's Walk. ⟨Song.⟩ Written by Mark Lorne & Carl Howard. [With separate voice part.] 2 pt. *Francis, Day & Hunter: London*, [1902.] fol.   **H. 3985. o. (20.)**

— Moonbeams. [Song.] Written by W. Pink, *etc. Francis, Day & Hunter: London*, 1892. fol.   **H. 3602. (16.)**

— More Trouble in Store for someone. ⟨Song.⟩ Written by John P. Harrington, *etc.* [Staff and tonic sol-fa notation. Voice part.] *Francis, Day & Hunter: London*, [1904.] *s. sh.* fol.   **H. 3985. o. (21.)**

— More Trouble in Store for someone, *etc.* ⟨Song.⟩ [With separate voice part.] 2 pt. *Francis, Day & Hunter: London*, [1904.] fol.   **H. 3985. o. (22.)**

— The Mother Tongue. [Song.] Written by A. Hall, *etc. Francis, Day & Hunter: London*, 1899. *s. sh.* fol.   **H. 3602. b. (37.)**

— Music, sweet Music. ⟨Song.⟩ Written by John P. Harrington, *etc.* [Staff and tonic sol-fa notation. Voice part.] *Francis, Day & Hunter: London*, [1901.] *s. sh.* fol.   **H. 3985. o. (23.)**

— Music, sweet Music, *etc.* ⟨Song.⟩ [With separate voice part.] 2 pt. *Francis, Day & Hunter: London*, [1901.] fol.   **H. 3985. o. (24.)**

— My Boy! [Song.] Written by C. Wilmott, *etc. Francis, Day & Hunter: London*, 1899. *s. sh.* fol.   **H. 3602. b. (38.)**

— My Gal, or my Sweetheart's my Mammy ... [Songs.] Written by J. P. Harrington. *Mocatta & Co.: London*, 1894. fol.   **H. 3602. a. (26.)**

— My Gardenful of Love. [Song.] Written by J. P. Harrington. *Francis, Day & Hunter: London*, 1897. *s. sh.* fol.   **H. 3602. (105.)**

— My Irish "Pet Name" Girl. ⟨Song.⟩ Written by John P. Harrington, *etc.* [Staff and tonic sol-fa notation. Voice part.] *Francis, Day & Hunter: London*, [1903.] *s. sh.* fol.   **H. 3985. o. (25.)**

— My Irish "Pet Name" Girl, *etc.* ⟨Song.⟩ [With separate voice part.] 2 pt. *Francis, Day & Hunter: London*, [1903.] fol.   **H. 3985. o. (26.)**

— My Japanese Charmer. ⟨Song.⟩ Written by John P. Harrington, *etc.* [Staff and tonic sol-fa notation. Voice part.] *Francis, Day & Hunter: London*, [1904.] *s. sh.* fol.   **H. 3985. o. (27.)**

— My Japanese Charmer, *etc.* ⟨Song.⟩ [With separate voice part.] 2 pt. *Francis, Day & Hunter: London*, [1904.] fol.   **H. 3985. o. (28.)**

— My Lady Loo. [Song.] Written by C. Wilmott. *Francis, Day & Hunter: London*, 1897. *s. sh.* fol.   **H. 3602. (106.)**

— My little Prairie Flower! ⟨Song.⟩ Written by John P. Harrington, *etc.* [Staff and tonic sol-fa notation. Voice part.] *Francis, Day & Hunter: London*, [1903.] *s. sh.* fol.   **H. 3985. o. (29.)**

LE BRUNN (GEORGE)

— My little Prairie Flower! *etc.* ⟨Song.⟩ [With separate voice part.] 2 pt. *Francis, Day & Hunter: London*, [1903.] fol.   **H. 3985. o. (30.)**

— My Lot. [Song.] Written by W. Pink. *Francis, Day & Hunter: London*, 1897. *s. sh.* fol.   **H. 3602. (107.)**

— My next-door Neighbour's Gardin. [Song.] Written by E. Bateman and G. Elen. *Francis, Day & Hunter: London*, 1900. fol.   **H. 3602. b. (39.)**

— My old Man. [Song.] Written by H. King, *etc. Francis Bros. & Day: London*, [1889.] fol.   **H. 1260. m. (43.)**

— My own little Lily of Killarney. ⟨Song.⟩ Written by J. P. Harrington, *etc.* [Staff and tonic sol-fa notation. Voice part.] *Francis, Day & Hunter: London*, [1904.] *s. sh.* fol.   **H. 3985. o. (31.)**

— My own little Lily of Killarney, *etc.* ⟨Song.⟩ [With separate voice part.] 2 pt. *Francis, Day & Hunter: London*, [1904.] fol.   **H. 3985. o. (32.)**

— My Pale-face Queen. ⟨Song.⟩ Written by John P. Harrington, *etc.* [Staff and tonic sol-fa notation. Voice part.] *Francis, Day & Hunter: London*, [1905.] *s. sh.* fol.   **H. 3985. o. (33.)**

— My Pale-face Queen, *etc.* ⟨Song.⟩ [With separate voice part.] 2 pt. *Francis, Day & Hunter: London*, [1905.] fol.   **H. 3985. o. (34.)**

— My Post is here! [Song.] Written by J. P. Harrington. *Francis, Day & Hunter: London*, 1894. *s. sh.* fol.   **H. 3602. (108.)**

— My Second Time on Earth. [Song.] Written by R. Morton. *Francis, Day & Hunter: London*, 1897. *s. sh.* fol.   **H. 3602. (109.)**

— My Son. [Song.] Written by E. W. Rogers, *etc. Francis, Day & Hunter: London* [1890.] fol.   **H. 3602. (17.)**

— My Whistling Gal. [Song.] Written by J. P. Harrington. *Francis, Day & Hunter: London*, 1897. *s. sh.* fol.   **H. 3602. (110.)**

— Naughty, naughty, naughty. Words by John P. Harrington. [Song. With separate voice part.] 2 pt. *Hopwood & Crew.: London*, [1904.] fol.   **H. 3985. o. (35.)**

— The Navvy's Motor Ride. ⟨Song.⟩ Written by J. P. Harrington, *etc.* [Staff and tonic sol-fa notation. Voice parts.] *Francis, Day & Hunter: London*, [1904.] *s. sh.* fol.   **H. 3985. o. (36.)**

— The Navvy's Motor Ride, *etc.* ⟨Song.⟩ [With separate voice part.] 2 pt. *Francis, Day & Hunter: London*, [1904.] fol.   **H. 3985. o. (37.)**

— Neighbours—simply Neighbours! [Song.] Written by J. P. Harrington. *Francis, Day & Hunter: London*, 1896. *s. sh.* fol.   **H. 3602. (111.)**

— Never introduce your Bloke, to your Lady Friend. [Song.] Words by John P. Harrington. pp. 5. *Maurice Shapiro: [New York,* 1907.] fol.   **H. 3985. o. (38.)**

— Never mind the Moon, John. [Song.] Written by W. Pink. *Francis, Day & Hunter: London*, 1896. *s. sh.* fol.   **H. 3602. (112.)**

— A Nice quiet Week. [Song.] Written by J. P. Harrington. *Francis, Day & Hunter: London*, 1893. fol.   **H. 3602. a. (27.)**

— The Nightingale and the Star. ⟨Song.⟩ Written by John P. Harrington. [Staff and tonic sol-fa notation. Voice part.] *Francis, Day & Hunter: London*, [1903.] *s. sh.* fol.   **H. 3985. o. (39.)**

— The Nightingale and the Star, *etc.* ⟨Song.⟩ [With separate voice part.] 2 pt. *Francis, Day & Hunter: London*, [1903.] fol.   **H. 3985. o. (40.)**

LE BRUNN (George)

— No, 'Arry, don't ask me to marry. [Song.] Written by Harry Castling. pp. 4. *Francis, Day & Hunter: London*, [1893.] 4°.
H. 3980. pp. (48.)

— Norah from Killarney ... ⟨Song.⟩ Written by J. P. Harrington, *etc.* [Staff and tonic sol-fa notation. Voice part.] *Francis, Day & Hunter: London*, [1905.] *s. sh.* fol. **H. 3985. o. (41.)**

— Norah from Killarney, *etc.* ⟨Song.⟩ [With separate voice part.] 2 pt. *Francis, Day & Hunter: London*, [1905.] fol.
H. 3985. o. (42.)

— Not while de Coons am about, Sammie! [Song.] Written by J. P. Harrington. *Francis, Day & Hunter: London*, 1897. *s. sh.* fol. **H. 3602. (113.)**

— Now be aisy, Ma'am. ⟨Song.⟩ Written by J. P. Harrington, *etc.* [Staff and tonic sol-fa notation. Voice part.] *Francis, Day & Hunter: London*, [1901.] *s. sh.* fol. **H. 3985. o. (43.)**

— Now be aisy, Ma'am, *etc.* ⟨Song.⟩ [With separate voice part.] 2 pt. *Francis, Day & Hunter: London*, [1901.] fol.
H. 3985. o. (44.)

— Oh, Dinah, Dear! ... Ballad. Written by J. P. Harrington. *Francis, Day & Hunter: London*, 1896. *s. sh.* fol.
H. 3602. (114.)

— Oh! Don't it tickle you? [Song.] Words by W. Pink. *Francis, Day & Hunter: London*, 1896. *s. sh.* fol. **H. 3602. (115.)**

— Oh! for the Jubilee! [Song.] Written by A. West, *etc. Francis Bros. & Day: London*, [1887.] fol. **H. 1260. f. (40.)**

— Oh, Girls! what am I to do with it? ⟨Song.⟩ Written by John P. Harrington, *etc.* [Staff and tonic sol-fa notation. Voice part.] *Francis, Day & Hunter: London*, [1904.] *s. sh.* fol.
H. 3985. o. (45.)

— Oh, Girls! what am I to do with it? *etc.* ⟨Song.⟩ [With separate voice part.] 2 pt. *Francis, Day & Hunter: London*, [1904.] fol.
H. 3985. o. (46.)

— "Oh, isn't it singular!" ⟨Song.⟩ Written by J. P. Harrington, *etc.* [Staff and tonic sol-fa notation. Voice part.] *Francis, Day & Hunter: London*, [1903.] *s. sh.* fol. **H. 3985. o. (47.)**

— "Oh, isn't it singular!" *etc.* ⟨Song.⟩ [With separate voice part.] 2 pt. *Francis, Day & Hunter: London*, [1903.] fol.
H. 3985. o. (48.)

— Oh! the Coronation. ⟨Song.⟩ Written by J. P. Harrington, *etc.* [Staff and tonic sol-fa notation. Voice part.] *Francis, Day & Hunter: London*, [1902.] *s. sh.* fol. **H. 3985. o. (49.)**

— Oh! the Coronation, *etc.* ⟨Song.⟩ [With separate voice part.] 2 pt. *Francis, Day & Hunter: London*, [1902.] fol.
H. 3985. o. (50.)

— Old Joe Blake. [Song.] Written by W. Pink. *Francis, Day & Hunter: London*, 1894. *s. sh.* fol. **H. 3602. (116.)**

— A 'Oliday on one Pound ten. ⟨Song.⟩ Written by Edgar Bateman, *etc.* [Staff and tonic sol-fa notation. Voice part.] *Francis, Day & Hunter: London*, [1901.] *s. sh.* fol.
H. 3985. n. (9.)

— A 'Oliday on one Pound ten, *etc.* ⟨Song.⟩ pp. 5. *Francis, Day & Hunter: London*, [1901.] fol. **H. 3985. n. (10.)**

— On Sunday. ⟨Song.⟩ Written by John P. Harrington, *etc.* [Staff and tonic sol-fa notation. Voice part.] *Francis, Day & Hunter: London*, [1902.] *s. sh.* fol. **H. 3985. o. (51.)**

— On Sunday, *etc.* ⟨Song.⟩ [With separate voice part.] 2 pt. *Francis, Day & Hunter: London*, [1902.] fol.
H. 3985. o. (52.)

— One at a time. [Song.] Written by Murray & Leigh, *etc. Francis, Day & Hunter: London*, 1899. *s. sh.* fol.
H. 3602. b. (40.)

LE BRUNN (George)

— "One little lonely Star." ⟨Song.⟩ Written by John P. Harrington, *etc.* [With separate voice part.] 2 pt. *Monte Carlo Publishing Co.: London*, [1906.] fol.
M. C. P. Co. Sixpenny Successes. no. 46. **H. 3985. o. (53.)**

— One of the Dandy Fifth ... [Song.] Written by F. W. Leigh, *etc. Howard & Co.: London*, 1898. fol. **H. 3602. b. (41.)**

— Only a Saturday Soldier. [Song.] Written by A. Hall, *etc. Francis, Day & Hunter: London*, 1898. *s. sh.* fol.
H. 3602. b. (43.)

— The Only Friend 'e 'ad. [Song.] Written by H. Castling. *Francis, Day & Hunter: London*, 1896. *s. sh.* fol.
H. 3602. (117.)

— The Only Way. [Song.] Written by J. P. Harrington. *Francis, Day & Hunter: London*, 1901. fol. **H. 3602. b. (42.)**

— Our 'Ouse is our own. ⟨Song.⟩ Written by Fred W. Leigh, *etc.* [Staff and tonic sol-fa notation. Voice part.] *Francis, Day & Hunter: London*, [1902.] *s. sh.* fol. **H. 3985. o. (54.)**

— Our 'Ouse is our own, *etc.* ⟨Song.⟩ [With separate voice part.] 2 pt. *Francis, Day & Hunter: London*, [1902.] fol.
H. 3985. o. (55.)

— Our 'Ouseboat! ⟨Song.⟩ Written by John P. Harrington, *etc.* [Staff and tonic sol-fa notation. Voice part.] *Francis, Day & Hunter: London*, [1902.] *s. sh.* fol. **H. 3985. o. (56.)**

— Our 'Ouseboat! *etc.* ⟨Song.⟩ [With separate voice part.] 2 pt. *Francis, Day & Hunter: London*, [1902.] fol.
H. 3985. o. (57.)

— Our stuck-up little Square. [Song.] Written by E. Bateman. *Francis, Day & Hunter: London*, 1896. *s. sh.* fol.
H. 3602. (110.)

— Over & over again.—Comic Song.—Written by C. Cornell, *etc. Francis Bros. & Day: London*, [1886.] fol.
H. 1260. f. (41.)

— Over the Sticks. [Song.] Written by W. Pink. *Francis, Day & Hunter: London*, 1897. *s. sh.* fol. **H. 3602. (118.)**

— Over the Sticks. Galop. [P. F.] *Francis, Day & Hunter: London*, 1897. fol. **h. 3286. g. (22.)**

— 'Ow's this for a Start. [Song.] Written by R. P. Weston & F. W. Leigh, *etc. Francis, Day & Hunter: London*, 1899. *s. sh.* fol. **H. 3602. b. (44.)**

— Perhaps! P'raps not? [Song.] Written by R. Morton. *Francis, Day & Hunter: London*, 1894. *s. sh.* fol. **H. 3602. (120.)**

— P'r'aps you've seen the Pictures. ⟨Song.⟩ Written by John P. Harrington, *etc.* [Staff and tonic sol-fa notation. Voice part.] *Francis, Day & Hunter: London*, [1903.] *s. sh.* fol.
H. 3985. o. (58.)

— P'r'aps you've seen the Pictures *etc.* ⟨Song.⟩ [With separate voice part.] 2 pt. *Francis, Day & Hunter: London*, [1903.] fol.
H. 3985. o. (59.)

— The Peri—the Pierrot—and the Pier! ⟨Song.⟩ Written by John P. Harrington. [Staff and tonic sol-fa notation. Voice part.] *Francis, Day & Hunter: London*, [1904.] *s. sh.* fol.
H. 3985. o. (60.)

— The Peri—the Pierrot—and the Pier! *etc.* ⟨Song.⟩ [With separate voice part.] 2 pt. *Francis, Day & Hunter: London*, [1904.] fol. **H. 3985. o. (61.)**

— The Piccaninny Chickabiddy Coon. Plantation Song. Written by W. Burnot. With additional accompaniment for Banjo (by N. Greenop). *J. A. Turner: London*, 1898. fol.
H. 3602. b. (45.)

— Play us an old "Come all ye". [Song.] Written by A. Hall. *Francis, Day & Hunter: London*, 1896. fol. **H. 3602. a. (28.)**

LE BRUNN (George)

— Pong, pinga, pong. [Song.] Written by J. P. Harrington. (Arranged for Banjo (Mandoline) by E. Forman.) *Francis Bros. & Day: London*, [1890.] fol.　　**H. 3602. (18.)**

— The Poster on the Wall. [Song.] Written by A. J. Morris, *etc. Francis, Day & Hunter: London*, 1899. *s. sh.* fol.
　　H. 3602. b. (47.)

— Practical Impossibilities. [Song.] Written by J. H. Clarendon. *Francis, Day & Hunter: London*, 1898. *s. sh.* fol.
　　H. 3602. (121.)

— Pretty little Maidens' Polka, *etc.* [P. F.] *Francis, Day & Hunter: London*, 1893. fol.　　**h. 3285. q. (15.)**

— The Pretty little Maidens' Sea-Trip. [Song.] Written by J. P. Harrington, *etc. Francis, Day & Hunter: London*, 1893. fol.
　　H. 3602. (19.)

— The Pretty Maid was young and fair. [Song.] Written by J. P. Harrington. *Francis, Day & Hunter: London*. 1893. fol.
　　H. 3602. a. (29.)

— Proud of her Irish Boy. [Song.] Written by A. Hall, *etc. Francis, Day & Hunter: London*, 1898. *s. sh.* fol.
　　H. 3602. b. (46.)

— Pull the String. Song and Dance. Written by L. Barclay. *Francis, Day & Hunter: London*, 1897. *s. sh.* fol.
　　H. 3602. (122.)

— Queen of the Coral Isles! ⟨Song.⟩ Written by John P. Harrington. [Staff and tonic sol-fa notation. Voice part.] *Francis, Day & Hunter: London*, [1905.] *s. sh.* fol.
　　H. 3985. o. (62.)

— Queen of the Coral Isles! *etc.* ⟨Song.⟩ [With separate voice part.] 2 pt. *Francis, Day & Hunter: London*, [1905.] fol.
　　H. 3985. o. (63.)

— The Real Susie Tusie. [Song.] Written by E. Turner. *Francis, Day & Hunter: London*, 1894. *s. sh.* fol.　**H. 3602. (123.)**

— "Remember me to Mother dear!" ⟨Song.⟩ Written by J. P. Harrington. pp. 3. *Monte Carlo Publishing Co.: London*, [1905.] fol.
M. C. P. Co. Sixpenny Successes. no. 4.　　**H. 3985. o. (64.)**

— Remember me to mother dear! [Song.] Written by John P. Harrington. [c. 1905.] fol.
A pirated edition.　　**H. 1848. b. (16.)**

— The Rich Girl and the Poor. [Song.] Written by J. P. Harrington. *Francis, Day & Hunter: London*, 1895. *s. sh.* fol.
　　H. 3602. (124.)

— Riding on the District Railway. [Song.] Written by A. J. Morris. *Francis, Day & Hunter: London*, 1894. *s. sh.* fol.
　　H. 3602. (125.)

— Right across the Bridge.—Parody,—written by F. Bowyer, *etc. Francis Bros. & Day: London*, [1889.] fol.　**H. 1260. f. (24.)**

— The Road to Ruin. [Song.] Written by F. Bowyer, *etc. Francis Bros. & Day: London*, [1889.] fol.　**H. 1260. m. (44.)**

— The Royal Fusiliers. *See* infra: [The 7th Royal Fusiliers.]

— Sadie. ⟨[Song from] "The Little Duchess," a musical comedy in three acts, [mainly composed] by Reginald de Koven.⟩ Words by J. P. Harrington. pp. 5. *Edward Schuberth & Co.: New York, London*, [1901.] fol.　**H. 3985. p. (1.)**

— Sadie. Sung ... in The Little Duchess ... Arr. by Ludomir Thomas. [Orchestral parts.] 17 pt. *In:* KOVEN (H. L. R. de) [The Little Duchess.—Banjo Serenade.] Entreacte. [1901.] 4°.
　　g. 1800. (170.)

LE BRUNN (George)

— Sadie. Song in "The Little Duchess" ... Leo [or rather, George] Le Brunn. Arr. by Ludomir Thomas. ⟨Solo B♭ cornet [and military band parts].⟩ 26 pt. *In:* KOVEN (H. L. R. de) [The Little Duchess.—Banjo Serenade.] Entr'acte—Chloe I'm waitin'. [1902.] 8°.　　**f. 800. (738.)**

— Sailing through the Air. ⟨Song.⟩ Written by J. P. Harrington, *etc.* [Staff and tonic sol-fa notation. Voice part.] *Francis, Day & Hunter: London*, [1901.] *s. sh.* fol.　**H. 3985. p. (2.)**

— Sailing through the Air, *etc.* ⟨Song.⟩ [With separate voice part.] 2 pt. *Francis, Day & Hunter: London*, [1901.] fol.
　　H. 3985. p. (3.)

— Sally wasn't a Lady. [Song.] Written by J. P. Harrington. *Francis, Day & Hunter: London*, 1897. *s. sh.* fol.
　　H. 3602. (126.)

— Salute my Bicycle! [Song.] Written by J. P. Harrington. *Francis, Day & Hunter: London*, 1895. *s. sh.* fol.
　　H. 3602. (127.)

— The Sawdust Chest. [Song.] Written by H. H. Greenbank. *Francis Bros. & Day: London*, [1889.] fol.　**H. 1260. m. (45.)**

— Schoolmates. [Song.] Written by T. Le Brunn and H. Leighton. *A. Cary: London*, [1892.] fol.　**H. 3602. (20.)**

— Seeing Life. [Song.] Written by J. P. Harrington, *etc. Francis Bros. & Day: London*, [1889.] fol.　**H. 1260. m. (46.)**

— The Seven Ages of Man. [Song.] Written by J. P. Harrington, *etc. Francis Bros. & Day: London*, [1888.] fol.
　　H. 1260. f. (42.)

— The 7th Royal Fusiliers. A story of Inkerman. [Song.] Words by Wal Pink, *etc.* pp. 9. *Francis, Day & Hunter: London*, [1892.] fol.　　**H. 3980. pp. (49.)**

— Royal Fusiliers. (City of London regiment.) "The Seventh Royal Fusiliers." ⟨Regimental quick march⟩ ... Arranged [for military band] by B. E. Hicks. [Parts.] 20 pt. *Boosey & Hawkes: London*, [1966.] obl. 8°.　　**h. 3210. j. (59.)**

— The Royal Fusiliers ... March, founded on C. Godfrey's ... Song [or rather, on the song sung by C. Godfrey. P. F.]. *Francis, Day & Hunter: London*, 1893. fol.　**h. 3285. q. (16.)**

— The Royal Fusilier's March arranged as a Banjo Solo, *etc.* 1893. *See* FRANCIS AND DAY. Francis & Day's Banjo Gems. No. 18. [1890, *etc.*] fol.　　**h. 1980. (2.)**

— The Seventh Royal Fusiliers. Waltz, founded on C. Godfrey's latest successes, *etc.* [P. F.] *Francis, Day & Hunter: London*, 1893. fol.　　**h. 3285. q. (17.)**

— The Shadow on the Blind ... ⟨Song.⟩ Written by John P. Harrington. [Staff and tonic sol-fa notation. Voice part.] *Francis, Day & Hunter: London*, [1905.] *s. sh.* fol.
　　H. 3985. p. (4.)

— The Shadow on the Blind, *etc.* ⟨Song.⟩ [With separate voice part.] 2 pt. *Francis, Day & Hunter: London*, [1905.] fol.
　　H. 3985. p. (5.)

— She'd changed her Mind ... Song. Written by J. P. Harrington and T. Conley, *etc. Francis, Day & Hunter: London*, 1899. *s. sh.* fol.　　**H. 3602. b. (48.)**

— She'd never been there before ... [Song.] Words by Murray and Leigh. *W. B. Gray & Co.: New York*, 1897. fol.
　　H. 3602. a. (30.)

— She's my Love! ... [Song.] Written by C. W. Wilmott. *B. Mocatta & Co.: London*, 1896. fol.　**H. 3602. a. (31.)**

— She taught him a Thing or two, too! ... ⟨Song.⟩ Written by Fred. W. Leigh, *etc.* [Staff and tonic sol-fa notation. Voice part.] *Francis, Day & Hunter: London*, [1904.] *s. sh.* fol.
　　H. 3985. p. (6.)

LE BRUNN (GEORGE)

— She taught him a Thing or two, too! *etc.* ⟨Song.⟩ [With separate voice part.] 2 pt. *Francis, Day & Hunter: London,* [1904.] fol. **H. 3985. p. (7.)**

— She wears no Crown of Gold. [Song.] Written by Murray and Leigh, *etc. Francis, Day & Hunter: London,* 1898. *s. sh.* fol. **H. 3602. b. (49.)**

— She would marry anything with Trousers on ... [Song.] Written by L. Barclay, *etc. Francis, Day & Hunter: London,* 1898. *s. sh.* fol. **H. 3602. b. (51.)**

— Shipmates and Messmates. [Song.] Written by W. T. Lytton. *Francis, Day & Hunter: London,* [1891.] fol. **H. 3602. (21.)**

— The Shop Girl. [Song.] Written by J. P. Harrington. *Francis, Day & Hunter: London,* 1895. *s. sh.* fol. **H. 3602. (128.)**

— The Shop-Walker. *See* MEISSLER (J.) The Shop-Walker. Polka on the ... song ... by G. Le Brunn. 1892. fol. **h. 3604. a. (15.)**

— Siberia, or a Daughter's Devotion. [Song.] Written by W. Pink. *Francis, Day, & Hunter: London,* 1893. fol. **H. 3602. a. (32.)**

— The Silk Dress and the cotton Frock. ⟨Song.⟩ Written by J. P. Harrington. [Staff and tonic sol-fa notation. Voice part.] *Francis, Day & Hunter: London,* [1904.] *s. sh.* fol. **H. 3985. p. (8.)**

— The Silk Dress and the cotton Frock, *etc.* ⟨Song.⟩ [With separate voice part.] 2 pt. *Francis, Day & Hunter: London,* [1904.] fol. **H. 3985. p. (9.)**

— Silly Fool. [Song.] Written by J. P. Harrington. *Francis, Day & Hunter: London,* 1893. fol. **H. 3602. a. (33.)**

— Sing a Song to me, Mother. [Song.] Written by A. Hall. *Francis, Day & Hunter: London,* 1897. *s. sh.* fol. **H. 3602. (129.)**

— Sisters! [Song.] Written by J. P. Harrington. *Francis, Day, & Hunter: London,* 1893. fol. **H. 3602. a. (34.)**

— Six little yaller Gals an' one little Coon. ⟨Song.⟩ Written by John P. Harrington. [Staff and tonic sol-fa notation. Voice part.] *Francis, Day & Hunter: London,* [1904.] *s. sh.* fol. **H. 3985. p. (10.)**

— Six little yaller Gals an' one little Coon, *etc.* ⟨Song.⟩ [With separate voice part.] 2 pt. *Francis, Day & Hunter: London,* [1904.] fol. **H. 3985. p. (11.)**

— Sleep! Sleep! He's always got his Eyes shut. ⟨Song.⟩ Written by Murray and Leigh, *etc.* [Staff and tonic sol-fa notation. Voice part.] *Francis, Day & Hunter: London,* [1901.] *s. sh.* fol. **H. 3985. p. (12.)**

— Sleep! Sleep! He's always got his eyes shut, *etc.* ⟨Song.⟩ [With separate voice part.] 2 pt. *Francis, Day & Hunter: London,* [1901.] fol. **H. 3985. p. (13.)**

— The Sleepin' Beauty. [Song.] Written by E. Bateman. *Francis, Day, & Hunter: London,* 1896. *s. sh.* fol. **H. 3602. (130.)**

— The Smile. [Song.] Written by A. J. Morris, *etc. H. Beresford: London,* [1892.] fol. **H. 3602. (22.)**

— So he did. [Song.] Written by J. P. Harrington, *etc. Hopwood & Crew: London,* [1888.] fol. **H. 1260. f. (43.)**

— So her Sister says. [Song.] Written by J. P. Harrington. *Hopwood & Crew: London,* [1894.] fol. **H. 3602. a. (35.)**

— The Soldiers' Promenade. ⟨Song.⟩ Written by J. P. Harrington, *etc.* [Staff and tonic sol-fa notation. Voice part.] *Francis, Day & Hunter: London,* [1904.] *s. sh.* fol. **H. 3985. p. (14.)**

LE BRUNN (GEORGE)

— The Soldiers' Promenade, *etc.* ⟨Song.⟩ [With separate voice part.] 2 pt. *Francis, Day & Hunter: London,* [1904.] fol. **H. 3985. p. (15.)**

— Somebody's Baby Boy. [Song.] Written by A. Hall, *etc. Francis, Day & Hunter: London,* 1898. *s. sh.* fol. **H. 3602. b. (50.)**

— Something to play with. [Song.] Written by W. C. Lytton, *etc. H. Beresford: London,* [1892.] fol. **H. 3602. (23.)**

— Sometimes! ⟨Song.⟩ Written by John P. Harrington, *etc.* [Staff and tonic sol-fa notation. Voice part.] *Francis, Day & Hunter: London,* [1902.] *s. sh.* fol. **H. 3985. p. (16.)**

— Sometimes! *etc.* ⟨Song.⟩ [With separate voice part.] 2 pt. *Francis, Day & Hunter: London,* [1902.] fol. **H. 3985. p. (17.)**

— The Song of the Thrush. [Song.] Written by W. Hastings. *Francis, Day, & Hunter: London,* 1897. *s. sh.* fol. **H. 3602. (131.)**

— "Spring-time is Ring-time." ⟨Song.⟩ Written by J. P. Harrington, *etc.* [Staff and tonic sol-fa notation. Voice part.] *Francis, Day & Hunter: London,* [1905.] *s. sh.* fol. **H. 3985. p. (18.)**

— Spring-time is Ring-time, *etc.* ⟨Song.⟩ [With separate voice part.] 2 pt. *Francis, Day & Hunter: London,* [1905.] fol. **H. 3985. p. (19.)**

— The Stars are Angel-faces ... ⟨Song.⟩ Written by J. P. Harrington, *etc.* [Staff and tonic sol-fa notation. Voice part.] *Francis, Day & Hunter: London,* [1905.] *s. sh.* fol. **H. 3985. p. (20.)**

— The Stars are Angel-faces, *etc.* ⟨Song.⟩ [With separate voice part.] 2 pt. *Francis, Day & Hunter: London,* [1905.] fol. **H. 3985. p. (21.)**

— Stick to me and the Kids! [Song.] Written by W. Pink. *Francis, Day, & Hunter: London,* 1897. *s. sh.* fol. **H. 3602. (132.)**

— The Story of the Stars. [Song.] Written by A. Hall. *Francis, Day & Hunter: London,* 1897. *s. sh.* fol. **H. 3602. (133.)**

— Such a Don, don't you know! [Song.] Written by R. Morton. *Francis, Day & Hunter: London,* 1895. *s. sh.* fol. **H. 3602. (134.)**

— Such a very, very fine old Man. [Song.] Written by A. Hall, *etc. Francis, Day & Hunter: London,* 1899. *s. sh.* fol. **H. 3602. b. (52.)**

— Sunshine and Shadow. [Song.] Written by A. J. Morris. *Francis, Day, & Hunter: London,* 1894. *s. sh.* fol. **H. 3602. (135.)**

— Sweethearts once. [Song.] Written by L. Barclay. *Francis, Day & Hunter: London,* 1899. fol. **H. 3602. b. (53.)**

— Take it off! [Song.] Written by H. Hunter, *etc. Francis, Day & Hunter: London,* 1899. *s. sh.* fol. **H. 3602. b. (54.)**

— The Tale of the Skirt. ⟨Song.⟩ Written by Fred W. Leigh, *etc.* [Staff and tonic sol-fa notation. Voice part.] *Francis, Day & Hunter: London,* [1904.] *s. sh.* fol. **H. 3985. p. (22.)**

— The Tale of the Skirt, *etc.* ⟨Song.⟩ [With separate voice part.] 2 pt. *Francis, Day & Hunter: London,* [1904.] fol. **H. 3985. p. (23.)**

— Talk about a big Responsibility. [Song.] Written by Murray and Leigh. *Francis, Day, & Hunter: London,* 1898. *s. sh.* fol. **H. 3602. (136.)**

— That Boy is only seven Years of age. [Song.] Written by G. Rollit, *etc. Francis, Day & Hunter: London,* 1899. *s. sh.* fol. **H. 3602. b. (55.)**

LE BRUNN (George)

— That's one of your Girls. ⟨Song.⟩ Written by W. T. Lytton, *etc.* pp. 5. *Hopwood & Crew: London*, [1901.] fol.
H. 3985. p. (24.)

— "That's 'ow we doos it in the Mile End Road!" ... ⟨Song.⟩ Written by John P. Harrington. [Staff and tonic sol-fa notation. Voice part.] *Francis, Day & Hunter: London*, [1905.] *s. sh.* fol.
H. 3985. p. (25.)

— "That's 'ow we dooes it in the Mile End Road!" *etc.* ⟨Song.⟩ [With separate voice part.] 2 pt. *Francis, Day & Hunter: London*, [1905.] fol.
H. 3985. p. (26.)

— That's the Cause of it. [Song.] Written by C. Wilmott, *etc. Francis, Day & Hunter: London*, [1893.] fol.
H. 3602. (24.)

— That's what the World is in need of to-day. [Song.] Written by A. J. Morris. *Francis, Day, & Hunter: London*, 1896. *s. sh.* fol.
H. 3602. (137.)

— That's when you cheer, Boys, cheer! [Song.] Written by J. P. Harrington. *Francis, Day, & Hunter: London*, 1895. *s. sh.* fol.
H. 3602. (138.)

— That shows what a Woman can do. ⟨Song.⟩ Written by John P. Harrington, *etc.* [Staff and tonic sol-fa notation. Voice part.] *Francis, Day & Hunter: London*, [1904.] *s. sh.* fol.
H. 3985. p. (27.)

— That shows what a Woman can do, *etc.* ⟨[Song.] [With separate voice part.] 2 pt. *Francis, Day & Hunter: London*, [1904.] fol.
H. 3985. p. (28.)

— That was a Bloomer. [Song.] Written by H. Castling. *Francis, Day, & Hunter: London*, 1896. *s. sh.* fol.
H. 3602. (139.)

— Their Heads nestled closer together. [Song.] Written by W. Pink. *Francis, Day, & Hunter: London*, 1894. *s. sh.* fol.
H. 3602. (140.)

— [Then you wink the other Eye.] When the Winkle-Man goes by! Parody ... words by W. T. Lytton, *etc.* ... (When the Winkle-Man goes by ... with Banjo accompaniment by P. Bradley.) 2 no. *Marshalls: London*, [1891.] fol.
H. 3602. (29.)

— [Then you wink the other Eye.] *See* Saint Quentin (Edward) *pseud.* "Wink the other Eye." Schottische. On the ... songs "Then you wink the other Eye" [by G. Le Brunn] & "They're after me". [c. 1885.] fol.
H. 1650. ff. (11.)

— There'll be no Beano there. [Song.] Written by F. Perry and C. Ridgwell, *etc. Francis, Day & Hunter: London*, 1898. *s. sh.* fol.
H. 3602. b. (56.)

— There's always 'alf a Pint of Beer for him. [Song.] Written by E. Bateman, *etc. Francis, Day & Hunter: London*, 1899. *s. sh.* fol.
H. 3602. b. (57.)

— There was Hooligan. [Song.] Written by A. Hall. *Francis, Day, & Hunter: London*, 1896. *s. sh.* fol. **H. 3602. a. (36.)**

— There was something on his Mind. ⟨Song.⟩ Written by Fred W. Leigh, *etc.* [Staff and tonic sol-fa notation. Voice part.] *Francis, Day & Hunter: London*, [1903.] *s. sh.* fol.
H. 3985. p. (29.)

— There was something on his Mind, *etc.* ⟨Song.⟩ [With separate voice part.] 2 pt. *Francis, Day & Hunter: London*, [1903.] fol.
H. 3985. p. (30.)

— There won't be any Annual. ⟨Song.⟩ Written by J. P. Harrington, *etc.* [Staff and tonic sol-fa notation. Voice part.] *Francis, Day & Hunter: London*, [1901.] *s. sh.* fol.
H. 3985. p. (31.)

— There won't be any Annual, *etc.* ⟨Song.⟩ [With separate voice part.] 2 pt. *Francis, Day & Hunter: London*, [1901.] fol.
H. 3985. p. (32.)

LE BRUNN (George)

— They bunged him into my Growler ... [Song.] Written by J. P. Harrington. *Francis, Day, & Hunter: London*, 1896. *s. sh.* fol.
H. 3602. a. (37.)

— They left no Stone unturned. [Song.] Written by J. P. Harrington. *Francis, Day & Hunter: London*, 1900. fol.
H. 3602. b. (58.)

— They walked for Miles and Miles. ⟨Song.⟩ Written by J. P. Harrington. [Staff and tonic sol-fa notation. Voice part.] *Francis, Day & Hunter: London*, [1904.] *s. sh.* fol.
H. 3985. p. (33.)

— They walked for Miles and Miles, *etc.* ⟨Song.⟩ [With separate voice part.] 2 pt. *Francis, Day & Hunter: London*, [1904.] fol.
H. 3985. p. (34.)

— A Thing you can't buy with Gold! Song. Written by J. P. Harrington. *Francis, Day & Hunter: London*, 1900. fol.
H. 3602. b. (59.)

— Think I'd marry a Girl! [Song.] Written by J. P. Harrington, *etc. Francis, Day & Hunter: London*, 1900. *s. sh.* fol.
H. 3602. b. (60.)

— This is the Way they go. [Song.] Written by J. P. Harrington, *etc. Francis, Day & Hunter: London*, 1899. *s. sh.* fol.
H. 3602. b. (61.)

— Those great, big Eyes. ⟨[Song from] "The Little Duchess," a musical comedy in three acts, [mainly composed] by Reginald de Koven.⟩ Words by Harry B. Smith. pp. 5. *Edward Schuberth & Co.: New York, London*, [1901.] fol.
H. 3985. p. (35.)

— Three little Chambermaids. [Song.] Written by A. Hall. *Francis, Day, & Hunter: London*, 1897. *s. sh.* fol.
H. 3602. a. (38.)

— Till a Woman comes between. ⟨Song.⟩ Written by John P. Harrington, *etc.* [Staff and tonic sol-fa notation. Voice part.] *Francis, Day & Hunter: London*, [1901.] *s. sh.* fol.
H. 3985. p. (36.)

— Till a Woman comes between, *etc.* ⟨Song.⟩ [With separate voice part.] 2 pt. *Francis, Day & Hunter: London*, [1901.] fol.
H. 3985. p. (37.)

— Tilly the Typress ... ⟨Song.⟩ Written by J. P. Harrington. [Staff and tonic sol-fa notation. Voice part.] *Francis, Day & Hunter: London*, [1902.] *s. sh.* fol. **H. 3985. p. (38.)**

— Tilly the Typress, *etc.* ⟨Song.⟩ [With separate voice part.] 2 pt. *Francis, Day & Hunter: London*, [1902.] fol.
H. 3985. p. (39.)

— To-night! To-night! To-night! ... Song. Written by J. P. Harrington. *Francis, Day, & Hunter: London*, 1897. *s. sh.* fol.
H. 3602. a. (39.)

— Tra-la-la, Tra-la-lay ... [Song.] Written by H. Adams, *etc. Howard & Co.: London*, [1887.] fol. **H. 1260. f. (44.)**

— Tricky little Trilby. [Song.] Written by J. P. Harrington. *Francis, Day, & Hunter: London*, 1895. *s. sh.* fol.
H. 3602. a. (40.)

— Trilby. Polka March, *etc.* [P. F.] *Francis, Day & Hunter: London*, 1895. fol. **H. 3286. g. (23.)**

— 'Twas the last, last Kiss! ⟨Song.⟩ Written by John P. Harrington, *etc.* [Staff and tonic sol-fa notation. Voice part.] *Francis, Day & Hunter: London*, [1904.] *s. sh.* fol.
H. 3985. p. (40.)

— 'Twas the last, last Kiss! *etc.* ⟨Song.⟩ [With separate voice part.] 2 pt. *Francis, Day & Hunter: London*, [1904.] fol.
H. 3985. p. (41.)

— Twiggy voo? [Song.] Written by R. Morton, *etc. Francis, Day & Hunter: London*, 1892. fol. **H. 3602. (25.)**

LE BRUNN (George)

— Two can live cheaper than one. [Song.] Written by
E. Bateman. *Francis, Day, & Hunter: London*, 1897. *s. sh.* fol.
H. 3602. a. (41.)

— Two Eyes to see with. [Song.] Written by A. Hall, *etc.*
Francis, Day & Hunter: London, 1898. *s. sh.* fol.
H. 3602. b. (62.)

— Two little Vagabonds. [Song.] Written by P. Pelham. *Francis,
Day, & Hunter: London*, 1896. *s. sh.* fol. **H. 3602. a. (42.)**

— Two little Vagabonds. [Song.] Written by W. Pink. *Francis,
Day, & Hunter: London*, 1897. *s. sh.* fol. **H. 3602. a. (43.)**

— Two Maiden Aunts. [Song.] Written by A. R. Marshall.
Francis, Day, & Hunter: London, 1894. *s. sh.* fol.
H. 3602. a. (44.)

— Two on a Swing. ⟨Song.⟩ Written by John P. Harrington.
[Staff and tonic sol-fa notation. Voice part.] *Francis, Day
& Hunter: London*, [1904.] *s. sh.* fol.
H. 3985. p. (42.)

— Two on a Swing, *etc.* ⟨Song.⟩ [With separate voice part.] 2 pt.
Francis, Day & Hunter: London, [1904.] fol.
H. 3985. p. (43.)

— Uncle Joe's Spree, or Hi! Boys, Hi! Boys … [Song.] Written
by E. W. Rogers, *etc. Francis, Day & Hunter: London*, [1891.]
fol. **H. 3602. (9.)**

— [Another edition. Uncle Joe's Spree.] Hi! Boys, Hi! Boys, *etc.*
Francis, Day & Hunter: London, [1891.] fol. **H. 3602. (10.)**

— Uncle Tom. [Song.] Written by J. P. Harrington. *B. Mocatta
& Co.: London*, 1895. fol. **H. 3602. a. (47.)**

— The Union Jack. [Song.] Written by C. Wilmott. *Francis,
Day, & Hunter: London*, 1895. *s. sh.* fol. **H. 3602. a. (48.)**

— The Union Jack. ⟨Song.⟩ Written by Charles Wilmott, *etc.*
pp. 4. *Francis, Day & Hunter: London*, [1895.] fol.
h. 721. ww. (10.)

— Up go the Fireworks. [Song.] Written by W. Pink, *etc.*
Francis, Day & Hunter: London, 1893. fol. **H. 3602. (26.)**

— Vat ze English call ze — … [Song.] Written by M. Tressor.
Francis, Day, & Hunter: London, 1897. *s. sh.* fol.
H. 3602. a. (45.)

— Victoria, a Name that will never die. Song. Written by
T. Edwards. (Arranged by W. H. Middleton.) *Hopwood
& Crew: London*, [1901.] fol. **H. 1799. cc. (54.)**

— Victoria, the Mother of our Nation. [Song.] Written by
P. Pelham. *Francis, Day, & Hunter: London*, 1896. *s. sh.* fol.
H. 3602. a. (46.)

— Waitin' for ma bonnie Jean. ⟨Song.⟩ Written by John P.
Harrington. [With separate voice part.] 2 pt. *Monte Carlo
Publishing Co.: London*, [1906.] fol.
M. C. P. Co. Sixpenny Successes. no. 13. **H. 3985. p. (44.)**

— We all of us know what that means … [Song.] Written by
J. P. Harrington, *etc. Francis, Day & Hunter: London*, [1891.]
fol. **H. 3602. (4.)**

— We all went Home in a Cab. [Song.] Words by H. Wincott,
etc. C. Sheard & Co.: London, 1892. fol. **H. 3602. (27.)**

— We did have a lively Time. [Song.] Written by J. P.
Harrington, *etc. Francis, Day & Hunter: London*, [1890.] fol.
H. 3602. (28.)

— We've all had 'em. [Song.] Written by E. W. Rogers, *etc.*
Francis Bros. & Day: London, [1889.] fol. **H. 1260. m. (47.)**

— The Wedding March! ⟨Song.⟩ Written by John P. Harrington,
etc. [Staff and tonic sol-fa notation. Voice part.] *Francis,
Day & Hunter: London*, [1902.] *s. sh.* fol. **H. 3985. p. (45.)**

LE BRUNN (George)

— The Wedding March! *etc.* ⟨Song.⟩ [With separate voice part.]
2 pt. *Francis, Day & Hunter: London*, [1902.] fol.
H. 3985. p. (46.)

— What Britishers are made of! [Song.] Written by J. P.
Harrington. *Francis, Day, & Hunter: London*, 1894. *s. sh.* fol.
H. 3602. a. (49.)

— What did it cost to paint it? [Song.] Written by H. Castling.
Francis, Day, & Hunter: London, 1897. *s. sh.* fol.
H. 3602. a. (50.)

— What did the Lady do? [Song.] Written by A. Nicholls, *etc.*
Francis, Day & Hunter: London, 1899. *s. sh.* fol.
H. 3602. b. (63.)

— What is that without any Hands? [Song.] Written by
J. Tabrar, *etc. Francis, Day & Hunter: London*, 1898. *s. sh.*
fol. **H. 3602. b. (64.)**

— What will poor Callaghan do? [Song.] Written by T. Conley,
etc. Francis, Day & Hunter: London, 1899. *s. sh.* fol.
H. 3602. b. (65.)

— What will the Neighbours say? [Song.] Written by J. P.
Harrington, *etc. Francis, Day & Hunter: London*, 1900. fol.
H. 3602. b. (66.)

— When a Child. [Song.] Words by W. Pink. *Francis, Day,
& Hunter: London*, 1894. *s. sh.* fol. **H. 3602. a. (53.)**

— When I come sailing back to you. ⟨Song.⟩ Written by Edgar
Bateman. [Staff and tonic sol-fa notation. Voice part.]
Francis, Day & Hunter: London, [1903.] *s. sh.* fol.
H. 3985. p. (47.)

— When I come sailing back to you, *etc.* ⟨Song.⟩ [With separate
voice part.] 2 pt. *Francis, Day & Hunter: London*, [1903.] fol.
H. 3985. p. (48.)

— When the Leaves are falling. ⟨Song.⟩ Written by John P.
Harrington, *etc.* [Staff and tonic sol-fa notation. Voice part.]
Francis, Day & Hunter: London, [1904.] *s. sh.* fol.
H. 3985. p. (49.)

— When the Leaves are falling, *etc.* ⟨Song.⟩ [With separate voice
part.] 2 pt. *Francis, Day & Hunter: London*, [1904.] fol.
H. 3985. p. (50.)

— When the Missis is out. [Song.] Written by W. Pink. *Francis,
Day, & Hunter: London*, 1893. fol. **H. 3602. a. (54.)**

— When the Squire brought home his Bride! Ballad. Words by
J. P. Harrington. *Francis, Day, & Hunter: London*, 1894. *s. sh.*
fol. **H. 3602. a. (55.)**

— Where are all the Irishmen? [Song.] Written by A. Hall, *etc.*
Francis, Day & Hunter: London, 1899. *s. sh.* fol.
H. 3602. b. (67.)

— Where does true Happiness lie? [Song.] Written by A. Hall.
Francis, Day, & Hunter: London, 1897. *s. sh.* fol.
H. 3602. a. (51.)

— Where shall we go to now. [Song.] Written by H. Wincott
& H. Castling. *Howard & Co.: London*, [1896.] fol.
H. 3602. a. (56.)

— Whistling Willie. [Song.] Written by A. Hall, *etc. Francis,
Day & Hunter: London*, 1899. *s. sh.* fol. **H. 3602. b. (68.)**

— "Who are you getting at, eh?" [Song.] Words by John P.
Harrington. pp. 5. *Maurice Shapiro: New York*, [1907.] fol.
H. 3985. p. (51.)

— Why do the Boys run after the Girls? ⟨Song.⟩ Written by
J. P. Harrington, *etc.* [Staff and tonic sol-fa notation. Voice
part.] *Francis, Day & Hunter: London*, [1904.] *s. sh.* fol.
H. 3985. p. (52.)

LE BRUNN (George)

— Why do the Boys run after the Girls? *etc.* ⟨Song.⟩ [With separate voice part.] 2 pt. *Francis, Day & Hunter: London,* [1904.] fol.   **H. 3985. p. (53.)**

— Why should we wait till we're old? ⟨Song.⟩ Written by John P. Harrington, *etc.* [Staff and tonic sol-fa notation. Voice part.] *Francis, Day & Hunter: London,* [1904.] *s. sh.* fol.   **H. 3985. p. (54.)**

— Why should we wait till we're old? *etc.* ⟨Song.⟩ [With separate voice part.] 2 pt. *Francis, Day & Hunter: London,* [1904.] fol.   **H. 3985. p. (55.)**

— Why shouldn't I love my little Girl? ⟨Song.⟩ Written by John P. Harrington, *etc.* [Staff and tonic sol-fa notation. Voice part.] *Francis, Day & Hunter: London,* [1903.] *s. sh.* fol.   **H. 3985. p. (56.)**

— Why shouldn't I love my little Girl? *etc.* ⟨Song.⟩ [With separate voice part.] 2 pt. *Francis, Day & Hunter: London,* [1903.] fol.   **H. 3985. p. (57.)**

— Wide. [Song.] Written by H. Castling. *Howard & Co.: London,* [1896.] fol.   **H. 3602. a. (57.)**

— The Wild Man of Borneo ... [Song.] Arranged by G. Le Brunn. pp. 4. *Francis, Day & Hunter: London,* [1890.] fol.   **H. 3980. pp. (50.)**

— The Women of to-morrow. [Song.] Written by J. P. Harrington, *etc. Francis, Day & Hunter: London,* 1901. fol.   **H. 3602. b. (69.)**

— Won't you buy, Sir? [Song.] Written by J. P. Harrington, *etc. Francis, Day & Hunter: London,* 1900. *s. sh.* fol.   **H. 3602. b. (70.)**

— Won't you love me? won't you? [Song.] Written by R. Morton, *etc. Francis, Day & Hunter: London,* 1898. *s. sh.* fol.   **H. 3602. b. (71.)**

— Wot cher, Polly! [Song.] Written by A. J. Morris. *Francis, Day & Hunter: London,* 1895. *s. sh.* fol.   **H. 3602. a. (52.)**

— The Wrong Girl. [Song.] Written by J. P. Harrington. *Francis, Day, & Hunter: London,* 1895. *s. sh.* fol.   **H. 3602. a. (58.)**

— Yea, verily, verily o! ⟨Song.⟩ Written by J. P. Harrington, *etc.* [Staff and tonic sol-fa notation. Voice part.] *Francis, Day & Hunter: London,* [1904.] *s. sh.* fol.   **H. 3985. p. (58.)**

— Yea, verily, verily o! *etc.* ⟨Song.⟩ [With separate voice part.] 2 pt. *Francis, Day & Hunter: London,* [1904.] fol.   **H. 3985. p. (59.)**

— "You ain't ashamed o' me, are you, Bill?" ... ⟨Song.⟩ Written by J. P. Harrington, *etc.* [Staff and tonic sol-fa notation. Voice part.] *Francis, Day & Hunter: London,* [1904.] *s. sh.* fol.   **H. 3985. p. (60.)**

— You ain't ashamed o' me, are you, Bill? *etc.* ⟨Song. Gentleman's version.⟩ [With separate voice part.] 2 pt. *Francis, Day & Hunter: London,* [1904.] fol. *The verso of the titlepage bears the words headed "Lady's version".*   **H. 3985. p. (61.)**

— You can get a Sweetheart any Day ... [Song.] Written by J. P. Harrington, *etc. Francis, Day & Hunter: London,* 1901. fol.   **H. 3602. b. (72.)**

— You can get a Sweetheart any Day (but not another Mother). [Song.] Written by J. P. Harrington. [c. 1905.] fol. *A pirated edition.*   **H. 1848. b. (17.)**

— "You might be a white Man's Wife." ⟨Song.⟩ Written by John P. Harrington, *etc.* [Staff and tonic sol-fa notation. Voice part.] *Francis, Day & Hunter: London,* [1905.] *s. sh.* fol.   **H. 3985. p. (62.)**

LE BRUNN (George)

— "You might be a white Man's Wife," *etc.* ⟨Song.⟩ [With separate voice part.] 2 pt. *Francis, Day & Hunter: London,* [1905.] fol.   **H. 3985. p. (63.)**

— You must go. [Song.] Written by J. P. Harrington, *etc. Francis Bros. & Day: London,* [1889.] fol.   **H. 1260. m. (48.)**

— You're a J. J. J. [Song.] Written by W. Pink. *Francis, Day, & Hunter: London,* 1897. *s. sh.* fol.   **H. 3602. a. (59.)**

— "You're a Thing of the Past." ⟨Song.⟩ Written by John P. Harrington. [With separate voice part.] 2 pt. *Monte Carlo Publishing Co.: London,* [1906.] fol. *M. C. P. Co. Sixpenny Successes. no.* 14.   **H. 3985. p. (64.)**

— You're my Gal — you're my Dinah! ⟨Song.⟩ Written by John P. Harrington, *etc.* [Staff and tonic sol-fa notation. Voice part.] *Francis, Day & Hunter: London,* [1905.] *s. sh.* fol.   **H. 3985. p. (65.)**

— You're my Gal — you're my Dinah! *etc.* ⟨Song.⟩ [With separate voice part.] 2 pt. *Francis, Day & Hunter: London,* [1905.] fol.   **H. 3985. p. (66.)**

— "You're not the only Rosebud" ... ⟨Song.⟩ Written by J. P. Harrington. [Staff and tonic sol-fa notation. Voice part.] *Francis, Day & Hunter: London,* [1905.] *s. sh.* fol.   **H. 3985. p. (67.)**

— You've got to have a lot more yet. [Song.] Written by E. Bateman, *etc. Francis, Day & Hunter: London,* 1899. *s. sh.* fol.   **H. 3602. b. (73.)**

— "Young Men Lodgers." [Song.] Words by John P. Harrington. pp. 5. *Maurice Shapiro:* [*New York,* 1907.] fol.   **H. 3985. p. (68.)**

— Zanana! (A romance of the backwoods.) ⟨Song.⟩ Written by John P. Harrington, *etc.* [Staff and tonic sol-fa notation. Voice part.] *Francis, Day & Hunter: London,* [1905.] *s. sh.* fol.   **H. 3985. p. (69.)**

— Zanana! *etc.* ⟨Song.⟩ [With separate voice part.] 2 pt. *Francis, Day & Hunter: London,* [1905.] fol.   **H. 3985. p. (70.)**

— *See* BODEN (Harry) Up he went like a Rocket, *etc.* [Song.] ⟨Arranged by G. LeBrunn.⟩ [1890.] fol.   **H. 3980. d. (29.)**

— *See* CASTLING (Harry) We've got quite enough of our own ... [Song.] Arranged by G. Le Brunn, *etc.* [1897.] fol.   **H. 3980. h. (61.)**

— *See* CHAPLIN (Charles) Every-Day Life, *etc.* ⟨Arranged by G. Le Brunn.⟩ [1891.] fol.   **H. 3980. i. (4.)**

— *See* DANCE (G.) Angels without Wings [song], *etc.* (Arranged by G. Le Brunn.) [1887.] fol.   **H. 1260. c. (32.)**

— *See* EGERTON (Frank) She's not a Princess, *etc.* [Song.] ⟨Arranged by G. Le Brunn.⟩ [1890.] fol.   **H. 3980. q. (56.)**

— *See* HARRINGTON (John P.) Of course! [Song.] Written and composed by J. P. Harrington, J. F. Lambe and G. Le Brunn, *etc.* [1899.] *s. sh.* fol.   **H. 3980. dd. (4.)**

— *See* HARRINGTON (John P.) and LE BRUNN (G.) John Bull's Christmas Tree ... ⟨Song.⟩ Written and composed by J. P. Harrington & G. Le Brunn, *etc.* [1902.] *s. sh.* fol.   **H. 3984. l. (30.)**

— *See* HARRINGTON (John P.) and LE BRUNN (G.) John Bull's Christmas Tree ... ⟨Song.⟩ Written and composed by J. P. Harrington and G. Le Brunn. [1902.] fol.   **H. 3984. l. (31.)**

— *See* HARRINGTON (John P.) and LE BRUNN (G.) The Whistling Bluecoat Boy, *etc.* [Song.] [1899.] *s. sh.* fol.   **H. 3980. dd. (5.)**

— *See* MURRAY (Fred) What a Kid 'e is. ⟨Song.⟩ Written and composed by Murray ... and Le Brunn, *etc.* [1902.] *s. sh.* fol.   **H. 3986. l. (26.)**

LE BRUNN (George)

— See Murray (Fred) What a Kid 'e is. ⟨Song.⟩ Written and composed by Murray ... and Le Brunn. [1902.] fol.

H. 3986. l. (27.)

— See Nolan (M.) Little Annie Rooney, etc. (Arranged by G. Le Brunn.) [1889.] fol. **H. 1260. h. (34.)**

— See Pink (Wal) and Le Brunn (G.) The Story of a Kiss, etc. ⟨Song.⟩ [1892.] fol. **H. 3981. j. (27.)**

— See Rolmaz (James) Norah Delaney, etc. [Song.] ⟨Arr. by G. Le Brunn.⟩ [1891.] fol. **H. 3981. q. (5.)**

— See Seldon (A.) Waltzing as she is waltzed, etc. (Arranged by G. Le Brunn.) [1889.] fol. **H. 1260. m. (57.)**

— See Stamford (John J.) Don't you heed what the young Men tell you, etc. ⟨Song. Arranged by G. Le Brunn.⟩ [1891.] fol. **H. 3981. bb. (19.)**

— See Tabrar (Joseph) Maid of London, ere we part. (Comedy song.) By J. Tabrar, J. P. Harrington and G. Le Brunn, etc. [1896.] s. sh. fol. **H. 3981. gg. (77.)**

— See Tabrar (Joseph) You can't stop a Girl from thinking! By J. Tabrar, J. P. Harrington and G. Le Brunn, etc. [Song.] [1897.] s. sh. fol. **H. 3981. gg. (78.)**

— See West (Arthur) Drink up, Boys, etc. ⟨Song. Arranged by G. Le Brunn.⟩ [1890.] fol. **H. 3981. qq. (7.)**

— See West (Arthur) Now, what will become of poor old Ireland? etc. ⟨Song. Arranged by G. Le Brunn.⟩ [1891.] fol. **H. 3981. qq. (30.)**

— See West (Arthur) Rootity-toot, she plays the Flute, etc. (Arranged by G. Le Brunn.) [1888.] fol. **H. 1260. l. (23.)**

LE BRUNN (Leo)

— See Le Brunn (George)

LE BRUNN (Thomas)

— At the Queen's Command. Written by Charles Williams. [Song. Staff and tonic sol-fa notation. Voice part.] Francis, Day & Hunter: London, [1898.] s. sh. fol. **H. 3980. pp. (51.)**

— Baby's Good-Night. Lullaby, written by M. Arnold. A. Cary: London, [1892.] fol. **H. 1797. o. (34.)**

— Beside the River. Ballad. The words written and the music composed by Thomas le Brunn. pp. 4. T. Hamilton & Cᵒ: London, [c. 1910.] fol. **H. 1654. qq. (28.)**

— Come back to Mother and me. ⟨Song.⟩ Written and composed by T. Le Brunn, etc. [Staff and tonic sol-fa notation. Voice part.] Francis, Day & Hunter: London, [1902.] s. sh. fol. **H. 3985. p. (71.)**

— Come back to Mother and me, etc. ⟨Song. Arranged by H. E. Pether.⟩ [With separate voice part.] 2 pt. Francis, Day & Hunter: London, [1902.] fol. **H. 3985. p. (72.)**

— The Convict's Wife. ⟨Song.⟩ Written and composed by T. Le Brunn. [Staff and tonic sol-fa notation. Voice part.] Francis, Day & Hunter: London, [1901.] s. sh. fol. **H. 3985. p. (73.)**

— Don't cry, Mamma. Written by Geo. A. Stevens, etc. [Song. Staff and tonic sol-fa notation. Voice part.] Francis, Day & Hunter: London, [1898.] s. sh. fol. **H. 3980. pp. (52.)**

— The Heart that clings to you still. ⟨Song.⟩ Written and composed by T. Le Brunn. [With separate voice part.] 2 pt. Francis, Day & Hunter: London, [1901.] fol. **H. 3985. p. (74.)**

— Julie, ma Queen of Tennessee. ⟨Song.⟩ Written and composed by T. Le Brunn. pp. 5. Francis, Day & Hunter: London, [1901.] fol. **H. 3985. p. (75.)**

LE BRUNN (Thomas)

— Kind Mr. Postman. ⟨Song.⟩ Written by Frank W. Carter, etc. [Staff and tonic sol-fa notation. Voice part.] Francis, Day & Hunter: London, [1901.] s. sh. fol. **H. 3985. p. (76.)**

— Kind Mr. Postman, etc. ⟨Song.⟩ [With separate voice part.] 2 pt. Francis, Day & Hunter: London, [1901.] fol. **H. 3985. p. (77.)**

— The Mother's Message. Written & composed by T. Le Brunn. pp. 6. W. Paxton: London, [1902.] fol. **H. 3985. p. (78.)**

— My Heart's own Queen. [Song.] Written by C. Williams. Howard & Co.: London, [1897.] fol. **H. 1798. u. (37.)**

— The Racing Crack. Written ... by Forbes Dawson. [Song. Staff and tonic sol-fa notation. Voice part.] Francis, Day & Hunter: London, [1897.] s. sh. fol. **H. 3980. pp. (53.)**

— Red Riding-Hood. Written and composed by T. Le Brunn, etc. [Song. Staff and tonic sol-fa notation. Voice part.] Francis, Day & Hunter: London, [1898.] s. sh. fol. **H. 3980. pp. (54.)**

— Underneath an Apple Tree. [Song.] Words by Charles Tracey. pp. 4. Frank Dean & Co.: London, [1898.] fol. **H. 3980. pp. (55.)**

— You're still the same to me. ⟨Song.⟩ Written and composed by T. Le Brunn. [Staff and tonic sol-fa notation. Voice part.] Francis, Day & Hunter: London, [1904.] s. sh. fol. **H. 3985. p. (79.)**

— You're still the same to me, etc. ⟨Song.⟩ [With separate voice part.] 2 pt. Francis, Day & Hunter: London, [1904.] fol. **H. 3985. p. (80.)**

LE CALSI (J.)

— See Li Calsi (G.)

LE CAMUS (J. P.)

— Les ages de l'amour; Romance. Paris, [1830?] fol. **H. 1665. (9.)**

— The Art of Singing; a method, in three parts, on an entirely new plan of vocalization, etc. ⟨In English & French. Second edition.⟩ [With a portrait.] pp. 212. Duff & Cᵒ: London, [c. 1835.] fol.
Imperfect; wanting pp. 141, 142. **H. 2245. q.**

— The Bard, a periodical Publication of English, French & Italian vocal & instrumental music ... with accompaniments for the piano forte & harp, etc. ⟨Nᵒ [ᴹˢ 1.].⟩ The Author: London, [c. 1830.] fol. **H. 1652. dd. (5.)**

— The muse of grief at the tomb of George the fourth. A grand lyric scene for one, two, or three voices ad libitum, with an accompaniment for the Pianoforte or harp. London, [1830.] fol. **H. 1665. (10.)**

— Le Reduit Obscur. Pour deux voix ad libitum, avec accompagnement de Pianoforte, ou harpe. Paris, [1830?] fol. **H. 1665. (12.)**

LE CAMUS (Sebastien)

— See Parodies. Parodies spirituelles ... sur des airs choisis de Messieurs Le Camus, Lambert, etc. 1717. obl. 4°. **Hirsch iii. 977.**

LE CARPENTIER (Adolphe Clair)

— L'Africaine, opéra de G. Meyerbeer. 201 et 202 Bagatelle. [P. F.] 2 no. Paris, [1866.] fol. **h. 637. a. (4.)**

— L'Africaine, opéra de Meyerbeer, quadrille, etc. [P. F.] Paris, [1866.] obl. fol. **e. 217. b. (28.)**

LE CARPENTIER (ADOLPHE CLAIR)

— Album des Enfants pour Piano. *Paris,* [1855?] fol.
h. 637. b.

— 115ᵉ Bagatelle sur Stella, ou les contrebandiers, musique de Pugni. *London,* [1850.] fol. **h. 637. (7.)**

— Trois Bagatelles pour le Piano à quatre mains, composées sur des Motifs des Huguenots de Meyerbeer. 3 no. *Maurice Schlesinger: Paris,* [1836.] fol. **R.M. 25. i. 8. (13.)**

— 2 bagatelles, sur le Pardon de Ploërmel de Meyerbeer pour piano. 2 no. *Paris,* [1859.] fol. **h. 637. (18.)**

— Les Bouquets de Fanchette. Fantaisie, *etc.* [P. F.] *Paris,* [1869.] fol. **h. 637. a. (6.)**

— La Chasse du Jeune Henri, de Méhul. Rondo pour piano. [Solo and duet.] 2 no. *Paris,* [1885.] fol. **h. 637. c. (4.)**

— La Circassienne, opéra de D. F. E. Auber, petite fantaisie pour Piano. *London,* [1861.] fol. **h. 1460. v. (5.)**

— Divertissement de salon sur le Cor des Alpes, mélodie de Proch, pour piano ... Op. 49. pp. 10. *Chez A. Meissonnier et J. L. Heugel: Paris,* [c. 1840.] fol. **h. 60. bb. (10.)**

— Divertissement de salon sur Le Cor des Alpes, mélodie de Proch, pour piano ... Op. 49. pp. 10. *Chez les fils de B. Schott: Mayence,* [1843.] fol. **h. 61. r. (14.)**

— Divertissement pour le Piano à quatre mains sur des motifs de l'opéra Guido et Ginévra, de F. Halévy. *Leipzig,* [1840?] fol. **h. 637. c. (2.)**

— Divertissement sur la chanson, Le Roi d'Yvetot, pour le Forte Piano. Op. 67. *London,* [1842.] fol. **h. 702. (8.)**

— Divertissement pour le Piano à quatre mains sur des motifs de l'opéra Les Treize, de F. Halévy. 3ᵐᵉ Divertissement. *Paris,* [1840?] fol. **h. 637. c. (1.)**

— Éléments du Piano à quatre mains: Études de la Mesure ... op. 232. *Paris,* [1861.] fol. **h. 1050.**

— Eléments du Piano à quatre mains, *etc.* Op. 232. *London,* [1861.] fol. **h. 637. a. (1.)**

— L'Enfant et l'Alouette, fantaisie facile sur les motifs de L. Peuchot. [P. F.] *Paris,* [1869.] fol. **h. 637. a. (7.)**

— 25 Études Dialoguées (sans octaves) composées pour Piano à quatre mains. Op. 239. *Paris,* [1861.] fol. **h. 637. a. (2.)**

— Fantaisie sur Anna Bolena de G. Donizetti pour Piano et Violon concertants ... Op. 205. *A. Cotelle: Paris,* [1860?] fol. **h. 1608. k. (10.)**

— Fantaisie sur Don Giovanni de Mozart pour Piano et Violon concertants ... Op. 207. *Paris,* [1860?] fol. **h. 1608. k. (11.)**

— Fantaisie sur L'Elisire d'amore de G. Donizetti pour piano et violon concertants ... Op. 182. *A. Cotelle: Paris,* [1860?] fol. **h. 1608. k. (8.)**

— Fantaisie brillante sur Faust, opéra de C. Gounod, pour le Piano. *London,* [1860.] fol. **h. 1460. v. (4.)**

— Fantaisie sur Les Puritains de Bellini pour piano et violon concertants ... Op. 204. *Paris,* [1860?] fol. **h. 1608. k. (9.)**

— Fantaisie from the opera Queen Topaze [by V. Massé. P. F.]. Op. 201. *London,* [1861.] fol. **h. 1460. v. (3.)**

— Fantaisie sur Richard Cœur de Lion de Grétry pour piano et violon concertants ... Op. 181. *Paris,* [1860?] fol. **h. 1608. k. (7.)**

— Fantaisie sur Semiramide de Rossini pour piano et violon ... Op. 208. *Paris,* [1860?] fol. **h. 1608. k. (12.)**

LE CARPENTIER (ADOLPHE CLAIR)

— Fantaisie brillante sur "Le silence des nuits et amour et fanatisme" d'A. de Carayon La Tour, pour piano. Op. 176. *London,* [1853.] fol. **h. 637. (5.)**

— Fantaisie élégante sur les Vêpres siciliennes de Verdi. Pour le piano. *London,* [1856.] fol. **h. 637. (13.)**

— Le festival des enfans. Collection de danses modernes très faciles pour le piano. Op. 164. 6 no. *London,* [1854.] fol. **h. 637. (12.)**

— La Fiancée du Roi de Garbe, opéra comique de D. F. E. Auber. Fantaisie pour Piano. *Paris,* [1864.] fol. **h. 637. a. (3.)**

— Le Fifre Enchanté de J. Offenbach. Petite fantaisie. [P. F.] *Paris,* [1869.] fol. **h. 637. a. (5.)**

— L'incomparable mirobolanpouff ... Quadrille ... pour le Piano. *Paris,* [1857.] *obl.* fol. **e. 40. (14.)**

— Les Jolies Fleurettes. 12 petites recréations, sur des motifs de Bellini et Donizetti, pour le Pianoforte, *etc.* 12 no. *Wessel & Co.: London,* [1851.] fol. **h. 637. (1.)**

— Juvenile Ball quadrille ... and the Alpensänger's march. [P. F.] *London,* [1855.] fol.
No. 256 of the "Musical Bouquet". **H. 2345.**

— Manon Lescaut, opéra comique de D. F. E. Auber, 171ᵐᵉ bagatelle pour piano par A. Le Carpentier. *Paris,* [1856.] fol. **h. 637. (17.)**

— Manon Lescaut, quadrille sur l'opéra de D. F. E. Auber. [P. F., with accompaniment.] *Paris,* [1856.] *obl.* fol. **e. 38. (12.)**

— Méthode théorique et pratique d'Orgue-Harmonium. Op. 260. *Paris,* [1860?] fol. **h. 2509.**

— Metodo de Piano para los niños. *Paris,* [1869.] fol. *Libro 1°. of "Curso practico de Piano".* **h. 637. a. (8.)**

— Mirella, petite fantaisie facile sur l'opéra de C. Gounod, pour Piano. *London,* [1864.] fol. **h. 1460. v. (6.)**

— Le Nid des Colibris. Esquisse. [P. F.] *Paris,* [1872.] fol. **h. 637. a. (9.)**

— Non più mesta, the celebrated finale, from the opera of Cenerentola, composed by Rossini, arranged with variations by A. Le Carpentier. [P. F.] Op. 4. pp. 4. *J. Duncombe: London,* [c. 1840.] fol. **h. 1203. dd. (14.)**

— Oberon, Fantasia [on C. M. F. E. von Weber's opera] for the Pianoforte. *London,* [1859.] fol. **h. 637. (14.)**

— The Ourika polka. [P. F.] *London,* [1855.] fol. *No. 291 of the "Musical Bouquet".* **H. 2345.**

— Petite Fantaisie pour le piano sur le choeur des gardes chasse du songe d'une nuit d'été, d'A. Thomas. Op. 159. *London,* [1854.] fol. **h. 637. (6.)**

— Petite Fantaisie sur "Bonsoir Mr. Pantalon," opéra comique d'A. Grisar ... pour le piano. Op. 160. *London,* [1854.] fol. **h. 637. (2.)**

— Trois petites fantaisies dansantes sur l'opéra de A. Limnander, Le Chateau de la Barbe-Bleue, pour le piano. Op. 167. *London,* [1854.] fol. **h. 637. (3.)**

— Deux petits souvenirs à Malibran et Stockhausen. Récréations musicales pour le piano forte. N° 1. "We dearly love to see again." Tyrolienne chantée par Madᵉ Malibran. N° 2. "Tyrolienne" chantée par Madᵉ Stockhausen. no. 1. *Wessel & Cⁱ: London,* [1836.] fol. *Imperfect; wanting no. 2.* **h. 723. bb. (32.)**

— Les reines de Venise, petite fantaisie brillante, pour piano, sur des motifs de L. Bordèse. *London,* [1854.] fol. **h. 637. (4.)**

LE CARPENTIER (Adolphe Clair)

— La Ronde des Farfadets. Danse fantastique. [P. F.] *Paris,* [1872.] fol. **h. 637. a. (10.)**

— Rose des Bois, valse gracieuse. [P. F.] *Paris,* [1872.] fol. **h. 637. a. (11.)**

— Le Sergent de la Banlieue. Chanson [begins: "C'est tout d'mêm'ben amusant"]. Paroles d'Aristide Le Carpentier. *Paris,* [1835?] fol. **G. 553. (20.)**

— Short Vocal Exercises with pianoforte accompaniment, *etc. Mayence,* (1884.) *obl.* fol. **E. 601. h. (13.)**

— Si j'étais Roi, d'A. Adam. 204ᵉ. & 205ᵉ. Bagatelles pour Piano à quatre mains. *Paris,* [1876.] fol. **h. 637. a. (12.)**

— Tarentelle Napolitaine ... pour le piano. Op. 178. *Paris,* [1854.] fol. **h. 637. (8.)**

— Tarentelle Napolitaine pour le piano forte. Op. 178. *London,* [1854.] fol. **h. 637. (9.)**

— "La Tenerezza" mélodie de Mᵐᵉ. Brambilla, variée pour le piano par A. Le Carpentier. Op. 177. *London,* [1854.] fol. **h. 637. (10.)**

— La tenerezza ... mélodie de Madame Brambilla, variée pour le piano par A. Le Carpentier. Op. 177. *Paris,* [1854.] fol. **h. 637. (11.)**

— Les universelles. 3 Polkas nationales pour le Piano. Op. 92. *London,* [1845.] fol. **h. 935. (8.)**

— *See* BILSE (B.) [Sturm Galop.] "Il Furioso" Sturm Marsch-Galop de B. Bilse, pour le Piano Forte par A. le Carpentier, *etc.* [1853.] fol. **h. 975. (37.)**

— *See* LECHNER (J.) Suite aux Bagatelles de Le Carpentier. [1886.] fol. **h. 637. c. (3.)**

— *See* VIALON (A.) La danse pour tous, quadrille ... arrangé facilement ... par A. Le Carpentier. [1857.] *obl.* fol. **e. 40. (15.)**

— *See* VIALON (A.) Les forgerons ... Rondo-galop pour le piano, par A. Le Carpentier. [1857.] fol. **h. 637. (16.)**

— *See* VIALON (A.) La promenade sur l'eau ... Rondo-barcarolle pour piano, par A. Le Carpentier. [1857.] fol. **h. 637. (15.)**

LE CARRON (Victor)

— The New Zealanders' Farewell to Egypt. Military March with chorus in "Soldiers" Maori. [P. F.] *West & Co.: London,* 1916. fol. **h. 3284. nn. (28.)**

LECERF (Justus Amadeus)

— Neun Gesaenge zu Goethe's Faust, für Stimme und Pianoforte gesetzt, *etc.* 2 Hft. *Berlin,* [1830?] *obl.* fol. **E. 711.**

LECHALLIER ( )

— Les Adieux à Roselle. Romance ... Paroles de Mr. Armand-Gouffé. *Paris,* [1820?] fol. **G. 806. j. (49.)**

— Elle n'est plus. Romance [begins: "Plus de repos"] de Mr. Maigeon. *Paris,* [1825?] fol. **G. 806. j. (48.)**

LECHEV (Boyan)

— *See* PIPKOV (L.) Соната за цигулка и пиано, *etc.* (Op. 7. Редактор на цигулковата партия Б. Лечев.) 1955. 4°. **g. 896. b. (3.)**

LE CHEVALLIER (Amédée)

— Scelta delle più belle Ariette, e Canzocine Italiane, de' più famosi Autori ... Accommodate al suono di Flauto, Violino, & altri Stromenti, racolte d'A. Le Chevallier. (Violino Primo.) (Basso Continuo.) 2 pt. *P. & J. Blaeu: Amsterdam,* 1691. *obl.* 4°. **C. 404. (3.)**

— *See* LULLI (G. B.) Les Trios des Opéra de Monsieur de Lully, mis en ordre pour les concerts, *etc.* [Arranged, with a preface, by A. Le Chevallier.] 1690. (1691.) *obl.* 4°. **C. 404. (1.)**

— *See* ROSIERS (C.) Pièces Choisies ... Mises en ordre par A. Le Chevallier, *etc.* 1691. *obl.* 4°. **C. 404. (2.)**

LECHNER (J.)

— Suite aux Bagatelles de Le Carpentier. 20 no. *Paris,* [1886.] fol. **h. 637. c. (3.)**

LECHNER (Johannes)

— Lebe wohl. *See* infra: Wanderlieder ... Op. 5. No. 1.

— Morgenlied. *See* infra: Wanderlieder ... Op. 5. No. 3.

— Scheiden und Meiden. *See* infra: Wanderlieder ... Op. 5. No. 2.

— Wanderlieder. Gedichte von L. Uhland für eine Singstimme mit Pianofortebegleitung. Op. 5. No. 1. Lebewohl. No. 2. Scheiden und Meiden. No. 3. Morgenlied. 3 no. *Berlin,* [1885.] fol. **H. 2836. h. (33.)**

LECHNER (Konrad)

— Es taget vor dem Walde und andere alte Weisen für Singstimmen, Blockflöten oder andere Instrumente (auch Hausorgel oder Cembalo). [Score and part for recorders.] 2 pt. *Bärenreiter: Kassel, etc.,* [1960.] *obl.* 8°. **B. 418. l. (1.)**

— Kleine Tanz- und Spielstücke für eine Blockflöte. (Fidel, Gambe, kleine Pauke ad lib.) pp. 16. *Bärenreiter: Kassel, etc.,* [1960.] *obl.* 8°. **a. 40. n. (13.)**

— Volkslied-Improvisationen für eine Blockflöte (oder ein anderes Melodie-Instrument). pp. 16. *Bärenreiter: Kassel, etc.,* [1960.] *obl.* 8°. **A. 1115. (8.)**

LECHNER (Leonhard)

— Werke ... Herausgegeben von Konrad Ameln. [With facsimiles.]

Bd. 1. Motectæ sacræ quatuor, quinque et sex vocum, 1575 ... Herausgegeben von Ludwig Finscher. pp. 193. 1956.

Bd. 2. Newe Teutsche Lieder zu drey Stimmen ... Herausgegeben von Uwe Martin. pp. xvi. 71. 1969.

Bd. 3. Newe Teutsche Lieder mit vier und fünff Stimmen. 1577 ... Herausgegeben von Uwe Martin. pp. 79. 1954.

Bd. 4. Sanctissimae Virginis Mariæ canticum secundum octo vulgares tonos quatuor vocibus. 1578. Herausgegeben von Walther Lipphardt. pp. xvii. 48. 1960.

Bd. 5. Newe teutsche Lieder mit fünff Stimmen. Con alchuni madrigali. 1579. Herausgegeben von Konrad Ameln. pp. xviii. 101. 1970.

Bd. 7. Newe Teutsche Lieder mit fünff und vier Stimmen. 1582. Herausgegeben von Konrad Ameln. pp. xix. 139. 1974.

Bd. 8. Liber missarum sex et quinque vocum adjunctis aliquot introitibus in præcipua festa, 1584. Herausgegeben von Walther Lipphardt. pp. xxiii. 197. 1964.

Bd. 9. Neue lustige Teutscher Lieder nach Art der Welschen Canzonen, 1586/1588 ...

LECHNER (Leonhard)

    herausgegeben von Ernst Fritz Schmid. pp. xv. 65.
1955.

Bd. 11. Neue geistliche und weltliche teutsche Lieder mit
fünff und vier Stimmen. 1589. Herausgegeben von
Konrad Ameln. pp. xv. 111. 1980.

Bd. 12. Historia der Passion und Leidens unsers einigen
Erlösers und Seligmachers Jesu Christi. 1593.
Herausgegeben von K. Ameln. pp. xii. 45. 1960.

Bd. 13. Neue Gaistliche und weltliche Teutsche Gesang
sampt zwayen Lateinischen mit vier und fünf
Stimmen aus der posthumen Handschrift von
1606. Herausgegeben von Walther Lipphardt. pp.
xx. 79. 1973.

Bärenreiter-Verlag: Kassel, Basel, 1954, *etc.* 8°.   **F. 58.**

— Drei Volksliedsätze für drei und vier gleiche Stimmen a
cappella. [No. 1.] Jagen, Hetzen und Federspiel. [No. 2.] Grün
ist der Mai. [No. 3.] Mein grosse Lieb, die macht mich blind.
⟨Dichter unbekannt.⟩. pp. 6. *C. F. Peters: Frankfurt,* [1959.] 8°.
Part of "Das Singwerk".   **E. 724. c. (8.)**

— Benedicamus patrem et filium cum sancto spiritu. *See infra:*
[Motectae sacrae.]

— Deutsche Sprüche von Leben und Tod. Aus der posthumen
Handschrift von 1606. Für vierstimmigen gemischten Chor
... Herausgegeben von ... Walther Lipphardt. pp. 18.
Bärenreiter: Kassel, etc., [1971.] 8°.
Part of "Chor-Archiv".   **F. 1199. qq. (2.)**

— Harmoniæ miscellæ Cantionum Sacrarum, ab Exquisitissimis
Ætatis Nostræ Musicis cum Quinque & Sex vocibus
concinnatæ ... editæ studio Leonardi Lechneri, *etc.* Cantus.
(Altus.) (Tenor.) (Basis.) (Quinta (Sexta) Vox.) 6 pt. *Typis
Gerlachianis: Noribergæ,* 1583. *obl.* 4°.
*The Tenor part alone is dated. The composers named in this
collection are: O. de Lasso, P. de Monte, C. de Rore, Hannibal
Paduano, I. P. Prænestinus, I. de Wert, A. Gabrieli, F. de
Lasso, C. Porta, M. A. Ingegnerius, H. Stabilis, I. Guami,
A. Gabrieli, A. Morari, L. Lechner, Don Ferdinandus de las
Infantas, G. Prevost, A. Gorswinus, T. Riccius, G. Florius,
A. Ferabosco, H. Baccusius and H. Meloni.*   **A. 249. c.**

— [Another copy. Cantus. (Altus.) (Tenor.) (Basis.) (Sexta Vox.)]
    A. 249. f.

— Das Hohelied Salomonis. Aus der posthumen Handschrift
von 1606. Für vierstimmigen gemischten Chor ...
Herausgegeben von ... Walther Lipphardt. pp. 19.
Bärenreiter: Kassel, etc., [1971.] 8°.
Part of "Chor-Archiv".   **F. 1199. qq. (1.)**

— Lustige teutsche Lieder. *See infra:* [Neue lustige teutsche
Lieder.]

— Magnificat primi toni. *See infra:* [Sanctissimae Virginis
Mariae canticum.]

— Liber Missarum Sex et Quinque Vocum ... Adjunctis aliquot
Introitibus in præcipua festa ... iisque Sex & Quinque
vocum, *etc.* Cantus. (Altus.) (Basis.) (Quinta & Sexta Vox.)
4 pt. *Typis Gerlachianis: Norimbergae,* 1584. *obl.* 4°.
    A. 249. d.

— [Liber missarum.] Missa prima Domine Dominus noster. Für
sechsstimmigen gemischten Chor. Herausgegeben von
Walther Lipphardt. pp. 28. *Bärenreiter: Kassel, etc.,* [1964.]
8°.
Part of "Chor Archiv".   **F. 274. rr. (1.)**

— Motectæ Sacræ, Quatuor, Quinque, et Sex Vocum, ita
compositae, ut non solum viua voce commodissime cantari,
sed etiam ad omnis generis instrumenta optimè adhiberi
possint ... Addita est in fine Motecta octo vocum, *etc.* Altus.
*Impressæ ... in Officina typographica Katharinæ, Theodorici
Gerlachij relictæ Viduæ, & Hæredum Ioannis Montani:
Noribergæ,* 1576. *obl.* 4°.   **A. 249.**

LECHNER (Leonhard)

— [Motectae sacrae.] Benedicamus patrem et filium cum sancto
spiritu, *etc.* [S.A.T.T.] pp. 6. *Bärenreiter-Verlag: Kassel,* 1968.
8°.   **E. 1439. r. (17.)**

— Neue lustige Teutsche Lieder, nach art der Welschen
Canzonen, mit vier Stimmen componirt ... Mit etlichen
neuen Compositionen ... gemehret. Secunda Vox. *Gedruckt
durch Katharinam Gerlachin: Nürmberg,* 1588. *obl.* 4°.
    A. 249. e.

— [Neue lustige teutsche Lieder.] Lustige teutsche Lieder für
vierstimmigen Chor. Herausgegeben von Ernst Fritz Schmid.
[A selection.] pp. 19. *Bärenreiter: Kassel, etc.,* [1959.] 8°.
Part of "Chor-Archiv".   **E. 724. d. (5.)**

— [Neue lustige teutsche Lieder. No. 1, 3, 6, 7, 13, 16.] Six
Lieder ... For four voices or instruments. ⟨[Edited by]
Bernard Thomas. [Texts translated by] Alan Robson.⟩ pp. 11.
London Pro Musica Edition: [*London,* 1979.] 4°.
[*Thesaurus musicus.* 14.]   **g. 1374. j.**

— Newe Teutsche Lieder, mit Vier vnd Fünff Stimmen, Welche
ganz lieblich zusingen, auch auff allerley Instrumenten
zugebrauchen, *etc.* Discant. (Altus.) (Tenor.) (Basis.) (Quinta
Vox.) 5 pt. *Gedruckt durch Nicolaum Knorrn: Nürnberg,*
1577. *obl.* 4°.   **A. 249. a.**

— Sacrarum Cantionum, Quinque et Sex Vocum, Liber
Secundus, *etc.* Altus. *In Officina Catharinæ Gerlachin, &
Hæredum Iohannis Montani: Noribergæ,* 1581. *obl.* 4°.
    A. 249. b.

— [Sanctissimae Virginis Mariae canticum.] Magnificat primi
toni. Für vierstimmigen Chor. Herausgegeben von Walther
Lipphardt. pp. 8. *Bärenreiter: Kassel, etc.,* [1960.] 8°.
Part of "Chor-Archiv".   **F. 1176. jj. (8.)**

— Wann kommen wird mein' letzte Stund'. [Motet for four
voices.] [1908.] *See* THIEL (C.) Auswahl hervorragender
Meisterwerke, *etc.* Band II. No. 10. [1898, *etc.*] 8°.   **F. 1767.**

— *See* REGNARD (J.) Newe Teutsche Lieder ... mit fünff
Stimmen gesetzet, durch Leonardum Lechnerum, *etc.* 1579.
obl. 4°.   **A. 369. c.**

LECHNER (Lothar)

— Mein Weihnachtsbuch. 33 Weihnachtslieder mit
vollständigen Texten für Klavier zwei- und vierhändig sehr
leicht gesetzt von L. Lechner. pp. 47. *B. Schott's Söhne:
Mainz,* [1950.] 4°.   **g. 1128. i. (4.)**

— *See* CZERNIK (W.) Morinell. (Kleiner Regenpfeifer.)
⟨Accordeon-Spezialstimme: L. Lechner.⟩ [1959.] 4°. [*Schott's
Domesticum. no.* 541.]   **g. 1053. a.**

— *See* DVOŘÁK (A.) Humoreske. Humoresque ... Opus 101.
Nr. 7. Erleichtert von L. Lechner. Piano. [1955.] 4°.
    g. 1160. c. (10.)

— *See* KAESTNER (H.) and LECHNER (L.) Leichte Spielstücke aus
dem 17. und 18. Jahrhundert ... Für Sopranflöte und Klavier
... Herausgegeben ... H. Kaestner/L. Lechner. [1957.] *obl.* 8°.
    b. 411. (10.)

— *See* MOZART (W. A.) [Männer suchen stets zu naschen.
K. 433.] Warnung ... Gesang und Klavier, *etc.* ⟨Neuausgabe
von L. Lechner.⟩ [1963.] 4°.   **G. 537. d. (3.)**

— *See* RUHRMANN (F.) Alte Weihnachtslieder ... für
Altblockflöte mit Klavier. Bearbeitet von L. Lechner. [1963.]
obl. 8°.   **B. 742. q.**

— *See* WINKLER (G.) Südliches Temperament, *etc.* [The
accordion and saxophone parts arranged by L. Lechner.]
[1954.] 4°. [*Schott's Domesticum, no.* 559.]   **g. 1053. a.**

LÉCHOPIÉ (Pierre Martin Nicolas)

— 3 Duos pour deux Violons. Op. 23.   *Paris*, [1825?] fol.

g. 421. j. (2.)

LECLAIR (Jean Marie)

— Jean-Marie Leclair. [A biographical sketch and a thematic catalogue of his works by A. Bachmann. With a portrait. Extracted from an unidentified periodical.] *Fr.* [1913.] 4°.
The name of the author and date of publication are given in a MS. note.   **Hirsch 171.**

— First Steps to the Art of playing classical music. 24 Pieces by J. M. Le Clair, arranged for the Pianoforte by V. Moret. 2 bk. *St. Cecilia Music Publishing Co.: London*, [1891.] 8°.   **e. 454.**

— Minuet [Sonata. Op. 5. No. 9] and Hunting Scene. Menuet et Chasse. For Wind Quintet ... Arranged by O. Mueller. [Parts.] *See* QUINTETS. Quintets for Wind Instruments, *etc.* [No. 3.] 1937. 4°.   **g. 417. z. (1.)**

— Allegro di Ballo. *See* infra: [Sonatas. Book 4. Op. 9. No. 12.]

— Le Beaujoyeux. *See* infra: [Sonatas. Book 4. Op. 9. No. 7. — Giga.]

Concertos. Op. 7

— Ier et IIme (IIIeme et IVme — Veme et VIme) concerto a tré violino, alto, basso, per organo, é violoncello ... Premiere partie. Oeuvre VIIme. On trouvera deux parties de basse. [Parts.] 3 no. 18 pt.   *Chez l'auteur, etc.: Paris*, [1737?] fol.   **g. 220. g. (1.)**

— Six Concerto e Tre Violini, Alto e Basso per Organo a Violoncello. Composés par M^r Le Clair l'Aîné. Gravés par son Epouse ... Premiere Partie. Œuvre VIIme. [Parts.]   *Chez l'Auteur: Paris*, [1740?] fol.   **g. 220. c.**

— [No. 2.] Concerto pour violon en ré majeur, *etc.* ⟨Révision et réalisation J. F. Paillard.⟩ [Score.] pp. 35.   *Éditions Costallat: Paris*, [1962.] 4°.
Part of "Archives de la musique instrumentale".

g. 420. qq. (8.)

— [No. 3.] Konzert C-dur ... für Flöte oder Violine oder Oboe, Streicher und Generalbass. Herausgegeben und bearbeitet von Gustav Scheck und Hugo Ruf. [Score.] pp. 31.   *Deutscher Ricordi Verlag: Lörrach*, [1956.] 4°.
Florilegium musicum. no. 6.   **g. 1620. d. (1.)**

— [No. 3.] Concerto en do majeur pour flûte solo, deux violons, alto et la basse continue. ⟨Réalisation de Claude Crussard.⟩ [Score and parts.] 6 pt.   *Édition Fœtisch: Lausanne*, 1964. 4°.
[Flores musicae. 14.]   **G. 519. y.**

— [No. 3.] Concerto en ut-majeur. Pour flûte ou hautbois et orchestre à cordes. Reconstitution par Fernand Oubradous. [P. F. score and part.] 2 pt.   *Éditions musicales transatlantiques: Paris*, [1963.] 4°.   **g. 70. aa. (7.)**

— [No. 4.] Concerto en fa majeur pour violon solo, deux violons, alto et la basse continue. ⟨Réalisation de Claude Crussard.⟩ [Score and parts.] 6 pt.   *Édition Fœtisch: Lausanne*, 1960. 4°.
[Flores musicæ. 10.]   **G. 519. y.**

— [No. 5.] Konzert A-moll für Violine, Streichorchester und Basso continuo. Concerto in A minor ... Herausgegeben von ... Hugo Ruf. [With a portrait. Score.] pp. 46.   *Nagels Verlag: Kassel*, [1963.] 4°.
Nagels Musik-Archiv. 209.   **g. 1620. r. (6.)**

— [No. 6.] Concerto n° 6 en la-majeur pour violon et orchestre à cordes. Reconstitution par Fernand Oubradous. [Score.] pp. 52.   *Éditions musicales transatlantiques: Paris*, [1958.] 8°.
Part of "Collection Fernand Oubradous".   **d. 135. l. (3.)**

LECLAIR (Jean Marie)

Concertos. Op. 10

— VI concerto a tré violini, alto, e basso per organo, e violoncello ... Gravés par son épouse ... On trouvera deux parties de basse. Parte seconda. Ouvre Xme. [Parts.] 6 pt.   *Chez l'auteur, etc.: Paris*, [1744?] fol.   **g. 220. g. (2.)**

— [No. 1.] Concerto für Violine, Streicher und Basso continuo ... Bearbeitet von Frederick F. Polnauer. Partitur, *etc.* pp. 35. *B. Schott's Söhne: Mainz*, [1968.] 4°.
Part of "Concertino".   **g. 1067. s. (6.)**

— [No. 2.] Concerto pour violon en la majeur, *etc.* ⟨Révision et réalisation J. F. Paillard.⟩ [Score.] pp. 32.   *Éditions Costallat: Paris*, [1963.] 4°.   **g. 1620. t. (4.)**

— [No. 6.] Concerto pour violon en sol mineur, *etc.* ⟨Révision et réalisation J. F. Paillard.⟩ [Score.] pp. 47.   *Éditions Costallat: Paris*, [1963.] 4°.
Archives de la musique instrumentale. 5.   **g. 1780. v. (11.)**

— Dance Provencale. *See* infra: [Trio.—Tambourin 2.]

— Six duets for two Violins. *See* infra: Sonates à deux violons sans basse. Op. 3.

— Entrée. *See* infra: [Sonatas. Book 1. Op. 1. No. 8.—Vivace.]

— Fête champêtre. Rondeau. Leclair- [transcribed for violin or violoncello and piano by A.] Trowell. (Edition for Violin by G. C. Trowell.)   *Schott & Co.: London*, 1926. fol.
[Oeuvres Classiques. Première Série. No. 7.]   **h. 1738. c.**

— Une Fleur du Passé. Andante d'une Sonate de Leclair (1720) arrangé pour Violon avec accomp^t. de Piano par V. Moret. *London*, [1877.] fol.   **h. 1608. q. (37.)**

— Musette. *See* infra: [Sonatas. Book 1. Op. 1. No. 8.]

— Ouvertures et sonates en trio pour deux violons, avec la basse continuë. Composées par M. Leclair l'aîné. Gravées par son épouse ... Œuvre XIIIe. [Parts.] 3 pt.   *Chez l'auteur, etc.: Paris*, [1753.] fol.   **g. 220. h.**

— [Ouvertures et sonates en trio. Op. 13. Ouvertura 1. Sonata 1.] Two Trio Sonatas. For two violins and basso continuo. Edited by Graham Sadler, *etc.* [Score and parts.] 7 pt. *Oxford University Press: London*, [1976.] 4°.
[Musica da camera. no. 38.]
The parts for the Ouvertura and the Sonata are printed separately.   **g. 935.**

— Première récréation de musique. Op. VI. Für zwei Violinen und Basso continuo ... Herausgegeben von ... Hugo Ruf. [Score and parts.] 4 pt.   *Bärenreiter: Kassel, etc.*, 1976. 4°.
Hortus musicus. 225.   **f. 388. d. (2.)**

— Deuxième récréation de musique. Op. VIII. Für zwei Querflöten oder Violinen und Basso continuo ... Herausgegeben von ... Hugo Ruf. [With a portrait. Score and parts.] 4 pt.   *Bärenreiter: Kassel, etc.*, [1967.] 4°.

g. 1067. h. (8.)

— Sarabande et Allemande. [Violin and P. F.] 1924. *See* MOFFAT (A. E.) French 18th Century Violin Pieces ... 15. 1919, *etc.* fol.   **h. 1684. g. (1.)**

— Scylla et Glaucus. [For airs published anonymously:] *See* SCYLLA.

— Scylla et Glaucus. Tragédie ... Representée pour la premiere fois ... le 4e octobre 1746, *etc.* [Score.] pp. xxviii. 1–168. *Chez l'auteur, etc.: Paris*, [1746?] fol.
Imperfect; wanting pp. 169, 170, *supplied in photostat facsimile.*

H. 230. z.

LECLAIR (Jean Marie)

— [Scylla et Glaucus.] Suite d'orchestre tirée de l'opéra Scylla et
Glaucus, pour orchestre à cordes ... Réalisation et revision
de ... Laurence Boulay. Partition, *etc.* pp. 48. *Hawkes &
Son: London*, [1956.] 4°. **g. 727. rr. (2.)**

— [Sonatas. Bk. 2. Op. 2. No. 8, Bk. 3. Op. 5. No. 1.—Allegro.]
Sarabanda et Bravura. *See* MORET (V.) Un souvenir du temps
de Louis XV. [1878.] fol. **h. 1494. v. (9.)**

— [Sonatas. Bk. 1. Op. 1. No. 3, 4 and 8; Bk 3. Op. 5. No. 4.]
Pièces en duo, pour Violon et Violoncelle avec Clavecin ou
Piano. [No. 1.] Gavotte. [No. 2.] Menuet. [No. 3.] Musette.
[No. 4.] Chaconne ... avec les doigtés, les coups d'archet ...
qui conviennent à l'interprétation de ces Œuvres par
C. Bouvet. Réalisation de la Basse chiffrée par J. Jemain.
E. Demets: Paris, [1906.] fol.
Part of the "Répertoire de la Fondation J.-S. Bach".
h. 420. (2.)

— Zwei Sonaten für Flöte oder Violine und Klavier ... Nr. 1,
E moll ... 2, G dur ... [Op. 9. No. 7.] Aussetzung des
bezifferten Basses von ... H. Bouillard. *B. Schott's Söhne:
Mainz und Leipzig*, 1931. 4°.
No. 2 only. **g. 70. h. (14.)**

— Sonatas for Violin and Basso continuo. Opus 5, opus 9, and
opus 15 ... Edited by Robert E. Preston. [With facsimiles.
Scores and parts.] 4 vol. 12 pt. *A-R Editions: New Haven*,
[1968–71.] 4°.
[*Recent Researches in the Music of the Baroque Era. vol.* 4, 5,
10, 11.] **G. 1490.**

Sonatas. Bk. 1. Op. 1

— Premier Livre de Sonates à Violon Seul avec la Basse
Continue ... Gravées par L. Hue, *etc.* *Chez le Sr Boivin:
Paris*, 1723. fol. **i. 8. a. (1.)**

— [Another copy.] **Hirsch III. 357. (1.)**

— [No. 2.] Sonate C-Dur ... für Querflöte und Basso continuo.
Cembalo (Pianoforte), Violoncello (Viola da gamba) ad lib
... Herausgegeben von Hugo Ruf. [Score and part.] 2 pt.
B. Schott's Söhne: Mainz, [1967.] 4°.
Part of "Il Flauto traverso". **g. 70. ll. (4.)**

— [No. 2.] Gavotte, *etc.* [P. F. and violin, violoncello or flute.]
See TRANSCRIPTIONS. Transcriptions classiques, *etc.* No. 13.
[1873–86.] fol. **h. 1752.**

— [No. 2.] Gavotte célèbre. *See* HERMAN (A.) Cinq Pièces, *etc.*
No. 3. [1875.] fol. **h. 1620. b. (7.)**

— [No. 5.] Sonata in A, *etc.* [Violin and P. F.] *See* MOFFAT
(A. E.) Kammer-Sonaten, *etc.* No. 5. (1909, 10.) fol.
h. 1684. d. (3.)

— [No. 8.] Musette ... Arr. [for 2 violins, violoncello ad lib., and
P. F.] by J. W. Slatter. *B. Schott's Söhne: Mainz, etc.*, (1912.)
fol.
Part of "Transcriptions de Morceaux classiques et modernes".
h. 2842. a. (12.)

— [No. 8.] Musette. Arranged for flute and piano by Georges
Barrère. [Score and part.] 2 pt. *G. Schirmer: New York;
Chappell & Co.: London; London* [printed, 1964.] 4°.
g. 70. u. (5.)

— [No. 8.—Vivace.] Entrée. [Violin and P. F.] *See* MOFFAT (A. E.)
Masterpieces, *etc.* No. 1. 1919. 4°. **g. 500. b. (13.)**

Sonatas. Bk. 2. Op. 2

— Second Livre de Sonates pour le Violon et pour la Flute
Traversiere avec la Basse Continue ... Gravées par Mlle
Louise Roussel. *Chez l'Auteur: Paris*, [1725?] fol.
i. 8. a. (2.)

— [Another copy.] **Hirsch III. 357. (2.)**

LECLAIR (Jean Marie)

— Zwölf Sonaten für Violine und Generalbass, nebst einem
Trio für Violine, Violoncell und Generalbass ... Mit einem
ausgesetzten Generalbass herausgegeben von R. Eitner.
Breitkopf & Härtel: Leipzig, 1903. fol.
[*Publikation aelterer praktischer und theoretischer Musikwerke.
Band XXVII.*] **Ac. 5144/2.**

— [No. 1.] Andante. [Violoncello and P. F.] *See* SWERT (J. de)
Collection de Morceaux choisis des maîtres classiques ...
Suite III. Nr. 15. [1881.] fol. **g. 523. a.**

— [No. 2.] Sonata, *etc.* [Violin and P. F.] (1912.) *See* MOFFAT
(A. E.) Kammer-Sonaten, *etc.* No. 22. (1909, *etc.*) fol.
h. 1684. d. (3.)

— [No. 4.] Sonate IV. D. [1894.] *See* JENSEN (G.) Classische Violin
Musik, *etc.* Hft. 25. [1890, *etc.*] 4°. **g. 986.**

— [No. 4.] Sarabande und Tambourin. D moll. [Violin and P. F.]
See RIES (Franz) Album Blätter ... No. 11. [1884.] fol.
h. 1609. v. (16.)

— [No. 4.] Sarabanda & Tambourino. [Violin and P. F.] [1892.]
See JENSEN (G.) Vortragsstudien, *etc.* No. 4. [1892, *etc.*] fol.
h. 1628.

— [No. 4.] Sarabande and Tambourin. [Violin and P. F.]
Wickins & Co.: London, [1896.] fol.
No. 42 of "Wickins' Violin Literature". **h. 1743. (13.)**

— [No. 4.] Sarabande and Tambourin ... for Violin and
Pianoforte. 1901. *See* WILHELMJ (A. E. D. F. V.) and
BROWN (J.) A Modern School for the Violin. No. 27. 1898,
etc. 4°. **h. 1748. a.**

— [No. 4.] Sarabande et Tambourin ... Arranged by H. Tolhurst.
[Violin and P. F.] *W. Paxton & Co.: London*, 1926. 4°.
Part of the "Anthology of Violin Music". **g. 505. nn. (13.)**

— [No. 4.] Tambourin. [Violin and P. F.] [1904.] *See*
HERMANN (F.) Morceaux Favoris, *etc.* No. 138. [1886, *etc.*] fol.
h. 1621. b.

— [No. 6.] *See* ALARD (D.) Les Maîtres Classiques du Violon.
No. 54. [1862, *etc.*] fol. **h. 1605. a.**

— [No. 7.] Gigue ... Arranged (for Flute or Violin and Piano)
by G. Barrère. *G. Schirmer: New York*, 1928. 4°.
g. 70. h. (3.)

— [No. 7.] Gigue. Arranged for flute and piano by Georges
Barrère. [Score and part.] 2 pt. *G. Schirmer: New York;
Chappell & Co.: London; London* [printed, 1964.] 4°.
g. 70. u. (4.)

— [No. 8.] Sonate à trois pour Violon ou Flute, Viole de Gambe
ou Violoncelle, et Clavecin ou Piano ... avec les doigtés, les
coups d'archet ... qui conviennent à l'interprétation de cette
Œuvre par C. Bouvet. Réalisation de la Basse chiffrée par
J. Jemain. *E. Demets: Paris*, 1905. fol.
Part of the "Répertoire de la Fondation J.-S. Bach".
h. 420. (1.)

— [No. 8.] Trio-Sonate ... D dur ... für Violine oder Flöte, Viola
da Gamba, oder Violoncelle, und Cembalo, oder Klavier ...
Bearbeitet und herausgegeben von C. Döbereiner. 2 no.
B. Schott's Söhne: Mainz, 1929. 4°. **g. 417. o. (4.)**

— [No. 8.] Sonate à trois avec une flûte allemande ou un violon,
une viole et le clavecin. ⟨Réalisation de Claude Crussard.⟩
[Score and parts.] 3 pt. *Édition Fœtisch: Lausanne*, [1955.] 4°.
[*Flores musicæ.* 5.] **G. 519. y.**

— [No. 8.] Triosonate D-Dur ... für Violine oder Querflöte,
Viola da gamba (Violoncello) und Basso continuo ...
Herausgegeben von Hugo Ruf. [Score and parts.] 5 pt.
B. Schott's Söhne: Mainz, etc, [1968.] 4°.
Part of "Antiqua". **g. 1067. s. (5.)**

LECLAIR (Jean Marie)

— [No. 8.] Sarabande, *etc.* [2 violins, violoncello and P. F.] (1912.) *See* Moffat (A. E.) Transcriptionen klassischer Stücke, *etc.* No. 34. [1891, *etc.*] fol.   **h. 1684. (2.)**

Sonatas. Bk. 3. Op. 5

— Troisième livre de sonates à violon seul avec la basse continue ... Gravé par Mme Leclair ... Oeuvre v. [Score.] pp. 82. *Chez l'auteur: Paris*, [1723?] fol.
The date in the privilege is 1723.   **Hirsch III. 357. (3.)**

— [A reissue.] Troisième livre de sonates à violon seul avec la basse continue ... Gravées par Mme Leclaire ... Œuvre v. *Paris*, [1735?] fol.
Without the leaves containing the dedication and titlepage.   **g. 220. a.**

— [No. 1.—Allegro.] Toccata ... for the Violin. Edited ... and an accompaniment for the Pianoforte adapted by J. J. Poole. *J. J. Poole: London*, 1899. fol.   **h. 1612. c. (32.)**

— [No. 4.—Aria.] Cantilena. [Violoncello and P. F.] *See* Lee (S.) Souvenir des anciens Maîtres ... No. 3. [1885.] fol.   **h. 1875. b. (2.)**

— [No. 5.] Sonate H-moll für Violine and Basso continuo. Sonata in B minor. For violin and thorough bass. Herausgegeben von ... Hugo Ruf, *etc.* [Score and part.] 2 pt. *Bärenreiter: Kassel, etc.*, [1958.] 4°.   **h. 1613. l. (3.)**

— [No. 6.] Sonate vi. (Le Tombeau.) *See* Alard (D.) Les Maîtres Classiques du Violon. No. 4. [1862, *etc.*] fol.   **h. 1605. a.**

— [No. 6.] Sonate genannt Le Tombeau, für Violine, *etc. See* David (F.) Die hohe Schule des Violinspiels. No. 5. [1867.] fol.   **h. 1618. b.**

— [No. 6.] Le Tombeau. Sonate à violon seul avec la Basse continue. Œuvre v. No. vi. [1894.] *See* Jensen (G.) Classische Violin Musik, *etc.* Hft. 28. [1890, *etc.*] 4°.   **g. 986.**

— [No. 6.] Gavotta graziosa ... in freier Uebertragung für Pianoforte von G. Jensen. [1897.] *See* Perles. Perles Musicales, *etc.* No. 13. [1890, *etc.*] fol.   **h. 3270.**

— [No. 6.] Gavotte from the Sonata in C minor, Le Tombeau. Arranged by K. Simpson. (Scored for 3 Violins, Violoncello (Bass) and Piano.) *Hinrichsen Edition: London*, 1938. 8°. *Part of the "School Orchestra Series".*   **e. 688. j. (15.)**

— [No. 7.] Sonate A-moll für Violine und Basso continuo ... Herausgegeben von ... Hugo Ruf, *etc.* [Score and part.] 2 pt. *Bärenreiter: Kassel, etc.*, [1961.] fol.   **g. 500. hh. (11.)**

— [No. 9.] Andante, Gavotta e Minuetto. [Violin and P. F.] [1894.] *See* Jensen (G.) Vortragsstudien, *etc.* No. 18. [1892, *etc.*] fol.   **h. 1628.**

— [No. 9.] Gavotte. [Violoncello and P. F.] *See* Schroeder (C.) Vortragsstudien, *etc.* No. 38. [1894, *etc.*] fol.   **g. 800. a.**

— [No. 10.] Sonata x, Book III. Continuo realization by A. G. Dechaume. [Score.] *In:* The Score. no. 3. pp. 10–19. 1950. 8°.   **P. P. 1945. abe.**

— [No. 10.] Tambourin. *See* Kreisler (F.) Meisterwerke der Violine mit Klavier-Begleitung, *etc.* No. 3. (1913.) fol.   **h. 1694. (1.)**

— [No. 10.] Le Tambourin ... [Violoncello and P. F.] Arrangement by A. Moffat [or rather, T. Nachèz]. (1912.) *See* Moffat (A. E.) Klassische Stücke, *etc.* No. 21. (1911, 12.) fol.   **h. 1684. e. (1.)**

— [No. 10.] *See* Wagner (O.) Tambourin ... Souvenir de J. M. Le Clair, *etc.* [1884.] fol.   **h. 3689. (22.)**

— [No. 11.] Giga. *See* Elman (M.) Succès Classiques pour Violon et Piano. No. 11. (1910.) fol.   **g. 505. dd. (35.)**

LECLAIR (Jean Marie)

— [No. 12.] Sonate für Violine, *etc. See* David (F.) Die hohe Schule des Violinspiels. No. 6. [1867.] fol.   **h. 1618. b.**

— [No. 12.] Sonate für Violine mit beziffertem Bass. Bearbeitet von Ferdinand David. Neue revidierte Ausgabe von Henri Petri. [Score.] pp. 17. *Breitkopf & Härtel: Leipzig*, [c. 1910.] fol.
Die hohe Schule des Violinspiels. no. 6.   **h. 1613. n. (4.)**

— [No. 12.] Largo. [Violoncello and P. F.] [1897.] *See* Schroeder (C.) Vortragsstudien, *etc.* No. 52. [1894, *etc.*] fol.   **g. 800. a.**

Sonatas. Bk. 4. Op. 9

— Quatrième livre de sonates à violon seul avec la basse continue ... Gravées par Mme Le Clair ... Œuvre ix. [Score.] pp. 75. *Chez l'auteur: Paris*, [1745?] fol.
With the bookplate of Michael Christian Festing.   **Hirsch III. 357. (4.)**

— Quatrième Livre de Sonates à Violon Seul avec la Basse Continue ... Gravées par Mme Le Clair ... Œuvre ix. *Chez l'Auteur: Paris*, [1745?] fol.
Imperfect; wanting pp. 4, 5, which have been supplied in MS.   **i. 8.**

— [No. 1, 12, 4, 3, 5 and 6.] Six Solos for a Violin with a Bass for the Harpsichord or Violoncello. Opera Seconda. *Printed for I. Walsh: London*, [1755.] fol.   **g. 220.**

— [Another copy.]   **g. 223. y. (3.)**

— [No. 2, 7.] Sonate e-Moll ⟨G-Dur⟩ ... für Querflöte und Basso continuo ... Herausgegeben von Hugo Ruf. [Scores and parts.] 2 no. 6 pt. *B. Schott's Söhne: Mainz*, [1968.] 4°. *Part of "Il Flauto traverso".*   **g. 70. ll. (3.)**

— [No. 2.] Sonata [E minor] ... Edited by Frederick F. Polnauer. [Score and parts.] 3 pt. *J. & W. Chester: London*, [1970.] 4°. *Part of "Continuo Series".*   **g. 223. oo. (9.)**

— [No. 3.] Sonate III., *etc.* [Violin and P. F.] *See* Alard (J. D.) Les Maîtres classiques du Violon, *etc.* No. 24. [1862, *etc.*] fol.   **h. 1605. a.**

— [No. 3.] *See* Moffat (A. E.) Meister-Schule der alten Zeit, *etc.* No. 4. 1899. fol.   **h. 1684. a.**

— [No. 3.] Sonata III. in D for Violin with Accompaniment of Piano. Edited and fingered by L. Lichtenberg, with a biographical sketch of the author by R. Aldrich. *G. Schirmer: New York*, 1903. 4°.
Schirmer's Library of Musical Classics, Vol. 722.   **g. 223. k. (18.)**

— [No. 3.] Sonata III in D for the Violin with Piano accompaniment. Edited and fingered by Leopold Lichtenberg. With a biographical sketch of the author by Richard Aldrich. [Score and part.] 2 pt. *G. Schirmer: New York; Chappell & Co.: London;* [London printed, 1952.] 4°. *Schirmer's Library of musical Classics. vol. 722.*   **g. 500. z. (1.)**

— [No. 3.] Sonate D-Dur ... für Violine und Basso continuo ... Herausgegeben von Frederick F. Polnauer. [Score, and parts for violin and violoncello.] 3 pt. *B. Schott's Söhne: Mainz*, [1968.] 4°. *Part of "Violin Bibliothek Schott".*   **g. 500. tt. (3.)**

— [No. 3.] Sarabande et Tambourin. [Violin and P. F.] *Laudy & Co.: London*, [1900.] fol.
Collection de Morceaux classiques et modernes, etc. No. 35.   **h. 1754. (35.)**

— [No. 3.] Sarabande & Tambourin. [Violoncello & P. F.] *See* Schroeder (C.) Vortragsstudien, *etc.* No. 5. [1894, *etc.*] fol.   **g. 800. a.**

— [No. 3.] Sarabanda, *etc.* [Violoncello and P. F.] *See* Moffat (A. E.) Klassische Stücke ... Op. 17. No. 10. [1891.] fol.   **h. 1684. (1.)**

LECLAIR (JEAN MARIE)

— [No. 5.] Sonate a-Moll ... für Violine und Basso continuo ... Herausgegeben von Frederick F. Polnauer. [Score and parts.] 3 pt.   *B. Schott's Söhne: Mainz*, [1969.] 4°.
Part of "Violin Bibliothek Schott".   **g. 500. uu. (3.)**

— [No. 7.] Sonata F-dur für Sopranblockflöte und Klaiver, *etc.* ⟨Rev. Fritz Koschinsky.⟩ [Score and part.] 2 pt.   *Otto Heinrich Noetzel Verlag: Wilhelmshaven, etc.*, [1961.] 4°.
g. 109. r. (6.)

— [No. 7.—Giga.] Le Beaujoyeux. Gigue. [Violin and P. F.] 1924.
See MOFFAT (A. E.) French 18th Century Violin Pieces ... 19. 1919, *etc.* fol.   **h. 1684. g. (1.)**

— [No. 12.] Allegro di Ballo ... Arr. par A. Moffat. (Violine & Piano.)   *Schott & Co.: London*, 1929. 4°.
[*Sonaten-Studien. No.* 15.]   **h. 1684. b. (1.)**

— Sonate a violon seul et basse continue. Ouvrage postume ⟨xvᵉ⟩ de M. Leclair l'ainé. Gravée par sa veuve. pp. 7.   *Chez Mᵐᵉ la Vᵉ Leclair: Paris; M. Castaud: Lyon*, [1767.] fol.
P. 1. bears the autograph signature of J. B. Cartier.   **i. 8. b.**

Sonates à deux violons sans basse. Op. 3

— Sonates à Deux Violons sans Basse ... Gravées par Mˡˡᵉ L. Roussel. Troisième Oeuvre.   *Chez l'Auteur: Paris*, 1730. fol.
g. 220. b.

— Six Sonatas for two Violins. [Parts.]   *Printed for I. Walsh: London*, [1744.] fol.
With MS. notes by Alfred Moffat.   **g. 220. d.**

— Sonates a deux violons sans basse. Composées par Mʳ Leclair l'ainé, gravées par Mᵐᵉ son épouse ... Troisieme oeuvre, *etc.* [Parts.] 2 pt.   *Chez l'auteur, etc.: Paris*, [c. 1760.] fol.
h. 210. n. (4.)

— Six Duets for two Violins.   *Cambridge*, [1803?] fol.
h. 210. a. (9.)

— [No. 2, 6, 4.] Three Original Sonatas for two Violins. (Edited by E. Herrmann.)   *Hinrichsen Edition: London*, [1938.] 4°.
Hinrichsen Edition, No. 15.   **g. 218. g. (8.)**

— [No. 2, 6, 4.] 3 original Sonaten für 2 Violinen. ⟨Herausgegeben von Carl Herrmann.⟩ [Parts.] 2 pt.   *Hinrichsen Edition:* [*London*, 1957.] 4°.
g. 218. j. (8.)

— Second Livre de Sonates à Deux Violons sans Basse ... Gravées par Mᵐᵉ son Epouse ... Oeuvre xiiᵉ, *etc.* [Parts.]   *Chez l'Auteur: Paris*, [1750?] fol.   **g. 220. e.**

— [Sonates à deux violons sans basse. Op. 12.] A 2ᵈ Set of six Sonatas for two Violins ... Opera terza. [Parts.] 2 pt.   *Printed for I. Walsh: London*, [1757.] fol.   **g. 220. i.**

Sonates en trio. Op. 4

— Sonates en trio. Pour deux violons, et la basse continue ... Oeuvre iv. [Parts.] 3 pt.   *Chez l'auteur, etc.: Paris*, [c. 1730.] fol.   **g. 220. f.**

— [No. 2.] Trio Sonata in B flat major for 2 Violins, Violoncello, ad lib., & Piano. Arranged and edited by A. Moffat. [P. F. score and parts.]   *A. Lengnick & Co.: London*, 1934. 4°.
g. 417. r. (10.)

— [No. 3.] Trio Sonata in D minor for 2 Violins, Violoncello, ad lib., & Piano. Arranged and edited by A. Moffat. [P. F. score and parts.]   *A. Lengnick & Co.: London*, 1934. 4°.
g. 417. r. (11.)

— [No. 4.] Sonate en trio pour deux violons et la basse continue. ⟨Réalisation de Claude Crussard.⟩ [Score and parts.] 3 pt.   *Édition Fœtisch: Lausanne*, [1955.] 4°.
[*Flores musicœ.* 4.] *The violin parts are printed in score.*
G. 519. y.

LECLAIR (JEAN MARIE)

— [No. 6.] Sonata ... A-dur für zwei Violinen und Basso continuo, *etc.* ⟨Herausgegeben von Anne Majewski. Partitur, Stimmen.⟩ 4 pt.   *Edizioni Pegasus, etc.: Locarno, etc.*, [1977.] 4°.   **g. 422. kk. (2.)**

— [Trio.—Tambourin 2.] Dance Provencale. Arranged for clarinet and piano by Paul Smim. [Score and part.] 2 pt.   *Galliard: London*, [1963.] 4°.   **h. 2189. m. (3.)**

— *See* BARDI (B.) Three Sinfoniettas for Strings. Completed from fragments ... [No. 2.] J. M. Leclair, *etc.* [1935?] fol.
H. 3417. (12.)

— *See* DAVID (F.) Vorstudien ... aus Werken berühmter Meister, *etc.* [1872, *etc.*] fol.   **h. 1618. c.**

— *See* HAIGH (T.) *of Manchester.* A divertimento ... from the works of Corelli ... and Leclair, *etc.* [1817?] fol.   **h. 291. (1.)**

LECLAIRE (HENRI)

— The Butterfly—Le Papillon errant—for Flute & Pianoforte.   *Rudall, Carte & Co.: London & Dublin*, (1905.) fol.
Part of the "Flute Players' Journal".   **h. 232. g. (15.)**

— L'Espérance ... for Flute and Pianoforte, *etc.*   *Rudall, Carte & Co.: London & Dublin*, (1912.) fol.
Part of "Leaflets. A Journal of Music," etc.   **h. 2103. a. (31.)**

— Eva. Pensée romantique. [Flute and P. F.]   *Rudall, Carte & Co.: London & Dublin*, (1911.) fol.
Part of "Leaflets. A Journal of Music," etc.   **h. 2103. a. (25.)**

— Fantasia on Airs from E. German's ... Opera "A Princes of Kensington," for Flute & Pianoforte.   *Rudall, Carte & Co.: London & Dublin*, (1903.) fol.
Part of the "Flute Players' Journal. Second Series".
h. 232. g. (29.)

— Fond Memories. Melody. [Flute and P. F.]   *Rudall, Carte & Co.: London*, [1899.] fol.
Part of "Leaflets. A Journal of Music," etc.   **h. 2103. (25.)**

— Jeannette. Pensée romantique. [Flute and P. F.]   *Rudall, Carte & Co.: London*, (1904.) fol.
Part of "Leaflets. A Journal of Music," etc.   **h. 2103. a. (11.)**

— Mountain Echoes.—Switzerland.—[Flute and P. F.]   *Rudall, Carte & Co.: London*, [1900.] fol.
Part of "Leaflets. A Journal of Music," etc.   **h. 2103. a. (12.)**

— The Rose of Persia. Fantasia on Airs from Sir A. Sullivan's Opera, for Flute & Pianoforte.   *Rudall, Carte & Co.: London*, [1900.] fol.
Part of the "Flute Players' Journal. Second Series".
h. 232. g. (30.)

— Sérénade. [Flute and P. F.]   *Rudall, Carte & Co.: London & Dublin*, (1910.) fol.
Part of "Leaflets. A Journal of Music," etc.   **h. 2103. a. (26.)**

— Souvenir de Seville. Serenade for Flute & Pianoforte.   *Rudall, Carte & Co.: London*, [1897.] fol.
Part of the "Flute Player's Journal".   **h. 232. b. (27.)**

— Venetian Love Song. [Flute and P. F.]   *Rudall, Carte & Co.: London*, [1899.] fol.
Part of "Leaflets. A Journal of Music," etc.   **h. 2103. (26.)**

— A Village Sabbath Morn. [Flute and P. F.]   *Rudall, Carte & Co.: London*, [1900.] fol.
Part of "Leaflets. A Journal of Music," etc.   **h. 2103. (27.)**

LECLARE (CHRÉTIENNE)

— The Hinxworth Barn Dance, for the Pianoforte.   *J. & W. Chester: Brighton*, [1902.] fol.   **h. 3286. y. (30.)**

LE CLERC (   ) *Organiste des Révérends Pères de la Mercy*

— 1 ⟨2⟩ cayer de pièces d'orgue, entrée de chœur, offertoires, élévations, versets, et fugues. 2 no. *Chez Frère: Paris,* [c. 1800.] *obl.* fol.   **e. 54.**

— Journal de pièces d'orgue. no. 2, 6–8. *Chez Frere: Paris,* [c. 1790.] *obl.* 4°.   **e. 54. a.**

— Recueil de noël variés pour l'orgue ou le clavecin. Avec un carillon des morts pour le Jour de la Toussaint. Arrangée par M^r Le Clerc. pp. 23. *Chez le Sr Frere: Paris,* [c. 1800.] *obl.* 4°.   **e. 54. b.**

LECLERC (ALPHONSE)

— Les cadeaux de noce. Fantaisie à la valse. [P. F.] *London,* [1858.] fol.   **h. 977. f. (27.)**

— Old dog Tray, Polka. [On American melody by S. C. Foster. P. F.] *London,* [1858.] fol.   **h. 977. f. (28.)**

LECLERC (JEAN)

— Premier Recueil de Contre Danses ... avec la Basse Continue et chiffrée. Receuilly et mis en ordre par M^r Le Clerc. Gravées par M^de Le clair. pp. 100. *Chez Le S^r Le clerc: Paris,* [c. 1730.] fol.   **h. 422.**

— Troisième recüeil de contre danses ... avec la basse continüe et chifrée. Recueilly et mis en ordre par M^r Le Clerc, *etc.* pp. 71–100. *Chez le S^r Le Clerc: Paris,* 1737. fol.
    A reissue of the corresponding pages of the preceding.   **h. 422. a. (1.)**

— Quatrieme recüeil de contredanses ... avec la basse continüe et chiffrée. Receüilly [*sic*] et mis en ordre par M^r Le Clerc, *etc.* pp. 101–130. *Chez le S^r Le Clerc: Paris,* [c. 1740.] fol.   **h. 422. a. (2.)**

— Cinquieme recüeil de contredanses ... avec la basse continüe et chiffrée. Receüilly [*sic*] et mis en ordre par Mr Leclerc, *etc.* pp. 131–162. *Chez Mr Leclerc: Paris,* [c. 1740.] fol.   **h. 422. a. (3.)**

— Sixieme recüeil de contredanses ... avec la basse continüe et chiffrée. Receüilly [*sic*] et mis en ordre par M^r Le Clerc. pp. 163–197. *Chez M^r Le Clerc: Paris,* [c. 1740.] fol.   **h. 422. a. (4.)**

— Huitieme recueil de contredanses pour les violons, flûtes et hautbois. Recüeilli & mis en ordre par M^r Le Clerc. pp. 237–274. *Chez le S^r Le Clerc: Paris,* 1744. fol.   **h. 422. a. (5.)**

— Neufieme recüeil de contredanses pour les violons, flûtes, et hautbois. Recüeillie [*sic*] et mis en ordre par Mr Leclerc. pp. 275–292. *Chez le S^r Le Clerc: Paris,* 1745. fol.   **h. 422. a. (6.)**

— Nouveaux menuets françois et italiens ... avec la basse continue et chiffrées [*sic*] ... Recueillis et mis en ordre par M^r Le Clerc ... xieme recüeil. pp. 22. *Chez le ... S^r Le Clerc: Paris,* [c. 1740.] fol.   **h. 422. a. (7.)**

— Six sonates à deux flûtes sans basse ... Œuvre 1er ... Gravé par Melle Vendome. [Score.] pp. 33. *Chez le Sr Maupetit: Paris; chez Monsieur de Brotonne: Lyon,* [1745?] fol.   **g. 70. m. (1.)**

LE CLERC (VICTOR)

— On dirait qu'c'est toi! Chansonnette ... Paroles de Eugène Lemercier. [Melody only.] *G. Ondet: Paris,* [c. 1895.] 8°.   **E. 270. cc. (13.)**

LE CLERCQ (JEAN) *pseud.* [i.e. FREDERIC MULLEN.]

— Chant poétique. Rêverie pour pianoforte. *W. Paxton & Co.: London,* 1916. fol.   **h. 3284. nn. (29.)**

LE CLERCQ (JEAN) *pseud.* [i.e. FREDERIC MULLEN.]

— Feuilles volantes (Falling Leaves). Valse brillante for pianoforte. pp. 7. *W. Paxton: London,* [1916.] fol.   **h. 3866. i. (21.)**

— Love Birds. Duo d'amour for pianoforte. *W. Paxton & Co.: London,* 1916. fol.   **h. 3284. nn. (30.)**

— Piorella. Air de ballet for pianoforte. *W. Paxton & Co.: London,* 1916. fol.   **h. 3284. nn. (31.)**

— Songe d'orient. Valse. ⟨Piano solo.⟩ pp. 5. *W. Paxton: London,* [1919.] fol.   **h. 3866. i. (22.)**

— La Vallière.—Danse d'autrefois.—Pour pianoforte. *W. Paxton & Co.: London,* 1916. fol.   **h. 3284. nn. (32.)**

LE CLERE (VICTOIRE) *Madame*

— The Virgin's First Love. A Favorite Ariette. With an Accompaniment for the Harp or Piano Forte and German Flute. The Melody by Madame V. Le Clere, adapted to English Words & the Accompaniments by an Eminent Composer. *L. Lavenu: London,* [1800?] fol.   **G. 800. m. (37.)**

LE CLERQ (GUS)

— *See* BAYNES (Sydney) and LE CLERQ (G.) Lassie o' the Dee, *etc.* ⟨Song.⟩ [1907.] fol.   **H. 3982. k. (52.)**

— *See* BAYNES (Sydney) and LE CLERQ (G.) Lassie o' the Dee. ⟨Song.⟩ Written and composed by S. Baynes and G. Le Clerq. [1907.] *s. sh.* fol.   **H. 3982. k. (51.)**

LE COAT (G.)

— Kanæouennou Kristen ... Chants chrétiens, édités et composés par G. Le Coat ... avec les vieux Airs Bretons, recueillis, transcrits et harmonisés par Rev. Dr. Bullinger, *etc.* *Paris, etc.,* 1899. 4°.   **B. 372.**

LECOCQ (ALEXANDRE CHARLES)

— New and popular Dance Music by ... Lecocq, *etc.* *See* CHAPPELL AND CO. Chappell's Musical Magazine. No. 109. [1861, *etc.*] 4°.   **F. 161.**

— Ali-Baba. Opéra-Comique en 3 actes et 8 tableaux de A. Vanloo et W. Busnach. Partition chant & piano transcrite par L. Roques. *Choudens: Paris,* (1887.) 8°.   **F. 443. k.**

— Allegretto pour violoncelle ou violon et piano. *Paris,* [1885.] fol.   **h. 3106. a. (3.)**

— L'Amour et son Carquois. Opéra Bouffe en 2 Actes, paroles de P. Marquet. Partition chant et piano, *etc.* *L. Bathlot: Paris,* [1868.] 8°.   **F. 443. m.**

— L'Amoureuse. [Song, begins: "Quand il est là".] Paroles de H. Meilhac. *Paris,* [1879.] fol.   **H. 582. a. (3.)**

— Andante Nuptial. [Violin and organ.] *See infra:* Deux morceaux religieux ... No. 1.

— L'Arbre de Noël. Féerie ... de M. M. Leterrier, Vanloo & A. Mortier ... N° 1. Rondeau de la poupée. Soprano ... N° 2. Polka chantée de la montreuse d'ours. Soprano ... N° 3. Le Noël des petits enfants à 1–2 et 3 voix, *etc.* 3 no. *Heugel & fils: Paris,* [1881.] fol.   **H. 582. a. (4.)**

— L'Arbre de Noël. Féerie ... 1. Rondeau de La Poupée parlante ... 2. Polka de La Montreuse d'ours ... Mezzo-soprano ... 3. Le Noël des petits enfants, à 1, 2 et 3 voix. 3 no. *Heugel & fils: Paris,* [c. 1885.] fol.
     H. 582. d. (18.)

— [L'Arbre de Noël.] *See* ARBAN (J. J. B. L.) L'Arbre de Noël, quadrille, *etc.* [1881.] *obl.* fol.   **e. 272. k. (1.)**

LECOCQ (Alexandre Charles)

— Le Baiser à la porte. Opérette de salon. Paroles de Jules de la Guette ... Partition chant et piano et dialogue intercalé. pp. 40. *Choudens fils: Paris*, [c. 1890.] 8°. **F. 443. s.**

— Balladine. Chanson de Pifferaro [begins: "Ma mère? hélas! je n'en ai pas"]. Paroles de S. Bordèse. *Paris*, [1885.] fol. **H. 582. a. (14.)**

— Barbe-bleue. Ballet pantomime avec chœurs en trois tableaux de Richard O'Monroy ... Partition complète. [Vocal score.] pp. 119. *Choudens: Paris*, [1898.] 8°. **F. 443. u.**

— Le Barbier de Trouville, bluette bouffe en 1 acte. Paroles de Mr. Jaime. Partition Chant et Piano. *Paris*, [1872.] 8°. **F. 36. c.**

— Le Beau Dunois, opéra-bouffe en un acte. Paroles de MM. H. Chivot & A. Duru. Partition Piano et Chant réduite par L. Roques. *Paris*, [1870.] 8°. **F. 36. b.**

— La Belle au bois dormant. Opéra-comique en 3 actes et 4 tableaux de A. Vanloo & G. Duval ... Partition chant et piano. pp. 276. *Choudens: Paris*, [1900.] 4°. **F. 443. w.**

— La Belle au bois dormant. Opéra-comique en 3 actes et 4 tableaux de A. Vanloo & G. Duval ... Partition chant et piano. ⟨2ᵐᵉ édition.⟩ pp. 284. *Choudens: Paris*, [c. 1905.] 8°. **F. 443. t. (1.)**

— La Belle au bois dormant. Opéra-comique ... Ballet pour piano. pp. 17. *Choudens: Paris*, [c. 1905.] 8°. **F. 443. t. (2.)**

— Berceuse [begins: "Brises de l'Océan"]. Paroles de A. Aubert. *Paris*, [1875.] fol. **H. 1777. h. (38.)**

The Black Prince

— The Brighton Boatman, *etc. London*, [1875.] fol. **H. 582. (24.)**

— Cigars and Guitars ... Bolero [begins: "Know'st thou the land"] ... written by H. B. Farnie. *London*, [1874.] fol. **H. 582. (20.)**

— Nice day for a sail ... Boatmen's chorus [begins: "We see as how"] ... written by H. B. Farnie. *London*, [1874.] fol. **H. 582. (17.)**

— The Rose and the Glove. Romance [begins: "Dainty little glove"] ... written by H. B. Farnie. *London*, [1874.] fol. **H. 582. (19.)**

— Two Loves. [Song, begins: "One lover sought".] Written by H. B. Farnie. *London*, [1874.] fol. **H. 582. (18.)**

— You, 'tis You ... Quintette. *London*, [1874.] fol. **H. 582. (21.)**

— The Bridal Chorus. *See* infra: [Le grand Casimir.]

— The Brighton Boatman. *See* supra: [The Black Prince.]

La Camargo

— La Camargo, opéra comique en trois actes. Paroles de MM. A. Vanloo et E. Leterrier. Partition Chant & Piano arrangée par L. Roques. *Paris*, [1879.] 8°. **F. 36. u.**

— La Camargo. Opéra comique ... Partition pour Piano seul, arrangée par L. Roques. *Paris*, [1879.] 8°. **f. 270. l.**

— La Camargo ... Morceaux détachés transcrits ... pour Piano seul par A. Croisez. 8 no. *Paris*, [1879.] fol. **h. 1493. n. (27.)**

— Airs ... arrangés pour Cornet seul par Bryart. *Paris*, [1879.] fol. **h. 2284. b. (12.)**

— Airs ... arrangés pour Flûte seule par G. Garibaldi. *Paris*, [1879.] fol. **h. 2140. g. (5.)**

LECOCQ (Alexandre Charles)

— Airs ... arrangés pour Violon seul par J. de Brayer. *Paris*, [1879.] fol. **h. 1609. m. (8.)**

— *See* ARBAN (J. J. B. L.) La Camargo ... polka, *etc.* [1879.] fol. **h. 3317. (28.)**

— *See* ARBAN (J. J. B. L.) La Camargo ... quadrille, *etc.* [1879.] *obl.* fol. **e. 272. h. (9.)**

— *See* BULL (G.) Transcription facile ... sur La Camargo, *etc.* [1879.] fol. **h. 1493. c. (23.)**

— *See* DERANSART (E.) La Camargo ... quadrille, *etc.* [1879.] *obl.* fol. **e. 272. h. (19.)**

— *See* DESSAUX (L.) La Camargo ... quadrille. [1878.] *obl.* fol. **e. 272. h. (27.)**

— *See* ETTLING (E.) La Camargo ... suite de valses. [1879.] *obl.* fol. **e. 272. h. (30.)**

— *See* HESS (J. C.) Fantaisie élégante ... sur La Camargo, *etc.* [1879.] fol. **h. 1493. l. (7.)**

— *See* HUBANS (C.) La Camargo ... polka-mazurka. [1879.] fol. **h. 1493. l. (28.)**

— *See* MARX (H.) La Camargo ... quadrille. [1879.] *obl.* fol. **e. 272. i. (3.)**

— *See* MÉTRA (J. L. O.) La Camargo quadrille. [1879.] *obl.* fol. **e. 272. j. (30.)**

— *See* MÉTRA (J. L. O.) Suite de valses sur La Camargo, *etc.* [1879.] *obl.* fol. **e. 272. i. (11.)**

— *See* RENAUD DE VILBAC (A. Z. C.) La Camargo ... duo facile, *etc.* [1879.] fol. **h. 1228. l. (29.)**

— *See* ROQUES (L.) Polka brillante sur La Camargo, *etc.* [1879.] fol. **h. 1493. t. (21.)**

— *See* RUMMEL (J.) La Camargo ... fantaisie pour Piano. [1879.] fol. **h. 523. g. (10.)**

— Capriccio pour Piano. *Paris*, [1875.] fol. **h. 3106. (4.)**

— Les Cent Vierges, opéra bouffe en 3 actes. Paroles de Clairville, Chivot & Duru. Partition Chant et Piano. *Paris*, [1872.] 8°. **F. 36. e.**

— [Les Cent Vierges.] The Island of Bachelors. Comic opera ... arranged for Pianoforte solo. *London*, [1874.] 4°. **f. 270. (1.)**

— [Les Cent Vierges.] *See* DESSAUX (L.) Les Cent Vierges ... quadrille, *etc.* [1876.] *obl.* fol. **e. 272. e. (5.)**

— Chanson de table du XVIIIᵉ. siècle, d'après un manuscrit de l'époque. *Paris*, [1883.] fol. **H. 582. a. (12.)**

— Chansons de Gavroche. Victor Hugo (Les Misérables). I. Où vont les belles filles? II. Quand irons-nous dans la forêt? 2 no. *Heugel & cie.: Paris*, [1910.] fol. **H. 582. d. (13.)**

— Cigars and Guitars. *See* supra: [The Black Prince.]

— Clairette. *See* infra: [La Fille de Madame Angot.]

— La Clochette. Conte [begins: "Dans la Touraine, un galant jouvenceau"], paroles de W. Busnach d'après La Fontaine. *Paris*, 1885. fol. **H. 582. a. (8.)**

Le Cœur et la Main

— [For songs, etc. interpolated in the English version, "Incognita":] *See* YVOLDE, *pseud.*

— Le Cœur et la Main. Opéra comique ... Orchestre. *Paris*, [1882.] fol. **h. 1580. c.**

LECOCQ (ALEXANDRE CHARLES)

— Le Cœur et la Main. Opéra comique en 3 actes. Paroles de MM. Nuitter & Beaumont. Partition Chant & Piano arrangée par L. Roques. *Paris*, [1883.] 8°.　　　**F. 443. d.**

— Incognita. A Comic Opera in three Acts ... English Libretto ... by F. C. Burnand. Lyrics by H. Greenbank. *Hopwood & Crew: London*, [1893.] 4°.　　　**F. 443. n.**

— Le Cœur et la Main ... Partition Piano seul arrangée par L. Roques. *Paris*, [1883.] 8°.　　　**f. 270. t.**

— Incognita ... Arranged for the pianoforte by R. Wood. *Hopwood & Crew: London*, (1892.) 4°.　　　**f. 270. z.**

— Chant National.—Dernier final. [Brass band parts.] *Paris*, [1883.] fol.　　　**f. 245. g. (6.)**

— Le Cœur et la Main ... Morceaux détachés, transcrits et arrangés pour piano seul par A. Croisez. 6 no. *Paris*, [1883.] fol.　　　**h. 1259. b. (18.)**

— Selection from ... 'Incognita' for the pianoforte by C. Godfrey J^r. *Hopwood & Crew: London*, [1893.] fol.　　　**h. 1489. s. (27.)**

— Airs ... arrangés pour Cornet seul par E. Guilbaut. *Paris*, [1883.] fol.　　　**h. 2202. c. (15.)**

— Airs ... arrangés pour Flûte seule par G. Gariboldi. *Brandus et Cie.: Paris*, [1883.] fol.　　　**h. 3106. a. (6.)**

— Airs ... arrangés pour Violon seul par A. Müller. *Paris*, [1883.] fol.　　　**h. 1608. l. (10.)**

— [Au soldat, après la parade.] Comrades fill. Drinking Song, *etc. Hopwood & Crew: London*, [1893.] fol.　　　**H. 582. (35.)**

— [Par toi, divine créature.] I love you only, only you. Romance, *etc. Hopwood & Crew: London*, [1894.] fol.　　　**H. 582. (34.)**

— [Un soir, Pérez le capitaine.] What Life is so bright. Bolero, *etc. Hopwood & Crew: London*, [1893.] fol.　　　**H. 582. (32.)**

— [Y avait un jour dans l'infant'rie.] Mercedes is a gipsy charming. Song of the Helmet, *etc. Hopwood & Crew: London*, [1893.] fol.　　　**H. 582. (33.)**

— *See* ARBAN (J. J. B. L.) Le Cœur & la Main ... quadrille, *etc.* [1883.] *obl.* fol.　　　**e. 272. m. (3.)**

— *See* ARBAN (J. J. B. L.) Polka de l'Infante ... sur des motifs de Le Cœur et la Main. [1883.] fol.　　　**h. 3317. (39.)**

— *See* BULL (G.) Transcription ... sur l'opéra comique, *etc.* [1883.] fol.　　　**h. 3358. a. (8.)**

— *See* COOTE (C.) *the Younger.* Incognita. Lancers ... on ... Lecocq's ... Opera, *etc.* [1893.] fol.　　　**h. 2948. d. (7.)**

— *See* CRAMER (H.) Bouquet de Mélodies ... Le Cœur et la Main, *etc.* [1883.] fol.　　　**h. 371. c. (15.)**

— *See* GENG (C.) Micaela valse ... sur des motifs de Le Cœur et la Main, *etc.* [1883.] fol.　　　**h. 3276. d. (8.)**

— *See* GOBBAERTS (J. L.) Fantaisie brillante ... sur Le Cœur et la Main, *etc.* [1883.] fol.　　　**h. 2974. b. (36.)**

— *See* HERMAN (A.) Fantaisie ... sur Le Cœur et la Main, de C. Lecocq. [1888.] fol.　　　**h. 1620. f. (1.)**

— *See* HESS (J. C.) Divertissement ... sur Le Cœur et la Main, *etc.* [1883.] fol.　　　**h. 3276. e. (28.)**

— *See* HUBANS (C.) Polka-mazurka sur des motifs de Le Cœur et la Main, *etc.* [1883.] fol.　　　**h. 3276. e. (55.)**

— *See* LECHNER (J.) Suite aux Bagatelles ... No. 104. [1886.] fol.　　　**h. 637. c. (3.)**

LECOCQ (ALEXANDRE CHARLES)

— *See* MARX (M.) Le Cœur et la Main ... quadrille, *etc.* [1883.] *obl.* fol.　　　**e. 272. m. (26.)**

— *See* MÉTRA (J. L. O.) Le Cœur et la Main ... quadrille, *etc.* [1883.] *obl.* fol.　　　**e. 272. m. (30.)**

— *See* NUYENS (H.) Valse ... Le Cœur & la Main, *etc.* [1883.] fol.　　　**h. 3276. h. (34.)**

— *See* RENAUD DE VILBAC (A. Z. C.) Duo facile pour piano à 4 mains sur Le Cœur et la Main, *etc.* [1883.] fol.　　　**h. 1228. n. (30.)**

— *See* ROQUES (J. L.) Polka ... sur des motifs de Le Cœur et la Main, *etc.* [1883.] fol.　　　**h. 3285. d. (19.)**

— *See* SHAW (S.) Fantasia on melodies from ... "Incognita," *etc.* [1893.] fol.　　　**h. 1608. z. (25.)**

— *See* SMALLWOOD (F.) Fantasia on Lecocq's Opera, *etc.* [1893.] fol.　　　**h. 1412. v. (8.)**

— *See* STREABBOG (L.) *pseud.* Petite fantaisie pour piano sur Le Cœur et la Main, *etc.* [1883.] fol.　　　**h. 3197. c. (16.)**

— *See* TAVAN (Émile) Fantaisie sur Le cœur et la main ... de Ch. Lecocq, pour le piano. [c. 1910.] fol.　　　**h. 1226. i. (14.)**

— Comrades fill. *See* supra: [Le Cœur et la Main.—Au soldat, après la parade.]

— Cydalise. Gavotte. Partition d'orchestre. *Brandus et Cie.: Paris*, [1887.] 8°.　　　**e. 666. i. (5.)**

— Cydalise. Gavotte pour piano. *Paris*, 1885. fol.　　　**h. 3106. a. (4.)**

— Le Cygne. Ballet-pantomime en un acte de Catulle Mendès ... Partition piano solo. pp. 87. *Heugel & c^{ie}: Paris*, [1899.] 8°.　　　**f. 270. aa.**

— Day and Night. *See* infra: [La Petite Mariée.—Couplets du Jour et de la Nuit.]

— The Days of old. *See* infra: [Giroflé-Girofla.—Nos ancêtres étaient sages.]

— Desdémone. Scène Lyrique [begins: "Sérénité des nuits, viens apaiser mon âme"], poésie de J. Barbier. *Paris*, [1884.] fol.　　　**H. 582. a. (13.)**

— Le Docteur Miracle, opéra-comique en 1 acte ... Paroles de MM. L. Battu & L. Halévy. Partition Chant et Piano. *Paris*, [1877.] 8°.　　　**F. 36. r.**

— The Elopement. *See* infra: [La Petite Mariée.—Couplets de l'Enlèvement.]

— En revenant de la Bastille. Chansonette. Paroles de J. de la Guette. *Paris*, [1867.] fol.　　　**H. 1774. e. (21.)**

— Ere Love could see. *See* infra: [Le Jour et la Nuit.—Selections.]

— Étoile[s] Filante[s] (Falling Star) set of valses. [Orchestral parts.] *London*, [1877.] 8°.　　　**f. 410. (16.)**

— [Étoiles Filantes.] Falling Stars. [P. F.] *London*, [1874.] fol.　　　**h. 1482. z. (4.)**

— Étoiles Filantes, suite de valses. [P. F.] *Paris*, [1874.] *obl.* fol.　　　**e. 272. b. (17.)**

— 6 fables de Lafontaine, *etc.* pp. 32. *R. Legouix: Paris*, [c. 1920.] fol.　　　**H. 582. d. (16.)**

— Fair summer eve. *See* infra: [Fleur de Thé.—En tous pays l'homme est un être.]

LECOCQ (ALEXANDRE CHARLES)

— La Famille de Gabrielle. Chanson [begins: "Maman est un' femme très sévère"], paroles de W. Busnach. *Paris*, 1885. fol.
H. 582. a. (10.)

— Fan-Fan, morceau de salon. [P. F.] *London*, [1874.] fol.
h. 1482. z. (3.)

— Fantasia galop. [P. F.] *London*, [1874.] fol. **h. 1482. z. (2.)**

— Les Fantoccini. Ballet pantomime. [P. F.] *Paris*, [1876.] fol.
h. 3106. (5.)

— The Farewell Duet. *See* infra: [La Marjolaine.—Je ne suis plus.]

La Fille de Madame Angot

— La Fille de Madame Angot. Opéra-comique en 3 actes. Paroles de Mrs Clairville, Siraudin & Koning. Partition Chant & Piano arrangée par H. Nuyens. pp. 263. *Brandus & c^{ie}.: Paris*, [1873.] 8°. **F. 36. f.**

— La Fille de Madame Angot. Opéra comique en 3 actes, paroles de … Clairville, Siraudin & Koning … Partition Chant & Piano, arrangée par H. Nuyens. pp. 269. *Brandus & Cie.: Paris*, [1873.] 8°. **R.M. 26. f. 2.**

— La Fille de Madame Angot … Translated into English by H. J. Byron. [Vocal score.] *London*, [1875.] 8°. *Boosey & Co's "Royal edition".* **E. 93. p.**

— La Fille de Madame Angot … Pianoforte solo. *See* BOOSEY AND CO. Boosey's Musical Cabinet. No. 179. [1861, *etc.*] 4°.
F. 160.

— Lecocq's popular comic Opera, La Fille de Madame Angot, arranged for the Pianoforte. pp. 56. *Boosey & Co.: London, New York*, [c. 1875.] 4°. **f. 65. e. (1.)**

— La Fille de Mme. Angot. Opéra comique en trois actes … pour le Piano à quatre mains par J. Rummel. *Paris*, [1877.] *obl.* fol. **e. 908.**

— La Fille de Madame Angot. Opéra comique en trois actes … Edition illustrée de costumes coloriées … de vignettes … des portraits et des autographes des auteurs de la musique et du Livret, accompagnée de la musique gravée des principaux airs, *etc. Paris, Bruxelles*, 1875. 8°. *Part of the "Bibliothèque des Succes Dramatiques".*
11739. g. 2.

— Selection, *etc.* [Military band parts.] 25 pt. *Boosey & Co.: London*, [1879.] fol. [*Boosé's military Journal. ser.* 55. *no.* 5.] **h. 1549.**

— Transcription facile pour Piano. *London*, [1873.] fol.
h. 1484. c. (32.)

— La Fille de Mme. Angot … Morceau détachés transcrits et arrangés pour Piano seul par A. Croisez. 12 no. *Paris*, [1874.] fol. **h. 3106. (1.)**

— The Favorite Airs, from La Fille de Madame Angot [by A. C. Lecocq] … arranged as a piano forte duet by Michael Watson. [c. 1880.] fol. *See* WATSON (William M.)
g. 1138. zz. (17.)

— Selection … for pianoforte by Cramer. Newly revised & edited. *Boosey & Co.: London, etc.*, 1919. fol.
h. 3865. c. (4.)

— Selection, *etc.* [Cornet and P. F.] [1889?] *See* BOOSEY AND CO. Boosey's Cornet Miscellany, *etc.* No. 32. [1856, *etc.*] fol.
h. 2277.

— Mélange sur La Fille de Madame Angot pour hautbois et piano. *Paris*, [1884.] fol. **h. 3106. a. (2.)**

— La Fille de Madame Angot. Selection, arranged [for P. F. and violin] by H. Basquit. [1886.] *See* BOOSEY AND CO. Boosey's Violin Miscellany, *etc.* No. 20. [1886, *etc.*] fol. **h. 1653.**

LECOCQ (ALEXANDRE CHARLES)

— Clairette. Ballade [begins: "Charming Clairette"]. Words by J. Oxenford. *London*, [1874.] fol. **H. 582. (4.)**

— [Elle est tellement innocente.] She is so innocent. [Four-part song.] S.S.A.A., a capella … Arr. G. Pitcher. *C. C. Birchard & Co.: [Boston,]* 1928. 8°. **F. 217. c. (25.)**

— La Fille de Madame Angot … Gavotte, *etc.* [P. F.] *[Paris,]* 1898. 8°. *Supplement to "L'Illustration," No.* 2908. **P.P. 4283. m. (3.)**

— Ma femme est blonde. [Song, begins: "Elle était brune".] Paroles de G. Nadaud adaptées sur le Chœur des Conspirateurs. *Paris*, [1874.] fol. **H. 1777. h. (34.)**

— [Marchande de Marée.] Légende de la Mère Angot. [Song.] *London*, [1873.] fol. **H. 582. (3.)**

— [Marchande de Marée.] The Tale of a Shah. [Song, begins: "A Shah renowned in story".] Written by H. S. Leigh. *London*, [1877.] fol. **H. 582. (27.)**

— [Tournez, tournez.] Valse chantée. *Paris*, [1873.] fol.
H. 1777. h. (31.)

— *See* ALBERT (C. L. N. d') [La Fille de Madame Angot Lancers.] Lancers.—[On melodies from Lecocq's opera] "La Fille de Madame Angot" … Arranged [for military band] by F. Godfrey. [1874.] fol. [*Army Journal. no.* 97.] **h. 1562.**

— *See* ALBERT (C. L. N. d') La Fille de Madame Angot lancers, *etc.* [P. F. solo and duet.] [1873.] fol. **h. 825. b. (3.)**

— *See* ARBAN (J. J. B. L.) La Fille de Madame Angot quadrille, *etc.* [1873.] fol. **h. 1482. a. (8.)**

— *See* BRISSON (F.) La Fille de Madame Angot … fantaisie, *etc.* [1873.] fol. **h. 1487. b. (10.)**

— *See* BRYART (J.) La Fille de Madame Angot … fantaisie pour Cornet, *etc.* [1875.] fol. **h. 2202. b. (2.)**

— *See* COOTE (Charles) *the Elder.* La Fille de Madame Angot quadrille (valse) on Lecocq's … opera. [P. F.] [1873.] fol.
h. 2947. c. (2.)

— *See* COOTE (Charles) *the Elder.* Quadrille "La Fille de Madame Angot". [Based on melodies from the comic opera by C. Lecocq.] [Military band.] [1874.] fol. [*Boosé's supplemental military Journal. no.* 265.] **h. 1544.**

— *See* COOTE (Charles) *the Elder.* La Fille de Madame Angot. Quadrille. [1875?] fol. **h. 721. l. (24.)**

— *See* CRAMER (W. O.) Bouquet de mélodies de La Fille, *etc.* [1873.] fol. **h. 3380. (22.)**

— *See* DESSAUX (L.) La Fille de Madame Angot, quadrille, *etc.* [1875.] *obl.* fol. **e. 272. e. (1.)**

— *See* FAHRBACH (P.) Angot. Walzer, *etc.* [1876.] fol.
h. 1493. g. (32.)

— *See* FRAMBACH (J. B.) Angot-Lanciers, *etc.* [1873.] *obl.* fol.
e. 272. a. (33.)

— *See* GARIBOLDI (G.) La Fille de Madame Angot … Caprice … pour Piano et Flûte. [1874.] fol. **h. 2096. (2.)**

— *See* GODFREY (C.) *the Younger.* Clairette waltz on airs from Lecocq's … opera, *etc.* [1874.] fol. **h. 2931. a. (29.)**

— *See* GUNG'L (J.) Marsch über Motive aus Lecocq's Oper, *etc.* [1874.] fol. **h. 3048. b. (1.)**

— *See* HERMAN (A.) La Fille de Mme. Angot … fantaisie, *etc.* [1874.] fol. **h. 1620. b. (5.)**

— *See* KUHE (W.) La Fille de Madame Angot. Fantasia on Lecocq's … Opera, for the Pianoforte. **h. 3283. jj. (21.)**

LECOCQ (Alexandre Charles)

— *See* Lamotte (A.) Angot polka, *etc.* [1873.] fol.
  h. 1487. o. (29.)

— *See* Lebeau (A.) La Fille de Mme. Angot. Transcription pour Orgue-Harmonium. [1875.] fol.
  h. 3105. (32.)

— *See* Lechner (J.) Suite aux Bagatelles, *etc.* No. 87. [1886.] fol.
  h. 637. c. (3.)

— *See* Leybach (J.) La Fille de Mme. Angot, fantaisie brillante, *etc.* [1874.] fol.
  h. 1299. b. (21.)

— *See* Luigini (F.) La Fille de Madame Angot ... quadrille. [1874.] *obl.* fol.
  e. 272. b. (23.)

— *See* Marx (H.) La Fille ... quadrille, *etc.* [1874.] 8°.
  c. 120. (5.)

— *See* Marx (H.) Le Rêve de Mme Angot, quadrille, *etc.* [1874.] *obl.* fol.
  e. 272. b. (26.)

— *See* Quadrille. Quadrille, Valse, Polka, Polka-Mazurka sur La Fille de Madame Angot, *etc.* [1874.] 8°.
  e. 370. a. (10.)

— *See* Renaud de Vilbac (A. Z. C.) Souvenir de la Fille de Mme. Angot ... pour Piano, *etc.* [1874.] fol.
  h. 1483. g. (38.)

— *See* Rummel (J.) La Fille de Mme. Angot ... fantaisie, *etc.* [1873.] fol.
  h. 523. f. (5.)

— *See* Saro (H.) La Fille de Madame Angot ... Marsch. [1876.] fol.
  h. 3192. (9.)

— *See* Singelée (J. B.) La Fille de Madame Angot ... Fantaisie pour Violon, *etc.* [1875.] fol.
  h. 1726. a. (12.)

— *See* Strauss (Eduard) Angot-Quadrille, nach Motiven der komischen Oper von Ch. Lecocq "Mamsell Angot, die Tochter der Halle" für Pianoforte ... Op. 110. [1874.] fol.
  h. 3209. d. (23.)

— *See* Talexy (A.) La Fille de Madame Angot ... mazurka, *etc.* [1873.] fol.
  h. 1483. m. (1.)

— *See* Valiquet (H.) La Fille de Mme. Angot ... valse, *etc.* [1874.] fol.
  h. 3231. (7.)

— *See* Valiquet (H.) Quadrille sur ... La Fille, *etc.* [1874.] *obl.* fol.
  e. 272. c. (31.)

Fleur de Thé

— Fleur de Thé. Opéra-bouffe en 3 Actes. Paroles de A. Duru et H. Chivot. Partition Chant et Piano. *Paris*, [1868.] 8°.
  F. 36.

— Fleur de Thé. Opéra-bouffe ... Airs detachés, avec accomp^l. de Piano. No. 1, 4, 6–10. *Paris*, [1868.] fol.
  Imperfect; wanting all the other no. **H. 2827. a. (15.)**

— Selection from ... "Fleur de thé". Arranged [for military band] by Fred Godfrey. [Parts.] 24 pt. *S. A. Chappell: London*, [1873.] fol.
  [Army Journal. no. 94.] **h. 1562.**

— [Césarine à mes vœux docile.] 'Tis only a poor little flower. Romance ... Words by C. J. Rowe. *London*, [1871.] fol.
  H. 1775. u. (7.)

— [En tous pays l'homme est un être.] Fair summer eve. Air ... words by C. J. Rowe. *London*, [1871.] fol. **H. 1775. u. (6.)**

— *See* Albert (C. d') Fleur de Thé ... quadrille. [1875.] fol.
  h. 825. b. (5.)

— *See* Cramer (H.) Bouquet de Mélodies de Fleur de Thé, *etc.* [1868.] fol.
  h. 371. (19.)

— *See* Roques (J. L.) Clicquot polka, sur des thèmes de Fleur de thé ... arrangée pour le piano par L. Roques, *etc.* [c. 1870.] fol.
  h. 975. kk. (1.)

LECOCQ (Alexandre Charles)

— Fleurs nipponnes. [Songs.] Poésies de André Alexandre. pp. 47. *Heugel & cie.: Paris*, [1903.] 4°. **H. 582. d. (14.)**

— Fleurs parisiennes. Huit mélodies pour chant avec accompagnement de piano. Poésies d'André Alexandre, *etc.* pp. 47. *Choudens: Paris*, [1905.] 4°. **H. 582. d. (15.)**

— Les Foins. Idylle [begins: "Viens donc couper les foins"], poésie de P. Choudens. *Paris*, [1884.] fol. **H. 582. a. (6.)**

— Fricassée. [P. F. With a portrait.] *In:* La Danse. pp. 141–145. [1888.] fol. **H. 2349. b.**

— Gandolpho. Operette en un acte. Paroles de Chivot et Daru. Partition Chant et Piano. *Paris*, [1869.] 8°. **F. 36. a.**

— [Gandolpho.] Stenio's serenade. [Song, begins: "Oh! Nina dearest"] ... Words adapted from the French by L. K. Times. *London*, [1870.] fol. **H. 1775. u. (5.)**

— Gavotte pour Piano. *Paris*, [1868.] fol. **h. 1462. r. (28.)**

— Gavotte (en Sol mineur) pour Piano. *Londres*, [1874.] fol.
  h. 1482. z. (1.)

— La Géante. *See infra:* Six morceaux caractéristiques. 2.

— Gentle Phœbe. Song [begins: "Ah! I remember"]. Written by H. B. Farnie. *London*, [1881.] fol. **H. 1787. j. (22.)**

Giroflé-Girofla

— Giroflé-Girofla, komische Oper in drei Acten von A. Vanloo und E. Leterrier. Partitur. *Braunschweig*, [1874.] fol.
  H. 582. b.

— Giroflé-Girofla, opéra-bouffe en trois actes ... Partition chant et Piano arrangée par Nuyens. *Paris*, [1874.] 8°.
  F. 36. h.

— Giroflé-Girofla, opera-bouffe en 3 actes ... Partition Chant et Piano arrangée par L. Roques. *Paris*, [1874.] 8°. **F. 36. i.**

— Giroflé-Girofla, opéra bouffe en 3 actes. Paroles de MM. A. Vanloo & E. Leterrier. [Vocal score.] *London*, [1874.] 8°.
  F. 36. g.

— Lecocq's popular opera-bouffe ... arranged for the Pianoforte. *London*, [1874.] 4°. **f. 270. d.**

— Giroflé-Girofla, opéra-bouffe ... Partition Piano seul arrangée par L. Roques. *Paris*, [1875.] 8°. **f. 270. b.**

— Giroflé-Girofla, complete for the Violin. *London*, [1874.] 8°.
  f. 270. a.

— Selection ... arranged by J. Rivière. [Brass band parts.] *London*, [1877.] 8°. **f. 413. b. (30.)**

— Selection ... [arranged by] J. Rivière. [Fife and drum band parts.] *London*, [1877.] 8°. **f. 414. (37.)**

— Selection ... for Octuor by J. Riviere. *London*, [1877.] 8°.
  f. 411. b. (11.)

— Giroflé-Girofla ... Morceaux détachés transcrits et arrangés pour Piano seul par A. Croisez. 10 no. *Paris*, [1875.] fol.
  h. 3106. (3.)

— Je vous présente un père. Couplets. *London*, [1874.] fol.
  H. 582. (7.)

— [Je vous présente un père.] A Happy Father. Song. *London*, [1874.] fol. **H. 582. (12.)**

— Ma belle Girofla. Duo. *London*, [1874.] fol. **H. 582. (9.)**

— [Ma belle Girofla.] My Girofla, my bride. Duet. *London*, [1874.] fol. **H. 582. (10.)**

— Ma belle Girofla ... pour Piano. [1875.] fol. *See* Jungmann (A.) **h. 847. a. (38.)**

LECOCQ (Alexandre Charles)

— [Ma belle Girofla.] *See* Arban (J. J. B. L.) Ma belle Girofla, polka mazurka, *etc.* [1875.] fol.　　　　**h. 3317. (14.)**

— Matamoros, grand capitaine, extrait du quintette … pour voix seule. *London*, [1874.] 8°.　　　　**H. 582. (5.)**

— [Mon père est un très-gros banquier.] My Father is a banker old … Song. *London*, [1874.] fol.　　　　**H. 582. (16.)**

— Nos Ancêtres étaient sages. Chanson avec chœur ad libitum. *London*, [1874.] fol.　　　　**H. 582. (6.)**

— [Nos ancêtres étaient sages.] The Days of old. Song. *London*, [1874.] fol.　　　　**H. 582. (11.)**

— Pauvres victimes que nous sommes. Couplets. *Paris*, [1875.] fol.　　　　**H. 1777. h. (35.)**

— Père adoré. Couplets. *London*, [1874.] fol.　　　　**H. 582. (8.)**

— [Père adoré.] Here's Giroflé. Valse. *London*, [1874.] fol.　　　　**H. 582. (14.)**

— Giroflé-Girofla polka. [P. F.] *London*, [1874.] fol.　　　　**h. 1482. z. (5.)**

— Le Punch scintille en reflets bleus. Brindisi. *London*, [1874.] fol.　　　　**H. 582. (10.)**

— [Le Punch scintille.] See how it sparkles. Drinking song. *London*, [1874.] fol.　　　　**H. 582. (13.)**

— *See* Arban (J. J. B. L.) Polka des Pirates, *etc.* [1875.] fol.　　　　**h. 3317. (13.)**

— *See* Arban (J. J. B. L.) Quadrille "Giroflé," *etc.* [1875.] *obl.* fol.　　　　**e. 272. d. (3.)**

— *See* Arban (J. J. B. L.) Girofla quadrille, *etc.* [1875.] *obl.* fol.　　　　**e. 272. d. (4.)**

— *See* Battmann (J. L.) Mélange pour Piano sur … Giroflé-Girofla, *etc.* [1875.] fol.　　　　**h. 3009. a. (25.)**

— *See* Brisson (F.) Giroflé-Girofla … illustration pour Piano, *etc.* [1875.] fol.　　　　**h. 1487. b. (13.)**

— *See* Bryant (J.) Giroflé-Girofla … fantaisie pour Cornet, *etc.* [1875.] fol.　　　　**h. 2202. b. (3.)**

— *See* Bull (G.) Giroflé-Girofla … transcription … pour Piano. [1875.] fol.　　　　**h. 1487. b. (23.)**

— *See* Coote (C.) *the Elder.* Giroflé-Girofla. Quadrille (valse), *etc.* [1874.] fol.　　　　**h. 2947. c. (4.)**

— *See* Cramer (W. O.) Bouquet of melodies on Lecocq's opera, *etc.* [1874.] fol.　　　　**h. 3380. (23.)**

— *See* Deransart (E.) Polka-Mazurka … sur les motifs de Giroflé-Girofla, *etc.* [1875.] fol.　　　　**h. 1487. e. (24.)**

— *See* Dessaux (L.) Quadrille … sur … Giroflé-Girofla, *etc.* [1875.] *obl.* fol.　　　　**e. 272. e. (4.)**

— *See* Dufils (L.) Giroflé-Girofla … quadrille, *etc.* [1875.] *obl.* fol.　　　　**e. 272. e. (11.)**

— *See* Ettling (E.) Grande suite de valses … sur … Giroflé-Girofla, *etc.* [1875.] *obl.* fol.　　　　**e. 272. e. (27.)**

— *See* Frambach (J. B.) Giroflé-Lanciers, *etc.* [1875.] *obl.* fol.　　　　**e. 272. e. (33.)**

— *See* Gariboldi (G.) Fantaisie de salon pour Flûte … sur des motifs de Giroflé-Girofla, *etc.* [1875.] fol.　　　　**h. 2096. (5.)**

— *See* Godfrey (C.) *the Younger.* Giroflé-Girofla lancers (galop), *etc.* [1874.] fol.　　　　**h. 2931. a. (31.)**

— *See* Hartmann (F.) Giroflé-Girofla … fantaisie pour Violon, *etc.* [1874.] fol.　　　　**h. 1609. g. (31.)**

LECOCQ (Alexandre Charles)

— *See* Hawkes (W. H.) Giroflé-Girofla quick march, *etc.* [1877.] 8°.　　　　**f. 413. b. (10.)**

— *See* Krug (D.) Giroflé-Girofla … fantaisie brillante, *etc.* [1875.] fol.　　　　**h. 3093. (21.)**

— *See* Kuhe (W.) Giroflé-Girofla, fantasia, *etc.* [1874.] fol.　　　　**h. 755. g. (8.)**

— *See* Lechner (J.) Suite aux Bagatelles … No. 99. [1886.] fol.　　　　**h. 637. c. (3.)**

— *See* Luigini (F.) Fantaisie sur les motifs de Giroflé-Girofla, *etc.* [1875.] fol.　　　　**h. 1487. q. (30.)**

— *See* Marx (H.) Giroflé-Girofla … quadrille, *etc.* [1875.] *obl.* fol.　　　　**e. 272. f. (18.)**

— *See* Métra (J. L. O.) Giroflé … suite de valses. [1875.] *obl.* fol.　　　　**e. 272. f. (27.)**

— *See* Nuyens (H.) Galop (valse) de Giroflé-Girofla, *etc.* [1875.] fol.　　　　**h. 1487. t. (27.)**

— *See* Renaud de Vilbac (A. Z. C.) Giroflé-Girofla, fantasia, *etc.* [1874.] fol.　　　　**h. 1483. g. (39.)**

— *See* Richards (H. B.) Celebrated Sextett from Giroflé-Girofla … for the Pianoforte. [1874.] fol.　　　　**h. 760. h. (17.)**

— *See* Rivière (J.) Fantasia from C. Lecocq's Opera, *etc.* [1877.] 8°.　　　　**f. 413. d. (1.)**

— *See* Rivière (J.) Giroflé Girofla Quadrille, *etc.* [1887.] 8°.　　　　**f. 410. l. (3.)**

— *See* Rivière (J.) Giroflé-Girofla, set of valses, *etc.* [1877.] 8°.　　　　**f. 410. a. (7.)**

— *See* Roques (L.) Grande polka sur … Giroflé-Girofla, *etc.* [1875.] fol.　　　　**h. 1487. x. (21.)**

— *See* Sivrai (J. de) Giroflé-Girofla, fantaisie brillante, *etc.* [1875.] fol.　　　　**h. 3186. a. (35.)**

— *See* Smallwood (W.) Six Airs from Giroflé-Girofla … for the Pianoforte. [1874.] fol.　　　　**h. 1412. d. (38.)**

— *See* Strauss (Eduard) Giroflé-Girofla. Quadrille nach Motiven über Lecocq's Oper, *etc.* ⟨Op. 122.⟩ [1875?] fol.　　　　**h. 3209. d. (26.)**

— *See* Strauss (Eduard) Giroflé-Girofla. Walzer nach Motiven über Lecocq's Oper … Op. 123. [1875.] fol.　　**h. 3209. e. (29.)**

— *See* Talexy (A.) Polka-mazurka … sur … Giroflé-Girofla, *etc.* [1875.] fol.　　　　**h. 764. c. (28.)**

— *See* Valiquet (H.) Giroflé-Girofla … Trois danses faciles, *etc.* [1875.] fol.　　　　**h. 3231. (9.)**

— *See* Valiquet (H.) Petit Bouquet de mélodies sur Giroflé-Girofla, *etc.* [1875.] fol.　　　　**h. 3231. (8.)**

— *See* Watson (W. M.) Popular Fantasia on Giroflé-Girofla, *etc.* [1874.] fol.　　　　**h. 3242. a. (7.)**

———————

— Le Goût du néant. *See* infra: Six morceaux caractéristiques. 5.

Le Grand Casimir

— Le Grand Casimir. Opérette en 3 actes de MM. J. Prével et A. de Saint-Albin. Partition Chant et Piano, arrangée par M. Boullard. *Paris*, [1879.] 8°.　　　　**F. 36. v.**

— [Le Grand Casimir.] The Great Casimir … Operetta in 3 acts. English adaptation by H. S. Leigh. *London*, [1881.] 4°.　　　　**F. 36. y.**

LECOCQ (Alexandre Charles)

— Le Grand Casimir. Opérette en 3 actes. [Orchestral parts.]
Paris, [1879.] fol.   **h. 1580. a.**

— Le Grand Casimir ... Partition Piano seul arrangée par
M. Boullard. *Paris*, [1879.] 8°.   **f. 270. m.**

— The Great Casimir ... Piano score. *London*, [1881.] 4°.
                                                          f. 270. p.

— Selection, "The Great Casimir," *etc.* [Military band parts.]
25 pt. *Boosey & Co.: London*, 1879. fol.
[*C. Boosé's supplemental military Journal. no.* 300.]   **h. 1544.**

— Grand Selection ... Selected and arranged [for military band]
by Charles Godfrey ... Conductor [and parts]. 27 pt. *Lafleur
& Son: London*, [1880.] fol.
[*Orpheus. no.* 15.]   **h. 1548.**

— Airs ... arrangés pour Cornet seul par Bryart. *Paris*, [1879.]
fol.   **h. 2284. b. (13.)**

— Airs ... arrangés pour Flûte seule par G. Garibaldi. *Paris*,
[1879.] fol.   **h. 2140. g. (6.)**

— Airs ... arrangés pour Violon seul par J. de Brayer. *Paris*,
[1879.] fol.   **h. 1609. m. (9.)**

— The Bridal Chorus. [1899.] *See* CHORAL. Choral Gems.
Secular, *etc.* No. 7. [1898–99.] 4°.   **F. 451.**

— *See* ARBAN (J. J. B. L.) Le Grand Casimir ... quadrille. [1879.]
obl. fol.   **e. 272. h. (12.)**

— *See* BULL (G.) Transcription facile ... sur Le Grand Casimir,
etc. [1879.] fol.   **h. 1493. c. (24.)**

— *See* GRENVILLE (A.) Le Grand Casimir. Lancers. [On Lecocq's
opera.] [1888.] 8°.   **e. 79. f. (9.)**

— *See* HESS (J. C.) Morceau de salon ... sur Le Grand Casimir,
etc. [1879.] fol.   **h. 1493. l. (9.)**

— *See* MÉTRA (J. L. O.) Le Grand Casimir ... valses. [1879.] *obl.*
fol.   **e. 272. j. (29.)**

— *See* RIVIÈRE (J.) Le Grand Casimir pas redoublé, *etc.* [1880.]
8°.   **f. 412. l. (18.)**

— *See* RUMMEL (J.) Le Grand Casimir ... bouquet de melodies,
etc. [1879.] fol.   **h. 523. g. (14.)**

— *See* VIZENTINI (A.) Polka sur les motifs du Grand Casimir,
etc. [1879.] fol.   **h. 1493. x. (28.)**

— A Happy Father. *See* supra: [Giroflé-Girofla.—Je vous
présente un père.]

— Harmonie du soir. *See* infra: Six morceaux caractéristiques.
3.

— Here's Giroflé. *See* supra: [Giroflé-Girofla.—Père adoré.]

— Histoire de 3 Bluets. [Song, begins: "Trois gentils bluets".]
Poësie de G. Boyer. *Paris*, [1883.] fol.   **H. 582. a. (5.)**

— The Hunter. Song [begins: "I am a dweller"]. Poetry by
W. J. Westbrook. *London*, [1873.] fol.   **H. 582. (1.)**

— I love you only, only you. *See* supra: [Le Cœur et la Main.—
Par toi, divine créature.]

— I. Idylle printanière ... II. Suzette et Suzon. [Songs.] Poésie de
Victor Hugo. no. 2. *Heugel & cie.: Paris*, [1910.] fol.
Imperfect; wanting no. 1.   **H. 582. d. (5.)**

— In a Village once lived a Maiden. *See* infra: [La Princesse des
Canaries.—Bolero.]

— Incognita. *See* supra: [Le Cœur et la Main.]

LECOCQ (Alexandre Charles)

— L'Ingénue de Fontenay-sous-Bois. [Song, begins: "Pour ma
naiv' té".] Paroles de A. Decourcelle et W. Busnach. *Paris*,
[1876.] fol.   **H. 1777. h. (39.)**

— L'Invitation au voyage. *See* infra: Six morceaux
caractéristiques. 4.

— The Island of Bachelors. *See* supra: [Les Cent Vierges.]

— J'ai manqué le train. Chansonnette [begins: "Quand, pour
épouser la jeun' fille"], paroles d'A. Millaud. *Paris*, 1885.
fol.   **H. 582. a. (11.)**

Janot

— Janot. Opéra comique en 3 actes. Paroles de MM. H. Meilhac
et L. Halévy ... Partition Chant et Piano arrangée par
L. Roques. *Paris*, [1881.] 8°.   **F. 36. z.**

— Janot, opéra comique en 3 actes ... Partition Piano seul
arrangée par L. Roques. *Paris*, [1881.] 8°. **f. 270. q.**

— *See* ARBAN (J. J. B. L.) Polka des Tambours ... sur ... Janot,
etc. [1881.] fol.   **h. 3317. (34.)**

— *See* ARBAN (J. J. B. L.) Janot ... quadrille, *etc.* [1881.] *obl.* fol.
                                               e. 272. l. (2.)

— *See* CROISEZ (A.) Fantaisie–souvenir ... sur ... Janot, *etc.*
[1881.] fol.   **h. 1259. b. (10.)**

— *See* MARX (H.) Janot ... quadrille, *etc.* [1881.] *obl.* fol.
                                               e. 272. l. (15.)

— *See* MÉTRA (J. L. O.) Janot ... suite de valses. [1881.] *obl.* fol.
                                               e. 272. l. (18.)

— *See* NUYENS (H.) Valse ... sur des motifs de Janot, *etc.* [1881.]
fol.   **h. 3272. l. (32.)**

— *See* ROQUES (L.) Parade-polka sur ... Janot, *etc.* [1881.] fol.
                                               h. 3272. n. (16.)

— Je vous présente un père. *See* supra: [Giroflé-Girofla.]

La Jolie Persane

— La Jolie Persane. Opéra comique en 3 actes. Paroles de MM.
E. Leterrier & A. Vanloo ... Partition Chant et Piano
arrangée par L. Roques. *Paris*, [1879.] 8°. **F. 36. x.**

— La Jolie Persane. Opéra comique en trois actes. Paroles de
MM. E. Leterrier and A. Vanloo. [Orchestral parts.] *Paris*,
[1880.] fol.   **h. 1580. b.**

— La Jolie Persane ... Partition Piano seul arrangée par
L. Roques. *Paris*, [1880.] 8°.   **f. 270. o.**

— Grand Selection ... Selected and arranged [for military band]
by Charles Godfrey. [Parts.] 24 pt. *Lafleur & Son: London*,
[1883.] fol.
[*Orpheus. no.* 36.]   **h. 1548.**

— La Jolie Persane ... Airs pour Flûte seule par G. Gariboldi.
Paris, [1880.] fol.   **h. 2096. b. (2.)**

— La Jolie Persane ... Air pour Violon seul par J. de Brayer.
Paris, [1880.] fol.   **h. 1609. q. (9.)**

— *See* ARBAN (J. J. B. L.) Polka brillante sur ... La Jolie Persane,
etc. [1880.] fol.   **h. 3317. (33.)**

— *See* ARBAN (J. J. B. L.) La Jolie Persane ... quadrille, *etc.*
[1880.] *obl.* fol.   **e. 272. j. (5.)**

— *See* BULL (G.) La Jolie Persane ... fantaisie, *etc.* [1880.] fol.
                                               h. 3272. b. (19.)

— *See* DERANSART (E.) Polka mazurka sur La Jolie Persane, *etc.*
[1880.] fol.   **h. 3272. d. (17.)**

LECOCQ (Alexandre Charles)

— *See* Herman (A.) Chanson de la Jolie Persane ... pour Violon, *etc.* [1880.] fol. **h. 1620. e. (5.)**

— *See* Marx (H.) La Jolie Persane ... quadrille. [1880.] *obl.* fol. **e. 272. j. (28.)**

— *See* Métra (J. L. O.) La Jolie Persane ... valses. [1880.] *obl.* fol. **e. 272. j. (35.)**

— *See* Roques (L.) Polka de salon sur La Jolie Persane, *etc.* [1880.] fol. **h. 3272. n. (14.)**

Le Jour et la Nuit

— Le Jour et la Nuit. Opéra bouffe en 3 actes. Paroles de MM. A. Vanlos et E. Leterrier ... Partition Chant et Piano arrangée par L. Roques. *Paris*, [1882.] 8°. **F. 443. b.**

— Manola. Comic opera in 3 acts. The English adaptation by H. B. Farnie. *London*, [1882.] 4°. **F. 443. c.**

— Le Jour et la Nuit ... Partition Piano solo arrangée par L. Roques. *Paris*, [1882.] 8°. **f. 270. s.**

— Manola ... Piano score. *London*, [1882.] 4°. **f. 270. r.**

— Ere Love could see. (Snake song.)—Procrastination. Song.— Song of the Onion.—Woman. Song.—Two Birds. Duet. Written by H. B. Farnie. 5 no. *London*, [1882.] fol. **H. 1787. j. (23.)**

— Grand Selection "Manola". ⟨Arranged [for military band] by Kappey.⟩ [Parts.] 26 pt. *Boosey & Co.: London*, [1882.] fol. [*Boosé's military Journal. ser.* 72. *no.* 4.] **h. 1549.**

— Le Jour et la Nuit ... Morceaux détachés ... arrangés pour Piano seul par A. Croisez. 8 no. *Paris*, [1882.] fol. **h. 3276. g. (11.)**

— Manola. ... A selection ... arranged for the Pianoforte by H. Parker. [Solo and duet.] 2 no. *London*, [1882.] fol. **h. 3159. (14.)**

— Manola ... arranged for Violin, Flute, Flageolet, Clarinet, Concertina or Cornet by E. Audibert. *London*, [1882.] 8°. **e. 316. (7.)**

— Airs de l'opéra ... arrangés pour Cornet seul par E. Guilbaut. *Paris*, [1882.] fol. **h. 2202. c. (16.)**

— Airs de l'opéra ... arrangés pour Flûte seule par G. Gariboldi. *Paris*, [1882.] fol. **h. 2140. k. (19.)**

— Airs de l'opéra ... arrangés pour Violon seul par A. Müller. *Paris*, [1882.] fol. **h. 1608. l. (11.)**

— *See* Arban (J. J. B. L.) Les Gais Portugais polka sur des motifs de Le Jour et la Nuit. [1882.] fol. **h. 3317. (38.)**

— *See* Arban (J. J. B. L.) Le Jour et la Nuit ... quadrille, *etc.* [1882.] *obl.* fol. **e. 272. l. (4.)**

— *See* Arban (J. J. B. L.) Le Jour et la Nuit, Opéra-Comique de Ch. Lecocq. Quadrille par Arban. [1882.] 8°. **e. 665. b. (8.)**

— *See* Bull (G.) Le Jour et la Nuit, transcription facile, *etc.* [1882.] fol. **h. 3358. a. (1.)**

— *See* Burty (M.) Transcription brillante ... sur le Jour et la Nuit, *etc.* [1882.] fol. **h. 3276. a. (39.)**

— *See* Cramer (N.) Le Jour & la Nuit ... bouquet de mélodies, *etc.* [1882.] fol. **h. 3276. b. (19.)**

— *See* Fruehling (M.) Manola ... waltzes, *etc.* [1882.] fol. **h. 3275. f. (71.)**

— *See* Geng (C.) Manola-valse sur ... Le Jour et la Nuit, *etc.* [1882.] fol. **e. 272. m. (21.)**

— *See* Herman (A.) Fantaisie ... sur Le Jour et la Nuit, de C. Lecocq. [1888.] fol. **h. 1620. f. (2.)**

LECOCQ (Alexandre Charles)

— *See* Hess (J. C.) La Jour et la Nuit, fantaisie, *etc.* [1882.] fol. **h. 3276. e. (26.)**

— *See* Hubans (C.) Le Jour et la Nuit, polka-mazurka, *etc.* [1882.] fol. **h. 3276. e. (54.)**

— *See* Kuhe (W.) Manola, fantasia, *etc.* [1882.] fol. **h. 755. h. (21.)**

— *See* Lechner (J.) Suite aux Bagatelles ... No. 97. [1886.] fol. **h. 637. c. (3.)**

— *See* Leybach (J.) Fantaisie brillante ... sur Le Jour & la Nuit, *etc.* [1882.] fol. **h. 1299. g. (31.)**

— *See* Marriott (C. H. R.) Manola ... lancers, *etc.* [1882.] fol. **h. 3275. k. (19.)**

— *See* Marx (H.) Le Jour et la Nuit ... quadrille, *etc.* [1882.] *obl.* fol. **e. 272. l. (16.)**

— *See* Métra (J. L. O.) Le Jour et la Nuit ... quadrille. [1882.] *obl.* fol. **e. 272. l. (21.)**

— *See* Métra (J. L. O.) Suite de valses ... sur Le Jour et la Nuit, *etc.* [1882.] *obl.* fol. **e. 272. l. (22.)**

— *See* Neustedt (C.) Chanson Indienne, fantaisie-transcription ... sur Le Jour et La Nuit, *etc.* [1882.] fol. **h. 485. d. (28.)**

— *See* Nuyens (H.) Valse ... sur Le Jour et la Nuit, *etc.* [1882.] fol. **h. 3276. h. (33.)**

— *See* Roques (L.) Polka Portugais sur ... Le Jour et la Nuit, *etc.* [1882.] fol. **h. 3272. n. (18.)**

— *See* Tavan (Émile) Fantaisie sur Le jour et la nuit ... de Ch. Lecocq, pour le piano. [c. 1905.] fol. **h. 1226. i. (15.)**

— Les Jumeaux de Bergame. Opéra comique en un acte arrangé par William Busnach d'après la comédie de Florian. Partition d'orchestre. pp. 170. *Brandus & c^{ie}: Paris*, [1884.] 8°. **F. 443. f.**

— [Another copy.] **Hirsch ii. 507.**

— Les Jumeaux de Bergame. Opéra comique en un acte arrangé par William Busnach d'après la comédie de Florian. Partition chant et piano arrangée par l'auteur. pp. 70. *Brandus & c^{ie}: Paris*, [1876.] 8°. **F. 36. m.**

— [Les Jumeaux de Bergame.] *See* Lechner (J.) Suite aux Bagatelles ... No. 92. [1886.] fol. **h. 637. c. (3.)**

Kosiki

— Kosiki. Opéra comique en 3 actes. Paroles de MM. W. Busnach et A. Liorat. Partition Chant et Piano arrangée par L. Roques. *Paris*, [1877.] 8°. **F. 36. p.**

— Kosiki. Opéra comique en 3 actes ... Partition pour Piano seul arrangée par L. Roques. *Paris*, [1877.] 8°. **f. 270. h.**

— Kosiki, opéra-comique ... Morceaux détachés transcrits et arrangés pour Piano seul par A. Croisez. 10 no. *Paris*, [1877.] fol. **h. 3106. (8.)**

— *See* Arban (J. J. B. L.) Kosiki polka, *etc.* [1877.] fol. **h. 3317. (18.)**

— *See* Arban (J. J. B. L.) Kosiki ... quadrille, *etc.* [1877.] *obl.* fol. **e. 272. d. (17.)**

— *See* Bull (G.) Valse ... sur Kosiki. [1877.] fol. **h. 1493. c. (20.)**

— *See* Deransart (E.) Kosiki ... quadrille. [1877.] *obl.* fol. **e. 272. d. (41.)**

— *See* Dessaux (L.) Kosiki ... quadrille, *etc.* [1877.] *obl.* fol. **e. 272. e. (8.)**

LECOCQ (Alexandre Charles)

— *See* ETTLING (E.) Suite de valses sur Kosiki, *etc.* [1877.] *obl.* fol.   **e. 272. e. (30.)**

— *See* MARX (H.) Quadrille sur Kosiki, *etc.* [1877.] *obl.* fol.   **e. 272. f. (21.)**

— *See* MÉTRA (J. L. O.) Suite de valses ... sur Kosiki, *etc.* [1877.] *obl.* fol.   **e. 272. f. (38.)**

— *See* ROQUES (L.) Polka-Mazurka sur ... Kosiki, *etc.* [1877.] fol.   **h. 1487. x. (29.)**

— *See* RUMMEL (J.) Kosiki ... Bouquet de mélodies, *etc.* [1877.] fol.   **h. 523. f. (23.)**

— *See* RUMMEL (J.) Kosiki ... duo pour Piano, *etc.* [1877.] fol.   **h. 523. f. (25.)**

— Le Langage des Yeux. [Song, begins: "Je sais un aimable langage".] Paroles de MM. J. Prével & St. Albin. *Paris,* [1874.] fol.   **H. 1777. h. (33.)**

— Une Larme de tes yeux. Mélodie. [Begins: "J'aime ta parole".] Paroles de L. Montini. *Paris,* [1872.] fol.   **H. 1777. h. (30.)**

— La Leçon d'Amour. Couplets [begins: "Allons, je vois qu'il faut tout vous apprendre"], paroles de W. Busnach. *Paris,* 1885. fol.   **H. 582. a. (9.)**

— Légende de la Mère Angot. *See* supra: [La Fille de Madame Angot.—Marchande de Marée.]

— Lettre d'une Cousine à son Cousin. [Song, begins: "Je ne voulais pas".] Paroles de H. Meilhac. *Paris,* [1875.] fol.   **H. 1777. h. (37.)**

— Liline et Valentin, opérette de salon, paroles de Jules de la Guette ... Partition chant et piano et dialogue intercalé, *etc.* pp. 36. *E. Gérard et cᵉ: Paris,* [1865?] 8°.   **E. 270. qq. (1.)**

— The Lily and the Rose. *See* infra: [Les Prés St. Gervais.—Je vais vous débrouiller la chose.]

— The Little Duke. *See* infra: Le Petit Duc.

— Ma belle Girofla. *See* supra: [Giroflé-Girofla.]

— Ma Femme est blonde. *See* supra: [La Fille de Madame Angot.]

— Manola. *See* supra: Le Jour et la Nuit.

— Marche nuptiale d'une poupée ... Partition d'orchestre. *Paris,* 1885. 8°.   **e. 666. e. (9.)**

— Marche Nuptiale d'une poupée, pour piano. *Paris,* 1885. fol.   **h. 3106. a. (5.)**

La Marjolaine

— La Marjolaine. Opéra-bouffe en 3 actes. Paroles de MM. A. Vanloo & E. Leterrier. Partition pour Chant & Piano arrangée par L. Rocques. *Paris,* [1877.] 8°.   **F. 36. q.**

— La Marjolaine. Opéra-bouffe en 3 actes. [Orchestral parts.] *Paris,* [1877.] fol.   **h. 1580.**

— La Marjolaine, opéra-bouffe en 3 actes ... Partition pour Piano seul arrangée par L. Roques. *Paris,* [1877.] 8°.   **f. 270. i.**

— La Marjolaine, opera bouffe ... arranged for Pianoforte solo. *London,* [1877.] 4°.   **f. 270. j.**

— La Marjolaine. Opéra bouffe en trois actes. [10 detached pieces.] *Paris,* [1877.] fol.   **H. 582. a. (2.)**

— [Ah! plaignez la misère.] Un P'tit Sou. Song. *London,* [1878.] fol.   **H. 582. (31.)**

LECOCQ (Alexandre Charles)

— [Je ne suis plus.] The Farewell duet. (Le Duo des Adieux.) [Begins: "No more am I".] *London,* [1877.] fol.   **H. 582. (28.)**

— [Jeunes filles selon l'usage.] See the prize of virtue. Song [begins: "Of the custom"]. *London,* [1878.] fol.   **H. 582. (29.)**

— [Magu'lonne allant à la fontaine.] She lost her way. Song [begins: "Margu'lonne to the well"]. *London,* [1878.] fol.   **H. 582. (30.)**

— *See* ARBAN (J. J. B. L.) Coucou polka from C. Lecocq's opera, *etc.* [1877.] fol.   **h. 1482. a. (12.)**

— *See* ARBAN (J. J. B. L.) La Marjolaine ... quadrille. [1877.] *obl.* fol.   **e. 272. d. (18.)**

— *See* BULL (G.) Souvenirs de la Marjolaine, *etc.* [1877.] fol.   **h. 1493. c. (21.)**

— *See* DESSAUX (L.) La Marjolaine ... quadrille, *etc.* [1877.] *obl.* fol.   **e. 272. e. (9.)**

— *See* FOUQUE (P. O.) La Marjolaine ... fantaisie, *etc.* [1877.] fol.   **h. 1493. h. (27.)**

— *See* LAMOTHE (G.) La Marjolaine ... waltzes, *etc.* [1877.] fol.   **h. 3100. c. (12.)**

— *See* MARX (H.) La Marjolaine ... quadrille. [1877.] *obl.* fol.   **e. 272. f. (22.)**

— *See* MÉTRA (J. L. O.) Suite de valses ... sur la Marjolaine, *etc.* [1877.] *obl.* fol.   **e. 272. f. (41.)**

— *See* ROQUES (L.) Polka mazurka sur ... La Marjolaine, *etc.* [1877.] fol.   **h. 1493. t. (19.)**

— *See* RUMMEL (J.) La Marjolaine ... Bouquet de melodies, *etc.* [1877.] fol.   **h. 523. f. (27.)**

— *See* RUMMEL (J.) La Marjolaine ... Duo pour Piano à quatre mains. [1878.] fol.   **h. 523. g. (1.)**

— Matamoros, grand capitaine. *See* supra: [Giroflé-Girofla.]

— Deux Mazurkas pour Piano. *Paris,* [1874.] fol.   **h. 3106. (2.)**

— Mercedes is a Gipsy charming. *See* supra: [Le Cœur et la Main.—Y avait un jour dans l'infant'rie.]

— Mes Loisirs. 12 morceaux pour piano. *G. Legouix: Paris,* [1888.] 4°.   **f. 270. y.**

— Miettes Musicales, esquisses de genre pour Piano. Op. 21. *Paris,* [1875.] 4°.   **g. 442. b. (6.)**

— Miettes musicales pour Piano. 4 Liv. *Paris,* [1877.] fol.   **h. 3106. (7.)**

— Six morceaux caractéristiques pour chant et piano, sur des poésies de Ch. Baudelaire, Leconte de L'Isle et X ... 1. La Vipère ... 2. La Géante ... 3. Harmonie du soir ... 4. L'Invitation au voyage ... 5. Le Goût du néant ... 6. Sérénade mélancolique, *etc.* 6 no. *Choudens fils: Paris,* [c. 1890.] fol.   **H. 582. d. (17.)**

— Deux Morceaux religieux pour violon et orgue ou piano. 2 no. *Paris,* [1883.] fol.   **h. 3106. a. (1.)**

— My Castle in Spain. [Song, begins: "The Cottage where I live".] Words by L. H. F. Du Terreaux. *London,* [1874.] fol.   **H. 582. (2.)**

— My excellent Friend. Duet. *See* infra: [La Princesse des Canaries.—Bonjour, Général Bombardos.]

— My Father is a banker old. *See* supra: [Giroflé-Girofla.—Mon père est un très-gros banquier.]

LECOCQ (ALEXANDRE CHARLES)

— My Girofla, my bride. *See* supra: [Giroflé-Girofla.—Ma belle Girofla.]

— My New Maid, operetta, written by H. B. Farnie. *See* FARNIE (H. B.) Cramer's Opera Bouffe Cabinet. No. 3. [1874.] 4°.　**F. 157.**

— My New Maid. Opera in one act, written by H. B. Farnie. *See* FARNIE (H. B.) Cramer's Opera-Comique Cabinet ... No. 6. [1874, *etc.*] 4°.　**F. 159.**

— Le Myosotis. Opérette-bouffe en un acte. Paroles de Cham et W. Busnach. Partition Chant et Piano. *Paris*, [1866.] 8°.　**F. 443.**

— Le Myosotis. Opérette-bouffe, *etc. Paris*, [1875.] 8°.　**F. 443. a.**

— Nice day for a sail. *See* supra: [The Black Prince.]

— The Nightingale. *See* infra: [La Petite Mariée. — Le Rossignol.]

— Ninette. Opéra-comique en 3 actes de Charles Clairville ... Partition chant et piano. pp. 243. *Choudens: Paris*, [1896.] 8°.　**F. 443. v.**

— Ninette. Opéra-comique en trois actes, poème de C. Clairville. Duo—Acte II., *etc.* [Begins: "Si j'étais le soleil".] [*Paris*], 1896. 8°. *Supplement to "L'Illustration," No.* 2769.　**P. P. 4283. m. (3.)**

— Nos Ancêtres étaient sages. *See* supra: [Giroflé-Girofla.]

— Offertoire. [Violin and organ.] *See* supra: Deux Morceaux religieux ... No. 2.

L'Oiseau Bleu

— L'Oiseau Bleu. Opéra comique en 3 actes de Duru & Chivot. Partition Chant & Piano transcrite par L. Roques. *Paris*, [1884.] 8°.　**F. 443. g.**

— L'Oiseau Bleu ... Partition Piano seul. *Paris*, [1884.] 8°.　**f. 270. v.**

— L'Oiseau Bleu. Polka-Mazurka pour piano par G. Geng. *Paris*, [1884.] fol.　**h. 3285. a. (65.)**

— L'Oiseau Bleu ... Polka pour piano par E. Deransart. *Paris*, [1884.] fol.　**h. 3285. a. (14.)**

— *See* BULL (G.) Les Succès Lyriques ... No. 41. L'Oiseau Bleu. Fantaisie. [1884.] fol.　**h. 3358. a. (7.)**

— *See* MÉTRA (J. L. O.) L'Oiseau Bleu ... Quadrille. [1884.] *obl.* fol.　**e. 283. c. (18.)**

— *See* MÉTRA (J. L. O.) L'Oiseau Bleu ... Suite de valses. [1884.] *obl.* fol.　**e. 283. c. (19.)**

— *See* RENAUD DE VILBAC (A. Z. C.) Bouquets de mélodies. L'Oiseau Bleu ... pour piano en 2 suites. [1883.] fol.　**h. 1228. n. (15.)**

— *See* ROQUES (L. J.) and RUMMEL (J.) Récréations mélodiques. Collection de Mosaïques pour piano ... No. 22. L'Oiseau bleu [by A. Zimmer]. [1884.] fol.　**h. 523. h. (4.)**

Ondines au Champagne

— The Sea Nymphs: a romance of the tidal train. Written by H. B. Farnie. *See* FARNIE (H. B.) Cramer's Opera-Comique Cabinet ... No. 7. [1874, *etc.*] 4°.　**F. 159.**

— Ondines au Champagne. Opérette en un acte. Paroles de MMrs. H. Lefebvre & J. Pélissié. Partition Chant et Piano. *Paris*, [1876.] 8°.　**F. 36. l.**

— The Sea Nymphs. A romance of the tidal train. Written by H. B. Farnie. *London*, [1877.] 4°. *One of "Metzler & Co's Opera Bouffe series".*　**F. 155. (8.)**

LECOCQ (ALEXANDRE CHARLES)

— Fleur de Corail valse. [P. F.] *London*, [1877.] fol.　**h. 1482. z. (7.)**

— *See* GODFREY (C.) *the Younger.* Sea Nymphs quadrille, *etc.* [1877.] fol.　**h. 2931. b. (2.)**

— *See* LAMOTHE (G.) Coquillette polka sur l'opérette, *etc.* [1876.] fol.　**h. 3100. (45.)**

— *See* MARX (H.) Ondines au Champagne, quadrille, *etc.* [1876.] *obl.* fol.　**e. 272. f. (19.)**

— *See* STERN (G.) Valse ... sur les motifs de l'opérette, *etc.* [1876.] fol.　**h. 1488. (13.)**

— Où vont les belles filles? *See* supra: Chansons de Gavroche I.

— Parade-marche. Allegro militaire pour piano. pp. 7. *J. Hamelle: Paris*, [c. 1905.] fol.　**g. 1138. gg. (16.)**

— Pauvre victimes que nous sommes. *See* supra: [Giroflé-Girofla.]

— Pepita. Comic opera. *See* infra: [La Princesse des Canaries.]

— Père adoré. *See* supra: [Giroflé-Girofla.]

Le Petit Duc

— Le Petit Duc, opéra comique en trois actes. Paroles de MM. H. Meilhac et L. Halévy. Partition Chant & Piano arrangée par L. Roques. *Paris*, [1878.] 8°.　**F. 36. s.**

— The Little Duke. Comic opera in 3 acts. The English words by S. Rowe and B. Rowe ... Vocal score. *London*, [1878.] 4°.　**F. 36. t.**

— Le Petit Duc. Opéra comique en trois actes ... Partition pour Piano seul arrangée par L. Roques. *Paris*, [1878.] 8°.　**f. 270. k.**

— Airs ... arrangés pour Cornet seul par Bryart. *Paris*, [1878.] fol.　**h. 2284. b. (11.)**

— Airs ... arrangés pour Flûte seule par Garibaldi. *Paris*, [1878.] fol.　**h. 2140. g. (4.)**

— Airs ... arrangés pour Violon seul par J. de Brayer. *Paris*, [1878.] fol.　**h. 1609. m. (7.)**

— Le Petit Duc ... Morceaux détachés transcrits ... pour Piano seul par A. Croisez. 6 no. *Paris*, [1879.] fol.　**h. 1493. n. (26.)**

— [La Leçon de chant.] The Singing Lesson ... Edited and arranged by Gerald Cockshott. (Unison.) [Staff and tonic sol-fa notation.] pp. 4. *Alfred Lengnick & Co.: South Croydon*, [1970.] 8°. *Part of "Zenith choral Library".*　**E. 812. k. (33.)**

— *See* ARBAN (J. J. B. L.) Le Petit Duc ... polka, *etc.* [1878.] fol.　**h. 3317. (26.)**

— *See* ARBAN (J. J. B. L.) Le Petit Duc ... quadrille, *etc.* [1878.] *obl.* fol.　**e. 272. h. (7.)**

— *See* BATTMANN (J. L.) Le Petit Duc ... fantaisie facile, *etc.* [1878.] fol.　**h. 3009. b. (7.)**

— *See* BULL (G.) Le Petit Duc ... transcription facile, *etc.* [1878.] fol.　**h. 1493. c. (22.)**

— *See* CRAMER (H.) The Little Duke ... bouquet of melodies, *etc.* [1878.] fol.　**h. 1494. e. (33.)**

— *See* DESSAUX (L.) Le Petit Duc ... quadrille. [1878.] *obl.* fol.　**e. 272. h. (26.)**

— *See* ETTLING (E.) Suite de valses sur le Petit Duc, *etc.* [1878.] *obl.* fol.　**e. 272. h. (29.)**

LECOCQ (ALEXANDRE CHARLES)

— *See* HERMAN (A.) Le Petit Duc ... divertissement ... pour Violon, *etc.* [1878.] fol.   **h. 1620. c. (8.)**

— *See* HERMAN (J.) Le Petit duc ... fantaisie, *etc.* [1878.] fol.   **h. 2100. (10.)**

— *See* HESS (J. C.) Le Petit Duc ... fantaisie, *etc.* [1878.] fol.   **h. 1493. l. (3.)**

— *See* HUBANS (C.) Le Petit Duc ... polka-mazurka, *etc.* [1878.] fol.   **h. 1493. l. (25.)**

— *See* LECHNER (J.) Suite aux Bagatelles ... No. 95. [1886.] fol.   **h. 637. c. (3.)**

— *See* MARX (H.) Le Petit Duc ... quadrille, *etc.* [1878.] *obl.* fol.   **e. 272. i. (2.)**

— *See* MÉTRA (J. L. O.) Suite de valses sur le Petit Duc, *etc.* [1878.] *obl.* fol.   **e. 272. i. (9.)**

— *See* MONIOT (E.) Le Petit Duc ... fantaisie brillante, *etc.* [1878.] fol.   **h. 1493. q. (17.)**

— *See* NEUSTEDT (C.) Le Petit Duc ... fantaisie-gavotte, *etc.* [1878.] fol.   **h. 485. d. (16.)**

— *See* NUYENS (H.) Valse ... sur Le Petit Duc, *etc.* [1878.] fol.   **h. 1493. r. (12.)**

— *See* RENAUD DE VILBAC (A. Z. C.) Le Petit Duc ... duo pour Piano, *etc.* [1878.] fol.   **h. 1228. l. (25.)**

— *See* RIVIÈRE (J.) The Little Duke ... quadrille, *etc.* [1878.] fol.   **h. 1495. (14.)**

— *See* ROQUES (L.) Le Petit Duc ... polka, *etc.* [1878.] fol.   **h. 1493. t. (20.)**

— *See* RUMMEL (J.) Le Petit Duc ... Bouquet de mélodies, *etc.* [1878.] fol.   **h. 523. g. (2.)**

— *See* RUMMEL (J.) Le Petit Duc ... fantaisie pour Piano. [1878.] fol.   **h. 523. g. (4.)**

— Un P'tit Sou. *See supra*: [La Marjolaine.—Ah! plaignez la misère.]

La Petite Mademoiselle

— La Petite Mademoiselle. Opéra comique en trois actes de MM. H. Meilhac et L. Halévy. Partition Chant et Piano arrangée par L. Roques. *Paris*, [1879.] 8°.   **F. 36. w.**

— La Petite Mademoiselle ... English words by H. S. Leigh. *J. Williams: London*, [1880?] 4°.   **F. 443. p.**

— La Petite Mademoiselle. Opéra comique en trois actes ... Partition pour Piano seul arrangée par L. Roques. *Paris*, [1879.] 8°.   **f. 270. n.**

— [Ne faisons pas de bruit and Comment! tout seul?] [1899.] *See* CHORAL. Choral Gems. Secular, *etc.* No. 9, 13. [1898–99.] 4°.   **F. 451.**

— Grand selection ... Selected and arranged [for military band] by Charles Godfrey. ⟨Conductor [and parts].⟩ 27 pt. *Lafleur & Son: London*, [1880.] fol. [*Orpheus. no.* 19.]   **h. 1548.**

— Selection ... by Hare. [Reed band parts.] *London*, [1880.] 8°.   **f. 401. p. (21.)**

— A grand selection ... arranged ... for the Piano by C. Godfrey. *London*, [1881.] fol.   **h. 3275. j. (24.)**

— La Petite Mademoiselle. Valse. [Orchestral parts.] *J. Williams: London*, [1888.] 8°.   **e. 79. g. (16.)**

LECOCQ (ALEXANDRE CHARLES)

— [Arrivé dans Bordeaux.] When I am far away. [Violin and P. F.] *See* PALMER (E. D.) Popular Transcriptions, *etc.* No. 2. [1892.] fol.   **h. 1683. (1.)**

— *See* ARBAN (J. J. B. L.) La Petite Mademoiselle ... quadrille. [1879.] *obl.* fol.   **e. 272. j. (1.)**

— *See* HERMAN (A.) La Petite Mademoiselle ... Fantaisie pour le Violon, *etc.* [1880.] fol.   **h. 1620. e. (1.)**

— *See* MARX (H.) La Petite Mademoiselle ... quadrille. [1879.] *obl.* fol.   **e. 272. j. (26.)**

— *See* MÉTRA (J. L. O.) La Petite Mademoiselle ... valses, *etc.* [1879.] *obl.* fol.   **e. 272. j. (32.)**

— *See* NUYENS (H.) Valse ... sur La Petite Mademoiselle, *etc.* [1880.] fol.   **h. 1493. r. (13.)**

— *See* RENAUD DE VILBAC (A. Z. C.) La Petite Mademoiselle ... duo facile, *etc.* [1879.] fol.   **h. 1228. l. (35.)**

— *See* ROQUES (L.) La Petite Mademoiselle ... polka, *etc.* [1879.] fol.   **h. 1493. t. (22.)**

— *See* RUMMEL (J.) La Petite Mademoiselle ... bouquet de mélodies, *etc.* [1879.] fol.   **h. 523. g. (26.)**

— *See* VIZENTINI (A.) Polka-mazurka sur La Petite Mademoiselle, *etc.* [1879.] fol.   **h. 1493. x. (29.)**

La Petite Mariée

— La Petite Mariée, opéra bouffe en trois actes. Paroles de MM. E. Leterrier & A. Vanloo. Partition Chant et Piano arrangée par L. Roques. *Paris*, [1876.] 8°.   **F. 36. o.**

— The Scarlet Feather. Comic opera, English Libretto by H. Greenbank, from the French of MM. Leterrier and Vanloo ... With additional numbers by L. Monckton. Vocal Score. *Hopwood & Crew: London*, [1897.] 4°.   **F. 443. q.**

— La Petite Mariée ... Partition pour Piano seul arrangée par L. Roques. *Paris*, [1876.] 8°.   **f. 270. f.**

— La Petite Mariée, opéra bouffe ... arranged for Pianoforte solo. *London*, [1876.] 4°.   **f. 270. e.**

— Selection ... arranged by E. Audibert. [Orchestral parts.] *London*, [1876.] 8°. *Part of the "Alliance Musicale".*   **f. 400. k. (6.)**

— Selection, *etc.* [Military band parts.] 25 pt. *Boosey & Co.: London*, [1876.] fol. [*Boosé's military Journal. ser.* 61 *no.* 1.]   **h. 1549.**

— La Petite Mariée ... Morceaux détachés transcrits et arrangés pour Piano seul par A. Croisez. 12 no. *Paris*, [1876.] fol.   **h. 3106. (6.)**

— Selection ... by E. Audibert. [P. F.] *London*, [1876.] 8°. *No.* 377 *of the "Alliance Musicale. Album Bijou".*   **f. 406.**

— Selection from ... The Scarlet Feather. Selected and arranged for the Pianoforte by C. Godfrey, Junr. *Hopwood & Crew: London*, [1901.] fol.   **h. 3282. w. (36.)**

— Airs ... arrangés pour Cornet seul. *Paris*, [1876.] fol.   **h. 2202. b. (12.)**

— Airs ... arrangés pour Flûte seule. *Paris*, [1876.] fol.   **h. 2140. e. (10.)**

— Airs ... arrangés pour Violon seul. *Paris*, [1876.] fol.   **h. 1609. f. (7.)**

— [Couplets de l'Enlèvement.] The Elopement. [Song, begins: "Indeed I can't help laughing." – "Vraiment j'en ris".] (The English words by F. Lyster.) *London*, [1876.] fol.   **H. 582. (26.)**

LECOCQ (Alexandre Charles)

— [Couplets du Jour et de la Nuit.] Day and Night. [Song, begins: By day, you must know." "Le Jour vois tu".] (The English words by F. Lyster.) *London*, [1876.] fol.
H. 582. (25.)

— [Le Rossignol.] The Nightingale. Song from ... The Scarlet Feather, *etc. Hopwood & Crew: London*, [1901.] fol.
H. 582. a. (20.)

La Petite Mariée.—Appendix

— Quadrille [by Arban]. Valse [by E. Ettling] Polka-Mazurka [by L. Roques] sur La Petite Mariée ... Arrangés pour Cornet seul, Flûte seul, Violin seul. 12 no. *Brandus et Cᵉ.: Paris*, [1876.] 8°.
f. 420. a. (3.)

— *See* ARBAN (J. J. B. L.) La Petite Mariée ... polka, *etc.* [1876.] fol.
h. 3317. (16.)

— *See* ARBAN (J. J. B. L.) La Petite Mariée ... quadrille, *etc.* [1876.] *obl.* fol.
e. 272. d. (13.)

— *See* BULL (G.) La Petite Mariée ... transcription facile, *etc.* [1876.] fol.
h. 1493. c. (19.)

— *See* COOTE (C.) *the Elder.* La Petite Mariée quadrille, *etc.* [1876.] fol.
h. 2947. c. (11.)

— *See* COOTE (C.) *the Younger.* The Scarlet Feather. Quadrilles (Waltz) on Melodies from Lecocq's opera, *etc.* [1901.] fol.
h. 2948. e. (5.)

— *See* CRAMER (H.) La Petite Mariée ... pot pourri, *etc.* [1877.] fol.
h. 371. c. (7.)

— *See* DERANSART (E.) La Petite Mariée ... quadrille, *etc.* [1876.] *obl.* fol.
e. 272. d. (37.)

— *See* DESSAUX (L.) La Petite Mariée ... quadrille, *etc.* [1876.] *obl.* fol.
e. 272. e. (6.)

— *See* DUFILS (L.) La Petite Mariée ... quadrille, *etc.* [1876.] *obl.* fol.
e. 272. e. (23.)

— *See* DUFILS (L.) Polka sur La Petite Mariée, *etc.* [1876.] fol.
h. 3417. (20.)

— *See* ETTLING (E.) La Petite Mariée ... suite de valses. [1876.] *obl.* fol.
e. 272. e. (29.)

— *See* GARIBOLDI (G.) La Petite Mariée ... fantaisie ... pour Flûte, *etc.* [1876.] fol.
h. 2096. (7.)

— *See* GODFREY (A. F.) La Petite Mariée ... waltzes, *etc.* [1876.] fol.
h. 3046. a. (6.)

— *See* HARE (E. C. F.) La Petite Mariée quick step. [1877.] 8°.
f. 403. c. (32.)

— *See* HERMAN (A.) La Petite Mariée ... Morceau de salon pour Violon et Piano. [1876.] fol.
h. 1620. c. (2.)

— *See* KUHE (W.) La Petite Mariée, fantasia brillante ... for the Pianoforte. [1876.] fol.
h. 755. g. (16.)

— *See* LAMOTHE (G.) La Petite Mariée ... fantaisie brillante, *etc.* [1876.] fol.
h. 3100. (54.)

— *See* LECHNER (J.) Suite aux Bagatelles ... No. 101. [1886.] fol.
h. 637. c. (3.)

— *See* LUIGINI (F.) Petite fantaisie ... sur La Petite Mariée, *etc.* [1876.] fol.
h. 1487. q. (31.)

— *See* MARX (H.) La Petite Mariée ... quadrille. [1876.] *obl.* fol.
e. 272. f. (20.)

— *See* MÉTRA (J. L. O.) La Petite Mariée ... suite de valses. [1876.] *obl.* fol.
e. 272. f. (29.)

— *See* NEUSTEDT (C.) La Petite Mariée ... fantaisie transcription, *etc.* [1876.] fol.
h. 485. b. (53.)

LECOCQ (Alexandre Charles)

— *See* NUYENS (H.) La Petite Mariée ... valse brillante, *etc.* [1876.] fol.
h. 1487. t. (30.)

— *See* RENAUD DE VILBAC (A. Z. C.) La Petite Mariée ... duo facile, *etc.* [1879.] fol.
h. 1228. l. (31.)

— *See* RIVIÈRE (J.) La Petite Mariée, fantasia, *etc.* [1877.] 8°.
f. 413. d. (10.)

— *See* ROQUES (L.) La Petite Mariée ... polka-mazurka. [1876.] fol.
h. 1487. x. (27.)

— *See* SNYDERS (E.) La Petite Mariée ... Divertissement pour Piano. [1877.] fol.
h. 1493. v. (40.)

— *See* STRAUSS (Eduard) Quadrille nach Motiven der Lecocq'schen Operette Graziella (La Petite mariée) ... Op. 148 ... Ausg. für Pfte. zu 2 Hdn. [1876.] fol.
h. 3209. f. (21.)

— *See* TALEXY (A.) La Petite Mariée ... fantaisie-mazurka, *etc.* [1876.] fol.
h. 764. c. (33.)

— *See* VALIQUET (H.) La Petite Mariée ... Trois danses faciles. [1876.] fol.
h. 3231. (10.)

— Les Petits Enfants. [Song, begins: "Repondez moi".] Paroles de Jean Marie. *Paris*, [1877.] fol.
H. 582. a. (1.)

— Plutus. Opéra Comique en trois actes. Poème de MM. A. Millaud & G. Jollivet. Partition Chant & Piano réduite par A. Bazille. *Paris*, 1886. 8°.
F. 443. h.

Le Pompon

— Le Pompon, opéra comique en 3 actes. Paroles de MMrs. H. Chivot & A. Duru ... Partition Chant & Piano arrangée par L. Roques. *Paris*, [1875.] 8°.
F. 36. n.

— Le Pompon. Opéra comique ... Partition pour Piano seul arrangée par L. Roques. *Paris*, [1876.] 8°.
f. 270. g.

— Selection ... Arr. by Kappey. [Military band parts.] 25 pt. *Boosey & Co.: London*, [1879.] fol.
[*Boosé's military Journal.* ser. 67. no. 3.]
h. 1549.

— *See* ARBAN (J. J. B. L.) Quadrille sur le Pompon, *etc.* [1876.] *obl.* fol.
e. 272. d. (7.)

— *See* DERANSART (E.) Polka mazurka sur les motifs du Pompon. [1876.] fol.
h. 1493. e. (23.)

— *See* DUFILS (L.) Le Pompon ... quadrille. [1876.] *obl.* fol.
e. 272. e. (19.)

— *See* ROQUES (L.) Pompon-Polka, *etc.* [1876.] fol.
h. 1487. x. (25.)

— *See* RUMMEL (J.) Le Pompon ... bouquet de mélodies, *etc.* [1876.] fol.
h. 523. f. (15.)

— Prelude. [P. F.] *See* PIANO. Six Piano Pieces, *etc.* No. 1. [1894.] fol.
h. 3278. d. (1.)

Les Prés St. Gervais

— Les Prés St. Gervais, opéra comique en 3 actes. Paroles de MM. V. Sardou et P. Gille. Partition Chant & Piano arrangée par Renaud de Vilbac. *Paris*, [1874.] 8°.
F. 36. j.

— Les Prés St. Gervais, comic opera in 3 acts ... Translated into English by R. Reece. [Vocal score.] *London*, [1874.] 8°.
F. 36. k.

— Les Prés St. Gervais, comic opera, arranged for the Pianoforte. *London*, [1874.] 4°.
f. 270. (2.)

LECOCQ (ALEXANDRE CHARLES)

— Les Prés St. Gervais. Opéra comique en 3 actes ... Partition Piano seul arrangée par Renaud de Vilbac. *Paris*, [1875.] fol.
f. 270. c.

— Les Prés St. Gervais ... comic opera ... for the Violin. *London*, [1875.] 8°. **f. 380. (5.)**

— Les Prés St. Gervais. Comic opera in three acts, words by R. Reece. [10 detached vocal no.] *London*, [1875.] fol.
H. 582. (23.)

— Selection ... arranged by Audibert. [Orchestral parts.] *London*, [1875.] 8°.
Part of the "Alliance Musicale". **f. 400. (1.)**

— Selection from ... "Les Près S¹ Gervais". Arranged [for military band] by Fred Godfrey. [Parts.] 24 pt. *S. A. Chappell: London*, [1875.] fol.
[Army Journal. no. 103.] **h. 1562.**

— Selection, *etc.* [Military band parts.] 21 pt. *Boosey & Co.: London*, [1875.] fol.
[Boosé's supplemental military Journal. no. 271.] Without titlepage. The title is taken from the head of p. 1 of the first clarinet part. **h. 1544.**

— Les Prés S¹. Gervais galop. [P. F.] *London*, [1874.] fol.
h. 1482. z. (6.)

— Selection ... arranged by Audibert. [P. F.] *London*, [1875.] 8°.
No. 281 of the "Alliance Musicale. Album Bijou". **f. 406.**

— Overture. [Octet band parts.] *London*, [1877.] 8°.
f. 411. b. (12.)

— [Je vais vous débrouiller la chose.] The Lily and the Rose. Ballad [begins: "Listen to me"]. *London*, [1874.] fol.
H. 582. (22.)

— [Je vais vous débrouiller la chose.] *See* RIVIÈRE (J.) The Lily and the Rose, from C. Lecocq's opera, *etc.* [1877.] 8°.
f. 412. f. (25.)

Les Prés St. Gervais.—Appendix

— *See* ARBAN (J. J. B. L.) Les Prés St. Gervais quadrille, *etc.* [1874.] fol. **h. 1482. a. (9.)**

— *See* ARBAN (J. J. B. L.) Les Prés St. Gervais ... quadrille, *etc.* [1875.] *obl.* fol. **e. 272. d. (1.)**

— *See* ARBAN (J. J. B. L.) Les Prés St. Gervais quadrille, *etc.* [1877.] 8°. **f. 412. (3.)**

— *See* BOULLARD (M.) Friquette polka-mazurka des Prés St. Gervais, *etc.* [1875.] fol. **h. 1487. a. (54.)**

— *See* COOTE (C.) *the Elder.* Les Prés St. Gervais lancers, *etc.* [1874.] fol. **h. 2947. c. (5.)**

— *See* CRAMER (A.) Les Prés St. Gervais ... Mosaïque. [1875.] 8°. **h. 1487. d. (21.)**

— *See* CRAMER (W. O.) Bouquet of melodies on Lecocq's comic opera, *etc.* [1875.] fol. **h. 3380. (24.)**

— *See* DERANSART (E.) Les Prés St. Gervais ... quadrille, *etc.* [1875.] *obl.* fol. **e. 272. d. (31.)**

— *See* DUFILS (L.) Les Prés St. Gervais ... polka. [1875.] fol. **h. 3417. (12.)**

— *See* DUFILS (L.) Les Prés St. Gervais ... valse, *etc.* [1875.] *obl.* fol. **e. 272. e. (14.)**

— *See* DUFILS (L.) Les Prés St. Gervais valse, *etc.* [1875.] fol. **h. 1482. k. (24.)**

— *See* FANTON (E.) Les Prés St. Gervais ... Transcription facile. [P. F.] [1875.] fol. **h. 1487. h. (1.)**

LECOCQ (ALEXANDRE CHARLES)

— *See* FANTON (E.) Les Prés St. Gervais ... easy transcriptions. [P. F.] [1875.] fol. **h. 1482. m. (5.)**

— *See* GODFREY (Adolphus F.) Quick March (N° 1) ... Based on melodies from "Les Près St. Gervais" by A. C. Lecocq. Arranged for military band by] F. Godfrey. [1875.] *obl.* 8°. *[Army Journal. no. 104.]* **h. 1562.**

— *See* GODFREY (Adolphus F.) Quick March [on melodies] from Lecocq's opera "Les Près S¹ Gervais". [Arranged for military band by] F. Godfrey. [1875.] 8°. *[Army Journal. no. 107.]*
h. 1562.

— *See* GODFREY (C.) *the Younger.* Près St. Gervais quick march, *etc.* [1875.] 8°. **f. 401. (15.)**

— *See* GODFREY (C.) *the Younger.* Grand Fantasia from Lecocq's Près St. Gervais. [1875.] 8°. **f. 401. (16.)**

— *See* KUHE (W.) Les Prés St. Gervais, fantasia, *etc.* [1874.] fol.
h. 755. g. (11.)

— *See* MÉTRA (J. L. O.) Les Prés St. Gervais ... quadrille, *etc.* [1875.] *obl.* fol. **e. 272. f. (25.)**

— *See* RENAUD DE VILBAC (A. Z. C.) Les Prés St. Gervais ... Bouquet de mélodies, *etc.* [1875.] fol. **h. 1228. m. (1.)**

— *See* RENAUD DE VILBAC (A. Z. C.) Les Prés St. Gervais ... mosaique, *etc.* [1875.] fol. **h. 1483. g. (41.)**

— *See* RIVIÈRE (J.) Le Régiment de Conti quick march from C. Lecocq's opera, *etc.* [1877.] 8°. **f. 413. d. (24.)**

— *See* ROQUES (L.) Les Prés St. Gervais ... polka, *etc.* [1875.] fol. **h. 1487. x. (23.)**

— *See* WATSON (W. M.) Popular Fantaisia on Les Prés St. Gervais, *etc.* [1875.] fol. **h. 3242. a. (24.)**

La Princesse des Canaries

— La Princesse des Canaries. Opéra bouffe en 3 actes de Chivot et Duru. Partition Chant et Piano trancrite par L. Roques. *Paris*, [1883.] 8°. **F. 443. e.**

— Pepita. Comic opera ... adapted from the French of Chivot & Duru by Mostyn Tedde. *London*, [1887.] 4°. **F. 443. j.**

— La Princesse des Canaries ... Partition Piano solo arrangée par A. Choudens. *Paris*, [1883.] 8°. **f. 270. u.**

— Pepita. Comic opera ... Pianoforte solo. *Chappell & Co.: London*, [1887.] 4°. **f. 270. x.**

— Pepita ... Winterbottom's Selection. Arranged for orchestra by John Pougher. [Orchestral parts.] 16 pt. *Chappell & Co.: London*, [1888.] 8°.
[Chappell & Co.'s Operatic and popular Selections for Orchestra by various Composers. no. 7.] **f. 424.**

— Selection from ... Pepita, for the pianoforte by W. Winterbottom. *Chappell & Co.: London*, [1888.] fol.
h. 3106. a. (8.)

— [Bolero.] In a Village once lived a Maiden. The Bolero from ... Pepita. *Chappell & Co.: London*, [1888.] fol.
This song was adapted to new music for the English version of the opera. **H. 582. a. (19.)**

— [Bonjour, Général Bombardos.] My excellent Friend. Duet, from ... Pepita, *etc.* *Chappell & Co.: London*, [1888.] fol.
H. 582. a. (18.)

— March from ... Pepita, arranged for pianoforte by E. R. Terry. *Chappell & Co.: London*, [1888.] fol. **h. 3106. a. (7.)**

— [Marche des toréadors.] The Toreadors. Quick march from ... "Pepita". [Arrd. by] A. Morelli. [Parts for fife and drum band.] 8 pt. *J. A. Lafleur & Son: London*, [1892.] 8°.
f. 800. (802.)

LECOCQ (Alexandre Charles)

— La Princesse des Canaries. Marche des Toréadors. *See* BULL (G.) Les Succès Lyriques ... No. 35. [1883.] fol.
h. 3358. a. (7.)

— [Marchons d'un air conquérant.] Shoulder to Shoulder. Quick march from ... "Pepita". [Arrd. by] A. Morelli. [Parts for fife and drum band.] 8 pt. *J. A. Lafleur & Son: London*, [1892.] 8°.
f. 800. (803.)

— La Princesse des Canaries. Polka des Généraux pour piano par Deransart. *Paris*, [1883.] fol.
h. 3285. a. (18.)

— [Qu'il est fier et splendide.] Toreador's song ... from ... Pepita, *etc. Chappell & Co.: London*, [1888.] fol.
H. 582. a. (17.)

La Princesse des Canaries. — Appendix

— *See* ARBAN (J. J. B. L.) La Princesse ... quadrille, *etc.* [1883.] *obl.* fol.
e. 272. m. (7.)

— *See* BUCALOSSI (P.) Pepita. Lancers. [On Lecocq's "La Princesse des Canaries". Orchestral parts.] [1887.] 8°. [*CHAPPELL AND CO. Popular Quadrilles, etc. no.* 200.]
e. 249.

— *See* BUCALOSSI (P.) Pepita Lancers, *etc.* [On Lecocq's "La Princesse des Canaries".] [1888.] fol.
h. 3004. b. (31.)

— *See* BUCALOSSI (P.) Pepita. Waltz. [On Lecocq's "La Princesse des Canaries". Orchestral parts.] [1887.] 8°. [*CHAPPELL AND Co. Popular Quadrilles, etc. no.* 199.]
e. 249.

— *See* BUCALOSSI (P.) Pepita Valse ... [on Lecocq's "La Princesse des Canaries"]. [1887.] fol.
h. 3004. a. (9.)

— *See* BULL (G.) Les Succès Lyriques ... No. 36. La Princesse des Canaries. Fantaisie. [1883.] fol.
h. 3358. a. (7.)

— *See* BURTY (M.) La Princesse des Canaries. Opéra Bouffe ... Fantaisie ... pour piano, *etc.* [1883.] fol.
h. 3280. b. (32.)

— *See* COOTE (C.) *the Younger.* Pepita. Quadrille. [On Lecocq's opera "La Princesse des Canaries". Orchestral parts.] [1887.] 8°. [*CHAPPELL AND Co. Popular Quadrilles, etc. no.* 201]
e. 249.

— *See* COOTE (C.) *the Younger.* Pepita Quadrille. [On Lecocq's opera "La Princesse des Canaries".] [1887–8.] fol.
h. 2948. c. (22.)

— *See* COOTE (C.) *the Younger.* La Princesse des Canaries ... Quadrille, *etc.* [1883.] fol.
h. 2948. c. (25.)

— *See* FARMER (H.) Pepita. Fantasia [on Lecocq's 'Princesse des Canaries'], *etc.* [1888.] fol.
h. 211. e. (9.)

— *See* MÉTRA (J. L. O.) La Princesse ... quadrille, *etc.* [1883.] *obl.* fol.
e. 272. m. (31.)

— *See* MÉTRA (J. L. O.) La Princesse ... valse, *etc.* [1883.] *obl.* fol.
e. 272. m. (33.)

— *See* MILTON (C.) La Princesse ... polka-mazurka, *etc.* [1883.] fol.
h. 3276. h. (9.)

— *See* RENAUD DE VILBAC (A. Z. C.) Bouquets de mélodies. La Princesse des Canaries ... pour piano en 2 suites. [1883.] fol.
h. 1228. n. (25.)

— *See* RUMMEL (J.) and MILTON (C.) Perles Enfantines ... No. 26. [1883.] fol.
h. 523. h. (5.)

— *See* SMALLWOOD (W.) Fantasia on Lecocq's ... opera, Pepita, *etc.* [1888.] fol.
h. 1412. m. (18.)

— *See* SMITH (B.) Pepita. Fantasia on C. Lecocq's ... opera, *etc.* [1888.] fol.
h. 3025. b. (30.)

— Procrastination. *See* supra: [Le Jour et la Nuit. — Selections.]

LECOCQ (Alexandre Charles)

— Le Punch scintille en reflets bleus. *See* supra: [Giroflé-Girofla.]

— Quand irons-nous dans la forêt? *See* supra: Chansons de Gavroche. II.

— Le Rajah de Mysore. Opérette bouffe en un acte ... paroles de A. Duru et H. Chivot. Partition piano et chant. *L. Bathlot: Paris*, [1869.] 8°.
F. 443. l.

— [Le Rajah de Mysore.] *See* LACOMBE (A.) Le Rajah de Mysore, fantaisie, *etc.* [1876.] fol.
h. 1482. y. (2.)

— Le Renard et les Raisins. Fable de la Fontaine [begins: "Certain renard gascon"]. *Paris*, 1885. fol.
H. 582. a. (7.)

— Reproches. Étude pour piano. pp. 7. *J. Hamelle: Paris*, [c. 1905.] fol.
g. 1138. gg. (17.)

— Retained on both sides. Operetta in one act written by H. B. Farnie. *London*, [1875.] 4°.
One of "Metzler & Co.'s Opera Bouffe series". **F. 155. (9.)**

— Le Rêve de Mme. Angot. [Song, begins: "J'ai rêvé".] Paroles de Clairville. *Paris*, [1874.] fol.
H. 1777. h. (32.)

— The Rose and the Glove. *See* supra: [The Black Prince.]

— Rose de France. Valse pour piano. *Metzler & Co.: London*, [1889.] fol.
h. 3106. a. (9.)

— Rose-mousse. Pièce en un acte de MM. André Alexandre et Peter Carin ... Partition chant et piano. pp. 49. *Choudens: Paris*, [1904.] 8°.
F. 1256. k.

— Le Roussotte ... Musique de MM. Hervi, C. Lecocq, *etc.* [1881.] 8°. *See* HERVÉ (F.) *pseud.* **F. 35. n.**

— Le Ruisseau. Lamento [begins: "Coule toujours charmant ruisseau"], paroles de S. Bordèse. *Paris*, [1885.] fol.
H. 582. a. (16.)

— Ruse d'Amour. Saynête en vers de S. Bordèse. Partition pour Chant et Piano. [*Paris*,] 1897. 8°.
Supplement to "L'Illustration," No. 2861. **P. P. 4283. m. (3.)**

— La Saison d'aimer. Mélodie. Poésie de Jacques Normand. [Score and voice part.] 2 pt. *Ph. Maquet: Paris*, [c. 1895.] fol.
H. 582. d. (1.)

— Sans défauts, ou Je ne suis pas bête. Bavardage. [Song.] Paroles de M****. [Score and voice part.] 2 pt. *Petit Aîné: Paris*, [c. 1865.] fol.
H. 582. d. (2.)

— The Scarlet Feather. *See* supra: [La Petite Mariée.]

— Scène de Phèdre de Racine. Édition Chant et Piano. *Paris*, [1883.] 8°.
F. 1273. g. (5.)

— Scherzo. [P. F.] *See* PIANO. Six Piano Pieces, *etc.* No. 3. [1894.] fol.
h. 3278. d. (1.)

— The Sea Nymphs. A romance, *etc. See* supra: [Les Ondines au Champagne.]

— See how it sparkles. *See* supra: [Giroflé-Girofla. — Le Punch scintille.]

— See the prize of virtue. *See* supra: [La Marjolaine. — Jeunes filles selon l'usage.]

— Sérénade mélancolique. *See* supra: Six morceaux caractéristiques. 6.

— She is so innocent. *See* supra: [La Fille de Madame Angot. — Elle est tellement innocente.]

— She lost her way. *See* supra: [La Marjolaine. — Magu'lonne allant à la fontaine.]

— The Singing Lesson. *See* supra: [Le Petit duc. — La Leçon de chant.]

LECOCQ (Alexandre Charles)

— Le Soldat de Floréal. Chanson militaire. Poésie d'Armand Silvestre. pp. 7. *G. Le Gouix: Paris*, [c. 1895.] fol.
H. 582. d. (3.)

— Song of the Onion. *See* supra: [Le Jour et la Nuit.]

— Sous un pommier ... Scène comique de MM. Émile Thierry et J. de la Guette. [Score and voice part.] 2 pt. *Alfr: Ikelmer et cie.: Paris*, [c. 1865.] fol.
H. 582. d. (4.)

— Stenio's serenade. *See* supra: [Gandolpho.]

— Suzette et Suzon. *See* supra: Idylle printanière.

— Ta porte est close. Aubade. Poésie de Victor Hugo ... N° 1 en sol. Baryton ou mezzo-soprano, *etc.* pp. 5. *Alphonse Leduc: Paris*, [c. 1875.] fol.
H. 582. d. (6.)

— Ta porte est close. Aubade. Poésie de V. Hugo. *Paris*, [1876.] fol.
H. 1777. h. (38.)

— The Tale of a Shah. *See* supra: [La Fille de Madame Angot.—Marchande de Marée.]

— Le Testament de Monsieur de Crac, opéra-bouffe en 1 acte. Paroles de J. Moinaux ... Partition chant et Piano arrangée par L. Roques. *Paris*, [1872.] fol.
F. 36. d.

— 'Tis only a poor little flower. Romance. *See* supra: [Fleur de Thé.—Césarine à mes vœux docile.]

— Les Tonneliers. Duo, tenor et baryton. Paroles de Jules de la Guette. pp. 5. *Colombier: Paris*, [c. 1865.] fol.
H. 582. d. (7.)

— Le Trahison de Pan. Opéra-comique en 1 acte, poème de Stéphan Bordèse ... Piano et chant. pp. 88. *Max Eschig: Paris*, [1912.] 4°.
H. 582. c.

— Les Trois Nids. Couplets [begins: "Jamais elle ne raille"], poésie de V. Hugo. *Paris*, [1885.] fol. **H. 582. a. (15.)**

— Two Birds. *See* supra: [Le Jour et la Nuit.]

— Two Loves. *See* supra: [The Black Prince.]

— Valse Fin de Siècle, pour le Piano. [*Paris*,] 1899. 8°. *Supplement to "L'Illustration," No.* 2922. **P. P. 4283. m. (3.)**

La Vie Mondaine

— La Vie Mondaine. Opéra bouffe en 4 actes. Paroles de MM. P. Ferrier et É. de Najac. Partition chant & piano. *Paris*, 1885. 8°.
F. 443. i.

— La Vie Mondaine. ... Partition piano seul. *Paris*, 1885. 8°.
f. 270. w.

— *See* ARBAN (J. J. B. L.) Je suis de Chicago. Polka ... sur des motifs de La Vie Mondaine, *etc.* 1885. fol. **h. 3285. (19.)**

— *See* ARBAN (J. J. B. L.) La Vie Mondaine ... Quadrille pour le piano, *etc.* 1885. *obl.* fol. **e. 272. n. (5.)**

— *See* BULL (G.) Fantaisie ... pour piano sur La Vie Mondaine, *etc.* 1885. fol. **h. 3358. a. (12.)**

— *See* CRAMER (H.) Bouquet de Mélodies ... de la Vie Mondaine, *etc.* [1885.] fol. **h. 371. c. (16.)**

— *See* GENG (C.) Georgette, valse sur des motifs de La Vie Mondaine, *etc.* 1885. *obl.* fol. **e. 272. n. (22.)**

— *See* NUYENS (H.) Valse ... pour piano sur des motifs de La Vie Mondaine, *etc.* [1885.] fol. **h. 3280. n. (22.)**

— La Vipère. *See* supra: Six morceaux caractéristiques. 1.

LECOCQ (Alexandre Charles)

— Vireli et virelette. ⟨Chanson.⟩ Paroles de Stéphan Bordèse. pp. 5. *A. Quinzard & cie.: Paris*, [c. 1910.] fol. *A slip bearing the imprint of Henri Gregh et fils has been pasted over the original imprint.* **H. 582. d. (8.)**

— Vive le boxe! Anglomanie ... [Song.] Paroles de Mr Rphe de Lacroix. *Émile Chatot: Paris*, [c. 1860.] fol. **H. 582. d. (9.)**

— La Volière. Opéra-comique en 3 actes, *etc.* ⟨Partition chant & piano transcrite par L. Roque [i. e. Jean Léon Roques].⟩ pp. 225. *Choudens père & fils: Paris*, [1888?] 8°. **F. 36. aa.**

— La Volière. Opéra-Comique en 3 actes de Nuitter et Beaumont. Partition chant et piano transcrite par L. Roque[s]. 2e Édition. *Choudens: Paris*, [c. 1890.] 8°. **F. 443. o.**

— Vous en souvenez-vous, mignonne? [Song.] Poésie de A. Kermor. pp. 7. *G. Ricordi & c.: Milan, etc.*, [c. 1890.] fol. **H. 582. d. (11.)**

— Vous qui savez ce qu'il en est. Chanson ... Paroles de L. Houssot. *L. Bathlot: Paris*, [c. 1870.] fol. **H. 582. d. (10.)**

— What Life is so bright. *See* supra: [Le Cœur et la Main.—Un soir, Pérez le capitaine.—Selections.]

— When I am far away. *See* supra: [La Petite Mademoiselle.—Arrivé dans Bordeaux.]

— Woman. *See* supra: [Le Jour et la Nuit.]

— Yetta. Opéra comique en 3 actes de F. Beissier. Partition piano et chant. *Choudens: Paris*, 1903. 8°. **F. 443. r.**

— Les Yeux de ma mie. Mélodie pour une voix avec accompt de piano. Poésie de Georges Dupré, *etc.* pp. 5. *J. Hamelle: Paris*, [1902.] fol. **H. 582. d. (12.)**

— You 'tis you. *See* supra: [The Black Prince.]

APPENDIX

— *See* CONTES. Contes Mystiques ... Musique de ... C. Lecocq, *etc.* 1890. 8°. **F. 970.**

— *See* DUNI (E. R.) La Clochette ... Partition Piano et Chant arrangée par C. Lecocq. [1910.] 8°. **F. 690. x. (2.)**

— *See* GUTELLO ( ) Lecocq-Walzer ... sur les ... motifs de C. Lecocq, *etc.* 1885. *obl.* fol. **e. 272. n. (24.)**

— *See* HARE (E. C. F.) "Mr. Cracked" galop on Lecocq's melodies. [1875.] 8°. **f. 403. (29.)**

— *See* MONSIGNY (P. A.) On ne s'avise jamais de tout ... Partition Piano et Chant arrangée par C. Lecocq. [1910.] 8°. **F. 690. x. (3.)**

— *See* MOZART (W. A.) [Sonatas. P. F. and violin. K. 7.] Sonate inachevée pour le clavecin ou pianoforte avec accompagnt. de violon ... Nouvelle édition revue et corrigée par C. Lecocq, *etc.* [1880?] fol. **Hirsch M. 1111.**

— *See* RAMEAU (J. P.) Castor et Pollux ... Partition arrangée ... par C. Lecocq. [1878.] 8°. **F. 866.**

LECOCQ (Alexandre Charles) and ELLIOTT (Lionel)

— My Uncle, the Ghost. A Musical Joke, in one Act. Libretto by H. Lathair. *J. Williams: London*, [1892?] 4°.
F. 689. (8.)

LECOCQ (Charles)

— *See* LECOCQ (Alexandre C.)

LE COCQ (François)

— Recueil des pièces de guitare. 1729. ⟨Réédition anastatique d'après l'exemplaire conservé à la Bibliothèque du Conservatoir [*sic*] royal de musique de Bruxelles sous la cote

LE COCQ (FRANÇOIS)

5.615.) pp. 122. *Éditions culture et civilisation: Bruxelles,*
1979. fol.
[*Thesaurus musicus. Nova series. ser. A.* 1.] **G. 80.**

LECOCQ (HENRI)

— L'Automne. Chanson [begins: "Déjà la nuit égale au jour"],
paroles et musique de H. Lecocq. *Paris,* [1886.] fol.
H. 2836. h. (34.)

LECOCQ (J.) and BESOZZI (L. D.)

— La Chapelle au Couvent. Publication spéciale de musique
religieuse [by L. Gastinel and J. Franck] pour voix de
femmes, sur la direction de J. Lecocq et L. D. Besozzi. 14 no.
Paris, [1867.] fol. **H. 1031.**

LECOCQ (MAURICE) *pseud.* [i. e. JEAN LOUIS GOBBAERTS.]

— Aimons-nous. Valse pour piano. *Bruxelles,* [1884.] fol.
h. 3285. b. (52.)

— Aimons nous. Valse ... pour piano. *A. Mahillon: Bruxelles,*
[1888.] fol. **h. 3281. l. (14.)**

— Aimons nous. Valse ... Piano Solo, *etc. E. Ascherberg &*
Co.: London, 1897. fol. **h. 3286. r. (5.)**

— L'Aubépine. Valse. [P. F.] *Bruxelles,* [1883.] fol.
h. 3285. b. (48.)

— Causerie d'oiseaux. Imitation pour piano. *Bruxelles,* [1884.]
fol. **h. 3280. k. (38.)**

— Coquelicots et Bluets. Polka-Mazurka. [P. F.] *Bruxelles,*
[1883.] fol. **h. 3285. b. (49.)**

— Gavotte Clémentine, *etc.* [P. F.] *St. Cecilia Music Publishing*
Co.: London, [1893.] fol. · **g. 605. f. (9.)**

— La Japonaise. Polka. [P. F.] *Bruxelles,* [1884.] fol.
h. 3285. b. (53.)

— Le Mail Coach, galop pour Piano. *Bruxelles,* [1882.] fol.
h. 3276. g. (12.)

— Le Mail Coach. Galop pour piano, *etc.* (Le Mail Coach ...
arr. par R. de Vilbac.) [Duet.] 2 no. *St. Cecilia Music*
Publishing Co.: London, [1893.] fol. **h. 3285. q. (18.)**

— La Malle Américane. Galop de bravoure pour piano.
Bruxelles, [1883.] fol. **h. 3285. b. (50.)**

— Le Retour des hirondelles. Galop. [P. F.] *Bruxelles,* [1884.]
fol. **h. 3285. b. (54.)**

— Sur la glace. Mazurka brillante pour piano. *Bruxelles,* [1884.]
fol. **h. 3285. b. (55.)**

— La Troïka. Galop Russe. [P. F.] *Bruxelles,* [1883.] fol.
h. 3285. b. (51.)

— Tyrolienne favorite. [P. F.] *Bruxelles,* [1884.] fol.
h. 3280. k. (39.)

— Tyrolienne favorite. [P. F.] *St. Cecilia Music Publishing Co.:*
London, [1893.] fol. **g. 605. f. (10.)**

LE COMPASSEUR (FERNAND)

— L'Amour et la Chasse, suite de valses. [P. F.] *Bruxelles,*
[1879.] *obl.* fol. **e. 272. j. (25.)**

— Flon-Flon polka pour le Piano. *Bruxelles,* [1879.] fol.
h. 1493. n. (28.)

— Patrie, marche pour Piano. *Bruxelles,* [1879.] fol.
h. 1493. n. (29.)

LECOMTE (ADOLPHE)

— *See* GOUËT (A.) Le Bonheur n'est pas au parloir ...
Accompagnement de Piano par A. Lecomte. [1840?] fol.
G. 540. (17.)

— *See* GOUËT (A.) Lucette ... Accompagnement de Piano par
A. Lecomte. [1840?] fol. **G. 540. (18.)**

LECOMTE (LOUISE)

— Il ne me regarde jamais. Boléro [begins: "On le contemple"].
Paris, [1835?] fol. **G. 542. (57.)**

— Le Lac ... Barcarolle [begins: "Accours, mon Héloïse"].
[*Paris,* 1830?] fol. **G. 551. (63.)**

— L'Oraison. Romance ... Paroles de Mme Desbordes Walmore.
H. Meissonnier: Paris, [1832?] fol. **G. 561. c. (22.)**

LECOMTE (PAUL)

— Belle Jeunesse. Valse lente. [P. F.] *Francis, Day & Hunter:*
London, 1909. fol.
Two copies, with different titlepages. **h. 3286. uu. (43.)**

LEÇON

— Le [*sic*] Leçon. Romance. *See* COUDRAY (G. T. du)

— La Leçon. Comédie. *See* DALAYRAC (N.)

— La Leçon. Romance. *See* PANSERON (A. M.)

— La Leçon d'Amour. [Song.] *See* DURAND (M. A.)

— La Leçon d'Amour. Couplets. *See* LECOCQ (A. C.)

— Leçon d'histoire. [Song.] *See* GEORGES (A.) Chants de
Rhénanie ... IV.

— La Leçon d'Inconstance. Valse. *See* PEELLAERT (A. de)

— La Leçon de Chant. Canon. *See* POURTET (N.)

— La Leçon de Chant. Opéra comique. *See* LAURENT DE RILLÉ
(F. A.)

— La Leçon de Charité. Mélodie. *See* GREGH (L.)

— La Leçon de Géographie. [Song.] *See* CŒDÈS (A.)

— La Leçon de Lecture. Chansonnette. *See* MEYER (C.)

— La Leçon de Piano. Chansonnette. *See* POURNY (C.)

— La Leçon de Valse du petit François. Chansonnette. *See*
BEAUPLAN (A. de) *pseud.*

— La Leçon du Caniche. Chansonnette. *See* PESSARD (E.) Deux
Chansonnettes. No. 1.

— La Leçon Galante. [Song.] *See* DÉCOUVREZ. Decouvrez un
tendre mistère. [1785?] 8°. **B. 362. e. (109.)**

— La Leçon Inutile. Romance. *See* SALVO (de) *Marquis.*

— La Leçon Savoyarde. Chansonnette. *See* THÉVENAU (A.)

— La Leçon Tyrolienne. Chansonnette. *See* BEAUPLAN (A. de)
pseud.

— La Leçon tyrolienne. Chansonnette. *See* SAGRINI (L.)

LEÇONS

— Les Leçons d'Anglais. Chansonnette. *See* CHASSAIGNE (F.)

— Leçons d'Épicure, ou l'Aimable Philosphie. [Song.] *See*
AMOUR. L'Amour est un bien suprême, *etc.* [1785?] 8°.
B. 362. a. (182.)

LEÇONS

— Vingt leçons de solfège modernes dans les sept clés (sans changement de clés) d'auteurs différents. (Claude Arrien —Georges Dandelot—Georges Hugon—Olivier Messiaen—Marc Starominsky.) pp. 54. *Henry Lemoine & c^{ie}: Paris, Bruxelles,* [1934.] 4°.　　　　**G. 844. n. (1.)**

— Les Leçons du Grand Papa. [Song.] *See* BERRETTONI (A.) La Semaine Musicale. No. 2.

LE COQ ( ) of Arras

— Le Parfait Biberon. Chanson ... Les paroles sont de Mr Bracheu. [*Paris,*] 1745. s. sh. 4°.
Mercure de France, Dec., 1745.　　　　**297. c. 4.**

LE CORBEILLER (CHARLES)

— Caprice original pour piano. Op. 30. *Paris,* [1854.] fol.
　　　　h. 1342. (4.)

— Caprice original pour le piano. Op. 30. *Paris,* [1855.] fol.
　　　　h. 1342. (3.)

— Le Château des Fleurs quadrille. [P. F.] *London,* [1855.] fol.
No. 341 of the "Musical Bouquet".　　　　**H. 2345.**

— "Le Châtelet" Fantaisie sur un Thème original pour le Piano Forte. Op. 20. *London,* [1852.] fol.　　　　**h. 723. l. (27.)**

— Le collier de perles, valses pour piano. *London,* [1853.] fol.
　　　　h. 964. (4.)

— Le Cotillon, suite de valses transcrites pour le Piano. *Paris,* [1869.] fol.　　　　**f. 131. b. (7.)**

— "La Dauphine." Premier Nocturne pour le Pianoforte. Op. 16. *London,* [1852.] fol.　　　　**h. 723. l. (26.)**

— Une Entrevue. Opérette. Paroles de A. Liorat. [Vocal score.] *Paris,* [1871.] 8°.　　　　**F. 807.**

— Fantaisie pour piano sur une barcarolle favorite. Op. 16. *London,* [1853.] fol.　　　　**h. 723. l. (25.)**

— Les Gouttes d'Or, rêverie pour Piano. *Paris,* [1869.] fol.
　　　　h. 1462. r. (29.)

— Le Jardin d'Hiver quadrille. [P. F.] *London,* [1855.] fol.
No. 354 of the "Musical Bouquet".　　　　**H. 2345.**

— Marche militaire pour le piano. Op. 28. *London,* [1854.] fol.
　　　　h. 723. l. (29.)

— Nicette valse pour piano. *London,* [1853.] fol.　　**h. 964. (3.)**

— Nizza, polka pour piano. *London,* [1853.] fol.　　**h. 964. (5.)**

— Pensez à moi, redowa-mélodie pour piano. *Paris,* [1854.] fol.
　　　　h. 1342. (2.)

— Pensez à moi, redowa-mélodie pour piano. *Paris,* [1855.] fol.
　　　　h. 1342. (1.)

— Les Postillons du Roy, galop-fantaisie pour Piano. *Paris,* [1876.] fol.　　　　**h. 1493. n. (30.)**

— Procida, tarentelle pour Piano. *Paris,* [1879.] fol.
　　　　h. 1493. n. (31.)

— Rêve d'Azur, mélodie pour Piano. Op. 27. *London,* [1854.] fol.　　　　**h. 723. l. (28.)**

— Le réveil, aubade pour piano. Op. 32. *Paris,* [1855.] fol.
　　　　h. 1342. (7.)

— Le réveil, aubade pour piano. Op. 32. *London,* [1855.] fol.
　　　　h. 1342. (8.)

— Rondoletto sur un motif original pour piano. Op. 31. *Paris,* [1855.] fol.　　　　**h. 1342. (5.)**

LE CORBEILLER (CHARLES)

— Rondoletto sur un motif original pour Piano, *etc.* Op. 31. *London,* [1855.] fol.　　　　**h. 1342. (6.)**

— Le Tapis Vert quadrille. [P. F.] *London,* [1855.] fol.
No. 342 of the "Musical Bouquet".　　　　**H. 2345.**

— Voici l'Avril! Sérénade du Passant [begins: "Mignonne"]. Poésie de F. Coppée. *Paris,* [1870.] fol.　　**H. 1774. e. (22.)**

— *See* LESUEUR (J. F.) Oratorio ou Messe de Noel ... Revu par C. Le Corbeiller. [1870?] 8°.　　　　**E. 543. b.**

LE CORDIER (ARMANDINE)

— Paris-Plage. Etaples. Valse pour le piano. *Paris,* [1883.] fol.
　　　　h. 3285. b. (56.)

LE COUPPEY (FÉLIX)

— Selected Studies. [P. F.] (Graded ... & edited by T. F. Dunhill.) 2 bk. *Augener: London,* 1917. 4°.　　**g. 337. oo. (5.)**

— Eight tuneful pieces for beginners ... Edited by T. F. Dunhill. [P. F.] *Augener: London,* 1917. 4°.　　　**g. 603. vv. (6.)**

— A. B. C. du piano, méthode pour les commençans ... A. B. C. des Pianoforte, *etc. Fr. & Ger. Leipzig,* [1859.] fol.
　　　　h. 1032. (1.)

— A. B. C. of the Pianoforte, a method for beginners. *Paris,* [1877.] fol.　　　　**h. 1493. n. (32.)**

— L'Agilité. 25 progressive Studies for the Piano. Op. 20. Edited and revised by T. F. Dunhill. *Augener: London,* (1914.) 4°.
　　　　g. 337. ff. (8.)

— L'Agilité. 25 progressive studies for the piano. Op. 20. *J. Williams: London,* 1919. 4°.　　　　**g. 337. tt. (2.)**

— L'Agilité. ⟨Op. 20.⟩ Twenty-five progressive piano studies for mechanism and light touch. pp. 37. *G. Schirmer: New York; Chappell & Co.: London;* [*London* printed, 1951.] 4°.
Schirmer's Library of musical Classics. vol. 67.　**g. 338. o. (2.)**

— L'Alphabet, 25 études très faciles pour piano, *etc.* Op. 17. *Paris,* [1856.] fol.　　　　**h. 1032. (2.)**

— The Alphabet. 25 easy Studies for small hands for the Pianoforte. Op. 17. (Revised, phrased and fingered by O. Thümer.) *Augener: London,* [1907.] 4°.　**g. 543. kk. (6.)**

— The Alphabet. 25 easy Studies for Piano. (Op. 17.) 2 bk. *Laudy & Co.: London,* [1912.] fol.　　　　**h. 3821. c. (4.)**

— The Alphabet ... 25 very easy studies for the piano. Op. 17. *J. Williams: London,* 1915. 4°.　　　　**g. 761. s. (5.)**

— The Alphabet. ⟨Op. 17.⟩ Twenty-five very easy studies for the piano (for small hands). Edited and fingered by Wm. Scharfenberg. pp. 27. *G. Schirmer: New York; Chappell & Co.: London;* [*London* printed, 1950.] 4°.
Schirmer's Library of musical Classics. vol. 430.
　　　　g. 338. o. (3.)

— [L'Alphabet. Op. 17.] Six Studies. [P. F.] *Augener & Co.: London,* [1886.] fol.
Part of E. Pauer's "Pianoforte Library".　　　**h. 3649. (3.)**

— L'Art du piano. 50 études prises dans les œuvres des maîtres les plus célèbres et annotées par F. Le Couppey. *See infra:* École Normale du Piano ... No. 1.

— De l'enseignement du Piano; conseils aux jeunes professeurs. *Paris,* 1865. 8°.　　　　**7895. aa. 59.**

— Le Décaméron. 10 études difficiles prises dans les œuvres de divers auteurs et annotées par F. Le Couppey. *See infra:* École Normale du Piano ... No. 6.

LE COUPPEY (FÉLIX)

— École du mécanisme, 15 séries d'exercices pour acquérir la souplesse, l'égalité de force et l'indépendance des doigts, *etc.* ⟨Piano.⟩ pp. 41. *J. Hamelle: Paris,* [c. 1885.] fol.

h. 62. m. (7.)

— École Normale du Piano. Ouvrages annotés et doigtés par F. Le Couppey. no. 1–6, 8, 9. *Paris,* [1876–86.] 4°. *Imperfect; wanting no. 7. Part of the Format Lemoine.*

g. 326.

— Grétry. Les Deux Avares ... Transcription pour Piano. *London,* [1875.] fol. **h. 1482. z. (8.)**

— In the Woods. [P. F.] [1901.] *See* KUHLSTROM (E.) Daisy Chains, *etc.* No. 10. [1901, *etc.*] fol. **g. 1186. a.**

— Introduction à l'Art du Piano. 30 études prises dans les œuvres des maitres les plus célèbres et annotées par F. Le Couppey. *See* supra: École Normale du Piano ... No. 2.

— Les Matinées Musicales. 12 Morceaux de Salon pris dans les œuvres des maitres les plus célèbres, transcrits pour piano et annotés par F. Le Couppey. *See* supra: École Normale du Piano. ... No. 4.

— Mélodie and Bourrée. [P. F.] [1912.] *See* DUNHILL (T. F.) and VOLK (W. A.) Recreative Pieces, *etc.* Series 1. No. 6a. (1912, *etc.*) fol. **h. 2912. a.**

— [Préface à la vélocité de Czerny. Op. 26.] Fifteen Preparatory Studies to Czerny's "School of Velocity". For the piano. pp. 29. *G. Schirmer: New York: Chappell & Co.: London;* [*London* printed, 1952.] 4°. *Schirmer's Library of musical Classics. vol. 69.* **g. 338. q. (7.)**

— Préliminaires de l'Art du Piano. 20 morceaux faciles pris dans les œuvres des maitres les plus célèbres et annotés par F. Le Couppey. *See* supra: École Normale du Piano ... No. 3.

— Fifteen Preparatory Studies to Czerny's "School of Velocity". *See* supra: [Préface à la vélocité de Czerny. Op. 26.]

— Le Recueil des Enfants. 20 morceaux très faciles à deux, à trois et à quatre mains. *See* supra: École Normale du Piano ... No. 8.

— Le Recueil des Pianistes. 12 morceaux de concert pris dans les œuvres des maitres les plus célèbres et annotés par F. Le Couppey. *See* supra: École Normale du Piano ... No. 5.

— *See* BEETHOVEN (L. van) [Variations. P. F. K.-H. 70.] La Molinara. Thème varié, *etc.* [Edited by F. Le Couppey.] [1860?] fol. **Hirsch M. 1294. (5.)**

— *See* FIELD (John) 2 nocturnes. [No. 1, 5. Edited by F. Le Couppey.] [c. 1880.] fol. **h. 3465. t. (1.)**

— *See* HAYDN (F. J.) [Quartet. Op. 50. No. 1.] Adagio ... transcribed by F. Le Couppey. [1876.] fol. **h. 3035. b. (7.)**

— *See* MENDELSSOHN-BARTHOLDY (J. L. F.) [Quartet. Op. 12.] Canzonetta ... transcrite ... par F. Le Couppey. [1877.] fol. **h. 575. n. (1.)**

LECOURT (PIERRE)

— Concerto pour le clavecin ou forte-piano, avec accompagnement de deux violons, alto, et basse, flûtes et cors, ad libitum ... Œuvre Iᵉʳ. ⟨Gravé par Mᵉˡˡᵉ de Gendron.⟩ [Parts.] *Chez Mʳ Boyer: Paris,* [c. 1790.] fol. *Imperfect; the clavecin part only.* **g. 996. b. (7.)**

LECOUVREUR (BENOIT)

— Le Gorlitza, polka Livonienne de M. A. Varin, composée ... par B. Lecouvreur. [P. F.] *London,* [1851.] fol. **h. 964. (6.)**

— Les Marionettes Schottisch. [P. F.] *London,* [1853.] fol. **h. 975. e. (32.)**

LE CRAS (THOMAS LEWIS)

— Four Carol Descants. First Set, *etc. J. Curwen & Sons: London,* 1934. 8°. [*Church Choralist. No. 707.*] **E. 1330.**

— Five Carol Descants. [No. 1.] Good King Wenceslas. [No. 2.] In dulci jubilo. [No. 3.] Angels from the Realms of Glory. [No. 4.] Greensleeves. [No. 5.] I saw three Ships. pp. 11. *J. Curwen & Sons: London,* [1949.] 8°. [*Church Choralist. no. 789.*] **E. 1330.**

— Twenty-four Descants to popular Hymn Tunes by T. L. Le Cras. *J. Curwen & Sons: London,* 1929. 8°. [*Church Choralist. No. 671.*] **E. 1330.**

— Second Set of Twenty-four Descants to popular Hymn Tunes, *etc. J. Curwen & Sons: London,* 1935. 8°. [*Church Choralist. No. 710.*] **E. 1330.**

— A Legend of Mullaghmast. Old Irish Air. [Words by] A. Gillington. Arranged for S. S. C. by T. H. Le Cras. *J. Curwen & Sons: London,* 1923. 8°. [*Choruses for equal voices. No. 1599.*] **E. 861.**

— A Legend of Mullaghmast. Unison Song ... Old Irish Air. Arr. T. L. Le Cras. *J. Curwen & Sons: London,* 1925. 8°. [*Choruses for equal voices. No. 1668.*] **E. 861.**

— Londonderry Air. [Song.] Arr. T. L. Le Cras. Poem by I. Gass. *J. Curwen & Sons: London,* 1938. 4°. **G. 981. r. (12.)**

— *See* JAMES (J.) [Hen wlad fy nhadau.] Land of my Fathers ... Arranged with Descant by T. L. Le Cras, *etc.* 1936. 8°. [*Choruses for equal Voices. No. 1948.*] **E. 861.**

— *See* SHARP (Cecil J.) Widdecome Fair ... Devonshire folk song ... Arranged by C. J. Sharp. ⟨Alternative chorus by T. Le Cras.⟩ [1967.] 8°. [*Choruses for equal Voices.* 2650.] **E. 861.**

— *See* TAYLOR (S. C.) Drake's Drum. Arranged for ... mixed voices by T. L. Le Cras, *etc.* 1923. 8°. [*Choral Handbook. No. 1169.*] **E. 862.**

LE CROIX (JEAN)

— Sleep, my little blue-eyed Treasure. Ballad, words by A. W. French. *C. Sheard: London,* [1880.] fol. *No. 5974 of the Musical Bouquet.* **H. 2345.**

LECTIO

— Lectio libri sapientiae. Cantate. *See* GHEDINI (Giorgio F.)

LECTURE

— De Lecture. Plantation Song. *See* GATTY, afterwards SCOTT-GATTY (*Sir* Alfred S.) Plantation Songs ... No. 10.

— La Lecture du Bulletin. Romance. *See* PLANTADE (C. H.)

— Lecture du Soir. [Song.] *See* ENGEL (C.) *of the Library of Congress.* Trois Sonnets. 1.

— A Lecture on Fashions. Song. *See* HOOK (J.)

LECUONA (ERNESTO)

— Album No. 3. Danzas Afro-Cubanas. [P. F.] *Lecuona: Habana,* 1930. 4°. **g. 230. g. (10.)**

— Always in my Heart. (Chorus for S. A. T. B.) Lyric by Kim Gannon ... Arranged by Harry R. Wilson. pp. 9. *Southern Music Publishing Co.: New York,* [1957.] 8°. [*Latin American choral Perennials. ser. 1. 6.*] **E. 1860.**

LÉCUREUX (THÉODORE MARIE)

— L'Appel des Pâtres, chant Breton transcrit et varié pour Piano. *Paris,* [1866.] fol. **h. 849. (7.)**

LÉCUREUX (Théodore Marie)

— Barcarolle. Caprice pour Piano. *Paris*, [1867.] fol.
h. 849. (9.)

— Berceuse pour piano. *H. Heugel: Paris*, [1887.] fol.
h. 3281. l. (15.)

— Le chant du cygne, Mélodie dramatique, pour Piano. Op. 14. *Paris*, [1857.] fol.
h. 849. (1.)

— Le Chemin du Pardon, scène Bretonne pour Piano. *Paris*, [1863.] fol.
h. 849. (4.)

— Cristal de Roche, polka mazurka pour le piano. *Paris*, [1876.] fol.
h. 849. (12.)

— Le départ des moissonneurs, esquisse villageoise, pour Piano. Op. 15. *Paris*, [1857.] fol.
h. 849. (2.)

— Etude trémolo, extraite des Etudes caractéristiques. [P. F.] *Paris*, [1866.] fol.
h. 849. (6.)

— La Légende de St. Nicolas, de A. Gouzier, bluette pastorale pour Piano. *Paris*, [1865.] fol.
h. 849. (5.)

— Marche Slave, étude en octaves. [P. F.] *Paris*, [1873.] fol
h. 849. (11.)

— Trois morceaux de Salon ... pour le Piano. *Paris*, [1861.] fol.
h. 849. (3.)

— Soirée Bohémienne, mélodie et mazurke. [P. F.] *Paris*, [1868.] fol.
h. 849. (10.)

— Souvenir de Nantes, impromptu pour Piano. *Paris*, [1873.] fol.
h. 849. (13.)

— Valse Allemande pour Piano. *Paris*, [1866.] fol. **h. 849. (8.)**

LED

— Led Astray. Ballad. *See* VIOLETTA.

— Led by a Father's gentle hand. [Hymn.] *See* REECE (L.)

— Led into Light. Song. *See* BUCALOSSI (P.)

— Led on. [Sacred song.] *See* BRACKETT (F. H.)

LÉDA

— Léda. Cantatille. *See* MOURET (J. J.)

LEDBETTER (Huddie)

— Leadbelly. A collection of ... songs by H. Ledbetter. Edited by John A. Lomax and Alan Lomax. Hally Wood, music editor. Special note on Leadbelly's 12-string guitar by Pete Seeger. pp. 80. *Folkways Music Publishers: New York*, [1959.] 8°.
D. 836. dd. (1.)

— [Another copy.]
A microfilm.
Mic. A. 1748. (2.)

— The Leadbelly Songbook. (The ballads, blues and folksongs of Huddie Ledbetter.) Edited by Moses Asch and Alan Lomax. [Melodies only.] pp. 96. *Oak Publications: New York*, [1962.] 8°.
A microfilm.
Mic. A. 1748. (3.)

— The Leadbelly Legend. A collection of world-famous songs by H. Ledbetter. Edited by John A. Lomax and Alan Lomax. Hally Wood, music editor. Special note on Leadbelly's 12-string guitar by Pete Seeger. (Revised and augmented edition.) pp. 96. *Folkways Music Publishers: New York*, [1965.] 8°.
D. 836. n. (5.)

— 43 Huddie Ledbetter Songs, including all the songs from the Paramount picture Leadbelly. [With portraits.] pp. 128. *Folkways Music: New York*, [1976.] 4°. **G. 1277. o. (2.)**

LEDBETTER (Steven)

— *See* MARENZIO (Luca) The Secular Works. Edited by S. Ledbetter and P. Myers, *etc.* 1977, *etc.* 4°. **F. 1953. b.**

LEDDOU (G. F. H.)

— High Pressure galop. [P. F.] *London*, [1874.] 8°. *No. 166 of the "Alliance Musicale. Album Bijou".* **f. 406.**

LEDEČ (Jan)

— *See* JANÁČEK (L.) Vlči stopa, *etc.* (Ženský sbor s průvodem klavíru. K vydáni připravil J. Ledeč.) [1968.] 8°.
G. 1087. j. (3.)

LEDERER (Charles I.)

— Barcarolle. Song, English words by E. W. Bryant, German words and music by C. I. Lederer. 2 no. [In F and E flat.] *E. Ascherberg & Co.: London*, 1905. fol. **H. 1794. k. (56.)**

— Charm me, once more. Song, words by P. Robinson. *Ascherberg, Hopwood & Crew: London*, 1907. fol.
H. 1794. vv. (24.)

— Love's Measure.—Masslose Liebe.—[Song.] English words by P. Pinkerton, German words and music by C. I. Lederer. 2 no. [In C and E flat.] *E. Ascherberg & Co.: London*, 1905. fol. **H. 1794. k. (57.)**

— Four Lyrics with English & German words. [No. 1. Love's Greeting.—Liebes-Gruss.—German words by Schlosser. English version by P. Pinkerton. No. 2. The Clown's Serenade ... German words ... by C. I. Lederer. English words by E. W. Bryant. No. 3. Sadness.—Wehmuth.— German words after T. Koerner. English version by P. Pinkerton. No. 4. By the Fireside ... Am Kamine ... German words from H. Heine's Auto-da-fè. English version by P. Pinkerton.] 2 no. [In E flat and G.] *E. Ascherberg & Co.: London*, 1905 (1906). fol. **H. 1794. k. (58.)**

LEDERER (Dezsö)

— Berceuse Slave, pour Violon et Piano. *Laudy & Co.: London*, (1908.) fol. **g. 505. w. (29.)**

— Kuiawiak, pour Violon et Piano. *Laudy & Co.: London*, (1908.) fol. **g. 505. w. (30.)**

— Deuxième Mazurka, pour Violon avec Accompagnement de Piano. *Enoch & Cie.: Paris*, 1907. fol. **h. 1612. p. (22.)**

— Mélodie pour Violon et Piano. [*Paris*,] 1903. 8°. *Supplement to "L'Illustration," No.* 3132. **P. P. 4283. m. (3.)**

— Minuetto, pour Violon avec Accompagnement de Piano. *Enoch & Cie.: Paris*, 1907. fol. **h. 1612. p. (23.)**

— Six Morceaux très facile ... pour piano et violon. (Op. 101.) 1. Barcarolle ... 2. 2me Berceuse ... 3. Cavatine ... 4. Petite marche ... 5. Rêve d'enfant ... 6. Romance, *etc.* 6 no. *J. Williams: London*, 1917. fol. **h. 1612. hh. (7.)**

— Pensée joyeuse ... pour violon avec accompagnement de piano. Op. 95. *J. Williams: London*, 1914. fol.
h. 1612. hh. (8.)

— 2 poèmes hongrois pour violon avec accompagnement de piano (ou d'orchestre) ... Op. 16. [Score and part.] no. 2. *Enoch & c^ie: Paris*, [1899.] fol. *Imperfect; wanting no.* 1. **H. 1860. ee. (3.)**

LEDERER (George W.)

— The Lily's Promenade. [Song.] Words by Ernest Hanegan. pp. 2–5. *Jos. W. Stern & Co.: [New York*, 1903.] fol. *Pp. 3 and 4 have been misimposed.* **H. 3985. q. (1.)**

LEDERER (George W.)

— My little Child. Lullaby, words by S. Rosenfeld.
M. Witmark & Sons: New York, 1894. fol.　　**H. 1798. u. (38.)**

— Some beautiful Day. [Song.] Lyrics by George V. Hobart.
pp. 4.　*Jos. W. Stern & Co.:* [*New York*, 1903.] fol.
H. 3985. q. (2.)

— The Wild Rose. *See* Jerome (B. M.) The Wild Rose. Selection
for Piano on the ... Songs from G. W. Lederer's Musical
Gaiety, *etc.*　1902. fol.　　**h. 3282. jj. (38.)**

LEDERER (Joseph)

— Apparatus musicus, oder: Musikalischer Vorrath, enthaltend
18. Verse, 17. Präambulen, Menuet, Trio, 3. Sonaten, eine Art
von Rondeau mit 5. Variationen, eine Cantate in Partitur von
Canto Solo, Violin Solo, Orgel Solo, und Violoncello, *etc.*
pp. 40.　*Johann Jakob Lotter: Augsburg*, 1781. fol.
Hirsch III. 358.

— Fünf Vespern samt fünf andern Psalmen ... einem besondern
Magnificat, und einem Stabat Mater ... bestehend in
Discant, Alt, Tenor, Bass, zweyen Violinen, zweyen
Waldhörnern, Orgel und Violone, *etc.* 10 pt.　*Zu finden bey
dem Author: Ulm*, 1780. fol.　　**H. 3160. a.**

— Fünf Vespern ... Zwote Auflage. 10 pt.　*Bey J. J. Lotter und
Sohn: Augsburg*, 1789. fol.　　**H. 3160.**

LEDERER (R.)

— Ausgewählte Werke ... J. Staden, *etc.* (Zweiter Teil ...
Ausarbeitung des Basso Continuo von R. Lederer.) 1907. *See*
Denkmaeler. Denkmäler deutscher Tonkunst. Zweite Folge.
Denkmäler der Tonkunst in Bayern, *etc.* Achter Jahrgang. I.
Band. 1900, *etc.* fol.　　**H. 993. a.**

LEDERER (Victor)

— Ueber Heimat und Ursprung der mehrstimmigen Tonkunst.
Ein Beitrag zür Musik- und Allgemeinen Kulturgeschichte
des Mittelalters. Vorrede: Keltische Renaissance. (Erster
Band.) pp. xiv. 429.　*C. F. W. Siegel: Leipzig*, 1906. 8°.
7899. k. 45.

LEDESMA (Dámaso)

— Folk-Lore ó Cancionero Salmantino, *etc.* pp. 261.　*Imprenta
Alemana: Madrid*, 1907. fol.　　**G. 1013.**

— [Another copy.]　　**G. 1013. a.**

LEDESMA (Mariano Rodriguez de)

— Amo te solo. Notturno for two voices; the poetry from
Metastasio.　*London*, [1826.] fol.　　**H. 1675. (17.)**

— Seis canciones españolas con accompañamiento de
pianoforte ó harpa ... por M. de L. [i. e. M. R. de Ledesma.]
Sechs spanische Lieder, *etc.* Span. & Ger. pp. 21.　[c. 1810.]
obl. fol. *See* L., M. de.　　**E. 270. l. (2.)**

— Ch' io mai vi possa. Arietta; the poetry from Metastasio.
London, [1826.] fol.　　**H. 1675. (13.)**

— Da quel sembiante. Arietta; the poetry from Metastasio.
London, [1826.] fol.　　**H. 1675. (15.)**

— Dov'è il mio bene. Terzetto.　*London*, [1825?] fol.
G. 806. c. (16.)

— In te spero. Arietta; the poetry from Metastasio.　*London*,
[1826.] fol.　　**H. 1675. (18.)**

— Three Italian Ariettes, with an accompaniment for Spanish
guitar, and piano forte, *etc.* pp. 12.　*Monzani & Hill: London*,
[c. 1815.] fol.　　**H. 1860. ss. (5.)**

LEDESMA (Mariano Rodriguez de)

— Three Italian arietts ... Set 3ʳᵈ.　*London*, [1815?] fol.
G. 805. p. (2.)

— Three Italian notturnos, for two voices.　*London*, [1830.] fol.
H. 1675. (10.)

— Martial Divertimento, for piano forte & flute. [Score and
part.] 2 pt.　*Monzani & Hill:* [*London*, c. 1815.] fol.
h. 250. w. (5.)

— La Nebbia. Canzonetta.　*London*, [1815?] fol.
G. 809. b. (5.)

— El Pescador. Der Fischer. [Song, with guitar and P. F.
accompaniment.] *Span. & Ger.* [*Breitkopf und Haertel:
Leipzig*, 1814.] 4°.
[*Beylage zur Allgemeinen musikalischen Zeitung. Jahrg.* 16.
no. 4.]　　**P. P. 1945.**

— Più non si trovano. Arietta; the poetry from Metastasio.
London, [1826.] fol.　　**H. 1675. (14.)**

— Principes persecuti sunt. Salmo 3° de Nona (à 4 voces con
accompañamiento de orquesta). *See* Eslava (M. H.) Lira
Sacro Hispana, *etc.* Sigl. xix. Ser. 1ª. Tom. 2°. [1869.] fol.
H. 4.

— Se mai turbo il tuo riposo. Canzonetta; the poetry from
Metastasio.　*London*, [1826.] fol.　　**H. 1675. (16.)**

— Tardi s'avvede. Arietta; the poetry from Metastasio.
London, [1826.] fol.　　**H. 1675. (12.)**

— Trova un sol. Canzonetta; the poetry from Metastasio.
London, [1826.] fol.　　**H. 1675. (11.)**

— Trova un sol mia bella Clori, canzonetta, the poetry from
Metastasio. pp. 3.　*R. Mills: London*, [c. 1855.] fol.
H. 345. k. (25.)

— Vorrei di te fidarmi, arietta with an accompaniment for the
piano forte.　*London*, [1850?] fol.　　**H. 2827. f. (22.)**

LEDESMA (Nicolas)

— Stabat Mater à tres voces con accompanamiento de cuarteto,
etc. See Eslava (M. H.) Lira Sacro-Hispana, *etc.* Sigl. xix.
Ser. 1ª. Tom. 2°. [1869.] fol.　　**H. 4.**

LEDGE

— The Ledge. Opera. *See* Bennett (Richard R.)

LEDGER (Philip Stevens)

— Twenty-four Anthems for sopranos and altos (three or more
parts). Edited by Philip Ledger. pp. 99.　*Oxford University
Press: London*, [1973.] 8°.
[*Anthems for Choirs.* 3.]　　**D. 684. i.**

— Twenty-four Anthems for sopranos & altos (unison and
two-part). Edited by Philip Ledger. pp. 107.　*Oxford
University Press: London*, [1973.] 8°.
[*Anthems for Choirs.* 2.]　　**D. 684. i.**

— Two Carols. Arranged by Philip Ledger. [Mixed chorus and
organ.] 1. Silent Night. (Unaccompanied.) 2. On Christmas
Night. (Accompanied.) pp. 11.　*Oxford University Press:
London*, [1978.] 8°.
[*Oxford choral Songs.* X265.]　　**F. 1777. m.**

— Three Carols for Christmas. Arranged for mixed voices by
Philip Ledger. I saw three Ships. ⟨English traditional carol.⟩
Unaccompanied. Away in a Manger. ⟨Words anon. Tune by
W. J. Kirkpatrick.⟩ Unaccompanied. Come leave your Sheep.
⟨French traditional carol.⟩ Accompanied. pp. 12.　*Oxford
University Press: London*, [1976.] 8°.　　**F. 1892. e. (14.)**

LEDGER (Philip Stevens)

— Six Carols with Descants. Arranged by Philip Ledger. For mixed voices and organ. pp. 16. *Oxford University Press: London*, [1975.] 8°.   **E. 460. pp. (11.)**

— Chester Carol. (Qui creavit coelum.) ⟨S. A. T. B. [and organ.]⟩ Chester MS., c. 1425. Translated, adapted, and arranged by Philip Ledger. pp. 3. *Oxford University Press: London*, [1976.] 8°.
[*Oxford choral Songs. X*261.]   **F. 1777. m.**

— I will lift up mine Eyes. [Words] from Psalm 121. ⟨S. A. T. B.⟩ pp. 3. *Oxford University Press: London*, [1963.] 8°.
[*Oxford Anthems. A*192.]   **F. 1776.**

— The Oxford Book of English Madrigals. Edited by Philip Ledger. pp. 403. *Oxford University Press: London*, [1978.] 8°.   **D. 227. a.**

— The Oxford Book of English Madrigals. Edited by Philip Ledger ⟨[with] Andrew Parker⟩. pp. 403. *Oxford University Press: London*, [1978.] 8°.   **D. 227. b.**

— *See* Byrd (William) [*Smaller Collections.*] Prelude, Fantasia, Miserere (1) and (2), Gloria tibi trinitas, Ut re mee fa sol la, Veni creator spiritus (1) and (2). Edited by P. Ledger. [1968.] *obl.* 4°. [*Tallis to Wesley. no.* 8.]   **e. 1093. gg.**

— *See* Jackson (Francis A.) Anthems for Choirs ... Edited by F. Jackson ⟨P. Ledger⟩. [1973, *etc.*] 8°.   **D. 684. i.**

— *See* Purcell (Henry) [Beati omnes qui timent Dominum.] How blest are they ... Wedding anthem for mixed voices and soprano and bass soli with organ ... Realized ... by P. Ledger and Imogen Holst. [1968.] 8°. [*Oxford Anthems. A*245.]   **F. 1176.**

— *See* Purcell (Henry) The Fairy Queen ... Harpsichord part realized by P. Ledger, *etc.* 1970. 4°.   **F. 659. n. (1.)**

— *See* Purcell (Henry) King Arthur. An entirely new version ... realised by P. Ledger, *etc.* ⟨Vocal score.⟩ [1974.] 4°.   **G. 103. r.**

— *See* Purcell (Henry) King Arthur. An entirely new version ... realised by P. Ledger, *etc.* ⟨Chorus part.⟩ [1974.] 4°.   **F. 659. r. (1.)**

— *See* Warlike. Warlike Musick ... Marches and trumpet tunes for flute, or oboe, or violin, and basso continuo. Edited by P. Ledger, *etc.* [1974.] 4°.   **g. 270. mm. (6.)**

LE DHUY (Adolphe)

— Nocturne Espagnol brillant composé pour la Guitare. *Paris*, [1835?] fol.   **h. 259. c. (13.)**

— Petite fantaisie pour la guitarre sur l'air "Happy land". [Composed by E. F. Rimbault.] *London*, [1847.] fol.   **h. 139. (16.)**

— Va pensiero. Romance de l'opéra de Nino [by F. G. F. Verdi] arrangée pour guitarre et Piano par A. le Dhuy. *London*, [1847.] fol.   **h. 139. (17.)**

LEDI

— Леди Макбет Мценского уезда. Опера. *See* Shostakovich (D. D.)

LEDIA

— Ledia. Opera séria. *See* Zubiaurre (V.)

LEDINGHAM (W.)

— *See* Archibald (J.) O bonnie blooms the Whin ootbye Strathlene ... Arranged by W. Ledingham. [1914.] fol.   **H. 1792. mm. (1.)**

LEDINGTON (Stanley)

— Let all the World. Anthem for S. A. T. B. [Words by] George Herbert. pp. 4. *H. W. Gray Co.: New York*, [1959.] 8°.   **E. 335. x. (29.)**

LEDLIE (James C.)

— When does the spring seem sweetest. (Desiderium.) Song, words by M. Le B. Kennedy. *London*, [1882.] fol.   **H. 1787. j. (24.)**

LE DOUX (   )

— L'Esperance. [Contre danse. For two violins.] *Chez Frère: [Paris*, 1800?] 8°.   **b. 40. (22.)**

— Le Nauffrage. [Contre danse. For two violins.] *Chez Frère: [Paris*, 1800?] 8°.   **b. 40. (23.)**

— La Sara. [Contre danse. For two violins.] *Chez Frère: [Paris*, 1800?] 8°.   **b. 40. (24.)**

— La Sevère. [Contre danse. For two violins.] *Chez Frère: [Paris*, 1800?] 8°.   **b. 40. (25.)**

LEDSAM (John)

— The Fuzileers Quadrilles ... as performed by the band of the Royal Fuzileers ... To which is added the favorite waltz of Le Petit chaperon rouge. Arranged for the piano forte by John Ledsam. pp. 9. *Penson & Robertson: Edinburgh*, [WM 1820.] fol.   **h. 2605. ii. (13.)**

LEDSHAM (Emma Scarr)

— The Dying Flag Bearer. [Song, begins: "Comrade, do not move me".] *Cleveland* [*Ohio*, 1864.] fol.   **H. 1780. f. (12.)**

LEDSHAM (James Boardman)

— Ledsham's Code Tonic Sol-fa Time and Tune Tests, *etc.* [1894.] 8°. *See* Speight (C.)   **C. 1269. (3.)**

LEDSHAM (Samuel)

— Hear the Word of the Lord. Anthem, *etc. Weekes & Co.: London*, [1896.] 8°.   **E. 602. l. (32.)**

LEDUC (Alphonse)

— Twelve Drawing Room Pieces for the Pianoforte, by ... Leduc, *etc. See* Boosey and Co. Boosey's Musical Cabinet. No. 11. [1861, *etc.*] 4°.   **F. 160.**

— A. S. A. R. Marie Henriette Duchesse de Brabant, Valse brillante pour Piano. *Paris*, [1858.] fol.   **h. 912. (18.)**

— À son Altesse Royale Henriette, Duchesse de Brabant. Valse brillante. ⟨Pour piano.⟩ pp. 7. *Robert Cocks & Cᵒ: London*, [1858.] fol.   **h. 61. qq. (7.)**

— À son Altesse Royale Henriette, Duchesse de Brabant, Valse brillante pour Piano. *London*, [1858.] fol.   **h. 912. (16.)**

— À son altesse royale Henriette Duchesse de Brabant, valse brillante [as a duet] pour piano. *London*, [1858.] fol.   **h. 912. (17.)**

— Les abeilles, 3 petites fantaisies pour piano. Op. 157. 3 no. *London*, [1856.] fol.   **h. 619. (31.)**

— Les abeilles, 3 petites fantaisies pour piano. Op. 157. 3 no. *Paris*, [1856.] fol.   **h. 616. (16.)**

— Adélaïde-Victoria d'Angleterre. Valse brillante pour le Piano. *Paris*, [1859.] fol.   **h. 619. e. (3.)**

LEDUC (ALPHONSE)

— Adelaïde Victoria, Princesse Royale de Prusse. Valse brillante pour piano. (No. 1 easy edition.) *London*, [1860.] fol.
h. 912. (10.)

— Adelaïde-Victoria, Princesse Royale de Prussia. Valse brillante pour piano. (No. 2, brilliant edition.) *London*, [1860.] fol.
h. 912. (11.)

— Adelaïde-Victoria, Princesse Royale de Prusse. Valse brillante pour piano. (No. 3 Duett.) *London*, [1860.] fol.
h. 912. (13.)

— Adieu, bords chéris de la Seine. Fantaisie. *See* infra: 2 Fantaisies élégantes sur deux Romances de F. Bérat. Op. 186. No. 1.

— L'Adieu de F. Schubert, pour le Piano. *See* infra: Deux Mélodies, *etc.* No. 2.

— Agnès Sorel. Quadrille historique pour le Piano. pp. 5. *Chez T. Boosey: London*, [1848.] fol.
h. 947. (43.)

— Agnès Sorel. Quadrille historique. [P. F.] pp. 5. *D'Almaine & Co.: London*, [1850.] fol.
h. 947. (42.)

— Agnes-Sorel, quadrille historique pour le piano. pp. 5. *Leoni Lee & Coxhead: London*, [1851.] fol.
h. 964. (12.)

— Agnès Sorel. Quadrille historique pour le piano, *etc.* pp. 5. *D'Almaine & Cᵒ: London*, [1854.] fol.
h. 722. t. (11.)

— Agnès Sorel, quadrille historique, pour le piano. pp. 5. *Leader & Cock: London*, [1854.] fol.
h. 617. (27.)

— Agnes Sorel quadrille historique. [P. F.] *London*, [1855.] fol. *No. 213 of the "Musical Bouquet".*
H. 2345.

— Agnès Sorel, quadrille historique, pour le piano. pp. 5. *J. Lawson: London*, [c. 1855.] fol.
h. 723. ll. (16.)

— Agnès Sorel. Quadrille historique pour le Piano. pp. 5. *W. Williams & Co.: London*, [1861.] fol.
h. 619. c. (27.)

— Agnes Sorel quadrille. [P. F.] *George Bell: Leeds*, [1871.] fol.
h. 1485. s. (40.)

— Agnes Sorel quadrille. [P. F.] *London*, [1879.] fol. *No. 315 of C. Boosey's "Universal" music.*
H. 2324.

— Agnes Sorel quadrille, edited by R. Sestini. *Alphonse Bertini: London*, [1880.] fol.
h. 1494. p. (39.)

— Agnes Sorel. Quadrille. [P. F.] *Rivière & Hawkes: London*, [1887.] fol.
h. 975. u. (57.)

— Agnes Sorel. Quadrille historique, pour le piano. pp. 5. *F. Pitman Hart & Cᵒ: London*, [c. 1890.] fol. h. 3870. hh. (1.)

— Agnes Sorel Quadrilles. [P. F.] *E. Donajowski: London*, [1898.] fol. *Popular Dance Music, etc. No. 47.*
h. 3299. a.

— Agnès Sorel, quadrille pour le piano. [Duet.] pp. 11. *D'Almaine & Co.: London*, [1850.] fol.
h. 964. (27.)

— Agnès Sorel, quadrille, arranged for two performers on the piano forte by A. Schubert. pp. 11. *Leoni Lee & Coxhead: London*, [1851.] fol.
h. 969. (21.)

— Agnès Sorel. Quadrille historique pour le Piano. [Duet.] pp. 11. *W. Williams & Co.: London*, [1861.] fol.
h. 619. c. (26.)

— Agnes Sorel. Quadrille. Arrᵈ. by S. V. Balfour. [Orchestral parts.] *Rivière & Hawkes: London*, [1887.] 8°. e. 370. g. (2.)

— Agnes Sorel. Quadrille ... Arrᵈ. by J. Hartmann. [Reed band parts.] *Rivière & Hawkes: London*, [1887.] 8°.
e. 372. e. (18.)

— Aimez-moi, Valse brillante, pour le Piano. *London*, [1857.] fol.
h. 912. (1.)

LEDUC (ALPHONSE)

— Aladin, ou la Lampe Merveilleuse. Quadrille brillant sur des motifs de A. Pilati. [P. F. with accompaniments for violin, cornet and flute.] *Paris*, [1864.] *obl.* fol.
e. 290. (16.)

— L'Albanaise, schottisch, pour le piano, *etc. London*, [1858.] fol.
h. 913. (22.)

— L'Albanaise, Schottisch, pour le Piano. *Paris*, [1858.] fol.
h. 913. (21.)

— Alexandrowna. Valse brillante pour Piano. *London*, [1865.] fol.
h. 619. d. (22.)

— Alexandrowna de Russie. Valse brillante pour le Piano. *Paris*, [1865.] fol.
h. 619. e. (36.)

— L'Allégresse. Valse brillante. [P. F.] *London*, [1862.] fol.
h. 619. c. (47.)

— L'Allégresse. Valse brillante. [P. F.] *Paris*, [1862.] fol.
h. 619. e. (16.)

— L'Allemande, fantaisie pour Piano. Op. 85. *Paris*, [1840?] fol.
g. 270. d. (28.)

— Allons prier! Duettino [begins: "La nuit"], paroles de J. B. Vasseur. *Paris*, [1867.] fol.
H. 2623. a. (29.)

— [Allons prier.] The Hour of Prayer, vocal duet [begins: "The moon has lit"], the poetry by W. Hills. *London*, [1868.] fol.
H. 2623. (16.)

— L'Américaine. [Fantasia for P. F. on "Yankee Doodle".] *See* infra: 3 Petites Fantaisies. Op. 184. No. 2.

— L'Amitié et L'Amour. Variations concertante pour le Piano à quatre mains. Op. 60. *London*, [1849.] fol.
h. 715. (27.)

— L'Andalouse, Varsoviana pour piano. *London*, [1856.] fol.
h. 913. (25.)

— L'Andalouse, Varsoviana pour le piano. *Paris*, [1856.] fol.
h. 913. (26.)

— Anna Bolena, Opéra de G. Donizetti, fantaisie pour Piano ... Op. 204. *A. Leduc: Paris*, [1872.] fol. h. 619. f. (11.)

— The Aquarium, *etc. London*, [1867.] fol. h. 619. d. (33.)

— L'Aquarium. Six bluettes musicales pour Piano. Op. 199. *Paris*, [1867.] fol.
h. 619. e. (55.)

— L'Arabesque des jeunes élèves. Fantaisie gracieuse sur une thême Arabe, pour piano. *London*, [1853.] fol. h. 617. (4.)

— L'Arlésienne. Polka Mazurka ... pour le Piano. *London*, [1867.] fol.
h. 619. d. (34.)

— Aurora. Fantaisie sur une Valse de Labitzki. *See* infra: Trois petites Fantaisies élégantes. Op. 190. No. 1.

— L'Aurore d'un beau jour, fantaisie pastorale pour piano. *Paris*, [1855.] fol.
h. 616. (1.)

— L'aurore d'un beau jour, fantaisie pastorale pour piano. *London*, [1855.] fol.
h. 619. (2.)

— Bagatelle sur [l']opéra comique de L. Clapisson "Les trois Nicolas," pour piano, *etc. London*, [1859.] fol.
h. 619. a. (22.)

— Bagatelle sur les Trois Nicolas, opéra comique de L. Clapisson pour Piano. *Paris*, [1859.] fol. h. 619. b. (13.)

— 4 Bagatelles ... pour piano [on the operas, "Les Huguenots", "La Favorite", "Robert le Diable" and "Guillaume Tell"]. *Paris*, [1854.] fol.
h. 618. (1.)

— Le Baise Main. Quadrille élégant pour le Piano. [With accompaniments for violin, cornet and flute.] *Paris*, [1867.] *obl.* fol.
e. 290. (19.)

LEDUC (ALPHONSE)

— Un bal à la cour, quadrille brillant pour piano [with accompaniment for cornet]. *London*, [1856.] fol.
h. 619. (13.)

— Un bal à la cour, quadrille pour le piano. [With accompaniments for violin, cornet and flute.] *Paris*, [1856.] fol.
e. 38. (13.)

— Un bal chez Grand'maman, quadrille mignon pour piano. *London*, [1856.] fol.
h. 911. (1.)

— Un bal chez grand'maman, quadrille mignon pour le piano. [With violin, flute, and cornet accompaniment.] *Paris*, [1856.] fol.
e. 70. (2.)

— Le Bananier. Quadrille Créole sur les motifs de L. M. Gottschalk … pour Piano. *London*, [1860.] fol.
h. 619. c. (23.)

— Le Bananier. Quadrille Créole (sur un motif) de L. M. Gottschalk. Orchestré de L. Waldteufel. *Paris*, [1859.] *obl.* fol.
e. 70. (16.)

— Barbe-bleue. Quadrille historique pour le Piano Forte [as a solo and duet]. *London*, [1844.] fol.
h. 932. (31.)

— [Barbe-bleue.] The Blue Beard Quadrille. [P. F.] *Musical Bouquet Office: London*, [1854?] fol.
[*Musical Bouquet. no.* 335.]
H. 2345. a.

— [Barbe-bleue.] The Bluebeard quadrille. [P. F.] *London*, [1855.] fol.
No. 335 *of the "Musical Bouquet".*
H. 2345.

— Barcarolle. Op. 195. *See* infra: Les Pâquerettes. No. 3.

— Barcarolle. Op. 199. No. 6. *See* supra: L'Aquarium. No. 6.

— [La Bataille d'Austerlitz.] The battle of Austerlitz quadrille. [P. F.] *London*, [1855.] fol.
No. 357 *of the "Musical Bouquet".*
H. 2345.

— La Bataille d'Austerlitz, quadrille historique [arranged for reed band by] P. Clodomir. *Paris*, [1882.] 8°.
e. 372. a. (3.)

— La bataille d'Inkermann, quadrille pour le piano [with accompaniments for flute, violin and cornet]. *Paris*, [1854.] *obl.* fol.
e. 38. (16.)

— La bataille d'Jéna, quadrille historique pour le piano. *London*, [1853.] fol.
h. 964. (14.)

— Bataille de Friedland, quadrille historique pour le piano. *London*, [1853.] fol.
h. 617. (28.)

— Bataille de la Tchernaia, quadrille. [P. F.] *London*, [1855.] fol.
h. 619. (9.)

— Bataille de la Tchernaia, quadrille. [P. F. with accompaniments.] *Paris*, [1855.] *obl.* fol.
e. 38. (17.)

— Bataille de Magenta, quadrille historique et militaire … pour le piano, *etc.* [Solo.] *London*, [1859.] fol.
h. 911. (2.)

— Bataille de Magenta, quadrille historique … pour le piano. *Paris*, [1859.] fol.
e. 70. (24.)

— Bataille de Magenta, quadrille … pour le piano. [Duet.] *London*, [1859.] fol.
h. 911. (3.)

— Bataille de Marengo, quadrille historique, pour piano. *London*, [1851.] fol.
h. 964. (11.)

— Bataille de Marignan. Quadrille. *See* infra: Melegnano.

— Bataille de Montebello, quadrille historique … pour le piano. *Paris*, [1859.] fol.
e. 70. (26.)

— Bataille de Montebello … quadrille historique … pour le piano, *etc.* [Solo.] *London*, [1859.] fol.
h. 911. (4.)

LEDUC (ALPHONSE)

— Bataille de Montebello … quadrille … pour le piano. [Duet.] *London*, [1859.] fol.
h. 911. (5.)

— Bataille de Palestro. Quadrille. *See* infra: Palestro.

— Bataille de Solferino, quadrille historique et militaire … pour le piano, *etc.* [Solo.] *London*, [1859.] fol.
h. 911. (6.)

— Bataille de Solferino. Quadrille historique et militaire. [P. F. with accompaniments for flute, violin, cornet and bass.] *Paris*, [1859.] *obl.* fol.
e. 70. (28.)

— Bataille de Solferino, quadrille … pour le piano. [Duet.] *London*, [1859.] fol.
h. 911. (7.)

— Bataille de Wagram, quadrille historique pour piano. *London*, [1851.] fol.
h. 964. (8.)

— La Bavarde, chansonnette [begins: "Ma mère"], paroles de T. Julian. *Paris*, [1868.] fol.
H. 2623. a. (33.)

— La Belle de Mai et le Seigneur. Romance [begins: "Que demandez vous"], paroles de T. Julian. *Paris*, [1867.] fol.
H. 2623. a. (31.)

— La belle Gabrielle, polka mazurka. [P. F.] *London*, [1858.] fol.
h. 913. (1.)

— La belle Gabrielle, polka mazurka … pour le piano. *Paris*, [1859.] fol.
h. 913. (2.)

— Le Berger, chansonnette [begins: "Je suis berger"] … Paroles de T. Julian. *Paris*, [1867.] fol.
H. 2623. a. (32.)

— Bienfait porte Bonheur, romance [begins: "Un soir"], paroles d'H. Guérin. *Paris*, [1866.] fol.
H. 2623. a. (17.)

— Le bijou perdu. Quadrille sur des motifs d'A. Adam, pour le Piano. *London*, [1857.] fol.
h. 911. (8.)

— Le bijou perdu, Polka-Mazurka [on A. C. Adam's opera]. [P. F.] *Paris*, [1857.] fol.
h. 917. (3.)

— Le Bivouac. Petite Fantaisie militaire, pour Piano. *London*, [1865.] fol.
h. 619. d. (23.)

— Le Bivouac. Mélodie de Kücken. Petite Fantaisie militaire pour Piano. *Paris*, [1865.] fol.
h. 619. e. (41.)

— Blondinette. *See* infra: La Faneuse.

— The Blue Beard quadrille. *See* supra: [Barbe-bleue.]

— Les bluets, valse pour le piano. *London*, [1852.] fol.
h. 964. (26.)

— Bolero Espagnol, Fantaisie pour Piano. *London*, [1860.] fol.
h. 619. a. (13.)

— Bonaparte en Egypte, quadrille historique pour le piano. No. 1 solo, No. 2 duet. 2 no. *London*, [1852.] fol.
h. 964. (22.)

— Les Bords de la Marne. Valse gracieuse pour le Piano. *Paris*, [1863.] fol.
h. 619. e. (18.)

— Les bords de la Meuse, Valse gracieuse, pour le Piano. *Paris*, [1858.] fol.
h. 912. (2.)

— Les bords de la Meuse. Valse gracieuse, pour le Piano. *London*, [1858.] fol.
h. 912. (3.)

— Les bords de la Neva, valse brillante, pour piano. *London*, [1854.] fol.
h. 617. (36.)

— Les bords du Cher, valse brillante pour piano. *London*, [1853.] fol.
h. 964. (17.)

— Les bords du Loiret, valse élégante, pour le piano. *London*, [1853.] fol.
h. 617. (42.)

— Les bords du Rhin, polka pour le piano. *London*, [1853.] fol.
h. 964. (20.)

LEDUC (Alphonse)

— Les bords du Rhone, fantaisie valse, pour le piano. Op. 119. *London*, [1854.] fol. **h. 618. (7.)**

— La Bouquetière de Marly, chansonnette [begins: "Fleurissez vous"], paroles de T. Julian. *Paris*, [1865.] fol. **H. 2623. a. (2.)**

— [La Bouquetière de Marly.] The Village Flower Girl, song [begins: "Young men"] written by G. Linley. *London*, [1865.] fol. **H. 2623. (7.)**

— La Bouquetière de Marly ... pour le Piano. [1864.] fol. *See* WOHLFAHRT (H.) **h. 3245. (5.)**

— Brises des Alpes. 6 petites fantaisies, pour le Piano. Op. 153. 6 no. *London*, [1853.] fol. **h. 618. (13.)**

— Le camp de Châlons, Quadrille militaire. [P. F.] *London*, [1857.] fol. **h. 911. (9.)**

— Le camp de Châlons, Quadrille militaire. [P. F.] *Paris*, [1857.] fol. **e. 70. (29.)**

— Le camp du drab d'or, quadrille, chevaleresque, pour le piano. *London*, [1851.] fol. **h. 964. (10.)**

— The Camptown Races. Fantasia ... on ... melodies of the Christy Minstrels, for the Pianoforte. *London*, [1860.] fol. **h. 619. c. (4.)**

— The Camptown Races. Fantasia ... for the Pianoforte. *Paris*, [1860.] fol. **h. 619. c. (13.)**

— Le Captif Délivré, romance [begins: "Petit oiseau"], paroles de V. Déo. *Paris*, [1865.] fol. **H. 2623. a. (3.)**

— [Le Captif délivré.] Come sing with me, song [begins: "Tell me"] written by W. Hills. *London*, [1868.] fol. **H. 2623. (4.)**

— Le Carillonneur de Vendôme, chansonnette [begins: "Orléans"], paroles de T. Julian. *Paris*, [1867.] fol. **H. 2623. a. (27.)**

— Le Carnaval de Venise, fantaisie brillante pour piano. *London*, [1854.] fol. **h. 617. (3.)**

— Le Carnaval de Venise, fantaisie brillante pour piano. *Paris*, [1855.] fol. **h. 616. (2.)**

— La Castillanne. Valse espagnole, pour le piano. *London*, [1852.] fol. **h. 617. (40.)**

— Cecilia, valse mignonne pour le piano. *London*, [1853.] fol. **h. 964. (19.)**

— Les Cerises, valse brillante ... pour le Piano. *See* BURLINGTON. The Burlington Album, 1863. No. 6. [1862.] fol. **h. 1240.**

— Chanson Espagnole. *See* supra: L'Aquarium. No. 5.

— Chanson Montagnarde. *See* supra: L'Aquarium No. 4.

— Charles-Quint. Quadrille historique pour Piano. [With accompaniments for violin, cornet and flute.] *Paris*, [1865.] *obl.* fol. **e. 290. (24.)**

— La Chasse. Morceau de genre pour le Piano. *See* infra: 2 Morceaux de genre. Op. 191. No. 1.

— La Chasse au Tigre. Quadrille brillant. [P. F., with accompaniments for violin, cornet and flute.] *Paris*, [1862.] fol. **e. 290. (8.)**

— [La Chasse au Tigre.] The Tiger Hunt, Quadrille for the Pianoforte. *London*, [1862.] fol. **h. 619. d. (4.)**

— La Chasse impériale, quadrille brillant pour piano. *London*, [1856.] fol. **h. 911. (10.)**

LEDUC (Alphonse)

— La chasse impériale, quadrille pour piano [with violin, flute and cornet accompaniments]. *Paris*, [1856.] fol. **e. 70. (17.)**

— Le chateau d'Asnières. Polka originale, pour le Piano. *London*, [1853.] fol. **h. 617. (16.)**

— Château d'Heidelberg. Polka brillante pour le Piano. *Paris*, [1863.] fol. **h. 619. e. (22.)**

— Le Château d'Heidelberg. Polka brillante. [P. F.] *London*, [1863.] fol. **h. 619. c. (38.)**

— Le Château de Blois, quadrille historique pour piano. *London*, [1858.] fol. **h. 911. (11.)**

— Le château de Blois, quadrille. [P. F. with accompaniments for cornet, violin, and flute.] *Paris*, [1859.] fol. **e. 70. (30.)**

— Le Château de Chantilly, quadrille pour piano. *London*, [1856.] fol. **h. 911. (12.)**

— Le château de Chantilly, quadrille pour le piano [with violin, flute, and cornet accompaniments]. *Paris*, [1856.] fol. **e. 70. (3.)**

— Le chateau de Compiègne, quadrille élégant pour le piano. *London*, [1854.] fol. **h. 617. (29.)**

— Le Chateau de Compiègne, quadrille pour le piano [with accompaniments]. *Paris*, [1855.] *obl.* fol. **e. 38. (18.)**

— Le chateau de Fontainebleau, quadrille pour le piano. *London*, [1851.] fol. **h. 964. (29.)**

— Le Château de Pierrefonds. Quadrille élégant pour piano. *Paris*, [1859.] *obl.* fol. **e. 70. (4.)**

— Le Château de Pierrefonds. Quadrille ... pour Piano. *London*, [1860.] fol. **h. 911. (40.)**

— Le Château de Rambouillet quadrille. [P. F.] *London*, [1855.] fol. *No. 337 of the "Musical Bouquet".* **H. 2345.**

— Le chateau de St. Cloud, quadrille pour le piano. [With accompaniment for cornet.] *London*, [1856.] fol. **h. 619. (14.)**

— Le chateau de St. Cloud, quadrille pour le piano. [With accompaniments for violin, cornet and flute.] *Paris*, [1856.] fol. **e. 38. (24.)**

— Le Château de St. Germain. Quadrille brillant pour le piano. *Paris*, [1860.] *obl.* fol. **e. 70. (18.)**

— Le Château de St. Germain. Quadrille brillant pour Piano. *London*, [1860.] fol. **h. 619. c. (24.)**

— Le Chateau de Versailles, quadrille élégant pour le piano [with an accompaniment for the cornet à pistons]. *London*, [1853.] fol. **h. 617. (25.)**

— Le chateau de Windsor, quadrille brillant pour le piano. *London*, [1853.] fol. **h. 964. (13.)**

La Châtelaine

— La chatelaine [by J. Rosenthal?, arranged as a] Fantaisie à la Valse pour le Piano. *London*, [1853.] fol. **h. 618. (4.)**

— La Châtelaine, fantaisie à la valse, pour piano. *Campbell, Ransford & Co.: London*, [1854.] fol. *Forming part of a collection entitled on the cover, "Campbell, Ransford and Co's series of admired works for the pianoforte".* **h. 1368. (5.)**

— La Chatelaine, fantaisie à la valse. [P. F.] *R. Addison & Co.: London*, [1855.] fol. **h. 619. (3.)**

— La Chatelaine. [Fantasia. P. F.] *Leoni Lee: London*, [1855.] fol. **h. 619. (4.)**

LEDUC (Alphonse)

— La Châtelaine, fantaisie à la valse. [P. F.] *London*, [1855.] fol.
No. 595, 596 of the "Musical Bouquet". **H. 2345.**

— La Châtelaine, fantaisie à la valse. [P. F.] pp. 7. *B. Williams: London*, [c. 1855.] fol. **h. 61. oo. (4.)**

— La Châtelaine, fantaisie à la valse. [P. F.] *W. Williams: [London, 1858.]* fol. **h. 619. b. (15.)**

— La Châtelaine. Fantaisie à la Valse, pour le Piano Forte. *Leader & Cock: London*, [1858.] fol. **h. 912. (4.)**

— La Châtelaine. Fantaisie à la valse. [P. F.] *Brewer & Co.: London*, [1859.] fol. **h. 619. c. (19.)**

— La Chatelaine, fantaisie à la valse pour piano. pp. 7. *Ashdown & Parry: London*, [c. 1865.] fol. **h. 3870. uu. (17.)**

— La Chatelaine. Fantaisie à la valse pour le Piano. *J. W. Trayhearne: London*, [1867.] fol. **h. 619. d. (30.)**

— La Châtelaine. Fantaisie à la valse. [P. F.] *George Bell: Leeds*, [1869.] fol. **h. 619. d. (41.)**

— La Chatelaine. Fantaisie à la valse, pour forte piano. ⟨Op. 139. New edition, revised and fingered by W. Vincent Wallace.⟩ pp. 7. *Robert Cocks & Cⁱ: London*, [c. 1870.] fol. [*W. Vincent Wallace's Edition of standard Piano Forte Works. no. 9.*] **h. 628. e.**

— La Châtelaine, pour Piano. *J. Bath: London*, [1873.] fol. **h. 1482. z. (9.)**

— La Châtelaine, fantaisie à la valse pour Piano. *Willey & Co.: London*, [1873.] fol. **h. 1482. z. (10.)**

— La Châtelaine, valse sentimentale. [P. F.] pp. 4. *Howard & Co.: London*, [1876.] fol. **h. 1482. z. (11.)**

— [Another edition.] La châtelaine, *etc.* pp. 5. *Howard & Co.: London*, [1876.] fol. **h. 1482. z. (12.)**

— La Chatelaine. Fantaisie à la valse. [P. F.] *A. Bertini: London*, [1879.] fol. **h. 1484. s. (30.)**

— La Châtelaine. [P. F.] *London*, [1879.] fol. *No. 320 of C. Boosey's "Universal" music.* **H. 2324.**

— La Châtelaine. For the Pianoforte. *W. Marshall & Co.: London*, [1880.] fol. **h. 1494. p. (40.)**

— La Châtelaine. Fantaisie à la valse pour le piano. pp. 9. *F. Amos & Cⁱ: London; Leipzig printed*, [1886?] fol. *Part of "The Oxford Edition".* **h. 61. pp. (3.)**

— La Châtelaine. Fantaisie à la valse. [P. F.] pp. 4. *W. Paxton: London*, [c. 1890.] fol. **h. 3870. uu. (16.)**

— La chatelaine [arranged for two performers, as a] fantaisie à la valse pour le piano par A. Leduc. *London*, [1854.] fol. **h. 618. (3.)**

— Fantaisie, La Chatelaine, arrangé à quatre mains par J. Rummel. *London*, [1855.] fol. **h. 523. (1.)**

— Fantaisie, la Châtelaine ... arrangé [P. F.] à quatre mains par J. Rummel. *London*, [1858.] fol. **h. 619. a. (19.)**

— La Châtelaine, arranged as a [P. F.] duet by E. F. Rimbault. *Chappell & Co.: London*, [1874.] fol. **h. 486. c. (9.)**

— La Châtelaine. Fantaisie à la valse. Arranged as a duet by P. Jackman. *R. Cocks & Co.: London*, [1894.] fol. **h. 3290. l. (26.)**

— Les Chauffeurs. Quadrille brillant pour Piano. [With accompaniments for violin, cornet and flute.] *Paris*, [1866.] *obl.* fol. **e. 290. (28.)**

— Chaume et Manoir, romance [begins: "Le petit chaume"], paroles d'H. Guérir. *Paris*, [1865.] fol. **H. 2623. a. (4.)**

LEDUC (Alphonse)

— Les Chevau-Légers. Quadrille brillant pour le Piano. [With accompaniments for violin, cornet and flute.] *Paris*, [1867.] *obl.* fol. **e. 290. (20.)**

— Les Chevaux de Bois. Quadrille mignon ... pour le Piano. [With accompaniments for violin, cornet and flute.] *Paris*, [1863.] *obl.* fol. **e. 290. (11.)**

— Les Chevaux de Bois, chansonnette [begins: "Entrez"], paroles de T. Julian. *Paris*, [1865.] fol. **H. 2623. a. (12.)**

— La Chevrière du Mont Aventin. Chanson tyrolienne [begins: "Je suis chevrière"], paroles de T. Julian. *Paris*, [1865.] fol. **H. 2623. a. (8.)**

— [La Chevrière du Mont Aventin.] The Mountain Queen, song [begins: "Not a care"] written by Mrs. W. Hills. *London*, [1865.] fol. **H. 2623. (10.)**

— La Chevrière du Mont Aventin. *See* DELASEURIE (A.) La Chevrière ... pour Piano. [1866.] fol. **h. 3021. a. (35.)**

— Le chien, quadrille mignon pour le piano. *Londres, Paris*, [1858.] fol. **e. 70. (5.)**

— [Le chien.] Our Pet quadrilles [P. F.] *London*, [1858.] fol. **h. 911. (22.)**

— [Le chien.] Our Pet quadrilles. [P. F. duet.] *London*, [1858.] fol. **h. 911. (23.)**

— [Le chien.] Rondo on "Our Pet" Quadrille. [P. F. solo and duet.] *See* SMALLWOOD (W.) Home Treasures, *etc.* No. 55. [1872, *etc.*] fol. **h. 1412. o.**

— Le Clairon, chansonnette [begins: "Je suis clairon"], paroles de T. Julian. *Paris*, [1866.] fol. **H. 2623. a. (18.)**

— Coeur de Lion. Quadrille. *See infra:* Duguesclin.

— Le Collier de Corail. Schottisch pour le Piano. *Paris*, [1861.] fol. **h. 619. e. (10.)**

— [Le Collier de Corail.] The Coral Necklace. Schottisch for the Pianoforte. *London*, [1861.] fol. **h. 619. c. (36.)**

— Come, my way. *See infra:* Hymne à la Vierge.

— Come sing with me. *See supra:* Le Captif Délivré.

— Coquetterie, chansonnette, paroles de T. Julian. *Paris*, [1867.] fol. **H. 2623. a. (21.)**

— The Corsair quadrille. [P. F.] *London*, [1855.] fol. *No. 346 of the "Musical Bouquet".* **H. 2345.**

— Le Corsaire breton. ⟨Op. 89.⟩ Quadrille brillant ... pour le piano à 4 mains. pp. 11. *Chez A. Leduc: Paris*, [c. 1855.] *obl.* fol. **f. 770. aa. (5.)**

— La couronne d'or, polka-mazurka pour le piano. No. 1 en feuille, No. 2 en morceau. 2 no. *Paris*, [1855.] fol. **h. 616. (5.)**

— Le Couronnement, Quadrille pour le Piano. *London*, [1857.] fol. **h. 911. (13.)**

— [La Course au Clocher.] The Steeple Chase. Quadrille. [P. F.] *London*, [1862.] fol. **h. 619. d. (3.)**

— La Course au Clocher. Quadrille mignon pour le Piano. [With accompaniments for violin, flute and cornet.] *Paris*, [1862.] *obl.* fol. **e. 290. (9.)**

— La Course aux Cerceaux. Quadrille Mignon. [P. F. with accompaniments for flute, violin, cornet and bass.] *Paris*, [1859.] *obl.* fol. **e. 70. (6.)**

— La Course aux cerceaux. Quadrille mignon pour Piano. *London*, [1860.] fol. **h. 911. (41.)**

LEDUC (ALPHONSE)

— La Croix au drapeau. Polka ... pour Piano. (Edition No. 1, "en feuille".) *London*, [1860.] fol.   **h. 913. (3*.)**

— La Croix au drapeau Polka ... pour piano. (Edition no. 2, "en morceau".) *London*, [1860.] fol.   **h. 913. (3**.)**

— La dame aux camélias, quadrille pour le piano. *London*, [1852.] fol.   **h. 964. (21.)**

— La dame aux camélias, schottisch pour le piano. *London*, [1852.] fol.   **h. 964. (25.)**

— La Dame aux Camélias schottisch ... arr. [for military band] par P. Clodomir. *Paris*, [1879.] 8°.   **e. 372. (6.)**

— La dame aux perles, polka élégante, pour le piano. *London*, [1853.] fol.   **h. 617. (18.)**

— Les dames de Florence, valses brillantes for the pianoforte. *London*, [1851.] fol.   **h. 964. (7.)**

— Darling Nelly Gray. Fantasia [on B. R. Hanby's song] ... for the Pianoforte. *London*, [1860.] fol.   **h. 619. c. (8.)**

— Darling Nelly Gray. Fantasia ... for the Pianoforte. *Paris*, [1860.] fol.   **h. 619. c. (17.)**

— Dear Morn of Life. *See* infra: Travaille Enfant.

— Le Départ de l'Helvétie. Fantaisie brillante pour Piano. *London*, [1862.] fol.   **h. 619. c. (48.)**

— Le Départ de l'Helvétie. Fantaisie brillante sur un Romance de F. Masini pour le Piano. Op. 18. *Paris*, [1862.] fol.   **h. 619. e. (12.)**

— Le départ du village, fantaisie brillante pour le piano forte. Op. 67. *London*, [1858.] fol.   **h. 619. b. (8.)**

— Le départ du village; fantaisie brillante pour piano. Op. 175. *London*, [1859.] fol.   **h. 619. a. (9.)**

— Deux amis. 2 petites Fantaisies. Op. 155. 2 no. *London*, [1853.] fol.   **h. 618. (14.)**

— Diana, valse sentimentale, pour le piano. *London*, [1854.] fol.   **h. 617. (37.)**

— La distribution des drapeaux, quadrille historique, pour le piano. No. 1 solo, No. 2 duet. 2 no. *London*, [1852.] fol.   **h. 964. (24.)**

— Don Quichotte, quadrille brillant pour le Piano Forte edited by J. Mc.Calla. *London*, [1844.] fol.   **h. 932. (30.)**

— Dona Maria II., valse brillante pour le piano. Difficult edition. *London*, [1858.] fol.   **h. 912. (13.)**

— Doña Maria II., valse brillante pour piano. *Paris*, [1859.] fol.   **h. 912. (15.)**

— Dona Maria II., valse brillante pour le piano. Easy edition. *London*, [1858.] fol.   **h. 912. (12.)**

— Dona Maria II., valse brillante pour le piano [as a duet]. *London*, [1858.] fol.   **h. 912. (14.)**

— Douce Pensée. 5e. Nocturne pour Piano. Op. 188. *Paris*, [1861.] fol.   **h. 619. e. (4.)**

— Douce Pensée. Nocturne pour Piano. Op. 188. *London*, [1861.] fol.   **h. 619. c. (29.)**

— Doux Espoir. 4e. nocturne pour Piano. *London*, [1859.] fol.   **h. 619. b. (17.)**

— Doux Espoir, Quatrième nocturne pour Piano. *London*, [1860.] fol.   **h. 619. a. (14.)**

— Le Doux Repos, nocturne à deux voix [begins: "Quand la nuit"], paroles de T. Julian. *Paris*, [1866.] fol.   **H. 2623. a. (19.)**

LEDUC (ALPHONSE)

— Les Dragons de l'Impératrice, Quadrille brillant, pour le Piano. *London*, [1858.] fol.   **h. 911. (14.)**

— Les dragons de l'Impératrice, Quadrille brillant [for the piano, with flute, violin, and cornet accompaniments]. *Paris*, [1858.] *obl*. fol.   **e. 70. (19.)**

— La Duchesse Constantin de Russie. Valse brillante pour Piano. *London*, [1862.] fol.   **h. 619. c. (49.)**

— Duchesse Constantin de Russie. Valse brillante pour le Piano. *Paris*, [1862.] fol.   **h. 619. e. (14.)**

— La Duchesse de Chevreuse, polka brillante ... pour piano. *London*, [1858.] fol.   **h. 913. (4.)**

— La duchesse de Chevreuse, polka brillante ... pour le piano. *Paris*, [1859.] fol.   **h. 913. (5.)**

— Duchesse de Manchester. Valse brillante pour Piano. *London*, [1861.] fol.   **h. 619. c. (37.)**

— Duchesse de Manchester. Valse brillante pour Piano. Edition difficile. *Paris*, [1861.] fol.   **h. 619. e. (33.)**

— Duchesse Olga, valse brillante pour piano. *London*, [1859.] fol.   **h. 912. (19.)**

— Duchesse Olga, valse brillante pour piano, *etc.* [Edition difficile.] *Paris*, [1859.] fol.   **h. 912. (20.)**

— Duguesclin. Quadrille historique ... pour Piano. *Paris*, [1861.] *obl*. fol.   **e. 290. (1.)**

— [Duguesclin.] Coeur de Lion. Quadrille. [P. F.] *London*, [1861.] fol.   **h. 619. c. (28.)**

— Duo brillant et concertant pour deux pianos. Op. 60 bis. *London*, [1855.] fol.   **h. 619. (25.)**

— Duo brillant et concertant pour deux pianos. Op. 60 bis. *Paris*, [1855.] fol.   **h. 616. (14.)**

— Les échos de la Loire. Quadrille pour le Piano. *London*, [1857.] fol.   **h. 911. (15.)**

— Les échos de la Loire. Quadrille pour le Piano. *Paris*, [1857.] fol.   **e. 70. (7.)**

— Les échos du Mont Blanc, quadrille pour piano [with accompaniment for cornet]. *London*, [1856.] fol.   **h. 619. (15.)**

— Les échos du Mont Blanc, quadrille pour le piano. [With accompaniments for violin, cornet and flute.] *Paris*, [1856.] fol.   **e. 38. (25.)**

— Les échos du Rhin, quadrille élégant [P. F.]. *London*, [1859.] fol.   **h. 911. (16.)**

— Les échos du Rhin. Quadrille élégant ... pour le piano [with accompaniments for violin, flute, and cornet], *etc.* *Paris*, [1859.] fol.   **e. 70. (8.)**

— L'écrin musical 5 petites Fantaisies pour le piano. Op. 149. 5 no. *London*, [1852.] fol.   **h. 618. (11.)**

— L'écrin musicale ... [melodies by Carafa di Colobrano and others arranged] pour Piano. Op. 149. 5 no. *Chappell & Co.: London*, [1857.] fol.   **h. 619. a. (1.)**

— L'Ecrin Musicale ... No. 4. La Topaze. *London*, [1860.] fol. *Imperfect; wanting the other no.*   **h. 619. c. (2.)**

— L'Ecrin Musicale, 5 petites fantasias pour le Piano. 5 no. *London*, [1874.] fol. *No. 2377–2381 of the "Musical Bouquet".*   **H. 2345.**

— L'Électrique. Quadrille brillant ... pour le Piano. [With accompaniments for violin, flute, cornet, whip and bells.] *Paris*, [1863.] *obl*. fol.   **e. 290. (12.)**

LEDUC (ALPHONSE)

— L'élégante amazone, schottisch pour le piano. *Paris*, [1854.] fol.   **h. 617. (13.)**

— Elisabeth d'Autriche, valse pour le piano, *etc. London*, [1856.] fol.   **h. 619. (23.)**

— Elisabeth d'Autriche, valse brillante pour piano. (Edition difficile.) *Paris*, [1856.] fol.   **h. 616. (10.)**

— Elisabeth d'Autriche, valse brillante pour le piano. (Edition facile.) *Paris*, [1856.] fol.   **h. 616. (9.)**

— Elizabeth, polka de salon pour Piano à six mains. *Paris*, [1868.] fol.   **h. 619. f. (3.)**

— Ella Leene. Fantasia (sur un motif de F. Buckley) ... for the Pianoforte. *London*, [1860.] fol.   **h. 619. c. (11.)**

— Ella Leene. Fantasia ... for the Pianoforte. *Paris*, [1860.] fol.   **h. 619. e. (20.)**

— L'Éloge des larmes de F. Schubert, pour le Piano. *See* infra: Deux Mélodies ... No. 1.

— Empereurs et Rois. Quadrille historique pour Piano. *London*, [1867.] *obl.* fol.   **e. 290. (34.)**

— En avant, fantaisie alla militare pour piano, sur une chansonnette de C. Larsonneur. *London*, [1855.] fol.   **h. 619. (26.)**

— En Poste. Polka brillante pour le Piano. *London*, [1865.] fol.   **h. 619. d. (25.)**

— En Poste. Polka brillante pour Piano. [With accompaniments for violin, cornet, flute, whip and bells.] *Paris*, [1865.] fol.   **h. 619. e. (42.)**

— En Vendanges. Quadrille champêtre pour Piano. [With accompaniments for violin, cornet and flute.] *Paris*, [1866.] *obl.* fol.   **e. 290. (32.)**

— L'Enjouée, valse mignonne pour le Piano. *Paris*, [1872.] fol.   **h. 619. f. (12.)**

— Entrée à Milan. Polka militaire, pour le piano, *etc. London*, [1859.] fol.   **h. 913. (7.)**

— Entrée à Milan, polka militaire, pour piano. *Paris*, [1859.] fol.   **h. 913. (6.)**

— Ernesta, valse mignonne pour le piano. *London*, [1855.] fol.   **h. 619. (24.)**

— Ernesta, valse mignonne, pour le piano. *Paris*, [1855.] fol.   **h. 616. (11.)**

— L'Espagnol. Fantaisie pour Piano Forte. *London*, [1849.] fol.   **h. 715. (30.)**

— L'Espagnole, fantasia for the Pianoforte. *London*, [1856.] fol. *No.* 1059, 1060 *of the "Musical Bouquet".*   **H. 2345.**

— L'Etat Major. Polka militaire. *Paris*, [1863.] fol.   **h. 619. e. (19.)**

— L'Étoile d'Or. Polka-mazurka pour le Piano. [With accompaniments for violin, cornet and flute.] *Paris*, [1867.] fol.   **h. 619. e. (50.)**

— L'étoile du bal. Polka mazurka, pour le piano. *Paris*, [1858.] fol.   **h. 913. (8.)**

— L'Etoile du matin, schottisch élégante pour le piano. No. 1 en feuille. No. 2 en morceau. No. 3 à 4 mains. 3 no. *Paris*, [1855.] fol.   **h. 616. (8.)**

— Les étoiles, opéra ballet de A. Pilati, quadrille brillant pour piano par A. Leduc. *London*, [1854.] fol.   **h. 617. (30.)**

— L'éventail, polka mazurka, pour le piano. *Paris*, [1854.] fol.   **h. 617. (21.)**

LEDUC (ALPHONSE)

— Exposition universelle, quadrille historique pour piano. *London*, [1855.] fol.   **h. 619. (16.)**

— Exposition Universelle, Paris 1855, quadrille historique pour le piano. *Paris*, [1855.] fol.   **e. 38. (26.)**

— The express quadrilles, (gare que je passe) quadrille à grande vitesse ... for the Piano Forte. *London*, [1853.] fol.   **h. 617. (26.)**

— The Fair Dane. Brilliant Waltz ... for Pianoforte. *London*, [1862.] fol.   **h. 619. d. (8.)**

— The fall of Sebastopol, quadrille. [P. F.] *London*, [1855.] fol.   **h. 619. (11.)**

— La Faneuse, chansonnette, paroles de T. Julian. *Paris*, [1865.] fol.   **H. 2623. a. (5.)**

— [La Faneuse.] Blondinette. Song [begins: "Oh! blythe"] written by G. Linley. *London*, [1865.] fol.   **H. 2623. (3.)**

— [La Faneuse.] Blondinette. Mélodie ... pour le Piano. *London*, [1865.] fol.   **h. 619. d. (24.)**

— La Faneuse ... Petite Fantaisie pour Piano. *Paris*, [1865.] fol.   **h. 619. e. (43.)**

— Fantaisie sur Follette de A. Thys, pour piano. Op. 104. *London*, [1856.] fol.   **h. 619. (29.)**

— Fantaisie sur Follette de A. Thys, pour piano. [Op. 104.] *London*, [1855.] fol.   **h. 619. (28.)**

— Fantaisie brillante sur l'opéra La Part du diable de D. F. E. Auber pour piano ... Op. 110. pp. 11. *E. Troupenas et c^{ie}: Paris*, [c. 1840.] fol.   **h. 721. uu. (15.)**

— Fantaisie brillante, sur Beatrice di Tenda, de Bellini, pour piano. Op. 112. *London*, [1854.] fol.   **h. 618. (5.)**

— Fantaisie brillante, sur Nenni—da! de A. Thys, pour piano. Op. 115. *London*, [1854.] fol.   **h. 618. (6.)**

— Deux fantaisies sur Cenerentola [by G. A. Rossini] et Crociato [by G. Meyerbeer] pour piano. Op. 145. 2 no. *London*, [1854.] fol.   **h. 618. (8.)**

— Fantasia brillante [from G. A. Rossini's opera] Cenerentola, for the Piano Forte. *London*, [1857.] fol.   **h. 619. a. (18.)**

— Fantaisie brillante, de Rossini's Semiramide, pour le piano. Op. 147. *London*, [1854.] fol.   **h. 618. (10.)**

— 3 Fantaisies élégantes ... pour le piano. Op. 151. 3 no. *London*, [1852.] fol.   **h. 618. (12.)**

— Fantaisie brillante sur [the composition of C. G. Reissiger known as] la dernière pensée de C. M. von Weber pour piano. Op. 158. *London*, [1855.] fol.   **h. 619. (32.)**

— Fantaisie brillante sur la dernière pensée de C. M von Weber pour piano. Op. 158. *Paris*, [1855.] fol.   **h. 616. (17.)**

— 3 Fantaisies gracieuses pour piano. Op. 163. 3 no. *Paris*, [1855.] fol.   **h. 616. (18.)**

— 3 Fantaisies gracieuses pour piano. Op. 163. 3 no. *London*, [1855.] fol.   **h. 619. (1.)**

— 3 Fantaisies ... arrangées pour piano à quatre mains par C. Czerny. Op. 163. 3 no. *London*, [1856.] fol.   **h. 514. (3.)**

— 3 Fantaisies gracieuses, arrangées pour piano à quatre mains par C. Czerny. Op. 163. 3 no. *Paris*, [1856.] fol.   **h. 515. (3.)**

— 2 Fantaisies élégantes sur deux Romances de F. Bérat. Op. 186. *Paris*, [1861.] fol.   **h. 619. e. (34.)**

— [2 fantaisies élégantes. Op. 186. No. 1.] Adieu, bords chéris de la Seine. Fantaisie élégante pour le Piano. Op. 186. *London*, [1861.] fol.   **h. 619. c. (35.)**

LEDUC (ALPHONSE)

— [2 fantaisies élégantes. Op. 186. No. 2.] La Montagnarde au Départ. Fantaisie élégante pour le Piano. *London*, [1861.] fol. **h. 619. c. (42.)**

— 3 Fantaisies élégantes, pour le Piano. Op. 198. *Paris*, [1867.] fol. **h. 619. e. (54.)**

— [Fantasia on] Partant pour la Syrie, Mélodie de la reine Hortense. Fantaisie élégante pour Piano. *London*, [1853] fol. **h. 617. (1.)**

— Fantasia on Partant pour la Syrie. [P. F.] *London*, [1854.] fol. *No. 359 of the "Musical Bouquet".* **H. 2345.**

— Fête at Venise. Quadrille, composed for the Pianoforte. *London*, [1862.] fol. **h. 619. c. (50.)**

— Une Fête au Lido. Quadrille brillant. [P. F., with accompaniment for violin, cornet and flute.] *Paris*, [1862.] *obl.* fol. **e. 290. (7.)**

— Une Fête Champêtre. Rondo villageois pour le Piano. *See* infra: 2 Morceaux de genre ... Op. 191. No. 2.

— La Fête des Lanternes. Quadrille Chinois ... pour le Piano. [With accompaniments for violin, flute and cornet.] *Paris*, [1865.] *obl.* fol. **e. 290. (29.)**

— Les fêtes de Cherbourg, quadrille historique pour piano. *London*, [1858.] fol. **h. 911. (17.)**

— Les fêtes de Cherbourg, quadrille ... pour piano [with accompaniments for cornet, violin, and flute]. *Paris*, [1859.] fol. **e. 70. (31.)**

— Feux-Follets, valse brillante pour Piano. *Paris*, [1869.] fol. **h. 619. f. (7.)**

— The Field of the Cloth of Gold, quadrille for the Piano Forte. *London*, [1868.] fol. **h. 619. d. (38.)**

— Les Fifres de la Garde. Quadrille militaire ... pour le Piano. [With accompaniments for violin, flute and cornet.] *Paris*, [1863.] *obl.* fol. **e. 290. (13.)**

— La Fille de la nuit. Grande valse pour le Piano Forte. *London*, [1853.] fol. **h. 617. (41.)**

— La Fille de la Vallée, d'A. Delatour. *See* supra: 3 Fantaisies élégantes. Op. 198. No. 3.

— Fleur de noblesse, valse brillante, pour le piano. *London*, [1854.] fol. **h. 617. (38.)**

— Fleur de noblesse, valse brillante, pour le piano. *London*, [1858.] fol. **h. 912. (5.)**

— Fleur de Noblesse. [P. F.] *See* SMALLWOOD (W.) Little Footprints, *etc.* No. 23. [1900–2.] fol. **h. 1412. w. (1.)**

— Fleur des Champs, valse mignonne pour le piano. *Paris*, [1854.] fol. **h. 617. (45.)**

— Fleurs d'Espagne. 3 Petites Fantaisies pour Piano. 3 no. *Paris*, [1859.] fol. **h. 619. b. (16.)**

— Le Florian des jeunes pianistes. 6 Fabliaux ou petites fantaisies, soigneusement doigtées pour le piano. [With text by Florian.] Op. 161. *Paris*, [1854.] fol. **h. 618. (15.)**

— Florian, six fables or fantasias carefully fingered for the pianoforte. Op. 161. *London*, [1854.] fol. *This edition is without the text by Florian.* **h. 618. (16.)**

— La flotte Anglo-Française quadrille maritime, pour le piano. *London*, [1854.] fol. **h. 617. (31.)**

— La flotte anglo-française, quadrille maritime, pour le piano. *Paris*, [1854.] *obl.* fol. **e. 38. (14.)**

— La Flotte Cuirassée. Quadrille maritime pour Piano. *Paris*, [1866.] *obl.* fol. **e. 290. (30.)**

LEDUC (ALPHONSE)

— La Folie. Polka brillante ... pour le Piano. *London*, [1865.] fol. **h. 619. d. (20.)**

— La Folie. Polka brillante ... pour le Piano. *Paris*, [1865.] fol. **h. 619. e. (37.)**

— La Française. Fantaisie brillante. [P. F.] *See* SOIRÉES. Les Soirées de Salon, *etc.* No. 20. [1847–55.] fol. **h. 525. (7.)**

— La Française. Fantaisie brillante pour le Piano Forte. Op. 108. *London*, [1848.] fol. **h. 715. (28.)**

— La Française, fantaisie brillante, pour pianoforte. *London*, [1853.] fol. **h. 617. (2.)**

— La Française, fantasia brillante. [P. F.] *London*, [1855.] fol. *No. 543, 544 of the "Musical Bouquet".* **H. 2345.**

— La Française, fantaisie brillante pour piano à quatre mains. Op. 108. *London*, [1855.] fol. **h. 619. (30.)**

— La Française, fantaisie brillante pour piano à quatre mains. Op. 108. *Paris*, [1855.] fol. **h. 616. (15.)**

— [La Française.] Lizette ... set to Leduc's ... air "La Française" [begins: "Two years and am I changed"]. Poetry by J. J. Lonsdale. *London*, [1874.] fol. *No. 2665, 2666 of the "Musical Bouquet".* **H. 2345.**

— Francis the First quadrille. [P. F.] *London*, [1855.] fol. *No. 288 of the "Musical Bouquet".* **H. 2345.**

— Les Francs-Tireurs, quadrille brillant pour Piano. *Paris*, [1872.] *obl.* fol. **e. 272. b. (19.)**

— The French March for the piano forte. *Paris*, [1854.] fol. **h. 617. (5.)**

— The French march founded on "Partant pour la Syrie" [the melody by Hortense, Queen Consort of Louis, King of Holland] for the Piano forte. *London*, [1854.] fol. **h. 617. (6.)**

— Le Furet. Quadrille mignon pour le Piano. [With accompaniments for violin, cornet and flute.] *Paris*, [1861.] *obl.* fol. **e. 290. (4.)**

— [Le Furet.] Hunt the Slipper. Juvenile Quadrille ... for the Pianoforte. *London*, [1861.] fol. **h. 619. c. (40.)**

— La Gallegada, Fantaisie Espagnole pour Piano. *London*, [1860.] fol. **h. 619. a. (12.)**

— La Gazza Ladra, fantaisie [on G. A. Rossini's opera] pour piano forte. *London*, [1854.] fol. **h. 618. (9.)**

— La Gazza Ladra, fantaisie [on G. A. Rossini's opera], pour Pianoforte. *London*, [1868.] fol. **h. 619. d. (36.)**

— Gentle Annie. Fantasia (on S. C. Foster's ... melody) ... for the Pianoforte. *London*, [1860.] fol. **h. 619. c. (9.)**

— Gentle Annie. Fantasia ... for the Pianoforte. *Paris*, [1860.] fol. **h. 619. e. (32.)**

— La Gerbe d'or, Schottisch originale pour le piano. *Paris*, [1854.] fol. **h. 617. (14.)**

— Good news from home. Fantasia ... for the Pianoforte. *London*, [1859.] fol. **h. 619. b. (10.)**

— Good news from home. Première Fantaisie pour le Piano. *Paris*, [1859.] fol. **h. 619. a. (15.)**

— Grand Mère est toujours là! Chansonnette [begins: "Voyez vous"], paroles de M. Constantin. *Paris*, [1865.] fol. **H. 2623. a. (6.)**

— [Grand Mère est toujours là.] The Saraband, song [begins: "I've wandered"] written by W. Hills. *London*, [1865.] fol. **H. 2623. (5.)**

LEDUC (ALPHONSE)

— [Grand Mère est toujours là.] *See* DELASEURIE (A.) Grand Mère ... fantaisie, *etc.* [1868.] fol.   **h. 3021. a. (36.)**

— Les Guérillas, quadrille brillant pour Piano. *Paris*, [1868.] *obl.* fol.   **e. 217. b. (29.)**

— L'Hortensia. Valse gracieuse pour Piano. *London*, [1861.] fol.   **h. 619. c. (32.)**

— L'Hortensia. Valse gracieuse pour Piano. *Paris*, [1861.] fol.   **h. 619. e. (6.)**

— The Hour of Prayer. *See* supra: Allons prier.

— Hunt the Slipper. Quadrille. *See* supra: Le Furet.

— Hymne à la Vierge, chœur à trois voix [begins: "Gloire à vous"]. (Paroles de T. Julian.) *Paris*, [1866.] fol.   **H. 2623. a. (10.)**

— [Hymne à la Vierge.] Come, my way, my truth, my life, hymn for three voices ... arranged and adapted to the words of G. Herbert ... by W. Hills. *London*, [1867.] fol.   **H. 2623. (12.)**

— I'm off to Charlestown. Fantasia ... on ... melodies of the Christy Minstrels, for the Pianoforte. *London*, [1860.] fol.   **h. 619. c. (5.)**

— I'm off to Charlestown. Fantasia ... for the Pianoforte. *Paris*, [1860.] fol.   **h. 619. c. (14.)**

— Il m'a quitté. Romance. Paroles de Mr. Hortensius de S¹. A ... *Paris*, [1835?] fol.   **G. 556. (57.)**

— L'Illustration musicale, 12 operatic fantasias, on motivos from the most favorite operas. [P. F.] Op. 164. 12 no. *London*, [1854.] fol.   **h. 618. (17.)**

— L'Illustration musicale, 12 operatic fantasias on motivos from the most favorite operas. Op. 164. 12 no. *Paris*, [1855.] fol.   **h. 616. (19.)**

— L'Impératrice, grande valse pour piano. *London*, [1853.] fol.   **h. 617. (43.)**

— Impérial Galop pour le Piano. *Paris*, [1864.] fol.   **h. 619. e. (28.)**

— The Imperial Galop ... for the Pianoforte. *London*, [1864.] fol.   **h. 619. d. (14.)**

— Imperial grand march of Napoleon the first, arranged for the piano-forte. *London*, [1854.] fol.   **h. 617. (8.)**

— Imperial grand march of Napoleon the first, arranged for the piano forte. *Paris*, [1854.] fol.   **h. 617. (7.)**

— L'Italienne. Fantaisie pour Piano Forte. *London*, [1849.] fol.   **h. 715. (29.)**

— L'Italienne, fantasia for the Pianoforte. *London*, [1855.] fol. *No. 790, 791 of the "Musical Bouquet".*   **H. 2345.**

— [L'Italienne.] Fantaisie brillante pour piano-forte. *London*, [1856.] fol.   **h. 619. (5.)**

— J's'rai Rentier, chansonnette [begins: "Mon père voudrait"], paroles de T. Julian. *Paris*, [1867.] fol.   **H. 2623. a. (22.)**

— Le Jardin de la Reine. Quadrille gracieux ... pour Piano. *London*, [1861.] fol.   **h. 619. c. (31.)**

— Le Jardin de la Reine. Quadrille gracieux ... pour le Piano. [With accompaniments for violin, cornet and flute.] *Paris*, [1861.] *obl.* fol.   **e. 290. (3.)**

— Le Jardin sous les Toits, chansonnette [begins: "Tombez, Tombez"], paroles de T. Julian. *Paris*, [1866.] fol.   **H. 2623. a. (13.)**

LEDUC (ALPHONSE)

— [Le Jardin sous les Toits.] Pearls of the Morning, song [begins: "Welcome"], written by W. Hills. [Adapted to the song "Le Jardin," *etc.*] *London*, [1866.] fol.   **H. 2623. (14.)**

— Le Jardin sous les Toits. *See* supra: 3 Fantaisies élégantes. Op. 198. No. 1.

Jenny la Meunière

— Jenny la Meunière, chansonnette [begins: "Venez tous"], paroles de M. T. Julian. *Paris*, [1864.] fol.   **H. 2623. a. (1.)**

— Jenny of the Mill. ⟨In A.⟩ *London*, [1864.] fol.   **H. 2623. (2.)**

— Jenny of the Mill. Song [begins: "There's a breeze"], written by G. Linley. ⟨In G.⟩ *London*, [1864.] fol.   **H. 2623. (1.)**

— Jenny of the Mill. Ballad, *etc.* pp. 7. *Robert Cocks & Co.: London*, [1865?] fol.   **H. 1652. v. (10.)**

— Jenny ... for the Piano. [1865.] fol. *See* RICHARDS (H. B.)   **h. 760. f. (43.)**

— Jenny of the Mill. [P. F. solo and duet.] *See* SMALLWOOD (W.) Home Treasures, *etc.* No. 41. [1872, *etc.*] fol.   **h. 1412. o.**

— Jenny of the Mill. [P. F. solo and duet.] *See* SMALLWOOD (W.) Little Buds, *etc.* No. 41. [1874, *etc.*] fol.   **h. 1412. p.**

— Jenny la Meunière ... Transcription de la chansonnette, *etc.* [1882.] fol. *See* BATTMANN (J. L.)   **h. 3009. b. (19.)**

— Jenny of the Mill. Fantaisie ... for the Pianoforte. *London*, [1864.] fol.   **h. 619. d. (17.)**

— Jenny la Meunière. Fantaisie brillante pour Piano. Op. 197. *Paris*, [1864.] fol.   **h. 619. e. (35.)**

— Les jeunes parisiennes, quadrille élégant pour le piano. *London*, [1853.] fol.   **h. 617. (32.)**

— Jeunesse de Turenne. Quadrille brillant. [P. F.] *London*, [1850.] fol.   **h. 947. (41.)**

— Jeunesse et Vieillesse, chansonnette [begins: "Dites-moi"] ... Paroles de T. Julian. *London*, [1868.] fol.   **H. 2623. a. (34.)**

— Joli petit Mouton. Fantaisie sur une Romance de Sieg. *See* infra: Trois petites Fantaisies élégantes. Op. 190. No. 3.

— La Jolie Fileuse. Polka brillante ... pour le Piano. *Paris*, [1862.] fol.   **h. 619. e. (15.)**

— [La Jolie Fileuse.] The Sensation Polka. For the Pianoforte. *London*, [1862.] fol.   **h. 619. d. (2.)**

— Les jolies femmes de Paris, polka élégante, pour le piano. *London*, [1855.] fol.   **h. 619. (12.)**

— Les jolies femmes de Paris, polka élégante pour le piano. *Paris*, [1855.] fol.   **h. 616. (6.)**

— La Jota. Fantaisie sur un air Espanol. *See* infra: Trois petites Fantaisies élégantes. Op. 190. No. 2.

— Le Joueur de Hautbois, pastorale [begins: "Je reconnais"] ... Paroles de T. Julian. *Paris*, [1867.] fol.   **H. 2623. a. (30.)**

— Joyeux Colibris, valse chantée [begins: "Chantez"], paroles de T. Julian. *Paris*, [1867.] fol.   **H. 2623. a. (35.)**

— Kiss me quick and go. Fantasia [on F. Buckley's song] for the Pianoforte. *London*, [1860.] fol.   **h. 619. c. (7.)**

— Kiss me quick and go. Fantasia ... for the Pianoforte. *Paris*, [1860.] fol.   **h. 619. c. (16.)**

— Laissez les roses aux rosiers. Fantaisie brillante pour Piano. Op. 170. *Paris*, [1858.] fol.   **h. 619. a. (6.)**

LEDUC (ALPHONSE)

— Laissez les roses aux rosiers. Fantaisie brillante pour le Piano. Op. 170. *London*, [1858.] fol.   **h. 619. b. (5.)**

— The Lancers, Polka Anglaise. [P. F.] *London*, [1857.] fol.   **h. 913. (9.)**

— Les Lanciers de la reine, Quadrille original, nouvelle théorie à 16 ou 8 personnes ... pour le Piano. (Explication des nouvelles figures par Renausy.) *Paris*, [1857.] obl. fol.   **e. 70. (20.)**

— [Les Lanciers de la reine.] The Queen's Lancers, a new set of Quadrilles. [P. F.] *London*, [1857.] fol.   **h. 911. (28.)**

— [Les Lanciers de la reine.] The Queen's Lancers, a New Set of Quadrilles, for eight or sixteen persons. [P. F. duet.] *London*, [1857.] fol.   **h. 911. (29.)**

— Une Larme d'Enfant! Mélodie [begins: "C'était à Cologne"], paroles d'A. Joly. *Paris*, [1866.] fol.   **H. 2623. a. (11.)**

— [Une Larme d'Enfant.] Not a Month ago, song [begins: "Take, O take"], poetry written by W. Hills. [Adapted to "Une Larme," *etc.*] *London*, [1866.] fol.   **H. 2623. (13.)**

— La Legion d'Honneur. Polka brillante pour Piano. [With accompaniments for violin, cornet and flute.] *Paris*, [1867.] fol.   **h. 619. e. (53.)**

— Lettre à Monsieur le Soleil. [Song, begins: "Ce billet".] Paroles de T. Julian. *Paris*, [1873.] fol.   **H. 2623. a. (39.)**

— Lilla's a lady, petite fantaisie à la valse pour piano. *London*, [1855.] fol.   **h. 619. (7.)**

— Lilla's a lady, petite fantaisie à la valse pour piano. *Paris*, [1855.] fol.   **h. 616. (3.)**

— The Lily was the only flower. Fantasia ... for the Pianoforte. *Paris*, [1861.] fol.   **h. 619. e. (11.)**

— The Lily was the only flower. Fantasia on the melody (by F. Buckley) ... arranged for the Pianoforte. *London*, [1861.] fol.   **h. 619. c. (44.)**

— The little drummer. Song. *See* infra: [Le petit tambourin.]

— Les Loups de Mer. Quadrille maritime pour Piano. [With accompaniments for violin, cornet and flute.] *Paris*, [1865.] obl. fol.   **e. 290. (26.)**

— Ma Mère, mélodie [begins: "Splendide mot"], paroles de J. Colvé. *Paris*, [1867.] fol.   **H. 2623. a. (28.)**

— Madrid, polka mazurka pour Piano. *London*, [1868.] fol.   **h. 619. d. (39.)**

— La Madrilena, Fantaisie Espagnole pour Piano. *London*, [1860.] fol.   **h. 619. a. (11.)**

— Maison à louer. Fantaisie [for P. F., on an air] de J. B. Katto. *See* infra: 3 Petites Fantaisies. Op. 184. No. 1.

— The Malakhoff quadrilles. [P. F.] *London*, [1855.] fol.   **h. 619. (10.)**

— Le Marchand d'habits. Scène comique. [Song.] Paroles d'Alfred Deschamps. pp. 3. *Alphonse Leduc: Paris*, [1850?] fol.   **Hirsch M. 1296. (5.)**

— Marche Autrichienne. *See* supra: L'Aquarium. No. 2.

— Marche Militaire. *See* infra: Les Pâquerettes. No. 6.

— Margaret of Anjou quadrilles. [P. F.] *London*, [1855.] fol. *No. 258 of the "Musical Bouquet".*   **H. 2345.**

— Marguerite de Navarre, Quadrille historique, pour le piano [with an accompaniment for the cornet à pistons]. *London*, [1853.] fol.   **h. 617. (23.)**

LEDUC (ALPHONSE)

— Marguerite de Valois, quadrille pour le Piano. *London*, [1851.] fol.   **h. 964. (28.)**

— Les Marguerites, valse gracieuse, pour le piano. *London*, [1854.] fol.   **h. 617. (39.)**

— Marie Alboni, valse pour le Piano. *Paris*, [1855.] fol. *Forming part of a collection entitled: "Les Perles du Théatre,"* etc.   **h. 619. e. (51.)**

— Marie Alboni, valse pour piano. *London*, [1855.] fol.   **h. 619. (22.)**

— Le Mât de Cocagne, quadrille mignon pour le piano, *etc.* [With accompaniments for violin, cornet, and flute.] *Paris*, [1859.] fol.   **e. 70. (9.)**

— [Le Mât de Cocagne.] The village fair quadrilles. [P. F.] *London*, [1859.] fol.   **h. 911. (38.)**

— The May Pole Quadrille. *See* infra: Le Petit Tambourin.

— Le Médaillon, polka-mazurka, pour le piano. *Paris*, [1854.] fol.   **h. 617. (20.)**

— Melegnano. Quadrille militaire pour Piano. *London*, [1860.] fol.   **h. 619. c. (20.)**

— [Melegnano.] Bataille de Marignan. Quadrille historique & militaire pour le piano. *Paris*, [1860.] obl. fol.   **e. 70. (25.)**

— Mélodie Allemande. [Fantasia for P. F.] *See* infra: 3 Petites Fantaisies. Op. 184. No. 3.

— Mélodie de F. Kücken transcrite pour le Piano. *Paris*, [1865.] fol.   **h. 619. e. (40.)**

— Mélodie de F. Kücken. Transcrite pour le Piano. *London*, [1865.] fol.   **h. 619. d. (19.)**

— Mélodie de L. van Beethoven transcrite pour le Piano. *Paris*, [1865.] fol.   **h. 619. e. (39.)**

— Mélodie de L. van Beethoven pour le Piano. *London*, [1865.] fol.   **h. 619. d. (18.)**

— Deux Mélodies de F. Schubert. Transcriptions pour le Piano. Op. 193. *Paris*, [1863.] fol.   **h. 619. e. (24.)**

— [2 Mélodies ... Op. 193. No. 1.] L'Éloge des Larmes de F. Schubert. [P. F.] *London*, [1863.] fol.   **h. 619. d. (13.)**

— [2 Mélodies ... Op. 193. No. 2.] L'Adieu de F. Schubert. [P. F.] Op. 193. *London*, [1863.] fol.   **h. 619. c. (39.)**

— La Merveilleuse. Polka brillante pour le Piano. *Paris*, [1861.] fol.   **h. 619. e. (9.)**

— La Merveilleuse. Polka brillante pour le Piano. *London*, [1861.] fol.   **h. 619. c. (41.)**

— Le Messager du Printemps. Polka Gracieuse pour Piano. [With accompaniment for violin, cornet and flute.] *Paris*, [1866.] fol.   **h. 619. e. (47.)**

— [Le Messager du Printemps.] The Messenger of Spring. Polka gracieuse. [P. F. with accompaniments for violin, cornet and flute.] *London*, [1866.] fol.   **h. 619. d. (27.)**

— Méthode de piano. 35ᵉ edition. *Paris*, [1884.] fol.   **h. 3820. c. (16.)**

— Método de piano. 35ᵉ edicion ... con el concurso de H. d'Aubel. *Paris*, [1886.] fol.   **h. 3820. d. (13.)**

— Le Meunier et le Meunier. Quadrille brillant sur des motifs de P. Henrion. [P. F. with accompaniments for violin, cornet and flute.] *Paris*, [1865.] obl. fol.   **e. 290. (27.)**

— La Meunière et le Meunier. Quadrille brillant, *etc.* *London*, [1865.] fol.   **h. 619. d. (26.)**

LEDUC (Alphonse)

— La Mi-Carême. Quadrille ... pour le Piano. *Paris*, [1863.] *obl.* fol.　　　　　　　　　　　　　　　　**e. 290. (14.)**

— Michel-Ange, quadrille brillant pour Piano. *Paris*, [1873.] *obl.* fol.　　　　　　　　　　　　　　　**e. 272. b. (21.)**

— Minnie Clyde. Fantasia on the melody as sung by Christy's Minstrels, arranged for the Pianoforte. *London*, [1861.] fol.　　　　　　　　　　　　　　　**h. 619. c. (46.)**

— Le mirroir, polka mazurka, pour le piano. *London*, [1853.] fol.　　　　　　　　　　　　　　　**h. 617. (19.)**

— La Montagnarde au Départ. Fantaisie. *See* supra: 2 Fantaisies élégantes sur deux Romances de F. Bérat. Op. 186. No. 2.

— Les montagnes russes, Quadrille pour le Piano. *Paris*, [1857.] *obl.* fol.　　　　　　　　　　　　　　　**e. 70. (10.)**

— Les montagnes Russes, Quadrille pour le Piano. *London*, [1857.] fol.　　　　　　　　　　　　　　　**h. 911. (19.)**

— 2 Morceaux de genre pour le Piano. Op. 191. *Paris*, [1863.] fol.　　　　　　　　　　　　　　　**h. 619. e. (20.)**

— [2 Morceaux de genre, *etc.* Op. 191. No. 1.] La Chasse. (Morceau de genre.) Op. 191. [P. F.] *London*, [1863.] fol.　　　　　　　　　　　　　　　**h. 619. d. (9.)**

— [2 Morceaux de genre, *etc.* Op. 191. No. 2.] Une Fête Champêtre. Rondo Villageois. Op. 191. [P. F.] *London*, [1863.] fol.　　　　　　　　　　　　　　　**h. 619. d. (10.)**

— The Mountain Queen. *See* supra: La Chevrière du Mont Aventin.

— Quadrille "Les Mousquetaires de la Reine". Opéra d'Halévy par A. Leduc. [P. F.] *See* WESSEL AND CO. Les Soirées de Londres, *etc.* No. 65. [1851, *etc.*] fol.　　**H. 1385.**

— Les Muletiers. Quadrille pour Piano. [With accompaniments for violin, flute and cornet.] *Paris*, [1864.] *obl.* fol.　　　　　　　　　　　　　　　**e. 290. (18.)**

— La Neige. Polka brillante pour Piano. *Paris*, [1866.] fol.　　　　　　　　　　　　　　　**h. 619. e. (44.)**

— Nelly was a lady. Fantasia ... on ... melodies of the Christy Minstrels, for the Pianoforte. *London*, [1860.] fol.　　　　　　　　　　　　　　　**h. 619. c. (6.)**

— Nelly was a lady. Fantasia ... for the Pianoforte. *Paris*, [1860.] fol.　　　　　　　　　　　　　　　**h. 619. c. (15.)**

— Le Nid de l'Hirondelle, romance [begins: "Enfants, gardez vous"], paroles de Mr. E. Dufour. *Paris*, [1866.] fol.　　　　　　　　　　　　　　　**H. 2623. a. (14.)**

— Le Nid de la fauvette. Romance de la Faridondaine d'A. de Groot. Fantaisie élégante pour Piano. pp. 7. *O. Legouix: Paris*, [1859.] fol.　　　　　　　　**h. 619. b. (14.)**

— Le Nid de la fauvette, romance favorite, transcrite en forme de fantaisie par A. Leduc. [P. F.] *London*, [1859.] fol.　　　　　　　　　　　　　　　**h. 619. a. (23.)**

— Le Nid des Fauvettes, romance [begins: "Dans les aubépines"]. Poésie de T. Julian. *Paris*, [1867.] fol.　　　　　　　　　　　　　　　**H. 2623. a. (23.)**

— La Niobé, 3ᵉ fantaisie brillante pour le Piano. Op. 145. *London*, [1868.] fol.　　　　　　　**h. 619. d. (37.)**

— Not a Month ago. *See* supra: Une Larme d'Enfant.

— Notre Dame de la Mer! Marine [begins: "Vogue mon beau navire"], paroles de T. Julian. *Paris*, [1866.] fol.　　　　　　　　　　　　　　　**H. 2623. a. (20.)**

LEDUC (Alphonse)

— Notre Dame des Bouquets, legende bretonne [begins: "Cueillons"], paroles de T. Julian. *Paris*, [1868.] fol.　　　　　　　　　　　　　　　**H. 2623. a. (36.)**

— La Nouvelle St. Hubert, quadrille des chasseurs pour Piano. *Paris*, [1868.] *obl.* fol.　　　　**e. 217. b. (30.)**

— Now Winter flies. *See* infra: Le Printemps.

— Odessa. Polka Mazurka. *See* infra: Les Pâquerettes. No. 4.

— Les oeufs de Paques, quadrille mignon pour le piano. [With accompaniments for violin, cornet and flute.] *Paris*, [1856.] fol.　　　　　　　　　　　　　　　**e. 38. (27.)**

— Les oeufs de Paques, quadrille mignon pour piano [with accompaniment for cornet]. *London*, [1856.] fol.　　　　　　　　　　　　　　　**h. 619. (17.)**

— L'oiseau bleu ... fantaisie brillante (sur la romance de A. Thys) pour piano. Op. 176. *London*, [1858.] fol.　　　　　　　　　　　　　　　**h. 619. b. (9.)**

— L'oiseau bleu de A. Thys, fantaisie brillante pour piano par A. Leduc. Op. 176. *Paris*, [1859.] fol.　　**h. 619. a. (10.)**

— L'Oiseau des Bois, chanson [begins: "Oh! chante"], paroles des V. Déo. *Paris*, [1865.] fol.　　**H. 2623. a. (7.)**

— [L'Oiseau des Bois.] Softly the Chimes are ringing, song [begins: "Sadly the maid"] written by G. Linley. *London*, [1865.] fol.　　　　　　　　　　**H. 2623. (6.)**

— Les Ombres Chinoises. Quadrille mignon pour le Piano. [With accompaniments for violin, cornet and flute.] *Paris*, [1867.] *obl.* fol.　　　　　　　　　**e. 290. (21.)**

— L'oracle des champs, schottisch pour le piano. *London*, [1853.] fol.　　　　　　　　　　　　　　　**h. 964. (16.)**

— "Our Pet." Quadrille. *See* supra: Le Chien.

— La Paix, quadrille historique et militaire pour le piano. [With accompaniments for violin, cornet and flute.] *Paris*, [1856.] fol.　　　　　　　　　　　　　　　**e. 38. (21.)**

— [La Paix.] Peace, historical and military quadrille for the piano forte. *London*, [1856.] fol.　　**h. 619. (18.)**

— [La Paix.] Peace, historical and military quadrille for the piano forte [as a duet]. *London*, [1856.] fol.　　**h. 619. (19.)**

— Le palais de l'Industrie, valse brillante pour le piano. *Paris*, [1855.] fol.　　　　　　　　**h. 616. (12.)**

— Palestro. Quadrille militaire pour le Piano. *London*, [1860.] fol.　　　　　　　　　　　　**h. 619. c. (21.)**

— [Palestro.] Bataille de Palestro. Quadrille historique & militaire. *Paris*, [1860.] *obl.* fol.　　**e. 70. (27.)**

— Les Pâquerettes. Six esquisses musicales ... pour les petites mains pour Piano. *Paris*, [1863.] fol.　**h. 619. e. (25.)**

— La Parade. Quadrille sur des Rondes enfantines ... pour le Piano. [With accompaniments for violin, cornet and flute.] *Paris*, [1863.] *obl.* fol.　　　　　**e. 290. (15.)**

— Le Paradis des Enfants. Quadrille mignon ... pour le Piano. *Paris*, [1865.] *obl.* fol.　　　　**e. 290. (25.)**

— Partant pour la Syrie. *See* supra: Fantasia on Partant pour la Syrie.

— La Parure de Val, Polka ... pour le Piano. *Paris*, [1861.] fol.　　　　　　　　　　　　**h. 619. e. (5.)**

— Pas redoublé. *See* supra: L'Aquarium. No. 3.

— Passage du Mont St. Bernard. Quadrille historique ... pour le Piano. [With accompaniments for violin, flute and cornet.] *Paris*, [1862.] *obl.* fol.　　　　　**e. 290. (10.)**

LEDUC (Alphonse)

— Passage du Mont St. Bernard. Quadrille historique ... pour Piano. *London*, [1862.] fol.　　**h. 619. c. (18.)**

— Pastorale et Tyrolienne pour le Piano à six mains. *Paris*, [1859.] fol.　　**h. 619. b. (18.)**

— Pastorale et Tyrolienne pour le Piano à six mains. *London*, [1859.] fol.　　**h. 619. a. (24.)**

— Le Pâtre des Alpes, chansonnette [begins: "Mes brebis"]. paroles de T. Julian. *Paris*, [1867.] fol.　　**H. 2623. a. (24.)**

— Pearls of Dew. Polka Mazurka ... for the Pianoforte. *London*, [1862.] fol.　　**h. 619. d. (1.)**

— Pearls of Dew, polka mazurka. [P. F.] *Cincinnati*, [1864.] fol.　　**h. 1459. g. (9.)**

— Pearls of the Morning. *See* supra: Le Jardin sous les Toits.

— La perle de Castille, polka brillante pour le piano ... en morceau. *Paris*, [1855.] fol.　　**h. 616. (7.)**

— La Perle du Nord, varsoviana pour le piano. *Paris*, [1854.] fol.　　**h. 617. (12.)**

— Perles de Rosée. Polka-Mazurka ... pour le Piano. *Paris*, [1862.] fol.　　**h. 619. e. (17.)**

— Le Petit Diable, polka mignonne pour Piano. *Paris*, [1873.] fol.　　**h. 619. f. (14.)**

— Le petit rémouleur ... Polka mignonne, pour le Piano. *London*, [1857.] fol.　　**h. 913. (12.)**

— Le petit sorcier. Quadrille mignon pour le Piano [with accompaniments for violin, flute and cornet]. *Paris*, [1857.] *obl.* fol.　　**e. 70. (11.)**

— [Le petit sorcier.] The little wizard, Quadrilles, Le pettit [*sic*] sorcier, for the Piano. *London*, [1857.] fol.　　**h. 911. (18.)**

— Le Petit Tambourin. Quadrille villageois pour le Piano. [With accompaniments for violin, cornet and flute.] *Paris*, [1861.] *obl.* fol.　　**e. 290. (2.)**

— [Le petit tambourin.] The May Pole Quadrille for the Pianoforte. *London*, [1861.] fol.　　**h. 619. c. (33.)**

— [Le petit tambourin.] The Little Drummer. Song [begins: "At the break"], written by G. Linley. *London*, [1865.] fol.　　**H. 2623. (9.)**

— Le Petit Trianon, quadrille mignon pour le piano. *London*, [1851.] fol.　　**h. 964. (9.)**

— La Petite bouquetière. Quadrille mignon ... Pour le piano. pp. 5. [*A. Leduc: Paris*, c. 1855.] *obl.* fol. *The imprint is cropped.*　　**f. 770. aa. (2.)**

— La petite cendrillon, quadrille pour piano. *London*, [1854.] fol.　　**h. 617. (33.)**

— La petite Cendrillon, quadrille mignon, pour le piano. *Paris*, [1855.] *obl.* fol.　　**e. 38. (28.)**

— La Petite Chevrière, quadrille mignon pour Piano. *Paris*, [1872.] *obl.* fol.　　**e. 272. b. (20.)**

— Petite fantaisie mignonne sur Oberon de Weber. Pour piano, *etc. London*, [1858.] fol.　　**h. 619. a. (20.)**

— Petite fantaisie mignonne sur Oberon de Weber pour piano (à quatre mains). *London*, [1858.] fol.　　**h. 619. a. (21.)**

— La Petite Fête d'Hiver. Quadrille mignon ... pour le Piano. [With accompaniments for violin, flute and cornet.] *Paris*, [1866.] *obl.* fol.　　**e. 290. (31.)**

— Petite fleur des bois, de F. Masini, caprice pour piano par A. Leduc. Op. 174. *London*, [1858.] fol.　　**h. 619. b. (7.)**

LEDUC (Alphonse)

— Petite fleur des Bois, de F. Masini, caprice pour piano par A. Leduc. Op. 174. *Paris*, [1859.] fol.　　**h. 619. a. (8.)**

— Petite fleur des bois, de F. Masini, caprice [as a duet] pour piano, *etc.* Op. 174. *London*, [1858.] fol.　　**h. 619. b. (7b.)**

— La petite magicienne, polka. [P. F.] *London*, [1858.] fol.　　**h. 913. (10.)**

— La petite magicienne, polka mignonne ... pour piano. *Paris*, [1859.] fol.　　**h. 913. (11.)**

— La Petite Retraite. Quadrille mignon ... pour le Piano. [With accompaniments for violin, cornet and flute.] *Paris*, [1864.] *obl.* fol.　　**e. 290. (17.)**

— La Petite Suissesse. Polka mignonne pour le Piano. *London*, [1860.] fol.　　**h. 619. c. (22.)**

— La petite Suisesse. Polka mignonne pour le piano. (Édition no. 2, "en morceau".) *London*, [1860.] fol.　　**h. 913. (12*.)**

— Quatre petites fantaisies élégantes sur des thêmes favoris des opéras. [P. F.] 4 no. *London*, [1855.] fol.　　**h. 619. (6.)**

— 2 petites fantaisies sur des motifs de l'opéra Si j'étais roi, d'A. Adam, pour piano. Op. 166. 2 no. *Paris*, [1856.] fol.　　**h. 619. a. (3.)**

— 2 [petites] Fantaisies sur des motifs de l'opéra Si j'étais roi, d'A. Adam, pour piano. *London*, [1856.] fol.　　**h. 619. b. (2.)**

— 3 Petites Fantaisies ... pour le Piano. Op. 184. *London*, [1860.] fol.　　**h. 619. c. (25.)**

— 3 petites Fantaisies pour piano. Op. 184. *Paris*, [1860.] fol.　　**h. 619. a. (14*.)**

— Trois petites Fantaisies élégantes ... pour la Piano. Op. 190. *Paris*, [1862.] fol.　　**h. 619. e. (13.)**

— [3 petites fantaisies élégantes, *etc.* Op. 190. No. 1.] Aurora. Fantaisie pour Piano. Op. 190. No. 1. *London*, [1862.] fol.　　**h. 619. d. (5.)**

— [3 petites fantaisies élégantes, *etc.* Op. 190. No. 2.] La Jota. Air Espagnol. Fantaisie pour Piano. Op. 190. *London*, [1862.] fol.　　**h. 619. d. (6.)**

— Les Petites Folles quadrille pour Piano avec acc^nts ad lib. *Paris*, [1840?] *obl.* fol.　　**e. 272. (8.)**

— Les petites glaneuses, quadrille Mignon pour le piano. *London*, [1852.] fol.　　**h. 964. (23.)**

— Les Petits Acrobates, quadrille mignon pour Piano. *Paris*, [1872.] *obl.* fol.　　**e. 272. b. (18.)**

— Les Petits Bateaux, quadrille mignon pour le Piano. *Paris*, [1867.] *obl.* fol.　　**e. 217. b. (31.)**

— Les petits Bretons, quadrille mignon pour le piano. *London*, [1858.] fol.　　**h. 911. (20.)**

— Les petits Bretons, quadrille ... pour le piano. *Paris*, [1859.] fol.　　**e. 70. (12.)**

— Les petits Bretons, quadrille mignon. [P. F. duet] *London*, [1858.] fol.　　**h. 911. (21.)**

— Les Petits Chinois. Quadrille mignon. [P. F. with accompaniments for violin, cornet and flute.] *Paris*, [1867.] *obl.* fol.　　**e. 290. (22.)**

— Les petits Ecossais, quadrille mignon, pour le piano. [With accompaniments for flute, violin and cornet.] *Paris*, [1855.] *obl.* fol.　　**e. 38. (29.)**

— Les Petits Musettes. Quadrille mignon ... pour le Piano. [With accompaniments for violin, cornet and flute.] *Paris*, [1865.] *obl.* fol.　　**e. 290. (23.)**

LEDUC (ALPHONSE)

— Les petits patineurs, quadrille mignon, pour le piano. *London*, [1853.] fol. **h. 617. (34.)**

— Les Petits Zouaves. Quadrille mignon pour Piano. *Paris*, [1866.] *obl.* fol. **e. 290. (33.)**

— La Peur. Duettino [begins: "Dans les bois"]. Paroles de T. Julian. *Paris*, [1873.] fol. **H. 2623. a. (38.)**

— Pierre le Grand, quadrille historique pour le piano. *London*, [1855.] fol. **h. 619. (20.)**

— Les plaisirs de la pension, quadrille mignon, pour le piano. *London*, [1853.] fol. **h. 964. (15.)**

— Le Pluie de Dragées. Polka mignonne pour le Piano. *Paris*, [1867.] fol. **h. 619. e. (52.)**

— Polka brillante, sur Si j'étais roi [by A. Adam], pour le Piano. *London*, [1857.] fol. **h. 913. (17.)**

— Polka brillante sur l'opéra Si j'étais roi, d'A. Adam, pour le Piano. *Paris*, [1857.] fol. **h. 913. (18.)**

— Polka des Hussards pour Piano. *Paris*, [1868.] fol. **h. 619. f. (4.)**

— Polka des Hussars pour Piano. *London*, [1870.] fol. **h. 1485. s. (39.)**

— Polka des Roses pour Piano. *Paris*, [1867.] fol. **h. 619. f. (2.)**

— Le Postillon du Roi, quadrille brillant pour le Piano. *Paris*, [1845?] *obl.* fol. **e. 272. (10.)**

— Le Postillon quadrille. [P. F.] *London*, [1855.] fol. *No. 273 of the "Musical Bouquet".* **H. 2345.**

— 24 Préludes dans tous les Tons ... pour Piano. *Paris*, [1859.] fol. **h. 619. a. (5*.)**

— 24 Preludes in all the major & minor keys composed for the Pianoforte. *London*, [1860.] fol. **h. 619. a. (5**.)**

— Le premier ami, quadrille mignon, pour le piano [with an accompaniment for the cornet à pistons]. *London*, [1853.] fol. **h. 617. (24.)**

— Les premières roses, suite de valses pour le piano. *London*, [1859.] fol. **h. 912. (6.)**

— Les premières roses, suite de valses pour le piano, *etc. Paris*, [1859.] fol. **e. 70. (1.)**

— Pretty Polly, Quadrille mignon pour le Piano. *Paris*, [1858.] *obl.* fol. **e. 70. (13.)**

— Pretty Polly Quadrilles. [P. F.] *London*, [1858.] fol. **h. 911. (24.)**

— Pretty Polly Quadrilles. [P. F. duet.] *London*, [1858.] fol. **h. 911. (25.)**

— Priez pour elle, fantaisie élégante. [P. F.] Op. 172. *London*, [1858.] fol. **h. 619. b. (6.)**

— Priez pour elle, fantaisie élégante pour piano. Op. 172. *Paris*, [1859.] fol. **h. 619. a. (7.)**

— The Princess of Wales. *See* infra: [La Princesse de Galles.]

— La Princesse Alexandra de Danemark. Valse brillante pour le Piano. *Paris*, [1864.] fol. **h. 619. e. (27.)**

— La Princesse de Galles. Valse brillante pour Piano. *Paris*, [1866.] fol. **h. 619. e. (46.)**

— [La Princesse de Galles.] The Princess of Wales. Valse brillante pour Piano. *London*, [1866.] fol. **h. 619. d. (29.)**

— La Princesse Michel. Valse brillante pour le Piano. *Paris*, [1863.] *obl.* **h. 619. e. (21.)**

LEDUC (ALPHONSE)

— Le Printemps, chansonnette [begins: "Adieu! l'hiver"], paroles de T. Julian. *Paris*, [1866.] fol. **H. 2623. a. (15.)**

— [Le Printemps.] Now Winter flies, song, English version written by W. Hills. *London*, [1867.] fol. **H. 2623. (15.)**

— Le Printemps. *See* supra: 3 Fantaisies élégantes. Op. 198. No. 2.

— La prise de Sebastopol, quadrille. [P. F. with accompaniments.] *Paris*, [1855.] *obl.* fol. **e. 38. (20.)**

— Pussy, Quadrille mignon pour le Piano. *Paris*, [1857.] *obl.* fol. **e. 70. (14.)**

— The Pussy Quadrille ... for the Pianoforte. *London*, [1857.] fol. **h. 911. (26.)**

— The Pussy Quadrille. [P. F. duet.] *London*, [1857.] fol. **h. 911. (27.)**

— Les 4 fils Aymon. Quadrille pour le piano sur des motifs de W. Balfe. pp. 5. *Chez les fils de B. Schott: Mayence*, [1845.] *obl.* fol. **Hirsch M. 1291. (7.)**

— Le Rapide, galop brillant pour Piano. *Paris*, [1869.] fol. **h. 619. f. (8.)**

— Les rayons d'or, 3 petites Fantaisies pour Piano. Op. 167. 3 no. *Paris*, [1857.] fol. **h. 619. a. (4.)**

— Les rayons d'or, 3 petites Fantaisies pour Piano. Op. 167. 3 no. *London*, [1857.] fol. **h. 619. b. (3.)**

— Redowa nationale, fleur des salons, pour le piano. *Paris*, [1854.] fol. **h. 617. (15.)**

— Le Régent de France. Polka brillante pour Piano. [With accompaniments for violin, cornet and flute.] *Paris*, [1866.] fol. **h. 619. e. (48.)**

— La reine d'Angleterre, polka brillante, pour le piano. *London*, [1853.] fol. **h. 617. (17.)**

— La Reine de Portugal. Valse brillante pour Piano. Édition difficile. *Paris*, [1863.] fol. **h. 619. e. (23.)**

— La Reine de Portugal. Valse brillante. [P. F.] *London*, [1863.] fol. **h. 619. d. (12.)**

— Reine des Belges. Valse brillante pour Piano. *Paris*, [1867.] fol. **h. 619. d. (31.)**

— La Résille. Polka-mazurka pour Piano. *Paris*, [1865.] fol. **h. 619. e. (38.)**

— La Résille. Polka-mazurka pour Piano. *London*, [1865.] fol. **h. 619. d. (21.)**

— Le Retour au Nid, romance [begins: "Écoute, enfant"], paroles d'E. Dufour. *Paris*, [1868.] fol. **H. 2623. a. (37.)**

— Le retour au pays, fantaisie à la valse, for the piano forte. Op. 103. *London*, [1854.] fol. **h. 618. (2.)**

— Le retour au pays, fantaisie à la valse, pour piano. *London*, [1855.] fol. **h. 619. (27.)**

— Retour d'Italie. Quadrille historique et militaire. *Paris*, [1859.] *obl.* fol. **e. 70. (32.)**

— Retour d'Italie. Quadrille ... pour piano. Solo. *London*, [1859.] fol. **h. 911. (30.)**

— Retour d'Italie. Quadrille ... pour piano. Duet. *London*, [1859.] fol. **h. 911. (31.)**

— Retour de Crimée, quadrille militaire pour le piano. [With accompaniments for violin, cornet and flute.] *Paris*, [1856.] fol. **e. 38. (22.)**

— Retour de Crimée, quadrille pour le piano. *London*, [1856.] fol. **h. 619. (21.)**

373

LEDUC (ALPHONSE)

— Le Retour des Hirondelles, valse brillante pour Piano. *Paris*, [1868.] fol.   **h. 619. f. (5.)**

— Return of the Swallows, waltz for the Piano. *London*, [1868.] fol. *A simplified version of the preceding.*   **h. 619. d. (35.)**

— Un Rêve à Venise. Caprice nocturne pour Piano. Op. 196. *Paris*, [1864.] fol.   **h. 619. e. (29.)**

— Un Rêve à Venise. Caprice Nocturne pour Piano. *London*, [1864.] fol.   **h. 619. d. (16.)**

— Rêverie au bal, valse sentimentale pour piano. *Paris*, [1858.] fol.   **h. 916. (8.)**

— Rêverie au bal. Valse sentimentale, pour Piano. *London*, [1858.] fol.   **h. 916. (7.)**

— Rêverie-Barcarolle pour Piano. *Paris*, [1873.] fol.   **h. 619. f. (13.)**

— Une revue aux Tuilleries, quadrille militaire, pour piano [with accompaniments]. *Paris*, [1854.] *obl.* fol.   **e. 38. (23.)**

— Les rives de la Rance, valse élégante, pour le piano. *Paris*, [1854.] fol.   **h. 617. (44.)**

— Le roi de la fève, quadrille mignon pour le piano. *London*, [1858.] fol.   **h. 911. (32.)**

— Le roi de la fève, quadrille ... pour le piano. *Paris*, [1859.] fol.   **e. 70. (15.)**

— Le roi de la fève, quadrille mignon. [P. F. duet.] *London*, [1858.] fol.   **h. 911. (33.)**

— Une Romance de Sieg. Fantaisie pour Piano. Op. 190. No. 3. *London*, [1862.] fol.   **h. 619. d. (7.)**

— Romanza. Op. 195. *See* supra: Les Pâquerettes. No. 5.

— Ronde des Montagnes. *See* supra: Les Pâquerettes. No. 2.

— La Rose de Florence, polka mazurka pour le piano. *Paris*, [1856.] fol.   **h. 913. (13.)**

— La rose de Florence, polka mazurka pour piano. *London*, [1856.] fol.   **h. 913. (14.)**

— La Rose des Alpes, valse sentimentale pour le piano. N°. 1 en feuille. N°. 2 en morceau. 2 no. *Paris*, [1855.] fol.   **h. 616. (13.)**

— Rose-Pompon Valse. *See* supra: Les Pâquerettes. No. 1.

— Rosette. Schottische. [Fife and drum band parts.] *London*, [1877.] 8°.   **f. 414. a. (46.)**

— Le Rossignol et la Fauvette, chansonnette [begins: "Le jour vient"] paroles de C. de Charlemagne. *Paris*, [1865.] fol.   **H. 2623. a. (9.)**

— [Le rossignol et la fauvette.] Sweet Philomel, song [begins: "'Tis sweet"] written by Mrs. W. Hills. *London*, [1865.] fol.   **H. 2623. (11.)**

— Royale Victoria, valse brillante pour piano. *Paris*, [1856.] fol.   **h. 912. (22.)**

— Royale Victoria, valse brillante pour piano. *London*, [1856.] fol.   **h. 912. (21.)**

— Le Ruban d'Honneur, romance [begins: "Embrasse moi"], paroles d'E. Potier. *Paris*, [1867.] fol.   **H. 2623. a. (25.)**

— The Saraband. *See* supra: Grand Mère est toujours là.

— The Sardinian march, arranged for the pianoforte by A. Leduc. *Paris*, [1856.] fol.   **h. 616. (4.)**

— The Sardinian march, arranged for the piano forte by A. Leduc. *London*, [1856.] fol.   **h. 619. (8.)**

LEDUC (ALPHONSE)

— Schoenbrunn, Polka brillante, pour le Piano. *Paris*, [1857.] fol.   **h. 913. (16.)**

— Leduc's Schoenbrunn polka. [P. F.] *London*, [1858.] fol.   **h. 913. (15.)**

— Schottisch Pompadour, pour le piano. *Paris*, [1856.] fol.   **h. 913. (24.)**

— Schottisch Pompadour, pour piano. *London*, [1856.] fol.   **h. 913. (23.)**

— Sémiramis. Fantaisie brillante [on G. A. Rossini's opera] pour le Piano, à six mains. *Paris*, [1861.] fol.   **h. 619. e. (8.)**

— The Sensation Polka. *See* supra: La Jolie Fileuse.

— La sentinelle, polka militaire pour le piano. *Paris*, [1854.] fol.   **h. 617. (22.)**

— Si j'étais roi, quadrille pour piano [on A. Adam's opera]. *Paris*, [1856.] fol.   **e. 70. (21.)**

— "Si j'étais roi," quadrille brillant (sur des motifs de l'opéra d'A. Adam) pour piano. *London*, [1856.] fol.   **h. 911. (34.)**

— La siège de Sébastopol, quadrille pour le piano [with accompaniment]. *Paris*, [1855.] *obl.* fol.   **e. 38. (15.)**

— The Snow polka for Piano. *London*, [1868.] fol.   **h. 619. d. (40.)**

— Softly the chimes are ringing. *See* supra: L'Oiseau des Bois.

— Trois Sonates pour la Guitare. Œuvre 1. *Nantes*, [1825?] fol.   **h. 3213. k. (8.)**

— Le Songe, polka-mazurka ... pour Piano. *Paris*, [1868.] fol.   **h. 619. f. (6.)**

— Le Songe, polka mazurka ... pour Piano. *London*, [1869.] fol.   **h. 619. d. (42.)**

— Souvenir de Bruxelles, Quadrille brillant, pour le Piano. *Paris*, [1858.] *obl.* fol.   **e. 70. (22.)**

— Souvenir de Bruxelles, Quadrille brillant pour le Piano. *London*, [1858.] fol.   **h. 911. (35.)**

— Souvenir de Maintenon. Polka Mazurka pour piano. (Edition no. 1, "en feuille".) *London*, [1860.] fol.   **h. 913. (18*.)**

— Souvenir de Maintenon. Polka Mazurka pour piano. (Edition no. 2, "en morceau".) *London*, [1860.] fol.   **h. 913. (18**.)**

— Souvenir de Marly. Polka-mazurka pour le piano. *Paris*, [1861.] fol.   **h. 619. e. (7.)**

— Souvenir de Marly. Polka-mazurka pour Piano. *London*, [1861.] fol.   **h. 619. e. (34.)**

— Souvenir de Nantes, quadrille brillant pour piano. *London*, [1858.] fol.   **h. 911. (36.)**

— Souvenir de Nantes, quadrille ... pour le piano. *Paris*, [1859.] fol.   **e. 70. (23.)**

— Souvenir de Ratisbonne, quadrille militaire pour le piano [with violin, flute and cornet accompaniments.] *Paris*, [1856.] fol.   **e. 70. (33.)**

— Souvenir de Ratisbonne, quadrille militaire pour piano. *London*, [1856.] fol.   **h. 911. (36a.)**

— Souvenir de Strasbourg. Quadrille brillant pour Piano. *Paris*, [1861.] *obl.* fol.   **e. 290. (5.)**

— [Another copy.]   **e. 290. (6.)**

— Souvenir de Vienne, Fantaisie élégante pour Piano. Op. 168. *Paris*, [1857.] fol.   **h. 619. a. (5.)**

LEDUC (ALPHONSE)

— Souvenir de Vienne, Fantaisie élégante pour Piano. Op. 168. *London*, [1858.] fol.   **h. 619. b. (4.)**

— Souvenir du Théatre Italien. [Operatic fantasias.] [P. F.] Op. 165. 6 no.   *R. Cocks & Co.: London*, [1855.] fol.   **h. 619. (33.)**

— Souvenir du Théatre Italien. [Fantasias on various operas.] Pour le piano, *etc.* N°. 1–6.   *Paris*, [1855.] fol.   **h. 616. (20.)**

— Souvenirs d'enfance, 3 bluettes pour piano. Op. 165. 3 no. *Paris*, [1856.] fol.   **h. 619. a. (2.)**

— Souvenirs d'enfance, 3 bluettes pour piano. 3 no.   *London*, [1856.] fol.   **h. 619. b. (1.)**

— Souvenirs de Clisson, quadrille ... pour le Piano avec accomp^{ts}.   *Paris*, [1845?] *obl.* fol.   **e. 272. (9.)**

— Speranza. Romance Nocturne pour Piano. Op. 192.   *Paris*, [1863.] fol.   **h. 619. e. (26.)**

— Speranza. Romance-Nocturne. Op. 192. [P. F.]   *London*, [1863.] fol.   **h. 619. d. (11.)**

— Star of the evening. Song & chorus. Deuxième Fantaisie pour le Piano.   *Paris*, [1859.] fol.   **h. 619. a. (16.)**

— Star of the evening. Fantasia arranged for the Pianoforte. *London*, [1859.] fol.   **h. 619. b. (11.)**

— The Steeple Chase Quadrille. *See* supra: La Course au Clocher.

— Strasbourg. Quadrille brillant pour le Piano.   *London*, [1861.] fol.   **h. 619. c. (43.)**

— Sweet Philomel. *See* supra: Le rossignol et la fauvette.

— Sympathie Française. Grande Valse pour Piano.   *Dover*, [1857.] fol.   **h. 912. (9.)**

— Taïaut! Taïaut! polka pour Piano.   *Paris*, [1869.] fol.   **h. 619. f. (9.)**

— [Taïaut! Taïaut!] Tally-Ho! polka pour Piano.   *London*, [1869.] fol.   **h. 619. d. (44.)**

— Toc!!! Toc!!! quadrille brillant, pour piano.   *London*, [1853.] fol.   **h. 617. (35.)**

— The Toc! Toc! quadrille. [P. F.]   *London*, [1855.] fol. *No. 226 of the "Musical Bouquet".*   **H. 2345.**

— [Toc! Toc!] The most celebrated Quadrilles ... for the Pianoforte, composed by A. Leduc. No. 4. Toc, Toc. *London*, [1858.] fol.
    h. 619. c. (1.)

— La Toilette. Polka pour Piano.   *London*, [1861.] fol.
    h. 619. c. (30.)

— La Topaze. *See* supra: L'Écrin musicale. No. 4.

— La tour Malakoff, quadrille. [P. F. with accompaniments.] *Paris*, [1855.] *obl.* fol.   **e. 38. (19.)**

— [Le Tournoi.] The Tournament Polka ... for the Piano. *London*, [1864.] fol.   **h. 619. d. (15.)**

— Le Tournoi. Polka brillante pour le Piano.   *Paris*, [1864.] fol.
    h. 619. e. (30.)

— Les Tourterelles. Valse gracieuse pour Piano.   *Paris*, [1866.] fol.   **h. 619. e. (45.)**

— Le Traineau, polka-mazurka pour le piano.   *London*, [1853.] fol.   **h. 964. (18.)**

— Transcription de l'air de Chérubin, des Noces de Figaro de Mozart, pour Piano. *London*, [1869.] fol.   **h. 619. d. (43.)**

LEDUC (ALPHONSE)

— Transcription de l'air de Chérubin [Voi che sapete] des Noces de Figaro, de Mozart, pour Piano.   *Paris*, [1869.] fol.
    h. 619. f. (10.)

— [Travaille Enfant.] Dear Morn of Life. Song, written by W. Hills.   *London*, [1865.] fol.   **H. 2623. (8.)**

— Premier trio concertant ... pour piano, flute & basson ... Op. 66. [Parts.] 3 pt.   *A. Petit: Paris*, [c. 1830.] fol.
    h. 1568. n. (2.)

— Les Trois Cousines, 1er. Quadrille pour Piano à six mains. *Paris*, [1867.] fol.   **h. 619. f. (1.)**

— Les Trois Cousines. Quadrille pour Piano à six mains. *London*, [1867.] fol.   **h. 619. d. (32.)**

— Le trompette, polka militaire pour le piano.   *Paris*, [1856.] fol.   **h. 913. (19.)**

— Le Trompette, polka militaire. [P. F.]   *London*, [1856.] fol.
    h. 913. (20.)

— Valse mignonne. Op. 199. No. 1. *See* supra: L'Aquarium. No. 1.

— Varsoviana des dames, avec la théorie de cette danse, composée et orchestrée par E. Depas, composée pour le piano par A. Leduc. [*Paris*, 1854.] fol.   **h. 617. (10.)**

— Varsoviana nationale ... For the piano-forte. pp. 5.   *Robert Cocks & Co.: London*, [1855?] fol.   **h. 721. n. (24.)**

— La Vie d'une Rose, romance [begins: "Je fais"], paroles d'E. Potier.   *London*, [1867.] fol.   **H. 2623. a. (26.)**

— Le vieux Paris, Quadrille historique, pour le Piano.   *Paris*, [1857.] *obl.* fol.   **e. 70. (34.)**

— Le vieux Paris. Quadrille historique pour le Piano.   *London*, [1857.] fol.   **h. 911. (37.)**

— The Village Fair quadrilles. *See* supra: Le Mât de Cocagne.

— The Village Flower Girl. *See* supra: La Bouquetière de Marly.

— La Voile Égarée. Fantaisie dramatique pour Piano.   *Paris*, [1866.] fol.   **h. 619. e. (49.)**

— La voiture aux chèvres. Quadrille pour le Piano.   *London*, [1857.] fol.   **h. 911. (39.)**

— La Voiture aux Chèvres, chansonnette [begins: "Tu vois"], paroles de T. Julian.   *Paris*, [1866.] fol.   **H. 2623. a. (16.)**

— Wait for the Waggon. Fantasia ... for the Pianoforte.   *Paris*, [1860.] fol.   **h. 619. e. (1.)**

— Wait for the Waggon. Fantasia [on G. P. Knauff's song] ... for the Pianoforte. *London*, [1860.] fol.   **h. 619. c. (10.)**

— The Wandering Heart. Fantasia transcribed for the Pianoforte. *London*, [1866.] fol.   **h. 619. d. (28.)**

— We are coming, sister Mary. Fantasia [on E. P. Christy's song] ... for the Pianoforte. *Paris*, [1860.] fol.   **h. 619. c. (12.)**

— We are coming, sister Mary. Fantasia [on E. P. Christy's song] for the Pianoforte. *London*, [1860.] fol.   **h. 619. c. (3.)**

— Where the Bee sucks. (Dr. Arne.) Fantasia for the Pianoforte. *London*, [1861.] fol.   **h. 619. c. (45.)**

— Willie we have miss'd you. Troisième Fantaisie pour le Piano [on S. C. Foster's song]. *Paris*, [1859.] fol.   **h. 619. a. (17.)**

— Willie we have miss'd you. Fantasia ... [on S. C. Foster's song] for the Pianoforte. *London*, [1859.] fol.
    h. 619. b. (12.)

— Les Willis. Polka-mazurka pour le Piano.   *Paris*, [1864.] fol.
    h. 619. e. (31.)

LEDUC (Alphonse)

— *See* Bousquet (N.) Varsoviana de S^{te}. Cecile ... arrangée pour piano par A. Leduc. [1854.] fol.   **h. 617. (11.)**

— *See* Czerny (C.) [*Collections.*] The morning practice ... with the addition of four new exercises by A. Leduc. [1856.] fol.   **h. 1015. (2.)**

— *See* Czerny (C.) School of modern pianoforte playing, *etc.* ⟨With an appendix by A. Leduc.⟩ Op. 837. *London*, [1855.] fol.   **h. 1016. (2.)**

— *See* Czerny (C.) The new school of velocity (Op. 834) for the pianoforte. ⟨With an appendix by A. Leduc.⟩ 4 bk. *London*, [1855.] fol.   **h. 1015. (1.)**

— *See* Czerny (C.) Studies for the attainment of a practical knowledge of all the chords of through bass for the pianoforte ... With introductory exercises by A. Leduc. Op. 838. *London*, [1855.] fol.   **h. 1015. (4.)**

— *See* Czerny (C.) [40 tägliche Studien. Op. 337.] Exercices Journaliers pour piano ... Nouvelle édition ... augmentée de 4 exercices, écrits spécialement pour l'édition d'A. Leduc. [1887.] fol.   **h. 514. e. (11.)**

— *See* Czerny (C.) and Leduc (A.) 34 new daily exercises for the piano forte ... Composed by C. Czerny and A. Leduc. [1856.] fol.   **h. 1016. (5.)**

— *See* Delaseurie (A.) Mr. Briquet ... quadrille sur des romances de A. Leduc, *etc.* [1865.] *obl.* fol.   **e. 217. a. (6.)**

— *See* Depas (E.) and Leduc (A.) L'Arabesque des jeunes élèves, *etc.* [1854.] fol.   **h. 1610. (8.)**

— *See* Depas (E.) and Leduc (A.) La dame aux Camelias, *etc.* [1853.] fol.   **h. 1610. (7.)**

— *See* Depas (E.) and Leduc (A.) Protège le pécheur, *etc.* [1853.] fol.   **h. 1610. (6.)**

— *See* Garimond (H.) and Leduc (A.) Douze Fantaisies pour Hautbois et Piano, *etc.* [1874.] fol.   **h. 2665. (18.)**

— *See* Klosé (H. E.) and Leduc (A.) L'Adieu ... Fantaisie, *etc.* [1880.] fol.   **h. 3212. e. (24.)**

— *See* Klosé (H. E.) and Leduc (A.) Le Désir ... Fantaisie, *etc.* [1880.] fol.   **h. 3212. e. (23.)**

LEDUC (Ambroise)

— Tête à Tête. Polka. [P. F.] *B. Williams: London*, [1884.] fol.   **h. 975. u. (56.)**

LE DUC (Carl)

— Ah! keep the little faded Flower [by C. Bernstein] as a pianoforte duet. *C. Sheard: London*, [1876.] fol. *No.* 5664, 5 *of the "Musical Bouquet"*.   **H. 2345.**

— Belle Mahone [by J. H. MacNaughton] as a pianoforte duet by C. Le Duc. *C. Sheard: London*, [1876.] fol. *No.* 5646, 7 *of the "Musical Bouquet"*.   **H. 2345.**

— Belle Mahone's Reply [by C. Bernstein], as a pianoforte duet. *C. Sheard: London*, [1876.] fol. *No.* 5648, 9 *of the "Musical Bouquet"*.   **H. 2345.**

— Birdie's come, [by C. Bernstein] as a pianoforte duet. *C. Sheard: London*, [1876.] fol. *No.* 5660, 1 *of the "Musical Bouquet"*.   **H. 2345.**

— Come, Birdie, come, [by C. A. White] as a pianoforte duet. *C. Sheard: London*, [1876.] fol. *No.* 5658, 9 *of the "Musical Bouquet"*.   **H. 2345.**

— Far away, as a pianoforte duet. *C. Sheard: London*, [1876.] fol. *No.* 5650, 1 *of the "Musical Bouquet"*.   **H. 2345.**

LE DUC (Carl)

— Far away, yet ever near, [by C. Bernstein] as a pianoforte duet. *C. Sheard: London*, [1876.] fol. *No.* 5652, 3 *of the "Musical Bouquet"*.   **H. 2345.**

— March of the Men of Harlech, as a pianoforte duet. *C. Sheard: London*, [1876.] fol. *No.* 5668, 9 *of the "Musical Bouquet"*.   **H. 2345.**

— Mollie darling, [by W. S. Hays] as a pianoforte duet. *C. Sheard: London*, [1876.] fol. *No.* 5654, 5 *of the "Musical Bouquet"*.   **H. 2345.**

— Mollie's Answer, [by C. Bernstein] as a pianoforte duet. *C. Sheard: London*, [1876.] fol. *No.* 5656, 7 *of the "Musical Bouquet"*.   **H. 2345.**

— A Ray of Sunshine. Morceau de Salon pour Piano. *London*, [1874.] fol. *No.* 5462, 3 *of the "Musical Bouquet"*.   **H. 2345.**

— A Ray of Sunshine, morceau de salon pour Piano. *London*, [1874.] fol.   **h. 1482. z. (13.)**

— A Ray of Sunshine, morceau de salon ... pour Piano. *London*, [1877.] fol.   **h. 1482. z. (14.)**

— A Ray of Sunshine, morceau de salon pour Piano. *London*, [1878.] fol.   **h. 1494. p. (41.)**

— A Ray of Sunshine ... pour Piano. *London*, [1879.] fol.   **h. 1494. p. (42.)**

— A Ray of Sunsine for the Pianoforte. Edited by G. Rolande. *London*, [1880.] fol.   **h. 1494. p. (43.)**

— A Ray of Sunshine. Morceau de salon. [P. F.] pp. 4. *W. H. Broome: London*, [c. 1900.] fol.   **h. 1203. m. (3.)**

— A Ray of Sunshine. [P. F.] *See* Smallwood (W.) Little Footprints, *etc.* No. 2. [1900–2.] fol.   **h. 1412. w. (1.)**

— A Ray of Sunshine. Morceau de Salon ... pour piano. (Arranged as a duet by P. Jackman.) *R. Cocks & Co.: London*, [1894.] fol.   **h. 3290. l. (27.)**

— Silver Threads among the Gold [by H. P. Danks], as a pianoforte duet. *C. Sheard: London*, [1876.] fol. *No.* 5642, 3 *of the "Musical Bouquet"*.   **H. 2345.**

— 'Tis but a little faded Flower, [by J. R. Thomas] as a pianoforte duet. *C. Sheard: London*, [1876.] fol. *No.* 5662, 3 *of the "Musical Bouquet"*.   **H. 2345.**

— Uncle Tom's Cabin Quadrilles on popular melodies, *etc.* [P. F.] *C. Sheard: London*, [1879.] fol. *No.* 5878, 9 *of the "Musical Bouquet"*.   **H. 2345.**

— The Union Jack of Old England, [by C. Williams] as a pianoforte duet. *C. Sheard: London*, [1876.] fol. *No.* 5666, 7 *of the "Musical Bouquet"*.   **H. 2345.**

— What to us is silver Hair [by C. Bernstein] as a pianoforte duet. *C. Sheard: London*, [1876.] fol. *No.* 5644, 5 *of the "Musical Bouquet"*.   **H. 2345.**

LEDUC (Charles)

— Nuage d'Argent, polka brillante pour Piano. *Bruxelles*, [1882.] fol.   **h. 3276. g. (13.)**

LE DUC (E.)

— Fantasia—Highland Memories. Brass Band Score. *Wright & Round: Liverpool*, [1925.] *obl.* 4°.   **e. 503. (12.)**

— Fantasia—In Days of Old. Brass Band Score. *Wright & Round: Liverpool*, [1934.] *obl.* 4°.   **e. 503. c. (9.)**

LE DUC (Ernest)

— Juanita, polka de Salon. [P. F. with cornet accompaniment.]
London, [1854.] fol.   **h. 723. l. (30.)**

LE DUC (Philibert)

— Chansons et Lettres Patoises Bressanes, Bugeysiennes et
Dombistes, avec une Étude sur le Patois du Pays de Gex et la
Musique des Chansons. Textes recueillis, traduits et annotés
par P. Le Duc, *etc. F. Martin-Bottier: Bourg-en-Bresse*, 1881.
8°.   **11498. c. 24.**

— Les Noëls Bressans de Bourg, de Pont-de-Vaux et des
paroisses voisines ... suivis de six Noëls Bugistes, de trois
anciens Noëls français et des Airs en Musique: Corrigés sur
les premières éditions, traduits et annotés par P. Le Duc, *etc.*
Martin-Bottier: Bourg-en-Bresse, 1845. 8°.   **11498. c. 19.**

LEDUC (Simon)

— 2ᵉ concerto en ut majeur pour violon et orchestre.
Reconstitution par Fernand Oubradous. [Score.] pp. 36.
Éditions musicales transatlantiques: Paris, [1958.] 8°.
Part of "Collection Fernand Oubradous".   **d. 135. e. (2.)**

— Six easy Duets for two Violins, *etc. See infra*: [6 petits duos.
Op. 6.]

— Drei kleine Sonaten für zwei Violinen. *See infra*: [6 petits
duos. Op. 6.]

— [6 petits duos. Op. 6.] Six easy Duets for two Violins, *etc.*
⟨Violino secondo.⟩ *Printed by Longman and Broderip:
London*, [c. 1785.] fol.
Imperfect; wanting the violino primo part.   **g. 218. v. (5.)**

— [6 petits duos. Op. 6.] Drei kleine Sonaten für zwei Violinen.
Herausgegeben von Erich Doflein. [Score.] pp. 24. *B. Schott's
Söhne: Mainz und Leipzig; Schott & Co.: London*, [1941.] 4°.
                                                     g. 218. f. (6.)

— Vier Sonaten für Violine und Basso continuo. Erste
Neuausgabe für Violine und Pianoforte (Cembalo),
Violoncello (Viola da gamba) ad lib. von Elma Doflein. I.
Sonaten: A-Dur, Op. IV Nr. 1. F-Moll, Op. IV Nr. 6 ... II
Sonaten: D-Dur, Op. 1. Nr. 1. C-Moll, Op. IV Nr. 4, *etc.*
[Scores and parts.] *B. Schott's Söhne: Mainz*, [1964.] 4°.
Imperfect; wanting Hft. 2.   **g. 223. mm. (7.)**

— Second Livre de Sonates pour le Violon ... Oeuvre IV. *Ches
Mᵣ le Duc: Paris*, [1770?] fol.   **g. 422. a. (5.)**

— Sonate de violon, avec accompagnement de basse ... Oeuvre
posthume. ⟨Écrit par Ribiere.⟩ pp. 7. *Chez Le Duc: Paris*,
[c. 1780.] fol.
Plate number 56.   **g. 890. e. (2.)**

— Simphonie concertante pour deux violons. Cette simphonie
peut s'exécuter à petite et grande orchestre, les instrumens à
vent sont ad libitum. [Parts.] 16 pt. *Chez Mᵣ Henry: Paris*,
[1775?] fol.   **i. 173. ll.**

— Symphonie en ré-majeur. Reconstitution par Fernand
Oubradous, *etc.* [Score.] pp. 28. *Éditions musicales
transatlantiques: Paris*, [1957.] 8°.   **d. 134. xx. (2.)**

— Symphonie en mi bémol ... Reconstitution de Barry
S. Brook. [Score.] pp. 27. *In:* Brook (Barry S.) La Symphonie
française dans la seconde moitié du XVIIIᵉ siècle. tom. 3.
pp. 55–81. 1962. fol.   **Cup. 1254. z. 1/3.**

— Six Trio pour deux Violons et une Basse ... Oeuvre V. Gravé
par Mᵈᵉ la Veuve Le Clair. [Parts.] *Chés le Sᵣ Sieber: Paris*,
[1775?] fol.
*A slip pasted over the place of imprint bears the words
"Imported & Sold by Longman & Broderip ... London".*
                                                     g. 409. t. (4.)

— *See* Bach (J. C.) and Leduc (S.) Trois Symphonies à quatre
ou à huit parties, *etc.* [1780?] fol.   **R. M. 16. b. 17. (1.)**

LEDUC (Simon) and **GOSSEC** (François Joseph)

— Trois Sinfonies à deux Violons, Taille et Basse, Flûtes ou
Hautbois & Cors de Chasse ... Œuvre I. [Parts.] *J. Schmitt:
Amsterdam*, [1770?] fol.   **g. 257. a. (2.)**

LEDWARD (James)

— *See* Rietz (Julius) [Concert-Stück. Op. 33.] Concert Piece
Op. 33. For oboe & orchestra, *etc.* ⟨[Edited by] J. Ledward.⟩
[1975.] 4°.   **g. 1078. v. (6.)**

LEDYANOI

— Ледяной домъ. Опера. *See* Koreshchenko (Arseny N.)

LEE

-— The Lee Shore. Chorus. *See* Fletcher (P. E.)

— The Lee Shore. [Part-song.] *See* Harris (C.)

— The Lee Shore. Part Song. *See* Jenkins (D. C.)

— The Lee Shore. Romance. *See* Planquette (R.) [Surcouf.]

— The Lee Shore. Song. *See* S., A. M.

— The Lee Shore. Part-Song. *See* Taylor (S. C.)

LEE (   )

— Lee's Twelve Singing Lessons. [*Weekes & Co.: London*,
1904.] *obl.* 8°.   **C. 738. f. (1.)**

LEE (A. Larne)

— *See* Lee (A. Lorne)

LEE (A. Lorne)

— Crysanthemum [*sic*] Waltzes. [P. F.] pp. 5. *Jerome H. Remick
& Co.: Detroit, New York*, [1908.] fol.   **h. 4120. oo. (2.)**

— Fly-Paper Rag. [P. F.] *A. H. Goetting: Toronto*, [1909.] fol.
                                                     h. 4120. oo. (3.)

— I'm thinking of you. [Song.] pp. 5. *Jerome H. Remick & Co.:
Detroit, New York*, [1908.] fol.   **H. 3985. q. (3.)**

— Oh! for a mighty Revival. [Hymn, words and music] by
A. L. Lee. *A. L. Lee: Hamilton, Ontario*, 1909. 8°.
                                                     F. 1171. gg. (34.)

— Two Roses ... Song ... (Words and music by) A. L. Lee.
Toronto, 1910. *s. sh.* fol.
Part of "The Toronto World," July 17*th*, 1910.
                                                     I. 600. d. (167.)

LEE (Alexander)

— *See* Lee (George Alexander)

LEE (Alfred)

— Four ... Motto Songs. *See* Alexandra. The Alexandra Music
Books. No. 46. [1893.] fol.   **H. 2328.**

— The Alabama Claims ... A comic medley ... written by
F. W. Green. *London*, [1872.] fol.
No. 4997, 8 *of the "Musical Bouquet".*   **H. 2345.**

— Album of Jullien's ... Dances. 2 no. [Arranged by W. H.
Montgomery and A. Lee.] [1889.] *See* Victoria. The Victoria
Music Books. No. 166–7. [1878, *etc.*] fol.   **H. 2321.**

— Always do your Duty, Boy. Song & Chorus ... Words by
W. D. Spalding. *C. Sheard & Co.: London*, [1889.] fol.
No. 7780 *of the "Musical Bouquet".*   **H. 2345.**

LEE (Alfred)

— Always think before you speak ... Song [begins: "My advice if it you seek"] written by F. W. Green. *London*, [1872.] fol. *No.* 4863, 4 *of the "Musical Bouquet".* **H. 2345.**

— And so say all of us. [Song.] Written by H. Adams & A. Roberts, *etc. Hopwood & Crew: London*, [1882.] fol. **H. 1260. f. (45.)**

— Angel Echoes. Song & chorus [begins: "I hear them"] written by J. Bath. *London*, [1873.] fol. **H. 1561. (14.)**

— Angels guard my Baby Boy. Cradle Song, written by F. W. Green. *London*, [1874.] fol. *No.* 5381, 2 *of the "Musical Bouquet".* **H. 2345.**

— Annie's idea, varsoviana. [P. F.] *London*, [1874.] fol. *No.* 5130 *of the "Musical Bouquet".* **H. 2345.**

— Another new Bonnet for Mother. Comic Song, written by T. S. Lonsdale. *C. Sheard: London*, [1882.] fol. *No.* 6792, 3 *of the "Musical Bouquet".* **H. 2345.**

— Any body ill? ... Humorous song. *London*, [1872.] fol. *No.* 5008, 9 *of the "Musical Bouquet".* **H. 2345.**

— Arbitration ... [Song.] Written by F. W. Green. *London*, [1874.] fol. *No.* 5228, 9 *of the "Musical Bouquet".* **H. 2345.**

— The Autumn Manœuvres. Humorous song [begins: "Oh! the autumn manœuvres"], written by W. Mitchell. *London*, [1874.] fol. *No.* 5141, 2 *of the "Musical Bouquet".* **H. 2345.**

— Because she ain't built that Way. Comic Song, written by O. Allan. *C. Sheard & Co.: London*, [1889.] fol. *No.* 7791 *of the "Musical Bouquet".* **H. 2345.**

— Beware of the Ring. [Song, begins: "Whatever condition of life".] Written ... by H. Hunter. *London*, [1877.] fol. **H. 1561. (20.)**

— Billy Stutters ... [comic] Song, *etc. C. Sheard: London*, [1876.] fol. *No.* 5685, 6 *of the "Musical Bouquet".* **H. 2345.**

— The Boat of Joy. (New buffo song) ... written by H. Hunter. [Begins: "Leave the gun".] *London*, [1877.] fol. **H. 1561. (24.)**

— The Bond St. Beau. [Song, begins: "In Bond street".] Written by F. W. Green. *London*, [1873.] fol. **H. 1561. (11.)**

— The Boy from County Clare. [Song, begins: "My name is Pat".] Written by H. Hunter. *London*, [1877.] fol. **H. 1561. (23.)**

— The Brandy and Soda Brigade. [Song.] Written by J. W. Jones, *etc. Francis Bros. & Day: London*, [1886.] fol. **H. 1260. f. (46.)**

— Brass. [Song, begins: "I've never earned a penny".] Written by T. L. Clay. *London*, [1879.] fol. **H. 1783. o. (31.)**

— The Bridal Bell ... Ballad [begins: "Ding, ding, dong"] written by H. Martin. *London*, [1871.] fol. *No.* 4567, 8 *of the "Musical Bouquet".* **H. 2345.**

— Polka. "Cairo." (Conductor [and military band parts].) 26 pt. *In:* FLOTOW (F. F. A. von) *Baron.* [Jubel-Ouverture.] Overture, *etc.* 1896. fol. [*Boosey's military Journal. ser.* 101. *no.* 3.] **h. 1549.**

— Called Back ... Ballad ... Words by T. S. Lonsdale. *C. Sheard: London*, [1889.] fol. *No.* 7419, 20 *of the "Musical Bouquet".* **H. 2345.**

— Came the Lord of Lorne a wooing ... Ballad ... written by F. W. Green. *London*, [1871.] fol. *No.* 4634, 5 *of the "Musical Bouquet".* **H. 2345.**

LEE (Alfred)

— Captain Webb ... Song, *etc.* (Written by F. W. Green.) *C. Sheard: London*, [1876.] fol. *No.* 5569, 70 *of the "Musical Bouquet".* **H. 2345.**

— Champagne. [Song, begins: "Since Champagne Charlie first began".] Written by T. L. Clay. *London*, [1879.] fol. **H. 1783. o. (30.)**

— Champagne Charlie ... Comic Song, written ... by G. Leybourne. *C. Sheard: London*, [1867.] fol. *Imperfect; wanting the title page.* **H. 1650. e. (9.)**

— The Christmas Dinner ... Song ... words by T. S. Lonsdale. *C. Sheard: London*, [1884.] fol. *No.* 7013, 4 *of the "Musical Bouquet".* **H. 2345.**

— The Claimant's Woes. [Comic song.] Written by F. W. Green. *London*, [1874.] fol. *No.* 5413, 4 *of the "Musical Bouquet".* **H. 2345.**

— Come kiss let's be Friends. Ballad ... poetry by T. L. Clay. *C. Sheard: London*, [1880.] fol. *No.* 6217, 8 *of the "Musical Bouquet".* **H. 2345.**

— The Cricket on the Hearth ... Song, words by T. S. Lonsdale. *C. Sheard: London*, [1882.] fol. *No.* 6811, 2 *of the "Musical Bouquet".* **H. 2345.**

— The Darkie's Courtship. Song with chorus [begins: "About this darkie's courtship"] ... written by F. Green. *London*, [1874.] fol. *No.* 4538, 9 *of the "Musical Bouquet".* **H. 2345.**

— Dick Murphy of T. C. D. ... Song [begins: "I'm an undergrad"] written by H. Sweny. *London*, [1871.] fol. **H. 1561. (7.)**

— Doing the Academy, [comic song] written by T. L. Clay, *etc. C. Sheard: London*, [1879.] fol. *No.* 6073, 4 *of the "Musical Bouquet".* **H. 2345.**

— Dolly Varden ... Comic song [begins: "Oh! have you seen"] written by F. W. Green. *London*, [1872.] fol. *No.* 4877, 8 *of the "Musical Bouquet".* **H. 2345.**

— Don't let it happen again ... Song [begins: "Never to cry"] written by F. W. Green. *London*, [1872.] fol. *No.* 4889, 90 *of the "Musical Bouquet".* **H. 2345.**

— Don't tell the missis you have seen me here. [Song, begins: "I'm married".] (Written by F. W. Green.) *London*, [1878.] fol. **H. 1783. o. (27.)**

— Dora's Device ... Song [begins: "A gem of rare price"], written by W. Mitchell. *London*, [1874.] fol. *No.* 5124, 5 *of the "Musical Bouquet".* **H. 2345.**

— The Early Bird catches the worm ... Song [begins: "I'm fond of early rising"] written by F. W. Green. *London*, [1872.] fol. *No.* 4895, 6 *of the "Musical Bouquet".* **H. 2345.**

— England in Danger ... Song, written by O. Allan. *C. Sheard & Co.: London*, [1889.] fol. *No.* 7952, 3 *of the "Musical Bouquet".* **H. 2345.**

— England's Welcome to her Prince ... Song, *etc.* (Written by F. W. Green.) *C. Sheard: London*, [1876.] fol. *No.* 5600, 1 *of the "Musical Bouquet".* **H. 2345.**

— Farewell Annie dear ... Song and dance, written by H. Martin. *London*, [1874.] fol. *No.* 5087 *of the "Musical Bouquet".* **H. 2345.**

— Fishing from a punt at Teddington ... Song [begins: "There was Jones"] written by F. W. Green. *London*, [1872.] fol. *No.* 4926, 7 *of the "Musical Bouquet".* **H. 2345.**

— The Flying Trapeze. [Song.] Written ... by George Leybourne, *etc.* pp. 7. *C. Sheard: London*, [c. 1870.] fol. *The titlepage has been cropped.* **H. 1846. ww. (11.)**

LEE (Alfred)

— [The Flying Trapeze.] The Man on the flying Trapeze. An old circus song. Arranged by C. Wallis. pp. 5. 1934. 4°. *See* WALLIS (Chester)   **G. 981. m. (15.)**

— For my love he is late. Serenade [begins: "I leaned out of window"] written by J. Ingelow. *London*, [1871.] fol.
No. 4687, 8 *of the "Musical Bouquet".*   **H. 2345.**

— Forbidden Fruit. Comic song [begins: "When I was a boy"], written by J. F. Mc.Ardle. *London*, [1878.] fol.   **H. 1783. o. (28.)**

— The Gainsboro' Hat ... Comic Song ... written by F. W. Green. *C. Sheard: London*, [1877.] fol.
No. 5691, 2 *of the "Musical Bouquet".*   **H. 2345.**

— The Gallant 24th ... Song, written by F. W. Green. *C. Sheard: London*, [1879.] fol.
No. 5976, 7 *of the "Musical Bouquet".*   **H. 2345.**

— The General Election ... Song, written by L. Clay. *C. Sheard: London*, [1880.] fol.
No. 6229, 30 *of the "Musical Bouquet".*   **H. 2345.**

— The General Strike, a ... medley ... written by ... W. Burnot. *London*, [1874.] fol.
No. 5105, 6 *of the "Musical Bouquet".*   **H. 2345.**

— Get away Johnnie! [Song.] Written by J. W. Jones, *etc. Francis Bros & Day: London*, [1886.] fol.   **H. 1260. f. (47.)**

— God bless Prince Alfred's Bride. [Song.] Poetry by F. W. Green. *London*, [1874.] fol.
No. 5342, 3 *of the "Musical Bouquet".*   **H. 2345.**

— God help our Sister Isle. Song ... words by F. W. Green. *C. Sheard: London*, [1880.] fol.
No. 6215, 6 *of the "Musical Bouquet".*   **H. 2345.**

— Going to the Derby in a Four-in-hand. [Song, begins: "As we drive".] Written by F. W. Green. *London*, [1870.] fol.   **H. 1561. (5.)**

— Gone to the Bad ... Song, written by F. W. Green. *London*, [1874.] fol.
No. 5230, 1 *of the "Musical Bouquet".*   **H. 2345.**

— The Good Time is come. Song. Written by W. Mitchell. *London*, [1874.] fol.
No. 5206, 7 *of the "Musical Bouquet".*   **H. 2345.**

— Gordon, or, Too late! too late! Memorial Song, written by E. Letherbrow. *C. Sheard: London*, [1889.] fol.
No. 7493, 4 *of the "Musical Bouquet".*   **H. 2345.**

— The Grecian Bend ... Comic song [begins: "I'm glad to see you"] written by B. Walker. *London*, [1871.] fol.
No. 4371, 2 *of the "Musical Bouquet".*   **H. 2345.**

— Grumble away. Humorous song [begins: "I hate to hear folks grumble"] written by F. W. Green. *London*, [1872.] fol.
No. 5000, 1 *of the "Musical Bouquet".*   **H. 2345.**

— The Haw! Haw! Swell ... [Song.] Written by T. S. Lonsdale. *C. Sheard: London*, [1884.] fol.
No. 7090, 1 *of the "Musical Bouquet".*   **H. 2345.**

— He's as good as gold ... Song [begins: "My love is but a shepherd lad"] written by F. W. Green. *Leeds*, [1875.] fol.   **H. 1561. (17.)**

— Hearts of Iron. [Song, begins: "Arise, arise".] Written by E. J. Brown. *London*, [1879.] fol.   **H. 1783. o. (29.)**

— The Heavy Swell of the Sea. [Song, begins: "As you may suppose".] Written by T. L. Clay. *London*, [1879.] fol.   **H. 1783. o. (32.)**

— Higher up ... Song [begins: "Have you watched"] written by F. W. Green. *London*, [1872.] fol.
No. 4861, 2 *of the "Musical Bouquet".*   **H. 2345.**

LEE (Alfred)

— Hit the right nail on the head ... Song [begins: "How many people pass their lives"] written by F. W. Green. *London*, [1872.] fol.
No. 4875, 6 *of the "Musical Bouquet".*   **H. 2345.**

— Homeless. Song [begins: "Where do I journey"] written by F. W. Green. *London*, [1874.] fol.
No. 4704, 5 *of the "Musical Bouquet".*   **H. 2345.**

— The Host of the Lion & Lamb. [Song, begins: "A Briton I am".] Written by H. Hunter. *London*, [1877.] fol.   **H. 1561. (21.)**

— I always make myself at home ... Ballad [begins: "I hope, my friends"] written by C. Sansom. *London*, [1870.] fol.
No. 4453, 4 *of the "Musical Bouquet".*   **H. 2345.**

— I dreamt, my little boy, of thee ... Ballad ... written by F. W. Green. *London*, [1872.] fol.
No. 4938 *of the "Musical Bouquet".*   **H. 2345.**

— I'll paddle my own canoe. [Song, begins: "I left my loved and sacred home".] *London*, [1874.] fol.
No. 3904, 5 *of the "Musical Bouquet".*   **H. 2345.**

— I'll send you one by the Parcels' Post ... Song. Written by T. S. Lonsdale. *C. Sheard: London*, [1884.] fol.
No. 7086, 7 *of the "Musical Bouquet".*   **H. 2345.**

— I love my love ... Ballad, words by F. W. Green. *C. Sheard: London*, [1880.] fol.
No. 6213, 4 *of the "Musical Bouquet".*   **H. 2345.**

— I love thee more than I can say ... Ballad, words by F. W. Green. *C. Sheard: London*, [1880.] fol.
No. 6143, 4 *of the "Musical Bouquet".*   **H. 2345.**

— I'm a Don, I've got 'em on. [Comic song.] Written by T. S. Lonsdale. *C. Sheard: London*, [1880.] fol.
No. 6198, 9 *of the "Musical Bouquet".*   **H. 2345.**

— I'm happy since you still love me. [Song.] ... Words by J. Cuthbertson. *C. Sheard: London*, [1879.] fol.
No. 5928 *of the "Musical Bouquet".*   **H. 2345.**

— I will not heed her warning. [Song, begins: "Nay, I will not heed"] ... Written by W. Mitchell. *London*, [1874.] fol.
No. 5080 *of the "Musical Bouquet".*   **H. 2345.**

— I wish you all good night ... Song [begins: "To say good bye"] written by F. W. Green. *London*, [1872.] fol.
No. 4855, 6 *of the "Musical Bouquet".*   **H. 2345.**

— The Idol of the Day. (Par excellence.) [Song, begins: "I'm on the cards".] Written ... by ... Vance. *London*, [1869.] fol.   **H. 1561. (2.)**

— In a Fog ... Comic song [begins: "The fog was very thick"] written by F. W. Green. *London*, [1872.] fol.
No. 4951, 2 *of the "Musical Bouquet".*   **H. 2345.**

— Is the war to last for ever. Song, written by H. J. Whymark. *London*, [1871.] fol.
No. 4701, 2 *of the "Musical Bouquet".*   **H. 2345.**

— It's never too late to mend ... Song & chorus, words by F. W. Green. *C. Sheard: London*, [1880.] fol.
No. 6247 *of the "Musical Bouquet".*   **H. 2345.**

— It would not be surprising. Ballad [begins: "'Tis fair Spring time"]. Words by H. Hunter. *London*, [1877.] fol.   **H. 1561. (22.)**

— The Jolly Bohemians ... Song [begins: "We are gay Bohemians"] written by F. W. Green. *London*, [1874.] fol.
No. 4652, 3 *of the "Musical Bouquet".*   **H. 2345.**

— Jumbo's Jinks. A Comic Vocal Medley. (Written by F. W. Green. Arranged by A. Lee.) *C. Sheard: London*, [1882.] fol.
No. 6799, 800 *of the "Musical Bouquet".*   **H. 2345.**

LEE (Alfred)

— Kissi Kissi ... Comic Song, written by F. W. Green. *London,* [1874.] fol.
No. 5309, 10 *of the "Musical Bouquet".* **H. 2345.**

— Kissing in the Tunnel. [Song, begins: "You have asked me for a rhyme".] Words by W. Mitchell. *London,* [1874.] fol.
No. 5177, 8 *of the "Musical Bouquet".* **H. 2345.**

— The Knock-around Nigger ... Song. Written by M. Lane. *C. Sheard & Co.: London,* [1889.] fol.
No. 8061 *of the "Musical Bouquet".* **H. 2345.**

— Leaning on the Balcony ... Song [begins: "'Tis pleasant"] written by F. W. Green. *London,* [1872.] fol.
No. 4857, 8 *of the "Musical Bouquet".* **H. 2345.**

— The Legend of Love. Ballad, words by O. Allan. *C. Sheard & Co.: London,* [1889.] fol.
No. 8105 *of the "Musical Bouquet".* **H. 2345.**

— Let those laugh that lose ... Song [begins: "Now I'm a jolly sort of man"] written by H. J. Whymark. *London,* [1872.] fol.
No. 4900, 1 *of the "Musical Bouquet".* **H. 2345.**

— Lettice White. Song [begins: "My neighbour White"] written by J. Ingelow. *London,* [1871.] fol.
No. 4694, 5 *of the "Musical Bouquet".* **H. 2345.**

— Life and the Flower ... Song [begins: "I cast a flower upon the stream"], written by O. Allan. *London,* [1874.] fol.
No. 5179, 80 *of the "Musical Bouquet".* **H. 2345.**

— The Lion Hearts of England. National Song and Chorus, words by O. Allen. *C. Sheard: London,* [1884.] fol.
No. 7017, 8 *of the "Musical Bouquet".* **H. 2345.**

— The Little Coquette. [Song, begins: "Oh! how I love to flirt".] Written by F. W. Green. *London,* [1872.] fol.
No. 4869, 70 *of the "Musical Bouquet".* **H. 2345.**

— Little Snowball. Song, written by F. W. Green. *C. Sheard: London,* [1882.] fol.
No. 6818, 9 *of the "Musical Bouquet".* **H. 2345.**

— London Society. [Song, begins: "I think I've travelled everywhere".] ... Written ... by ... Vance. *London,* [1878.] fol. **H. 1783. o. (26.)**

— Look at the price of coals. [Song, begins: "I'm very unhappy".] Written by H. Hunter. *London,* [1877.] fol. **H. 1561. (30.)**

— Look before you leap. Motto Song & Chorus, written by F. W. Green. *C. Sheard: London,* [1880.] fol.
No. 6246 *of the "Musical Bouquet".* **H. 2345.**

— Lounging in the Aq. [Song, begins: "I've tried all kinds of gaiety".] Written by T. L. Clay. *London,* [1879.] fol. **H. 1783. o. (33.)**

— Love Lane. Ballad ... words by T. S. Lonsdale. *C. Sheard: London,* [1884.] fol.
No. 7024, 5 *of the "Musical Bouquet".* **H. 2345.**

— Love may be old, but his Heart's ever young ... Vocal Duet, words by F. W. Green. *C. Sheard: London,* [1884.] fol.
No. 7021, 2 *of the "Musical Bouquet".* **H. 2345.**

— Lucy's Advice ... Song [begins: "Oh! I never will marry"], written by W. Mitchell. *London,* [1874.] fol.
No. 5181, 2 *of the "Musical Bouquet".* **H. 2345.**

— Make hay while the sun shines ... Song [begins: "The happy spring and summer days"] written by F. W. Green. *London,* [1872.] fol.
No. 4871, 2 *of the "Musical Bouquet".* **H. 2345.**

— The Man on the flying Trapeze. *See* supra: [The Flying Trapeze.]

LEE (Alfred)

— Many happy returns of the day. Birthday song [begins: "We are gazing back"], written by W. Mitchell. *London,* [1874.] fol.
No. 5085, 6 *of the "Musical Bouquet".* **H. 2345.**

— May the present moment be the worst of our lives. Song [begins: "Dear friends"] written ... by Vance. *London,* [1870.] fol. **H. 1561. (3.)**

— Mercenary Jane ... Comic song [begins: "'Twas at a first-class eating-house"]. (Words by F. W. Green.) *London,* [1871.] fol.
No. 4986, 7 *of the "Musical Bouquet".* **H. 2345.**

— The Mermaid ... Comic song [begins: "'Twas in the Atlantic ocean"] written by W. M. Thackeray. *London,* [1871.] fol.
No. 4672, 3 *of the "Musical Bouquet".* **H. 2345.**

— The Merry New Year polka. [P. F.] *London,* [1881.] fol. **h. 3275. j. (25.)**

— The Military. A Serio-Comic Song ... written by T. S. Lonsdale. *C. Sheard: London,* [1880.] fol.
No. 6250, 1 *of the "Musical Bouquet".* **H. 2345.**

— Minnie Palmer Quadrilles. (Waltzes.) 2 no. [P. F.] *C. Sheard & Co.: London,* [1889.] fol.
No. 7838–41 *of the "Musical Bouquet".* **H. 2345.**

— Mother weep not for your boy. A song [begins: "Oh! mother"] ... written by Nella. *London,* [1871.] fol.
No. 4608, 9 *of the "Musical Bouquet".* **H. 2345.**

— Mother wouldn't let me. [Song.] Written by T. S. Lonsdale. *C. Sheard: London,* [1884.] fol.
No. 7003, 4 *of the "Musical Bouquet".* **H. 2345.**

— Mother's last Words ... Song & Chorus, written by F. W. Green. *C. Sheard: London,* [1874.] fol.
No. 5359 *of the "Musical Bouquet".* **H. 2345.**

— Mrs. Somebody swallowed a fly. [Song.] Written by F. W. Green. *London,* [1872.] fol. **H. 1561. (10.)**

— Mrs. Winslow's Soothing Syrup. Comic Song, *etc.* (Written by W. R. Gordon.) *C. Sheard: London,* [1877.] fol.
No. 5738, 9 *of the "Musical Bouquet".* **H. 2345.**

— Music from the Gold Sphere. [Song.] ... Written by F. W. Green. *C. Sheard: London,* [1874.] fol.
No. 5466 *of the "Musical Bouquet".* **H. 2345.**

— My Friend the Ma-jar. [Song.] Written by Walter Greenway. pp. 5. *Hopwood & Crew: London,* [c. 1870.] fol. **H. 1652. jj. (2.)**

— My Nancy Fair at the fancy fair. Song [begins: "Oh! if you visit"]. (Words by F. W. Green.) *London,* [1870.] fol. **H. 1561. (4.)**

— The New Electric Light ... Comic Song, written by F. W. Green. *C. Sheard: London,* [1879.] fol.
No. 5900, 1 *of the "Musical Bouquet".* **H. 2345.**

— The Night Birds. Song [written] by A. G. Vance. *London,* [1870.] fol. **H. 1561. (6.)**

— Not for Joseph ... Comic song, arranged ... by A. Lee. *London,* [1874.] fol.
No. 3994, 5 *of the "Musical Bouquet".* **H. 2345.**

— Now is not that like Roger ... Comic song [begins: "There's nothing new"] written by F. W. Green. *London,* [1872.] fol.
No. 4967 *of the "Musical Bouquet".* **H. 2345.**

— Oh! bid me not forget the Past ... Ballad, written by T. L. Clay. *C. Sheard: London,* [1880.] fol.
No. 6201 *of the "Musical Bouquet".* **H. 2345.**

LEE (Alfred)

— Oh, Fie! Diddledum ... [Song.] Words by T. S. Lonsdale.
C. Sheard: London, [1889.] fol.
No. 7531, 2 *of the "Musical Bouquet".* **H. 2345.**

— Oh! I've lost my Katie dear. [Song.] Written by F. Green.
London, [1873.] fol. **H. 1561. (15.)**

— The Old Church Spire ... Song & Chorus, written by F. Gray.
C. Sheard & Co.: London, [1889.] fol.
No. 7810 *of the "Musical Bouquet".* **H. 2345.**

— Old England shares thy Grief. Ballad ... written by F. W.
Green. *C. Sheard: London*, [1879.] fol.
No. 6035, 6 *of the "Musical Bouquet".* **H. 2345.**

— Old Friends. Lancers ... for the Pianoforte. *C. Sheard &
Co.: London*, [1889.] fol.
No. 7956, 7 *of the "Musical Bouquet".* **H. 2345.**

— The Old Village School. Song & Chorus, words by T. L. Clay.
C. Sheard: London, [1880.] fol.
No. 6219, 20 *of the "Musical Bouquet".* **H. 2345.**

— One story is good till another is told ... Song [begins: "I hear
a long story"] written by F. W. Green. *London*, [1872.] fol.
No. 4873, 4 *of the "Musical Bouquet".* **H. 2345.**

— Only once a year ... Song [begins: "To Brompton I was
going"] written by C. H. Witt. *London*, [1872.] fol.
No. 4960, 1 *of the "Musical Bouquet".* **H. 2345.**

— Our Brothers in the Mines. Song, written by F. W. Green.
C. Sheard: London, [1877.] fol.
No. 5754, 5 *of the "Musical Bouquet".* **H. 2345.**

— Our lost little one. Song with chorus [begins: "Bright
maybuds were springing"] written by F. Green. *London*,
[1871.] fol.
No. 4531, 2 *of the "Musical Bouquet".* **H. 2345.**

— Our Sailors on the Sea. Song, written by F. W. Green.
C. Sheard: London, [1874.] fol.
No. 5281, 2 *of the "Musical Bouquet".* **H. 2345.**

— Out with my gun in the morning. [Song, begins: "I live a
jovial country life".] Written by F. W. Green. *London*, [1873.]
fol. **H. 1561. (13.)**

— The Pantomime. Comic Vocal Medley, written by F. W.
Green. *C. Sheard: London*, [1880.] fol.
No. 6189, 90 *of the "Musical Bouquet".* **H. 2345.**

— Poor Jo. Song & Chorus, written by W. R. Gordon.
C. Sheard: London, [1876.] fol.
No. 5683, 4 *of the "Musical Bouquet".* **H. 2345.**

— Poor little Sue the quadroon ... Ballad [begins: "There's a
sad story told"] written by H. Hunter. *London*, [1877.] fol.
H. 1561. (25.)

— Pretty Puss ... Song [begins: "We live at home"] written by
F. W. Green. *London*, [1872.] fol.
No. 4841, 2 *of the "Musical Bouquet".* **H. 2345.**

— The Queen he swore to serve. Written by Frederick Bowyer,
etc. [Song. Staff and tonic sol-fa notation. Voice part.]
Francis, Day & Hunter: London, [1895.] *s. sh.* fol.
H. 3980. qq. (1.)

— Quite au fait. [Song, begins: "Well! here I am".] (Written by
S. Shenton.) *London*, [1876.] fol. **H. 1561. (19.)**

— The Right Man at the Helm. Patriotic Song ... written by
F. W. Green. *C. Sheard: London*, [1877.] fol.
No. 5716, 7 *of the "Musical Bouquet".* **H. 2345.**

— The Right Man in the right place ... Song [begins: "I'm
going to sing"] written by F. W. Green. *London*, [1872.] fol.
No. 4891, 2 *of the "Musical Bouquet".* **H. 2345.**

LEE (Alfred)

— The Royal Wild Beast Show galop. [P. F.] *London*, [1870.]
fol.
No. 4367, 8 *of the "Musical Bouquet".* **H. 2345.**

— Said the Pot to the Kettle. [Song.] Written by F. W. Green and
T. L. Clay. *Hopwood & Crew: London*, [1882.] fol.
H. 1260. f. (48.)

— Sally Wade's choice. [Song.] Written ... by H. Hunter.
London, [1877.] fol. **H. 1561. (29.)**

— The Same Knock may come at your Door. A Proverb in
Song, words by F. W. Green. *C. Sheard: London*, [1882.] fol.
No. 6824, 5 *of the "Musical Bouquet".* **H. 2345.**

— Saved, though the Ship was lost at Sea ... [Song.] Words by
O. Allan. *C. Sheard & Co.: London*, [1889.] fol.
No. 7834, 5 *of the "Musical Bouquet".* **H. 2345.**

— Say so saucy Sue. [Song, begins: "Miss Susan Simpkins".]
Written ... by H. Hunter. *London*, [1877.] fol.
H. 1561. (27.)

— The School Board ... A comic medley ... written by F. W.
Green. *London*, [1872.] fol.
No. 5032, 3 *of the "Musical Bouquet".* **H. 2345.**

— Serjeant Sharp of Lincoln's Inn. [Song, begins: "Ahem!
ahem!"] Written by W. Greenaway. *London*, [1872.] fol.
H. 1561. (9.)

— The Shah's Visit to England ... Vocal Medley. *C. Sheard:
London*, [1874.] fol.
No. 5340, 1 *of the "Musical Bouquet".* **H. 2345.**

— She comes, fair star. (La Mandoline.) ... Serenade [begins:
"Where all is calm"] written by F. W. Green. *London*, [1871.]
fol.
No. 4650, 1 *of the "Musical Bouquet".* **H. 2345.**

— She did ... Comic song [begins: "I dearly loved"]. (Written
by F. W. Green.) *London*, [1874.] fol.
No. 4616 *of the "Musical Bouquet".* **H. 2345.**

— She's as good as gold ... Song [begins: "Though fond of
jollity"] written by F. W. Green. *Leeds*, [1875.] fol.
H. 1561. (18.)

— She's the Apple of my Eye ... Song and Chorus, written by
F. W. Green. *C. Sheard: London*, [1874.] fol.
No. 5250, 1 *of the "Musical Bouquet".* **H. 2345.**

— Signals of Distress. Ballad, the words by O. Allan. *C. Sheard
& Co.: London*, [1889.] fol.
No. 8106 *of the "Musical Bouquet".* **H. 2345.**

— Skating on the Rink. Comic Song, written by F. W. Green.
C. Sheard: London, [1876.] fol.
No. 5590, 1 *of the "Musical Bouquet".* **H. 2345.**

— Song of the Conscript [begins: "Waving on high"] ... written
by F. W. Green. *London*, [1874.] fol.
No. 4628, 9 *of the "Musical Bouquet".* **H. 2345.**

— The Spelling Bee. Comic Vocal Medley, written by F. W.
Green. *C. Sheard: London*, [1876.] fol.
No. 5592, 3 *of the "Musical Bouquet".* **H. 2345.**

— The Spirit of the Deep galop. [P. F.] *London*, [1876.] fol.
h. 1482. z. (15.)

— Spooning on the Sands ... Comic song [begins: "Who
doesn't love to wander"] written by F. W. Green. *London*,
[1874.] fol.
No. 4827, 8 *of the "Musical Bouquet".* **H. 2345.**

— Stout and Bitter. [Song, begins: "I tasted have".] Written by
J. Jones. *London*, [1873.] fol. **H. 1561. (16.)**

LEE (ALFRED)

— The Stowaway. [Song.] ... Written by F. W. Green.
C. Sheard: London, [1882.] fol.
No. 6733, 4 *of the "Musical Bouquet".* **H. 2345.**

— Strike the iron while it's hot ... Song, written by F. W. Green.
London, [1872.] fol.
No. 4879, 80 *of the "Musical Bouquet".* **H. 2345.**

— Tambo Sambo. [Song, begins: "There was a saucy nigger".]
Written by H. Hunter. *London*, [1877.] fol. **H. 1561. (26.)**

— A Tear for Beaconsfield. Ballad ... written by F. W. Green.
C. Sheard: London, [1881.] fol.
No. 6620, 1 *of the "Musical Bouquet".* **H. 2345.**

— Tell me Darling, tell me truly ... Song. Written by O. Allan.
C. Sheard: London, [1874.] fol.
No. 5187, 8 *of the "Musical Bouquet".* **H. 2345.**

— Then I'll prove to my true Love untrue ... Comic Song,
written by A. Thurville. *C. Sheard: London*, [1881.] fol.
No. 6503, 4 *of the "Musical Bouquet".* **H. 2345.**

— They have found me a home. Song with chorus [begins:
"Saved from the pitiless rain"] ... written by F. W. Green.
London, [1872.] fol.
No. 4903 *of the "Musical Bouquet".* **H. 2345.**

— They have written a letter from home. [Song, begins: "Oh!
heed not the tears"] ... Written by F. W. Green. *London*,
[1872.] fol.
No. 4902 *of the "Musical Bouquet".* **H. 2345.**

— Three Acres and a Cow! Song, written by O. Allan.
C. Sheard: London, [1889.] fol.
No. 7640 *of the "Musical Bouquet".* **H. 2345.**

— Three jolly Humbugs ... Humorous Song, written by F. W.
Green. *C. Sheard: London*, [1874.] fol.
No. 5238, 9 *of the "Musical Bouquet".* **H. 2345.**

— The Three Sailors of Bristol Citee. Humorous song [begins:
"There were three sailors"] written by Thackeray. *London*,
[1872.] fol.
No. 5034, 5 *of the "Musical Bouquet".* **H. 2345.**

— The Tichborne Trial ... Comic vocal medley ... written by
F. W. Green. *London*, [1872.] fol.
No. 4962, 3 *of the "Musical Bouquet".* **H. 2345.**

— 'Tis Angel Voices that we hear. [Song.] ... Words by O. Allan.
C. Sheard & Co.: London, [1889.] fol.
No. 8102 *of the "Musical Bouquet".* **H. 2345.**

— Toothpick and Crutch. [Song, begins: "I'm one of those
enchanting youths".] Written by T. L. Clay. *London*, [1879.]
fol. **H. 1783. o. (34.)**

— Treading on dangerous ground. [Song, begins: "That speech
is but silver".] Written ... by H. Hunter. *London*, [1877.] fol.
H. 1561. (28.)

— The Uhlan's Farewell. [Song, begins: "Speak to me
Gretchen"] ... Written by Nella. *London*, [1874.] fol.
No. 4626, 7 *of the "Musical Bouquet".* **H. 2345.**

— The Um-ber-el-la Mender. [Song, begins: "Now when you
look at me".] Written ... by G. Leybourne. *London*, [1865.]
fol. **H. 1561. (1.)**

— Up in the Monument, [song] written by Frank W. Green, *etc.*
pp. 5. *Hopwood and Crew: London*, [c. 1870.] fol.
Cropped. **H. 1652. v. (29.)**

— Wait till the violets blow. Ballad with chorus [begins: "'Twas
autumn"] written by F. W. Green. *London*, [1872.] fol.
No. 4904, 5 *of the "Musical Bouquet".* **H. 2345.**

— Walking in the Zoo. [Song, begins: "The Stilton, sir".]
Written by H. W. Sweny. *London*, [1871.] fol. **H. 1561. (8.)**

LEE (ALFRED)

— The Walking Wedding. [Song.] ⟨Words by "Perroquet".⟩ pp. 5.
Charles Sheard & Co.: London, [c. 1895.] fol.
H. 1654. qq. (30.)

— We are going away to Manga. (Song of the African Slave.)
Written by H. Martin. *London*, [1874.] fol.
No. 5107 *of the "Musical Bouquet".* **H. 2345.**

— We'll fight for our honour ... Song [begins: "'Tis scarcely
wise"] ... written by Nella. *London*, [1871.] fol.
No. 4646, 7 *of the "Musical Bouquet".* **H. 2345.**

— Wearily waiting for him to return. Ballad with chorus
[begins: "A lone mother sat"] ... written by F. W. Green.
London, [1871.] fol.
No. 4640, 1 *of the "Musical Bouquet".* **H. 2345.**

— Welcome, White Wings! ... Song, words by O. Allan.
C. Sheard: London, [1889.] fol.
No. 7778 *of the "Musical Bouquet".* **H. 2345.**

— When all this uproar is over ... Comic song [begins: "I'm
fond of taking it easy"] written by C. Browne. *London*,
[1874.] fol.
No. 4780, 1 *of the "Musical Bouquet".* **H. 2345.**

— When my ship comes home. Buffo song [begins: "I'm sadly
out of spirits"] written by F. W. Green. *London*, [1873.] fol.
H. 1561. (12.)

— When you wash a Nigger white. Comic Song. (Written by
F. W. Green.) *C. Sheard: London*, [1874.] fol.
No. 5493, 4 *of the "Musical Bouquet".* **H. 2345.**

— Why rouse the British lion ... Song [begins: "What means
this talk"] written by F. W. Green. *London*, [1871.] fol.
No. 4667, 8 *of the "Musical Bouquet".* **H. 2345.**

— Wo-oh! Emma! ... Comic Song ... written by O. Allen.
C. Sheard: London, [1878.] fol.
No. 5800 *of the "Musical Bouquet".* **H. 2345.**

— Would you be surprised to hear ... Comic song, written by
F. W. Green. *London*, [1874.] fol.
No. 4797, 8 *of the "Musical Bouquet".* **H. 2345.**

— The Wreck of the Northfleet ... Recitative and Aria, written
by W. R. Gordon. *C. Sheard: London*, [1874.] fol.
No. 5254, 5 *of the "Musical Bouquet".* **H. 2345.**

— The Wreck of the Princess Alice ... Song, written by W. R.
Gordon. *C. Sheard: London*, [1878.] fol.
No. 5862, 3 *of the "Musical Bouquet".* **H. 2345.**

— Yes, I love you very dearly. [Song.] ... Poetry by F. W. Green.
C. Sheard: London, [1874.] fol.
No. 5464 *of the "Musical Bouquet".* **H. 2345.**

— Yo, heave ho! on we gaily go ... Ballad [begins: "I left my
little Polly"] written by F. W. Green. *London*, [1871.] fol.
No. 4529, 30 *of the "Musical Bouquet".* **H. 2345.**

— You'll be sorry for this ... Comic Song, written by W. R.
Gordon. *C. Sheard: London*, [1876.] fol.
No. 5594, 5 *of the "Musical Bouquet".* **H. 2345.**

— *See* BASS (Tom) The Bill Poster or "Stick 'em up Bill" ...
[Song.] Arranged by A. Lee. [1892.] fol. **H. 3980. c. (1.)**

— *See* BELASCO (F.) Creep into Bed, my Baby, *etc.* (Arranged ...
by A. Lee.) [1889.] fol. **H. 2345.**

— *See* BURNOT (W.) The Duchess of Devonshire ... Arranged
by A. Lee. [1877.] fol. **H. 1778. e. (71.)**

— *See* DAVIS (A.) Baby's laughing in her Sleep ... Arranged by
A. Lee. [1889.] fol. **H. 2345.**

— *See* FAGAN (Barney) I love only one Love. ⟨Song and chorus.⟩
Arranged by A. Lee, *etc.* [1900.] fol. **H. 1601. oo. (11.)**

LEE (Alfred)

— *See* HULSE (E. H.) The Rockaway Quickstep March. (Arranged by A. Lee.) [1889.] fol. **H. 2345.**

— *See* JULLIEN (L. A.) Jullien's celebrated Dance Compositions. (Arranged ... by A. Lee.) [1889.] fol. **H. 2345.**

— *See* MAGUIRE (T.) Bold Robert Emmett ... Arranged by A. Lee. [1903.] fol. **H. 1799. ww. (57.)**

— *See* MAGUIRE (T.) Where, oh! where is my Norah? Ballad, *etc.* (Arranged by A. Lee.) 1891. fol. **H. 1797. p. (43.)**

— *See* MAGUIRE (T.) Where, oh, where is my Norah ... Arranged by A. Lee. [1903.] fol. **H. 1799. ww. (61.)**

— *See* OSBORNE (C.) What do they do with the old 'uns? [Song.] (Arranged by A. Lee.) 1892. fol. **H. 3710. (18.)**

— *See* PLEON (Harry) [Mock Melodrama.] Harry Pleon's Mock Melodrama, *etc.* ⟨Song. Arranged by A. Lee.⟩ [1892.] fol. **H. 3981. j. (32.)**

— *See* SELBY (Arthur) The Brick went up, *etc.* ⟨Song. Arranged by A. Lee.⟩ [1892.] fol. **H. 3981. v. (1.)**

— *See* SIMMONS (E. K.) Good Bye, *etc.* (Arranged by A. Lee.) [1881.] fol. **H. 2345.**

— *See* TABRAR (J.) Sleeping in the Air, *etc.* (Arranged by A. Lee.) 1892. fol. **H. 3850. (43.)**

— *See* WEST (Arthur) I'll give him "Ta-ra-ra boom-de-ay", *etc.* ⟨Song. Arranged by A. Lee.⟩ [1892.] fol. **H. 3981. qq. (15.)**

LEE (Alfred) and HARRIGAN (E.)

— Hildebrandt Montrose, [comic song] written by E. Harrigan. *C. Sheard: London*, [1876.] fol. *No. 5687, 8 of the "Musical Bouquet".* **H. 2345.**

— Hildebrandt Montrose. *See* BERNSTEIN (C.) Hildebrandt Montrose & E. Harrigan's Polka [on A. Lee's song]. [1877.] fol. **H. 2345.**

LEE (Ambrose)

— The Bold Young Volunteer. Patriotic Song ... words and music by A. Lee. *Forsyth Brothers: London*, [1886.] fol. **H. 1788. v. (14.)**

LEE (Amelia W. Lelièvre)

— Sunrise Waltz. [P. F.] *A. Eady & Co.: Auckland*, 1910. fol. **h. 3283. jj. (40.)**

— Tantum ergo. Soprano solo with Organ or Piano accompt. *A. Eady & Co.: Auckland*, [1909.] fol. **H. 1187. rr. (8.)**

LEE (Annie)

— A Fantasia à la valse, for the Pianoforte. *London*, [1860.] fol. **h. 1460. v. (7.)**

— The Military March, composed for the Pianoforte. *London*, [1862.] fol. **h. 1460. v. (8.)**

— The Penrhyn quadrilles. [P. F.] *London*, [1857.] fol. **h. 919. (7.)**

— The railway galop ... for the pianoforte, *etc. London*, [1858.] fol. **h. 919. (8.)**

— The victor waltzes ... for the pianoforte. *London*, [1858.] fol. **h. 919. (9.)**

— The victory polka. [P. F.] *London*, [1856.] fol. **h. 976. d. (25.)**

LEE (Arthur)

— The Cape Union Sight Singer through Song. A Graduated Course of Songs & Melodious Exercises in Tonic Sol-fa notation. Edited by A. Lee ... Based ... upon "Sight Singing through Song from the Staff Notation," by R. Dunstan. (Complete edition.) *Schofield & Sims: Huddersfield*, [1913.] 8°. *Part of the "S. & S. Series".* **D. 803.**

— Hester. Song, the words by C. Lamb. *Novello and Co.: London*, 1921. 4°. **G. 426. r. (3.)**

— The Southern Cross Chorister. Parts I. and II. Pianoforte edition, with hints to teachers. Edited by A. Lee. *J. Curwen & Sons: London*, [1907.] 8°. **F. 1668.**

— The Southern Cross Chorister. The work for the junior and elementary certificates of Tonic Sol-fa College. Edited by A. Lee. 2 pt. *J. Curwen & Sons: London*, [1906?] 8°. *Without titlepage. The title is taken from the cover.* **B. 880. o. (2.)**

— [Another edition.] The Southern Cross Chorister. The Work for the Junior and Elementary (for the Intermediate) Certificates of the Tonic Sol-fa College. Edited by A. Lee. 2 pt. *J. Curwen & Sons: London*, [1907.] 8°. **D. 789. d. (2.)**

— The Southern Cross Chorister. Part 1. The Work for the Junior and Elementary Certificates of the Tonic Sol-fa College. Edited by A. Lee. *J. Curwen & Sons: London*, [1906.] 8°. **D. 789. d. (1.)**

— The Southern Cross Chorister ... Extra Part. For Schools of the Lower Grades. Edited by A. Lee. [Tonic sol-fa notation.] *J. Curwen & Sons: London*, [1907.] 8°. **D. 837. a. (3.)**

— *See* DUNSTAN (R.) and LEE (A.) A Collection of over 600 English and Dutch Songs, *etc.* [1914.] 8°. **F. 1707.**

LEE (Mrs Arthur Carey)

— The Tomahawk polka. [P. F.] *London*, [1868.] fol. **h. 1485. s. (41.)**

LEE (Aylmer)

— The Steamer steamed away. ⟨Song.⟩ Written and composed by A. Lee, Maurice Scott & John Neat. *B. Feldman & Co.: London*, [1907.] 4°. **H. 3985. q. (4.)**

LEE (Aylmer) and SCOTT (Maurice)

— Kiss me Georgie, do ... ⟨Song.⟩ Written and composed by A. Lee & M. Scott. pp. 3. *Shapiro von Tilzer Music Co.: London*, [1908.] 4°. **H. 3985. q. (5.)**

LEE (B. Sandberg)

— Te Deum laudamus ... in ... C, for Baritone Solo and Chorus. *Weekes & Co.: London*, [1903.] 8°. **F. 1169. c. (17.)**

LEE (B. Watt)

— A Bachelor Life for me! Humorous song. Written & composed by B. W. Lee. pp. 5. *J. Bath: London*, [1899.] fol. **H. 3980. qq. (2.)**

— Bubbles!—Humorous song. Written & composed by B. W. Lee. pp. 5. *J. Bath: London*, [1899.] fol. **H. 3980. qq. (3.)**

— Much the same to-day! Humorous song. Written & composed by B. W. Lee. pp. 5. *J. Bath: London*, [1900.] fol. **H. 3985. q. (6.)**

LEE (Mrs Baker P.)

— *See* LEE (Lulu Skinner) *Mrs.*

LEE (Bernard)

— A choice collection of twenty airs for the single and double flageolet. *London*, [1821?] *obl.* 4°. **b. 60. (5.)**

—— A complete preceptor for the quadrille flageolet. *London*, [1833.] fol. **h. 1160. (1.)**

— Three concertante duets for two flutes. Op. 1. *London*, [1818.] fol. **h. 1160. (2.)**

— Dear Harp of sweet Erin. Ballad ... written by Miss Chapman. pp. 3. *Printed by Phillips & Mayhew: London*, [WM 1819.] fol. **H. 1652. ll. (24.)**

— A Fantasia for the Flute, with an accompaniment for the Pianoforte. *London*, [1835?] fol. **h. 250. a. (4.)**

— The National Waltz, arranged with variations for the Flute and an accompaniment for the Pianoforte. *London*, [1835?] fol. **g. 280. b. (7.)**

LEE (Bert)

— "Hi! there! whoa!" ... ⟨Song.⟩ Written and composed by B. Lee. [Staff and tonic sol-fa notation. Voice part.] *Francis, Day & Hunter: London, New York*, [1908.] *s. sh.* fol. **H. 3985. q. (7.)**

— "Hi! there! whoa!" *etc.* ⟨Song.⟩ [With separate voice part.] 2 pt. *Francis, Day & Hunter: London*, [1908.] fol. **H. 3985. q. (8.)**

— Hope for the best. ⟨Song.⟩ Written and composed by B. Lee. *B. Feldman & Co.: London*, [1908.] 4°. **H. 3985. q. (9.)**

— What's the matter with Father? [Song.] Words and music by B. Lee, *etc.* [With separate voice part.] 2 pt. *W. Paxton; Price & Reynolds: London*, [1908.] fol. *Price & Reynolds' Sixpenny Series. no.* 134. **H. 3985. q. (10.)**

— "What would the Congregation say?" ... ⟨Song.⟩ Written and composed by B. Lee. [Staff and tonic sol-fa notation. Voice part.] *Francis, Day & Hunter: London*, [1908.] *s. sh.* fol. **H. 3985. q. (11.)**

— "What would the Congregation say?" *etc.* ⟨Song.⟩ [With separate voice part.] 2 pt. *Francis, Day & Hunter: London*, [1908.] fol. **H. 3985. q. (12.)**

— *See* ALLANDALE (Fred) and LEE (B.) All the Time is Summertime with you. ⟨Song.⟩ Written and composed by F. Allandale and B. Lee. [1911.] fol. **H. 3988. oo. (44.)**

— *See* ALLEN (Andrew N.) and LEE (B.) All the old Cocks are very busy crowing ... [Song.] Written & composed by A. Allen and B. Lee. [1916.] fol. **H. 3988. pp. (6.)**

— *See* ALLEN (Andrew N.) and LEE (B.) You can't do without a Bit of Love. ⟨Song.⟩ Written and composed by A. Allen and B. Lee. [1916.] fol. **H. 3988. pp. (7.)**

— *See* ARTHURS (George) and LEE (B.) Let's pretend we're married. ⟨Song.⟩ Written and composed by G. Arthurs & B. Lee. [1913.] 4°. **H. 3988. uu. (56.)**

— *See* ARTHURS (George) and LEE (B.) Mister Goldberg's Jewsharp Band. Song ... Written and composed by G. Arthurs and B. Lee. [1912.] fol. **H. 3988. uu. (57.)**

— *See* ARTHURS (George) and LEE (B.) "Sweet Eileen O'Shea" ... ⟨Song.⟩ Written and composed by G. Arthurs and B. Lee. [1912.] fol. **H. 3988. uu. (58.)**

— *See* ARTHURS (George) and LEE (B.) Timothy Green. ⟨Song.⟩ Written and composed by G. Arthurs and B. Lee, *etc.* [1913.] fol. **H. 3988. uu. (59.)**

— *See* DAVID (Worton) In the Valley of the Moon. ⟨Song.⟩ Words and music by W. David, B. Lee, *etc.* [1916.] fol. **H. 3990. yy. (18.)**

LEE (Bert)

— *See* DAVID (Worton) Poppy. ⟨Song.⟩ Written and composed by W. David, B. Lee, *etc.* [1914.] fol. **H. 3990. yy. (21.)**

— *See* DAVID (Worton) Something's always happening by the Seaside. ⟨Song.⟩ Written and composed by W. David, B. Lee, *etc.* [1914.] fol. **H. 3990. yy. (24.)**

— *See* DAVID (Worton) Stand in the Corner and be a good Boy. ⟨Song.⟩ Written by W. David, B. Lee, *etc.* [1914.] fol. **H. 3990. yy. (25.)**

— *See* DAVID (Worton) Sweet Kathleen ... ⟨Song.⟩ Written & composed by W. David, B. Lee, *etc.* [1910.] fol. **H. 3990. yy. (27.)**

— *See* DAVID (Worton) Wedding Cake. ⟨Song.⟩ Written and composed by W. David ... and B. Lee, *etc.* [1915.] fol. **H. 3990. yy. (28.)**

—— [For editions and arrangements of songs written and composed by B. Lee in sole collaboration with Worton David:] *See* DAVID (Worton) and LEE (B.)

— *See* GREY (C.) and LEE (B.) The Miner's Story, *etc.* 1915. fol. **H. 2087. (133.)**

— *See* KAPS (K.) *pseud.* Lonely. Waltz including B. Lee's Songs, "I feel so lonely" and "No more stopping out late". 1911. fol. **h. 681. b. (35.)**

— *See* PETHER (H. E.) Blighty March. Founded on Weston and Lee's ... song Blighty, *etc.* 1916. fol. **h. 3284. tt. (6.)**

— *See* SMITH (C.) [Back again.] Selection on melodies by C. Smith ... B. Lee, *etc.* 1919. fol. **h. 3284. xx. (38.)**

— *See* SMITH (C.) Cheep. Selection by C. Smith ... B. Lee, *etc.* 1917. fol. **h. 3284. xx. (39.)**

LEE (Bo Luen)

— *See* LI (Bao-lian)

LEE (Bob)

— *See* ANGUS (Colin S.) and LEE (B.) I'm going to marry Mary in the Morning. [Song.] Written & composed by C. S. Angus and B. Lee, *etc.* [1914.] fol. **H. 3988. ss. (19.)**

LEE, afterwards STEMBRIDGE (Carolyn)

— Five Villancicos. For 3 & 4 voices and/or instruments. ⟨From a manuscript in the archive of Segovia Cathedral.⟩ Edited by Carolyn Lee. pp. 12. *Antico Edition: Lustleigh*, [1976.] 4°. **G. 383. mm. (11.)**

LEE (Carrington)

— Cradle Song. "Hush thee my darling," written by E. Fitzball. *London*, [1878.] fol. **H. 1785. o. (35.)**

— The Last Letter. Song [begins: "The days are waning fast"]. Words by R. Reece. *London*, [1878.] fol. **H. 1783. o. (36.)**

LEE (Charles)

— Spring. Song. *London*, [1882.] fol. **H. 1787. j. (25.)**

LEE (Clifford Bernard)

— *See* DITTERS VON DITTERSDORF (Carl) Concertos for double Bass and Orchestra. ⟨Krebs 171, 172. Piano reduction by C. Lee.⟩ [1978.] 4°. **g. 867. h. (3.)**

— *See* KEYPER (F. A. L. J.) Romance and Rondo for Double Bass and Orchestra. ⟨Edited by R. Slatford. Piano reduction by C. Lee.⟩ [1975.] 4°. **g. 867. d. (4.)**

LEE (D.)

— A Grand triumphal March ... For the piano forte. pp. 7.
Chappell and Co.: London, [c. 1815.] fol.   **h. 60. f. (21.)**

LEE (DAI-KEONG)

— Incantation and Dance. For violin and piano. (Violin part
edited by Patricia Travers.) [Score and part.] 2 pt.
G. Schirmer: New York, [1950.] 4°.   **g. 500. ii. (12.)**

LEE (DAVID)

— "Away from him I love;" ballad, the words by W. J. Millson.
London, [1847.] fol.   **H. 1704. (39.)**

— "Come to the cloud capt mountains [*sic*]," [song,] written by
Miss Pardoe. *London*, [1833.] fol.   **H. 1288. (17.)**

— Come to the cloud capt mountain. [Song.] The poetry by Miss
Pardoe. pp. 5. *G. S. Tregear: London*, [1855.] fol.
    H. 1758. (27.)

— "Ho! for merry England;" national ballad, the words by
Miss Pardoe. pp. 5. *Tregear & Lewis: London*, [1833?] fol.
    H. 1288. (15.)

— I'll have a lover in spite of them all, ballad, words by
E. Davids. [Begins: "The girls of the village all tell me I'm
jealous".] *London*, [1854.] fol.   **H. 1758. (28.)**

— The mermaid's cave, [song] written by Miss Pardoe. pp. 5.
Tregear & Lewis: London, [1833?] fol.   **H. 1288. (12.)**

— The Mermaid's Cave, *etc.* *London*, [1865.] fol.
    H. 1772. r. (26.)

— "My own one," [song] written by Miss Pardoe. pp. 5.
Tregear & Lewis: London, [1833?] fol.   **H. 1288. (19.)**

— "Oh! must we part to-night;" a ballad, written by Miss
Pardoe. pp. 5. *Tregear & Lewis: London*, [1843?] fol.
    H. 1288. (14.)

— Oh! must we part tonight, a ballad ... written by Miss
Pardoe. *London*, [1854.] fol.   **H. 1758. (26.)**

— O must we part tonight. Ballad. *London*, [1864.] fol.
    H. 1772. r. (25.)

— The poet's bride, [song] written by Miss Pardoe. pp. 5.
Tregear & Lewis: London, [1833?] fol.   **H. 1288. (16.)**

— "The red and the blue," song written by Miss Pardoe. pp. 5.
Tregear & Lewis: London, [1833?] fol.   **H. 1288. (18.)**

— The red and the blue, song ... written by Miss Pardoe.
London, [1854.] fol.   **H. 1758. (25.)**

— A set of Turkish melodies. The poetry by Maurice Dowling,
etc. *A. Lee & Lee: London*, [1830?] 4°.   **E. 1732.**

— Songs for the Army. Song for the Canteen, the words by
R. G. Pigot. pp. 5. *The Author: London*, [1842.] fol.
    H. 1288. (10.)

— "The Thames;" a national song, the words by R. G. Pigot.
pp. 6. *The author: London*, [1842.] fol.   **H. 1288. (9.)**

— The united service; a national song, the words by R. G. Pigot.
pp. 6. *The Author: London*, [1842.] fol.   **H. 1288. (11.)**

— The wandering fairy; ballad [begins: "I've left my fairy
haunts"]. *London*, [1846.] fol.   **H. 1704. (38.)**

— "Write to me, love;" a ballad, written by Miss Pardoe. pp. 5.
Tregear & Lewis: London, [1843?] fol.   **H. 1288. (13.)**

— *See* HORN (C. E.) Horn's Alpine Waltz, arranged ... by
D. Lee. [1843.] fol.   **h. 932. (15.)**

LEE (DAVID) and LEE (GEORGE ALEXANDER)

— Songs for the Army. [Words] by Richard Greville Pigot. With
symphonies and accompaniments by D. and A. Lee. no. 1.
The Author: London, 1841. fol.   **H. 1653. bb.**

— [Another copy.]
Containing 10 songs with separate title-pages and pagination.
    R. M. 13. f. 10.

— Songs for the Army. By R. G. Pigot. [Melodies only.] pp. 32.
The Author: London, [1842.] 16°.   **A. 451.**

LEE (DORA)

— Sea Horses. Unison Song for children, poem and music by
D. Lee. *J. Curwen & Sons: London*, 1926. 8°.
[*Choruses for equal voices. No.* 1670.]   **E. 861.**

LEE (DOROTHY)

— L'Heure brève. *See infra*: [One fleeting Hour.]

— I gathered a Rose. A Song with violin or cello obbligato,
words by E. M. Stuart. *S. Fox Pub. Co.: Cleveland*, 1917. fol.
    H. 1846. x. (40.)

— I love you more. Song with violin or cello obbligato, words
by E. Edson. *S. Fox Pub. Co.: Cleveland, New York*, 1921. 4°.
    G. 426. r. (5.)

— The Monkey-Man. [Song.] Words by E. V. Cooke. *S. Fox
Pub. Co.: Cleveland*, 1918. fol.   **H. 1846. x. (41.)**

— My Dreams. Song with violin or cello obligato, words by
F. G. Bowles. *S. Fox Pub. Co.: Cleveland, etc.*, 1916. fol.
    H. 1846. x. (42.)

— One Fleeting Hour. Song, with Violin or Cello obligato,
words by K. Fuhrmann. Extra High, High, Medium, Low,
Extra Low. 5 no. *S. Fox Pub. Co.: Cleveland*, (1915.) fol.
    H. 1793. s. (37.)

— [Another copy.]
With a different title-page.   **H. 1846. x. (43.)**

— [One fleeting Hour.] L'Heure brève ... Chanson avec violon
ou violoncelle obligato ... Paroles françaises d'A. Larrieu.
S. Fox Pub. Co.: Cleveland, New York, 1920. 4°.
    G. 426. r. (4.)

— When you are truly mine. Song, with violin or cello
obbligato, words by E. M. Stuart. *S. Fox Pub. Co.: Cleveland,
etc.*, 1917. fol.   **H. 1846. x. (44.)**

LEE (DOUGLAS ALLEN)

— *See* NICHELMANN (Christoph) Clavier Concertos in E major
and A major. Edited by D. A. Lee. [1977.] 4°. [*Recent
Researches in the Music of the Classical Era. vol.* 6.]
    g. 1490. c.

LEE (EASTEN)

— Auldstane. Polka March. [Two mandolines and P. F.] *Barnes
& Mullins: Bournemouth*, [1896.] fol.   **h. 188. e. (29.)**

LEE (EDOUARD)

— La Bayamesa, ballade pour le piano ... Op. 7. *Brunswick*,
[1859.] fol.   **h. 1487. p. (18.)**

— Souvenance. Rêverie intime pour le Piano. Op. 6. *Brunswick*,
[1859.] fol.   **h. 1487. p. (17.)**

LEE (ERNEST MARKHAM)

— Abide with me. Two-part Anthem. Words by H. F. Lyte, *etc.*
Banks & Son: York, 1941. 8°.
York Series, No. 1470.   **F. 231. mm. (22.)**

LEE (ERNEST MARKHAM)

— Admirals all. [For S. C. Words by] Henry Newbolt. pp. 6. *J. Curwen & Sons: London*, [1910.] 8°. [*Choruses for equal Voices. no.* 1228.] **E. 861.**

— Alice in Wonderland. Twelve easy duets for pianoforte. 2 bk. *Anglo French Music Co.: London*, 1923. 4°. **g. 1123. (3.)**

— Arcady. Unison song, words by Margaret Rose. pp. 7. *Leonard, Gould & Bolttler: London*, [1953.] 8°. [*Leonard, Gould & Boltzler's Library of unison and Part-songs for Schools. no.* 87.] **F. 1843.**

— At Dusk. [P. F.] *J. Curwen & Sons: London*, 1923. 4°. *Part of "Selected Pianoforte Music. Edited by E. Fowles".* **g. 1127. dd. (3.)**

— At Home and Abroad. 6 pianoforte pieces. *A. Lengnick & Co.: London*, 1919. 4°. **g. 1129. h. (29.)**

— At the Pantomime. Six very easy Pianoforte Pieces, *etc.* *A. Lengnick & Co.: London*, 1914. 4°. **g. 1129. b. (10.)**

— Aubade. [Organ.] *J. B. Cramer & Co.: London*, 1941. 4°. [*Cramer's Library of Organ Music by British Composers. Set* 7. *No.* 6.] **g. 1353.**

— Balletto. An easy Suite for Pianoforte, *etc.* *J. B. Cramer & Co.: London*, 1926. 4°. *Part of the "Library Edition".* **g. 1125. t. (8.)**

— Be merry and wise. Christmas ... Carol. [Staff and tonic sol-fa notation.] [1896?] *See* CHORAL. Choral Leaflets. No. 129. [1882, *etc.*] *s. sh.* 4°. **F. 569.**

— Benedictus ... in ... C. 1909. *See* NOVELLO AND CO. Novello's Parish Choir Book, *etc.* No. 804. [1866, *etc.*] 8°. **E. 618.**

— Blessed be the Lord my Strength. Full Anthem for four voices, *etc.* 1903. *See* NOVELLO AND CO. Novello's Collection of Anthems, *etc.* No. 770. [1876, *etc.*] 8°. **E. 618. a.**

— Blessed be the Lord my Strength ... Anthem, *etc.* [1904.] *See* NOVELLO AND CO. Novello's Tonic Sol-fa Series. No. 1396. [1876, *etc.*] 4°. **B. 885.**

— Boating Song. [Song, words by] A. B. Cooper. *J. Curwen & Sons: London*, [1899.] 8°. *Unison Songs, No.* 33. **E. 812.**

— Markham Lee's Books for Beginners. A modern method of pianoforte instruction, *etc.* 3 bk. *Paterson Sons & Co.: Glasgow, etc.*, 1922. 4°. **g. 337. xx. (3.)**

— 1. Bourrée. 2. Minuet. 3. Gigue ... For Pipes. *J. B. Cramer & Co.: London*, 1941. 4°. *Music for Pipes. No.* 36. **g. 1087. a. (7.)**

— The Brown Bird's Lullaby. Unison song, word by Margaret Rose. pp. 4. *J. B. Cramer & Co.: London*, [1949.] 8°. [*Cramer's Library of Unison and Part-songs. no.* 219.] **E. 1678. a.**

— By the Wayside. Five pastorals for pianoforte. *A. Lengnick & Co.: London*, 1919. 4°. **g. 1129. h. (30.)**

— A Canary's Song. Unison Song, words by T. Wells. *Winthrop Rogers: London*, 1938. 8°. *Part of the "Winthrop Rogers Edition".* **E. 1830. e. (9.)**

— Capriccietto. [Organ.] *J. B. Cramer & Co.: London*, 1925. 4°. [*Cramer's Library of Organ Music. Set* 1. *No.* 7.] **g. 1353.**

— Changeable Blackbird. Two-part Song for Equal Voices ... Poem by U. Gwynne, *etc.* *J. Curwen & Sons: London*, 1935. 8°. [*Choruses for equal Voices. no.* 1900.] **E. 861.**

— The Change-Ringers. Two-part Song for equal voices, words by S. N. Sedgwick. *J. Williams: London*, 1919. 4°. *Collection of Two-part Songs for treble voices. Fourth Series. No.* 11. **F. 1681.**

LEE (ERNEST MARKHAM)

— Six Characteristic Pieces ... for the pianoforte. I. Dream fancies ... II. The Goblin walk. III. A sunny morning. IV. The wind in the trees. V. Polly's Lullaby. VI. March of the sprites. 6 no. *J. Williams: London*, 1916. fol. **h. 3284. nn. (33.)**

— The Chase of Life. Hunting Song, words by S. L. Sedgwick. *J. Williams: London*, 1919. 8°. *Unison School Songs. Series II, No.* 17. **F. 197. g.**

— Thirteen Christmas Carols. New and Old. Third Selection, arranged by E. M. Lee. *Banks & Son: York*, 1932. 8°. *York Series, No.* 1114. **F. 1176. i. (3.)**

— Cinderella. A Fairy Suite for pianoforte, *etc.* *A. Lengnick & Co.: London*, 1915. 4°. **g. 603. dd. (12.)**

— Cliff and Tide-rip. [P. F.] *Oxford University Press: London*, 1928. 4°. [*The Oxford Piano Series. No.* 112.] **g. 1231.**

— Colours. [Unison song, words by] U. Gwynne. *E. J. Arnold & Son: Leeds*, [1944.] 8°. *The Music Hour, No.* 15. **E. 1830. e. (54.)**

— Come Landlord, fill the flowing Bowl. Old English Song, arranged for Men's Voices ... [by] E. M. Lee. *Banks & Son: York*, 1932. 8°. *York Series, No.* 1115. **F. 638. e. (15.)**

— Come to the Land where the Pipers play. Two-part song, words by Margaret Rose. pp. 4. *Leonard, Gould & Boltler: London*, [1950.] 8°. [*Leonard, Gould & Boltzler's Library of unison and Part-songs for Schools. no.* 76.] **F. 1843.**

— Come unto these yellow Sands. Two-part Song for Equal Voices ... Poem by Shakespeare, *etc.* *J. Curwen & Sons: London*, 1935. 8°. [*Choruses for equal Voices. no.* 1901.] **E. 861.**

— Dance of the Sylphs. [P. F.] *J. Curwen & Sons: London*, 1923. fol. *Part of "Selected Pianoforte Music. Edited by E. Fowles".* **h. 3865. g. (10.)**

— Dance, ye merry Wavelets. [For S. C. Words by] A. B. Cooper. pp. 4. *J. Curwen & Sons: London; Leipzig* [printed, 1901.] 8°. [*Choruses for equal Voices. no.* 466.] **E. 861.**

— Dancing Lightly, for Pianoforte. *Chappell & Co.: London*, 1943. 4°. **f. 133. hh. (31.)**

— Dandelions. Unison Song for Juniors, words by T. Wells, *etc.* *J. Curwen & Sons: London*, 1939. 8°. [*Choruses for equal Voices. no.* 2018.] **E. 861.**

— The Day Thou gavest, Lord, is ended. An Anthem for Solo—soprano or tenor—and Chorus. [Words by] J. Ellerton. *Vincent Music Co.: London*, 1900. 8°. *Church Music. No.* 3. **F. 231. r. (18.)**

— Diversions. Four Pieces for Piano Duet, *etc.* *Murdoch, Murdoch & Co.: London*, 1930. 4°. **g. 1123. a. (14.)**

— Dreams. Two-part Song for Equal Voices ... Poem by W. Gwynne, *etc.* *J. Curwen & Sons: London*, 1935. 8°. [*Choruses for equal Voices. no.* 1899.] **E. 861.**

— Dreams & Delights. Five easy pieces for piano. *Anglo-French Music Co.: London*, 1918. 4°. **g. 603. xx. (7.)**

— The Dream-Seller. *See infra*: [A Poppyland Lullaby, and other Part-Songs.]

— Drop down, ye Heavens. Anthem, *etc.* *Morgan & Scott: London*, 1912. 8°. **F. 231. dd. (19.)**

— Drowsietown. Song, words by A. Hyatt. *Murdoch, Murdoch & Co.: London*, 1921. fol. **H. 1846. ll. (16.)**

LEE (ERNEST MARKHAM)

— An Eastern Dance and Chant. *See* infra: [A Modern Suite. No. 3.]

— Four Easy Pieces, First position, for violin and piano.
A. Lengnick & Co.: London, 1919. 4°.   **g. 500. e. (17.)**

— Six Easy Studies without octaves for pianoforte, *etc.*
Anglo-French Music Co.: London, 1919. 4°.   **g. 337. tt. (3.)**

— The Elder Tree. A Carol for Holy Week, words by
S. N. Sedgwick, *etc. S. P. C. K.: London*, 1933. 8°.
S. P. C. K. Church Music, No. 63.   **E. 602. ss. (11.)**

— Elfin Mount, after Hans Andersen. Six very easy pieces for
children, *etc.* [P. F.] *Murdoch, Murdoch & Co.: London*, 1922.
4°.   **g. 1125. q. (20.)**

— Explorations. A Second Set of Twelve Tests of Musical
Initiative & Intelligence, *etc. A. Lengnick & Co.: London*,
1932. 4°.   **g. 338. f. (8.)**

— Three Fancies for Pianoforte. [No. 1.] Bell Tower. [No. 2.]
Here sleeps Titania. [No. 3.] Gaudeamus. 3 no. *W. Rogers:
London*, 1926. 4°.   **g. 1127. dd. (4.)**

— Fiddle and I ... for Violin and Piano, *etc.* 4 bk. *J. Williams:
London*, 1919–34. 4°.   **g. 500. d. (8.)**

— Fight the good Fight. Anthem ... [Words by] J. S. B. Monsell,
etc. Banks & Son: York, 1934. 8°.
York Series, No. 1141.   **F. 231. ll. (17.)**

— A Flemish Lullaby. Song, words by A. H. Hyatt. *Murdoch,
Murdoch & Co.: London*, 1925. 4°.   **G. 1270. m. (2.)**

— Florestina. Intermezzo for Pianoforte. *A. Lengnick & Co.:
London*, 1928. fol.   **h. 3865. g. (38.)**

— Florestina. Intermezzo for Violin & Piano. *A. Lengnick &
Co.: London*, 1928. fol.   **h. 1613. g. (12.)**

— Folk Dances of the British Isles. Arranged and edited for
Piano Solo by E. M. Lee, *etc. A. Lengnick & Co.: London*,
1939. 4°.   **g. 822. i. (8.)**

— For a lost Eden. Lament for the piano. *J. Williams: London*,
1922. fol.   **h. 3865. c. (5.)**

— Frolics and Fancies. Five piano pieces for young players.
A. Lengnick & Co.: London, 1918. 4°.   **g. 1129. g. (8.)**

— Full Fathom five. Two-part Song ... Poem by Shakespeare,
etc. J. Curwen & Sons: London, 1936. 8°.
[*Choruses for equal Voices. no.* 1902.]   **E. 861.**

— The Gallant Fire Brigade. [Song.] Words by A. B. Cooper.
J. Curwen & Sons: London, [1899.] 8°.
Unison Songs, No. 31.   **E. 812.**

— Gallop away. Humorous Part-Song for Mixed Voices, *etc.
Banks & Son: York*, 1932. 8°.
York Series, No. 1110.   **F. 638. e. (16.)**

— The Gay Gordons. [For S. C. Words by] Henry Newbolt.
pp. 5. *J. Curwen & Sons: London*, [1910.] 8°.
[*Choruses for equal voices. no.* 1229.]   **E. 861.**

— The Gentle Maiden. Old Irish Air. Words by Harold
Boulton. Arranged for Male Voices by E. M. Lee. *J. B.
Cramer & Co.: London*, 1945. 8°.
[*Cramer's Choral Library B. No.* 18.]   **F. 157. g.**

— Glory to God in the Highest. Anthem for Christmas, *etc.*
1903. *See* NOVELLO AND CO. Novello's Collection of
Anthems, *etc.* No. 779. [1876, *etc.*] 8°.   **E. 618. a.**

— Glory to God in the Highest. Anthem, *etc.* [1904.] *See*
NOVELLO AND CO. Novello's Tonic Sol-fa Series. No. 1352.
[1876, *etc.*] 4°.   **B. 885.**

LEE (ERNEST MARKHAM)

— Go, lovely Rose. Part-Song for S. C. ... [Words by] E. Waller,
etc. J. Curwen & Sons: London, 1923. 8°.
[*Choruses for equal voices. no.* 1606.]   **E. 861.**

— The Golden Gate. Five joyous pieces for pianoforte, *etc.
A. Lengnick & Co.: London*, 1923. 4°.   **g. 1127. v. (24.)**

— Good-bye to the Town. Unison Song, words by A. Dobson.
Anglo-French Music Co.: London, 1924. 8°.   **E. 1766. x. (31.)**

— Graceful Dance. [P. F.] *J. Williams: London*, [1899.] fol.
        h. 3282. w. (37.)

— Graded Sight Tests for Pianoforte, *etc.* 3 bk. *A. Lengnick &
Co.: London*, 1926. 4°.   **g. 338. d. (5.)**

— Happy Maidens we. Chorus or Part Song for equal voices,
words by A. B. Cooper. *Stainer & Bell: London*, 1914. 8°.
Stainer & Bell's Part Songs for treble and alto voices, No. 73.
        F. 1137. a.

— He that loves a rosy Cheek. Three-part Song for S. S. C.,
unaccompanied, poem by T. Carew, *etc. J. Curwen & Sons:
London*, 1922. 8°.
[*Choruses for equal voices. no.* 1577.]   **E. 861.**

— Here a little Child I stand. Unison. [Words by] Herrick.
Oxford University Press: London, 1928. 8°.
[*The Oxford Choral Songs. No.* 84.]   **F. 1777. a.**

— Hey nonny no! Two-part Song, *etc. E. Ashdown: London*,
1928. 8°.   **E. 263. g. (60.)**

— Ho! Boys. [Unison song. Words by] R. G. Legge. pp. 7.
J. Curwen & Sons: London, [1904.] 8°.
[*Choruses for equal Voices. no.* 836.]   **E. 861.**

— Holiday Time. Four ... easy pianoforte duets. *A. Lengnick &
Co.: London*, 1919. 4°.   **g. 1129. q. (12.)**

— I shot an Arrow. The Arrow and the Song. Two-part Song
with Accompaniment for 1st and 2nd Violins, optional, and
Piano. Words by Longfellow. *Boosey & Hawkes: London*,
1932. 8°.
Part of "The Winthrop Rogers Edition of Choral Music".
        E. 263. i. (4.)

— I sing the Cross. [Anthem.] Words by K. White. Adapted and
arranged to the Londonderry Air by E. M. Lee. *Banks &
Son: York*, 1933. 8°.
York Series, No. 1113.   **F. 231. ll. (15.)**

— I will magnify Thee, O God. Full Anthem for four voices,
etc. 1903. *See* NOVELLO AND CO. Novello's Collection of
Anthems, *etc.* No. 780. [1876, *etc.*] 8°.   **E. 618. a.**

— In a Garden red. *See* infra: [The Mermaid. No. 2.]

— In Gavotte Style. *See* infra: [Four Short Pieces. No. 4.]

— In the North Country. Six impressions for pianoforte.
A. Lengnick & Co.: London, 1918. 4°.   **g. 603. ww. (12.)**

— John Peel. Version for more advanced Choralists. (Easy
version.) Arranged for Mixed Voices by E. M. Lee. *Banks &
Son: York*, 1933. 8°.
York Series, No. 1123.   **F. 638. e. (17.)**

— Jubilate. Three-part Song for female voices ... [Words by]
T. Moore. *E. Ashdown: London*, 1925. 8°.   **F. 328. z. (26.)**

— Keep on the Ball. [Song.] Words by A. B. Cooper. *J. Curwen
& Sons: London*, [1899.] 8°.
Unison Songs, No. 18.   **E. 812.**

— King Cricket. [Song, words by] A. B. Cooper. *J. Curwen &
Sons: London*, [1899.] 8°.
Unison Songs, No. 17.   **E. 812.**

LEE (ERNEST MARKHAM)

— King of Glory, King of Peace. Anthem for S. A. T. B., unaccompanied. Words by George Herbert. *Leonard, Gould & Bolttler: London*, 1945. 8°.
[*L. G. B. Choral Repertoire. No.* 46.] **F. 1843. a.**

— Three Settings of the Kyrie Eleison. *C. Vincent: London*, [1901.] 8°. **F. 1169. a. (27.)**

— The Land of Make-believe, *etc.* (Four Pieces for Pianoforte.) *W. Paxton & Co.: London*, 1928. 4°. **g. 1125. z. (31.)**

— Lavender. Unison song, words by Margaret Rose, *etc.* [Staff and tonic sol-fa notation.] pp. 4. *Elkin & Co.: London*, [1952.] 8°.
Elkin new choral Series. 2259. **E. 1830. e. (64.)**

— Lead, kindly Light. Anthem for S. A. T. B. [Words by] Cardinal Newman, *etc.* [Staff and tonic sol-fa notation.] pp. 7. *Banks & Son: York*, [1954.] 8°.
York Series, No. 1513. **E. 442. x. (20.)**

— The Leaves. [Unison song.] Words by Margaret Rose. [Staff and tonic sol-fa notation.] pp. 4. *Leonard, Gould & Bolttler: London*, [1952.] 8°.
[*Leonard, Gould & Bolttler's Library of unison and Part-songs for Schools. no.* 82.] **F. 1843.**

— Legend. [P. F.] *Murdoch, Murdoch & Co.: London*, 1928. 4°. **g. 1125. z. (32.)**

— The Lesson of Spring. Two-part Song for equal voices, words by S. N. Sedgwick. *J. Williams: London*, 1919. 4°.
Collection of Two-part Songs for treble voices. Fourth Series. No. 10. **F. 1681.**

— Light Heart. A merry Suite for String Orchestra ... Score. *A. Lengnick & Co.: London*, 1925. 4°. **g. 417. n. (5.)**

— Light Heart. A merry suite for string orchestra, *etc.* [Parts.] *A. Lengnick & Co.: London*, 1925. 4°. **h. 3210. h. (220.)**

— Light Heart. A merry suite for pianoforte, *etc. A. Lengnick & Co.: London*, 1925. 4°. **g. 1127. dd. (5.)**

— The Lightest, brightest Time. *See* infra: [A Poppyland Lullaby and other Part-Songs.]

— A Little Dance Set. Six easy pieces for pianoforte, *etc. Ascherberg, Hopwood & Crew: London*, 1923. 4°. **g. 1127. v. (25.)**

— Four Little Dances ... for pianoforte. *J. Williams: London*, 1917. 4°. **g. 603. vv. (7.)**

— Ten Little Pieces, *etc.* [P. F.] *Oxford University Press: London*, 1926. 4°.
[*The Oxford Piano Series. No.* 42.] **g. 1231.**

— Six Little Sketches ... for the pianoforte. *Stainer & Bell: London*, 1920. 4°. **g. 1125. c. (26.)**

— The Lizard. Unison Song for Juniors, words by T. Wells, *etc. J. Curwen & Sons: London*, 1939. 8°.
[*Choruses for equal Voices. no.* 2017.] **E. 861.**

— London River. Unison song, words by Margaret Rose, *etc.* [Staff and tonic sol-fa notation.] pp. 4. *Elkin & Co.: London*, [1952.] 8°.
Elkin new choral Series. 2261. **E. 1830. e. (65.)**

— The Londonderry Air. Easily arranged for the Pianoforte by E. M. Lee. *Murdoch, Murdoch & Co.: London*, 1928. 4°. **g. 822. d. (8.)**

— The Londonderry Air. Arranged for the Pianoforte by E. M. Lee. *Chappell & Co.: London*, 1943. 4°. **f. 133. hh. (32.)**

LEE (ERNEST MARKHAM)

— The Lord's Service. A simple setting of the service of the Holy Communion, with hymns and explanatory directions, in use at S. Mary's, Bishopstoke ... the hymns by the ... Bishop of Kingston-upon-Thames, *etc. A. R. Mowbray & Co.: London & Oxford*, [1915.] 8°. **B. 835. f. (2.)**

— The Lord's Service. A simple setting of the Service of the Holy Communion with Hymns and explanatory directions ... The hymns by the Right Rev. the Lord Bishop of Kingston-upon-Thames. *W. Paxton & Co.: London*, [1928.] 8°. **B. 512. p. (23.)**

— Loving Shepherd. Anthem ... [Words by] J. E. Leeson, *etc. Banks & Son: York*, 1934. 8°.
York Series, No. 1142. **F. 231. ll. (18.)**

— Magnificat and Nunc dimittis ... in ... C, *etc.* 1912. *See* NOVELLO AND CO. Novello's Parish Choir Book, *etc.* No. 885. [1866, *etc.*] 8°. **E. 618.**

— Magnificat and Nunc dimittis in D, *etc. Vincent Music Co.: London*, [1902.] 8°.
Church Music. No. 4. **E. 597. p. (19.)**

— Magnificat and Nunc dimittis, in D. [1909.] *See* NOVELLO AND CO. Novello's Parish Choir Book, *etc.* No. 810. [1866, *etc.*] 8°. **E. 618.**

— Magnificat and Nunc Dimittis in E flat. *C. Vincent: London*, 1899. 8°. **F. 1169. a. (26.)**

— Magnificat and Nunc dimittis, in E♭. [1909.] *See* NOVELLO AND CO. Novello's Parish Choir Book, *etc.* No. 809. [1866, *etc.*] 8°. **E. 618.**

— The Man in the Moon. Six little Pieces for the Pianoforte, *etc. Elkin & Co.: London*, 1926. 4°. **g. 1127. gg. (20.)**

— March. *See* infra: [Four Short Pieces. No. 1.]

— Six Marches for pianoforte. *A. Lengnick & Co.: London*, 1918. 4°. **g. 272. kk. (18.)**

— The Market Place. Unison Song, poem by C. F. Geere, *etc. J. Curwen & Sons: London*, 1933. 8°.
[*Choruses for equal Voices. no.* 1860.] **E. 861.**

— A May Madrigal. Two part Song for equal voices, words by A. H. Hyatt. *J. Williams: London*, 1920. 4°.
Collection of Two-part Songs for treble voices. Fourth Series. No. 23. **F. 1681.**

— The Mer-King's Palace. *See* infra: [The Mermaid. No. 1.]

— The Mermaid. After Hans Anderson [*sic*]. Five easy pianoforte pieces. *Gould & Bolttler: London*, 1924. 4°.
Educational Album Series, No. 3. **g. 1125. k. (10.)**

— [The Mermaid. No. 1.] The Mer-King's Palace. (For Piano.) *Leonard, Gould & Bolttler: London*, [1929.] 4°. **g. 1125. z. (33.)**

— [The Mermaid. No. 2.] In a Garden red. (For Piano.) *Leonard, Gould & Bolttler: London*, [1929.] 4°. **g. 1125. z. (30.)**

— Merry Dance. [P. F. duet.] *J. Curwen: London*, 1944. 4°.
Part of the "Festival Series of Pianoforte Duets". **g. 1123. c. (14.)**

— Merry Moments. *See* infra: [Summer Days. No. 1.]

— Four Modern Sonatinas ... for pianoforte, *etc.* 4 no. *A. Lengnick & Co.: London*, 1920. fol. **h. 3870. a. (24.)**

— A Modern Suite for pianoforte ... 1. Prelude. 2. Scherzino. 3. Eastern dance & Chant. 4. Romance. 5. Pier[r]ette & Pierrot. *A. Lengnick & Co.: London*, 1919. 4°. **g. 1129. l. (27.)**

— [A Modern Suite. No. 1.] Prelude for pianoforte. *A. Lengnick & Co.: London*, [1919.] fol. **h. 3870. a. (25.)**

LEE (ERNEST MARKHAM)

— [A Modern Suite. No. 3.] An Eastern Dance and Chant, for pianoforte. *A. Lengnick & Co.: London*, 1919. fol.
h. 3870. a. (26.)

— [A Modern Suite. No. 4.] Romance in G flat, for pianoforte. *A. Lengnick & Co.: London*, 1919. fol. **h. 3870. a. (27.)**

— Moorland and Torland. 6 sketches for pianoforte. *A. Lengnick & Co.: London*, 1916. 4°. **g. 272. hh. (12.)**

— Moorland and Torland ... Orch. by F. L. Taylor. [P. F. conductor and parts.] *A. Lengnick & Co.: [London,]* 1928. 4°.
h. 3210. h. (239.)

— The Morn of St. Valentine's Day. [Two-part song.] Words by A. Hyatt. *Stainer & Bell: London*, 1914. 8°.
Stainer & Bell's Part Songs for treble and alto voices, No. 74.
F. 1137. a.

— The Morning. Part-Song for Equal Voices ... Poem by A. Cunningham, *etc. J. Curwen & Sons: London*, 1931. 8°.
[Choruses for equal voices. no. 1798.] **E. 861.**

— Moto perpetuo ... For violin & piano. *A. Lengnick & Co.: London*, 1925. fol. **h. 1613. f. (24.)**

— The Music-Lover's Ear Tests and Book of Themes, *etc.* 2 pt. *Banks & Son: York*, [1933.] 8°. **D. 1085. d. (4.)**

— The Music-Lover's Sight Singing Tests and Book of Themes. Containing 150 melodies from classic and standard sources. *Banks & Son: York*, [1937.] 8°. **D. 1085. e. (6.)**

— My First Tunes. 14 very easy pianoforte pieces, *etc. A. Lengnick & Co.: London*, 1922. 4°. **g. 1127. g. (14.)**

— Naughty Mary. Humorous Part-Song for Mixed Voices, poem by T. Hook. *J. Curwen & Sons: London*, 1932. 8°.
[Choral Handbook. No. 1284.] **E. 862.**

— Nights in Venice. Three pieces for pianoforte. 1. Southern skies. 2. Carnival. 3. On the lagoon. *A. Lengnick & Co.: London*, 1922. 4°. **g. 1127. g. (15.)**

— Ninette. Graceful Dance for piano. *H. J. Reeks: London*, [1898.] fol. **h. 3282. f. (22.)**

— The North Wind. Unison song, words by Margaret Rose. pp. 4. *Leonard, Gould & Bolttler: London*, [1950.] 8°.
[Leonard, Gould & Bolttler's Library of unison and Part-songs for Schools. no. 77.] **F. 1843.**

— Novelettes. Five Pieces for the Piano. *International Music Co.: London*, 1928. 4°. **g. 1125. w. (22.)**

— Now thank we all our God. [Anthem.] Words from the German translated by Winkworth. *Banks & Son: York*, 1931. 8°.
York Series, No. 1084. **F. 1176. g. (26.)**

— Nursery Rhymes, arranged for pianoforte duet by E. M. Lee. *A. Lengnick & Co.: London*, 1921. 4°. **g. 1127. g. (16.)**

— 16 Nursery Rhymes very simply arranged for the Pianoforte by E. M. Lee. *A. Lengnick & Co.: London*, 1926. 4°.
g. 822. b. (6.)

— O sing unto the Lord. Easter anthem. [S. A. T. B.] Ps. xcviii., 1, 2, 5; Ps. cvii., 16; 1 Cor. xv., 18. pp. 7. *Musical News Syndicate: London*, [c. 1920.] 8°. **E. 442. aa. (35.)**

— An Ode in Honour of the Birth of the Prince Edward of York, by R. H. Manley, *etc.* [Chorus.] *Novello, Ewer and Co.: London & New York*, 1896. 8°. **F. 1273. z. (7.)**

— Ode to Saint Cecilia. [Song.] The words ... by Pope. *Novello and Co.: London*, [1906.] fol. **G. 807. jj. (50.)**

LEE (ERNEST MARKHAM)

— O'er the distant Hills. Two-part Song for equal voices, words and music by E. M. Lee. *J. Williams: London*, 1920. 4°.
Collection of Two-part Songs for treble voices. Fourth Series. No. 13. **F. 1681.**

— The Old Curiosity Shop. A little suite for pianoforte, *etc. A. Lengnick & Co.: London*, 1920. 4°. **g. 1129. t. (9.)**

— Old King Cole. Freely treated for Male Voices, T. T. B. B. *Banks & Son: York*, 1936. 8°.
York Series, No. 1250. **F. 638. g. (27.)**

— Old Meg. Part Song for Mixed Voices, words by A. Keats. *Banks & Son: York*, 1940. 8°.
York Series, No. 1388. **F. 638. i. (25.)**

— Old Tunes for young People, very simply arranged for the pianoforte by E. Markham Lee, *etc. J. Williams: London*, 1925. 4°. **g. 1125. k. (11.)**

— Out and About. A small Suite for boys & girls, *etc.* [P. F.] *E. Ashdown: London, etc.*, 1928. 4°. **g. 1125. w. (23.)**

— Over the Rim of the Sky. Unison song, words by Margaret Rose. pp. 4. *Leonard, Gould & Bolttler: London*, [1953.] 8°.
[Leonard, Gould & Bolttler's Library of unison and Part-songs for Schools. no. 86.] **F. 1843.**

— Overture alla marcia. [Organ.] *Novello and Co.: London*, 1904. *obl.* fol.
Original Compositions for the Organ, No. 321. **e. 1091.**

— Paris in Spring ... A Comic Opera in two acts, book and lyrics by Stanley Guise. [Vocal score.] *J. Curwen & Sons: London*, 1939. 4°. **F. 943. r. (3.)**

— Pastimes ... Violin & piano. *Gould & Bolttler: London*, 1924. 4°.
Educational Album Series, Book I. **g. 505. kk. (35.)**

— Pickwick. Six easy experiments in programme music ... for pianoforte, *etc. A. Lengnick & Co.: London*, 1920. 4°.
g. 1127. g. (17.)

— Picture Palaces. Five Sketches for Pianoforte. *Oxford University Press: London*, 1930. 4°. **g. 1125. ee. (10.)**

— [Four Pieces. No. 1.] Valse in G, *etc.* [Violin and P. F.] *J. Williams: London*, 1926. 4°.
Selected Pieces for the Violin, etc., Series I. No. 18.
g. 505. nn. (30.)

— [Four Pieces. No. 3.] Romance in F, *etc.* [Violin and P. F.] *J. Williams: London*, 1926. 4°.
Selected Pieces for the Violin, etc., Series I. No. 19
g. 505. nn. (31.)

— The Pigtail. Humorous Part Song for Mixed Voices. [Words by] W. M. Thackeray. *Banks & Son: York*, 1935. 8°.
York Series, No. 1213. **F. 638. g. (28.)**

— Pleasantries. Four easy pieces for the pianoforte, *etc. J. B. Cramer & Co.: London*, 1925. 4°. **g. 1125. q. (21.)**

A Poppyland Lullaby and other Part-Songs

— A Poppyland Lullaby and other Part-Songs for equal voices, words by A. H. Hyatt. *J. Curwen & Sons: London*, 1904. 8°.
E. 263. d. (33.)

— The Dream-Seller, *etc. J. Curwen & Sons: London*, [1921.] 8°.
[Choruses for equal Voices. no. 1559.] **E. 861.**

— The Dream Seller. Three-part Song, *etc. J. Curwen & Sons: London*, 1927. 8°.
[Choruses for equal Voices. no. 1731.] **E. 861.**

— The Lightest, brightest Time, *etc. J. Curwen & Sons: London*, [1921.] 8°.
[Choruses for equal Voices. no. 1560.] **E. 861.**

LEE (ERNEST MARKHAM)

— A Poppyland Lullaby, *etc. J. Curwen & Sons: London,*
[1924.] 8°.
[*Choruses for equal Voices. no.* 1609.]   **E. 861.**

— Snowdrop, *etc. J. Curwen & Sons: London,* [1924.] 8°.
[*Choruses for equal Voices. no.* 1610.]   **E. 861.**

— A Summer Impromptu, *etc. J. Curwen & Sons: London,*
[1924.] 8°.
[*Choruses for equal Voices. no.* 1612.]   **E. 861.**

— Tender Sleep enfold thee, *etc. J. Curwen & Sons: London,*
[1924.] 8°.
[*Choruses for equal Voices. no.* 1611.]   **E. 861.**

— Tender Sleep enfold thee. Part-Song for chorus of mixed
voices, unaccompanied, *etc. J. Curwen & Sons: London,*
1927. 8°.
[*Choral Handbook. No.* 1225.]   **E. 862.**

— Practice and Pleasure. Four study pieces for pianoforte.
No. 1. Chariot race ... No. 2. The bat ... No. 3. Puppet dance
... No. 4. An old water wheel, *etc.* 4 no. *A. Lengnick & Co.:*
London, 1915. fol.   **g. 606. bb. (23.)**

— Prelude. *See* supra: [A Modern Suite. No. 1.]

— Prelude, Romance and Irish Tune. A suite for piano duet.
A. Lengnick & Co.: London, 1924. 4°.   **g. 1123. (4.)**

— Two Preludes. For pianoforte ... I. Hesperis. II. Serapis. 2 no.
Murdoch, Murdoch & Co.: London, [1921.] fol.
h. 61. bb. (7.)

— The Primrose. Unison Song, words by D. Kean. *Paterson's*
Publications: London, Edinburgh, 1936. 8°.
The Lyric Collection of Choral Music, Secular. No. 1723.
E. 1830. c. (65.)

— Qui vive! in the Dawn. Part Song ... [Words by] Sir
G. Parker. 1914. *See* CHORAL. The Choral Handbook.
[No. 1040.] [1885, *etc.*] 8°.   **E. 862.**

— Raindrops. Unison Song, words by T. Wells. *Paterson's*
Publications: London, Edinburgh, 1936. 8°.
The Lyric Collection of Choral Music, Secular, No. 1722.
E. 1830. c. (66.)

— Reverie. [P. F.] *J. Curwen & Sons: London,* 1923. 4°.
Part of "Selected Pianoforte Music. Edited by E. Fowles".
g. 1127. dd. (6.)

— Reverie in A. [Organ.] *A. Abbott & Co.: London,* [1899.]
obl. fol.   **f. 314. t. (9.)**

— Rêverie, pour le violon avec accompagnement de piano.
J. Williams: London, 1920. fol.   **h. 1612. ll. (26.)**

— Rivers of Devon. Suite for Pianoforte, *etc. Goodwin & Tabb:*
London, 1929. 4°.   **g. 1125. bb. (25.)**

— Rivers of Devon. [String parts.] *Goodwin & Tabb:* [*London,*]
1929. 4°.
[*The English String Series. No.* 4.]   **g. 1236. d.**

— Romance in F. *See* supra: [Four Pieces. No. 3.]

— Romance in G flat. *See* supra: [A Modern Suite. No. 4.]

— The Rose and the Nightingale. [Two-part song.] Words by
P. J. Bailey. *Anglo-French Music Co.: London,* 1923. 8°.
F. 328. z. (27.)

— Rough Weather. [Unison song, words by] U. Gwynne.
E. J. Arnold & Son: Leeds, 1944. 8°.
The Music Hour, No. 16.   **E. 1830. e. (55.)**

LEE (ERNEST MARKHAM)

— Round the North Sea. Suite for Strings and Piano ... I. A
Chanty. II. Madame la Marquise. III. In the Fiords. IV.
Walloon ... Score ... Parts, *etc. Hawkes & Son: London,*
1933. 4°.   **g. 417. gg. (3.)**

— Roving Fancies. A Little Pianoforte Suite, *etc. Elkin & Co.:*
London, 1930. 4°.   **g. 1125. ee. (11.)**

— A Sailor's Hornpipe, for pianoforte. *A. Lengnick & Co.:*
London, 1917. fol.   **g. 606. bb. (24.)**

— Sailor's Song. [Song, words by] A. B. Cooper. *J. Curwen &*
Sons: London, [1899.] 8°.
Unison Songs, No. 34.   **E. 812.**

— Scherzo in A, for the Organ. *J. B. Cramer & Co.: London,*
1925. 4°.
[*Cramer's Library of Organ Music. Set* 1. *No.* 8.]   **g. 1353.**

— A Sea Song. Chorus for equal voices. [Words by]
A. B. Cooper. *Augener & Co.: London,* [1896.] 8°.
F. 328. a. (8.)

— Seamates bold. Part-Song for Men's Voices ... Poem by
J. Baillie, *etc. J. Curwen & Sons: London,* 1932. 8°.
[*The Apollo Club. No.* 691.]   **F. 667.**

— Semitones. Four easy pieces for violin ... and pianoforte, *etc.*
A. Lengnick & Co.: London, 1921. 4°.   **g. 500. h. (3.)**

— Serenade, for violin & piano. *J. Williams: London,* 1920. fol.
h. 1612. ll. (27.)

— Sérénade napolitaine pour Violon ou Violoncelle et Piano.
A. Lengnick & Co.: London, 1925. fol.   **h. 1612. mm. (24.)**

— Serenata. (1914.) *See* JOHNSON (B.) The Organ Recitalist, *etc.*
New Series. No. 39. (1912, *etc.*) 4°.   **f. 342. a.**

— She alone of Shepherdesses. ... Madrigal. [Staff and tonic
sol-fa notation.] [1897?] *See* CHORAL. Choral Leaflets.
No. 149. [1882, *etc.*] *s. sh.* 4°.   **F. 569.**

— The Shepherds' Holiday. Two-part Song for equal voices in
canon ... Poem by J. Shirley, *etc. J. Curwen & Sons: London,*
1922. 8°.
[*Choruses for equal Voices. no.* 1589.]   **E. 861.**

— Four Short Pieces for violin and piano. 1. March. 2. Minuet.
3. Valse. 4. In gavotte style. *J. Williams: London,* 1920. 4°.
g. 505. jj. (15.)

— [Four Short Pieces. No. 1.] March. [Violin and P. F.]
J. Williams: London, [1926.] 4°.
Selected Pieces for the Violin, etc., Series I. *No.* 7.
g. 505. nn. (25.)

— [Four Short Pieces. No. 4.] In Gavotte Style, *etc.* [Violin and
P. F.] *J. Williams: London,* [1926.] 4°.
Selected Pieces for the Violin, etc., Series I. *No.* 8.
g. 505. nn. (26.)

— Six Short Voluntaries for Organ, *etc.* pp. 15. *Alfred Lengnick*
& Co.: London, [1949.] 4°.   **g. 1380. w. (14.)**

— Shreds & Patches. Six easy pieces for the pianoforte, *etc.*
Ascherberg, Hopwood & Crew: London, 1922. 4°.
g. 1127. g. (18.)

— Sing we merrily. Prize Anthem. *Pilgrim Press: London,*
[1903.] 8°.
The "Pilgrim" Anthems. No. 7.   **E. 442. p. (34.)**

— 3 Sketches for violin & piano. 1. A stately dance. 2.
Barcarolle. 3. Merrymaking. *A. Lengnick & Co.: London,*
1925. 4°.   **g. 500. l. (5.)**

— Slow, slow, fresh Fount. Part Song for Ladies Voices ... with
Accompaniment for 1st and 2nd Violins, optional, and

LEE (Ernest Markham)

Piano. Words by Ben Jonson. *Boosey & Hawkes: London,* 1932. 8°.
Part of "The Winthrop Rogers Edition of Choral Music," etc.
F. 217. e. (39.)

— The Slumber River. Two-part Song for equal voices, words by S. N. Sedgwick. *J. Williams: London,* 1919. 4°.
Collection of Two-part Songs for treble voices. Fourth Series. No. 12. **F. 1681.**

— The Smart P. T. Solo, Chorus and Dance ... Words by A. B. Cooper. *J. Curwen & Sons: London,* 1899. fol.
H. 1984. c. (13.)

— Smugglers. Part Song for men's voices ... [Words by] F. Fox. *E. Ashdown: London,* 1926. 8°. **F. 163. w. (41.)**

— Smugglers. Part Song for Men's Voices, T. T. B. B. *Edwin Ashdown: London,* [1945.] 8°.
[*Enoch Choral Series. No.* 141.] **F. 1097.**

— The Snow Maiden. After a Russian legend. Suite for pianoforte, *etc. Ascherberg, Hopwood & Crew: London,* 1921. 4°. **g. 1127. g. (19.)**

— Snowdrop. *See* supra: [A Poppyland Lullaby and other Part-Songs.]

— Soldier's Song. [Song.] Words by A. B. Cooper. *J. Curwen & Sons: London,* [1899.] 8°.
Unison Songs, No. 32. **E. 812.**

— Soldiers of Christ, arise. Anthem for soprano, alto and bass. [Words by] C. Wesley, (1707–1788). pp. 6. *Banks & Son: York,* [1948.] 8°.
York Series, No. 1481. **F. 231. mm. (37.)**

— Three Sonatinas for pianoforte. 3 no. *J. Williams & Co.: London,* 1918. 4°. **g. 603. vv. (8.)**

— Three Sonatinas, *etc.* (Piano.) *J. Williams: London,* [1922.] 4°. **g. 1125. c. (27.)**

— A Song of Orthography. [Song. Words by] A. B. Cooper. pp. 3. *J. Curwen & Sons: London,* [1901.] 8°.
[*Choruses for equal Voices. no.* 557.] **E. 861.**

— Song of the Volga Boatmen, containing also an easy version of the same. Arranged by E. M. Lee. [P. F.] *Murdoch, Murdoch & Co.: London,* 1928. 4°. **g. 822. d. (9.)**

— Song of the Volga Boatmen containing also an easy version of the same. Arranged by E. M. Lee. *Chappell & Co.: London,* 1943. 4°. **f. 133. hh. (33.)**

— Two Songs, words by A. H. Hyatt. [No. 1.] Love's Melody ... [No. 2.] Rainbow-Time. *Chappell & Co.: London, etc.,* 1904. fol. **H. 1799. vv. (33.)**

— Spring and Summer. The Londonderry Air. Words by D. Kean. Arranged as a Two-part Song by E. M. Lee. *Banks & Son: York,* 1937. 8°.
York Series, No. 1269. **F. 1771. f. (3.)**

— Spring Joy. Two part Song ... [Words by] W. Wordsworth. *E. Ashdown: London,* 1925. 8°. **F. 328. z. (28.)**

— Step by Step. Ten easy and progressive Duets for young Pianists, *etc. International Music Co.: London,* 1927. 4°.
g. 1123. a. (1.)

— Summer Days. A little suite for the piano. 1. Merry moments. 2. Beneath the trees. 3. Valse. 4. Grasshoppers' march. 5. Summer reverie. 6. On the hill top. *J. Williams: London,* 1920. 4°. **g. 1129. v. (12.)**

— [Summer Days. No. 1.] Merry Moments, for the Piano. *J. Williams: London,* [1927.] 4°. **g. 1125. t. (9.)**

— A Summer Impromptu. *See* supra: [A Poppyland Lullaby and other Part-Songs.]

LEE (Ernest Markham)

— Summer is a merry Time. Canon for two equal voices with pianoforte accompaniment, words by Margaret Lyell. pp. 6. *J. Curwen & Sons: London,* [1949.] 8°.
[*Choruses for equal Voices. no.* 2177.] **E. 861.**

— Sunset and Evening Star. Nocturne for pianoforte. *A. Lengnick & Co.: London,* 1919. fol. **g. 606. bb. (25.)**

— Sweet Spirit, comfort me. Anthem ... Words by R. Herrick, *etc. J. Curwen & Sons: London,* 1941. 8°.
[*Church Choralist. No.* 763.] **E. 1330.**

— Te Deum laudamus ... in ... C. 1905. *See* NOVELLO AND CO. Novello's Parish Choir Book. No. 684. [1866, *etc.*] 8°.
E. 618.

— Tender Sleep enfold thee. *See* supra: [A Poppyland Lullaby and other Part Songs.]

— Twelve Tests of Musical Initiative, *etc. A. Lengnick & Co.: London,* 1930. 4°. **g. 338. f. (7.)**

— There was a great Earthquake. Anthem, *etc. J. Blackburn: Leeds,* [1924.] 8°.
The Classic Series, No. 142. **E. 1624.**

— There was a great Earthquake ... Tonic Sol-fa edition. *J. Blackburn: Leeds,* [1924.] 4°.
"Phlox" Sol-fa Series, No. 96. **C. 418.**

— Through the Glen. Part Song for men's voices, unaccompanied, poem by B. Gough, *etc. J. Curwen & Sons: London,* 1925. 8°.
[*The Apollo Club. No.* 625.] **F. 667.**

— To Celia. Two-part Song in canon for equal voices, words by B. Jonson. *J. Williams: London,* 1919. 4°.
Collection of Two-part Songs for treble voices. Fourth Series. No. 8. **F. 1681.**

— To the Cuckoo. [Three-part song.] Unaccompanied. Words by W. Wordsworth, *etc. Augener: London,* 1925. 8°.
F. 607. ii. (11.)

— To the Maypole. Elizabethan Folk Tune. Traditional. Arranged & edited for Piano by E. M. Lee. *Murdoch, Murdoch & Co.: London,* 1930. 4°. **g. 822. c. (27.)**

— Tristesse de Colombine. Valsette pour piano. *A. Lengnick & Co.: London,* 1915. fol. **g. 606. bb. (26.)**

— Tunes for two Players. Eight easy Pianoforte Duets, *etc. International Music Co.: London,* 1926. 4°. **g. 1123. a. (2.)**

— The Twilight Dustman. A Hush Song, words by A. H. Hyatt. *Murdoch, Murdoch & Co.: London,* 1921. fol.
H. 1846. ll. (17.)

— Under the greenwood Tree. [Unison song.] Words by Shakespeare. *Anglo-French Music Co.: London,* 1923. 8°.
E. 1766. x. (32.)

— Valse de Ballet. [P. F.] *C. Vincent: London,* 1900. 4°.
No. 212 *of the "New Century Series," etc.* **g. 1132.**

— Valse in G. *See* supra: [Four Pieces. No. 1.]

— Visions. Five easy pieces for young pianists, *etc. Murdoch, Murdoch & Co.: London,* 1924. 4°. **g. 1125. k. (12.)**

— The Water Babies. After Kingsley. Easy pieces ... for the pianoforte, *etc.* 2 bk. *Ascherberg, Hopwood & Crew: London,* 1925. 4°. **g. 1125. q. (22.)**

— West Country Suite. Orchestration by A. Oxenden. Piano Conductor [and parts]. *G. Ricordi & Co.: London,* 1940. 4°.
h. 3210. h. (839.)

— Westward Ho! Six easy tone poems for pianoforte, after Kingsley, *etc. E. Ashdown: London,* 1925. 4°.
g. 1125. q. (23.)

LEE (ERNEST MARKHAM)

— When Flower Time comes. 6 small pieces for pianoforte, *etc.*
A. Lengnick & Co.: London, 1924. 4°.   **g. 1127. v. (26.)**

— When the Children play. Six easy pianoforte pieces, *etc.*
Murdoch, Murdoch & Co.: London, 1921. 4°.
                                           g. 1127. dd. (7.)

— Where is He that is born? Anthem for Christmas. *A. Abbott
and Co.: London*, 1902. 8°.
The Ambrose Edition, etc. No. 65.   **F. 945.**

— Why seek ye the Living? Anthem for Easter. [1901.] *See*
PETTMAN (E.) The Parochial Anthem Book, *etc.* No. 27. [1895,
etc.] 8°.   **F. 1116. (2.)**

— Will o' the Wisp. Scherzo for pianoforte. *A. Lengnick & Co.:
London*, 1919. fol.   **h. 3870. a. (28.)**

— The Windy Hill. A little piano suite. *W. Rogers: London*,
1925. 4°.
New Century Edition, No. 80.   **g. 1127. dd. (8.)**

— Wistfulness ... For violin & piano. *A. Lengnick & Co.:
London*, 1925. fol.   **h. 1613. f. (25.)**

— The Wonderful Isles. Five fanciful pieces for pianoforte, *etc.*
A. Lengnick & Co.: London, 1923. 4°.   **g. 1127. v. (27.)**

— The Year's at the Spring. Two part Song, words by
R. Browning. *Anglo-French Music Co.: London*, 1924. 8°.
                                            F. 328. z. (29.)

— Youth's the Season made for Joys. Two-part song. Words
anon. pp. 4. *J. Curwen & Sons: London; Leipzig* [printed,
1896.] 8°.
[*Choruses for equal Voices. no.* 358.]   **E. 861.**

— *See* BACH (J. S.) [*Collected Works.—g.*] Second Year Bach for
Pianoforte Solo. Adapted ... by E. M. Lee, *etc.* 1936. 4°.
                                            g. 548. ee. (20.)

— *See* BACH (J. S.) [*Collected Works.—g.*] Four Dance Measures.
Arranged for Two Pianos by E. M. Lee. 1937. 4°.
                                            g. 548. ff. (1.)

— *See* BACH (J. S.) [*Collected Works.—g.*] First Year Bach ...
Adapted, arranged and edited by E. M. Lee, *etc.* 1945. 4°.
                                            g. 548. rr. (16.)

— *See* BACH (J. S.) [Also hat Gott ... Mein gläubiges Herz.] My
Heart ever faithful ... Arranged for four voices by E. M. Lee.
[1951.] 8°.   **F. 956. dd. (1.)**

— *See* BACH (J. S.) [Also hat Gott ... Mein gläubiges Herz.] My
Heart ever faithful. Arranged for Piano by E. M. Lee. [1946.]
4°.   **g. 548. rr. (21.)**

— *See* BACH (J. S.) [Zweistimmige Inventionen.] Invention in F
... Edited by E. M. Lee. 1936. 4°.   **g. 548. aa. (16.)**

— *See* BACH (J. S.) [Mer hahn en neue Oberkeet.] With Laughter
& Joy ... Arranged for Two Pianos by E. M. Lee. 1935. 4°.
                                            g. 548. bb. (10.)

— *See* BACH (J. S.) [Mer hahn en neue Oberkeet.] With Laughter
& Joy ... Arranged for Two Pianos by E. M. Lee. 1943. 4°.
                                            g. 548. rr. (9.)

— *See* BACH (J. S.) [Overture for Orchestra in D. No. 1.] Air.
Arranged for Piano by E. M. Lee. 1931. 4°. **g. 548. w. (13.)**

— *See* BACH (J. S.) [Overture for Orchestra in D. No. 1.] Air.
Arranged for Piano by E. M. Lee. 1943. 4°. **g. 548. rr. (10.)**

— *See* BEETHOVEN (L. van) [*Collected works.—c.*] Second Year
Beethoven ... Adapted ... by E. M. Lee, *etc.* 1938. 4°.
                                            g. 249. dd. (25.)

LEE (ERNEST MARKHAM)

— *See* BEETHOVEN (L. van) [Für Elise. K.-H. 59.] For Elise ...
Edited for Piano by E. M. Lee. 1930. 4°.   **g. 249. x. (19.)**

— *See* BEETHOVEN (L. van) [Für Elise. K.-H. 59.] For Elise ...
Phrased, fingered & edited for Piano by E. M. Lee. [1945.] 4°.
                                            g. 249. ii. (15.)

— *See* BEETHOVEN (L. van) [Sechs Menuette. K.-H. 10. No. 2.]
Beethoven's Minuet in G. Edited by E. M. Lee. 1928. 4°.
                                            g. 249. v. (8.)

— *See* BEETHOVEN (L. van) [Sechs Menuette. K.-H. 10. No. 2.]
Beethoven's Minuet in G. Edited by E. M. Lee. 1943. 4°.
                                            g. 249. ii. (9.)

— *See* BEETHOVEN (L. van) Rondo in C. Op. 51. No. 1. Edited by
E. M. Lee. 1932. 4°.   **g. 249. aa. (8.)**

— *See* BEETHOVEN (L. van) Rondo in C. Op. 51. No. 1. Edited by
E. M. Lee. [1945.] 4°.   **g. 249. ii. (16.)**

— *See* BERLIOZ (L. H.) [L'Enfance du Christ.—L'Adieu des
Bergers.] Hush! my Dear, lie still and slumber ... Adapted by
E. M. Lee. 1941. 8°.   **F. 1176. n. (36.)**

— *See* BRAHMS (J.) [*Collected Works.—b.*] First Year Brahms.
Pianoforte Solo ... edited by E. M. Lee. 1928. 4°.
                                            g. 609. g. (8.)

— *See* BRAHMS (J.) [Fünf Lieder. Op. 49. No. 4. Wiegenlied.—
Instrumental Arrangements.] Lullaby. Arranged for Piano by
E. M. Lee. 1930. 4°.   **g. 609. i. (3.)**

— *See* BRAHMS (J.) [Fünf Lieder. Op. 49. No. 4. Wiegenlied.—
Instrumental Arrangements.] Lullaby. Arranged ... by
E. M. Lee. 1943. 4°.   **g. 609. n. (4.)**

— *See* BULL (John) *Mus. Doc.* The King's Hunt ... Arranged for
Two Pianos by E. M. Lee. 1936. 4°.   **g. 1122. c. (15.)**

— *See* BULL (John) *Mus. Doc.* The King's Hunt ... Arranged ...
by E. M. Lee. [1946.] 4°.   **g. 1122. j. (3.)**

— *See* CHAIKOVSKY (P. I.) [*Collected Works.—b.*] First Year
Tchaikovsky for Pianoforte Solo. Adapted ... by E. M. Lee,
etc. 1935. 4°.   **g. 557. e. (36.)**

— *See* CHAIKOVSKY (P. I.) [Casse-Noisette.] Valse des Fleurs.
Arranged for Piano by E. M. Lee. 1938. 4°.   **g. 557. f. (11.)**

— *See* CHAIKOVSKY (P. I.) [Casse-Noisette.] Valse des Fleurs.
Arranged for Piano by E. M. Lee. [1944?] 4°. **g. 557. g. (15.)**

— *See* CHAIKOVSKY (P. I.) [12 Morceaux. Op. 40. No. 2.] Chanson
triste. Easily arranged for Piano by E. M. Lee. 1928. 4°.
                                            g. 557. d. (20.)

— *See* CHAIKOVSKY (P. I.) [12 Morceaux. Op. 40. No. 2.] Chanson
triste ... arranged for Piano by E. M. Lee. [1944.] 4°.
                                            g. 557. g. (27.)

— *See* CHAIKOVSKY (P. I.) [Souvenir de Hapsal. Op. 2. No. 3.]
Chant sans paroles. Easily arranged for Piano by E. M. Lee.
1928. 4°.   **g. 557. d. (21.)**

— *See* CHAIKOVSKY (P. I.) [Souvenir de Hapsal. Op. 2. No. 3.]
Chant sans paroles ... arranged for Piano by E. M. Lee.
[1944.] 4°.   **g. 557. g. (32.)**

— *See* CHOPIN (F. F.) [*Collected Works.—c.*] First Year Chopin.
Pianoforte Solo ... edited by E. M. Lee. 1928. 4°.
                                            g. 553. j. (14.)

— *See* DIBDIN (C.) The Waterman, or The Gardener's Daughter
... Music arranged by E. M. Lee, *etc.* 1928. 8°.
                                            E. 1592. jj. (2.)

— *See* GRIEG (E. H.) [Lyrische Stücke. Op. 12. No. 1, 2.] Waltz &
Watchman's Song ... Arranged ... by E. M. Lee. 1932. 4°.
                                            g. 1127. qq. (2.)

LEE (ERNEST MARKHAM)

— See HAENDEL (G. F.) [*Collected Works.—g.*] Second Year
Handel for Pianoforte Solo. Adapted ... by E. M. Lee, *etc.*
1937. 4°.   **g. 74. bb. (2.)**

— See HAENDEL (G. F.) [Berenice.—Overture.] Minuet ...
Arranged for Piano by E. M. Lee. 1929. 4°.   **g. 74. b. (13.)**

— See HAENDEL (G. F.) [Berenice.—Overture.] Minuet ...
Arranged ... by E. M. Lee. 1943. 4°.   **g. 74. hh. (8.)**

— See HAENDEL (G. F.) [Berenice.] Air. Demetrio's "Si tra i
ceppi" ... Arranged ... by E. M. Lee. 1939. 4°.
                                                   g. 74. ee. (7.)

— See HAENDEL (G. F.) [Berenice.] Air. Demetrio's "Se tra i
ceppi" ... Arranged ... by E. M. Lee. [1946.] 4°.
                                                   g. 74. kk. (1.)

— See HAENDEL (G. F.) [Joshua.] Oh had I Jubal's Lyre ... Arr.
... by E. M. Lee. 1938. 8°.   **E. 146. r. (3.)**

— See HAENDEL (G. F.) [Joshua.—O! had I Jubal's Lyre.] Jubal's
Lyre ... Arranged ... by E. M. Lee. 1938. 4°.   **g. 74. bb. (15.)**

— See HAENDEL (G. F.) [Joshua.—O! had I Jubal's Lyre.] Jubal's
Lyre ... Arranged for Two Pianos by E. M. Lee. [1945.] 4°.
                                                   g. 74. hh. (18.)

— See HAENDEL (G. F.) [Judas Maccabæus.] Come, ever smiling
Liberty ... Arranged ... by E. M. Lee. 1939. 8°.
                                                   E. 146. r. (4.)

— See HAENDEL (G. F.) [Judas Maccabæus.] See the conqu'ring
Hero comes ... Freely arranged for unison or massed singing
by E. M. Lee. [1947.] 8°.   **E. 146. r. (11.)**

— See HAENDEL (G. F.) [Serse.—Ombra mai fù.] Largo ...
Arranged for the Organ by E. M. Lee. 1944. 4°.
                                                   g. 74. ii. (3.)

— See HAENDEL (G. F.) [Fifteen Solos. Op. 1. No. 3. Allegro.]
The Tuneful Allegro. Arranged for Piano by E. M. Lee. 1929.
4°.   **g. 74. b. (18.)**

— See HAYDN (F. J.) [*Collected Works.—d.*] Second Year Haydn
for Pianoforte Solo. Adapted ... by E. M. Lee, *etc.* 1936. 4°.
                                                   g. 455. f. (12.)

— See MENDELSSOHN-BARTHOLDY (J. L. F.) [*Collected Works.—j.*]
First year Mendelssohn ... edited by E. M. Lee. 1927. 4°.
                                                   g. 635. o. (6.)

— See MENDELSSOHN-BARTHOLDY (J. L. F.) [Ein
Sommernachtstraum.—Hochzeitsmarsch.] Wedding March.
Arranged ... by E. M. Lee. 1944. 4°.   **g. 635. s. (4.)**

— See MOZART (W. A.) [Divertimento in D. K. 334.] Minuet ...
Arranged by E. M. Lee. 1928. 4°.   **g. 1018. f. (6.)**

— See MOZART (W. A.) [Divertimento in D. K. 334.] Minuet ...
Arranged ... by E. M. Lee. 1943. 4°.   **g. 1018. s. (3.)**

— See MOZART (W. A.) Fantasia in D minor. [K. 397.] Edited by
E. M. Lee. 1929. 4°.   **g. 1018. f. (8.)**

— See MOZART (W. A.) Fantasia in D minor. [K. 397.] Edited by
E. M. Lee. 1943. 4°.   **g. 1018. s. (5.)**

— See MOZART (W. A.) [Symphony in E flat. K. 543.] Minuet ...
Arranged for Piano by E. M. Lee. 1928. 4°.   **g. 1018. f. (12.)**

— See MOZART (W. A.) [Symphony in E flat. K. 543.] Minuet ...
Arranged ... by E. M. Lee. 1943. 4°.   **g. 1018. s. (4.)**

— See MOZART (W. A.) [Symphony in E flat. K. 543.] Celebrated
Minuet in E flat. Arranged for Piano Duet by E. M. Lee.
1938. 4°.   **g. 1018. n. (13.)**

— See PURCELL (H.) [*Collected Works.—c.*] First Year Purcell ...
Adapted ... by E. M. Lee. 1935. 4°.   **g. 25. d. (6.)**

LEE (ERNEST MARKHAM)

— See PURCELL (H.) [King Arthur.] Fairest Isle ... Edited by
E. M. Lee. 1937. 8°.   **F. 659. g. (4.)**

— See PURCELL (H.) [King Arthur.] Your Hay it is mow'd ...
Arranged as a Chorus ... by E. M. Lee, *etc.* 1936. 8°.
[*Choruses for equal Voices. no.* 1936.]   **E. 861.**

— See PURCELL (H.) Now that the Sun. *Evening Hymn, on a
Ground* ... Arr. for Four-part Choir by E. M. Lee. 1933. 8°.
                                                   F. 659. g. (2.)

— See PURCELL (H.) [Ode for Queen Mary's Birthday. 1694.]
Sound the Trumpet ... Arr. ... by E. M. Lee. 1936. 8°.
                                                   F. 659. g. (5.)

— See SCHUBERT (F. P.) [*Collected Works.—e.*] The Song Master.
Ten Songs ... Easily arranged for the Pianoforte by E. M.
Lee, *etc.* 1927. 4°.   **g. 567. e. (24.)**

— See SCHUBERT (F. P.) [*Collected Works.—e.*] The Song Master.
Ten Songs ... arranged ... by E. M. Lee. 1943. 4°.
                                                   g. 567. l. (16.)

— See SCHUBERT (F. P.) [*Collected Works.—g.*] First Year
Schubert. Pianoforte Solo ... edited by E. M. Lee. 1927. 4°.
                                                   g. 567. e. (23.)

— See SCHUBERT (F. P.) [*Collected Works.—g.*] Second Year
Schubert. Pianoforte Solo ... edited by E. M. Lee. 1928. 4°.
                                                   g. 567. h. (4.)

— See SCHUBERT (F. P.) [Drei Märsche. Op. 51. No. 1.] Marche
militaire. Edited by E. M. Lee. 1932. 4°.   **g. 567. j. (1.)**

— See SCHUBERT (F. P.) [Drei Märsche. Op. 51. No. 1.] Marche
Militaire ... Edited by E. M. Lee. 1943. 4°.   **g. 567. l. (21.)**

— See SCHUBERT (F. P.) [Rosamunde.] Ballet Music ... Arranged
for Piano by E. M. Lee. 1938. 4°.   **g. 567. k. (18.)**

— See SCHUBERT (F. P.) [Rosamunde.] Ballet Music ... Arranged
... by E. M. Lee. 1943. 4°.   **g. 567. l. (22.)**

— See SCHUBERT (F. P.) [Zwei Scherzi. No. 1.] Scherzo in B flat.
Edited by E. M. Lee. 1932. 4°.   **g. 567. i. (16.)**

— See SCHUBERT (F. P.) [Zwei Scherzi. No. 1.] Scherzo in B flat.
Edited by E. M. Lee. [1946?] 4°.   **g. 567. o. (7.)**

— See SCHUBERT (F. P.) [Schwanengesang.—No. 4. Ständchen.]
Serenade. Edited by E. M. Lee. 1932. 4°.   **g. 567. i. (17.)**

— See SCHUBERT (F. P.) [Schwanengesang.—No. 4. Ständchen.]
Serenade. Edited by E. M. Lee. 1946. 4°.   **g. 567. l. (29.)**

— See SCHUMANN (R. A.) [*Collected Works.—d.*] First Year
Schumann ... Adapted ... by E. M. Lee. 1927. 4°.
                                                   g. 715. h. (17.)

— See SCHUMANN (R. A.) [43 Clavierstücke für die Jugend.
Op. 68. Soldatenmarsch. Jägerliedchen.] Soldier's March &
Hunting Song ... Edited by E. M. Lee. 1932. 4°.
                                                   g. 715. k. (5.)

— See STRAUSS (J.) *the Younger.* [An der schönen blauen
Donau.] The Blue Danube Waltz. Arranged ... by E. M. Lee.
1934. 8°.   **F. 636. zz. (3.)**

— See STRAUSS (J.) *the Younger.* [Die Fledermaus.] Waltz ...
Arranged for Mixed Voices by E. M. Lee. 1939. 8°.
                                                   F. 638. i. (17.)

— See STRAUSS (J.) *the Younger.* [Wein, Weib und Gesang.]
Love's Refrain ... Arranged by E. M. Lee. 1937. 8°.
                                                   F. 638. h. (27.)

— See THOMAS (C. L. A.) [Mignon.] Gavotte ... Arranged ... by
E. M. Lee. 1938. 4°.   **g. 1127. xx. (27.)**

— See THOMAS (C. L. A.) [Mignon.] Gavotte ... Arranged ... by
E. M. Lee. [1946.] 4°.   **f. 133. ii. (20.)**

LEE (ERNEST MARKHAM)

— See WAGNER (W. R.) [Tannhäuser.—O! du mein holder
Abendstern.] O Star of Eve ... arranged ... by E. M. Lee.
1945. 8°. [*L. G. B. Choral Repertoire. No.* 47.]   **F. 1843. a.**

LEE (FROEBEL E.)

— The Blossom and the Bee. [Song.] Words and music by
F. E. Lee.   *T. Presser Co.: Philadelphia,* (1912.) fol.
H. 1723. s. (38.)

LEE (G. M.)

— Dominus custodiat introitum. Motet. [c. 1930.] *s. sh.* 8°.
F. 1196. w. (3.)

LEE (GARNETT)

— "I'm a lucky Coon." [Song.] Words by Al. Simonds.
Evans-Hill Co.: [*New York,* 1907.] 4°.   **H. 3985. q. (13.)**

LEE (GENEVIEVE KIMBER)

— Lady Bath. Schottische. [P. F.] pp. 5.   *Carl Fischer: New York,*
etc., [1909.] fol.   **h. 4120. oo. (4.)**

LEE (GEORGE)

— The Conisbro' Castle Polka. [P. F.] pp. 5.   *For the author:*
Sheffield, [c. 1870.] fol.   **h. 61. cc. (15.)**

LEE (GEORGE ALEXANDER)

— Seven Favourite Songs. See ALEXANDRA. The Alexandra
Music Books. No. 18. [1893.] fol.   **H. 2328.**

— Agar's prayer. No. 4 of Six Sabbath Songs.   *D'Almaine &*
Co.: London, [1851.] fol.   **H. 1290. (10.)**

—— [Alfred the Great.] The Music of Alfred the Great, or the
enchanted Standard ... arranged for the pianoforte (the
poetry by I. Pocock).   *London,* [1827?] fol.   **H. 627.**

— All around the ancient tree. Ballad written by J. W. Lake.
pp. 7.   *E. Ransford: London,* [1850.] fol.   **H. 1290. (34.)**

— Annie Bell ... Ballad, written by Mrs. Crawford. pp. 5.
D'Almaine & Co.: London, [1851.] fol.   **H. 1290. (12.)**

— At the Door of a Cottage, a fair Girl was spinning. [Song.]
The words written by W. H. Bellamy, *etc.* pp. 7.   *H. Tolkien:*
London, [c. 1840.] fol.   **G. 296. a. (17.)**

— Awake! awake! brave Scots to glory. Song. *See* infra:
[Malvina.]

— Away, away to the Mountain's Brow. *See* infra: [The Devil's
Brother.]

— The Banks of the Rhine, ballad. [Words by — Archer.] pp. 3.
Lewis & Co.: London, [1854.] fol.   **H. 1290. a. (16.)**

— Barney O'Toole, Irish ballad ... the words by S. Fearon.
pp. 7.   *E. Ransford: London,* [1847?] fol.   **G. 425. ss. (21.)**

— The Bavarian Girl's Song. Buy a Broom! The words by
D. A. O'Meara ... Arranged (and partly composed) ... by
A. Lee. pp. 6.   *Mayhew & C⁰: London,* [ᵂᴹ 1821.] fol.
H. 1653. h. (13.)

— The Bavarian girl's Duett ... Composed & arranged ... by
A. Lee. pp. 8.   *Mayhew & C⁰: London,* [ᵂᴹ 1824.] fol.
H. 2818. f. (26.)

— The Bavarian Girl's Song. Buy a Broom! ⟨The words by
D. A. O'Meara.⟩ ... Arranged ... by A. Lee. pp. 5.   *Mayhew &*
C⁰: London, [ᵂᴹ 1824.] fol.   **H. 1654. j. (10.)**

LEE (GEORGE ALEXANDER)

— Bavarian Girl's Song ... [Song.] Arranged and partly
composed by A. Lee. pp. 5.   [*London?,* ᵂᴹ 1827.] fol.
Without titlepage. The title has been taken from the head of
p. 1.   **H. 1980. o. (12.)**

— Bavarian Girl's song. (From Teutschland I come.)   *London,*
[1874.] fol.
No. 3393 *of the "Musical Bouquet".*   **H. 2345.**

— Bavarian Girl's Song. [With guitar accompaniment.] *See*
LAYS. Lays of Harmony, *etc.* No. 44. [1894.] fol.   **H. 2086.**

— "Be wise & never take a Wife," [song] as sung by Mʳˢ Browne
in the new grand melo-drama of Cagliostro. The words by
Butler Danvers ... Arranged & in part composed by
Alexander Lee. ⟨Flute, voice, piano forte.⟩ [Score.] pp. 9.
Bunting Walsh Pigott and Sherwin: Dublin, [c. 1825.] fol.
H. 1660. f. (6.)

— Beautiful Birds. [Song, begins: "Birds, beautiful bright".]
Words by M. McGill.   *Baltimore,* 1860. fol.
H. 1780. f. (13.)

— The beautiful flowers of May; a ballad [begins: "I wandered
forth"] ... the poetry by R. Raine.   *London,* [1845.] fol.
H. 1289. (24.)

— Beautiful May. Chansonette; the poetry by M. E. Cooke.
London, [1846.] fol.   **H. 1289. (26.)**

— The beautiful West. Ballad, the poetry by E. C. S. [Begins:
"Oh wilt thou still love me?"]   *London,* [1852.] fol.
H. 1735. (25.)

— Beauty's orders. Cavatina written by Shirley Brooks. pp. 6.
Jullien & Co.: London, [1847.] fol.   **H. 1290. (21.)**

— Believe me not false. Ballad ... written by E. M. Spencer.
London, [1845?] fol.   **H. 1288. a. (1.)**

— Bells at sunset. Song, written by F. E. Lacy. pp. 5.   *Leoni Lee*
& Coxhead: London, [1847.] fol.   **H. 1290. (17.)**

— The Bells, the Bells of evening; Ballad, the poetry by E. J.
Gill. pp. 5.   *Chappell: London,* [1841.] fol.   **H. 1287. (39.)**

— Bells upon the wind. *See* infra: [Lo Zingaro.]

— The better land. Song written by Mʳˢ. Hemans. [Begins: "I
hear thee speak of a better land".]   *London,* [1852.] fol.
H. 1735. (27.)

— The Bird of Love [song] ... the Poetry by ... Lord Byron, *etc.*
Goulding & D'Almaine: London, [1823?] fol.   **G. 383. h. (60.)**

— The Bird of Love, *etc.* [Song.] *In:* The Musical Bijou ... for
MDCCCXLVII. p. 36. [1847.] fol.   **H. 2330.**

— The bird of the Valley. Ballad, *etc.* ⟨written by E. J. Gill.⟩
pp. 5.   *D'Almaine & Co.: London,* [1850.] fol.   **H. 1290. (36.)**

— The blooming rose you gave me. Lovely Rosabella, Ballad ...
Poetry and music ... by A. Lee.   *H. Keeler: Bristol,* [1857.] fol.
H. 1290. a. (6.)

— Blue Bonnets over the Border, or March, march, Etterick &
Teviot-Dale ... Partly composed & arranged from the
original celebrated national air by A. Lee. pp. 7.   *I. Willis &*
C⁰: London, Dublin, [1826?] fol.   **H. 1652. mm. (20.)**

— Blue Bonnets over the Border. [Song.]   [*London,* 1830?] fol.
Imperfect; wanting the last leaf.   **H. 2815. f. (15.)**

— Blue Bonnets over the Border; or, March, march Ettrick &
Teviot-dale ... Words by Sir W. Scott ... The Music partly
composed & arranged from the orginal ... National Air, by
A. Lee. Third edition.   *I. Willis & Co.: London & Dublin,*
[1830?] fol.   **H. 1652. d. (46.)**

— Blue Bonnets over the border. [Song.]   *London,* [1874.] fol.
No. 3516 *of the "Musical Bouquet".*   **H. 2345.**

LEE (George Alexander)

— The Boatman's Daughter. The popular Nigger melody sung by the Ethiopian Serenaders ... arranged ... by A. Lee. *London*, [1847.] fol.   **H. 1435. (29.)**

— Bonnie Lad March. *See* infra: [Homage to Charlie.]

— The boundless sway of love; ballad, written by J. Churchill. pp. 7.   *J. Power: London*, [1834.] fol.   **H. 1287. (42.)**

— "Bright summer days are coming;" Chansonette, the poetry by F. Wilson. pp. 5.   *Lee: London*, [1843.] fol.   **H. 1288. (4.)**

— The Butterfly was a Gentleman. *See* infra: [The Loves of the Butterflies.]

— By the Waters of Babylon ... Duet. *In:* The Musical Bijou ... for MDCCCLI. pp. 78–82. [1851.] fol.   **H. 2330.**

— By the waters of Babylon — Duet. (The poetry by Lord Byron.)   *London*, [1852.] fol.   **H. 1735. (31.)**

— Canst thou ask me to forget. Ballad ... the poetry by R. F. Williams.   *London*, [1840?] fol.   **H. 2832. n. (2.)**

— Cheerful Melody. Chansonnette. ⟨Second edition.⟩ Written by F. W. N. Bayley.   *W. Williams & Co.: London*, [1859.] fol. *Imperfect, wanting pp.* 1–4, *for which another song has been substituted.*   **H. 1290. a. (9.)**

— Chime on chime on sweet Vesper Bell, barcarole, *etc.* pp. 5. *Lee: London*, [c. 1845.] fol.   **H. 1654. zz. (13.)**

— Cold was the night Wind. [Song. Words by] Rob¹ Southey. *In:* The Musical Bijou ... for MDCCCXLVII. p. 48. [1847.] fol.   **H. 2330.**

— Come away, come away, (the Mermaid's Song) the poetry by W. H. Bellamy. pp. 5.   *Cramer, Addison & Beale: London*, [1828.] fol.   **H. 1847. f. (9.)**

— Come away, come away, 'tis the Nightingale's Song. Cavatina ... The Poetry by Mrs. C. B. Wilson.   *P. E. Rowe: Pylmouth*, [1840?] fol.   **H. 1650. n. (18.)**

— Come away with me. Serenade.   *London*, [1845.] fol.   **H. 1289. (18.)**

— Come buy of me a Nosegay. [Song. Words] written by R. Nicholson. *In:* The Musical Bijou ... for MDCCCXLIX. pp. 52–56. [1849.] fol.   **H. 2330.**

— Come dwell with me, Ballad ... The poetry by T. Haynes Bayly. pp. 5.   *Goulding & D'Almaine: London*, [c. 1830.] fol.   **H. 1653. h. (14.)**

— Come dwell with me ... [Song.] The poetry by T. Haynes Bayly. Arranged as a duet by G. A. Hodson. pp. 5. *D'Almaine & Cᵒ: London*, [c. 1840.] fol. *Pp.* 3, 4 *are mutilated.*   **H. 1601. kk. (4.)**

— [Another issue.] Come dwell with me, composed by A. Lee arranged [as a duet] by G. A. Hodson.   *London*, [1840?] fol. *Imperfect; wanting title page.*   **G. 797. (21.)**

— Come dwell with me. [Song.] The poetry by T. H. Bayly. ⟨New & superior edition.⟩   *B. Williams: London*, [1863.] fol.   **H. 1290. a. (13.)**

— Come dwell with me ... Ballad.   *London*, [1874.] fol. *No.* 3775 *of the "Musical Bouquet".*   **H. 2345.**

— Come dwell with me ... for the Pianoforte. [1867.] fol. *See* MATTINI (F.)   **h. 3002. (6.)**

— Come, lady, come o'er the flowery heath. A ballad ... The poetry by A. Park.   *London*, [1830?] fol.   **G. 808. h. (26.)**

— Come o'er the Heather. *See* infra: [Malvina.]

— Come o'er the Hills with me, Serenade ... the poetry by Mrs. Jennings, *etc.   Schott & Co.: London*, [1850?] fol.   **H. 1652. m. (16.)**

LEE (George Alexander)

— "Come thou to me;" ballad, the words by Mrs. C. B. Wilson. pp. 7.   *Duff & Hodgson: London*, [1843.] fol.   **H. 1288. (2.)**

— Come to me again ... Ballad [begins: "I have sought thee"]. Poetry by T. H. Bayly.   *London*, [1874.] fol. *No.* 3777 *of the "Musical Bouquet".*   **H. 2345.**

— Come to my fairy Home deep in the chrystal Wave, canzonet ... The poetry by Mʳˢ Cornwell Baron Wilson. pp. 7.   *Metzler & Cᵒ, for the proprietors: London*, [c. 1840.] fol.   **H. 1289. a. (1.)**

— Come to the Gipsey's tent. Song ... selected and in part composed by Alexander Lee. pp. 7.   *D'Almaine & Co.: [London,]* 1850. fol.   **H. 1290. (38.)**

— Come where the aspens quiver. A ballad, the poetry by T. H. Bayly.   *London*, [1830?] fol.   **H. 2831. a. (11.)**

— "Come where the aspens quiver;" a ballad, arranged for the guitar by B. Sperati. pp. 5.   *D'Almaine & Co.: London*, [1843.] fol.   **H. 1288. (7.)**

— Come where the aspens quiver. Song.   *London*, [1874.] fol. *No.* 3375 *of the "Musical Bouquet".*   **H. 2345.**

— Como, Como, ballad. [The poetry by F. Enoch.] [Begins: "There is a city".]   *London*, [1852.] fol.   **H. 1735. (29.)**

— Como, Como exquisite Como, *etc.* [Song.] *In:* The Musical Bijou ... for MDCCCLII. pp. 83–88. [1852.] fol.   **H. 2330.**

— A complete course of instructions for singing, *etc.   London*, [1872.] fol.   **H. 1290. b.**

— Consider the Lilies. No. 1 of Six Sabbath Songs.   *D'Almaine & Co.: London*, [1850.] fol.   **H. 1290. (31.)**

— The Corsair. O'er the glad waters of the dark blue sea. Scena, the poetry by ... Lord Byron. pp. 8.   *Lee: London*, [c. 1840.] fol.   **H. 1289. a. (2.)**

— Cottage Vespers. [Song.]   *London*, [1835?] fol.   **H. 2835. c. (33.)**

— Could you but hear my lady sing. *See* infra: [Good Husbands make good Wives.]

— The Dark eyed Maid of Cadiz. ⟨[Song. Words] by Lord Byron.⟩ *In:* The Musical Bijou ... for MDCCCXXXIII. pp. 50–56. [1833.] 4°.   **F. 149.**

— The Daughters of my sunny Italy. Cavatina [begins: "Oh! wilt thou brave"].   *London*, [1840?] fol.   **H. 2832. o. (44.)**

— Day's Beams are over. ⟨[Song. Words] by Mrs. Cornwell Baron Wilson.⟩ *In:* The Musical Bijou ... for MDCCCXXXII. pp. 54–58. [1832.] 4°.   **F. 149.**

— "Daylight is on the sea;" serenade, the poetry by Mrs. C. B. Wilson.   *Liverpool*, [1844.] fol.   **H. 1289. (12.)**

— Daylight is on the sea. *See* HATTON (J. L.) A. Lee's ... song "Daylight is on the sea," arranged ... by J. L. Hatton. [1844.] fol.   **h. 702. (30.)**

— Daylight, love, is passed away. *See* infra: [The Devil's Brother.]

— The Days of young Romance. ⟨[Song. Words] by Fraser Bradshaw Smith.⟩ *In:* The Musical Bijou ... for MDCCCXXXV. pp. 2–7. [1835.] 4°.   **F. 149.**

— The Dear old scenes of home. Ballad. Poetry by G. J. O. Allmann. pp. 3.   *Lewis & Co.: London*, [1854.] fol.   **H. 1290. a. (15.)**

— Dearest Lady weep no more, new ballad, *etc.* pp. 5. *W. Wybrow: London*, [c. 1840.] fol.   **H. 1289. a. (3.)**

— The Deer Stalker, a ballad of the Highlands. The poetry by F. N. Bayly. pp. 7.   *B. Williams: London*, [1875.] fol.   **H. 1290. d. (6.)**

LEE (George Alexander)

The Devil's Brother

— Away, away to the Mountain's Brow, a Cavatina, *etc.* pp. 7. *Alexander Lee & Lee: London*, [c. 1830.] fol.
H. 2831. a. (12.)

— Away, away to the Mountain's Brow, a cavatina, *etc.* ⟨Tenth edition.⟩ pp. 7. *H. Wray: London*, [1832?] fol.
H. 1289. a. (4.)

— Away, away to the Mountain's Brow, a Cavatina, *etc.* ⟨Twelfth edition.⟩ pp. 7. *H. Wray: London*, [1833?] fol.
H. 1653. h. (15.)

— Away, away to the Mountain's Brow. A cavatina, *etc.* ⟨16ᵗʰ edition.⟩ pp. 7. *Lee: London*, [c. 1840.] fol. **H. 2815. f. (13.)**

— Away, away to the mountain's brow. ⟨Cavatina.⟩ pp. 4. *H. White & Son: London*, [1868.] fol. **H. 1290. a. (28.)**

— Away, away to the mountain's brow. Song. pp. 7. *Metzler & Cᵒ.: London*, [1874.] fol.
H. 1290. d. (3.)

— Away, away to the mountain's brow ... Cavatina. *London*, [1874.] fol.
No. 3506 of the "Musical Bouquet". **H. 2345.**

— Away to the mountain's brow. Song. pp. 4. *W. Marshall & Cᵒ.: London*, [1878.] fol.
H. 1290. d. (13.)

— Away, away to the Mountain's Brow ... Cavatina ... Arranged as a duett, for two performers on the piano forte, by Signor Corri. pp. 1–8. *H. Wray: London*, [1833?] fol. *Imperfect; wanting p. 9.* **H. 1289. a. (5.)**

— Away to the mountain's brow ... for Piano. [1866.] fol. *See* HIME (E. L.) **h. 983. (29.)**

— Daylight love is passed away ... Cavatina ... The poetry by R. Pigot. *London*, [1840?] fol. **G. 805. c. (7.)**

— Down where the blue bells grow. Ballad ... Poetry by J. Bruton. pp. 5. *D'Almaine & Co.: London*, [1851.] fol.
H. 1290. (15.)

— Down where the blue bells grow. Written by J. Bruton. ⟨Fifth edition.⟩ pp. 5. *D'Almaine & Co.: London*, 1851. fol.
H. 1290. (8.)

— Down where the Blue Bells grow, *etc.* [Song.] *In:* The Musical Bijou ... for MDCCCLI. pp. 7–11. [1851.] fol. **H. 2330.**

— Down where the Blue Bells grow, [song] written by J. Bruton, *etc.* pp. 5. *D'Almaine & Cᵒ: London*, [c. 1860.] fol.
H. 1870. aa. (11.)

— Down where the bluebells grow. Ballad, *etc.* pp. 5. *Robert Cocks & Co.: London*, [1867.] fol. **H. 1290. a. (23.)**

— Down where the blue bells ... for the Pianoforte. [1867.] fol. *See* WEST (G. F.) **h. 1395. b. (40.)**

— Down where the Blue-bells grow. [P. F. solo and duet.] *See* SMALLWOOD (W.) Home Treasures, *etc.* No. 35. [1872, *etc.*] fol.
h. 1412. o.

— Down where the Blue-Bells grow. [P. F. solo and duet.] *See* SMALLWOOD (W.) Little Buds, *etc.* No. 35. [1874, *etc.*] fol.
h. 1412. p.

— A Dream of the Past, *etc.* [Song.] *In:* The Musical Bijou ... for MDCCCXXXIX. pp. 6–10. [1839.] fol. **H. 2330.**

— A Dream of the Past, ballad ... The poetry by Charles Jefferys. pp. 6–10. *D'Almaine & Cᵒ: London*, [c. 1840.] fol. *Reissued from The Musical Bijou for 1839.* **H. 1289. a. (6.)**

— A Dream of the Past, ballad ... The poetry by Charles Jefferys. pp. 5. *D'Almaine & Cᵒ: London*, [c. 1840.] fol.
H. 1654. zz. (14.)

LEE (George Alexander)

— A Dream of the Past. Ballad. The poetry by C. Jeffreys. ⟨12ᵗʰ edition.⟩ pp. 5. *B. Williams: London*, [1870.] fol.
H. 1290. a. (34.)

— The Dryades, Duet the words by Mr. Spencer. pp. 9. *Duff & Hodgson: London*, [1847.] fol. **H. 1290. (24.)**

— The Dryades. Duet, *etc. See* DUETS. Vocal Duets, *etc.* No. 148. [1865? *etc.*] fol. **H. 2259.**

— Each Bower has Beauty for me. *See infra:* [The Loves of the Butterflies.]

— Each dew drop that falls. A ballad. *London*, [1830?] fol.
H. 2835. c. (34.)

— Eileen's Prayer. Ballad, written ... by J. H. Jewell. pp. 7. *Jewell and Letchford: London*, [1852?] fol. **G. 295. pp. (13.)**

— Ellen Mavourneen, ballad ... the poetry by R. Raine. [Begins: "Oh! Ellen, dear Ellen".] *London*, [1854.] fol.
H. 1758. (15.)

— England, dear England, the land of the free. ⟨Grand national song. Second edition.⟩ pp. 5. *Henry Keeler: Bristol*, [1857.] fol. **H. 1290. a. (4.)**

— Erin's lament. Mourn, lovely Erin, O'Connell's no more. Written by H. R. Addison. pp. 5. *Jullien & Co.: London*, [1847.] fol. **H. 1290. (22.)**

— Evening bells; duet. pp. 7. *Cramer, Addison & Beale: London*, [1838.] fol. **H. 1287. (31.)**

— Evening Bells. [For S. S.] pp. 3. *J. Curwen & Sons: London*, [1887.] 8°.
[*Choruses for equal Voices. no. 41.*] **E. 861.**

— The exile's song [begins: "I stand each day"], written by T. W. Hybart. *London*, [1846.] fol. **H. 1289. (25.)**

— The exiles or the chiming village bell, duet [begins: "They gaze upon the shore"], words by R. Raine. *London*, [1854.] fol. **H. 1758. (21.)**

— Fair Magiore [*sic*]. (The poetry by F. Enoch.) *London*, [1852.] fol. **H. 1735. (30.)**

— Fair Magiore [*sic*]!, *etc.* [Song.] *In:* The Musical Bijou for MDCCCLII. pp. 77–82. [1852.] fol. **H. 2330.**

— The Fairest Flower. *See infra:* [The Invincibles.]

The Fairy Lake

— The Fairy Lake or the Magic Veil, an opera in 3 acts. Adapted from the French "Le Lac des fées" by Charles Selby, *etc. W. J. Hammond: London*, [c. 1840.] fol.
No. 9 only. **G. 809. yy. (16.)**

— "I'll not beguile thee;" a ballad, with an accompaniment for the guitar by N. W. Gould. *London*, [1843.] fol.
H. 1289. (1.)

— I'll not beguile thee from thy home. Ballad. *London*, [1846.] fol. **H. 2832. e. (20.)**

— [Another edition.] I'll not beguile thee from thy Home. Ballad, *etc. C. Sheard & Co.: London*, [1889.] fol.
No. 7863 of the "Musical Bouquet". **H. 2345.**

— In our peaceful happy Home, Duet ... The poetry by Charles Selby, *etc.* pp. 5. *D'Almaine & Cᵒ: London*, [c. 1840.] fol.
H. 1980. bb. (9.)

— Fall not in Love. *See infra:* [The Invincibles.]

— [The Fancy Ball.] I never can forget thee. A ballad, from the Operetta of The Fancy Ball. Poetry by E. Morton. pp. 5. *J. Dean & Cᵒ.: London*, [1830.] fol. **H. 1287. (40.)**

LEE (George Alexander)

— [The Fancy Ball.] O, where are the Joys that once I knew, a ballad ... Poetry by Edwd Morton, *etc.* pp. 5. *J. Dean & Co: London*, [1832.] fol. **H. 1289. a. (7.)**

— [The Fancy Ball.] O where are the joys that once I knew ... Ballad. (Poetry by E. Morton.) *London*, [1835?] fol. **G. 809. b. (10.)**

— Farewell ye happy Hours, *etc.* [Song.] ⟨Words by Alfred Knott.⟩ pp. [5.] *B. Williams: London*, [c. 1850.] fol. **H. 1653. k. (26.)**

— [The First of May.] The Wild white Rose, a ballad sung ... in the new comedy called The First of May. ⟨The poetry by Isabel Hill.⟩ pp. 5. *H. Wray: London*, [1833?] fol. **H. 1289. a. (8.)**

— The Flower of Lammermoor, *etc.* [Song.] *In:* The Musical Bijou ... for MDCCCLI. pp. 27–31. [1851.] fol. **H. 2330.**

— The flower of Lammermoor. [Song.] Poetry by E. J. Gill. pp. 5. *D'Almaine & Co.: London*, [1851.] fol. **H. 1290. (13.)**

— The Flower of Lammermoor, *etc.* [Song, with P. F. accompaniment. pp. 5. [*D'Almaine & Co.: London*, 1851.] fol. *The imprint has been cropped. The verso of p. 5 bears an orchestral accompaniment in score.* **H. 1653. d. (8.)**

— Forest Flowers. A ballad [begins: "I've heard them lilting"]. The poetry by Miss J. Elliot. *London*, [1840?] fol. **H. 2835. (23.)**

— The Gay Troubadour. Ballad. *See infra:* [Sold for a Song.]

— The glory of all nations, or Victoria and England the land of the free. ⟨Grand national song.⟩ pp. 5. *H. Keeler: Bristol*, [1857.] fol. **H. 1290. a. (5.)**

— Go, cull your Roses. Ballad. pp. 5. *J. McDowell & Co.: London*, [1868.] fol. **H. 1290. a. (27.)**

— The Gondolette, cavatina ... The poetry by Charles Selby, *etc.* pp. 5. *Duff & Hodgson: London*, [1843.] fol. **H. 1289. a. (9.)**

— The Gondolette ... for the Piano. [1866.] fol. *See* HIME (E. L.) **h. 983. (31.)**

— [Good Husbands make good Wives.] Could you but hear my lady sing. A cavatina [begins: "Sweet are the beams"] ... written by J. B. Buckstone. *London*, [1830?] fol. **G. 809. b. (7.)**

— [Good Husbands make good Wives.] Woman loves ye best. Ballad [begins: "Who on earth"] ... written by J. B. Buckstone. *London*, [1835?] fol. **H. 2832. o. (43.)**

— Good Night, love, good night. [Song, written by R. Raine.] pp. 3. *Lewis & Co.: London*, [1854.] fol. **H. 1290. a. (14.)**

— The Good old Time, a ballad in the old style. ⟨[Words] by Thomas Haynes Bayly.⟩ *In:* The Musical Bijou ... for MDCCCXXXVI. pp. 12–19. [1836.] 4°. **F. 149.**

— The Gypsey's wild chaunt. *See infra:* [Lo Zingaro.]

— Happy Dreams. Ballad [begins: "Beautiful dreams"]. ⟨Words by M. M.⟩ pp. 11. *Samuel Brewer: London*, [1878.] fol. **H. 1290. d. (11.)**

— The happy loving Bride; chansonette [begins: "What care I"] ... the poetry by F. W. Hybart. *Leeds*, [1845.] fol. **H. 1289. (13.)**

— "Hark, 'tis the waterfall." Cavatina, the poetry by T. H. Bayly. pp. 7. *S. Chappell: London*, [1834.] fol. **H. 1287. (26.)**

— The Harp's wild notes. [Song,] poetry by E. Cook [begins: "A zephyr breath of wind is playing"]. *London*, [1845?] fol. **H. 1288. a. (2.)**

LEE (George Alexander)

— Haste to the Fairy Land with me, ballad ... in M^r. Buckstone's new operetta entitled I will be a Duchess! ... the poetry by J. Halford, *etc.* pp. 5. *W. J. Hammond: London*, [1839?] fol. **H. 1660. l. (20.)**

— The haunts of the Chamois, the wild haunts for me. Tyrolienne ... words by M^{rs}. Jennings. pp. 5. *Duff & Hodgson: London*, [1850?] fol. **H. 1290. (30.)**

— He comes not. [Song.] The poetry by Mrs. C. B. Wilson. *London*, [1840?] fol. **H. 2831. d. (13.)**

— He lives renown'd in Story, cavatina, *etc.* ⟨Written by Mrs Leoni Lee.⟩ pp. 6. *Mayhew & Co: London*, [^{WM} 1824.] fol. **H. 1289. a. (10.)**

— He wipes the tear from every eye. Vocal Duet. The poetry by M^{rs}. Mackinlay. [Begins: "When sore afflictions".] *London*, [1852.] fol. **H. 1735. (32.)**

— He wipes the tear from every eye. Sacred song. pp. 5. *Brewer & Co.: London*, [1874.] fol. **H. 1290. d. (4.)**

— He wipes the tear from every eye ... Trio. pp. 7. *Brewer & Co: London*, [1874.] fol. **H. 1290. d. (5.)**

— [Another edition.] He wipes the tear from ev'ry eye ... No. 1 in E flat. No. 2 in F. 2 no. *London*, [1883.] fol. **H. 1288. a. (9.)**

— He wipes the Tear from every Eye. Sacred Four-Part Song ... Arranged for 4 Voices by E. M. Lott, *etc. E. Ashdown: London*, [1885?] 8°. *Sacred Select Harmony, No. 26.* **F. 1146.**

— [A reissue.] He wipes the Tear from every Eye, *etc. Edwin Ashdown: London*, [c. 1900.] fol. **H. 1028. p. (6.)**

— [He wipes the Tear from every Eye.] "O Love Divine." Anthem adapted from the Sacred Song ... Words by G. [or rather, O.] W. Holmes. [1906.] *See* WOOD AND SONS. Wood's Collection of Glees, *etc.* No. 194. [1896, *etc.*] 8°. **E. 1689.**

— He wipes the Tear from every Eye. [Anthem.] Arr. by A. Leland [from the song by G. A. Lee]. 1913. 8°. *See* LELAND (A.) **F. 538. f. (38.)**

— He wipes the Tear from every Eye ... Choral Arrangement by J. Bell. *Caledonia Publishing Co.: Glasgow*, 1915. 8°. *New Part Songs, No. 62.* **F. 1171. ll. (22.)**

— He wipes the Tear from every Eye ... Arranged [for two voices] by Henry Geehl. pp. 5. *Edwin Ashdown: London*, [1949.] 8°. *[Ashdown vocal Duets. no. 237.]* **E. 1601.**

— He wipes the Tear from every Eye ... Choral arrangement by J. Bell. [Tonic sol-fa notation.] *Caledonia Publishing Co.: Glasgow*, 1915. 4°. *New Part Songs, No. 62.* **C. 745. f. (15.)**

— He wipes the tear from every eye ... for the Pianoforte. [1860.] fol. *See* RICHARDS (H. B.) **h. 760. e. (11.)**

— He wipes the tear from every eye ... for the Pianoforte. [1864.] fol. *See* STONE (J. T.) **h. 1403. c. (20.)**

— He wipes the tear from every eye ... for the Pianoforte. [1872.] fol. *See* SMALLWOOD (W.) **h. 1412. b. (26.)**

— He wipes the tear from every eye ... for the Pianoforte. [1878.] fol. *See* SMITH (B.) **h. 3025. b. (2.)**

— He wipes the Tear from ev'ry Eye, for the pianoforte, *etc.* [1883.] fol. *See* RICHARDS (H. B.) **h. 760. i. (14.)**

— He wipes the Tear from every Eye. Transcription. [Organ.] [1894.] *See* LOTT (E. M.) Popular Pieces, *etc.* No. 35. [1880, *etc.*] fol. **h. 2716. a. (1.)**

LEE (George Alexander)

— Her Smile's so soft & lovely. [Song.] The poetry by Butler Danvers ... Adapted to an original German air ... by Alexander Lee. pp. 7. *I. Willis & C[r]: Dublin, London*, [1829.] fol.   **H. 1660. f. (7.)**

— Here's a Health bonnie Scotland to thee. A ballad ... The poetry by W. H. Truman, *etc*. pp. 5. *A. Fleetwood: New York*, [c. 1830.] fol.   **H. 1660. m. (20.)**

— Here's a health, bonny Scotland, to thee ... Ballad. The poetry by W. H. Freeman. ⟨New & superior edition. In G.⟩ pp. 5. *B. Williams: London*, [1866.] fol.   **H. 1290. a. (19*.)**

— Here's a health bonny Scotland to thee ... Symphonies & accompaniments by J. Blockley. pp. 7. *John Blockley: London*, [1876.] fol.   **H. 1290. d. (9.)**

— Holy nature heavenly fair. Sacred Song. *London*, [1852.] fol.   **H. 1735. (24.)**

— Homage to Charlie, the celebrated Scotch Song of Bonnie Lad March ... Written by J. Churchill. pp. 5. *Mayhew & C[r].: London*, [[WM] 1824.] fol.   **G. 806. f. (44.)**

— [Another issue.] Bonnie Lad March, the celebrated Scotch Song Homage to Charlie, *etc*. pp. 5. *Mayhew & C[r]: London*, [[WM] 1824.] fol.   **H. 1653. h. (16.)**

— The Horticultural Wife. *See infra*: [The King's Gardener.]

— The Hunter's signal horn. *See* infra: [The Sublime and Beautiful.]

— Hurrah for the Bonnets of Blue. A Ballad ... Second edition. *I. Willis & Co.: London*, [1827?] fol.   **H. 1652. e. (5.)**

— Hurrah for the Bonnets of Blue. A Ballad ... Third edition. *I. Willis & Co.: London & Dublin*, [1827.] fol.   **G. 806. c. (18.)**

— Hurrah, for the bonnets of blue. Ballad. ⟨New edition.⟩ pp. 5. *B. Williams: London*, [1868.] fol.   **H. 1290. a. (25.)**

— Hurrah for the bonnets of blue ... Ballad. *London*, [1874.] fol.
No. 3394 *of the "Musical Bouquet".*   **H. 2345.**

— Hurrah for the Bonnets of Blue ... for the Pianoforte. [1861.] fol. *See* RICHARDS (H. B.)   **h. 760. f. (5.)**

— [Hurrah for the Bonnets of Blue.] *See* KNAPTON (Philip) Hurrah for the Bonnets of Blue ⟨composed by A. Lee⟩ ... arranged for the piano forte, with an introduction, variations & coda by P. Knapton. [1827.] fol.   **h. 61. ee. (10.)**

— [Hurrah for the Bonnets of Blue.] *See* KNAPTON (Philip) Hurrah for the Bonnets of Blue, an admired air ⟨composed by A. Lee⟩ ... Arranged for the piano forte ... by P. Knapton. [c. 1835.] fol.   **h. 724. r. (1.)**

— "Hurrah! for the jackets of blue;" a song. *Liverpool*, [1840?] fol.   **H. 1289. (11.)**

— [Another edition.] Hurrah for the Jackets of Blue, *etc*. *Sheard & Co.: London*, [1889.] fol.
No. 7871 *of the "Musical Bouquet".*   **H. 2345.**

— I am the mountain child. Chanzonette ... the poetry by J. H. Jewell. [Begins: "Free as the mountain fawn".] *London*, [1854.] fol.   **H. 1758. (17.)**

— I breathe no reproaches; ballad, the poetry by T. H. Bayly. pp. 5. *Metzler & C[r]., for the Proprietors: London*, [1834.] fol.   **H. 1287. (27.)**

— I have plucked the fairest flower ... Ballad, written by T. Morton. pp. 5. *Ransford & Son: London*, [1874.] fol.   **H. 1290. d. (1.)**

LEE (George Alexander)

— "I know he doth not love me;" ballad, the poetry by T. H. Bayly. pp. 5. *Metzler & C[r]., for the proprietors: London*, [1834.] fol.   **H. 1287. (30.)**

— I'll be a fairy, Cavatina. pp. 7. *Leader & Cock: London*, [1850.] fol.   **H. 1290. (37.)**

— I'll be no submissive Wife. *See infra*: [Love in a Cottage.]

— "I'll never be married again;" [song,] newly arranged, with symphonies and appropriate words, by A. Lee. *Liverpool*, [1844.] fol.   **H. 1289. (4.)**

— I'll not beguile thee from thy home. *See supra*: [The Fairy Lake.]

— I'll rove with thee near the Woodbine Bower. Cavatina the words by Lewellyn G. Plumer. *In:* The Musical Magazine. [Musical Supplement.] pp. 2–7. [1835.] 8°.   **P. P. 1945. ab.**

— I love all that thou lovest, a Ballad, *etc*. pp. 6. *In:* The Music Book. vol. 1. pt. 8. no. 2. [1847.] fol.   **H. 1249.**

— I love thee. Ballad, *etc*. *London*, [1850?] fol.
                                                  H. 2818. e. (10.)

— "I'm a poor shepherd maid," [song,] the poetry by C. Selby. *London*, [1844.] fol.   **H. 1289. (8.)**

— I'm a poor shepherd maid. Ballad, arranged for the spanish guitar by N. W. Gould. pp. 5. *D'Almaine & Co.: London*, [1847.] fol.   **H. 1290. (19.)**

— I'm a poor Shepherd Maid, *etc*. [Song.] pp. 5. *Brewer & C[r]: London*, [1855?] fol.   **H. 1653. d. (9.)**

— I'm a poor shepherd maid. ⟨Arranged as a vocal duet by E. J. Loder. 10th edition.⟩ pp. 5. *B. Williams: London*, [1867.] fol.   **H. 1290. a. (31.)**

— [I'm a poor shepherd maid.] *See* CZERNY (C.) Impromptu pastoral ... on the ... ballad, *etc*. [1845?] fol.   **h. 1480. e. (6.)**

— I met him in the happy throng. A ballad. *London*, [1830?] fol.   **H. 2815. g. (3.)**

— I never can forget thee. *See supra*: [The Fancy Ball.]

— "I sigh for the woods;" a ballad, the poetry by Miss T[odd?]. *Liverpool*, [1844.] fol.   **H. 1289. (7.)**

— I've a Harp for my Love. *See infra*: [Sold for a Song.]

— I've a lay for every clime. Ballad, the poetry by R. Nicholson. ⟨Fourth edition.⟩ pp. 5. *D'Almaine & Co.: London*, [1848.] fol.   **H. 1290. (26.)**

— "I've lived to hear your wedding bells." Ballad, the poetry by T. H. Bayly. *London*, [1844.] fol.   **H. 1289. (9.)**

— I've plucked the fairest flower. *See infra*: [The Invincibles.— The fairest flower.]

— I wandered with my love at morn, ballad, the words by J. Churchill. pp. 5. *S. Chappell: London*, [1827.] fol.
                                                  H. 1287. (41.)

— I will arise and go to my father. No. 6 of Six Sabbath Songs. pp. 7. *D'Almaine & Co.: London*, [1851.] fol.   **H. 1290. (11.)**

— I will be thine ... Song [begins: "By all the ties that bind us"] ... The words by T. H. Bayly. *London*, [1835?] fol.
                                                  H. 2835. b. (1.)

— "I will be true to thee." Chansonette, the poetry by G. D. Thompson. pp. 5. *Duff & Hodgson: London*, [1843.] fol.
                                                  H. 1288. (3.)

— In my own sweet native Vale, ballad, *etc*. pp. 5. *Leoni Lee: London*, [c. 1845.] fol.   **H. 1654. aa. (4.)**

— In our peaceful happy Home. *See* supra: [The Fairy Lake.]

LEE (GEORGE ALEXANDER)

The Invincibles

— The fairest Flower ... Ballad ... the poetry by T. Morton. Third Edition. *A. Lee: London*, [1828.] fol.

H. 1650. g. (25.)

— The Fairest Flower ... Ballad ... The poetry by Thomas Morton, *etc.* ⟨Fourth edition.⟩ pp. 5. *Alexander Lee & Lee: London*, [c. 1830.] fol. **H. 1601. n. (19.)**

— "The fairest flower," Ballad, in the musical farce of the Invincibles; arranged with an accompaniment for the Spanish guitar by B. Sperati. pp. 3. *D'Almaine & Cᵒ.: London*, [1843.] fol. **H. 1288. (5.)**

— [The fairest flower.] I've plucked the fairest flower ... Ballad. *London*, [1874.] fol.
No. 3359 of the "Musical Bouquet". **H. 2345.**

— [Fall not in Love.] O never fall in Love. Ballad ... the poetry by Thomas Morton, *etc.* pp. 5. *Alexander Lee & Lee: London*, [c. 1830.] fol. **H. 1860. bb. (8.)**

— Fall not in Love, ballad ... with an additional accompaniment ... for the Spanish guitar by B. Sperati. pp. 3. *D'Almaine & Cᵒ.: London*, [1843.] fol. **H. 1288. (6.)**

— The ivy and the oak, ballad. pp. 5. *B. Williams: London*, [1856.] fol. **H. 1290. a. (3.)**

— Kate Kearny. Favorite Irish air, the words by Lady Morgan. Symphonies and accompaniments by A. Lee. pp. 4. *D'Almaine & Cᵒ.: London*, [1837.] fol. **H. 1287. (38.)**

— Kate Kearney. Irish ballad ... The symphonies & accompaniments by A. Lee. ⟨Kate Kearney. Arranged as a vocal duet by E. I. Loder.⟩ ⟨Fifteenth edition.⟩ pp. 7. *D'Almaine & Cᵒ: London*, [1844.] fol. **H. 1654. aa. (16.)**

— Kate Kearney, *etc.* ⟨Sixteenth edition.⟩ pp. 6. *D'Almaine & Cᵒ: London*, [1857.] fol. **H. 1653. d. (10.)**

— Kate Kearney. Irish ballad, *etc.* ⟨New edition.⟩ pp. 6. *T. Bates: London*, [c. 1870.] fol. **H. 1289. a. (11.)**

— Kathleen's Reply to Terence's Farewell. Ballad written by T. E. Lacy. pp. 7. *Brewer & Co.: London*, [1872.] fol. **H. 1290. a. (36.)**

— [The King's Gardener.] The Horticultural Wife, a comic pathetic ballad of similes [begins: "She's my myrtle my geranium"] ... sung ... in C. Selby's ... Burletta ... adapted to an American air. *London*, [1839.] fol. **H. 1288. a. (3.)**

— The Kings of the Soil. Song. [Words anon.] pp. 3. *Lewis & Co.: London*, [1854.] fol. **H. 1290. a. (17.)**

— The Lad who wears the Pladdie. [Song.] *In:* The Musical Bijou ... for MDCCCXLIII. p. 14. [1843.] fol. **H. 2330.**

— The Lad who wears the pladdie. Ballad. pp. 5. *B. Williams: London*, [1868.] fol. **H. 1290. a. (26.)**

— The Lad who wears the pladdie ... Scotch song. *London*, [1874.] fol.
No. 3776 of the "Musical Bouquet". **H. 2345.**

— The Lady and the Mariner; a duet for two voices [begins: "Mariner, dost thou not fear"], the words by W. H. Bellamy. *London*, [1846.] fol. **H. 1289. (27.)**

— "Lady, when the moon is beaming." Canzonette. *London*, [1844.] fol. **H. 1289. (3.)**

— The Lass of Gourie, [song] ... Arranged by Alexander Lee. pp. 3. *H. Wray: London*, [1833?] fol. **H. 1289. a. (12.)**

— The Lass o' Gowrie ... Scotch ballad. (Arranged by A. Lee.) *J. Bath: London*, [1876.] fol. **H. 1290. d. (10.)**

LEE (GEORGE ALEXANDER)

— "Let love by love be guarded;" cavatina, the poetry by T. H. Bayly. pp. 7. *G. Luff: London*, [1834.] fol.

H. 1287. (34.)

— Let the Lasses merry be. Song. pp. 10. *Robert Cocks & Co.: London*, [1869.] fol. **H. 1290. a. (32.)**

— Lightly, lightly, swiftly follow [song], written by W. M. Tolkien. *London*, [1845.] fol. **H. 1289. (15.)**

— Lightly, lightly swiftly follow. Vocal Duet. ⟨3rd edition.⟩ pp. 7. *B. Williams: London*, [1867.] fol. **H. 1290. a. (20.)**

— Lightly tripping o'er the Mountain. Cavatina written by T. Morton. pp. 7. *W. Williams: London*, [1860.] fol.

H. 1290. a. (2.)

— Listen! tis the Nightingale. Grand scena ... The poetry by J. E. Carpenter. pp. 9. *E. Ransford: London*, [1850.] fol.

H. 1290. (32.)

— The Little Pigs, A favorite comic Glee ... Composed & arranged for three or four voices by A. Lee. pp. 8. *I. Willis: Dublin*, [c. 1820.] fol. **G. 807. d. (36.)**

— [Another copy.] **Mad. Soc. 59. (20.)**

— [A reissue.] The Little Pigs, *etc. London, Dublin*, [c. 1840.] fol.
H. 1202. v. (30.)

— Lo! on the mountain's height, or the Hunter's wild mountain lay ... Poetry by ... J. H. Jewell. pp. 7. *B. Williams: London*, [1851.] fol. **H. 1290. (2.)**

— [Love in a Cottage.] "I'll be no submissive Wife." ... Song in the Burletta "Love in a Cottage," the poetry by H. Bayly. ⟨New edition.⟩ pp. 7. *B. Williams: London*, [1860.] fol.

H. 1290. a. (1.)

— [Love in a Cottage. Another edition.] I'll be no submissive Wife ... Song. *C. Sheard & Co.: London*, [1889.] fol.
No. 7854 of the "Musical Bouquet". **H. 2345.**

— [Love in a Cottage.] Love in a Cottage for me, the favorite song ... the words by T. Haynes Bayly. pp. 5. *At Chappell's Music Circulating Library: London*, [1835?] fol.

H. 1660. m. (21.)

— Love in a Myrtle Bower. Ballad, *etc. Mori & Lavenu: London*, [1830?] fol. **H. 1652. d. (47.)**

— Love is blind. Ballad ... The words by Butler Danvers, *etc.* pp. 7. *Bunting Walsh Pigott & Sherwin: Dublin*, [c. 1825.] fol.

H. 1660. f. (8.)

The Loves of the Butterflies

— The Loves of the Butterflies. [Eight songs.] The poetry by Thomas Haynes Bayly. The music composed & selected by Alexander Lee. vol. I. *London*, [1828.] fol.
Imperfect; wanting pp. 33–36. **H. 1290. c.**

— The Butterfly was a Gentleman. Song ... The poetry by T. H. Bayly. *London*, [1830?] fol. **G. 806. c. (17.)**

— The Butterfly was a Gentleman. Song, *etc. H. Wray: London*, [1830?] fol. **H. 1650. n. (17.)**

— The Butterfly was a gentleman ... Ballad. *London*, [1874.] fol.
No. 3523 of the "Musical Bouquet". **H. 2345.**

— Each Bower has Beauty for me, ballad ... The poetry by Thomas H. Bayly ... The symphonies & accompaniments by Alexander Lee. pp. 41–45. *Alexander Lee & Lee: London*, [ᵂᴹ 1829.] fol. **G. 809. yy. (12.)**

— My own Blue Bell, Ballad, *etc. Alexander Lee & Lee: London*, [c. 1830.] fol. **H. 1653. y. (8.)**

LEE (George Alexander)

— "My own Blue Bell," the favorite ballad ... Arranged for the guitar in two different ways ... by B. Sperati. pp. 7. *D'Almaine & C': London*, [1843.] fol. **H. 1288. (8.)**

— My own Blue Bell, a ballad ... The poetry by T. H. Bayly ... The symphonies & accompaniments by A. Lee. ⟨8ᵗʰ edition.⟩ pp. 5. *D'Almaine & C': London*, [c. 1845.] fol. **H. 1654. zz. (15.)**

— My own Blue Bell ... Ballad, poetry by T. H. Bayly. pp. 4. *C. Sheard: London*, [1874.] fol. [*Musical Bouquet. no.* 3476.] **H. 2345.**

— My own Blue Bell ... Transcribed for the piano forte by F. Mattini. pp. 5. *Robert Cocks & C': London*, [1867.] fol. **h. 3002. (4.)**

— Round my own pretty Rose ... ballad ... The poetry by Thomas Haynes Bayly ... The music composed & arranged from a German air by Alexander Lee. *Alexander Lee & Lee: London*, [c. 1830.] fol. **H. 1289. a. (13.)**

— Round my own pretty Rose ... Ballad, written by T. H. Bayly. pp. 4. *C. Sheard: London*, [1874.] fol. [*Musical Bouquet. no.* 3770.] **H. 2345.**

— [Macgregor's Gathering.] The Moon's on the Lake ... Scotch song of the Macgregor's Gathering. Sung by Miss Paton and dedicated to Sir Walter Scott, (the author of the poetry) by Alexander Lee. pp. 6. *Mayhew & C': London*, [c. 1825.] fol. **H. 1289. a. (14.)**

— The McGregors' gathering, the poetry by Sir W. Scott. ⟨New edition.⟩ pp. 7. *B. Williams: London*, [1859.] fol. **H. 1290. a. (7.)**

— The Macgregors' Gathering. [Song.] *London*, [1874.] fol. *No.* 3880, 3881 *of the "Musical Bouquet".* **H. 2345.**

— The Macgregors' Gathering ... Scotch ballad. pp. 4. *Howard & C'.: London*, [1878.] fol. **H. 1290. d. (12.)**

— Macgregor's Gathering. [Song, with guitar accompaniment.] *See* Lays. Lays of Harmony, *etc.* No. 27. [1894.] fol. **H. 2086.**

— Macgregors' Gathering ... [Song.] Arranged by P. B. Kahn. *W. Rogers: London*, 1926. 4°. **G. 1275. w. (15.)**

— Macgregor's Gathering ... Arranged by W. Moodie [for S. C. T. B.]. [1902.] *See* Choral. The Choral Handbook. No. 585. [1885, *etc.*] 8°. **E. 862.**

— The MacGregor's Gathering. [For S. C.] pp. 7. *J. Curwen & Sons: London*, [1903.] 8°. [*Choruses for equal Voices. no.* 717.] **E. 861.**

— The MacGregors' Gathering. Arranged as a Part Song for mixed voices by H. S. Roberton, *etc. J. Curwen & Sons: London*, 1916. 8°. [*Choral Handbook. No.* 1077.] **E. 862.**

— [The Magic Horn.] Overture ... in the Grand Burlesque ... Music composed & selected by A. Lee. [P. F.] *See* Overtures. Overtures, *etc.* No. 81. [1877, *etc.*] fol. **h. 1423. a.**

— The Maid of Castalie. A ballad [begins: "There's not a spot"] ... The poetry by H. I. Bradfield. *London*, [1830?] fol. **G. 809. b. (9.)**

— The Maid of Kerry, Ballad ... The poetry by Mrs. Cornwell Baron Wilson. pp. 5. *Coventry & Hollier: London*, [c. 1835.] fol. **H. 1980. r. (30.)**

— The Maid of Kildare ... Irish ballad, the poetry by W. H. Bellamy. *London*, [1843.] fol. **H. 1289. (2.)**

— The Maid of Kildare, *etc.* [Song.] *In:* The Musical Bijou ... for MDCCCXLVI. p. 42. [1846.] fol. **H. 2330.**

LEE (George Alexander)

— The Maid of Kildare, Irish ballad. pp. 5. *Ashdown & Parry: London*, [1868.] fol. *Lays of Erin. no.* 1. **H. 1290. a. (24.)**

— [Another edition.] The Maid of Kildare, *etc. C. Sheard & Co.: London*, [1889.] fol. *No.* 7919 *of the "Musical Bouquet".* **H. 2345.**

— The maiden of Neath. (The poetry by E. H. Reed.) [Begins: "Alone thro' the valley at morning".] *London*, [1852.] fol. **H. 1735. (28.)**

— [Malvina.] Awake! awake! brave Scots to glory ... Song [adapted to the "Marseillaise"]. *Dublin*, [1826.] fol. **G. 807. d. (37.)**

— [Malvina.] Come o'er the Heather ... [Song.] The words and arrangement by Alexander Lee. pp. 4. *At M' Cullagh's Music Ware Room: Dublin*, [c. 1830.] fol. *P. 4 bears the words only of the song "Royal Charlie".* **H. 1289. a. (15.)**

— A Man's a Man for a' that, [song] as sung ... by Mʳ Graham. Composed & arranged for him by Alexʳ Lee. *I. Willis & C': Dublin, London*, [1829?] fol. **H. 1289. a. (16.)**

— A Man's a Man for a' that. [Song, begins: "Is there, for honest poverty". Words by R. Burns.] *London*, [1856.] fol. *No.* 475 *of the "Cyclopedia of Music. Miscellaneous Series of Songs".* **H. 2342.**

— March with the red & blue. Ballad [begins: "Clan Donnuil come"] ... The words by D. O'Meara. *London*, [1830?] fol. **H. 2815. g. (27.)**

— Mary O'More. [Song, begins: "I have loved thee".] *London*, [1846.] fol. *No.* 27 *of the "Musical Bouquet".* **H. 2345.**

— May, sweet May, a song, written by F. W. N. Bayley [begins: "Thou comest, and the blossoms of the earth"], *etc. London*, [1850?] fol. **H. 2818. e. (11.)**

— The mediator, sacred offering written by F. C. Lacy. [Begins: "He shall descend in gentle showers".] *London*, [1853.] fol. **H. 1735. (33.)**

— Meet me in the Willow Glen. *See* infra: [My Grandfather.]

— Melody floats on the evening breeze; duet for two voices, the words by N. M. J. Ratcliffe. *London*, [1845.] fol. **H. 1289. (21.)**

— Melody floats on the Evening Breeze. Duet, *etc. See* Duets. Vocal Duets, *etc.* No. 147. [1865? *etc.*] fol. **H. 2259.**

— The Memory of Thee. [Song.] Poetry by G. J. O. Allmann. pp. 3. *Lewis & Co.: London*, [1854.] fol. **H. 1290. a. (19.)**

— The Mermaid's Invitation. Cavatina [begins: "Oh come with me"]. pp. 7. *Duff & Hodgson: London*, [1849.] fol. **H. 1290. (27.)**

— Merrily o'er the waters blue. [Song.] Poetry by G. J. O. Allmann. pp. 3. *Lewis & Co.: London*, [1864.] fol. **H. 1290. a. (18.)**

— Merry I've been, and merry I'll be ... Song [begins: "I can never be sad"] ... written by T. H. Bayly. *London*, [1874.] fol. *No.* 3406 *of the "Musical Bouquet".* **H. 2345.**

— The merry month of May; or, the smiling morn. Trio. *Liverpool*, [1844.] fol. **H. 1289. (6.)**

— The Merry Sherwood Ranger ... Song [begins: "The lays of old famed stories"]. The poetry by J. Halford. *London*, [1846.] fol. *No.* 23 *of the "Musical Bouquet".* **H. 2345.**

LEE (George Alexander)

— The Merry Sherwood Ranger [song], *etc.* *J. Curwen & Sons: London*, [1903.] 8°.
Unison Songs, No. 56. **E. 812.**

— The Moon's on the Lake. *See* supra: [Macgregor's Gathering.]

— A mother's blessing, ballad, written by A. G. Duke. [Begins: "It hath passed".] *London*, [1854.] fol. **H. 1758. (19.)**

— A mother's gentle love. Posthumous ballad. (Poetry by M. Spencer.) pp. 5. *Duff & Hodgson: London*, [1862.] fol.
H. 1290. a. (12.)

— My fairy in the river, [song,] words by F. W. N. Bailey. pp. 5. *Henry Keeler: Bristol*, [1857.] fol. **H. 1290. a. (8.)**

My Grandfather

— Meet me in the Willow Glen, a ballad, sung ... in the opera of My Grandfather ... The poetry by Mrs Cornwell Baron Wilson. ⟨2nd edition.⟩ pp. 7. *Lee: London*, [c. 1840.] fol.
H. 1289. a. (18.)

— Meet me in the Willow Glen, *etc.* *Duff & Hodgson: London*, [c. 1860.] fol.
Alexander Lee's Vocal Music. Songs, cavatinas, duets, &c.
no. 2. **H. 1289. a. (17.)**

— Meet me in the willow glen, ballad, the poetry by Mrs. C. B. Wilson. ⟨New edition.⟩ pp. 5. *B. Williams: London*, [1867.] fol. **H. 1290. a. (22.)**

— Meet me in the willow glen ... Ballad. *London*, [1874.] fol.
No. 3374 *of the "Musical Bouquet"*. **H. 2345.**

— Meet me ... for Piano. [1866.] fol. *See* HIME (E. L.)
h. 983. (32.)

— Meet me ... pour le Piano. [1867.] fol. *See* MATTINI (F.)
h. 3002. (16.)

———

— My Heart is far away. Song [begins: "How sweetly breathes"]. pp. 5. *Brewer & Co.: London*, [1880.] fol.
H. 1290. d. (15.)

— My mothers plaintive Song. ⟨Written by J. E. Carpenter.⟩ pp. 5. *D'Almaine & Co.: London*, [1850.] fol. **H. 1290. (33.)**

— "My native bells;" chansonette, the words by Mrs. C. B. Wilson. pp. 5. *Duff & Hodgson: London*, 1842. fol.
H. 1288. (1.)

— My own Blue Bell. *See* supra: [Loves of the Butterflies.]

— My own! Oh, that's the name for thee, ballad, the poetry by T. H. Bayly. pp. 5. *G. Luff: London*, [1834.] fol.
H. 1287. (35.)

— My Village Girl, *etc.* [Song.] *In:* The Musical Bijou ... for MDCCCLI. pp. 45–50. [1851.] fol. **H. 2330.**

— My village girl. Ballad. Poetry by J. Bruton. pp. 7. *D'Almaine & Co.: London*, [1851.] fol. **H. 1290. (14.)**

— My Village Home; ballad [begins: "Dear Village"], the words by E. Ransford. *London*, [1845.] fol. **H. 1289. (16.)**

— [Another edition.] My Village Home, *etc.* *C. Sheard & Co.: London*, [1889.] fol.
No. 7926 *of the "Musical Bouquet"*. **H. 2345.**

— My Woodland Home, ballad ... Written by Ja^s Bruton. pp. 5. *T. E. Purday: London*, [c. 1840.] fol. **H. 1654. zz. (16.)**

— The Naiad's dance. Duet, the words by E. Gill. pp. 11. *Duff & Hodgson: London*, [1847.] fol. **H. 1290. (25.)**

— Napier the bold, a national song [begins: "To the nations"]. *London*, [1844.] fol. **H. 1289. (10.)**

LEE (George Alexander)

— Napolitaine; song, the words by E. J. Gill. *London*, [1846.] fol. **H. 1289. (28.)**

— Napolitaine. [Song.] *London*, [1858.] fol. **H. 1401. (22.)**

— Napolitaine. [Song.] *Chappell & Co.: London*, [1889.] fol.
H. 1788. v. (13.)

— [Another edition.] Napolitaine, *etc.* *C. Sheard & Co.: London*, [1889.] fol.
No. 7948 *of the "Musical Bouquet"*. **H. 2345.**

— Napolitaine, "I am dreaming of thee," Song and Chorus as sung by the Christy Minstrels (arranged by Professor Clare). *London*, [1858.] fol. **H. 1401. a. (33.)**

— The night lamps of heaven. Duet for two voices. The poetry by A. Knott. pp. 6. *B. Williams: London*, [1851.] fol.
H. 1290. (4.)

— Night's pale shining stars, ⟨duet⟩ for two voices. pp. 8. *B. Williams: London*, [1851.] fol. **H. 1290. (5.)**

— Norah Malone, Hibernian melody [begins: "Oh! bright is the sun"] ... the poetry by S. Fearon. *London*, [1845.] fol.
H. 1289. (17.)

— [The Nymph of the Grotto.] Time, time, time ... Ballad ... The poetry by W. Dimond. *London*, [1829.] fol.
G. 809. b. (14.)

— [The Nymph of the Grotto.] Time, Time, Time, ballad, the words by Dimond & Wilce. *London*, [1868.] fol.
H. 1290. a. (29.)

— Oh blame not my Lyre, a ballad ... Poetry by Mrs Cornwell Baron Wilson. pp. 5. *Geo. Shade: London; H. L. Shade: Dublin*, [c. 1835.] fol. **H. 1980. tt. (5.)**

— O canst thou not remember; duet, the words by E. J. Gill. *London*, [1845.] fol. **H. 1289. (20.)**

— "Oh! do not say forget her;" ballad, the poetry by T. H. Bayly. pp. 5. *Metzler & Co., for the proprietors: London*, [1834.] fol. **H. 1287. (29.)**

— Oh! give me the Cot. [Song.] The poetry by Mrs Crawford. *In:* The Musical Bijou ... for MDCCCLII. pp. 52–56. [1852.] fol.
H. 2330.

— Oh! how I lov'd and honor'd thee, a ballad. pp. 5. *Printed by W. Wybrow: London*, [c. 1850.] fol. **H. 1289. a. (19.)**

— O Love Divine. *See* supra: [He wipes the Tear from every Eye.]

— O never fall in Love. *See* supra: [The Invincibles.—Fall not in love.]

— "Oh! no, never name her to me," ballad, the poetry by T. H. Bayly. pp. 5. *Metzler & Co., for the proprietors: London*, [1834.] fol. **H. 1287. (28.)**

— Oh! sing from thy Spray, or My Jamie is far on the Sea. A ballad, *etc.* pp. 5. *Alexander Lee & Lee: London*, [c. 1830.] fol. **H. 3690. xx. (27.)**

— O there's a soft & pleasing hour. [Song.] *London*, [1830?] fol.
G. 805. c. (8.)

— O, where are the Joys that once I knew. *See* supra: [The Fancy Ball.]

— The Ocean flower gleaner. Song written by R. A. Philip. pp. 5. *D'Almaine & Co.: London*, [1850.] fol. **H. 1290. (39.)**

— O'er the blue Waters. *See* infra: [O'er the gold Waters.]

— O'er the gold Waters. ⟨[Song. Words] by Mrs. C. B. Wilson. *In:* The Musical Bijou ... for MDCCCXXXV. pp. 63–69. [1835.] 4°. **F. 149.**

LEE (George Alexander)

—— [O'er the gold Waters.] O'er the blue Waters. [Song. Words by] Mʳˢ C. B. Wilson. *In:* The Musical Bijou ... for MDCCCXLVII. pp. 17. [1847.] fol. **H. 2330.**

—— O'er the sea, come with me. Ballad, written by J. F. Haines. *London*, [1874.] fol.
No. 4131 *of the "Musical Bouquet".* **H. 2345.**

—— "O'er the Sea in my Fairy Boat," a ballad, as sung by Mʳˢ Waylett ... in the comedietta of Love and Mystery ... The poetry by J. T. Haines. pp. 5. *Royal Harmonic Institution: London*, [c. 1830.] fol. **H. 1654. cc. (10.)**

—— [O'er the Sea in my Fairy Boat.] *See* Cross (John H.) "O'er the Sea in my fairy Boat" ... ballad ... Arranged as a rondo, for the piano forte, *etc.* [1832?] fol. **h. 61. mm. (1.)**

—— The old Irish Gentleman; a national song [begins: "I love to hear"], the symphonies and accompaniments by A. Lee. pp. 5. *D'Almaine & Cⁿ.: London*, [1834.] fol. **H. 1287. (23.)**

—— The Old Irish Gentleman. [Song.] *In:* The Musical Bijou ... for MDCCCXLII. pp. 32, 33. [1842.] fol. **H. 2330.**

—— The old ivy'd Church [song,] the poetry by G. Cooke. pp. 7. *J. Alfred Novello: London*, [1849.] fol. **H. 1290. (28.)**

—— The Old Miller's Daughter. [Song.] The poetry by Ernest H. Reed. *In:* The Musical Bijou ... for MDCCCLII. pp. 26–30. [1852.] fol. **H. 2330.**

—— One careless word. [Song.] pp. 5. *Duff & Hodgson: London*, [1850.] fol. **H. 1290. (29.)**

—— One Morn I left my Boat. [Song. Words by] T. H. Bayly. *In:* The Musical Bijou ... for MDCCCXLIV. p. 12. [1844.] fol. **H. 2330.**

—— One silent tear. [Song.] pp. 5. *Duff & Hodgson: London*, [1851.] fol. **H. 1290. (1.)**

—— Our Sunny land. Duett ... the poetry by E. J. Gill. pp. 7. *D'Almaine & Co.: London*, [1850.] fol. **H. 1290. (35.)**

—— Our village home. Vocal Duet. ⟨Words by R. W. Sankey.⟩ pp. 5. *B. Williams: London*, [1851.] fol. **H. 1290. (3.)**

—— The Parting Souvenir. A song [begins: "To Julia's hand"] ... The words by S. Lover. *London*, [1840?] fol. **H. 2830. a. (50.)**

—— La Petite Bernoise ... Song [begins: "A poor Bernoise"]. ⟨The poetry by J. C. Churchill.⟩ *London*, [1830?] fol. **G. 806. c. (19.)**

—— Poor Mary [song, begins: "Her harp is hanging on the wall"], the poetry by J. Hurrey, *etc. London*, [1835?] fol. **H. 1288. a. (6.)**

—— [Poor Prince Charlie.] *See* Dibdin (M. A.) Variations for the Harp on A. Lee's Ballad, Poor Prince Charlie, *etc.* [1835?] fol. **h. 173. d. (8.)**

—— The poor Soldier boy. [Song.] pp. 7. *B. Williams: London*, [1851.] fol. **H. 1290. (6.)**

—— Pretty child, ballad ... poetry by E. H. Burrington. *London*, [1854.] fol. **H. 1758. (23.)**

—— Pretty maiden come wander with me, ballad, arranged by J. E. Loder. [Begins: "Oh come, for the lily is white on the lea".] *London*, [1856.] fol. **H. 1758. (22.)**

—— The Queen of the greenwood tree. *See* infra: [Lo Zingaro.]

—— Recollections of Shakspeare, dramatic overture for the Piano Forte. *London*, [1847.] fol. **h. 708. (18.)**

—— Rely not on beauty alone. A ballad, the poetry by C. Butler. *London*, [1830?] fol. **H. 2835. b. (2.)**

LEE (George Alexander)

—— The Rising of the Borderers. A ballad [begins: "Forward, forward"]. ⟨The poetry by F. W. Hohler.⟩ *London*, [1830?] fol. **H. 2832. q. (6.)**

—— The Rose is weeping. Serenade [begins: "The weary day"]. The poetry by Mrs. C. B. Wilson. *London*, [1840?] fol. **H. 2832. o. (41.)**

—— "The Rose of Berkeley vale;" ballad ... written by the Hon. G. F. Berkley. *London*, [1845.] fol. **H. 1289. (14.)**

—— Round my own pretty Rose. *See* supra: [Loves of the Butterflies.]

—— The Rover's Bride. A ballad ... the poetry by Thomas Haynes Bayly. ⟨Sixth edition.⟩ pp. 4. *H. Wray: London*, [c. 1833.] fol. **G. 809. cc. (22.)**

—— The Rover's Bride, a ballad, *etc.* ⟨7th edition.⟩ pp. 4. *H. Wray: London*, [1834?] fol. **H. 1847. m. (24.)**

—— The Rover's Bride, ballad, the poetry by T. H. Bayly. ⟨New edition.⟩ pp. 4. *B. Williams: London*, [1867.] fol. **H. 1290. a. (21.)**

—— The Rover's Bride ... Ballad, poetry by T. H. Bayly. *London*, [1874.] fol.
No. 4136 *of the "Musical Bouquet".* **H. 2345.**

—— Six Sacred Songs. The poetry by Miss R. Raine. *London*, [1852.] fol. **H. 1183. (34.)**

—— Rosa Raine's six sacred songs, *etc.* 6 pt. *London*, [1860.] fol. **H. 1187. a. (16.)**

—— The Silver Call. Duett for Soprano and Contralto, written by E. J. Gill. pp. 9. *Campbell, Ransford & Co.: London*, [1851.] fol. **H. 1290. (9.)**

—— Sing away, sing away, by day & by night. Ballad, *etc. London*, [1845?] fol. **H. 1288. a. (5.)**

—— The Sisters. *See* infra: [The Witness.]

Sold for a Song

—— The Gay Troubadour, ballad, from the Loves of lang syne, the poetry by Thomas H. Bayly, *etc.* ⟨Sung in the new interlude Sold for a song.⟩ pp. 5. *Alexander Lee & Lee: London*, [ᵂᴹ 1829.] fol. **H. 1289. a. (20.)**

—— "I've a Harp for my Love," the song of the French troubadour ... [Song.] The poetry by T. H. Bayly, *etc.* pp. 6. *Alexander Lee & Lee: London*, [ᵂᴹ 1829.] fol. **H. 1289. a. (21.)**

—— "The Soldier's Tear." A ballad ... ⟨Sung in the new interlude Sold for a Song.⟩ The poetry by Thomas Haynes Bayly. ⟨Third edition.⟩ pp. 4. *Alexander Lee & Lee: London*, [c. 1830.] fol. **H. 1601. n. (18.)**

—— "The Soldier's Tear." A ballad sung ... in the new interlude Sold for a Song. The poetry by Thomas Haynes Bayly. ⟨Fifth edition.⟩ pp. 4. *Alexander Lee & Lee: London*, [c. 1830.] fol. **H. 1653. e. (38.)**

—— The Soldiers Tear, a ballad ... The poetry by Thomas Haynes Bayly, *etc.* ⟨Sixth edition.⟩ pp. 4. *Alexander Lee & Lee: London*, [c. 1833.] fol. **H. 1289. a. (22.)**

—— The Soldier's Tear. [Song.] Sung in the opera of "Music & Prejudice," the words by Thos. H. Bayly. *John Cole: Baltimore*, [c. 1835.] fol.
Printed on blue paper. **H. 1653. i. (7.)**

—— The Soldier's Tear, ballad, sung ... in the new interlude Sold for a Song, *etc.* ⟨Tenth edition.⟩ pp. 4. *H. Wray: London*, [c. 1835.] fol. **H. 1980. o. (8.)**

LEE (GEORGE ALEXANDER)

— The Soldier's Tear, a national ballad ... The poetry by
Thomas Haynes Bayly, *etc.* ⟨17th edition.⟩ pp. 4. *Lee: London*,
[c. 1840.] fol. **H. 1654. zz. (17.)**

— The Soldier's Tear, a national Ballad, *etc.* ⟨17th edition.⟩ pp. 5.
Duff & Hodgson: London, [1845?] fol. **H. 1652. y. (37.)**

— The soldier's tear, the poetry by T. H. Bayly. ⟨New Edition.⟩
pp. 5. *B. Williams: London*, [1859.] fol. **H. 1290. a. (10.)**

— The Soldier's Tear. *See* CHAPPELL AND CO. Chappell's new
edition of popular songs. No. 15. [1864.] fol. **H. 2507. (1.)**

— The Soldier's Tear. Ballad. pp. 5. *Metzler & Co.: London*,
[1874.] fol. **H. 1290. d. (2.)**

— The Soldier's Tear ... Song. *London*, [1874.] fol.
No. 3358 *of the "Musical Bouquet".* **H. 2345.**

— The Soldier's Tear ... Song. pp. 4. *J. Bath: London*, [1876.]
fol. **H. 1290. d. (7.)**

— The Soldier's Tear ... Ballad. pp. 3. *W. Marshall & Cᵒ.:
London*, [1879.] fol. **H. 1290. d. (14.)**

— [Another edition.] The Soldier's Tear ... Accompaniment by
J. T. Lee. *Boosey & Co.: London*, [1880.] fol.
No. 18 *of the Ballad Concert Répertoire of Standard Songs.*
H. 1628. (18.)

— The Soldier's Tear ... for the Pianoforte. [1866.] fol. *See* HIME
(E. L.) **h. 983. (30.)**

— The Soldier's Tear ... for the Piano. [1866.] fol. *See*
KORNATZKI (F. V.) **h. 3086. (6.)**

— The Spaniard's serenade. [Song, begins: "Her bright eyes like
clouded stars."] ... The poetry by T. H. Bayly. *London*,
[1830?] fol. **H. 2835. c. (35.)**

— The Spaniard's Serenade. [Song. Words by] Florence Hoare.
pp. 4. *J. Curwen & Sons: London*, [1905.] 8°.
[*Choruses for equal Voices. no.* 907.] **E. 861.**

— The soldier's return, answer to the soldier's tear, poetry by
J. Duff. [Begins: "He sees again the village".] *London*,
[1855.] fol. **H. 1758. (16.)**

— The Soldier's Tear. *See* supra: [Sold for a Song.]

— The Soldier's Widow, "Cold was the night wind". A ballad,
the poetry by R. Southey. *London*, [1835?] fol.
G. 809. b. (11.)

— The Son of the Wave. [Song, begins: "The Life of a tar".] The
poetry by H. R. Addison. *London*, [1830?] fol.
G. 806. c. (20.)

— The Spaniard's serenade. *See* supra: [Sold for a Song.]

— "The Spirit of Good," cavatina ... Written by Edward
Mordaunt Spencer. pp. 7. *Joseph Williams: London*, [c. 1850.]
fol. **H. 1654. vv. (12.)**

— Spring, cavatina, *etc.* pp. 5. *Cramer, Addison & Beale:
London*, [1835.] fol. **H. 1289. a. (23.)**

— Star of Joy; song [begins: "In grief or joy"], the words by
E. J. Gill. *London*, [1845.] fol. **H. 1289. (19.)**

— "Strain of my Childhood;" romance, the poetry by
H. R. Addison. pp. 5. *S. Chappell: London*, [1834.] fol.
H. 1287. (24.)

— [The Sublime and Beautiful.] The Overture and the whole of
the music in the musical farce of The Sublime and Beautiful,
the poetry by T. Morton, *etc.* *A. Lee & Lee: London*, [1828.]
fol. **H. 627. a.**

LEE (GEORGE ALEXANDER)

— [The Sublime and Beautiful.] The hunter's signal horn ...
Song ... The poetry by T. Morton. *London*, [1828.] fol.
G. 809. b. (8.)

— Sweet Lady, good Night, serenade, *etc.* pp. 7. *B. Williams:
London*, [c. 1850.] fol. **G. 425. cc. (16.)**

— Sweet Mary, a cush-la ma-chree. [Song. Words by] Mʳˢ
Crawford. *In:* The Musical Bijou ... for MDCCCXLVII. p. 7.
[1847.] fol. **H. 2330.**

— The Swiss Exile. [Song, begins: "Far from my own fresh
lakes".] (Written by D. A. O'Meara.) *London*, [1830?] fol.
G. 809. b. (12.)

— [Swiss Swains.] Wilt thou dwell on the mountain with me ...
Duet. *London*, [1835?] fol. **H. 2831. j. (2.)**

— The Tear. [Song. Words by] Lord Byron. *In:* The Musical
Bijou ... for MDCCCXLVI. p. 46. [1846.] fol. **H. 2330.**

— There's not an Eye will weep for me ... [Song.] The poetry by
... Lord Byron, *etc.* pp. 9. *Goulding & D'Almaine: London*,
[c. 1840.] fol. **H. 1980. bb. (10.)**

— There's not an Eye will weep for me. [Song. Words by] Lord
Byron. *In:* The Musical Bijou ... for MDCCCXLVI. p. 4. [1846.]
fol. **H. 2330.**

— There's nothing true but Heaven, sacred song, written by
S. Farquharson. [Begins: "Oh! what is all this world
around".] *London*, [1852.] fol. **H. 1758. (24.)**

— Think of me. A duett [begins: "Go where the water glideth"]
... The words by A. Brooke. *London*, [1835?] fol.
H. 2831. j. (1.)

— This, this is the hour. A ballad ... The poetry by J. Halford.
Plymouth, [1840?] fol. **H. 2832. o. (42.)**

— Those bright blue eyes. Song, poetry by E. H. Reed. pp. 5.
Robert Cocks & Co.: London, [1867.] fol. **H. 1290. a. (30.)**

— Those tinkling bells ... Ballad [begins: "I am a wandering
Arab maid"] ... The poetry by J. T. Haines. *London*, [1835?]
fol. **G. 809. b. (13.)**

— Thou Queen of Beauty; ballad, written by E. H. Reed [begins:
"I saw thee first"]. *London*, [1853.] fol. **H. 1735. (23.)**

— "Thou wilt forget;" ballad, the words by W. H. Bellamy.
London, [1845.] fol. **H. 1289. (23.)**

— Though the day of my destiny's over. [Song.] The poetry by
Lord Byron. *London*, [1835?] fol. **H. 2834. (28.)**

— Three Times had the summons resounded afar. The
celebrated trumpet. Song ... Poetry by T. H. Bayly. pp. 5.
Alexander Lee & Lee: London, [1835?] fol. **H. 1290. a. (33.)**

— Time, time, time. *See* supra: [The Nymph of the Grotto.]

— 'Tis love's hallowed hour. Serenade [begins: "Awake thee"]
... The poetry by Mrs. C. B. Wilson. *London*, [1835?] fol.
H. 2832. n. (3.)

— The true heart of woman; duet [begins: "My friends"],
written by Mrs. C. B. Wilson. *Liverpool*, [1844.] fol.
H. 1289. (5.)

— Twilight deepens o'er the Green. Ballad ... the poetry by
Mrs. Cornwall Baron Wilson. *Charles Ollivier: London*,
[1843.] fol. **R. M. 14. b. 3. (8.)**

— 'Twixt the Cup and the Lip ... cavatina, written by Harry
Stoe van Dyk, sung by Madame Vestris ... in the revised
opera of John of Paris [by Sir H. R. Bishop], *etc.* pp. 5.
Mayhew & Cᵒ: London, [ᵂᴹ 1824.] fol. **H. 1289. a. (24.)**

— "Two minstrels of another land;" duet for two voices, the
words by E. J. Gill. *London*, [1845.] fol. **H. 1289. (22.)**

LEE (George Alexander)

— Two Minstrels of another land. [Song.] Arranged ... by F. Pelzer. *London*, [1858.] fol.
No. 21 of "Guitar Melodies".   **H. 2348.**

— The valley of Roses. Ballad, written by E. H. Reed. [Begins: "In the valley of roses".] *London*, [1852.] fol.
H. 1735. (26.)

— The Village Stream. A ballad. *London*, [1835?] fol.
H. 2832. o. (40.)

— The Warrior's Joy [Kriegers Lust], Grand German March [by J. Gung'l], arranged for the Piano Forte by A. Lee. *Bristol*, [1857.] fol.
h. 725. f. (25.)

— Waves of gold in music breaking, song, the words by Shirley Brooks. pp. 5. *Jullien & Co.: London*, [1847.] fol.
H. 1290. (20.)

— Waves of gold in music breaking. *See* Jullien (L. G.) Jullien & Co.'s collection of English ballads. No. 23. [1855.] fol.
H. 2828. b. (3.)

— What's a the steer kimmer, ballad. ⟨New edition.⟩ pp. 5. *B. Williams: London*, [1859.] fol.   **H. 1290. a. (11.)**

— What's a the steer kimmer, A. Lee's Scotch air arranged ... for the Pianoforte. *See* Glover (S.) [1858.] fol.   **h. 746. (4.)**

— What shall I do ... Song. *London*, [1830?] fol.
G. 809. b. (6.)

— When evening bells are chiming, a ballad. pp. 6. *W. Eavestaff: London*, [1834.] fol.   **H. 1287. (37.)**

— When I heard he was married, a Ballad ... The Poetry by T. H. Bayly, *etc. Lee: London*, [1835?] fol.   **G. 383. h. (61.)**

— When Maggie gangs awa, *etc.* [Song.] *In:* The Musical Bijou ... for MDCCCXLVII. p. 41. [1847.] fol.   **H. 2330.**

— When Maggie gangs awa. Ballad, the poetry by J. Hogg. pp. 7. *D'Almaine & Co.: London*, [1847.] fol.   **H. 1290. (18.)**

— When Maggie gangs awa. Scotch ballad ... arranged by J. Blockley. pp. 7. *John Blockley: London*, [1876.] fol.
H. 1290. d. (8.)

— When quiv'ring moonbeams glisten, Serenade ... the poetry by Florence Wilson. pp. 5. *D'Almaine & Co.: London*, [1851.] fol.
H. 1290. (7.)

— When Spring Time was shedding, ballad. pp. 4. *Alexander Lee & Lee: London*, [c. 1830.] fol.   **H. 1980. mm. (23.)**

— When streams in moonlight glisten. Duet, the poetry by F. H. Hybart. pp. 9. *E. Ransford: London*, [1847.] fol.
H. 1290. (23.)

— When the bright sun of love. A ballad. *Dublin*, [1825?] fol.
G. 807. d. (38.)

— When the Dew is on the Grass, a ballad, *etc.* pp. 5. *Printed for the proprietor by Geo. Shade: London; H. L. Shade: Dublin*, [1833?] fol.   **H. 1650. jj. (2.)**

— [A reissue.] When the dew is on the grass. A ballad [begins: "Softly, softly"]. *London*, [1835?] fol.   **G. 806. c. (21.)**

— When the dew is on the grass. A ballad. *London*, [1840?] fol.
H. 2815. f. (14.)

— When thou'rt away, ballad, the poetry by J. H. Jewell. *London*, [1854.] fol.   **H. 1758. (18.)**

— Where the blue bells grow. Song [begins: "I know a spot"], words by J. Bruton. *London*, [1885.] fol.   **H. 1288. a. (10.)**

— Where the Fairies love to stray, cavatina ... arranged by H. Foster. pp. 5. *Hutchings & Romer: London*, [1868.] fol.
H. 1290. a. (35.)

LEE (George Alexander)

— Where, where is the rover. *See* infra: [Lo Zingaro.]

— Who can see thee and not love. A ballad [begins: "With thine eyes"]. The words by C. Broad. *Dublin*, [1825?] fol.
G. 807. d. (39.)

— Who would not be a gipsy free, song ... the poetry by G. J. O. Allmann. *London*, [1854.] fol.   **H. 1758. (20.)**

— Who would not be a Gipsy free [song], *etc. J. Curwen & Sons: London*, [1903.] 8°.
Unison Songs, No. 68.   **E. 812.**

— Why dont they ask us to marry, a ballad ... The poetry by Butler Danvers, *etc.* pp. 4. *At E. McCullaghs Music Ware Room: Dublin*, [c. 1825.] fol.   **H. 1660. f. (9.)**

— Why will ye wear those ribbons. Ballad, written by T. H. Bayly. *London*, [1845?] fol.   **H. 1288. a. (8.)**

— [The Wigwam.] The wild free wind; Cora, the Indian Maiden's song, written by Shirley Brooks. pp. 5. *Leoni Lee & Coxhead: London*, [1847.] fol.   **H. 1290. (16.)**

— [The Wigwam.] [Another issue.] "The Wild free Wind." Cora, the Indian maiden's song, *etc. London*, [1847?] fol.
H. 1289. a. (25.)

— The Wild free Wind. *See* supra: [The Wigwam.]

— The Wild Mandoline. *See* infra: [Lo Zingaro.]

— The Wild white Rose. *See* supra: [The First of May.]

— "Wilt thou be my bride;" song, written by T. H. Bayly. pp. 5. *S. Chappell: London*, [1834.] fol.   **H. 1287. (25.)**

— Wilt thou dwell on the mountain with me. *See* supra: [Swiss Swains.]

— [The Witness.] The Sisters, a duett, as sung ... in the new melodrama of the Witness, the poetry by T. H. Bayly, *etc.* ⟨Vocal score.⟩ Arranged from the original orchestra score by M. Corri.⟩ pp. 7. *Alexander Lee & Lee: London*, [1829?] fol.
H. 1289. a. (26.)

— Woman loves ye best. *See* supra: [Good Husbands make good Wives.]

— The Woodland Cot, a ballad ... The words by Mʳˢ Butterworth. pp. 5. *Z. T. Purday: London*, [c. 1840.] fol.
H. 1654. zz. (18.)

— "Young Ellen Loraine," ballad, sung ... in the opera of Rosina [by William Shield], *etc.* ⟨Third edition.⟩ pp. 5. *Lee: London*, [c. 1840.] fol.   **H. 1289. a. (27.)**

Lo Zingaro

— Bells upon the wind. Ballad [begins: "That heavenly voice"] ... The poetry by H. R. Addison. *London*, [1837.] fol.
H. 2832. b. (1.)

— Bells upon the Wind, Ballad, *etc.* pp. 5. *Coventry & Hollier: London*, [c. 1840.] fol.   **H. 1860. oo. (4.)**

— Bells upon the Wind, *etc. C. Sheard & Co.: London*, [1889.] fol.
No. 7890 of the "Musical Bouquet".   **H. 2345.**

— The Queen of the greenwood tree. Ballad [begins: "Shall I dwell"] ... The poetry by H. R. Addison. *London*, [1835?] fol.   **H. 2832. o. (45.)**

— The Queen of the Greenwood Tree. [Song.] Arranged ... by F. Pelzer. *London*, [1858.] fol.
No. 2 of "Guitar Melodies".   **H. 2348.**

— [Sound the Tambourine.] The Gypsey's wild chaunt. Ballad ... the poetry by H. R. Addison, *etc. London*, [1833.] fol.
H. 1288. a. (4.)

LEE (George Alexander)

— [Sound the Tambourine.] *See* Cramer (Johann B.) The Gipsy Rondo for the Piano Forte. [c. 1860.] fol.　　**g. 451. r. (1.)**

— [Sound the Tambourine.] *See* Hodgson (C.) The Gypsey's wild chaunt ... for the pianoforte. [1835?] fol.

　　g. 270. i. (27.)

— Where, where is the rover. Ballad ... The poetry by H. R. Addison. *London*, [1833.] fol.　　**G. 807. b. (38.)**

— Where, where is the rover. [Song.] Arranged ... by F. Pelzer. *London*, [1858.] fol.
No. 4 *of "Guitar Melodies"*.　　**H. 2348.**

— Where, where is the Rover, *etc. C. Sheard & Co.: London*, [1889.] fol.
No. 7927 *of the "Musical Bouquet"*.　　**H. 2345.**

— The Wild Mandoline, a ballad ... The poetry by H. R. Addison ... with an accompaniment for the harp or piano forte. pp. 5. *J. Duff & Cº: London*, [1833?] fol.

　　H. 1289. a. (28.)

— *See* Adelaide (　　) *Mlle*. The Robe of Beauty. Ballad ... Arranged by A. Lee. [1840?] fol.　　**H. 1288. a. (7.)**

— *See* Auber (D. F. E.) [Fra Diavolo.—Chez Lorenzo, conservons l'espérance.] Vain are words ... adapted by A. Lee. [1830.] fol.　　**H. 1287. (33.)**

— *See* Auber (D. F. E.) [Fra Diavolo.—Oui, c'est demain.] But one day more, adapted by A. Lee. [1830.] fol.

　　H. 1287. (32.)

— *See* Barton (　　) *Major*. "Woman's Tear" ... arranged by A. Lee. [1843.] fol.　　**H. 1689. (26.)**

— *See* Elfin. [Elfin Crew.] Musical Entertainment. The Elfin Crew ... composed by S. Glover, (A. Lee, *etc*.) [1846.] fol.

　　H. 1369. (1.)

— *See* Hérold (L. J. F.) [Marie.—Je pars demain.] "Dry up your tears." Symphonies and accompaniments by A. Lee. [1834.] fol.　　**H. 1287. (36.)**

— *See* Lee (David) and Lee (G. A.) Songs for the Army ... With symphonies and accompaniments by D. and A. Lee, *etc*. 1841. fol.　　**H. 1653. bb.**

— *See* Lee (David) and Lee (G. A.) Songs for the army, *etc*. [1842.] 16°.　　**A. 451.**

— *See* Rossini (G. A.) [Guillaume Tell.—Toi que l'oiseau ne suivrait pas.] When Evening's breath of cooling balm. Duet ... arranged by A. Lee. [1852.] fol.　　**H. 1993. (32.)**

— *See* Smith (R. A.) Flowers of Scottish Song ... arranged ... by A. Lee. [1840?] fol.　　**H. 2108.**

— *See* Smith (R. A.) The Highland Harper's Song ... arranged ... by A. Lee. [1840?] fol.　　**H. 2831. b. (59.)**

— *See* Victorine (　　) *Madⁱˡᵉ*. Think of me, Mary ... arranged by A. Lee. [1849.] fol.　　**H. 1706. (50.)**

LEE (George Wadsworth)

— Preces and Responses. (The Apostles' Creed. The Lord's Prayer.) *W[eekes & Co.: London*, 1910]. 8°.

　　F. 1169. r. (18.)

LEE (Gertrude)

— Eglantine ... Dance for the Pianoforte. *E. Ashdown: London*, [1903.] fol.　　**g. 605. ee. (32.)**

LEE (Gwendoline)

— *See* Leigh (G.)

LEE (H.)

— The Mountain Rover ... [song] The Poetry by C. Mackay, *etc. H. Wray: London*, [1840?] fol.　　**H. 1650. n. (19.)**

LEE (Henry)

— Far away at heaven's gate ... Song and Chorus. (Written by W. J. Ryley.) *London*, [1878.] fol.　　**H. 1783. o. (37.)**

— Yes I know you fondly love me ... Song and chorus. (Written by W. J. Ryley.) *London*, [1878.] 8°.

　　H. 1783. o. (38.)

LEE (Irene)

— Plays for acting in the Infant School, *etc*. [Words by B. Belton and others. Music by I. Lee and D. H. Wassell.] *Sir I. Pitman & Sons: London, etc.*, 1932. 8°.　　**E. 1832.**

LEE (J.) *Composer of dance music*

— The Inseparables. Polka for two cornets ... Arrd. by A. Morelli. Solo B♭ cornet conductor [and wind band parts]. 33 pt. *J. R. Lafleur & Son: London*, [1892.] 8°.
Part of "Alliance Musicale".　　**f. 800. (804.)**

LEE (J.) *Editor*

— *See* Documentary. Documentary Dance Materials ... Editors: R. Lange, D. Baddeley-Lange, J. Lee. [1976, *etc*.] 4°.

　　g. 822. aa.

LEE (J. H.)

— Sight-Singing made easy. A progressive Manual, *etc. E. Ashdown: London*, [1889.] 8°.　　**E. 763. (5.)**

LEE (J. Haydn)

— Le Bonheur. Morceau. [P. F.] *West & Co.: London*, 1915. fol.
　　h. 3284. nn. (34.)

LEE (J. S.)

— The Bramham Moor ... Hunting song [begins: "Come fill up your glasses"]. Words by W. Pallin. *London*, [1880.] fol.
　　H. 1783. o. (40.)

— En Route. Quick March. [Reed band parts.] *London*, [1886.] *obl*. 4°.　　**a. 237. b. (4.)**

— A Falling Star. Song [begins: "A flash from heaven"]. Words by ... D. C. Budd. *London*, [1881.] fol.　　**H. 1787. j. (26.)**

— A Falling Star. Song, words by D. C. Budd. *J. B. Cramer & Co.: London*, [1883.] fol.　　**H. 1788. v. (15.)**

— Semplice gavotte. [Orchestral parts.] *London*, [1883.] 8°.
Part of the "Alliance Musicale".　　**f. 400. cc. (10.)**

— Semplice, Gavotte. Solo B♭ conductor & 1ˢᵗ cornet [and wind band parts]. 33 pt. *J. R. Lafleur & Son: London*, [1892.] 8°.
The conductor part is in duplicate.　　**f. 800. (805.)**

— Semplice. Gavotte. [P. F.] *London*, [1883.] 8°.
No. 785 *of the "Alliance Musicale, Album Bijou"*.　　**f. 406.**

— There are dark clouds in the East. Song, words by W. Pallin. *London*, [1879.] fol.　　**H. 1783. o. (39.)**

LEE (J. Watson)

— One hour with thee. Seul avec toi. Song ... with a Violoncello obbligato. Words by Sir W. Scott. (French version by R. S. Moffat.) *Glasgow*, [1874.] fol. **H. 1778. x. (59.)**

LEE (James)

— Apollo. Polka, for Banjo solo with 2nd Banjo & Piano accomp^t. *Barnes & Mullins: Bournemouth*, [1897.] fol. **h. 1971. c. (29.)**

LEE (James Turle)

— Aglaia polka. [P. F.] *London*, [1877.] fol. **h. 1482. z. (19.)**

— Alone. Song [begins: "In happy days"]. Words by R. Maries. *London*, [1877.] fol. **H. 1778. x. (54.)**

— The Claret-Cup quadrilles. [P. F.] *London*, [1877.] fol. **h. 1482. z. (18.)**

— Com' è gentil, Serenade from Donizetti's Don Pasquale, transcribed for the Piano Forte by J. T. Lee. *W. G. Hallifax & Co.: London*, [1877.] fol. **h. 1482. z. (16.)**

— Harvest Hymn [for S. A. T. B.], words by M. C. Gillington. 1892. *See* Periodical Publications.— *London*. The Lute, *etc.* No. 115. 1883–99. 8°. **P. P. 1945. hdc.**

— The Last Rose of Summer. [Words by] T. Moore, arranged for 4 Mixed Voices by T. Lee. 1899. *See* Periodical Publications.— *London*. The Lute, *etc.* No. 194. 1883–99. 8°. **P. P. 1945. hdc.**

— Mazurka for the Pianoforte. *London*, [1877.] fol. **h. 1482. z. (17.)**

— Mither blame me not. Song. *London*, [1877.] fol. **H. 1778. x. (55.)**

— Musings. Song [begins: "I sat and watched"] written by K. F. *London*, [1877.] fol. **H. 1778. x. (56.)**

— No love so sweet as thine. (Scheiden, Leiden.) Song [begins: "And art thou gone," — "Und bist du fern"]. The English version by K. Forrester. (German poetry by E. Geibel.) *London*, [1877.] fol. **H. 1778. x. (58.)**

— O give Thanks unto God. Anthem, *etc.* 1898. *See* Periodical Publications.— *London*. The Lute, *etc.* No. 190. 1883–99. 8°. **P. P. 1945. hdc.**

— O sing unto the Lord. Harvest Anthem, *etc. See* Periodical Publications.— *London*. The Lute, *etc.* No. 104. 1883–99. 8°. **P. P. 1945. hdc.**

— The Old Folks at Home. [Melody by S. C. Foster.]— Part-Song.—Arranged for 4 Male Voices by T. Lee. 1898. *See* Periodical Publications.— *London*. The Lute, *etc.* No. 191. 1883–99. 8°. **P. P. 1945. hdc.**

— Original Voluntaries, *etc.* [Organ.] [1905.] *See* Sanctuary. The Sanctuary Series, *etc.* Book 13. [1900, *etc.*] 4°. **g. 588.**

— The Snow King galop. [P. F.] *London*, [1877.] fol. **h. 1482. z. (20.)**

— Te Deum laudamus, in C. (1906.) *See* Choir. The Choir Journal, *etc.* No. 11. [1900–1906.] 8°. **F. 1700.**

— When twilight dews. Ballad, words by T. Moore. *London*, [1877.] fol. **H. 1778. x. (57.)**

— *See* Carey (H.) [*Doubtful and Supposititious Works.*] Sally in our Alley ... Accompaniments by J. T. Lee. [1880.] fol. **H. 1625. (17.)**

— *See* King (M. P.) and Braham (J.) *Public singer.* [The Americans.] The Anchor's weighed ... Accompaniments by J. T. Lee. [1880.] fol. **H. 1628. (12.)**

LEE (James Turle)

— *See* Lee (G. A.) The Soldier's Tear ... Accompaniments by J. T. Lee. [1880.] fol. **H. 1628. (18.)**

LEE (Job)

— In my Dreams. Polka, *etc.* [P. F.] *Spottiswoode & Co.: London*, [1894.] fol. **h. 3285. q. (19.)**

— Queen of the Moorlands. Valse. [P. F.] [*London?* 1894.] fol. **h. 3285. q. (20.)**

LEE (John)

— Bird of the wild wood. Song. *London*, [1874.] fol. **H. 2617. (10.)**

— The Chesterfield Schottische. [P. F.] *London*, [1864.] fol. **h. 3107. (1.)**

— Come, Love, when the moon is peeping. Serenade. *London*, [1862.] fol. **H. 2617. (3.)**

— Dick Turpin quadrille. [P. F.] *London*, [1864.] fol. **h. 3107. (3.)**

— Les élégantes Normans; a fourth set of quadrilles ... for the Piano Forte. *London*, [1844.] fol. **h. 932. (32.)**

— England, form! ... Song [begins: "Avenge, avenge"]. *London*, [1877.] fol. **H. 1783. o. (41.)**

— The English Rose mazurka. [P. F.] *London*, [1869.] fol. **h. 3107. (5.)**

— A favorite set of polkas arranged for the piano forte, *etc. London*, [1854.] fol. **h. 975. e. (33.)**

— Golden Clouds. Song [begins: "Sail on"] written by L. G. Lee. *London*, [1871.] fol. **H. 2617. (8.)**

— Hail to thy coming. Song [begins: "Bright day"]. *London*, [1869.] fol. **H. 2617. (6.)**

— The Highland Hunter; or, Royal Scotch Quadrilles ... for the Pianoforte. *London*, [1840.] fol. **h. 117. (15.)**

— The Last Out quadrille. [P. F.] *London*, [1864.] fol. **h. 3107. (2.)**

— The Merry Sunshine. Ballad [begins: "Oh! 'tis the merry"]. *London*, [1861.] fol. **H. 2617. (2.)**

— Onward, ever onward ... Song [begins: "As you journey"]. *London*, [1873.] fol. **H. 2617. (9.)**

— Ophelia valse. [P. F.] *London*, [1865.] fol. **h. 3107. (4.)**

— Our Gallant Riflemen. Song [begins: "Hark! hark!]. *London*, [1861.] fol. **H. 2617. (1.)**

— Rose of England. Glee. *London*, [1875.] fol. **H. 2617. (11.)**

— The Songs we sang together. Song. *London*, [1869.] fol. **H. 2617. (7.)**

— Summer Flowers are blooming. Ballad. *London*, [1862.] fol. **H. 2617. (4.)**

— The Voyage of Life. A service of song, *etc. London*, 1872. 8°. **D. 675. b. (7.)**

— The Voyage of Life ... Tonic Sol-Fa edition. *London*, [1874.] 8°. **D. 675. b. (8.)**

— The War Horse polka. [P. F.] *London*, [1869.] fol. **h. 3107. (6.)**

— Where are the Summer Roses. Ballad. *London*, [1865.] fol. **H. 2617. (5.)**

— *See* Thornhill (T.) M^{rs}. Connell o'Carle, harmonized by J. Lee. [1843.] fol. **H. 1692. (39.)**

LEE (JOHN) *Composer of church music*

— Adoro te devote. For S. A. or S. A. T. B. voices and organ. pp. 4. *Gregorian Institute of America: Toledo, Ohio*, [1955.] 8°.　　　　　　　　　　　　**F. 1175. dd. (11.)**

— Dialogue-Recessional. For organ. pp. 6. *J. Fischer & Bro.: Glen Rock, N. J.*, [1960.] 4°.　　　**g. 1380. xx. (5.)**

— Four Improvisations. For organ. pp. 9. *Gregorian Institute of America: Toledo, Ohio*, [1951.] fol.　　**g. 1380. ff. (19.)**

— Mass for the Dead and the Burial Service ... For unison, two or three equal voices with optional organ accompaniment. pp. 35. *Gregorian Institute of America: Toledo, Ohio*, [1965.] 8°.　　　　　　　　　　　　**F. 1183. (12.)**

— Mass in English. For unison voices. pp. 12. *Gregorian Institute of America: Toledo, Ohio*, [1963.] 8°. *Part of "Ecumenical music series".*　　**E. 274. ii. (10.)**

— Choral Mass in English. For S. A. T. B. voices. According to the official English text. pp. 19. *Gregorian Institute of America: Toledo, Ohio*, [1964.] 8°.　　**F. 274. uu. (3.)**

— Mass in English for Congregations and alternating Choir ad libitum, *etc.* pp. 10. *Gregorian Institute of America: Toledo, Ohio*, [1965.] 8°.　　　**F. 274. uu. (2.)**

— Second Mass in English for Congregations and alternating Choir ad lib. With the official English text. pp. 12. *Gregorian Institute of America: Toledo, Ohio*, [1964.] 8°.　　　　　　　　　　　　**F. 274. uu. (1.)**

— Mass in Honor of Our Lady—Help of Christians. (S. A. T. B.) pp. 28. *J. Fischer & Bro.: Glen Rock*, [1960.] 8°.　　　　　　　　　　　　**F. 1175. ii. (7.)**

— Mass in Honor of Saint Joseph. For S. A. T. B. voices and congregation ad libitum ... Organ accompaniment, *etc.* pp. 19. *Gregorian Institute of America: Toledo, Ohio*, [1966.] 8°.　　　　　　**F. 1183. g. (5.)**

— Mass in Honour of St. Joseph. For two equal voices with congregation ad lib. and organ accompaniment. pp. 16. *Gregorian Institute of America: Toledo, Ohio*, [1966.] 8°.　　　　　　　**F. 274. uu. (19.)**

— Two Motets. [By G. P. da Palestrina.] ⟨O loving Jesus. (O bone Jesu.) We adore you, O Christ. (Adoramus te Christe.)⟩ For S. A. T. B. choir and organ accompaniment ad libitum. Arranged by J. Lee. pp. 6. *Gregorian Institute of America: Toledo, Ohio*, [1966.] 8°.　　　**F. 1175. rr. (9.)**

— Two Motets in Honor of the blessed Virgin. Hail, holy Queen. ⟨Salve regina. Francesco Soriano.⟩ Hail, Queen of Heaven. ⟨Regina coeli laetare. Antonio Lotti.⟩ For S. A. T. B. choir and optional organ. Arranged by J. Lee. pp. 8. *Gregorian Institute of American: Toledo, Ohio*, [1967.] 8°.　　　　**E. 1439. s. (3.)**

— Eight Offertory Motets [by G. P. da Palestrina, G. Carissimi, C. Tye and others] and the Recessional Now thank we all our God [by J. Crüger]. For S. A. T. B. choir and organ accompaniment ad libitum. Compiled and arranged by J. Lee. pp. 31. *Gregorian Institute of America: Toledo, Ohio*, [1966.] 8°.　　　　　**F. 1175. rr. (10.)**

— Organ Suite. For low mass, *etc.* pp. 11. *Gregorian Institute of America: Toledo, Ohio*, [1954.] fol.　**g. 1380. ff. (20.)**

— Five Postludes. For organ. Fanfare—March—Fantasia— Epilogue—Toccata. pp. 11. *Gregorian Institute of America: Toledo, Ohio*, [1955.] fol.　　**g. 1380. ff. (21.)**

— Yours are the Heavens. Offertory for the third mass of Christmas for S. A. T. B. choir with organ accompaniment. pp. 4. *Gregorian Institute of America: Toledo, Ohio*, [1966.] 8°.　　　　　　　　**F. 1175. rr. (11.)**

LEE (JOHN) *Composer of flute music*

— Lee's Pocket Book for the German Flute or Violin, *etc.* [1780–88?] *obl.* 8°. *See* POCKET.　　　**a. 204.**

LEE (JOHN H.)

— "When I am far away from home." Song, written by A. Watt. *London*, [1865.] fol.　　　　**H. 1772. r. (27.)**

LEE (JOHN YORKEAT)

— Dat whistlin' yaller Dinah. Song with whistling refrain. ⟨Written and composed by J. Y. Lee. Music arranged by T. W. Garsberg.⟩ pp. 5. *White-Smith Music Pub. Co.:* [*Boston*, 1894.] fol.　　　　　　**H. 3980. qq. (4.)**

LEE (JOSEPH)

— *See* HAYDN (Franz J.) [Masses. Hob. XXII/10.—Et incarnatus est. Et vitam venturi saeculi.] "O Lord rebuke me not" ... with an accompaniment for the organ, arranged by J. Lee. [c. 1850.] fol.　　　　　**H. 2120. p. (10.)**

LEE (KANG DUK)

— Sae haneul. [For Korean instruments. Score.] *In:* ANTHOLOGY. Anthology of new Korean Music. vol. 1. pp. 6–41. 1962. 8°.　　　　　　　　　　　　**G. 1469. g.**

LEE (KATE)

— Three Songs. 1. The Angels are bending.—Cradle Song.— (Words by W. B. Yeats.) 2. Each on his own strict Line we move. (Words by M. Arnold.) 3. Do you ask what the Birds say? (Words by S. Coleridge.) *Bayley & Ferguson: London*, 1903. fol.　　　　　　**H. 1799. vv. (35.)**

— Two Songs. a. When two clasp Hands at parting. (Words translated from ... Heine by A. Kalisch.) b. Noon and Night. (Words by W. Toynbee.) *Bayley & Ferguson: London*, 1904. fol.　　　　　　　　　　**H. 1799. vv. (34.)**

— Songs for Children, words by H. Griffiths. *Bayley & Ferguson: London, Glasgow*, 1904. 4°.　　**G. 383. e. (2.)**

LEE (LEONI)

— *See* LEE (Louis L.)

LEE (LESTER)

— Meet Captain Kidd. [Operetta.] Lyrics by Bob Russell ... Book by Ed. Bradley. Arranged by Don Wilson. [Vocal score.] pp. 71. *Edwin H. Morris & Co.: New York*, [1954.] 8°.　　　　　　　　　　　　**F. 1267. gg. (3.)**

LEE (LIONEL)

— Summer Serenade. Song, the words by W. A. Barratt. ⟨In F. In D♭.⟩ 2 no. *London*, [1879.] fol.　**H. 1783. o. (42.)**

— Summer Serenade. [Violoncello and P. F.] *See* LEE (S.) Les Perles du Jour ... No. 10. [1883.] fol.　**h. 1875. c. (1.)**

LEE (LOU G.)

— The Inspiration March. Two-Step. [P. F.] *Whaley, Royce & Co.: Toronto*, 1896. fol.　　　　**h. 3286. g. (25.)**

— Mocha. March two-step. [P.F.] pp. 5. *Whaley, Royce & Co.: Winnipeg, Toronto*, [1908.] fol.　　**h. 4120. oo. (5.)**

LEE (LOUIS)

— Trois pièces gracieuses, pour le violoncelle, avec accompagnement de piano. Op. 12. 3 no. *Leipzig*, [1857.] fol.　　　　　　　　　　　　**h. 1851. c. (1.)**

LEE (Louis Leoni)

— Auld Lang Syne, the celebrated Song & Chorus, in the Opera of Rob Roy or Auld Lang Syne ... Harmonized by Mr L. Lee. *Phillips & Comp^y: London,* [1820?] fol. **H. 1652. n. (7.)**

— If ye a highland laddie meet ... Ballad. *London,* [1820?] fol. **H. 2835. b. (3.)**

— A nosegay once of varied flowers. Ballad ... the words ... by Miss Chapman, *etc. London,* [1825?] fol. **H. 2818. f. (27.)**

— The Rose that is free from a thorn. A ballad [begins: "How bright rose that day"], written by Miss Chapman. *London,* [1828?] fol. **G. 810. (41.)**

— The Snow on beds of roses ... Ballad, written by A. Bunn. *London,* [1820?] fol. **G. 810. (42.)**

LEE (Lulu Skinner) Mrs

— Life's Eden Rose. [Song.] Words and music by Mrs. B. P. Lee. *Mrs. B. P. Lee: Los Angeles,* (1913.) fol. **H. 1793. s. (36.)**

LEE (Mabel)

— Thirty Favorite Folk Tunes. Arranged with melody and chord accompaniment for analysis and transposition by M. Lee. *C. F. Summy Co.: Chicago,* 1927. 4°. **G. 981. f. (13.)**

LEE (Marion)

— Algerine Waltz, for the pianoforte. *Weekes & Co.: London,* [1886.] fol. **h. 975. v. (1.)**

LEE (Mathew K. Y.)

— *See* Li (Kuang-yeh)

LEE (Maurice)

— Ah! Cruel Parting. Volkslied aus Thüringen. Fantaisie. Op. 45. *See* infra: Fantaisies (Morceaux) de Salon. No. 14.

— Au Bord de la Fontaine. Romance-étude pour Piano. *London,* [1870.] fol. **h. 3108. (4.)**

— Azur, nocturne sentimentale pour Piano. *London,* [1871.] fol. **h. 3108. (5.)**

— Le Berger. Tyrolienne. [P. F.] *See* infra: Fantaisies (Morceaux) de Salon. No. 43.

— The Brook's Lullaby. Study for the Pianoforte. *See* infra: Fantaisies (Morceaux) de Salon. No. 36.

— Cantilena pour violon ou violoncelle ou flûte avec accompagnement de piano. *Augener & Co.: London,* [1894.] fol. **g. 505. m. (10.)**

— Célèbre Sérénade ... transcrit [*sic*] pour le Piano par M. Lee. [1870.] fol. *See* HAYDN (F. J.) [*Doubtful and Supposititious Works.*] [Quartets. Op. 3. No. 5.—Serenade.] **h. 3108. (3.)**

— Célèbre Sérénade de J. Haydn, transcrite pour Piano. *Paris,* [1870.] fol. **h. 1462. r. (32.)**

— Le Courier. Grand galop de concert. Op. 50. [P.F.] *See* infra: Fantaisies (Morceaux) de Salon. No. 20.

— Dernière Valse d'un Fou. Fantaisie ... Op. 32. *See* infra: Fantaisies (Morceaux) de Salon. No. 1.

— Echo du Ciel. Étude de Salon pour le piano. *See* also infra: Fantaisies (Morceaux) de Salon. No. 37.

— Echo du Ciel, étude de salon pour le Piano. *London,* [1879.] fol. **h. 1494. q. (4.)**

— L'Electricité. Étude de Salon pour piano. Op. 7. *See* also infra: Fantaisies (Morceaux) de Salon. No. 39.

— L'Electricité, étude de salon pour le Pianoforte. *London,* [1862.] fol. **h. 1460. v. (9.)**

LEE (Maurice)

— L'Electricité, étude de salon pour Piano. *London,* [1871.] fol. **h. 3108. (6.)**

— Études Chantantes pour Piano. 2 cah. *London,* [1879.] 4°. **g. 272. y. (10.)**

— Faint Heart.—Pas braves!—Song, the words by P. Carré. (English words by W. Grist.) *Augener & Co.: London,* [1892.] fol. **G. 807. h. (10.)**

— Fantaisie sur un ancien air français. [P. F.] *See* infra: Fantaisies (Morceaux) de Salon. No. 42.

— Fantaisies (Morceaux) de Salon pour le Piano. 44 no. *Augener & Co.: London,* [1875–83.] fol. **h. 3108. b.**

— Fête des Bayadères. [P.F.] *London,* [1874.] fol. **h. 3108. (8.)**

— Fleur de l'Âme, romance sans paroles ... pour Piano. *London,* [1872.] fol. **h. 3108. (7.)**

— Le Freyschütz de Weber. Prière et Choeur des Chasseurs pour Piano. *London,* [1867.] fol. **h. 3108. (1.)**

— Le Freyschütz de C.M. de Weber. Prière et Choeur des Chasseurs pour Piano. *Paris,* [1867.] fol. **h. 1462. r. (30.)**

— Gavotte de Louis Quinze. Op. 54. Pianoforte Solo. *See* also supra: Fantaisies (Morceaux) de Salon. No. 23.

— Gavotte de Louis Quinze. Piano solo & duet. 2 no. *London,* [1876.] fol. **h. 3108. (9.)**

— Gavotte de Louis XV. [P. F.] *See* SMALLWOOD (W.) Favorite Pieces, *etc.* No. 2. [1893.] fol. **h. 1412. v. (31.)**

— Gavotte de Louis Quinze. (Arranged for Harmonium by J. Löw.) *London,* [1879.] fol. **h. 2575. g. (21.)**

— Gavotte de Louis XV. (Op. 54.) [Violin and P. F.] [1904.] *See* HERMANN (F.) Morceaux Favoris, *etc.* No. 139. [1886, *etc.*] fol. **h. 1621. b.**

— Gavotte de Louis Quinze. [Violoncello and P. F.] *See* LEE (S.) Les Perles du Jour, *etc.* No. 2. [1883.] fol. **h. 1875. c. (1.)**

— Gavotte du Duc de Richelieu pour le piano. *See* also supra: Fantaisies (Morceaux) de Salon. No. 40.

— Gavotte du Duc de Richelieu pour le Piano. *London,* [1880.] fol. **h. 1494. q. (6.)**

— Gavotte du Duc de Richelieu, arranged by C. Godfrey. [Reed band parts.] *London,* [1881.] 4°. *Augener & Co.'s edition, No.* 7067. **g. 474. d. (4.)**

— Gavotte du Duc de Richelieu pour le Pianoforte & Flûte. *Augener & Co.: London,* [1881.] 4°. **h. 1509. q. (5.)**

— Gavotte du Duc de Richelieu pour le Pianoforte & Violin. *London,* [1881.] 4°. **g. 505. b. (6.)**

— Gavotte du Duc de Richelieu. [Violoncello and P. F.] *See* LEE (S.) Les Perles du Jour ... No. 11. [1883.] fol. **h. 1875. c. (1.)**

— Gavotte du Palais Royal. Edition pour 2 violons, viole & violoncelle ou orchestre d'accord. [Parts.] *Augener & Co.: London,* [1890.] 4°. **g. 474. e. (4.)**

— Graziella. Valse de Salon pour le piano. (Op. 53.) *See* also supra: Fantaisies (Morceaux) de Salon. No. 22.

— Long Ago, popular air arranged for small hands. [P.F.] *London,* [1879.] fol. **h. 1494. q. (3.)**

— May Day. Gavotte de Louis XVI. Arranged for 2 female voices by B. Lütgen [begins: "All the merry bells are ringing,"] words by E. Oxenford. *London,* [1886.] 8°. *No.* 4100 *of Augener & Co.'s edition.* **F. 1530. (14.)**

— Le Ménestrel Classique. 10 fragments ... transcrits ... pour le Piano. 10 no. *London,* [1877.] fol. **h. 3108. (11.)**

LEE (Maurice)

— Morceaux de Salon. *See* supra: Fantaisies (Morceaux) de Salon.

— La Napolitaine. Étude de Salon pour piano. *See* also supra: Fantaisies (Morceaux) de Salon. No. 38.

— La Napolitaine, étude de salon pour Piano. *London*, [1880.] fol.　　**h. 1494. q. (5.)**

— Le Papillon. Morceau pour Flûte avec accompagnement de piano. *Augener & Co.: London*, [1894.] fol.　**h. 2140. m. (7.)**

— Petit Caprice sur l'Opéra 'Joseph' de Méhul, pour le piano. *J. Heinz: Paris*, [1884.] fol.　　**g. 605. f. (11.)**

— Petites Soirées Musicales, Six Morceaux Mignons pour Piano et Violon Arrangés par M. Lee. 6 no. *J. Williams: London*, [1881.] fol.　　**h. 210. e. (22.)**

— Les Petits Concerts populaires. 4 Fantaisies mignonnes pour Piano. 4 no. *Paris*, [1867.] fol.　　**h. 1462. r. (31.)**

— Petits Concerts populaires. Trois fantaisies mignonnes. [P.F.] 3 no. *London*, [1867.] fol.　　**h. 3108. (2.)**

— Rêverie de Graziella pour piano. *J. Heinz: Paris*, [1884.] fol.　　**g. 605. f. (12.)**

— Robin Adair. [Fantasia. P. F.] Op. 37. *See* supra: Fantaisies (Morceaux) de Salon. No. 6.

— Rondoletto on an air by Mozart for the Pianoforte. *London*, [1879.] fol.　　**h. 1494. q. (2.)**

— Le Rossignol. Air Russe. [Fantasia. P. F.] Op. 40. *See* supra: Fantaisies (Morceaux) de Salon. No. 9.

— Russian Gipsy Songs. Fantasia. Op. 57. [P. F.] *See* supra: Fantaisies (Morceaux) de Salon. No. 26.

— Short operatic fantasias for the Pianoforte. 6 no. *London*, [1876.] fol.　　**h. 3108. (10.)**

— Souvenir de la Styrie. [P. F.] *See* supra: Fantaisies (Morceaux) de Salon. No. 33.

— Souvenir de Zillerthal. [P. F.] *See* supra: Fantaisies (Morceaux) de Salon. No. 44.

— Sylvana. Menuet. [Violoncello and P. F.] *See* LEE (S.) Les Perles du Jour ... No. 7. [1883.] fol.　**h. 1875. c. (1.)**

— Turkish War March. Pianoforte Solo. *See* supra: Fantaisies (Morceaux) de Salon. No. 34.

— Valse d'Amour pour piano. *See* also supra: Fantaisies (Morceaux) de Salon. No. 41.

— Valse d'Amour pour Piano. *London*, [1881.] fol.
　　h. 3273. a. (58.)

— Voix Celeste, andante by E. Batiste. Pianoforte fantasia. *London*, [1878.] fol.　　**h. 1494. q. (1.)**

— *See* BOCCHERINI (L.) [Quintet. Op. 13. No. 5.] Célèbre Minuet. Transcribed by M. Lee. [1900.] fol.　　**h. 1424.**

— *See* CORELLI (A.) [Sonatas. Op. 5. No. 9.] Gigue. Transcription by M. Lee. [1900.] fol.　　**h. 1424.**

— *See* GLUCK (C. W. von) [Don Juan.] Gavotte ... Transcribed by M. Lee. Op. 56. [1900.] fol.　　**h. 1424.**

LEE (Melville)

— Love's Device. Song [begins: "Gaily we strolled"] written by Gertrude. *Hereford*, [1877.] fol.　**H. 1778. x. (60.)**

LEE (N. H.)

— The Temple. Barn Dance. [P. F.] *Metzler & Co.: London*, [1897.] fol.　　**h. 3286. g. (26.)**

LEE (Noël E.)

— The Carrier. Unison Song for Children, words by Mrs. Washington-Metcalfe. *J. B. Cramer & Co.: London*, 1934. 4°.
[*Cramer's Library of Unison and Part Songs. No.* 113.]
　　E. 1678. a.

— Dialogues. For violin and piano. [Score and part.] 2 pt. *Theodore Presser Co.: Bryn Mawr, Pa.*, [1962.] 4°.
　　g. 223. hh. (2.)

— Sonatine. For piano solo. pp. 9. *Oxford University Press: London*, [1971.] 4°.　　**h. 60. n. (5.)**

LEE (Peggy)

— [The Lady and the Tramp.] From Walt Disney's Lady and the Tramp ... By P. Lee, S. Burke & O. Wallace. ⟨Piano selection arranged by Felton Rapley.⟩ pp. 7. *Walt Disney Music Co.: London*, [1955.] 4°.　　**g. 1425. c. (6.)**

LEE (Peggy) and **BARBOUR** (David)

— [It's a good Day.] *See* GERSHWIN (George) [The Shocking Miss Pilgrim.] For you, for me, for evermore ... and It's a good Day. ⟨By P. Lee and D. Barbour.⟩ [Orchestral parts.] [1947.] 8°.　　**E. 1897. a. (10.)**

LEE (Peter)

— A Conversation Piece, for two Persons to Sing and Play together, on one Harpsichord or Piano Forte. *Printed for the Author:* [*London*, 1787.] obl. fol.　　**e. 108. (10.)**

— Damon and Delia. A Favorite Rondou, *etc.* [*London*, 1786.] fol.　　**H. 1653. (34.)**

— [Another edition.] Damon and Delia, *etc. The Author: Putney*, [1785?] fol.　　**H. 2818. (14.)**

— A Small Collection of Hymns for the Organ or Harpsichord ... The Words by Dr Watts. *Holland & Co, for the Author: London*, [1785?] obl. 4°.　　**B. 788. (3.)**

— The Jolly Fellow. [Song.] *See* infra: The Tar in Distress.

— Six Progressive Lessons for the Harpsichord or Piano Forte, containing many Usefull passages, with the manner of fingering them. *Printed for the Author: Wandsworth*, [1785.] obl. fol.　　**e. 101. (5.)**

— [Six Progressive Lessons for the Harpsichord. No. 1.] Rigadoon. [P. F.] 1919. *See* ROWLEY (A.) Early English Harpsichord Music, *etc.* v. 1917, *etc.* 4°.　**g. 1236. a. (2.)**

— Rigadoon. *See* supra: [Six Progressive Lessons for the Harpsichord. No. 1.]

— Three Sonatas for the Harpsichord or Piano Forte, with an Accompanyment for a Violin or German Flute ... Op. 2^d. *Printed for the Author:* [*London*, 1786.] fol.　**h. 60. (5.)**

— The Tar in Distress. A Glee for 3 Voices, also adapted for the Piano Forte ... Written and Composed by P. Lee. (The Jolly Fellow. [Song.]) *Printed for the Author: London*, [1790?] fol.
　　G. 806. f. (45.)

— [Another copy.]　　**G. 806. e. (30.)**

— William & Mary, two favorite Rondos with an Accompaniment for a Violin, or German Flute ... Written and Composed by P. Lee. *Printed for the Author: London*, [1794.] fol.　　**G. 366. (28.)**

LEE (ROBERT CHARLES)

— *See* LISZT (F.) [*Collected Works.—b.*] Drei späte Klaviersütcke ... Erstausgabe ... Herausgegeben von ... R. C. Lee. [1969.] 4°.　　　　　　　　　　　　　　　**g. 547. x. (1.)**

LEE (RONNY)

— *See* RODGERS (Richard) The Sound of Music. Selection for guitar solo ... Arranged by R. Lee, *etc.* [1966.] 4°.
　　　　　　　　　　　　　　　g. 660. v. (14.)

LEE (RUPERT GODFREY)

— Christmas Plays for Children by M. Pemberton. Music and illustrations by R. G. Lee, *etc.　G. Routledge & Sons: London,* 1914. 8°.　　　　　　　　　**11778. g. 59.**

LEE (S. JACKSON)

— A Rose. Song, words by R. W. W. 2 no. [In D and F.] *Chappell & Co.: London, etc.,* 1914. fol.　　**H. 1793. s. (39.)**

LEE (SANG KYOO)

— Dawning. [For Korean instruments. Score.] *In:* ANTHOLOGY. Anthology of new Korean Music. vol. 2. pp. 31–85. 1965. 8°.
　　　　　　　　　　　　　　　G. 1469. g.

LEE (SCHUYLER C.)

— Nunc dimittis in A.　*W. Maxwell Music Co.: New York City,* (1914.) 8°.　　　　　　　　**F. 1169. w. (15.)**

LEE (SEBASTIAN)

— S. Lee's Technologie des Violoncellspiels (Violoncello Technics by S. Lee) revidirt und herausgegeben von H. Becker ... Methode, Op. 30. 40 leichte Etüden in der ersten Lage (with a 2nd Violoncello), Op. 70. 24 Melodische & progressive Uebungen (with a 2nd Violoncello), Op. 131. 40 Melodische & progressive Etüden (Suite I., II.), Op. 31. 5 no.　*Schott & Co.: London,* [1900–03.] fol.　　**h. 1875. d.**

— Adagio für zwei Violoncello aus Op. 39. No. 1 ... Arrangement für Violoncelle mit Begleitung des Pianoforte von C. Grimm.　*Leipzig,* [1875.] fol.　　**h. 1849. c. (4.)**

— Six Airs Nationaux pour le violoncelle avec accompagnement de piano. Op. 123. 2 Suites.　*London,* [1884.] 4°.
Augener & Co.'s edition, No. 7703A and 7703B.
　　　　　　　　　　　　　　　g. 514. f. (16.)

— Album pour Violoncelle et Piano, par Sebastian Lee. vol. I.(–III.) (Album pour Violoncelle et Piano, par Alfred Moffat. vol. IV.) (Album pour Violoncelle et Piano, arrangé par C. Schroeder. vol. V.) 5 vol.　*Augener & Co.: London,* [1890–1906.] 4°.　　　　　　**g. 514. i. (1.)**

— Berceuse. Op. 71. No. 2. [Violin and P. F.] *See* RITTER (E. W.) Les Succès du Salon, *etc.* No. 9. [1891, *etc.*] fol.　　**h. 3665. a.**

— Trois Duos faciles. Op. 124. 3 no. [Violin and violoncello.] *Mayence,* [1886.] fol.　　　　　　**h. 1875. b. (7.)**

— Duos for two Violoncellos ... Revised by O. Brückner. 2 bk. *Augener & Co.: London,* [1899.] 4°.　　**g. 510. b. (3.)**

— Trois Duos moyenne force. Op. 125. 3 no. [Violin and violoncello.] *Mayence,* [1886.] fol.　　**h. 1875. b. (8.)**

— École du violoncelliste. 4 oeuvres de duos pour deux violoncelles ... Op. 36. Trois duos ... 37. Trois duos ... 38. Trois duos ... 39. Trois duos, *etc.* [Parts.]　*Chez Breitkopf & Härtel: Leipzig,* [c. 1880.] fol.
Imperfect; op. 36 only.　　　　　　　**h. 4090. r. (5.)**

LEE (SEBASTIAN)

— [Études.] Twenty Studies. Op. 92, 76 & 105. Violoncello solo. (Edited by L. Lebell.)　*Augener & Co.: London,* 1917. 4°.
　　　　　　　　　　　　　　　g. 510. f. (8*.)

— Huit Etudes-Caprices pour Violoncelle. Op. 105.　*Paris,* [1876.] fol.　　　　　　　　**h. 1849. e. (3.)**

40 études mélodiques et progressives. Op. 31

— Forty Melodic and Progressive Études for Violoncello. Edited and fingered by Leo Schulz ... Biographical sketch of the composer by Richard Aldrich ... Book I (No. 1–22) ... Book II (No. 23–40), *etc.* 2 bk.　*G. Schirmer: New York; Chappell & Co.: London;* [*London* printed, 1950,51.] 4°. *Schirmer's Library of musical classics. vol.* 639, 640.
　　　　　　　　　　　　　　　h. 1870. f. (5.)

— Melodische Etüden für Violoncello ... Neu herausgegeben von Wolfgang Goldhan, *etc.* Hft. 1.　*Edition Peters: Leipzig,* [1966?] 4°.
Imperfect; wanting Hft. 2.　　　　　**g. 512. i. (11.)**

— [Cah. I.] *See* MICHAEL (P.) 16 Etüden ... für Violoncell—nach den Etüden. Op. 31. Heft I. von S. Lee, *etc.* [1906.] fol.
　　　　　　　　　　　　　　　h. 1851. d. (33*.)

— [No. 12, 15, 18.] 5 Exercises on Bowing, with Piano accompaniment. Dotzauer, Lee (I–III), Merk. (1911.) *See* FUCHS (C.) Violoncello Works, *etc.* No. 2. (1911,12.) fol.
　　　　　　　　　　　　　　　g. 510. e. (4.)

— [No. 23, 27–30, 34, 35.] Sept Pièces mélodiques ... pour violoncelle ou violon ou alto avec accompagnement de piano par J. B. Krall d'après les études mélodiques pour violoncelle seul. Op. 31. En deux cahiers. 6 no.　*Mayence,* [1885.] fol.
　　　　　　　　　　　　　　　h. 1875. b. (1.)

———

— Douze Études mélodiques pour le Violoncelle. (Op. 113.) *London,* [1881.] 4°.
Augener & Co.'s edition, No. 7776.　　**g. 514. f. (15.)**

— 24 Études mélodiques ... pour le Violoncelle avec accomp. d'un second Violoncell ... Op. 131.　*B. Schott's Söhne: Mayence,* [1888.] fol.　　　　　　**h. 1875. b. (8.)**

— Fantaisie sur La Juive, pour violoncelle avec accompagnem^t. de piano. Op. 128.　*Paris,* 1885. fol.　　**h. 1875. b. (5.)**

— Fantaisie sur des motifs d'Oberon, Euryanthe et de Preciosa de C. M. de Weber pour le violoncelle avec accomp^t. de piano. Oeuv. 51.　*Leipzig,* [1860?] fol.　　**h. 1875. b. (3.)**

— First Steps in Violoncello Playing. 50 easy Pieces in the first position, with 2nd Violoncello—ad lib— Op. 101.　*Augener: London,* [1909.] 4°.　　　　　　　**g. 514. l. (3.)**

— First Steps in Violoncello Playing, with 2nd cello, ad lib. Op. 101. (Revised and edited by L. Lebell.)　*Augener: London,* 1920. 4°.　　　　　　　**g. 514. p. (1.)**

— Gavotte pour Violoncelle avec accompagnement de Piano. *Hambourg,* [1880.] fol.　　　　　　**h. 1849. k. (14.)**

— Guide du jeune Violoncelliste. 40 Exercises journaliers pour Violoncelle ... Op. 82 & 83 ... Revue et doigtée par O. Brückner.　*Augener & Co.: London,* [1900.] 4°.
　　　　　　　　　　　　　　　g. 514. j. (7.)

— Méthode pratique pour le Violoncelle. (Praktische Violoncell-Schule.) Op. 30.　*Mayence,* [1850?] fol.
　　　　　　　　　　　　　　　h. 1870. (3.)

— Méthode pratique pour le Violoncelle.　*Mayence,* [1880.] fol.
　　　　　　　　　　　　　　　h. 1875.

— Méthode pour le Violoncelle ... revised and translated ... by J. Lidel.　*Mayence,* [1882.] fol.　　　**h. 1875. a.**

LEE (Sebastian)

— [Morceaux favoris pour Violoncelle et Piano. No. 1.] Prière du Soir. C. Reinecke. [Arranged by S. Lee.] [1904.] *See* Transcriptions. Transcriptions of Standard Vocal Works, *etc.* No. 17. [1904, *etc.*] fol.   **h. 1868.**

— [Morceaux favoris pour Violoncelle et Piano. No. 8.] Pur dicesti. Aria. A. Lotti. [Arranged by S. Lee.] [1904.] *See* Transcriptions. Transcriptions of Standard Vocal Works, *etc.* No. 11a. [1904, *etc.*] fol.   **h. 1868.**

— [Morceaux favoris pour Violoncelle et Piano. No. 14.] Nina. Siciliano. J. B. Pergolese. [Arranged by S. Lee.] [1904.] *See* Transcriptions. Transcriptions of Standard Vocal Works, *etc.* No. 15a. [1904, *etc.*] fol.   **h. 1868.**

— [Morceaux favoris pour Violoncelle et Piano. No. 17.] Romance. L. Spohr. [Arranged by S. Lee.] [1904.] *See* Transcriptions. Transcriptions of Standard Vocal Works, *etc.* No. 24. [1904, *etc.*] fol.   **h. 1868.**

— Les Perles du Jour, for Violoncello & Pianoforte. 12 no. *Augener & Co.: London*, [1883.] fol.   **h. 1875. c. (1.)**

— [Les Perles du Jour. No. 5.] Cujus animam. Air from Stabat Mater by Rossini. [Arranged by] S. Lee. [1904.] *See* Transcriptions. Transcriptions of Standard Vocal Works, *etc.* No. 18. [1904, *etc.*] fol.   **h. 1868.**

— [Les Perles du Jour. No. 12.] Serenade. By C. Gounod. Transcribed by S. Lee. [1904.] *See* Transcriptions. Transcriptions of Standard Vocal Works, *etc.* No. 6. [1904, *etc.*] fol.   **h. 1868.**

— 30 Präludien in allen Tonarten ... für das Violoncell. Op. 122, *etc. Hamburg*, [1885.] fol.   **h. 1875. b. (4.)**

— Soirées du Violoncelliste amateur. Collection de transcriptions faciles sur des opéras célèbres ... complétée par E. Gillet. 15 no. *Paris*, [1882.] fol. *Imperfect; no. 3, 4 and 8 only.*   **h. 1875. b. (6.)**

— Souvenir des anciens maîtres. Six morceaux pour violoncelle avec accompagnement de piano. 6 no. *Hambourg*, [1885.] fol.   **h. 1875. b. (2.)**

— L'Union. Caprice pour violoncelle avec acc^t de piano sur les mélodies Nella de Meyerbeer et Nizza de Rossini ... Op. 19. [Score.] pp. 11. *Chez Chabal: Paris*, [1840?] fol.   **h. 1871. a. (8.)**

— "Wie bist du meine Königin." Lied. J. Brahms. Arr. by S. Lee [for violoncello and P. F.]. [1904.] *See* Transcriptions. Transcriptions of Standard Vocal Works, *etc.* No. 3. [1904, *etc.*] fol.   **h. 1868.**

— *See* Dotzauer (J. J. F.) Quarante études ... Revues par S. Lee. [1881.] 4°.   **g. 514. f. (4.)**

— *See* Mendelssohn-Bartholdy (J.L.F.) [*Collected Works.—l.*] Trios des Amateurs ... par ... S. Lee, *etc.* [1879.] fol.   **h. 2851. c. (11.)**

— *See* Schubert (F.P.) [*Collected Works.—e.*] Les délices de Schubert ... German songs composed by F. Schubert, arranged for violoncello and piano by S.Lee. [1845, *etc.*] fol.   **h. 1932.**

— *See* Schumann (R. A.) 4 Lieder ... für Violoncell und Pianoforte eingerichtet von S. Lee. [1888.] fol.   **h. 88. g. (12.)**

— *See* Schumann (R. A.) [12 vierhändige Clavierstücke. Op. 85. No. 12.] Abendlied ... For cello and piano. (Arranged by S. Lee.) [1971.] 4°. [*Schott Cello Series. no. 16.*]   **g. 112. m.**

LEE (Seong cheon)

— Symphony for Daegeum, Piri and Gayageum. [Score.] *In:* Anthology. Anthology of new Korean Music. vol. 2. pp. 7–30. 1965. 8°.   **G. 1469. g.**

LEE (Soo za)

— Symphoy [*sic*] for Piri. [Score.] *In:* Anthology. Anthology of new Korean Music. vol. 1. pp. 60–77. 1962. 8°.   **G. 1469. g.**

LEE (T. Charles)

— Japanese Christmas Carol. For voices in unison. [Words by] Rev. S. Ojima. Tr. by Kate I. Hanson. Stanzas 2 & 3 by T. C. Lee. [Melody] traditional. Arranged by T. C. Lee. pp. 4. *H. W. Gray Co.: New York*, [1962.] 8°.   **F. 260. w. (26.)**

— Japanese Christmas Carol. For S.S.A. [Words by] Rev. S. Ojima. Tr. by Kate I. Hanson. Stanzas 2 & 3 by T. C. Lee. [Melody] traditional. Arranged by T. C. Lee. pp. 7. *H. W. Gray Co.: New York*, [1966.] 8°.   **F. 260. nn. (17.)**

— Japanese Christmas Carol. For S.A.T.B., with handbells (ad lib.). [Words by] Rev. S. Ojima. Tr. by Kate I. Hanson. Stanzas 2 & 3 by T. C. Lee. Traditional [melody]. Arr. by T. C. Lee. [Score.] pp. 7. *H. W. Gray Co.: New York*, [1970.] 8°.   **F. 260. ll. (15.)**

LEE (Theresa M. Y.)

— For Baby. (A guitar folio.) Selected & arranged by T. M. Y. Lee. [Tabulature.] pp. 48. *Hung Fai Company: Hong Kong*, [1977.] 8°.   **f. 530. a. (3.)**

LEE (Thomas)

— Festive March in C for the pianoforte. *E. Ashdown: London, etc.*, [1895.] fol.   **g. 605. f. (13.)**

— The Lord is my Shepherd. Anthem. *C. Vincent: London*, [1900.] 8°.   **F. 231. k. (18.)**

LEE (Turle)

— *See* Lee (J. T.)

LEE (Vedder)

— Aux Armes ... Polka March. [P. F.] *Moore, Smith & Co.: London*, [1895.] fol.   **h. 3285. q. (21.)**

— Barleycorn. Barn Dance. [P. F.] *J. & J. Hopkinson: London*, 1892. fol.   **h. 3285. q. (22.)**

— Le Sultan. Danse orientale. [P. F.] *Metzler & Co.: London*, 1895. fol.   **h. 1489. s. (28.)**

LEE (Victor)

— "The Voices of the Angels."—Lullaby.—Words by D. Smedt. *K. Dehnhoff: New York*, (1906.) fol.   **H. 1794. l. (1.)**

LEE (Walter H.)

— En Hâte. Galop. [P. F.] *W. D. Cubitt & Son: London*, [1883.] fol.   **h. 975. v. (2.)**

— Maraschino galop. [Orchestral parts.] *London*, [1879.] 8°. *Part of the "Alliance Musicale".*   **f. 400. s. (13.)**

— Maraschino galop. [Reed band parts.] *London*, [1878.] 8°. *Part of the "Alliance Musicale".*   **f. 401. k. (3.)**

— Maraschino galop, arranged by Hare. [Fife and drum band parts.] *London*, [1879.] 8°. *Part of the "Alliance Musicale".*   **f. 403. d. (45.)**

— Maraschino galop for the Pianoforte. *London*, [1878.] fol. *Part of the "Alliance Musicale".*   **h. 2915. a. (6.)**

— Maraschino galop. [P.F.] *London*, [1879.] 8°. *No. 539 of the "Alliance Musicale. Album Bijou".*   **f. 406.**

LEE (WALTER H.)

— The Royal Standard quick march. [Reed band parts.]
London, [1880.] 8°.
Part of the "Alliance Musicale".   **f. 401. o. (17.)**

LEE (WILLIAM)

— Benedicite, omnia opera ... in chant form. *Weekes & Co.:*
London, [1895.] 4°.   **E. 602. p. (16.)**

— An Evening Hymn. Words by Mrs. S. Noyes. *Weekes & Co.:*
London, [1906.] *s. sh.* 8°.   **D. 619. aa. (11.)**

— Evening Service ... in ... A. *Office of "The Organist":*
London, 1896. 8°.   **E. 605. h. (22.)**

— Glory to God in the Highest. Anthem for Christmas. Op. 11.
E. Donajowski: London, [1896.] 8°.
No. 25 of "Donajowski's Choir Music".   **F. 172. (25.)**

— Introduction and Variations, Lux Eoi, Sir A. Sullivan.
(Organ.) *B. Williams: London*, [1915?] *obl.* 4°.
No. 2 of "Cloister Echoes".   **f. 314. hh. (11.)**

— Memories of Childhood. Song, words by Mrs. E. Noyes.
Weekes & Co.: London, [1907.] fol.   **H. 1794. vv. (26.)**

— Six Sketches for the Organ. Op. 9. *E. Donajowski: London*,
[1895.] *obl.* fol.   **e. 120. b. (16.)**

— The Story of the Cross. [Hymns.] The words by E. Munro [or
rather, Monro]. *Weekes & Co.: London*, [1907.] 8°.
                  D. 619. z. (18.)

LEE (WILLIAM F.)

— Four Sketches for Brass. ⟨For brass choir and percussion.⟩
[Score and parts.] 18 pt. *Chas. H. Hansen Music Corp.:*
Miami Beach, [1969.] 8°.   **f. 760. z. (1.)**

LEE (WILLIAM HENRY MARKHAM)

— Connaught House School Song. [Four-part song.] The words
by W. W. Morrice. *Novello and Co.: London*, [1902.] 8°.
                  E. 1761. h. (15.)

— Dorset Men. Song, the poem by W. Barnes. *Boosey & Co.:*
London and New York, 1909. fol.   **H. 1794. vv. (25.)**

LEE (WINIFRED)

— The Spring is calling. Song, words and music by W. Lee.
3 no. [In C, D and E flat.] *J. B. Cramer & Co.: London*,
1915. fol.   **H. 1793. s. (40.)**

LEECH (FREDERICK)

— Good night, love! good night. Serenade [begins: "The doves
in the bough"] ... Words by D. Jerrold. [*London?* 1860?] fol.
                  H. 2827. d. (5.)

LEECH (HENRY R.)

— Forgotten Treasures, a series of rare ... classical works for
the Pianoforte. Edited by H. R. Leech. No. 1. *Birmingham*,
[1876.] fol.
No more published.   **h. 1448. e. (18.)**

LEECH (HILARY)

— *See* MOZART (W. A.) [Quintets. K. 452.] Quintett Es dur, *etc.*
⟨Herausgegeben von H. Leech.⟩ [1964.] 4°.   **g. 382. z. (1.)**

LEECH (PERCIVAL)

— Hark! Hark, my Soul! Anthem, words by Dr. F. W. Faber.
P. Leech: Hull, [1925.] 8°.   **D. 619. uu. (4.)**

LEECH (PERCIVAL)

— Sunbeams and Raindrops. Action Song for Children, words
by E. Davey. *P. Leech: Hull*, [1925.] 8°.   **D. 619. vv. (43.)**

— Sunday School Anniversary Hymns and Tunes, words by
E. Davey, *etc.* 8 set. *P. Leech: Hull*, [1924–31.] 8°.
                  D. 619. ww. (3.)

— Under the crimson Banner. Choral March, words by
E. Davey. *P. Leech: Hull*, [1925.] 8°.   **D. 619. uu. (5.)**

LEECHMAN (JOHN) *of London*

— The choral-book, a selection of sacred music ... arranged for
four voices, with appropriate psalms and hymns, *etc.*
London, [1855.] 8°.   **C. 556.**

LEECHMAN (JOHN) *of San Francisco*

— Laugh and the World laughs with you. Song, words by
Col. J. A. Joyce. *J. Church Co.: Cincinnati, etc.*, (1915.) fol.
                  G. 806. mm. (6.)

— Laugh and the World laughs with you. [Part-song for men's
voices.] *J. Church Co.: Cincinnati, etc.*, (1915.) 8°.
                  F. 163. r. (19.)

— The Recessional. Anthem, words by R. Kipling.
J. Leechman: San Francisco, 1906. 8°.   **F. 281. b. (31.)**

— Te Deum laudamus. Chorus for mixed voices, *etc.*
J. Leechman: San Francisco, 1913. 8°.   **F. 1169. u. (15.)**

LEEDAL (J. AINLEY)

— Love's Elysium.— Rêverie danseuse.— Waltz. [P. F.]
J. Bagshaw: Pateley Bridge, [1910.] fol.   **h. 3283. jj. (41.)**

LEEDAM (FRANK)

— A Mellow Melo-Drama. Being a compressed Act of an old
time Drama burlesqued in Song ... Written and composed by
F. Leedham. *Reynolds & Co.: London*, 1931. 4°.
[*Reynolds & Co.'s Concert Party Albums. No. 46.*]   **G. 821.**

— My Lady, Mary Ann. [Song.] Written by Stanley & Frank
Leedam. [With separate voice part.] 2 pt. *Hopwood & Crew:*
London, [1905.] fol.   **H. 3985. q. (14.)**

— She's not the only—. ⟨Song.⟩ Written and composed by
F. Leedam, *etc.* [Staff and tonic sol-fa notation. Voice part.]
Francis, Day & Hunter: London, [1904.] *s. sh.* fol.
                  H. 3985. q. (15.)

— She's not the only—. Humorous song, *etc.* [With separate
voice part.] 2 pt. *Francis, Day & Hunter: London*, [1904.] fol.
                  H. 3985. q. (16.)

— A Silly Song to sing. Humorous Duet ... written by A. S.
Leedam, *etc.* *Reynolds & Co.: London*, (1907.) fol.
                  H. 1794. vv. (27.)

— Two little Apples. ⟨Song.⟩ Written, composed ... by
F. Leedam, *etc.* [Staff and tonic sol-fa notation. Voice part.]
Francis, Day & Hunter: London, [1904.] *s. sh.* fol.
                  H. 3985. q. (17.)

— Two little Apples, *etc.* ⟨Song.⟩ [With separate voice part.] 2 pt.
Francis, Day & Hunter: London, [1904.] fol.
                  H. 3985. q. (18.)

— "Why don't you put one on?" ⟨Song.⟩ Written, composed ...
by F. Leedam, *etc.* [Staff and tonic sol-fa notation. Voice
part.] *Francis, Day & Hunter: London*, [1903.] *s. sh.* fol.
                  H. 3985. q. (19.)

— Why don't you put one on? *etc.* ⟨Song.⟩ [With separate voice
part.] 2 pt. *Francis, Day & Hunter: London*, [1903.] fol.
                  H. 3985. q. (20.)

LEE-DAVIES (L.)
— *See* DAVIES.

LEEDLE
— Leedle Schnapps. Song. *See* NORRIS (Harry B.)

— Leedle Yawcob Strauss. [Song.] *See* NEEDHAM (A. A.) Three Dialect Songs. No. 1.

LEEDS
— Leeds choral Series. *Leeds Music: London*, [1967, *etc.*] 8°.
    F. 1874. d.

— The Leeds Mission Tune-Book with Supplement. With a preface by the Rev. Samuel Bickersteth. pp. 210. *Richard Jackson: Leeds*, [1914.] 8°.
    B. 1170. q.

— Leeds University Song, 1919. *See* BARKER (A. F.)

— Leeds University Song Book. *See* LEEDS.— *University of Leeds.*

LEEDS.— *Church Institute*
— Leeds Church Institute. Hymns for Whitsuntide, 1908. *Leeds Church Institute: Leeds*, [1908.] 8°.
    D. 619. cc. (8.)

— Leeds Church Institute. Hymns for Whitsuntide, 1911. *Leeds Church Institute: Leeds*, [1911.] 8°.
    D. 619. jj. (10.)

— S. James' Church, Leeds. Hymns for Whitsuntide, 1912. *Leeds Church Institute: Leeds*, [1912.] 8°.
    D. 619. qq. (30.)

Leeds Musical Festival
— [For programmes of the Leeds Musical Festivals:] *See* PROGRAMMES.— *Leeds.*

— Leeds Triennial Musical Festival. 1892. Selection from the Works of G. F. Handel. [1892.] 8°. *See* HAENDEL (G. F.) [*Collected Works.—c.*]
    F. 249. c. (1.)

University of Leeds
— Leeds University Song Book. Compiled and edited by the Students' Union of the University of Leeds. *Printed by John Blackburn: Leeds*, 1922. 8°.
    B. 633.

LEEDS (AGNES HONORIA)
— My First Piano Lessons. (With illustrated notes.) *Novello & Co.: London*, 1903. *obl.* fol.
    f. 475.

LEEDS (FREDERIC)
— Benedicite, omnia opera … in … D. *Novello and Co.: London*, (1915.) 8°.
    F. 1169. w. (16.)

— Carmen Colfeianum. [Part-song.] Words by L. L. Duncan. *C. North: London*, 1897. 8°.
    F. 321. n. (23.)

— Colfe Sports' Song. [Song.] Words by L. L. Duncan, *etc.* [*L. L. Duncan: London*, 1907.] 8°.
Carmina Colfana, No. 3.
    D. 837. a. (4.)

— Dreams of thee. Song, with violoncello obbligato, words by T. K. Hervey. *Weekes & Co.: London*, [1888.] fol.
    H. 1788. v. (16.)

— Magnificat and Nunc Dimittis … in … B♭ for men's voices. *Novello, Ewer & Co.: London & New York*, 1874. 8°.
    F. 1170. k. (20.)

— "The Star of Faith." A Christmas Carol for treble voices, words by F. G. Attenborough. *Novello and Co.: London*, [1909.] 8°.
    C. 799. p. (20.)

LEEDS (FREDERIC)
— Te Deum laudamus. Chant setting in D flat. *G. Schirmer: London*, [1916.] 8°.
The Anglican Choir, No. 222.
    F. 1169. x. (11.)

LEEDS (GEOFFREY NORMAN)
— Elegy, for Organ. *Oxford University Press: London*, 1937. 4°.
    g. 575. mm. (21.)

— Music when soft Voices die. Four-part Song … Words by P. B. Shelley. *H. F. W. Deane & Sons: London*, 1929. 8°. [*The Year Book Press Series of Unison and Part-Songs. No.* 328.]
    F. 223.

— *See* PURCELL (H.) [*Doubtful and Supposititious Works.*] Trumpet Voluntary, *etc.* (Arranged by G. Leeds.) 1937. 4°.
    g. 25. d. (17.)

LEEDS (HENRY)
— Military Polka and Galopade, for the Piano Forte. *London*, [1849.] fol.
    h. 941. (22.)

— The Monabia Waltzes for the Piano Forte. *London*, [1850.] fol.
    h. 947. (44.)

LEEDS (RUTH)
— Five Fingerprints. For the young pianist, *etc.* pp. 11. *G. Schirmer: New York*, [1964.] 4°.
    g. 1129. gg. (8.)

LEEDY MANUFACTURING COMPANY
— Leedy Drum Corps Instruction Charts. Lesson One (–Twelve). Series One. *Leedy Mfg. Co.: Indianapolis*, 1928. *s. sh.* fol.
    i. 125.

LEEFLANG (A.)
— Io vivat, air varié pour le Pianoforte, *etc.* *Le Haye*, [1825?] fol.
    g. 272. b. (43.)

— Wilhelmus van Nassauwen & Al is de Prins ook nog zoo klein Al eren Zal hij Koning zijn. Met aangename Variatien voor de Piano Forto … Werk 23. *Bij L. Plattner: Rotterdam*, [1815?] fol.
    g. 443. j. (19.)

LEEFSON (MAURITS)
— Burlesque. Op. 19. No. 6. (Piano.) *J. H. Faunce Co.: Philadelphia*, (1912.) fol.
    h. 3284. g. (3.)

— Second … Canzonetta for Pianoforte, *etc.* *J. H. Faunce Co.: Philadelphia*, (1912.) fol.
    h. 3284. g. (1.)

— Carillon. The Chimes. Op. 19. No. 3, *etc.* (Piano.) *J. H. Faunce Co.: Philadelphia*, (1912.) fol.
    h. 3284. g. (2.)

— Two Compositions for Pianoforte. Op. 17. (No. 1.) The Mill. (No. 2.) The Miller Boys, *etc.* 2 no. *J. H. Faunce Co.: Philadelphia*, (1913.) fol.
    g. 606. n. (36.)

— Elementary Piano Method. Op. 20. (Piano Method. Part II. Op. 21.) (Part III. Op. 22.) 3 pt. *J. H. Faunce Co.: Philadelphia, etc.*, 1910–14. fol.
    h. 3820. y. (3.)

— Recollection of Childhood. Jugenderinnerungen. Five … Pieces for Pianoforte. Op. 18. (No. 1.) Grand Ma speaks. (No. 2.) Cuckoos and Nightingale. (No. 3.) May Pole Dance. (No. 4.) Brigand's Story. (No. 5.) Trouping [*sic*] of the Colours, *etc.* 5 no. *J. H. Faunce Co.: Philadelphia*, (1912.) fol.
    h. 3284. g. (4.)

— *See* HELLER (S.) [25 Études mélodiques. Op. 45. No. 2.] Avalanche. Edited … by M. Leefson. 1917. fol.
    h. 3870. f. (21.)

LEEFSON (Maurits)

— *See* Merkel (G. A.) [Bagatellen. Op. 81. No. 4. Schmetterling.] The Butterfly ... Edited ... by M. Leefson. 1917. fol.
g. 606. cc. (14.)

— *See* Pessard (E. L. F.) Mazurka de Concert ... Edited ... by M. Leefson. 1917. fol.
g. 606. dd. (13.)

— *See* Rakhmaninov (S. V.) [10 Préludes. Op. 23. No. 5.] Prélude ... Edited ... by M. Leefson. 1917. fol.
g. 606. dd. (28.)

— *See* Schulz-Weida (J.) [Jugendlieder ohne Worte. Op. 216. No. 1. Minnelied.] Love-Song ... Edited ... by M. Leefson. 1917. fol.
g. 606. ee. (34.)

— *See* Schumann (R. A.) [Albumblätter. Op. 124. No. 6. Wiegenliedchen.] Cradle Song ... Edited ... by M. Leefson. 1917. fol.
h. 3284. ww. (38.)

— *See* Schumann (R. A.) [43 Clavierstücke. Op. 68. Fröhlicher Landmann.] Happy Farmer ... Edited ... by M. Leefson. 1917. fol.
g. 606. ee. (35.)

LEEK (Teresa)

— My Darling. Song. *London*, [1881.] fol.
H. 1789. a. (34.)

LEELO

— Leelo. Rahvaluule. *See* Saar (M.)

LEENDERS (Maurice)

— La Vieille Chanson que tout le mond chante. Romance [begins: "O ma jeunesse"]. Paroles d'A. Houssaye. *Bruxelles*, 1860. fol.
H. 2830. d. (70.)

LEER (S. von)

— Trois Morceaux, for Violin and Piano. No. 1. Serenade. No. 2. Spring Song. No. 3. Danse in the ancient style. 3 no. *C. Woolhouse: London*, 1905. fol.
h. 1612. p. (24.)

— The New M. P. March. [P. F.] *C. Woolhouse: London*, 1906. fol.
h. 3283. p. (18.)

— Songe des Sirènes. Valse lente. [P. F.] *Price & Reynolds: London*, (1910.) fol.
h. 3286. uu. (44.)

LEERINK (Hans)

— *See* Coninck (Servaas de) Sonate in d ... voor altviool en continuo. [Edited by H. Leerink.] 1948. 4°.
g. 409. aa. (5.)

— *See* Telemann (G. P.) Sonate in D voor altviool en continuo, *etc.* [Edited by H. Leerink.] [c. 1950.] 4°.
g. 401. l. (3.)

LEES

— The Lees of Old Virginia. [Part-song.] *See* Edwards (Sherman) [1776.]

LEES (Benjamin)

— Collage. For string quartet, wind quintet and percussion. [Score.] pp. 37. *Boosey & Hawkes: New York*, [1978.] 8°. [*Hawkes Pocket Scores.* 819.]
E. 901.

— Oboe Concerto. Full score. pp. 72. *Boosey & Hawkes: London, etc.*, [1969.] fol.
h. 1564. h. (1.)

— Oboe Concerto. [Score.] pp. 72. *Boosey & Hawkes: London, etc.*, [1969.] 8°. [*Hawkes Pocket Scores. no.* 853.]
E. 901.

— Oboe Concerto. Oboe & piano. Piano reduction by Marcel G. Frank. [Score and part.] 2 pt. *Boosey & Hawkes: London, etc.*, [1967.] 4°.
g. 1078. m. (3.)

LEES (Benjamin)

— Concerto for Orchestra. Full score. pp. 126. *Boosey & Hawkes: London*, [1961.] 4°.
g. 1620. q. (9.)

— Concerto for String Quartet and Orchestra. Full score. pp. 113. *Boosey & Hawkes: London, etc.*, [1970.] fol.
h. 1568. z. (6.)

— Concerto for String Quartet & Orchestra. [Score.] pp. 113. *Boosey & Hawkes: London, etc.*, [1970.] 8°. [*Hawkes Pocket Scores. no.* 855.]
b. 211.

— Concerto for String Quartet and Orchestra. Piano reduction. [Score and parts.] 5 pt. *Boosey & Hawkes: London, etc.*, [1968.] 4°.
g. 1067. n. (5.)

— Violin Concerto. Full score. pp. 122. *Boosey & Hawkes: London, etc.*, [1966.] 4°.
g. 1620. qq. (6.)

— Violin Concerto. [Score.] pp. 122. *Boosey & Hawkes: London, etc.*, [1966.] 8°. [*Hawkes Pocket Scores. no.* 782.]
b. 211.

— Violin Concerto. Violin & piano. [Score and part.] 2 pt. *Boosey & Hawkes: London, etc.*, [1964.] 4°.
g. 223. ll. (11.)

— Cyprian Songs. Baritone and piano. ⟨Poems by Richard Nickson. [1.] From what green Island. [2.] Wake! for the Night of Shadows. [3.] Still is it as it was. [4.] Over me like soft Clouds.⟩ pp. 18. *Boosey & Hawkes: London, etc.*, [1960.] 4°.
G. 981. nn. (9.)

— Divertimento-burlesca. For chamber orchestra. Full score. pp. 119. *Hawkes & Son: London*, [1958.] 4°.
g. 1620. b. (1.)

— Duo for Flute and Clarinet. [Score.] *Boosey & Hawkes: [London*, 1967.] s. sh. 4°.
i. 260. (8.)

— Three Duos. For flute and clarinet. [Score.] pp. 4. *Boosey & Hawkes: London, etc.*, [1973.] 4°. Two copies.
g. 1780. tt. (13.)

— Fanfare for a Centennial. For brass, timpani and percussion. Full score [and parts]. 14 pt. *Boosey & Hawkes: London*, [1973.] 4°.
g. 860. ee. (4.)

— Fantasia. ⟨For piano.⟩ pp. 12. *Boosey & Hawkes: Lynbrook*, [1957.] 4°.
g. 1126. v. (5.)

— Interlude for String Orchestra. Full score. pp. 21. *Hawkes & Son: London*, [1960.] 4°.
g. 420. mm. (1.)

— Invenzione. Solo violin. pp. 10. *Boosey & Hawkes: London, etc.*, [1967.] 4°.
g. 422. t. (1.)

— Kaleidoscopes. Ten pieces for piano solo. pp. 13. *Hawkes & Son: London* [1959.] 4°.
g. 1128. ii. (8.)

— Two Miniatures. ⟨For wind quintet⟩ ... Flute, oboe, clarinet, horn and bassoon. [Score and parts.] 6 pt. *Boosey & Hawkes: [London*, 1974.] 4°.
g. 1667. c. (5.)

— Odyssey. Piano solo. pp. 12. *Boosey & Hawkes: London, etc.*, [1972.] 4°.
g. 1138. bb. (8.)

— Six ornamental Etudes. For pianoforte. pp. 23. *Boosey & Hawkes: London, etc.*, [1962.] 4°.
g. 272. ww. (3.)

— Three Preludes. Piano solo. pp. 20. *Boosey & Hawkes: London, etc.*, [1968.] 4°.
g. 1128. zz. (16.)

— Prologue, Capriccio and Epilogue. [For orchestra.] Full score. pp. 64. *Hawkes & Son: London*, [1961.] fol.
h. 1567. mm. (1.)

— String Quartet No. 1. [Score and parts.] 5 pt. *Boosey & Hawkes: [New York*, 1954.] 4°. *Fromm Music Foundation Series.* 5.
g. 417. rr. (1.)

— String Quartet N° 2. [Score.] pp. 45. *Boosey & Hawkes: London, etc.*, [1958.] 8°. [*Hawkes Pocket Scores. no.* 700.]
b. 211.

LEES (Benjamin)

— String Quartet N° 2. [Parts.] 4 pt. *Hawkes & Son: London,*
[1957.] 4°.   **g. 417. xx. (9.)**

— Piano Sonata No. 4. pp. 50. *Boosey & Hawkes: London, etc.,*
[1965.] 4°.   **g. 1138. j. (17.)**

— Sonata for two Pianos. pp. 46. *Boosey & Hawkes:* [*New York,*
1954.] 4°.
Fromm Music Foundation Series. 4. Two copies.
                                                              g. 1122. p. (5.)

— Sonata for Violin and Piano. No. 2. [Score and part.] 2 pt.
Boosey & Hawkes: London, etc., [1974.] fol.   **g. 422. p. (5.)**

— Sonata breve. ⟨Piano solo.⟩ pp. 24. *Boosey & Hawkes:*
Lynbrook, [1959.] 4°.   **g. 1128. bb. (13.)**

— Three Songs. For contralto and piano. Poems by Richard
Nickson and William Blake. pp. 19. *Boosey & Hawkes:*
London, etc., [1968.] 4°.   **G. 809. bb. (19.)**

— Songs of the Night. Words by Richard Nickson, *etc.* pp. 19.
Boosey & Hawkes: New York, [1958.] 4°.   **G. 1271. f. (21.)**

— Spectrum. For orchestra. [Score.] pp. 60. *Boosey & Hawkes:*
London, etc., [1978.] 8°.
[*Hawkes Pocket Scores.* 942.]   **E. 901.**

— Study No. 1. For unaccompanied cello. pp. 8. *Boosey &*
Hawkes: London, etc., [1972.] 4°.   **g. 511. r. (4.)**

— Symphony No. 2. Full score. pp. 115. *Hawkes & Son:*
London, [1959.] fol.   **h. 1568. k. (5.)**

— Symphony No. 3. [Score.] pp. 79. *Boosey & Hawkes: London,*
etc., [1975.] 8°.
[*Hawkes Pocket Scores. no.* 893.]   **b. 211.**

— The Trumpet of the Swan. For narrator and orchestra.
Narration by E. B. White, based on his book of the same
title. [Score.] pp. 30. *Boosey & Hawkes: London, etc.,* 1976.
8°.
[*Hawkes Pocket Scores. no.* 897.]   **E. 901.**

— Three Variables. For winds, horn and piano. Score [and
parts]. 5 pt. *Boosey & Hawkes: London,* [1964.] 4°.
                                                 h. 2784. hh. (4.)

— Variations for Piano and Orchestra ... Piano reduction.
[2 P.F. Score.] pp. 46. *Boosey & Hawkes: New York,* [1979.]
4°.   **g. 1529. aa. (9.)**

— Visions of Poets. A dramatic cantata for tenor and soprano
soli and chorus. Based on texts of Walt Whitman. Vocal
score. pp. 94. *Boosey & Hawkes: London, etc.,* [1965.] fol.
                                                 G. 1268. gg. (2.)

LEES (Ernest)

— Are we downhearted? Song, words and music by E. Lees, *etc.*
Warren & Phillips: London, 1914. fol.   **H. 1793. s. (42.)**

— Two Songs. [No. 1.] A Weary Lot is thine. (Scott.) [No. 2.] My
Luve's like a red, red Rose. (Burns.) *Novello and Co.:*
London, [1903.] fol.   **G. 807. z. (32.)**

LEES (George)

— Benedicite, omnia Opera ... set to Chants, with varied
accompaniments to unison verses. *Novello, Ewer and Co.:*
London & New York, [1890.] 8°.   **E. 597. m. (27.)**

— La Cascade d'Amour. Morceau brillant for the Pianoforte.
E. Donajowski: London, [1904.] fol.   **h. 3282. ww. (36.)**

— Click Clack. Polka. [P. F.] *Francis Bros. & Day: London,*
[1886.] fol.   **h. 975. v. (3.)**

— An Elf Dance for the pianoforte. *E. Donajowski: London,*
[1886.] fol.   **h. 1484. s. (31.)**

LEES (George)

— Grey Moors. Song, words by A. Hancock, *etc. Weekes &*
Co.: London, 1913. fol.   **H. 1793. s. (41.)**

— Love's Miracle. Song, words by M. Hedderwick, *etc. Weekes*
& Co.: London, 1913. fol.   **H. 1793. s. (43.)**

— Te Deum Laudamus ... in ... G. *Novello, Ewer & Co.:*
London & New York, [1887.] 8°.   **F. 1170. d. (16.)**

— Vesper, The Lord's Prayer, Commandments, Beatitudes,
Apostles' Creed. [S. A. T. B.] Words of Vesper by ... J. H.
Howard, *etc. W. Paxton & Co.:* [*London,* 1925.] 8°.
                                          E. 605. u. (15.)

LEES (Heath)

— Breathe on me Breath of God. Anthem for 3-part female
voice choir unaccompanied. ⟨Words by Edwin Hatch.⟩ [Staff
and tonic sol-fa notation.] pp. 4. *Roberton Publications:*
Wendover, [1976.] 8°.   **E. 460. pp. (12.)**

— Deep River. [Negro spiritual.] For full female voice choir
unaccompanied. Arranged by Heath Lees. [Staff and tonic
sol-fa notation.] pp. 4. *Roberton Publications: Wendover,*
[1974.] 8°.   **E. 1850. n. (8.)**

— Iona Boat Song. (For a dead king.) Unaccompanied female
choir [S.S.A.]. Words by Hugh S. Roberton. Traditional island
air ... arranged by Heath Lees. [Staff and tonic sol-fa
notation.] pp. 4. *Roberton Publications: Wendover,* [1976.] 8°.
                                          F. 217. x. (15.)

— Iona Boat Song. (For a dead king.) TTBB unaccompanied.
Words by Hugh S. Roberton. Traditional island air ...
arranged by Heath Lees. pp. 4. *Roberton Publications:*
Wendover, [1978.] 8°.   **F. 163. vv. (4.)**

— Two mediaeval Carols. 1. Nowell, Nowell. 2. Jesu, fili Dei.
For 4-part chorus of mixed voices unaccompanied. pp. 8.
Roberton Publications: Wendover, [1975.] 8°.
                                          E. 460. pp. (13.)

LEES (John) *Guitarist*

— [For songs by J. Lees contributed to albums of the group
"Barclay James Harvest":] *See* Barclay James Harvest.

LEES (John) *of Oldham*

— The Platt Memorial march. [P. F.] *Oldham,* [1878.] fol.
                                          h. 1494. q. (7.)

— Remember me, O Lord. Anthem. 1870. *See* Periodical
Publications.—*London.* The Choir, *etc.* No. 189. 1863–78. 4°.
                                          P. P. 1945. hc.

— While Shepherds. Carol. Arranged by J. Lees. [1908.] *See*
Wood and Sons. Wood's Collection of Glees, *etc.* No. 223[a].
[1896, *etc.*] 8°.   **E. 1689.**

LEES (John) *Organist*

— *See* Hymns. [*English.*] The Hymn Tunes of the Church of the
Brethren ... arranged [by J. Lees] for Four Voices in Score.
1824. *obl.* fol.   **E. 497. l.**

LEES (John Kenyon)

— The Balmoral Reel Book. A collection of the most admired
reels, strathspeys, country dances, schottisches, jigs,
quadrilles, hornpipes, polkas, etc. Arranged by J. Kenyon
Lees. [P.F.] pp. 52. *Bayley & Ferguson: London, Glasgow,*
[c. 1910.] fol.   **h. 975. mm. (1.)**

— The Golf Song Book. Edited by Rev. J. Kerr ... Music
[composed and arranged] by J. K. Lees. *J. K. Lees:*
Edinburgh, 1903. 8°.   **F. 637. ii. (2.)**

LEES (JOHN KENYON)

— Haidée Waltzes. [P.F.] pp. 11.　*W. J. Willcocks & C⁰: London,* [1887?] fol.　　　　　　　　　**h. 3870. yy. (8.)**

— Nap Polka. [P. F.]　*J. B. Cramer & Co.: London,* [1883.] fol.　　　　　　　　　**h. 975. v. (4.)**

— Old Edinburgh. Lancers. [Orchestral parts.]　*J. B. Cramer & Co.: London,* [1887.] 8°.　　　　**e. 665. g. (8.)**

— Old Edinburgh. Lancers on ... Scottish Airs. [P. F.]　*J. B. Cramer & Co.: London,* [1887.] fol.　　**h. 975. v. (6.)**

— Pen & Pencil. Waltzes. [P. F.]　*J. B. Cramer & Co.: London,* [1883.] fol.　　　　　　**h. 975. v. (5.)**

— *See* BURNS (Robert) *the Poet.* The Centenary Edition of the Songs of Burns, with symphonies and accompaniments by J.K. Lees, *etc.* ⟨New and revised edition.⟩ [c. 1920.] 4°.　　　　　　　　　　　　　**F. 1821. jj.**

— *See* TODD (George E.) Songs of Caledonia ... Pianoforte accompaniments by J.K. Lees. [c. 1900.] fol.　**H. 1248. ll. (1.)**

LEES (JOSEPH)

— The Lord's Prayer.—Key of D flat. [For four voices.] *J. Lees: Oldham,* [1904.] 8°.　　　**D. 619. v. (12.)**

— The Lord's Prayer. Arranged as a two-part song. [Staff and tonic sol-fa notation.] pp. 3.　*Ascherberg, Hopwood & Crew: London,* [1961.] 8°.
[*Ascherberg Series of Part-songs. no.* 550.]　**F. 1659. a.**

— Rest, weary Soul! [Hymn.] Words by H. L. L.　*Novello, Ewer and Co.: London and New York,* [1893.] *s. sh.* 8°.　　　　　　　　　　　　**D. 619. i. (15.)**

LEES (MARY)

— A Border Lament. Song, *etc.　Weekes & Co.: London,* [1908.] fol.　　　　　　　　　**H. 1794. vv. (28.)**

LEES (NEIL H.)

— The Aul' Drove Road. Song, words by A. MacCormack Thomson. pp. 5.　*Bosworth & Co.: London,* [1953.] 4°.　　　　　　　　　　　　**G. 1276. j. (19.)**

— The Glen o' Tum'lin' Waters. Song, words by A. MacCormack Thomson. pp. 5.　*Bosworth & Co.: London,* [1953.] 4°.　　　　　**G. 1276. j. (20.)**

— The Green Howm Lea. Words by A. MacCormack Thomson. [For S.S.A. Staff and tonic sol-fa notation.] pp. 4.　*Bosworth & Co.: London,* [1953.] 8°.　　**F. 217. n. (28.)**

LEES (NORMAN C.)

— *See* BEETHOVEN (L. van) Für Elise. [K.-H. 59.] Spanish guitar solo. Arr. by N. C. Lees. [1947.] fol.　**h. 400. o. (10.)**

LEES (P. J.)

— *See* DIBDIN (C.) [The Jubilee.] The Warwickshire Lad ... Arranged by P. J. Lees. 1931. 8°.　**E. 1830. b. (30.)**

LEES (SAMUEL)

— Two Christmas Carols. Words by ... O. M. Feilden.　*Novello & Co.: London,* [1901.] 8°.　　　**D. 620. y. (16.)**

— Magnificat and Nunc dimittis, *etc.　Novello & Co.: London,* [1913.] 8°.　　　　　　**F. 1169. v. (15.)**

— Old Rhymes with new Tunes, for piano. (Op. 4.) *A. Hammond & Co.: London,* [1922.] 4°.
The Academic Edition, No. 609.　　**g. 1130. r. (12.)**

LEES (T. A.)

— The Song of the Sword ... [Hymn.] Words by P. J. H. Kirner. *J. Bateman: London,* 1906. 8°.
Mission Band Leaflets, No. 1.　　**D. 619. z. (19.)**

LEES (WILLIAM HENRY)

— Vesper Hymn. To be sung after "The Blessing". [Begins: "Fast fades the Light".]　*Novello and Co.: London,* [1908.] *a card.*　　　　　　**I. 600. c. (217.)**

LEESE (H.)

— Bright Star of Hope, Valse élégante, for the Piano Forte, *etc.* pp. 5.　*Joseph Williams: London,* [c. 1855.] fol.　　　　　　　　　　　**h. 722. qq. (20.)**

— The Dora polka, for the Pianoforte.　*London,* [1865.] fol.　　　　　　　　　**h. 1460. v. (10.)**

LEESE (J.)

— The Elfin-King's March, for the pianoforte.　*E. Ashdown: London,* [1897.] fol.　　**g. 605. p. (22.)**

LEESE (L. E. S.)

— Vesper. Words ... by F. G. Attenborough, *etc.　Novello and Co.: London,* 1914. *a card.*　**I. 600. e. (117.)**

LEESE (WALTER A.)

— American National Hymn. Quartet for mixed Voices. (Words and Music by W. A. Leese.)　*S. Brainard's Sons Co.: Chicago,* 1898. 8°.　　　　　　　　**F. 321. m. (17.)**

LEESON (ALBERT)

— *See* CARYLL (Ivan) *pseud.* and MONCKTON (L.) "The Messenger Boy." Ivan Caryll and Lionel Monckton. (Second selection) ... Valse lente. "Mon secret." Mario Costa. Arranged [for military band] by A. Leeson. 1901. fol. [*Boosey's supplemental military Journal. no.* 430.]　**h. 1544.**

— *See* STUART (Leslie) *pseud.* Leslie Stuart's popular Songs. (Second selection.) [Arranged by] Ernest Allan. Arranged for military band by A. Leeson. 1902. fol.　[*Boosey's supplemental military Journal. no.* 437.]　　　　　　**h. 1544.**

LEESON (CECIL)

— *See* KREISLER (F.) Rondino on a Theme by Beethoven, for Saxophone and Piano. Arranged by C. Leeson. 1938. 4°.　　　　　　　　　　　　**g. 1112. a. (9.)**

LEESON (JOSEPH FREDERICK)

— Before Sebastopol. Hurrah! we grip the Tyrant now. National song ... The poetry by Gerald Massey, *etc.* pp. 5.　*J. Purdie: Edinburgh; Chappell: London,* [c. 1855.] fol.　　　　　　　　　　　**H. 1980. h. (13.)**

— Hark Comrades hark! Boat glee, for four voices, *etc.* pp. 11. *For the Author: Dublin,* [c. 1830.] fol.　**H. 1601. jj. (9.)**

— Hurrah! we grip the Tyrant now. *See* supra: Before Sebastopol.

— O sing to me the auld Scotch songs, ballad, the words by Bethune.　*London,* [1856.] fol.　　**H. 1758. (29.)**

— "O sing to me the auld Scotch songs," ballad, the words by the Rev. Dʳ. Bethune. Second edition.　*Manchester,* [1857.] fol.　　　　　　　　**H. 1771. l. (17.)**

— O sing to me the auld Scotch songs. [Song.] Written by ... Dr. Bethune.　*London,* [1876.] fol.　**H. 1778. x. (61.)**

LEESON (JOSEPH FREDERICK)

— [O sing to me the auld Scotch Sangs.] "The Auld Scotch Songs" ... Arr. for Chorus with Solo, by C. E. Allum. *G. Schirmer: New York*, (1907.) 8°.
G. Schirmer's Octavo Choruses for mixed voices, No. 4692.
F. 321. u. (21.)

LEESON (MICHAEL) and **VALE** (PETER)

— One Man Woman. [Song.] Words and music by Michael Leeson & Peter Vale. pp. 6. *Chappell: London*, [1980.] 4°.
F. 1680. ff. (10.)

LEESWOOD

— Leeswood. [Anthem.] *See* WOODCOCK (Edward W.)

LEETEL

— Leetel Frenchee. [Song.] *See* COX (G. W.)

LEETLE

— Leetle Jan. Song. *See* MOLLOY (J. L.)

— The Leetle Spanish Man. Humorous ballad. *See* L'AMANT (C.)

LEETLÜB, *pseud.* [i.e. BULTEEL.]

— No Surrender. Marche Funèbre, *etc.* [P. F.] *Weekes & Co.: London*, [1902.] fol. **h. 3282. kk. (26.)**

LEEUW (ANDREW DE)

— The Call of the Empire. March for piano. *Wellington Reeves Music Co.: London*, [1914.] fol. **h. 3284. nn. (35.)**

— Empire Day. March for Piano, *etc. Bach & Co.: London*, [1913.] fol. **g. 606. n. (37.)**

— Incidental and Dramatic Music for Pictures. 1st edition ... for piano. *Wellington Reeves Music Co.: London*, [1915.] 4°.
g. 603. gg. (11.)

— A New Year's Dream. Valse. [P. F.] *Wellington Reeves Music Co.: London*, 1914. fol. **h. 3284. nn. (36.)**

LEEUW (CORNELIS DE)

— [For editions of the Dutch Psalter as corrected by Cornelis de Leeuw and first published in 1662:] *See* PSALMS. [*Dutch.*]

— *See* PERS (D. P.) Bellerophon, of Lust tot Wysheyt ... op 't nieuw ... vermeedert ... De Musijck door C. de Leeuw gecorrigeert. 1669. 8°. **Case 64. b. 16. (1.)**

LEEUW (TON DE)

— Cinq études pour le piano (1951). pp. 9. *Donemus: Amsterdam*, [1977.] fol. **g. 1138. kk. (13.)**

LEEUWARDEN. — *Fryske Akademy.— Musicologysk Wurkforbân*

— Lieteboek. Algemiene samling fan âlde en nije Fryske sangen mei piano- en oargellieding. Forsoarge fan it Musicologisk Wurkforbân fan de Fryske Akademy. pp. 160. *R. van der Velde: Ljouwert; Brandenburgh & Co.: Snits*, [1948.] 4°.
G. 1012. a.

Fryske Akademy.— Musikologyske Wurkgroep

— Frysk Lieteboek. Samling fan alde en nije Fryske sangen mei piano-, oargel- en gitaarbegelieding. Fersoarge troch de Musikologyske Wurkgroep fan de Fryske Akademy. (B. Smilde, foarsitter. Th. P. A. Lambooij, skriuwer.) pp. 164. *A. J. Osinga: Boalsert*, 1979. 4°. **F. 1821. kk.**

LEEUWEN (ARY VAN)

— *See* BACH (C. P. E.) Sonate a moll für Flöte allein. Bearbeitet und bezeichnet von A. van Leeuwen. [c. 1950.] 4°.
g. 48. i. (8.)

— *See* BACH (J. S.) [Englische Suiten. No. III.] Gavotte e Musette ... Transcribed by A. van Leeuwen. 1939. 4°.
g. 548. ll. (22.)

— *See* BACH (Wilhelm F.) Sonate für 2 Flöten und Klavier ... [In D.] Herausgegeben und mit Generalbass versehen von A. van Leeuwen, *etc.* [c. 1975.] 4°. **g. 34. a. (2.)**

— *See* COUPERIN (L.) [*Doubtful and Supposititious Works.*] La Précieuse. Louis Couperin—Kreisler. Arranged for Flute and Piano by A. van Leeuwen. 1935. 4°. **g. 70. i. (9.)**

— *See* FRANCŒUR (F.) [*Doubtful and Supposititious Works.*] Siciliano and Rigaudon. (Francois Francœur—Kreisler. Arranged for Flute and Piano by A. van Leeuwen.) 1935. 4°.
g. 70. i. (10.)

— *See* KREISLER (F.) [Klassische Manuskripte. No. 10, 11, 12. Alt Wiener Tanzweisen. No. 1–3. Bearbeitungen für Flöte ... arrangiert von A. van Leeuwen. [1930.] 4°. **g. 70. h. (11.)**

— *See* KREISLER (F.) [Two Songs. No. 1. The Old Refrain.] Alter Refrain. Wiener Lied, Du alter Stefansturm ... Arranged for Flute and Piano by A. van Leeuwen. 1930. 4°.
g. 70. h. (12.)

— *See* SCARLATTI (A.) Solitudine avvenne. *Cantata.* Per soprano con flauto obligato ... Revisione e cadenza di A. van Leeuwen. [c. 1950.] 4°. **G. 770. oo. (2.)**

— *See* SCARLATTI (D.) Two Sonatas. Arranged for flute and harpsichord or piano by A. van Leeuwen, *etc.* [1953.] 4°.
g. 70. p. (14.)

LEEUWEN (M. VAN)

— *See* SCHUBERT (C.) *pseud.* Andante et Cavatine ... arranged by M. van Leeuwen. [1881.] 8°. **f. 400. dd. (11.)**

LEEVES (WILLIAM)
Auld Robin Gray

— Since Jenny she has married. *Jamie's Complaint*, or the Sequel to Auld Robin Gray. [Song.] Set to the Original Air [by W. Leeves], *etc.* [1780?] fol. *See* SINCE. **G. 311. (159.)**

— When the Sheep are in the fauld. *Auld Robin Gray, etc.* [1780?] fol. *See* WHEN. **G. 313. (177.)**

— Auld Robin Gray. [Song.] With the admir'd tune, *etc.* [c. 1780.] *s. sh.* fol. *See* YOUNG. Young Jamie lov'd me weel. **G. 426. kk. (96.)**

— When the Sheep are in the fauld, *etc.* [1782?] fol. *See* WHEN.
G. 383. i. (47.)

— When the Sheep are in the fauld, *etc.* [1785?] fol. *See* WHEN.
G. 383. i. (48.)

— Young Jamie lov'd me weel. *Auld Robin Gray*, with the new ... Tune. [1785?] *s. sh.* fol. *See* YOUNG. **H. 1601. a. (69.)**

— When the Sheep are in the fauld, *etc.* [1790?] fol. *See* WHEN.
H. 1651. b. (61.)

— Young Jamie lov'd me weel. *Auld Robin Gray.* [Song.] With the much admired tune. [c. 1790.] fol. *See* YOUNG.
G. 809. n. (12.)

— When the Sheep are in the Fauld. *Auld Robin Gray.* A favorite Scotch song. [c. 1800.] fol. *See* WHEN.
H. 1601. n. (14.)

— When the Sheep are in the Fauld. *Auld Robin Gray.* A favourite Scotch song. Set to the original favourite air. [c. 1800.] fol. *See* WHEN. **G. 426. pp. (24.)**

LEEVES (WILLIAM)

— Auld Robin Gray. [Song. 1812.] *See* infra: Six sacred airs, *etc.* 1812. fol.   **H. 1416. (1.)**

— Auld Robin Gray. A celebrated Scotch Air ... written [or rather, composed] by the Rev^d Mr. Leeves, & arranged with an accomp^t for the Piano Forte by T. B. Phipps. *G. Walker: London*, [1830?] fol.   **G. 385. ee. (19.)**

— Auld Robin Gray, a favorite Scotch song ... arranged with an accompaniment for the piano forte. pp. 3. [c. 1830.] fol. *See* WHEN. When the Sheep are in the Fauld.   **H. 1652. yy. (21.)**

— "Auld Robin Gray," the celebrated Scotch ballad, as sung by Miss Stephens. pp. 3. [c. 1830.] fol. *See* YOUNG. Young Jamie lov'd me well.   **G. 425. ff. (16.)**

— Auld Robin Gray, ballad. The poetry written by Lady Ann Lindsay ... The symphonies & accompaniments by E. I. Westrop. pp. 5. *Z. T. Purday: London*, [c. 1840.] fol.   **H. 1654. mm. (9.)**

— "Auld Robin Gray;" a ballad, written by Lady A. Lindsay, with the old Scottish tune "The Bridegroom greets," to which it was first adapted, and the more modern air as composed by the Rev^d. W.Leeves, edited, with a pianoforte accompaniment and an historical account of the words and music, by T. Oliphant. *London*, 1843. fol.   **H. 1416. (2.)**

— Auld Robin Gray ... arranged by G. F. Kemp. [1843.] fol. *See* KEMP (G. F.)   **H. 1342. (8.)**

— Auld Robin Gray ... Scotch Ballad ... Newly arranged by H. Schubert. [1854.] fol. *See* SCHUBERT (H.)   **H. 1254. (71.)**

— Auld Robin Gray ... arranged ... by Madame Sainton Dolby. [1865.] fol. *See* DOLBY, afterwards SAINTON (C.H.)   **H. 1772. h. (32.)**

— Auld Robin Gray, ballad, newly arranged by E. Land. *London*, [1868.] fol.   **H. 1559. a. (24.)**

— Auld Robin Gray. *See* WHEN. When the Sheep are in the fauld. [1872.] fol.   **H. 1791. a. (65.)**

— Auld Robin Gray ... (Edited by A. Dobigny.) [1876.] fol. *See* DOBIGNY (A.)   **H. 1778. k. (46.)**

— Auld Robin Gray. Scotch song. *See* YOUNG. Young Jamie lov'd me well. [1877.] fol.   **H. 2324.**

— Auld Robin Gray. Ballad. *London*, [1879.] fol.   **H. 1785. c. (31.)**

— Auld Robin Gray, as originally composed about the year 1770. (Words by Lady Anne Lindsay.) *Novello, Ewer & Co.: London*, [1888.] fol.   **H. 1788. v. (17.)**

— Auld Robin Gray ... harmonized for four voices. [1808.] fol. *See* KNYVETT (W.)   **H. 1220. (64.)**

— Auld Robin Gray. Arranged as a Trio, *etc. See* BANTOCK (*Sir* G.) Six Trios for female ... voices ... v, *etc.* 1908. 4°.   **F. 1689. (5.)**

— Auld Robin Gray. Arranged as a Trio ... by G. Bantock. [1927.] 4°. [*St. Cecilia. Series* 17. *No.* 5.] *See* BANTOCK (*Sir* G.) [Six Trios for female ... voices. No. 5.]   **F. 1526.**

— Auld Robin Gray, arranged for the Pianoforte. [1851.] fol. *See* OSBORNE (George A.)   **h. 641. (19.)**

— Auld Robin Gray, arranged for the piano forte, by G. A. Osborne. [1852?] fol. *See* OSBORNE (George A.)   **h. 62. t. (21.)**

— Auld Robin Gray. Transcribed for the Pianoforte ... by W. Coenen. [1868?] fol. *See* COENEN (W.)   **g. 232. a. (20.)**

— Auld Robin Gray ... for the Pianoforte. [1868.] fol. *See* FOWLES (A. G.)   **h. 2934. (8.)**

LEEVES (WILLIAM)

— Auld Robin Gray ... for the Pianoforte. [1873.] fol. *See* DONAJOWSKI (E.)   **h. 3413. a. (1.)**

— Auld Robin Gray transcribed for the Pianoforte. [1876.] fol. *See* DONAJOWSKI (E.)   **h. 3413. b. (10.)**

— The favorite air Auld Robin Gray ... for the Concertina. [1855.] fol. *See* LEA (H.)   **h. 2336. (17.)**

— The favorite air Auld Robin Gray ... for the guitar. [1835?] fol. *See* LEA (H.)   **h. 259. (3.)**

— *See* BOCHSA (R. N. C.) Grand Fantasia, *etc.* [1824.] fol.   **h. 163. (32.)**

— *See* BURROWES (J. F.) *the Elder.* [A Series of Caledonian Airs. No. 3.] Auld Robin Gray ... with variations for the Piano forte ... by J. F. Burrowes. [1824.] fol.   **h. 450. (21.)**

— *See* HAWLEY (L. E.) Ivanhoe a fanciful transcription ... for the Pianoforte. [1864.] fol.   **h. 1460. p. (50.)**

— *See* KALKBRENNER (F. W. M.) Auld Robin Gray, with variations for the Pianoforte by F. Kalkbrenner. [1845.] fol.   **h. 335. (8.)**

— *See* LINTER (R.) Auld Robin Gray ... with variations for the Pianoforte. [1850.] fol.   **h. 716. (4.)**

— *See* MEYER (F. C.) Auld Robin Gray; Divertimento for the harp. [1821.] fol.   **h. 150. (37.)**

— *See* POTTER (Philip C. H.) Impromptu on the favorite Scotch Air, Auld Robin Gray, for the Piano Forte, *etc.* [1826.] fol.   **h. 361. (5.)**

— The Pigeon. *See* WHY. Why tarries my Love ... An admired ... Song by the Author of Robin Gray, *etc.* [1784.] *s. sh.* 4°.   **P. P. 6154. k.**

— The Pigeon. [Song.] *See* WHY. Why tarries my Love? ... By the Author of Auld Robin Gray. [1790?] fol.   **G. 296. (16.)**

— [The Pigeon.] Why tarries my Love, *etc.* [Song.] [^WM 1794.] fol. *See* WHY.   **H. 1860. ww. (31.)**

— Six sacred airs, accompanied by a Piano Forte or harp, two of them by a violoncello obligato or violin, together with a corrected copy, in its original simplicity, of the well known ballad "Auld Robin Gray". *London*, 1812. fol.   **H. 1416. (1.)**

LEE-WARNER (ALEXANDRA)

— *See* WARNER.

LEEZIE

— Leezie Lindsay. Song. *See* COVER (L.)

— Leezie Lindsay. Song with Descant. *See* DUNHILL (T. F.) Arnold's Descant Series. No. 42.

— Leezie Lindsay. [Part-song.] *See* HEDGES (Anthony J.)

— Leezie Lindsay. [Ballad.] *See* KREISLER (F.)

— Leezie Lindsay. [Unison song.] *See* LAWSON (M. L.) The Songs of the North.

— Leezie Lindsay. [Part-song.] *See* SWEETING (E. T.)

— Leezie Lindsay. Chorus. *See* WARRELL (A. S.)

LEF'

— Lef' away. [Song.] *See* GUION (D. W.)

LE FANU (NICOLA)

— Abstracts and a Frame. For violin and piano. [Score and part.] 2 pt. *Novello: Borough Green*, [1976.] 4°.

g. 500. vv. (6.)

— But Stars remaining. For female voice (unaccompanied). 〈Words adapted from two poems by C. Day Lewis.〉 pp. 4. *Novello & Co.: [Borough Green, London,* 1973.] 4°.

F. 1875. o. (7.)

— Il Cantico dei cantici II. The Song of Songs, Ch. 2. Dramatic scena for female voice (unaccompanied). pp. 4. *Novello & Co.: [Borough Green, London,* 1973.] 4°. **F. 1875. o. (8.)**

— Chiaroscuro for Piano. pp. 24. *Novello & Co.: Borough Green, London,* [1972.] 4°. **f. 760. r. (9.)**

— Christ calls Man home. Processional, anthem, and recessional for two soprano soli and three SATB choirs with divisions (unaccompanied). Words medieval. pp. 39. *Novello: Borough Green,* [1977.] 4°. **F. 538. p. (5.)**

— The little Valleys. *See infra:* [The Valleys shall sing.]

— Quintet for Clarinet and String Quartet. [A facsimile of the composer's autograph. Score.] pp. 55. *Novello: Borough Green,* [1973.] 4°. **g. 420. ll. (6.)**

— Rondeaux. French medieval love poems for tenor voice and horn. [Score.] pp. 9. *Novello: Borough Green,* [1977.] 4°.

F. 1875. g. (8.)

— The Same Day dawns. Fragments from a book of songs for soprano and five players. 〈The words from poems in Tamil, Chinese, Japanese, Kannada and Akkadian.〉 Composer's facsimile score. *Eng.* pp. 31. *Novello: Borough Green,* [1977.] 4°. **F. 1875. g. (9.)**

— Soliloquy for Oboe solo. pp. 3. *Novello & Co.: [London,* 1970.] 4°. **g. 1078. l. (6.)**

— Songs and Sketches for Cellos. A suite of seven pieces for the cello class. [Score.] pp. 24. *Novello & Co.: Borough Green, London,* [1973.] 4°. **g. 512. m. (4.)**

— [The Valleys shall sing.] The little Valleys. Psalm 65, part of v. 9, v. 11 ... For female or boys' voices, SSSS (unaccompanied). pp. 8. *Novello & Co.: Borough Green,* [1975.] 8°.
[*Musical Times.* 1593.] **F. 280. n.**

— Variations for Oboe Quartet. [Score and parts.] 5 pt. *Novello & Co.: Borough Green, London,* [1971.] 4°. **g. 1078. i. (6.)**

— Verses from Psalm 90 ... For soprano solo and two choirs (unaccompanied), *etc.* pp. 4. *Novello & Company: Borough Green,* [1979.] 8°.
[*Musical Times.* 1636.] **F. 280. n.**

LEFAY (CHARLES)

— Ah! Ferdinand. Chansonnette comique [begins: "En descendant de Romainville"]. Paroles de G. Baron & H. d'Arsay. *Paris,* [1882.] fol. **H. 1793. d. (5.)**

— Eh bien, et Gugusse. Chanson [begins: "Tiens, c'est toi"]. Paroles de E. Aupto. *Paris,* [1880.] fol. **H. 1786. e. (22.)**

— Félicité. Polka ... arrangée pour piano par F. Hitz. *Paris,* [1885.] fol. **h. 3285. b. (57.)**

— Mon Homme et mon Chien. Chanson [begins: "L'autr'jour à la fêt"]. Paroles de E. Aupto. *Paris,* [1881.] fol.

H. 1786. e. (23.)

— Ohé! Conducteur. Chansonnette comique [begins: "L'autr' jour un oncle d'Amérique"]. Paroles de H. d'Arsay et G. Baron. *Paris,* [1882.] fol. **H. 1793. d. (6.)**

LEFÉBURE (ANDRÉ)

— L'Amour justifié. Concert. 1er divertissement à 2. voix pour un dessus & une haute-contre, avec simphonie. 〈P. L. Charpentier sculp.〉 [Score.] pp. 37. *Chez l'auteur, etc.: Paris,* [c. 1755.] fol.

H. 56. a. (7.)

— L'Amour Protecteur. Cantatille avec Symphonie, *etc. Chez l'Auteur: Paris,* [1755?] fol. **H. 56. (2.)**

— Andromède. Cantatille à voix seule avec simphonie, *etc.* 〈21e cantatille. Gravé par P. L. Charpentier.〉 [Score.] pp. 9. *Chez l'auteur, etc.: Paris,* [c. 1755.] fol. **H. 56. a. (5.)**

— Le Bouquet de l'amour. Cantatille avec symphonie ... 〈Ve cantatille.〉 Les parolles sont de Mr Heurtaux. Gravée par Mr De Mon Gaultier. [Score.] pp. 9. *Chez Mr de la Chevardiere, etc.: Paris,* [c. 1765.] fol. **H. 56. a. (4.)**

— Dans ce séjour. *Idée, tirée du Temple de Gnide.* Sur l'Air de la Musette de M. Lefebvre: Dans ce Verger, mon Berger &c. [Words.] Par M. Du. M. *[Paris,]* 1760. *s. sh.* 8°.
Mercure de France, July, 1760. **297. d. 24.**

— L'Heureux Dépit. Cantatille à Voix seule avec Simphonie. *Chez l'Auteur: Paris,* [1755?] fol. **H. 56. (1.)**

— Le Lever de l'Aurore. Cantatille avec simphonie, *etc.* 〈15e cantatille.〉 [Score.] pp. 10. *Chez l'auteur, etc.: Paris,* [c. 1755.] fol. **H. 56. a. (3.)**

— La Pensée. Cantatille à Voix Seule avec Simphonie, *etc. Chez l'Auteur: Paris,* [1755?] fol. **H. 56. (3.)**

— 1er(–12e) Recueil d'Ariettes, Airs tendres, Duo &c. avec Accompagnement. *Chés Mr de la Chevardière: Paris,* 1757–58. *obl.* fol.
The pagination is continuous. **R. M. 8. d. 7.**

— Le Rendés vous. Cantatille avec simphonie, *etc.* 〈14e cantatille.〉 [Score.] pp. 8. *Chez l'auteur, etc.: Paris,* [c. 1755.] fol. **H. 56. a. (2.)**

— La Retraite de Borée. Cantatille, à Voix seule avec Simphonie, *etc. Chés l'Auteur: Paris,* [1755?] fol.

H. 56. (4.)

— La Retraite de Borée, cantatille, à voix seule avec simphonie ... 〈VIIe cantatille.〉 Gravée par Mme Pradat. [Score.] pp. 8. *Chés Mr de la Chevardiere, etc.: Paris,* [c. 1765.] fol.

H. 56. a. (6.)

— La Rose. Cantatille à voix seule avec symphonie ... 〈Xe cantatille.〉 Gravée par Mdme Pradat. [Score.] pp. 8. *Chés Mr De la Chevardiere, etc.: Paris,* [c. 1765.] fol. **H. 56. a. (8.)**

— La Saison des plaisirs. Cantatille à voix seule auec symphonie ... 〈1ere cantatille.〉 Gravée par Melle Fauchoux. [Score.] pp. 9. *Chez Mr de la Chevardiere, etc.: Paris,* [c. 1765.] fol. **H. 56. a. (10.)**

— Sapho. Cantatille à voix seule avec symphonie ... 〈XIIeme〉 Gravée par Melle Vandôme. [Score.] pp. 7. *Chez l'auteur, etc.: Paris,* [c. 1755.] fol. **H. 56. a. (1.)**

— [A reissue.] Sapho. Cantatille, *etc. Chez Mr de la Chevardiere, etc.: Paris,* [c. 1765.] fol. **H. 56. a. (9.)**

LEFEBURE (P.)

— *See* BERR (F.) Méthode complète de clarinette ... Nouvelle édition entièrement revue annotée et augmentée par P. Lefebure, *etc.* [1956?] fol. **h. 1158. c.**

LEFÉBURE WÉLY (LOUIS JAMES ALFRED)

— Ten Nocturnes and Mazurkas for the Pianoforte by ... Wely, *etc. See* BOOSEY AND CO. Boosey's Musical Cabinet. No. 10. [1861, *etc.*] 4°. **F. 160.**

LEFÉBURE WÉLY (Louis James Alfred)

— A Series of Compositons for the Organ. Edited ... by
A. Whittingham. 16 no. *E. Ashdown: London*, [1886.] fol.
h. 2704. a. (3.)

— L'Adoration (andante célèbre de Lefébure-Wély) arranged
for Violoncello (Violin or Horn) and Piano by G. F. Cooke.
London, [1879.] fol. **h. 3213. q. (23.)**

— Aimons toujours! Mélodie. Poésie de Victor Hugo, *etc.* [Song.
With a portrait and a facsimile.] pp. 3. *In:* Album du Gaulois.
Vol. 1. [1869.] fol. **H. 2349. a.**

— Air Pompadour, caprice pour Orgue expressif. *Paris*, [1872.]
fol. **h. 2575. d. (8.)**

— Trois airs natinaux [*sic*]. Arrangés par Lefébure-Wély. ⟨N° 1.
La Marseillaise. Paroles et musique de Rouget de Lisle. Avec
les couplets autographes et le portrait de l'auteur.—N° 2. Le
Départ. N° 3. La Parisienne.⟩ no. 1. *Heugel & c^ie: Paris*,
[1870?] fol.
*Imperfect; wanting no. 2, 3. The portrait and the facsimile are
on a separate leaf bearing the imprint "Typographie Charles de
Mourges frères ... 1870".* **H. 1980. e. (9.)**

Andante

— The Hymn of Nuns, andante for the Organ. *London*, [1876.]
fol. **h. 2731. d. (33.)**

— Andante ... [in F] for the Organ. *J. Williams: London*,
[1897.] fol. **h. 2733. (1.)**

— The Hymn of Nuns. *See* PRIOR (M.) The Hymn of Nuns ...
for the Pianoforte. [1881.] fol. **h. 2704. o. (7.)**

— Chœur des Religieuses ... Andante ... transcribed for the
pianoforte by A. Whittingham. *R. Cocks & Co.: London*,
[1887.] fol. **h. 2704. a. (6.)**

— The Gift of Rest, Sacred Song, words by M. I. Ball, adapted
to the ... Andante. *R. Cocks & Co.: London*, [1887.] fol.
H. 879. e. (12.)

———————

— Andante, A flat. [Organ.] *See* BEST (W.T.) Cecilia, *etc.*
Book XXXII. [1883, *etc.*] obl. fol. **e. 1106.**

— Andantino. [Organ.] *See* BEST (W. T.) Cecilia, *etc.* Book XIII.
[1883, *etc.*] obl. fol. **e. 1106.**

— Les Anges. Romance ... Paroles de Mme Laure Jourdain.
⟨Acc^t [for guitar] par J^h Vimeux.⟩ *Chez Canaux: Paris*,
[c. 1840.] 8°. **E. 1717. l. (28.)**

— Après la victoire, marche pour piano. Op. 87. *London*,
[1855.] fol. **h. 1293. (7.)**

— Auré. *See* infra: La retraite militaire.

— Ave Maria. [Orchestral parts.] *London*, [1885.] 8°.
f. 410. k. (5.)

— Ave Maria, sur l'Adagio en Ut mineur de Beethoven. *Paris*,
[1876.] fol. **H. 1028. f. (26.)**

— Les babillardes, caprice, pour piano. Op. 117. *Paris*, [1858.]
fol. **h. 1293. a. (8.)**

— La Bergerie, scène champêtre pour Piano. Op. 138. *London*,
[1860.] fol. **h. 1293. b. (4.)**

— La Bergerie, scène champêtre pour piano ... Op. 138. pp. 9.
Joseph Williams: London, [c. 1860.] fol. **h. 61. u. (7.)**

— La Bergère. Scène champêtre pour Piano. *Paris*, [1860.] fol.
h. 1293. a. (22.)

— Boléro pour Piano. Op. 175. *Paris*, [1868.] fol.
h. 1293. c. (9.)

— Bourrée & La Danse des Paysans pour le Pianoforte.
London, [1877.] fol. **h. 1293. b. (23.)**

LEFÉBURE WÉLY (Louis James Alfred)

— La brise de Mai. Bluette pour piano. Op. 82. *London*, [1853.]
fol. **h. 1292. (24.)**

— Le Calme du Matin. *See* infra: [Deux mélodies. Op. 60.
No. 1.]

— Le Calme du soir. *See* infra: [Deux mélodies. Op. 60. No. 2.]

— Caprice de Salon, Qui s'y frotte s'y pique, pour Piano.
Op. 178. *Paris*, [1868.] fol. **h. 1293. c. (7.)**

— Caprice militaire pour le Piano à quatre mains. *Paris*, [1860.]
fol. **h. 1293. a. (17.)**

— Les Caquets du Couvent, esquise symphonique pour
Orgue-harmonium. *Paris*, [1868.] fol. **h. 2575. b. (19.)**

— Les Caquets du Couvent, esquisse symphonique pour Piano à
quatre mains. Op. 179. *Paris*, [1868.] fol. **h. 1293. c. (8.)**

— La Cascade, morceau de Salon. [P.F.] *London*, [1854.] fol.
h. 1292. (28.)

— [Another edition.] La cascade, morceau de salon. [P.F.]
London, [1854.] fol. **h. 1292. (30.)**

— [Another edition.] La cascade, morceau de salon. [P.F.]
London, [1854.] fol. **h. 1292. (29.)**

— La Cascade, morceau de Salon. [P.F.] *London*, [1855.] fol.
No. 668 of the "Musical Bouquet". **H. 2345.**

— La Cascade. Morceau de salon pour le Piano. *London*,
[1860.] fol. **h. 1293. b. (10.)**

— Chanson du Moulin, et Musique de Genève, deux petites
pièces de salon pour Piano. 2 no. *Paris*, [1868.] fol.
h. 1293. c. (15.)

— Le Chant du Cygne, romance sans paroles pour Harmonium.
Op. 190. *Paris*, [1870.] fol. **h. 2575. b. (20.)**

— La Chasse, fantaisie-valse pour Piano. Op. 135. *London*,
[1860.] fol. **h. 1293. b. (5.)**

— La Chasse. Fantaisie-Valse pour Piano. *Paris*, [1860.] fol.
h. 1293. a. (19.)

— Choeur des Religieuses. *See* supra: [Andante.]

Les Cloches du monastère

— Les Cloches du monastère. Nocturne pour piano ... Op. 54.
pp. 7. *Chez le suc^r de G. H. Hedler: Francfort s/M.*, [1850?]
fol. **Hirsch M. 1303. (12.)**

— Les Cloches du monastère, Nocturne pour Pianoforte. Op. 54.
pp. 7. *Chappell: London*, [1852.] fol. **h. 1292. (3.)**

— Les cloches du monastère; nocturne, pour le pianoforte.
Op. 54. pp. 7. *Wessel & Co.: London*, [1852.] fol.
h. 1292. (7.)

— Les Cloches du monastère. Nocturne pour le piano ...
Op. 54. pp. 7. *Chez Ed. Bote & G. Bock: Berlin, Posen*,
[1852?] fol. **h. 60. y. (5.)**

— Wély's nocturne, Op. 54. Edited and fingered by J. Benedict.
London, [1852.] fol.
No. 9 of the 2nd series of Benedict's pianoforte library.
h. 1233. b. (5.)

— Les cloches du monastère, *etc.* pp. 5. *T. E. Purday: London*,
[1853.] fol. **h. 1292. (2.)**

— Les cloches du monastère, *etc.* pp. 7. *D'Almaine & Co.:
London*, [1853.] fol. **h. 1292. (4.)**

— Les cloches du monastère, *etc.* pp. 7. *Boosey & Sons:
London*, [1853.] fol. **h. 1292. (5.)**

— Les cloches du monastère, *etc.* pp. 7. *R. Mills: London*,
[1853.] fol. **h. 1292. (6.)**

LEFÉBURE WÉLY (Louis James Alfred)

— Lefébure-Wély's "Les cloches du monastère," edited by L. Sloper. pp. 7. *Campbell, Ransford & Co.: London*, [1853.] fol.
[*E. Sloper's edition of Pianoforte works. No.* 33.]　　**h. 737.**

— Les cloches du Monastère, nocturne pour Piano. Op. 54. pp. 5. *Charles Jefferys: London*, [1854.] fol.　**h. 1292. (8.)**

— Les Cloches du Monastère, fantaisie brillante. [P.F.] *London*, [1855.] fol.
No. 505 *of the "Musical Bouquet".*　　**H. 2345.**

— Les Cloches du monastère, nocturne ... Op. 54. pp. 7. *Jewell & Letchford: London*, [c. 1855.] fol.　　**h. 3865. rr. (17.)**

— Les Cloches du monastère, nocturne pour le piano ... Op:54. 2ᵉ édition. pp. 9. *Alex. Grus aîné: Paris*, [c. 1855.] fol.
　　g. 352. ff. (9.)

— Les cloches du monastère, nocturne pour piano. Op. 54. pp. 5. *H. White & Son: London*, [1857.] fol.　**h. 1293. a. (1.)**

— Les Cloches du Monastère. [P.F.] pp. 5. *W. Williams & Co.: London*, [1860.] fol.　　**h. 1293. b. (2.)**

— Les Cloches du Monastère. Nocturne pour le Piano. Op. 54. pp. 5. *Chez les fils de B. Schott: Mayence*, [1863.] fol.
　　h. 1293. c. (2.)

— Les Cloches du Monastère. *See* SLOPER (E.H.L.) The Students' Library, *etc.* No. 57. [1863.] fol.　**h. 736. a. (30.)**

— Les Cloches du Monastère. Nocturne. [P.F.] pp. 7. *L'Enfant & Hodgkins: London*, [1864.] fol.　　**h. 1293. b. (12.)**

— Les Cloches du monastère. Nocturne pour piano. ⟨Op. 54. New edition, revised and fingered by W. Vincent Wallace.⟩ pp. 7. *Robert Cocks & Co.: London*, [c. 1870.] fol.
[*W. Vincent Wallace's Edition of Standard Piano Forte Works. no.* 8.]　　**h. 628. e.**

— Les Cloches du Monastère, pour le Piano. pp. 4. *E. Donajowski: London*, [1876.] fol.　　**h. 1293. b. (21.)**

— Les Cloches du Monastère. Nocturne. *See* RUMMEL (J.) Trois Pièces de Salon, *etc.* No. 1. [1877.] fol.　**h. 523. e. (30.)**

— Les Cloches du Monastère, fantaisie brillante. [P.F.] pp. 4. *Howard & Co.: London*, [1878.] fol.　　**h. 3275. j. (27.)**

— Les Cloches du Monastère ... for the Pianoforte. pp. 4. *W. Marshall & Co.: London*, [1878.] fol.　**h. 3275. j. (28.)**

— Les Cloches du Monastère, nocturne for the Pianoforte. *London*, [1879.] fol.
No. 576 *of C. Boosey's "Universal" music.*　　**H. 2324.**

— Les Cloches du Monastère. [P. F.] *See* DUFAURE (A.) Crotchets & Quavers, *etc.* No. 5. [1893.] fol.　　**h. 3416. c.**

— Les Cloches du Monastère ... Transcribed for the pianoforte by A. Dobigny. *E. Donajowski: London*, [1898.] fol.
　　h. 3282. f. (23.)

— Les Cloches du monastère. Nocturne for the pianoforte ... Op. 54. pp. 4. *W. H. Broome: London*, [c. 1900.] fol.
　　h. 3870. uu. (22.)

— Les Cloches du Monastère. Nocturne. [P.F.] pp. 5. *W. Paxton: London*, [c. 1900.] fol.
Part of "Macfarlane Edition".　　**h. 3870. uu. (3.)**

— Les Cloches du monastère, *etc.* [P. F.] *See* HEMERY (V.) Pleasing Fancies, *etc.* No. 5. [1901.] fol.　**h. 3528. b.**

— Les Cloches du monastère. Nocturne pour piano. ⟨Op. 54. Revised and fingered by W. Vincent Wallace.⟩ pp. 5. *William Reeves: London*, [c. 1910.] fol.　**h. 61. xx. (25.)**

— Les cloches du Monastère, arranged as a duet. [P. F.] pp. 9. *Campbell, Ransford & Co.: London*, [1854.] fol.　**h. 1292. (9.)**

LEFÉBURE WÉLY (Louis James Alfred)

— Lefébure-Wély's Les Cloches du monastère nocturne, arranged for two performers on the pianoforte by J. Rosenthal. Op. 119. pp. 13. *D'Almaine & Co.: London*, [1855.] fol.　　**h. 1272. (15.)**

— [Les] Cloches du monastère. [Op. 54.] Arrgd. by O. Barri. Piano conductor [and orchestral parts]. 18 pt. *J. R. Lafleur & Son: London*, [1892.] 8°.　　**f. 800. (806.)**

— Nocturne. Les Cloches du monastère ... [Op. 54.] Transcribed for military band by J. A. Kappey. [Parts.] 26 pt. *In:* BERGER (R.) Valse très lente. "Amoureuse," *etc.* 1902. fol. [*Boosey's military Journal. ser.* 112. *no.* 1.]　　**h. 1549.**

— Convent Bells. [Violin and P. F.] *See* STERKEL (C.) Duos, *etc.* No. 18. [1875–86.] fol.　　**h. 1722.**

— *See* BIRCH (W.H.) Les Cloches du Monastère polka, *etc.* [1856.] fol.　　**h. 2957. (2.)**

— La Clochette du pâtre, nocturne, pour piano ... Op. 102. pp. 9. *Chappell: London*, [1856.] fol.　**h. 61. oo. (5.)**

— La clochette du pâtre, nocturne pour piano. Op. 102. *Paris*, [1856.] fol.　　**h. 1293. (20.)**

— La clochette du Pâtre. *See* RICHARDS (H.B.) The pianist's album, *etc.* [1859.] fol.　　**h. 1390.**

— Wely's Clochette du Pâtre, arranged as a Pianoforte duet. *London*, [1860.] fol.　　**h. 1293. b. (3.)**

— La Clochette du Pâtre. *See* VIANESI (A.) Fanciulla che fai? [1872.] fol.　　**H. 2741. (17.)**

— Communion pour orgue. [1859.] *See* NIEDERMEYER (L.) La Maîtrise, *etc.* 3ᵐᵉ Année. Grande Maîtrise. No. 2. [1857–61.] fol.　　**H. 1237.**

— [Communion.] Andante, G major. [Organ.] *See* BEST (W. T.) Cecilia, *etc.* Book XXXII. [1883, *etc.*] *obl.* fol.　**e. 1106.**

— Concert à la pension, fantaisie à quatre mains. Op. 93. *Paris*, [1856.] fol.　　**h. 1293. (11.)**

— Concert à la pension, fantasia as a duet. [P.F.] Op. 93. *London*, [1856.] fol.　　**h. 1293. a. (2.)**

— Concertante school for the pianoforte, consisting of a collection of morceaux de genre, études de style, pièces caractéristiques ... for two performers on one pianoforte. *London*, [1854.] fol.　　**h. 1292. (38.)**

— Le Couronnement de la rosière, bluette pastorale pour piano. Op. 80. *London*, [1853.] fol.　　**h. 1292. (22.)**

— La Czarienne Marche. *See infra:* Pensées d'Album. No. 2.

— La danse des oiseaux, bluette pour piano. Op. 78. *London*, [1853.] fol.　　**h. 1292. (20.)**

— La Danse des paysans, for the pianoforte. *London*, [1854.] fol.　　**h. 1292. (31.)**

— Le Défilé, pas redoublé pour deux Pianos. Op. 180. *Paris*, [1868.] fol.　　**h. 1293. c. (12.)**

— Le Défilé ... à 4 mains. *Paris*, [1868.] fol.　**h. 1293. c. (13.)**

— Délaissée! Rêverie, pour piano. Op. 116. *Paris*, [1858.] fol.
　　h. 1293. a. (7.)

— The Derby Galop. *See infra:* Pensées d'Album. No. 6.

— Douce souvenance, nocturne. [P.F.] Op. 119. *Paris*, [1858.] fol.　　**h. 1293. a. (10.)**

— Duo brillant sur l'Opéra de H. Reber, le Père Gaillard, pour Piano à quatre mains. Op. 75. *London*, [1853.] fol.
　　h. 1292. (17.)

LEFÉBURE WÉLY (Louis James Alfred)

— Duo Symphonique pour deux Pianos. Op. 163. *Paris*, [1866.]
fol.   **h. 1293. c. (4.)**

— 2ème Duo Symphonique pour deux Pianos. Op. 181. *Paris*,
[1868.] fol.   **h. 1293. d.**

— Wély's Les échoes de la Loire. New edition. *London*, [1854.]
fol.   **h. 1292. (32.)**

— Elégie pour harmonium. Op. 96. *London*, [1856.] fol.
                                                h. 2575. (7.)

— Elégie pour orgue mélodium. Op. 96. *Paris*, [1856.] fol.
                                                h. 2575. (6.)

— Élégie. [Organ.] *See* BEST (W. T.) Cecilia, *etc.* Book XXXV.
[1883, *etc.*] *obl.* fol.   **e. 1106.**

— Élévation pour orgue. [1860.] *See* NIEDERMEYER (L.) La
Maîtrise, *etc.* 4ᵉ Année. No. 2. [1857–61.] 8°. **F. 623.**

— Esmeralda, caprice pour Piano. Op. 177. *Paris*, [1868.] fol.
                                                h. 1293. c. (11.)

— Étude, moyen-age, pour le piano. Op. 76. *London*, [1853.]
fol.   **h. 1292. (18.)**

— Trois études de Salon pour le Piano Forte. 3 no. *London*,
[1853.] fol.   **h. 1292. (37.)**

— 24 études mélodiques pour piano. *Paris*, [1860.] fol.
                                                h. 1077.

— Fantaisie sur la Flûte Enchantée de Mozart, pour Orgue
Harmonium. *Paris*, [1866.] fol.   **h. 2575. b. (17.)**

— Fantaisie sur les sabots de la marquise, opéra de
E. Boulanger pour piano à quatre mains. Op. 86. *London*,
[1855.] fol.   **h. 1293. (6.)**

— Fêtes de Noel, 3 fantaisies pour piano. Op. 129. 3 no.
London, [1858.] fol.   **h. 1293. a. (14.)**

— Fêtes des abeilles, caprice pour piano. Op. 127. *Londres*,
[1859.] fol.   **h. 1293. a. (12.)**

— Florence, mazurka, pour piano. Op. 100. *London*, [1856.] fol.
                                                h. 1293. a. (4.)

— [Florence.] Mazurka élégante, pour piano. Op. 100. *Paris*,
[1856.] fol.   **h. 1293. (18.)**

La garde montante

— La Garde Montante ... arranged by W. H. Montgomery.
[Orchestral parts.] *London*, [1879.] 8°.
Part of the "Alliance Musicale".   **f. 400. u. (11.)**

— La Garde montante. Caprice. [Op. 71.] [Parts for fife and
drum band.] 40 pt. *J. R. Lafleur & Son: London*, [1898.] 8°.
Part of "J. R. Lafleur & Son's Fife & Drum Journal".
Including several copies of various parts.   **f. 800. (807.)**

— La garde montante, caprice de genre pour piano. Op. 71.
London, [1855.] fol.   **h. 1293. (4.)**

— [Another edition.] La garde montante, caprice de genre pour
piano. Op. 71. *London*, [1855.] fol.   **h. 1293. (5.)**

— La Garde Montante, caprice de genre pour Piano. *London*,
[1855.] fol.
No. 775, 776 of the "Musical Bouquet".   **H. 2345.**

— La garde montante, caprice de genre, pour piano. Op. 71.
London, [1857.] fol.   **h. 1293. a. (1ᵇⁱˢ)**

— La Garde Montante ... arranged for the Pianoforte by
L. Williams. *London*, [1878.] fol.   **h. 3275. j. (26.)**

— La Garde Montante, caprice. [P.F.] *London*, [1880.] 8°.
No. 573 of the "Alliance Musicale. Album Bijou". **f. 406.**

LEFÉBURE WÉLY (Louis James Alfred)

— The gift of rest. *See* supra: [Andante.]

— Grande fantaisie de concert pour piano et melodium, sur des
motifs de Robin des Bois de C. M. Weber, *etc.* Op. 97. *Paris*,
[1856.] fol.   **h. 1293. (15.)**

— Grande valse pour piano. Op. 89. *London*, [1855.] fol.
                                                h. 1293. (9.)

— Les Grandes Orgues. Vade Mecum des églises, *etc. Paris*,
[1877.] 8°.   **f. 139.**

— Guillaume Tell [by G. A. Rossini] transcription pour Piano.
Paris, [1875.] fol.   **h. 1293. e. (1.)**

— La guirlande de Roses. 5 grandes valses brillantes pour le
piano à quatre mains. *London*, [1846.] fol.   **h. 939. (48.)**

— L'heure de l'Angelus, fantaisie pastorale pour Piano. Op. 136.
London, [1860.] fol.   **h. 1293. b. (6.)**

— L'heure de l'Angelus. Fantaisie pastorale pour Piano. *Paris*,
[1860.] fol.   **h. 1293. a. (20.)**

— L'heure de la prière, nocturne pour le piano-forte. *London*,
[1854.] fol.   **h. 1292. (33.)**

— Hop! Caprice brillant pour Piano. Op. 186. *Paris*, [1869.] fol.
                                                h. 1293. c. (16.)

— Hop, caprice brillant pour Piano. *London*, [1876.] fol.
                                                h. 1293. e. (6.)

— Hop. Caprice brillant. (Arranged as Pianoforte duet by
B. Tours.) *London*, [1877.] fol.   **h. 1293. e. (7.)**

— The Hymn of Nuns. *See* supra: [Andante.]

— Il Dort. Berceuse, pour Harmonium, Piano, Violon ou
Violoncelle. *Paris*, [1859.] fol.
No. 4 of "La Touraine au XVᵉ siècle".   **h. 3213. c. (17.)**

— Impressions de voyage, trois morceaux caractéristiques, pour
le piano. Op. 113, 114, 115. 3 no. *Paris*, [1858.] fol.
                                                h. 1293. a. (6.)

— Impromptu pour Piano. Op. 182. *London*, [1868.] fol.
                                                h. 1293. b. (14.)

— Impromptu pour Piano. Op. 182. *Paris*, [1868.] fol.
                                                h. 1293. c. (6.)

— Les jeunes recrues (the young recruits). Caprice militaire pour
piano. Op. 79. *London*, [1854.] fol.   **h. 1292. (21.)**

— Joséphine, Grand galop brillant, pour le piano forte. Op. 62.
London, [1852.] fol.   **h. 1292. (10.)**

— [Josephine.] Wély's Grand Galop brillant, Op. 62. Edited and
fingered by J. Benedict. *London*, [1852.] fol.
No. 10 of the 2nd series of Benedict's pianoforte library.
                                                h. 1233. b. (6.)

— [Josephine.] Grand galop brillante pour Piano. Op. 62.
London, [1856.] fol.
No. 1091, 1092 of the "Musical Bouquet".   **H. 2345.**

— Juanita, seguedille pour le piano-forte. *London*, [1854.] fol.
                                                h. 1292. (34.)

— Les Lagunes. Nocturnes. *See* infra: Pensées d'Album. No. 3.

— Larmes du coeur! (tears of the heart) romance sans paroles
pour le piano. Op. 84. *London*, [1854.] fol.   **h. 1292. (26.)**

— Leçons méthodiques pour Orgue-Mélodium. *Mayence*,
[1860?] fol.   **h. 2575. d. (9.)**

— The Madeleine. *See* infra: [Offertoires. Op. 35. no. 4.]

— La Marguerite. Romance ... Paroles de Mᵐᵉ Laure Jourdain.
⟨Accᵗ [for guitar] par Jʰ Vimeux.⟩ *Chez Canaux: Paris*,
[c. 1840.] 8°.   **E. 1717. l. (37.)**

LEFÉBURE WÉLY (Louis James Alfred)

— La Maritza, orientale pour Piano. *Paris,* [1864.] fol.
h. 1293. c. (3.)

Deux melodies. Op. 60

— Deux mélodies, nocturnes. No. 1. Le calme du matin. No. 2. Le calme du soir, pour piano. 2 no. *Chappell: London,* [1853.] fol.
Imperfect; wanting no. 1. h. 1458. d. (9.)

— Deux mélodies, nocturnes, No. 1. Le calme du matin. No. 2. Le calme du soir. 2 no. *London,* [1854.] fol. h. 1292. (27.)

— [No. 1.] Le Calme du Matin, nocturne No. 1 pour le Piano. *London,* [1855.] fol.
No. 681, 682 of the "Musical Bouquet". H. 2345.

— [No. 1.] Le calme du matin, nocturne pour piano. Op. 60. *D'Almaine & Co.: London,* [1857.] fol. h. 1458. d. (8.)

— [No. 2.] Le Calme du Soir, second nocturne. [P.F.] *London,* [1855.] fol.
No. 683 of the "Musical Bouquet". H. 2345.

— Mère et enfant, nocturne, pour piano. Op. 125. *Londres,* [1859.] fol. h. 1293. a. (11.)

— Méthode pour l'harmonium. pp. 25. *Chez S. Richault: Paris,* [c. 1845.] fol. h. 3819. e. (1.)

— Mignon, opéra d'A. Thomas, "Connais-tu le pays," romance paraphrase pour Violon, Orgue et Piano. *Paris,* [1867.] fol.
h. 2575. b. (18.)

— The Modern Organist, a collection of Organ pieces in all styles. The adaptation to English organs by W. T. Best. *London,* [1869.] *obl.* fol. e. 168. a.

— Six Morceaux, Elévation, Verset, Offertoire, Prélude, Communion, Marche. [Organ.] *Paris,* [1863.] *obl.* fol.
e. 174. b. (7.)

— Le Myosotis. Lied. *See* infra: Pensées d'Album. No. 5.

— Napoléon III., caprice militaire pour le Piano à quatre mains. Op. 132. *London,* [1860.] fol. h. 1293. b. (7.)

— Le nid des fauvettes (the tom-tit nest). Caprice de genre pour piano. Op. 83. *London,* [1854.] fol. h. 1292. (25.)

La Noce du village

— La Noce du village, presto, pour le piano, *etc.* pp. 5. *Cramer, Beale & Cᵒ.: London,* [1850?] fol. h. 62. ii. (6.)

— La noce du village pour le piano-forte. pp. 5. *R. Mills: London,* [1852.] fol. h. 1292. (35.)

— La noce du village for the pianoforte. *London,* [1852.] fol.
No. 1 of the "Modern Pianiste's Repertoire". h. 1447. (1.)

— Lefébure-Wély's "La noce au village," edited by L. Sloper. *London,* [1853.] fol.
[*L. Sloper's edition of Pianoforte works. No. 27.*] h. 737.

— La Noce du Village, fantasia. [P.F.] *London,* [1854.] fol.
No. 530 of the "Musical Bouquet". H. 2345.

— La Noce du Village, pour le Piano. *London,* [1859.] fol.
h. 1293. b. (1.)

— La Noce au Village. [P.F.] *London,* [1876.] fol.
h. 1293. b. (22.)

— La Noce du Village. *See* SCHUBERT (A.) L'Ecole d'Industrie, *etc.* No. 12. [1853.] fol. h. 787. (1.)

— Nuit d'Orient. Rêverie. *See* infra: Pensées d'Album. No. 1.

— O Salutaris. Solo de Basse. [1858.] *See* NIEDERMEYER (L.) La Maîtrise, *etc.* 2ᵉ Année. No. 9. [1857–61.] fol. H. 1237.

LEFÉBURE WÉLY (Louis James Alfred)

— O Salutaris, pour Soprano et Contralto, avec accompagnement d'Orgue, *etc.* [Words by St. Thomas Aquinas.] *Paris,* [1860?] fol. H. 1028. a. (4.)

— O Salutaris, pour Chant et Orgue. *Paris,* [1876.] fol.
H. 1028. f. (25.)

— O Salutaris. Solo de Soprano ou Ténor avec accompagnement d'orgue. *Paris,* [1885.] fol.
H. 1187. j. (16.)

— Six Offertoires for the organ. Op. 34. Edited ... by J. Partridge. 6 no. *E. Ashdown: London,* [1885.] fol.
h. 2704. a. (5.)

Offertoires. Op. 35

— "Offertoire," for the organ. Op. 35. Edited by W. Rea. 6 no. *London,* [1857.] fol. h. 2704.

— Original Compositions for the Organ. (Six grand Offertoires.) *London,* [1866.] *obl.* fol. e. 168.

— Grand Offertoires for the Organ ... Op. 35. Edited by H. Walton. *Boosey and Co.: London & New York,* [1877.] 4°. [*Boosey's Sacred Musical Cabinet. No. 7.*] F. 160. b.

— Six grand Offertoires for the organ ... transcribed, with pedal obbligato, by A. Whittingham. 6 no. *E. Ashdown: London,* [1886.] fol. h. 2704. a. (4.)

— Lefébure Wely's Grand Organ Offertoires, Op. 35. Arranged for the Harmonium by E. F. Rimbault. *Boosey and Co.: London & New York,* [1877.] 4°.
[*Boosey's Sacred Musical Cabinet. No. 6.*] F. 160. b.

— Wély's four grand Offertories (Op. 35), arranged (for the harmonium) by Dʳ. Rimbault. *See* CABINET. The Cabinet Organ Books. Vol. 16. [1886.] 4°. f. 318.

— [No. 2.] St. Eustache. Reminiscence for the pianoforte ... arranged by C. Mahler. *R. Cocks & Co.: London,* [1883.] fol.
h. 2704. a. (8.)

Offertoires. Op. 35. No. 4

— Offertoire in G for the Organ ... Abbreviated ... and edited by E. F. Rimbault. *London,* [1876.] fol. h. 2731. d. (32.)

— Lefébure Wély's ... Offertoire in G transcribed for the Pianoforte by E. M. Lott. *London,* [1873.] fol.
h. 2704. a. (2.)

— The Madeleine, characteristic piece for the Pianoforte, founded upon the Offertoire in G. *London,* [1874.] fol.
h. 1293. b. (19.)

— Offertoire in G. *See* SMALLWOOD (W.) St. Sulpice ... founded on ... Wély's ... Offertoire. [1877.] fol. h. 1412. j. (26.)

— Processional march for the Pianoforte, adapted from Wely's Offertoire in G by F. Lemoine. *London,* [1880.] fol.
h. 1494. q. (8.)

— Offertoire. No. 4. [P. F.] *See* PERCIVAL (F.) Sacred Lays, *etc.* No. 3. [1883.] fol. h. 3168. e. (1.)

— Wély's Madeleine, characteristic piece, arranged as a Pianoforte duet by F. Nava. *London,* [1875.] fol.
h. 1293. b. (20.)

— *See* SMITH (E. S.) Souvenir de la Madeleine, thêmes des Offertoires de Lefébure-Wély, *etc.* [1873.] fol.
h. 3024. d. (19.)

Offertoires. Op. 35. No. 5

— Lefébure Wély's ... Offertoire in A transcribed for the Pianoforte by E. M. Lott. *London,* [1874.] fol.
h. 2704. a. (1.)

LEFÉBURE WÉLY (Louis James Alfred)

— Offertoire. No. 5. [P. F.] *See* PERCIVAL (F.) Sacred Lays, *etc.*
No. 9. [1883.] fol.   **h. 3168. e. (1.)**

— Offertoire pour orgue. [1857.] *See* NIEDERMEYER (L.) La
Maîtrise, *etc.* 1re Année. No. 6. [1857–61.] fol.   **H. 1237.**

— Offertoire en forme d'une Marche. [Organ.] *See* SMALLWOOD
(W.) Celebrated Compositions, *etc.* First Series. No.19. [1893,
etc.] fol.   **h. 1412. t.**

— Ora pro me. Méditation en la majeur pour le Grand Orgue
avec pédale obligée. *See* PERIODICAL PUBLICATIONS.— *Paris.*
L'Illustration Musicale, *etc.* [No. 2.] 1863. 8°.   **P. P. 1948. t.**

— Original compositions for the organ. *See* supra: [Offertoires.
Op. 35.]

— Paolina, fantaisie-polka pour piano. *London,* [1854.] fol.
                                                      h. 1292. (36.)

— Les papillons d'or, nocturne brillant pour le piano. Op. 81.
London, [1853.] fol.   **h. 1292. (23.)**

— La Patrouille, caprice de genre ... transcrit pour Harmonium
seul par A. Parvy. *Paris,* [1878.] fol.   **h. 2575. h. (8.)**

— La Patrouille, caprice de genre ... transcrit pour Piano seul
par A. Parvy. *Paris,* [1878.] fol.   **h. 3272. j. (17.)**

— Pensées d'Album. [P.F.] 6 no. *London,* [1863.] fol.
                                                      h. 1293. b. (13.)

— Pensées intimes, romances sans paroles pour piano. Op. 91.
London, [1855.] fol.   **h. 1293. (10.)**

— Douze pensées musicales pour l'harmonium. 2 bk. Op. 28.
London, [1857.] fol.   **h. 2575. (4.)**

— Douze pensées musicales, pour l'harmonium ... Op. 28. 2 bk.
Brewer & C°: London, [1861.] fol.   **h. 3213. h. (13.)**

— Pensées Musicales for the Harmonium or American Organ.
Op. 28. 2 bk. *E. Donajowski: London,* [1892.] 4°.
                                                      g. 575. a. (3.)

— Pensées Musicales. A series of Movements for the American
Organ or Harmonium. *J. Curwen & Sons: London,* [1904.]
obl. 8°.   **b. 400. e. (5.)**

— Les Pifferari, aubade Italienne, pour piano. Op. 98. *Paris,*
[1856.] fol.   **h. 1293. (16.)**

— The Pilgrims' March, characteristic piece for the Pianoforte.
London, [1874.] fol.   **h. 1293. b. (17.)**

— Le Pré aux Clercs [by L. J. F. Hérold] grand duo brillant pour
le Piano. *Paris,* [1876.] fol.   **h. 1293. e. (3.)**

— Prière pour orgue. [1857.] *See* NIEDERMEYER (L.) La Maîtrise,
etc. 1re Année. No. 1. [1857–61.] fol.   **H. 1237.**

— [Prière.] Andante, *etc.* [Organ.] *See* BEST (W. T.) Cecilia, *etc.*
Book XI. [1883, *etc.*] obl. fol.   **e. 1106.**

— Un rayon de soleil, mélodie valse pour le piano. *Paris,*
[1856.] fol.   **h. 1293. (1.)**

— [Un rayon de soleil.] The sunbeam. [P.F.] *London,* [1856.] fol.
                                                      h. 1293. a. (15.)

— Recollections of Italy ... for the pianoforte. *See* RICHARDS
(H.B.) The pianist's album. [1853, *etc.*] fol.   **h. 1390.**

— Recollections of Italy, Venice, Milan, Rome, Naples. For the
pianoforte. Op. 20. 4 no. *London,* [1854.] fol.   **h. 1292. (1.)**

— Les Recruteurs, opéra comique en trois actes. Paroles de
Mrs. de Jallais et Vulpian ... réduit pour le Piano par Bazille.
Paris, [1861.] 8°.   **F. 808.**

LEFÉBURE WÉLY (Louis James Alfred)

— [Les Recruteurs.] *See* BURGMUELLER (J. J. F.) Les Recruteurs
... pour Piano. [1862.] fol.   **h. 567. (2.)**

— [Les Recruteurs.] *See* KETTERER (E.) Les Recruteurs ... pour
Piano. [1862.] fol.   **h. 1275. d. (18.)**

— Le Retour de l'Armée, marche triumphale pour le Piano à
quatre mains. Op. 133. *London,* [1860.] fol.   **h. 1293. b. (8.)**

— Le retour de l'armée. Marche triomphale pour le Piano à
quatre mains. *Paris,* [1860.] fol.   **h. 1293. a. (18.)**

La retraite militaire

— Auré, ou La Retraite Militaire. Caprice de genre pour le
Piano-Forte. Op. 65. *Wessel and Co.: London,* [1850?] fol.
                                                      R. M. 25. k. 9. (7.)

— La retraite militaire, caprice de genre pour piano. Op. 65.
London, [1852.] fol.   **h. 1292. (12.)**

— "Auré" ou la retraite militaire, caprice de Genre pour le
Pianoforte. Oeuv. 65. *London,* [1853.] fol.   **h. 1292. (14.)**

— La retraite militaire, caprice caractéristique pour Piano.
Op. 65. *London,* [1853.] fol.   **h. 1292. (13.)**

— La retraite militaire, caprice de genre, pour piano. Op. 65.
London, [1853.] fol.   **h. 1292. (11.)**

— Wely's La retraite militaire. *London,* [1854.] fol.
                                                      h. 1292. (15.)

— Wély's la retraite militaire. [P.F.] *London,* [1854.] fol.
                                                      h. 1292. (16.)

— Lefébure-Wély's "La Retraite Militaire" edited by L. Sloper.
Op. 65. [P. F.] *London,* [1854.] fol.
[*L. Sloper's edition of Pianoforte works. No. 45.*] **h. 737.**

— La retraite militaire. *See* SCHUBERT (A.) Récréations
modernes du pianiste, *etc.* No. 4. [1854.] fol.   **h. 787. (2.)**

— La Retraite Militaire. [P.F.] *London,* [1855.] fol.
No. 585, 86 of the "Musical Bouquet".   **H. 2345.**

— La retraite militaire, caprice de genre pour le piano. Op. 65.
London, [1856.] fol.   **h. 1293. (3.)**

— La Retraite Militaire, caprice de genre pour le Pianoforte.
Op. 65. *London,* [1869.] fol.   **h. 1293. b. (15.)**

— "La Retraite militaire." ⟨Fanfare.⟩ [Op. 65. Military band
parts.] 25 pt. *In:* FLOTOW (F. F. A. von) *Baron.* [Alessandro
Stradella.] Potpourri, *etc.* 1877. fol. [*Boose's supplemental
military Journal. no. 288.*]   **h. 1544.**

— Military Tattoo. "La Retraite militaire" ... [Op. 65.]
Transcribed for military band, with new ending by J. A.
Kappey. [Parts.] 26 pt. *In:* BERGER (R.) Valse très lente.
"Amoureuse," *etc.* 1902. fol. [*Boosey's military Journal.
ser. 112. no. 1.*]   **h. 1549.**

— Le Rêve de Cherubin, pour Piano. Op. 176. *Paris,* [1868.] fol.
                                                      h. 1293. c. (10.)

— Le reveil des anges, mélodie pour piano. Op. 99. *Paris,*
[1856.] fol.   **h. 1293. (17.)**

— Rêverie, andante pour piano. Op. 77. *London,* [1853.] fol.
                                                      h. 1292. (19.)

— Rêverie-mazurka pour piano. Op. 101. *London,* [1856.] fol.
                                                      h. 1293. a. (5.)

— Rêverie-Mazurka, pour piano. Op. 101. *Paris,* [1856.] fol.
                                                      h. 1293. (19.)

— Reviens à ta chaumière. Romance ... Paroles de Mme Laure
Jourdain. ⟨Acc^t [for guitar] par J^h Vimeux.⟩ *Chez Canaux:
Paris,* [c. 1840.] 8°.   **E. 1717. l. (40.)**

LEFÉBURE WÉLY (Louis James Alfred)

— Romance sans paroles, pour Piano. Op. 141. *Paris,* [1862.] fol.   **h. 1293. c. (1.)**

— 6 Romances sans paroles. [P.F.] Op. 160. 6 no. *Paris,* [1865.] fol.   **h. 1293. c. (14.)**

— Six Romances sans paroles pour Piano. 6 no. *London,* [1876.] fol.   **h. 1293. e. (4.)**

— Rome, la messe de minuit, pour le piano-forte. *London,* [1856.] fol.   **h. 1293. (2.)**

— Rome.—Milan. *See* RICHARDS (H.B.) The pianist's album, *etc.* [1853.] fol.   **h. 1390.**

— Rondo Polka pour Piano. *London,* [1864.] fol.   **h. 1293. b. (11.)**

— Roveredo, fantaisie tyrolinne [*sic*] pour Piano. Op. 137. *London,* [1860.] fol.   **h. 1293. b. (9.)**

— Roveredo. Fantaisie-Tyrolienne pour Piano. *Paris,* [1860.] fol.   **h. 1293. a. (21.)**

— St. Eustache. *See* supra: [Offertoires. Op. 35. no. 2.]

— La Sainte Chapelle. Vade Mecum de l'Organiste, *etc.* *Mayence,* [1877.] 8°.   **f. 139. a.**

— La sérénade du Gondolier, nocturne, pour piano. *London,* [1855.] fol.   **h. 1293. (8.)**

— Les Soirées de l'Organiste. Fantaisies de salon pour Harmonium. 20 no. *Paris,* [1877.] fol. *Imperfect; wanting no.* 1–8, 10–20.   **h. 3213. s. (1.)**

— Les Soirées Musicales. 14 Fantaisies pour le Piano à quatre mains. no. 1–4. *Paris,* [1864.] fol. *Imperfect; wanting all other no.*   **h. 1293. c. (17.)**

— The Sylph's Dance, characteristic piece for the Pianoforte. *London,* [1874.] fol.   **h. 1293. b. (18.)**

— Te voir toujours. Chansonnette … Paroles de Mme Laure Jourdain. ⟨Accompagnement de guitare, par J^h Vimeux.⟩ *Chez Canaux: Paris,* [c. 1840.] 8°.   **E. 1717. l. (39.)**

— Titania, fantaisie de concert pour Piano. Op. 170. *Paris,* [1867.] fol.   **h. 1293. c. (5.)**

— Titania, fantaisie de concert pour Piano. 2 no. *London,* [1873.] fol.   **h. 1293. b. (16.)**

— Titania, fantaisie de concert pour Piano. *London,* [1876.] fol.   **h. 1293. e. (5.)**

— La Touraine au xve. siècle. [Six duets for harmonium and piano.] *Paris,* [1859.] fol.   **h. 3213. c. (16.)**

— La Touraine au xve. siècle. Six duos … transcrits pour Piano seul par A.L. Parvy. *Paris,* [1878.] fol.   **h. 3272. j. (18.)**

— La Tunisienne, marche militaire, pour piano. Op. 118. *Paris,* [1858.] fol.   **h. 1293. a. (9.)**

— Valse des sylphes. [P. F.] *London,* [1859.] fol.   **h. 1293. a. (13.)**

— Les veilleurs de nuit, épisode musical, pour harmonium. Op. 95. *London,* [1856.] fol.   **h. 2575. (5.)**

— Les veilleurs de nuit, épisode musical pour piano. Op. 95. *London,* [1856.] fol.   **h. 1293. a. (3.)**

— Les veilleurs de nuit, episode musical pour piano. Op. 95. *Paris,* [1856.] fol.   **h. 1293. (14.)**

— Venite adoremus, chant de Noël, pour Piano. *Paris,* [1875.] fol.   **h. 1293. e. (2.)**

— Le Viennoise. Mazurka. *See* supra: Pensées d'Album. No. 4.

LEFÉBURE WÉLY (Louis James Alfred)

— Vivre & mourir. Romance … Paroles de Mme Laure Jourdain. ⟨Accompagnement de guitare, par J^h Vimeux.⟩ *Chez Canaux: Paris,* [c. 1840.] 8°. *The titlepage has been cropped.*   **E. 1717. l. (26.)**

— The Zuleika and the Emmeline polkas. [P.F.] *London,* [1855.] fol. *No. 244 of the "Musical Bouquet".*   **H. 2345.**

— *See* HYMNS. [*French.*] 80 Cantiques … avec accompagnement d'orgue … par … A. Lefébure-Wély, *etc.* [1886.] 8°.   **F. 322. a. (2.)**

— *See* PURCELL (A.) [*Collected Works.—c.*] Great Masters … arranged for Pianoforte … Selections from … Lefébure-Wély. Book 4, *etc.* [1907, *etc.*] 4°.   **g. 1330.**

— *See* RENAUD (A.) Communion, d'après Lefébure-Wély. Œuvre Posthume. 1894. *obl.* fol.   **e. 1091.**

— *See* RUDOLPHUS (C.) Wessel & Co.'s edition of a … method for the harmonium … compiled from the works of Lefébure-Wély, A. Miné, *etc.* [1854.] fol.   **h. 2501. (4.)**

— *See* VENZANO (L.) Célèbre valse, [arranged] pour piano par Lefébure-Wély. [1855.] fol.   **h. 1293. (12.)**

— *See* VENZANO (L.) Célèbre valse … pour piano par Lefébure-Wély. [1856.] fol.   **h. 1293. (13.)**

— *See* VENZANO (L.) La valse Venzano, arranged for the piano forte by Lefébure-Wély. [1856.] fol.   **h. 1293. a. (16.)**

LEFÉBURE-WÉLY (Louis James Alfred) and TRIEBERT (Charles Louis)

— Duo concertant pour piano & flute sur les motifs du Brasseur de Preston d'Ad. Adam, *etc.* [Score.] pp. 21. *Chez Richault: Paris,* [c. 1840.] fol.   **g. 934. ll. (9.)**

LEFEBVRE (Albert)

— L'Avenir de la France. Marche des bataillons scolaires. [P.F.] *Chez l'auteur:* [*Paris,* 1850?] fol.   **Hirsch M. 1298. (15.)**

LEFEBVRE (Channing)

— Alleluia! Sing Noel! Noel Maconnais. [Carol.] *H. W. Gray Co.: New York,* 1924. 8°.   **E. 602. kk. (22.)**

— At His Cradle. For Chorus of Men's Voices … Old French Carol … arranged by C. Lefebvre. *Galaxy Music Corporation: New York,* 1940. 8°.   **F. 260. c. (17.)**

— Benedicite omnia opera … in D flat. *H. W. Gray Co.: New York,* 1918. 8°.   **F. 1169. z. (12.)**

— Seven Caricatures. T.T.B.B. (A Humoresque showing how certain composers might have treated a 4 measure theme.) *G. Ricordi & Co.: New York,* 1927. 8°.   **F. 163. z. (42.)**

— Catalonian Christmas Carol. Cold December's Wintry Blast … English version by C. L. Arr. by C. Lefebvre. *H. W. Gray Co.: New York,* 1934. 8°.   **E. 602. tt. (16.)**

— Catalonian Christmas Carol. Winter with its Ice and Snow … English version by J. Phelps. Arr. by C. Lefebvre. *H. W. Gray Co.: New York,* 1933. 8°.   **E. 602. rr. (26.)**

— Three Characteristic Dance Rhythms. No. 1. Castanets and tambourines. (No. 2. Queues.) (No. 3. Petrouchka's wedding.) For three-part Chorus, women's voices. (Words and music by C. Lefebvre.) 3 no. *G. Ricordi & Co.: New York,* 1925. 8°.   **F. 217. (14.)**

— Christmas Eve … Christmas Carol for two Sopranos. Founded on an old Southern Melody by C. Lefebvre. *H. W. Gray Co.: New York,* 1934. 8°.   **E. 602. tt. (17.)**

LEFEBVRE (Channing)

— Eja, eja. To us in Bethlem City. For Chorus of Men's Voices with Soprano, or Tenor, Solo. German Folk Melody, from the Cölner Psalter, 1638. Arranged by C. Lefebvre. *Galaxy Music Corporation: New York*, 1941. 8°.   **E. 335. k. (31.)**

— Fishermen's Night Hymn. For Chorus of Men's Voices. [Words by] E. Clayton. Manx Folktune. Arranged by C. Lefebvre. *Galaxy Music Corporation: New York*, 1943. 8°.   **F. 1771. i. (34.)**

— The Flowers o' the Forest. For Chorus of Men's Voices. [Words by] J. Elliot. Old Scottish Melody. Arranged by C. Lefebvre. *Galaxy Music Corporation: New York*, 1940. 8°.   **F. 1771. h. (13.)**

— Fourteen Folk Tunes for young Men from America—Austria — England — Canada — Germany — Ireland — Russia — Scotland — Sicily — Slovakia — Sweden and Wales. Arranged for 3 part male chorus (t.b.b.) by C. Lefebvre. pp. 38. *Galaxy Music Corporation: New York*, [1947.] 8°.   **F. 1771. p. (3.)**

— Forever free. For Chorus of Men's Voices. [Words by] F. Downey. Ancient Dutch Melody. Arranged by C. Lefebvre. *Galaxy Music Corporation: New York*, 1941. 8°.   **F. 1771. h. (14.)**

— Forever free. For Chorus of Mixed Voices ... Ancient Dutch Melody. Arranged by C. Lefebvre. *Galaxy Music Corporation: New York*, 1942. 8°.   **E. 335. k. (32.)**

— Forever free. For Chorus of Women's Voices, Three Part, with Alto II, ad lib ... Ancient Dutch Melody. Arranged by C. Lefebvre. *Galaxy Music Corporation: New York*, 1943. 8°.   **F. 1771. i. (35.)**

— God rest you merry, Gentlemen. Old English Carol, arranged for Four Part Chorus by C. Lefebvre. *Stainer & Bell: London*, 1927. 8°.
Church Choir Library, No. 328.   **F. 1137. b.**

— God rest you merry, Gentlemen. Arr. by C. Lefebvre. (T. T. B. B.) (S. A. T. B.) 2 no. *G. Ricordi & Co.: New York*, 1927. 8°.   **E. 602. mm. (20.)**

— Good King Wenceslas. Old English carol. T.T.B.B. (Arr. by C. Lefebvre.) *G. Ricordi & Co.: New York*, 1927. 8°.   **E. 602. mm. (21.)**

— Greensleeves. Traditional English melody, freely arranged by C. Lefebvre ... Verses by William Chatterton Dix ... For chorus of male voices a cappella. pp. 5. *Galaxy Music Corporation: New York*, [1953.] 8°.   **F. 1771. p. (29.)**

— Here we come a-wassailing. For Chorus of Men's Voices. Old English Folk Melody freely arranged by C. Lefebvre. *Galaxy Music Corporation: New York*, 1941. 8°.   **F. 260. c. (23.)**

— Holly and the Ivy. Christmas Carol. Arranged by C. Lefebvre. T. T. B. B. *Galaxy Music Corporation: New York*, 1932. 8°.   **H. 602. qq. (19.)**

— The Holly and the Ivy. Old English Carol. Arr. [for S. S. A.] by C. Lefebvre. *Galaxy Music Corporation: New York*, [1932.] 8°.   **E. 602. qq. (50.)**

— Holly Day Holly Carol ... Old Cornish Carol. Arr. [for S. A. T. B.] by C. Lefebvre. *Galaxy Music Corporation: New York*, 1932. 8°.   **E. 602. qq. (51.)**

— Holly Day Holly Carol. For Chorus of Women's Voices. Old Cornish Carol arranged by C. Lefebvre. *Galaxy Music Corporation: New York*, 1939. 8°.   **F. 1176. m. (34.)**

— Three Irish Tunes. (Arr. by C. Lefebvre.) No. 1. Come rest in this bosom. (Words by T. Moore.) (No. 2. Rich and rare were the gems she wore. Words by T. Moore.) (No. 3. Cruiskeen lawn. The little jug.) T. T. B. B. 3 no. *G. Ricordi & Co.: New York*, 1927. 8°.   **F. 163. z. (43.)**

LEFEBVRE (Channing)

— Jubilate Deo ... In the key of C for S.A.T.B. pp. 6. *H. W. Gray Co.: New York*, [1958.] 8°.   **E. 335. v. (29.)**

— Ten Offertory Sentences, *etc. H. W. Gray Co.: New York*, 1924. 8°.   **E. 602. kk. (23.)**

— Old Carols for young Men. Arranged in Three Parts, T.T.B. ... by C. Lefebvre. *Galaxy Music Corporation: New York*, 1945. 8°.   **F. 260. d. (3.)**

— [A reissue.] Old Carols for young Men. Arranged in three parts (T.B.B.), *etc. Elkin & Co.: London*, [1958.] 8°.   **F. 260. h. (48.)**

— Orpheus with his Lute. For four-part chorus of men's voices a cappella ... [Words by] William Shakespeare. pp. 6. *G. Schirmer: New York*, [1958.] 8°.   **F. 163. oo. (13.)**

— Out of the orient crystal Skies. Falan-Tiding-Dido. For Chorus of Men's Voices with Soprano, or Tenor, Solo unaccompanied. Tyrolean Folk Melody arranged by C. Lefebvre. *Galaxy Music Corporation: New York*, 1941. 8°.   **F. 260. c. (24.)**

— See the destined Day arise! Anthem, *etc. H. W. Gray Co.: New York*, 1924. 8°.   **F. 281. zz. (28.)**

— Sing we merrily. A short festival anthem for S.A.T.B. From Psalm 81, v. 1–3. Psalm 148, v. 12. pp. 10. *H. W. Gray Co.: New York*, [1960.] 8°.   **E. 335. aa. (19.)**

— Two Swedish Melodies. [No. 1.] Hiking Song. Gångsång. [Words by] O. Thunman, English version by F. Downey. Swedish Folktune. Arranged [for T.T.B.B.] by C. Lefebvre. ([No. 2.] Student Song. Studentsång. [Words by] K. H. Sätherberg, English Version by F. Downey. [Music by] Prince Gustaf. Edited [for T.T.B.B.] by C. Lefebvre.) *Galaxy Music Corporation: New York*, 1940. 8°.   **F. 1771. h. (15.)**

— Te Deum laudamus. (Shortened form.) For mixed voices. pp. 11. *H. W. Gray Co.: New York*, [1957.] 8°.   **F. 1158. n. (22.)**

— Tuku, tuku, tuu I'm calling. Little Finnish Folk Song. English text by J. Teslof. Freely arranged [for S.S.A.] by C. Lefebvre. *Galaxy Music Corporation: New York*, 1937. 8°.   **F. 1771. e. (14.)**

— We greet you, Jesus. Polish Carol. Arranged for Solo Voice ... and Male Chorus. English version by E. B. Reed. Arranged by C. Lefebvre. *Stainer & Bell: London*, 1939. 8°.
Church Choir Library, No. 532.   **F. 1137. b.**

— *See* BACH (J. S.) [Uns ist ein Kind geboren.] Alleluia ... Arranged by C. Lefebvre. 1940. 8°.   **F. 956. y. (7.)**

— *See* BRAHMS (J.) The Thirteenth Psalm ... Edited by C. Lefebvre. 1940. 8°.   **F. 359. k. (34.)**

— *See* CHAIKOVSKY (P. I.) [7 Романсовъ. Op. 47. No. 5.] Pilgrim's Song ... Arranged ... by C. Lefebvre. 1942. 8°.   **F. 217. j. (42.)**

— *See* DELIBES (C. P. L.) [Lakmé.—Sous le dôme épais.] Flower Song from Lakmé ... Revised and edited by C. Lefebvre. 1934. 8°.   **E. 263. j. (32.)**

— *See* GAINES (Samuel R.) From old Russia ... Arranged by C. Lefebvre. 1946. 8°.   **F. 1744. g. (18.)**

— *See* GRUBER (F.X.) [Stille Nacht, heilige Nacht.] Silent Night ... (Adeste fideles) ... Descants and Accompaniment by C. Lefebvre. 1939. 8°.   **F. 1176. m. (35.)**

— *See* HAENDEL (G. F.) [Twelve Grand Concertos. Op. 6. No. 12.—Larghetto.] Father of Light. For chorus of male voices ... Arranged by C. Lefebvre, *etc.* [1950.] 8°.   **E. 146. r. (13.)**

LEFEBVRE (Channing)

— See HAENDEL (G. F.) [*Doubtful and Supposititious Works.*] [Dank sei dir, Herr.] Thanks be to Thee ... Arranged by C. Lefebvre, *etc.* 1941. 4°.　　　　　　**g. 74. ee. (22.)**

— See HAENDEL (G. F.) [*Doubtful and Supposititious Works.*] [Dank sei dir, Herr.] Thanks be to Thee ... Arranged by C. Lefebvre. 1941–42. 8°.　　　　　　**E. 146. q. (31.)**

— See HOLST (Gustavus T. von) Turn back O Man ... Arranged for chorus of male voices by C. Lefebvre. [1953.] 8°.　　　　　　**F. 1176. s. (16.)**

— See MENDELSSOHN-BARTHOLDY (J. L. F.) [6 Gesänge. Op. 34. No. 2. Auf Flügeln des Gesanges.] On Wings of Song. Arranged for male voices by C. Lefebvre. 1927. 8°.　　　　　　**F. 163. z. (46.)**

— See PALESTRINA (G. P. da) [Motettorum Quinque Vocibus Liber Quintus.] Exultate Deo ... Arr. by C. Lefebvre. 1933. 8°.　　　　　　**F. 23. k. (30.)**

— See SIBELIUS (J.) Onward, ye Peoples ... Men's Voices ... Arranged by C. Lefebvre. 1939. 8°.　　　　　　**F. 163. ii. (17.)**

— See SIBELIUS (J.) Onward, ye Peoples ... Mixed Voices ... Arranged by C. Lefebvre. 1939. 8°.　　　　　　**F. 1744. c. (39.)**

— See WOLF (H.) [Gedichte von Goethe. No. 35. Trunken müssen wir alle sein.] Drinking Song ... Arranged by C. Lefebvre. 1946. 8°.　　　　　　**F. 638. i. (59.)**

— See WOLF (H.) [6 Gedichte von Scheffel, Mörike, *etc.* No. 3. Biterolf.] The Crusader ... Arranged by C. Lefebvre. 1946. 8°.　　　　　　**F. 638. i. (60.)**

LEFEBVRE (Charles Édouard)

— Andantino pour Piano à quatre mains. *Paris,* [1870.] fol.　　　　　　**h. 1462. r. (33.)**

— Au Désert. Scène dramatique [begins: "Ella, la douce Ella"]. Paroles de P. de Choudens. *Paris,* [1882.] fol.　　　　　　**H. 1793. d. (7.)**

— L'Aurore. Mélodie [begins: "Viens, fuyons"]. Poésie de P. de Choudens. *Paris,* [1879.] fol.　　　　　　**H. 1781. i. (12.)**

— Berceuse [begins: "Prenez l'enfant"]. Poésie de G. Lafenestre. *Paris,* [1881.] fol.　　　　　　**H. 1786. e. (25.)**

— Dans la Steppe. [Song, begins: "Le printemps rit et l'air est doux!"] Poésie de H. Cazalis. *Paris,* [1885.] fol.　　　　　　**H. 2836. h. (35.)**

— Djelma. Opéra en trois actes, poème de C. Lomon. Partition chant et piano reduite par l'Auteur. *A. Durand et Fils: Paris,* 1894. 8°.　　　　　　**F. 809. b.**

— Djelma ... Phrase extraite du Duo du 1er Acte, *etc.* [Begins: "Tu sais trop bien".] [*Paris,*] 1894. 8°. *Supplement to "L'Illustration," No.* 2675.　　**P. P. 4283. m. (3.)**

— Espoir. Chœur avec Solo de Soprano [begins: "La détresse courbe nos âmes"]. Poésie de E. Guinand. *Paris,* [1883.] 8°.　　　　　　**F. 607. p. (12.)**

— Hymne, Prono volutus impetu, pour Contralto solo, chœur et orchestre. Partition Chant et Piano ... Traduction Française par Mr. P. Collin. *Paris,* [1882.] 8°.　　　　　　**F. 363. d. (8.)**

— Intermezzo pour Violon avec accompagnement ... de Piano. *Berlin & Posen,* [1881.] fol.　　　　　　**h. 1609. q. (8.)**

— Invocation. [Song, begins: "O mont de Sinaï".] Poésie de Racine. *Paris,* [1881.] fol.　　　　　　**H. 1786. e. (27.)**

— Jours d'Automne! [Song.] [*Paris,*] 1895. 8°. *Supplement to "L'Illustration," No.* 2727.　　**P. P. 4283. m. (3.)**

LEFEBVRE (Charles Édouard)

— Judith, drame lyrique en trois actes ... Poème de P. Collin. Partition Chant et Piano. *Paris,* [1877.] 8°.　　**F. 809.**

— Légende de Ste. Azénor. [Song, begins: "Le brick n'eut pas sitôt sombre".] Poésie de A. Theuriet. *Paris,* [1881.] fol.　　　　　　**H. 1786. e. (24.)**

— Marche pour le Piano. *Paris,* [1880.] fol.　　**h. 3272. j. (15.)**

— Mélodie pour le Piano. [*Paris,*] 1899. 8°. *Supplement to "L'Illustration," No.* 2938.　　**P. P. 4283. m. (3.)**

— Menuet pour le piano. Op. 60. *Paris,* [1883.] fol.　　　　　　**H. 3280. k. (40.)**

— Trois Pièces pour Violoncelle et Piano. *Berlin & Posen,* [1880.] fol.　　　　　　**h. 1849. k. (15.)**

— Pompei. [Song, begins: "Le volcan se dresse".] Poësie de E. Peveril. *Paris,* [1881.] fol.　　**H. 1786. e. (26.)**

— Pseaume XXIII pour Chœur, Solo et Orchestre. Partition Chant et Piano. *Paris,* [1876.] 8°.　　**F. 1075.**

— Il Ritorno. Canzonetta. *Choudens père et fils: Paris,* [1879.] fol. [*I Canti d'Italia. No.* 701.]　　**H. 345. c.**

— Romance pour le Violon avec accompagnement de Piano. *Paris,* [1878.] fol.　　　　　　**h. 1609. m. (10.)**

— Romance sans paroles pour le Piano. *Paris,* [1880.] fol.　　　　　　**h. 3272. j. (15.)**

— Salut à l'harmonie. Choeur à 4 voix d'hommes. Poésie de A. Lefebvre. *Paris,* [1883.] 8°.　　**E. 308. n. (25.)**

— Sérénade [begins: "Étoile dont la beauté luit"]. Poésie de H. Cazalis. *Paris,* [1877.] fol.　　**H. 1781. i. (11.)**

— Une Sérénade. Scène pour Orchestre. Op. 65 ... Réduction pour le piano à quatre mains. *Paris,* [1885.] fol.　　　　　　**h. 3290. c. (5.)**

— Suite pour flûte, hautbois, clarinette, cor et basson ... Op. 57. Partition réduite par l'auteur, *etc.* pp. 19. *J. Hamelle: Paris, Leipzig* [printed, c.1880.] 8°.　　**e. 668. x. (5.)**

— Le Trésor. Opéra comique. (Poëme de F. Coppée,) *etc. Paris,* [1884.] 8°.　　　　　　**F. 158. a. (4.)**

— Trio en ré mineur, pour piano, violon et violoncelle. 〈Op. 110.〉 [Score and parts.] 3 pt. *A. Noel: Paris,* [1902.] fol.　　　　　　**h. 2845. l. (2.)**

— Vision. Mélodie [begins: "Un songe m'enleva vers celle que j'adore"]. Sonnet de P. J. Pain, imitée de Pétrarque. *Paris,* [1885.] fol.　　　　　　**H. 2836. h. (36.)**

— Zaïre. Opéra en trois actes et cinq tableaux d'après la tragédie de Voltaire, par P. Collin. Partition chant et piano. *Paris,* [1887.] 8°.　　　　　　**F. 809. a.**

LE FEBVRE (Denis)

— Airs à boire à quatre parties. 〈Basse-contre.〉 *Robert Ballard: Paris,* 1660. *obl.* 8°. *Imperfect; wanting the other parts.*　　**A. 274. (1.)**

— Premier livre d'airs à quatre parties & la basse-continuë ... Basse-contre. *Robert Ballard: Paris,* 1660. *obl.* 8°. *Imperfect; wanting the other parts.*　　**A. 274. (2.)**

LE FEBVRE (François)

— Le Dieu Gard de la Ville de Paris, à Monseigneur de Guise ... à son retour de la prise de Calais, par Sonnets heroïques. Autheur François Habert de Berry. Auec vne chanson en l'honneur de mondict Seigneur de Guise, mise en musique par François Le Febure. *De l'imprimerie de la vefue de P. Attaingnant: Paris,* 1558. 8°.　　**238. m. 3. (4.)**

LEFEBVRE (François Charlemagne)

— [Les Noces de Gamache.] Ouverture et airs ... arrangés pour le Pianoforte. *Paris*, [1810?] fol.   **g. 443. d. (26.)**

— [Les Noces de Gamache.—Fandango.] *See* DALVIMARE (Martin P.) Fandango, air favori tiré du ballet des Noces de Gamache [by F.C. Lefebvre], *etc.* [1801.] fol.   **h. 173. b. (3.)**

— [Les Noces de Gamache.—Fandango.] *See* DALVIMARE (Martin P.) Fandango with Variations, for the harp, *etc.* [The theme from the ballet "Les Noces de Gamache" by F.C. Lefebvre.] [WM 1806.] fol.   **h. 2605. z. (10.)**

LEFEBVRE (H.)

— Dieu protége le Roi ... Air national anglais. Chœur, paroles de B. Sulte. Harmonisation de H. Lefebvre. *Le Passe-Temps: Montreal*, 1910. fol.   **H. 1792. r. (50.)**

LEFEBVRE (JULES)

— Une Nuit de carnaval. Quadrille brillant, pour piano, avec acc^t de flûte, violon, cornet à pistons et basse. 5 pt. *Petit aîné: Paris*, [c. 1860.] *obl.* fol. & *obl.* 8°.
Issued as music supplement to "La Musique populaire".   **P. P. 1948. s/2. (148.)**

LEFEBVRE (VICTOR)

— La Créole. Grande valse pour le piano. pp. 5. *Chez Ed. Bote & G. Bock: Berlin*, [1850?] fol.   **Hirsch M. 1303. (13.)**

LEFELD (JERZY)

— Sekstet Es-dur, op. 3. Partytura. pp. 132. *Towarzystwo wydawnicze muzyki polskiej: Warszawa*, 1929. 8°.   **d. 85. t. (1.)**

— *See* CHOPIN (F. F.) [*Collected Works.—a.*] Complete Works, *etc.* ⟨xv. Works for Piano and Orchestra. Piano arrangement by J. Lefeld.⟩ [1961.] fol.   **h. 472. c.**

— *See* SZYMANOWSKI (K.) Trzy kaprysy Paganiniego. Transkrypcja na skrzypce i fortepian, op. 40 ... Partię fortepianu przejrzał J. Lefeld. 1953. 4°.   **G. 1083. d. (3.)**

— *See* SZYMANOWSKI (K.) 2 pieśni kurpiowskie [op. 58. no. 2, 7] ... Transkrypcje na skrzypce i fortepian ułożyli ... I. Dubiska i J. Lefeld. [1947.] fol.   **g. 1250. d. (1.)**

LE FEUVRE (GUY)

— Arlette. [For songs by G. Le Feuvre published separately:] *See* LE FEUVRE (G.) and NOVELLO (I.)

— The Fairy Ring. *See* LE FEUVRE (G.) and NOVELLO (I.) [Arlette.]

— Love in my Heart is ringing. *See* LE FEUVRE (G.) and NOVELLO (I.) [Arlette.]

— Stage Love. *See* LE FEUVRE (G.) and NOVELLO (I.) [Arlette.]

LE FEUVRE (GUY) and **NOVELLO** (IVOR)

Arlette

— Arlette ... Operette in three acts, book by C. Ronald and L. Bouvet, translated by J. Levy ... lyrics by A. Ross and C. Grey. *B. Feldman & Co.: London*, 1917. 4°.   **G. 782. dd. (4.)**

— Selection ... Arranged by R. S. Stoddon. [P. F.] *B. Feldman & Co.: London*, 1917. fol.   **h. 3284. nn. (37.)**

— Arlette. Selection ... Arranged for military band by Dan Godfrey. ⟨Conductor [and parts].⟩ 27 pt. *Chappell & Co.: London*, [1918.] fol.
[*Chappell's Army Journal. no.* 457.]   **h. 1562.**

LE FEUVRE (GUY) and **NOVELLO** (IVOR)

— Cousinly Love. Trio, *etc. Ascherberg, Hopwood & Crew: London*, 1917. fol.   **H. 3670. (20.)**

— Didn't know the Way to. Duet, *etc. Ascherberg, Hopwood & Crew: London*, 1917. fol.   **H. 3670. (21.)**

— The Fairy Ring. Song, *etc. B. Feldman & Co.: London*, 1917. fol.   **H. 3670. a. (32.)**

— His Country first of all!—The People's King.—Song, *etc. Ascherberg, Hopwood & Crew: London*, 1917. fol.   **H. 3670. (22.)**

— It's just a Memory. Song, *etc. Ascherberg, Hopwood & Crew: London*, 1917. fol.   **H. 3670. (23.)**

— Love Bells. Song, *etc. Ascherberg, Hopwood & Crew: London*, 1917. fol.   **H. 3670. (24.)**

— Love in my Heart is ringing. Telephone Song, *etc. B. Feldman & Co.: London*, 1917. fol.   **H. 3670. a. (33.)**

— The Man of forty. Song, *etc. Ascherberg, Hopwood & Crew: London*, 1917. fol.   **H. 3670. (25.)**

— On the Staff. Song, *etc. Ascherberg, Hopwood & Crew: London*, 1917. fol.   **H. 3670. (26.)**

— Stage Love. Duet, *etc. B. Feldman & Co.: London*, 1917. fol.   **H. 3670. a. (34.)**

LE FEVRE (ACHILLE)

— Blessed is the Man, *etc.* [Anthem.] *W. Maxwell Music Co.: New York*, (1907.) 8°.   **F. 281. h. (23.)**

LEFÈVRE (ERNEST)

— Le Follet. Poème lyrique de P. Babier ... Mélodie, *etc.* [Begins: "Oh! comme tu t'achèves".] [*Paris*,] 1900. 8°.
Supplement to "L'Illustration," No. 2992.   **P. P. 4283. m. (3.)**

LEVÈVRE (FRÉDÉRIC)

— Pensez à moi. Waltz. [P. F.] *E. Donajowski: London*, [1888.] fol.   **h. 3285. q. (23.)**

LEFÈVRE (G.)

— *See* DUNKLER (É.) Au bord de la mer ... Transcription pour flûte et piano (par G. Lefèvre). [1885.] fol.   **h. 2050. a. (18.)**

— *See* DUNKLER (É.) Au bord de la mer ... Transcription pour alto [and P. F.] par G. Lefèvre. 1885. fol.   **h. 1785. a. (2.)**

LEFÈVRE (GEORGES)

— Chant des Prolétaires. Marche Internationale créée dans les réunions populaires [begins: "O travailleurs que la misère opprime"]. Paroles de A. Le Roy. *Paris*, [1880?] 8°.   **E. 308. q. (22.)**

LEFÈVRE (GUSTAVE)

— Traité d'Harmonie, *etc. École de Musique Classique: Paris*, 1889. 8°.   **7896. f. 32.**

— *See* PICCINI (N.) Didon. Tragédie lyrique ... réduite pour Piano et Chant par G. Lefèvre. [1881.] 8°.   **F. 699. k.**

— *See* PICCINI (N.) Roland. Tragédie lyrique ... Réduite pour Piano et Chant par G. Lefèvre. [1883.] 8°.   **F. 699. x.**

— *See* SALIERI (A.) Les Danaïdes. Tragédie lyrique ... réduite pour Piano et Chant par G. Lefèvre. [1881.] 8°.   **F. 699. l.**

LEFÈVRE (Jacques) *Musician to Louis XIII.*

— Aime-moi, Bergère. Chanson ... from 'Essai sur la Musique'
[by] J. B. de Laborde ... Edited by L. Benson. *See* ARION.
Arion, *etc.* [Vol. III. No. 45.] [1899.] 4°.   **G. 771.**

— Chambrière, chambrière. *See* infra: [Meslanges de musique.]

— [Las! il n'a nul mal.] The Pain of Love. Las! il n'a nul mal.
Song for Chorus of mixed voices. English version by
S. Spaeth ... Arranged by F. Damrosch. *G. Schirmer: New
York,* (1913.) 8°.   **F. 1744. b. (19.)**

— [Meslanges de musique.] Chambrière, chambrière.
Chambermaid, O chambermaid ... Edited by David Tunley.
Chanson for SAT (unaccompanied). *Fr. & Eng.* pp. 4.
Novello & Co.: Borough Green, [1974.] 8°.
[*Musical Times.* 1575.]   **F. 280. n.**

— [Meslanges de musique.] Tu ne l'entends pas. You're not
list'ning to me ... Edited by David Tunley. Chanson for SAT
(unaccompanied). *Fr. & Eng.* pp. 8. *Novello & Co.: Borough
Green,* [1974.] 8°.
[*Musical Times.* 1582.]   **F. 280. n.**

— Tu ne l'entends pas. *See* supra: [Meslanges de musique.]

LEFÈVRE (Jean Xavier)

— 4ᵉ et 6ᵉ concertos pour clarinette et orchestre. Édition par
Sherwood Dudley. [Score.] pp. iv. 123. *Heugel & cᵈᵉ: Paris,*
1975. 4°.
[*Le Pupitre.* 56.]   **G. 51.**

— Sixième concerto pour la clarinette, *etc.* [Parts.] 10 pt. *Chez
Jouve: Paris,* [c. 1805.] fol.   **h. 2177. b.**

— Six duo concertans pour deux clarinettes ... Œuvre IX de duo.
Gravé par Le Roy l'ainé. [Parts.] 2 pt. *Chez H. Naderman:
Paris,* [1810?] fol.   **h. 2189. i. (6.)**

— Six duos concertans pour deux clarinettes ... Œuvre 10ᵉ.
[Parts.] 2 pt. *Chez Naderman: Paris,* [1810?] fol.
    h. 2189. i. (7.)

— Six duos pour deux clarinettes ... Œuvre XI. [1ʳ, 2ᵉ] partie.
[Parts.] 4 pt. *Chez Janet: Paris,* [1810?] fol. **h. 2189. i. (8.)**

— Mère commune des humains. *Hymne à l'Agriculture,* par
Coupigny. *Au Magasin de Musique à l'usage des Fêtes
Nationales:* [Paris, 1796.] 8°.   **E. 1717. b. (32.)**

— Methode de clarinette (français et allemand), *etc.* pp. 80.
Chez J. André: Offenbach s∕m., [1805.] fol.
Lithographed throughout.   **h. 2177. a.**

— Metodo per clarinetto ... Edizione seconda ... con aggiunta
... di scale, salti e nuovi esercizi di Luigi Bassi. [With three
tablatures.] pp. 80. 99. 51. *G. Ricordi: Milano,* [1840?] fol.
    h. 2177.

— [Méthode de clarinette.] Sonata No. 1 ... For clarinet in B♭
and piano. Realised and edited by Georgina Dobrée. [Score
and part.] 2 pt. *Schott & Co.: London,* [1974.] 4°.
    g. 1104. aa. (5.)

— Trois Quatuors pour Clarinette, Violon, Alto et Basse ...
Œuvre 2ᵐᵉ de Quatuors. [Parts.] *Jouve: Paris,* [1803?] fol.
    R. M. 17. f. 8. (3.)

— Sonata in B flat. Opus 12. No. 1. For clarinet and piano.
Edited and realized by Georgina Dobrée. [Score and part.]
2 pt. *Oxford University Press: London,* [1973.] 4°.
    g. 1104. tt. (7.)

LEFÈVRE (Joseph)

— A Concise Method to attain the Art of playing on the Cistre,
etc. Longman and Broderip: London, [1787.] fol. **h. 1176.**

LEFEVRE (Simon)

— A. J. Zederymen, bestaande in Zangen en Gedigten. Verçiert
met Nieuwe Muzijk, *etc. Ian Rieuwertsz: t'Amsterdam,* 1656.
8°.   **A. 1167.**

LEFÈVRE (Théodore)

— [Caroline.] Un Jour pur éclairoit mon âme. Romance. [1789.]
8°. *See* CAROLINE.   **B. 362. a. (93.)**

— Le Prix, ou l'Embarras du Choix. [For songs, etc., published
anonymously:] *See* PRIX.

LEFÈVRE (Xavier)

— *See* LEFÈVRE (Jean X.)

LEFFLER (Carl Peter)

— Folkmusik från Norra Södermanland. Upptecknade af K. P.
Leffler. 2 pt. *Central-Tryckeriet: Stockholm,* 1899, 1900. 8°.
Bidrag till Södermanlands äldre kulturhistoria, etc., X., XI.
    010280. g.

— Om nyckelharpospelet på Skansen, *etc.* (Melodier.) *Ivar
Hæggström: Stockholm,* 1899. 8°.
No. 6 of "Bidrag till vår odlings häfder".   **10281. k. 2.**

LEFFLER (James Henry)

— The bee and the wasp. [Song, begins: "A wasp met a bee".]
London, [1818.] fol.   **H. 1675. (20.)**

— The Britannia in a Storm, [song,] *etc. Goulding, Phipps &
D'Almaine: London,* [1803.] fol.   **G. 383. h. (63.)**

— "Dicky White," [song,] the words and music by Mr. L. Senʳ.
London, [1807.] fol.   **H. 1675. (21.)**

— Anthem. I will arise and go to my Father, for four Voices,
etc. pp. 3. *Preston: London,* [ᵂᴹ1804.] fol. **G. 517. gg. (4.)**

— Lucy, a Ballad ... The Words by R. Bloomfield, *etc. Preston,
for the Author: London,* [1810?] fol.   **G. 383. h. (62.)**

— Morning and evening hymns [the words by Bishop T. Ken],
to which are added a few interludes, arranged by J. H.
Leffler. *London,* [1818.] fol.   **H. 1675. (19.)**

— O do not think because I smile. Canzonet, the words by
Mʳ F.L., *etc. Printed for the Author, by J. Balls: London,*
[ᵂᴹ1817.] fol.   **H. 1650. yy. (10.)**

— The Savoyard, divertimento for the piano forte, *etc.* pp. 7.
Preston: London, [c. 1815.] fol.   **h. 3865. oo. (17.)**

LEFFLER (Sidney H.)

— Constable Jackson. Song, words by C. Bingham, *etc.* 2 no. [In
G and A.] *J. B. Cramer & Co.: London,* 1907. fol.
    H. 1794. vv. (29.)

— Night of Stars. [Song.] Written and composed by S. H.
Leffler, *etc. Oetzmann & Sons: London,* [1907.] fol.
    H. 1794. vv. (30.)

LEFFTZ (Joseph)

— Das Volkslied im Elsass. *Éditions Alsatia: Colmar, etc.,*
1966, *etc.* 8°.   **F. 1885.**

LE FILS (   ) *L'Abbé*

— Principes du violon, pour apprendre le doigté de cet
instrument et les différends [*sic*] agréments dont il est
susceptible, *etc.* pp. 81. *Chez Des Lauriers: Paris,* [1770?] fol.
Engraved throughout.   **Hirsch I. 313.**

LEFKOFF (GERALD)

— Five Sixteenth Century Venetian Lute Books ... A dissertation ... by G. Lefkoff. [Transcriptions in staff notation, with commentary.] pp. xv. 208. *Catholic University of America Press: Washington, D.C.,* 1960. 8°.　　**d. 89.**

LEFKOVITCH (LEONARD)

— *See* ABEL (C. F.) [*Collections.*] Sonata and two other Pieces for Viola da Gamba solo, *etc.* ⟨Arranged by L. Lefkovitch.⟩ [1953.] 4°.　　**h. 1761. (6.)**

— *See* HOTTETERRE (J.) called *le Romain.* [Pièces pour la flûte traversière. Liv. 1. Op. 2.—Pièces à deux flûtes.] Duo and Rondeau. For two treble recorders. Edited and revised ... by L. Lefkovitch. [1957.] 4°. [*Schott's Recorder Library.* 38.]　　**g. 112. a.**

— *See* QUANTZ (J. J.) Trio Sonata in C ... Edited with realization of the figured bass by ... Walter Bergmann & L. Lefkovitch. [1958.] 4°.　　**g. 109. m. (2.)**

— *See* VALENTINE (Robert) Sonata No. 1 in F, for Oboe and Piano, *etc.* ⟨Edited for L. Lefkovitch and W. Bergmann.⟩ [1952.] 4°.　　**h. 2665. f. (16.)**

— *See* VALENTINE (Robert) [Another issue.] Sonata No. 1 in F. Edited and arranged from the figured bass edition by L. Lefkovitch and W. Bergmann.⟩ [1952.] 4°. [*Schott's Recorder Series. no.* 34.]　　**g. 112.**

— *See* VALENTINE (Robert) Sonata No. 8 in G, for Oboe and Piano, *etc.* ⟨Edited ... by L. Lefkovitch and W. Bergmann.⟩ [1951.] 4°.　　**h. 2665. f. (17.)**

— *See* VALENTINE (Robert) [Another issue.] Sonata No. 8 in G. Edited and arranged from the figured bass edition by L. Lefkovitch and W. Bergmann. [1951.] 4°. [*Schott's Recorder Series. no.* 33.]　　**g. 112.**

LEFKOWITZ (MURRAY)

— *See* LAWES (William) Select Consort Music. Transcribed and edited by M. Lefkowitz. 1963. fol. [*Musica Britannica.* 21.]　　**N. 10.**

— *See* LAWES (William) Trois masques à la cour de Charles 1ᵉʳ d'Angleterre ... Introductions, commentaries et transcriptions par M. Lefkowitz. 1970. 4°.　　**S. E. 74/156.**

LEFLAIVE (CHARLES)

— Songs of Hope. [Hymns.] Second edition. *G. Morrish: London,* 1915. 4°.　　**E .602. hh. (4.)**

LE FLEM (PAUL)

— Auccassin et Nicolette. Chantefable en un prologue et trois parties ... Ombres de Geo Dorival et Marc Bordry. Partition pour chant et piano réduite par l'auteur. pp. 52. *Édition mutuelle: Paris,* [1910.] 4°.
The titlepage bears a MS. dedication in the composer's autograph.　　**H. 232. k. (2.)**

— Quintette en mi mineur pour piano, 2 violons, alto et violoncelle. [Score and parts.] 5 pt. *Édition mutuelle: Paris,* [1911.] fol
The titlepage bears a MS. dedication in the composer's autograph.　　**h. 2782. v. (1.)**

— *See* PERNOT (H.) En Pays Turc. L'Île de Chio ... Avec 17 mélodies populaires (... notées par P. Le Flem), *etc.* 1903. 8°.　　**10126. e. 30.**

— *See* PERNOT (H.) Mélodies populaires grecques de l'Île de Chio ... mises en musique par P. Le Flem. 1903. 8°.　　**E. 1572.**

LE FLEMING (ANTONY)

— Jazz Fiddle, *etc.* ⟨Arrangements of great standards. Arr. Antony le Fleming.⟩ [Score and part.] 2 pt. *Chappell & Company: London,* 1979. 4°.　　**g. 500. vv. (8.)**

— Pop Moods. For young duettists, *etc.* [P.F.] pp. 16. *Chappell & Co.: London,* [1975.] 4°.　　**f. 65. ee. (7.)**

— Popfiddle. Easy arrangements for violin and piano by Antony le Fleming. [Score and part.] 2 pt. *Chappell & Company: Ilford,* [1976.] 4°.　　**g. 500. vv. (7.)**

— Suite for junior String Orchestra. ⟨Full score.⟩ pp. 20. *Chappell & Co.: London,* [1975.] 4°.　　**f. 390. ww. (5.)**

— Summer lazy Rag ... For recorders, strings, percussion and piano. ⟨Score and parts.⟩ 12 pt. *Chappell & Co.: London,* [1977.] 4°.　　**f. 246. ll. (5.)**

LE FLEMING (CHRISTOPHER)

— Air, Poppele, for Violon, or Violoncello, and Pianoforte. *J. & W. Chester: London,* 1937. fol.　　**h. 1612. pp. (5.)**

— Air and Dance. For violin (cello or oboe) and pianoforte. [Score and violin part.] 2 pt. *J. & W. Chester:* [1954.] 4°.
An earlier edition of the air, published separately with the title "Air, Poppele," is entered above.　　**g. 505. xx. (8.)**

— Beeches. *See* infra: Trees in the Valley. Op. 40. No. 2.

— The Birthright. [Unison song.] Words by E. Lewis. *J. B. Cramer & Co.: London,* 1936. 4°.
[*Cramer's Library of Unison and Part Songs. No.* 127.]　　**E. 1678. a.**

— Bramshaw Folly, for Pianoforte. *J. & W. Chester: London,* 1937. fol.　　**h. 3870. k. (4.)**

— A Children's Te Deum. ⟨Unison song.⟩ Words by Barbara Godlee. [Staff and tonic sol-fa notation.] pp. 5. *J. B. Cramer & Co.: London,* [1954.] 8°.
[*Cramer's Library of Unison and Part Songs. No.* 252.]　　**E. 1678. a.**

— Six Country Songs. ⟨Opus 34.⟩ For S.T. soli, S.A.T.B. chorus and orchestra. Words by Thomas Hardy. [Vocal score.] pp. 34. *Novello & Co.: London,* [1963.] 8°.　　**E. 271. b. (1.)**

— Cradle Song for Christmas. Words by E. Farjeon. *Oxford University Press: London,* 1929. 8°.
[*The Oxford Choral Songs. No.* 1024.]　　**F. 1777. a.**

— Day that I have loved. For three part chorus (S.S.A.) and two pianos (or one piano and strings). Words by Rupert Brooke. ⟨Vocal score.⟩ pp. 24. *J. & W. Chester: London,* [1951.] 8°.　　**F. 1267. y. (7.)**

— Day that I have loved. For Three Part Ladies Voices. With accompaniment of Two Pianos or One Piano and Strings. Words by Rupert Brooke ... Chorus Part. pp. 13. *J. & W. Chester: London,* 1946. 8°.
The chorus part only.　　**F. 638. i. (52.)**

— Deo gratias Anglia. Agincourt hymn circa 1425. The original version (partly for 2, partly for 3 voices) arranged for S.A.B. choirs ... with or without accompaniment. Arranged by C. Le Fleming. pp. 8. *Elkin & Co.: London,* [1961.] 8°.
Part of "The Elkin new choral Series".　　**F. 1171. ss. (7.)**

— The Echoing Green. A Children's Cantata in two parts. *J. & W. Chester: London,* 1933. 8°.　　**F. 1267. i. (5.)**

— Egypt's Might is tumbled down. Song. ⟨Words by Mary Coleridge.⟩ pp. 4. *J. & W. Chester: London,* [1949.] 4°.　　**G. 1270. ww. (46.)**

— The Elm. *See* infra: Trees in the Valley. Op. 40. No. 6.

— An Epitaph. *See* infra: Five Songs of Earth and Air. 3.

LE FLEMING (CHRISTOPHER)

— The Hills of Heaven. (Song.) Poem by M. Webb. *J. & W. Chester: London*, 1931. fol.   **H. 1860. h. (1.)**

— The Holly. *See* infra: Trees in the Valley. Op. 40. No. 3.

— Homage to Beatrix Potter. Six short pieces for wind ensemble (flute, oboe, 2 clarinets and bassoon), *etc.* [Score and parts.] 6 pt. *J. & W. Chester: London*, [1971.] 8°.   **f. 390. mm. (3.)**

— Hymnus, God be in my Head, for Voice and Pianoforte. (Words from the Sarum Primer, 1558.) *J. & W. Chester: London*, 1934. fol.   **H. 1186. f. (1.)**

— I love all beauteous Things. Unison Song with Descant, words by R. Bridges. Op. 12. No. 6. *J. B. Cramer & Co.: London*, 1943. 8°. [*Cramer's Library of Unison and Part Songs. No.* 197.]   **E. 1678. a.**

— I love all beauteous Things. Part-song S.A.T.B. with piano accompaniment, *etc.* [Staff and tonic sol-fa notation.] pp. 11. *J. B. Cramer & Co.: London*, [1955.] 8°. [*Cramer's choral Library B.* 58.]   **F. 157. g.**

— If it's ever Spring again. Song. (Words by T. Hardy. Opus 12. No. 5.) *J. & W. Chester: London*, 1943. 4°.   **G. 1270. tt. (34.)**

— In a sleepless Night. (Song.) Poem by W. H. H. *J. & W. Chester: London*, 1931. fol.   **H. 1860. h. (2.)**

— A King of so great Worth. (A Christmas carol.) Two-part (S.A.) with piano. Words by Winifred Fayerman. (Translated from a medieval French carol.) [Staff and tonic sol-fa notation.] pp. 4. *Elkin & Co.: London*, [1958.] 8°. *Elkin new choral Series.* 2515.   **F. 260. h. (47.)**

— Let Folly praise what Fancy loves. For unison singing, with descant. Words by the Blessed R. Southwell S. J. (1561–95). pp. 4. *Elkin & Co.: London*, [1960.] 8°. *Elkin new choral Series.* 2584.   **E. 812. b. (26.)**

— Lighten our Darkness. A Collect, S.A. or T.B. (Op. 12. No. 4.) *J. & W. Chester: London*, 1945. 8°.   **E. 602. ww. (15.)**

— Magnificat and Nunc dimittis in D, *etc.* (Op. 22.) pp. 16. *F. W. Dwelly:* [*London*, 1952.] 4°.   **F. 1176. q. (24.)**

— Magnificat and Nunc dimittis in D, *etc.* (Op. 22. S.A.T.B.) pp. 16. *Oxford University Press: London*, [1958.] 8°. [*Oxford Church Services. S.* 542.]   **F. 1777. c.**

— More Rounds and Canons. For voices and recorders. Compiled by C. Le Fleming. pp. 16. *Mills Music: London*, [1964.] 8°.   **F. 1196. l. (18.)**

— [Three Motets for Christmas. No. 1.] I sing of a Maiden. (S.S.A.T.B.B. (unacc.)) Words: anon. (15th century.) pp. 6. *Oxford University Press: London*, [1967.] 8°. [*Oxford Choral Songs. X* 165.]   **F. 1777. m.**

— [Three Motets for Christmas. No. 1.] [A reissue.] I sing of a Maiden, *etc. Roberton Publications: Wendover*, [1974.] 8°.   **F. 321. gg. (12.)**

— [Three Motets for Christmas. No. 2, 3.] Two Motets for Christmas. SSATBB unaccompanied. 1. The Changing Night. Words by Grace Armitage, *etc.* (2. Cradle Song. Words by Arthur Fforde.) pp. 12. *Roberton Publications: Wendover*, [1974.] 8°.   **E. 1439. q. (5.)**

— Nocturne. Tween-ea, for Pianoforte, *etc. J. & W. Chester: London*, 1933. fol.   **h. 3870. i. (16.)**

— O be joyful. Jubilate Deo. Set for S.A. choir. Psalm 100 as in the Book of Common Prayer. [Staff and tonic sol-fa notation.] pp. 4. *J. B. Cramer & Co.: London*, [1966.] 8°. [*Cramer's Library of Unison and Part Songs. No.* 318.]   **E. 1678. a.**

LE FLEMING (CHRISTOPHER)

— O mortal Folk, you may behold and see. (An epitaph.) Two-part song with pianoforte accompaniment, words by Stephen Hawes, d. 1523. Op. 16. No. 1. pp. 4. *J. Curwen & Sons: London*, [1947.] 8°. [*Choruses for equal Voices. no.* 2136.]   **E. 861.**

— O Waly, Waly. Somerset folk song for S.S.A. unaccompanied. Collected by Cecil Sharp and arranged by C. Le Fleming. [Staff and tonic sol-fa notation.] pp. 7. *Boosey & Hawkes: London*, [1955.] 8°. [*Boosey's modern Festival Series. no.* 233.]   **F. 160. f.**

— The Oak. *See* infra: Trees in the Valley. Op. 40. No. 8.

— Of all the Trees in England. *See* infra: Five Songs of Earth and Air. 1.

— The Old stone House. *See* infra: Five Songs of Earth and Air. 2.

— Once in a While. Song, words by B. Sievier. *Boosey & Co.:* [*London*,] 1935. 4°.   **G. 1275. pp. (7.)**

— The Peter Rabbit Music Books. For pianoforte ... With illustrations by Beatrix Potter, *etc.* 2 bk. *J. & W. Chester: London; Frederick Warne & C London, New York*, [1935.] 4°.   **g. 1129. ss.**

— Pilford Suite ... (For elementary string orchestra.) Score, *etc.* pp. 17. *J. B. Cramer: London*, [1950.] 4°.   **g. 727. n. (7.)**

— Pilford Suite ... Score ... Parts. [Revised edition.] 7 pt. *J. B. Cramer & Co.: London*, [1951.] 4°. *Part of the "Cramer School orchestral Series".*   **h. 3210. i. (111.)**

— The Plane. *See* infra: Trees in the Valley. Op. 40. No. 1.

— Poplars. *See* infra: Trees in the Valley. Op. 40. No. 7.

— Praise be to God. Three-part song. (S.S.A.) Words by E. M. Towner. [Staff and tonic sol-fa notation.] pp. 7. *Elkin & Co.: London*, [1959.] 8°. *Elkin new choral Series. no.* 2546.   **E. 442. z. (43.)**

— Prevent us, O Lord. (For S.S.A. unaccompanied.) Words from the Book of Common Prayer. pp. 3. *J. B. Cramer: London*, [1950.] 8°. *Unison Songs & Carols, etc. no.* 39.   **F. 1176. l. (30.)**

— Five Psalms for Soprano Solo, Chorus and Orchestra, *etc.* (Vocal score.) pp. 47. *J. & W. Chester: London*, [1947.] 8°.   **F. 1176. t. (1.)**

— [Five Psalms. No. 5.] O praise God in his Holiness. (Psalm 150.) Anthem for full choir with organ ... Revised and arranged by Laurence H. Davies. pp. 15. *J. & W. Chester: London*, [1966.] 8°. *Part of "Contemporary Church Music Series".*   **E. 442. hh. (4.)**

— Pull Devil—Pull Baker. A verse mime by K. M. Baxter. With music arranged from English traditional sources by Christopher Le Fleming. [Vocal score.] pp. 40. 1951. 4°. *See* LONDON.— *Religious Drama Society.*   **F. 1267. bb. (1.)**

— A Quiet Company. Song cycle for baritone or mezzo-soprano voice and pianoforte. Six epitaphs and a memorial inscription from "Ding Dong Bell" by Walter de la Mare ... Op. 18. pp. 19. *J. B. Cramer & Co.: London*, [1953.] 4°.   **F. 1196. a. (13.)**

— [A Quiet Company. Op. 18. No. 6.] Three Sisters, *etc.* [Song.] pp. 3. *J. B. Cramer & Co.: London*, [1961.] 4°.   **G. 1276. t. (15.)**

— The Ride by Nights. *See* infra: Five Songs of Earth and Air. 4.

LE FLEMING (CHRISTOPHER)

— Rounds & Canons. For voices and recorders. Compiled by
C. Le Fleming. Preface by Robert Salkeld. pp. 15. *Mills
Music: London*, [1961.] 8°.   **F. 1196. l. (7.)**

— St. David's. Part-song for S.A. and piano. Words by Eiluned
Lewis. pp. 7. *Novello & Co.: London*, [1961.] 8°.
[*Two-part Songs.* 371.]   **F. 280. e.**

— St. David's. Part-song for SATB and piano. Words by
Eiluned Lewis. pp. 7. *Novello & Co.: London*, [1964.] 8°.
[*Part-Song Book.* 1602.]   **F. 280. b.**

— Sheep Shearing. Dorset Folk Song. Arranged by C. Le
Fleming. *J. & W. Chester: London*, 1931. fol.
    H. 1248. d. (9.)

— The Silver Dove ... ⟨A morality with music.⟩ Words by K. M.
Baxter. Vocal score, *etc.* pp. 35. *Mills Music: London*, [1965.]
4°.   **G. 1268. rr. (1.)**

— The Silver Dove ... Chorus parts, *etc.* pp. 6. *Mills Music:
London*, [1965.] 8°.   **F. 1256. x. (7.)**

— Since we stay not here. Anthem for five-part mixed choir
unaccompanied. ⟨Words by Jeremy Taylor (from Holy
dying).⟩ pp. 11. *Roberton Publications: Wendover*, [1977.] 8°.
    E. 442. ee. (18.)

— Sing happy Child. Mezzo soprano solo and S.A.T.B. chorus.
Words by Eiluned Lewis. pp. 3. *J. B. Cramer & Co.: London*,
[1970.] 8°.
[*Cramer's choral Library. no.* 175.]   **F. 157. d.**

— The Singing Friar, for Tenor—or Light Baritone—Solo,
Chorus and Orchestra ... Words by Thomas Love Peacock,
etc. (Vocal Score.) *J. & W. Chester: London*, 1939. 8°.
    F. 607. ss. (8.)

— A Smuggler's Song. [Unison song, words by] Rudyard
Kipling. pp. 5. *Oxford University Press: London*, [1950.] 8°.
[*The Oxford Choral Songs. No.* 1222.]   **F. 1777. a.**

— A Smuggler's Song, *etc.* ⟨Two-part.⟩ pp. 6. *Oxford University
Press: London*, [1960.] 8°.
[*Oxford Choral Songs. T* 45.]   **F. 1777. m.**

— Four Songs from the Canterbury Tales. For unison voices
and piano. Words by Geoffrey Chaucer from the prologue to
The Canterbury Tales. ⟨1. When that Aprille. 2. The Nun's
Song. 3. The Clerk of Oxenford. 4. The Wife of Bath's Song.⟩
[Staff and tonic sol-fa notation.] 2 no. *Novello & Co.:
London*, [1962.] 8°.
[*School Songs.* 2061, 2062.]   **F. 280. d.**

— Five Songs of Earth and Air. Suite for women's voices. 1. Of
all the Trees. (Unison.) 2. The Old stone House. (Three part.)
3. An Epitaph. (Two part.) 4. The Ride by Nights. (Three
part.) 5. Wanderers. (Unison.) Poems by Walter de la Mare.
[Staff and tonic sol-fa notation.] no. 1, 3, 5. *J. B. Cramer &
Co.: London*, [1961.] 8°.
[*Cramer's Library of Unison and Part Songs. No.* 290–292.]
No. 2 *and* 4 *form no.* 92, 93 *of Cramer's choral Library B.*
    E. 1678. a.

— Five Songs of Earth and Air. Suite for women's voices. 1. Of
all the Trees. (Unison.) 2. Old Stone House. (Three part.)
3. An Epitaph. (Two part.) 4. The Ride by Nights. (Three
part.) 5. Wanderers. (Unison.) Poems by Walter de la Mare.
[Staff and tonic sol-fa notation.] no. 2, 4. *J. B. Cramer &
Co.: London*, [1961.] 8°.
[*Cramer's choral Library B. no.* 92, 93.] *No.* 1, 3 *and* 5 *form
no.* 290–292 *of Cramer's Library of Unison and Part Songs.*
    F. 157. g.

— Spring has now unwrapped the Flowers. (Flower carol.)
Words from Piae Cantiones 1582, trans. by Percy Dearmer
... Arranged by C. Le Fleming. ⟨S.S.A.⟩ [Staff and tonic sol-fa
notation.] pp. 7. *J. B. Cramer & Co.: London*, [1957.] 8°.
[*Cramer's choral Library B.* 72.]   **F. 157. g.**

LE FLEMING (CHRISTOPHER)

— Springtime. ⟨Two-part.⟩ Words by Grace Armitage. pp. 4.
Oxford University Press: London, [1967.] 8°.
[*Oxford Choral Songs. T* 88.]   **F. 1777. m.**

— Springtime. ⟨Unison.⟩ Words by Grace Armitage. pp. 4.
Oxford University Press: London, [1967.] 8°.
[*Oxford Choral Songs. U* 127.]   **F. 1777. m.**

— Squirrel Nutkin. A children's play. Adapted by Beatrix Potter
from her original story. Music adapted and arranged from
traditional tunes by C. Le Fleming. pp. 23. *Frederick Warne
& Co.: London, New York*, [1967.] 4°. **G. 1487. e. (2.)**

— Strings in the Earth and Air. Two-part song, words by James
Joyce. [Staff and tonic sol-fa notation.] pp. 4. *Elkin & Co.:
London*, [1955.] 8°.
Elkin new choral Series. no. 2384.   **E. 263. l. (35.)**

— Sunday Morning and Whistling Tune. Two pieces for piano,
etc. pp. 5. *Oxford University Press: London*, [1963.] 4°.
    g. 1128. ii. (18.)

— Sutton Valence Suite. Op. 25. For amateur and school
orchestra. Full score. pp. 52. *Boosey & Hawkes: London, etc.*,
[1963.] 4°.   **g. 860. j. (6.)**

— Te Deum and Benedictus ... in ... C ... Op. 27. [S.A.T.B.]
pp. 20. *Novello & Co.: London*, [1960.] 8°.
[*Parish Choir Book. no.* 1384.]   **E. 618.**

— Three Sisters. *See* supra: [A Quiet Company. Op. 18. No. 6.]

— To an Isle in the Water. (Song.) Poem by W. B. Yeats.
J. & W. Chester: London, 1931. fol. **H. 1860. h. (3.)**

— Three Traditional Tunes. Arranged for string quartet and
double bass (optional). Score, *etc.* pp. 13. *Novello & Co.:
London*, [1961.] 8°.   **e. 668. jj. (12.)**

— Trees in the Valley. Op. 40. Words by Grace Armitage. 1. The
Plane. Unison and piano ... 2. Beeches. Two-part or unison
and piano ... 3. The Holly. SSA and piano ... 4. The Willow.
Unison and piano ... 5. The Yew. SA and piano ... 6. The
Elm. SSA and piano ... 7. Poplars. Unison and piano ...
8. The Oak. Two-part or unison and piano. 8 no. *Boosey &
Hawkes:* [*London*, 1973.] 8°.
[*Boosey's modern festival Series no.* 847–854.] **F. 160. f.**

— Unseen Comradeship. Unison song ⟨with optional Descant⟩.
Words by Marion Sinclair. pp. 7. *J. B. Cramer & Co.:
London*, [1952.] 8°.
[*Cramer's Library of Unison and Part Songs. No.* 238.]
    E. 1678. a.

— Valley of Arun. Choral suite for baritone solo, SATB chorus
& orchestra. ⟨Opus 33. Words by Hilaire Belloc.⟩ [Vocal
score.] pp. 33. *Novello & Co.: London*, [1962.] 8°.
    E. 1500. j. (1.)

— Wanderers. *See* supra: Five Songs of Earth and Air. 5.

— When wintry Weather's all a-done. Two-part Song, words by
W. Barnes. *J. B. Cramer & Co.: London*, 1937. 4°.
[*Cramer's Library of Unison and Part Songs. No.* 137.]
    E. 1678. a.

— The Willow. *See* supra: Trees in the Valley. Op. 40. No. 4.

— The Wraggle taggle Gypsies, O! English folk-song for
unaccompanied voices. ⟨S.A.T.B.⟩ Arranged by C. Le Fleming.
pp. 8. *Oxford University Press: London*, [1950.] 8°.
[*Oxford Folk-song Series. no.* 49.]   **F. 1777. e.**

— The Yew. *See* supra: Trees in the Valley. Op. 40. No. 5.

— *See* BACH (J. S.) [*Collected Works.—g.*] Two Chorales ...
Adaptation for Two Pianofortes, four hands, by C. Le
Fleming. 1934. 4°.   **g. 548. y. (4.)**

LE FLEMING (CHRISTOPHER)

— *See* BACH (J. S.) [Clavierübung. Tl. 3.] Prelude and Fugue in E flat major. St. Anne ... Arr. C. Le Fleming. 1943. 4°.
g. 548. pp. (11.)

— *See* BACH (J. S.) Wachet auf, ruft uns die Stimme ... Arranged by C. Le Fleming. 1940. 4°.
g. 548. nn. (17.)

— *See* BACH (J. S.) [Was mir behagt.] Schafe können sicher weiden ... arranged ... by C. Le Fleming. 1940. 4°.
g. 548. nn. (16.)

— *See* STRAUSS (J.) *the Younger.* [An der schönen blauen Donau.] Donau Walzer ... Pianoforte transcription by C. Le Fleming. 1932. fol.
h. 3870. i. (4.)

— *See* STRAUSS (J.) *the Younger.* Geschichten aus [or rather, aus] dem Wiener Wald. (Op. 325.) Tales from the Vienna Woods ... Arranged for Two Pianos by C. Le Fleming. 1938. fol.
h. 3291. e. (7.)

— *See* SULLIVAN (*Sir* Arthur S.) The Mikado ... Arranged for school performance by C. Le Fleming, *etc.* 1975. 8°.
E. 504. g. (2.)

LEFNDEG

— *See* LLEFNDEG.

LEFORT (A.)

— Berceuse pour Violon & Piano. *Paris,* [1878.] fol.
h. 1609. m. (11.)

— 6 Morceaux pour violon avec accompagnement de piano. No. 1. Prière. No. 2. Petite Valse lente. No. 3. Barcarolle. No. 4. Chanson villageoise. No. 5. Barcelonnette. No. 6. Air de Ballet. *Durand & Schœnewerk: Paris,* [1886.] fol.
h. 1608. q. (38.)

— *See* BACH (J. S.) [6 Sonaten für Clavier und Violine.] 6 sonates ... Révision par Claude Debussy. ⟨Partie de violon révisée par A. Lefort.⟩ [1951.] 4°.
g. 699. x. (1.)

— *See* RENAUD DE VILBAC (A.Z.C.) 12 Duos pittoresques ... revus ... par A. Lefort. [1880.] fol.
h. 1715.

— *See* RENAUD DE VILBAC (A.Z.C.) and LEFORT (A.) Les Trios Dramatiques, *etc.* [1877.] 4°. [*Collection Litolff. vol.* 849, 850.]
g. 375.

— *See* VOGEL (A.) and LEFORT (A.) Le Concert au Salon, *etc.* [1881.] 4°. [*Collection Litolff. vol.* 581, 582, 873, 874, 1171, 1172, 1723, 1724.]
g. 375.

— *See* VOGEL (A.) and LEFORT (A.) Les Duos Dramatiques, *etc.* [1877.] 4°. [*Collection Litolff. vol.* 851–856, 1198, 1572.]
g. 375.

— *See* WEBER (C. M. F. E. von) [Aufforderung zum Tanz. Op. 65.] L'Invitation à la valse. Rondeau brillant ... Arrangé pour piano et violon par Vogel et A. Lefort. [1879.] 4°. [*Collection Litolff. vol.* 867.]
g. 375.

LEFORT (GEORGES)

— [La Bonne Année.] A Happy New Year [Song, begins: "A time of revel."] ... Written by H. B. Farnie. *London,* [1872.] fol.
H. 1775. u. (9.)

— The Early Leaflet. [Song.] *See* infra: [La première feuille.]

— The First Leaf of Spring. *See* infra: [La première feuille.]

— A Happy New Year. [Song.] *See* supra: [La Bonne Année.]

— [La Neige.] The Snow ... [Song, begins: "All bid me welcome".] The English words by M. X. Hayes. *London,* [1877.] fol.
H. 1778. y. (2.)

LEFORT (GEORGES)

La première feuille

— The Early Leaflet. (La première feuille.) [Song, begins: "Since the sun".] (English version by C. D'Arcy.) *London,* [1872.] fol.
H. 1775. u. (10.)

— The First Leaf. (La première feuille.) [Song.] Written by H. B. Farnie. *London,* [1872.] fol.
H. 1775. u. (8.)

— Spring's first leaf. Romance. English words by C. J. Rowe. *London,* [1873.] fol.
H. 1778. y. (1.)

— The First Leaf of Spring. [Song.] ... English version by Nella. *London,* [1874.] fol.
No. 5322, 23 *of the "Musical Bouquet".*
H. 2345.

— La Première Feuille. Romance. *Londres,* [1877.] fol.
H. 1785. c. (32.)

— The Snow. [Song.] *See* supra: [La Neige.]

LEFORT (JULES) *Composer of dance music*

— La Coquette. Deux Pas. [P. F.] *Boosey & Co.: London and New York,* 1907. fol.
h. 3286. ll. (23.)

— Deux pas. "La Coquette." J. Lefort. ⟨Arr. by M. Retford⟩ ... Valse. "C'est moi." A. Petromarchi. ⟨Arr. by M. Retford⟩ ... Duet. "Una Notte a Venezia." Lucantoni ... Danse nouvelle. "Mousmousse." Gimenez y Vives. ⟨Arr. by M. Retford.⟩ ⟨Conductor [and military band parts].⟩ 33 pt. *Boosey & Co.: London,* 1908. fol.
[*Boosey's military Journal. ser.* 125. *no.* 3.]
h. 1549.

— Idéale. Valse lente pour Piano. *Enoch & Sons: London,* 1906. fol.
h. 3286. ll. (24.)

LEFORT (JULES) *Teacher of singing*

— C. W. Glover's ... ballad, "'Tis hard to give the hand," transcribed for the Pianoforte. *London,* [1859.] fol.
h. 1460. v. (11.)

— De l'Émission de la Voix. *Paris,* [1868.] 8°.
F. 173.

— Méthode de Chant. *Paris,* [1874.] 4°.
G. 491.

LE FROID (   )

— Pourquoy venir troubler le repos de ma vie. *Air Nouveau.* [*Paris,* 1678.] *s. sh. obl.* 4°.
Nouveau Mercure Galant, May, 1678, *p.* 45.
P. P. 4482.

— Que sert à mon amour. *Air Nouveau.* [*Paris,*] 1679. *s. sh. obl.* 4°.
Nouveau Mercure Galant, June, 1679, *p.* 131.
P. P. 4482.

LE FROID DE MÉREAUX (JEAN AMÉDÉE)

— Au Bord de la Mer. Barcarolle pour Piano. *Paris,* [1861.] fol.
h. 1462. t. (27.)

— Barcarolle-étude. [P. F.] *In:* PERIODICAL PUBLICATIONS. — *Paris.* — *La Revue et gazette musicale.* Album des pianistes, *etc.* pp. 12–15. [c. 1845.] fol.
h. 1203. r. (9.)

— Une Chanson d'autrefois, arabesque pour Piano. *Paris,* [1861.] fol.
h. 1462. t. (26.)

— Les Clavecinistes de 1637 à 1790. 52 liv. (Histoire du Clavecin, portraits et biographies, *etc.*) *Heugel & Cie: Paris,* [1864–67.] fol.
h. 1052. c.

— Le Départ des Pélerins, caprice caractéristique pour le Piano. *Paris,* [1872.] fol.
h. 1487. s. (5.)

— Entr'acte-Gavotte de Mignon, opéra d'A. Thomas. Improvisata pour Piano. *Paris,* [1867.] fol.
h. 1462. t. (28.)

LE FROID DE MÉREAUX (Jean Amédée)

—— Grand Trio pour Piano, Violon & Violoncelle. Op. 102.
Paris, [1873.] fol.   **h. 2879.**

—— Grandes études pour piano en soixante caprices
caracteristiques dans le style libre et dans le style sévère.
Op. 63. 5 Liv.   *Paris*, [1855.] fol.   **h. 1052.**

—— Hymne de la Nuit pour Violoncelle et Piano ou Orgue.
Paris, [1877.] fol.   **h. 1849. h. (15.)**

—— Hymne du Matin pour Violon et Piano ou Orgue.   *Paris*,
[1877.] fol.   **h. 1609. m. (16.)**

—— Inquiétude, andante pour Piano.   *Paris*, [1861.] fol.
                                              h. 1462. t. (24.)

—— Mélodie. [P. F.] *In:* KEEPSAKE. Keepsake des pianistes, *etc.*
pp. 20–22. [1841.] fol.   **g. 442. dd. (10.)**

—— Quatuor pour deux Violons, Alto et Violoncelle.   *Paris*,
[1877.] fol.   **h. 2830. d. (10.)**

—— Romance-Étude pour le Piano.   *Paris*, [1861.] fol.
                                              h. 1462. t. (23.)

—— Souvenir de la Bastide, villanelle pour le Piano.   *Paris*,
[1872.] fol.   **h. 1487. s. (4.)**

—— "Sur l'eau qui te balance." Barcarolle de C. P. Lafont, variée
pour le piano ... Oe. 30. pp. 15.   *Chez Frédéric Hofmeister:
Leipzig*, [1831?] fol.   **h. 721. t. (15.)**

—— Transcriptions concertantes d'œuvres ... des grands maitres
... Duos, trios et quatuors pour Piano, orgue, violon et
violoncelle. 12 no.   *Paris*, [1861.] fol.   **h. 1052. a.**

—— 24 Transcriptions concertantes ... pour Piano et Orgue.
No. 13–24.   *Paris*, [1874.] fol.
Imperfect; wanting no. 1–12.   **h. 1458. i. (4.)**

—— Les Travestissements, gavotte variée pour Piano.   *Paris*,
[1861.] fol.   **h. 1462. t. (25.)**

—— *See* BERLIOZ (L. H.) L'enfance du Christ ... Transcription
pour le piano par A. Méreaux et T. Ritter, *etc.* [1855.] 8°.
                                                     F. 103. g.

—— *See* MEYERBEER (G.) [*Collections, Instrumental.*] Quarante
Mélodies ... arrangées ... par. A. Méreaux. [1879.] 8°.
                                                        f. 277.

LE FROID DE MÉREAUX (Joseph Nicolas)

—— Les Psaumes de David mis en vers Français ... Nouvelle
édition revue et corrigée par J. N. Méreaux.   *Paris*, 1829. 16°.
                                                  3434. aa. 10.

LE FROID DE MÉREAUX (Nicolas Jean)

—— Alexandre aux Indes. Opéra en trois actes ... Opera VI.
Représenté pour la premiere fois ... le ... 26 août 1783. Le
Poëme est de M. Morel. [Score.]   *Chez Des Lauriers: Paris*,
[1785.] fol.   **H. 507.**

—— [Alexandre aux Indes.] Quand le destin jaloux. *Air, etc.* 1784.
8°. *See* ALEXANDRE.   **B. 362. h. (39.)**

—— Arriettes de la Fête Donnés à Monsieur de La Garde ... Les
Parolles par Mr.*** [F. A. Quétant] ... Gravé par Mlle. Fleury.
pp. 8.   *Récoquilliée: [Paris*, 1770.] 8°.   **11738. m. 2. (1*.)**

—— Laurette. Comédie en un acte et en prose ... Opera III. Les
paroles sont de Mr Danzel de Malzeville ... Gravée par Mme
Lobry. [Score.] pp. 75.   *Chez Mmes Le Menu et Boyer: Paris*,
[1777.] fol.   **H. 507. a.**

—— [Oedipe à Thèbes.] Toccata ... Arranged by C. Dickinson.
C. F. Summy Co.: Chicago, (1909.) obl. fol.   **f. 314. y. (3.)**

LE FROID DE MÉREAUX (Nicolas Jean)

—— La Ressource Comique, Pièce en un Acte, mêlée d'Ariettes;
précédée d'un Prologue. [Words] Par M. Anseaume, *etc.*
Chez La Veuve Duchesne: Paris, 1772. 8°.   **11738. b. 15. (5.)**

—— Le Retour de la Tendresse, Comédie en un Acte et en vers,
mêlée d'Ariettes, *etc.* [Words by L. Anseaume.]   *Chez la
Veuve Duchesne: Paris*, 1774. 8°.   **11738. b. 15. (2.)**

LEFT

—— Left Alone. Song. *See* FERRARI (F. J.)

—— The Left-at-home Brigade. Song. *See* KENWAY (George)

—— The Left-Behind. Song. *See* HARTLEY (E. G.)

—— Left behind. Song. *See* MUSORGSKY (M. P.)

—— Left behind. [Song.] *See* OLIVER (H.)

—— Left behind. Song. *See* WEEKS (W.)

—— Left Book Club Musicians' Group. *See* ENGLAND.

—— Left! Left! Song. *See* DAMERELL (Stanley J.) and NEAT (J.)

—— Left of his own Accord. Song. *See* HALLIE (Dave)

—— Left on the Quay. Song. *See* PARKER (Henry T.)

—— Left—right! Song. *See* CONNOR (T. W.)

—— Left! Right! Song. *See* F., E.

—— Left, right. Song. *See* RUFFLE (J.)

—— Left-right March. [Song.] *See* SOUSA (John P.)

—— Left untold. Song. *See* COWEN (*Sir* F. H.)

—— Left us. Song. *See* PETHER (Henry E.)

LEFTWICH (Henry Thomas)

—— Jig for the pianoforte.   *E. Ashdown: London*, [1883.] fol.
                                              g. 543. j. (24.)

—— Now sing again ye happy birds. Spring song.   *London*,
[1864.] fol.   **H. 1772. r. (29.)**

—— Sleep my darling. Cradle song.   *London*, [1863.] fol.
                                              H. 1772. r. (28.)

—— Twelve Solos. A choice collection of operatic melodies ...
arranged with variations for the flute. 12 no.   *Clinton & Co.:
London*, [c. 1860.] fol.   **h. 2050. l. (3.)**

LEFTWICH (Vernon)

—— Autumn Leaves. Song, words by S. Wilbraham. 2 no. [In D
flat and D.]   *E. Ashdown: London*, 1906. fol.
                                              G. 805. mm. (27.)

—— Our Debt of Honour. [Musical monologue.] Written by
R. Leftwich, *etc. Reynolds & Co.: London*, 1914. fol.
Musical Monologues, No. 123.   **H. 2087.**

—— Two Songs. 1. Be true to me O Star. 2. Love's Supremacy.
Words by R. Croxton. 3 no. [Low, medium and high.]
E. Ashdown: London, 1907. fol.   **G. 805. mm. (28.)**

—— Were I the Flower. Song, words by R. Croxton. 2 no. [In C
and D.]   *E. Ashdown: London, etc.*, 1906. fol.
                                              G. 807. kk. (1.)

LEGA

—— La Lega. Dramma lirico. *See* JOSSE (G.)

—— La Lega Lombarda. Drama lirico. *See* COTTRAU (G.)

LEGA

— La Lega Lombarda. [Chorus.] *See* MARCARINI (G.) 5 Canti Corali.

LEGACIES

— Legacies. [Song.] *See* HILL (M. J.)

— Legacies. [Song.] *See* ROMA (C.)

LEGACY

— The Legacy. [Song.] *See* WHEN. When in death I shall calm recline. [1879.] fol. **H. 2324.**

— The Legacy. [Unison song.] *See* COLE (Hugo)

— The Legacy. [Song.] *See* MOORE (Thomas) *the Poet.* [A Selection of Irish Melodies. 2nd Number.—When in Death I shall calm recline.]

— The Legacy. Song. *See* WESTERNE (A.)

LEGAI (   )

— Lorsque sur ta musette. *Musette, etc. Gravée par Labassée. Imprimée par Torunelle:* [*Paris,*] 1757. *s. sh.* 8°. *Mercure de France, July,* 1757. **297. d. 8.**

LE GALLIENNE (DORIAN)

— Four Nursery Rhymes. Songs with pianoforte accompaniment ... Traditional words ... [No. 1.] I had a little Nut Tree. [No. 2.] There was a King. [No. 3.] Peter White. [No. 4.] Grey Goose & Gander. pp. 7. *Augener: London,* [1955.] 4°. **G. 1276. o. (5.)**

— Trio for Oboe, Violin and Viola ... Edited by Noël Nickson. (String parts bowed by John Glickman. Score.) pp. 28. *University of Western Australia, Department of Music: Nedlands,* [1976.] 8°. [*Studies in Music. no.* 10. *Supplement* (*Music Series* 9).] **P. 431/86.**

LEGARD (   )

— Recueil d'Airs François, et Italiens, avec un Accompagnement de Harpe ou de Clavecin, *etc. To be had at Mr Vogler's: London,* [1780.] fol. *This collection contains songs by Gluck, Piccini, Rauzzini, Albanese, Millico, Grétry, Bertoni, Edelman, Sacchini, Gazzaniga, Collizzi, Paesiello, Des Aides, d'Arondeau and Salieri.* **G. 295. a. (4.)**

LEGARDÈ (EUGENE)

— A Stray Thought. Rêverie pour Piano. *C. Begg & Co.: Dunedin,* (1910.) fol. **h. 3283. jj. 42.**

LEGARDE (MAURICE)

— *See* MEYERBEER (G.) [Les Huguenots.] Ouverture, *etc.* (Arr.: by M. Legarde.) [Military band.] 1906. fol. [*Boosey's military Journal. ser.* 121. *no.* 1.] **h. 1549.**

LEGARDE (PIERRE)

— Braga's Serenata ... arranged by P. Legarde. *See* RECREATIONS. Recreations for the Violin and Piano. No. 4. [1888.] fol. **h. 210. g. (33.)**

— The Court Minuet in A♭ for the Piano. *London,* [1879.] fol. **h. 1494. q. (9.)**

— Honour and Fame, march for the Piano. *London,* [1879.] fol. **h. 1494. q. (10.)**

LEGARDE (PIERRE)

— Pianoforte Sketches. *E. Donajowski: London,* [1901.] fol. *The Castle Series of Music Books, No.* 24. **h. 2924.**

— A Rambler's Sketches ... Easy Compositions for the pianoforte. no. 1–3. *W. Marshall & Co.: London,* [1880.] fol. *No more published.* **h. 1489. s. (29.)**

LEGARDO (JEAN)

— Daffodils. [P. F.] *Orpheus Music Publishing Co.: London,* 1911. fol. **h. 3284. g. (5.)**

— Rosebuds.—Valse etude.—[P. F.] *Orpheus Music Publishing Co.: London,* 1914. fol. **h. 3284. nn. (38.)**

LEGARÉ (ÉTIENNE)

— Recueil de Cantiques, anciens et nouveaux, en l'honneur de la Sainte Vierge, du Sacré-Cœur de Jésus, de Saint Joseph et de Sainte Anne, texte et musique, les Prières du Matin, du Soir, pour la Messe, la Confession et la Communion, *etc. J. A. Langlais & Fils: Québec,* 1908. 16°. **A. 499. h.**

LÉGAT DE FURCY (ANTOINE)

— L'Amant Indécis. Chanson. (Les paroles de M. P. M. B. L., *etc.*) [*Paris,*] 1767. *s. sh.* 8°. *Mercure de France, March,* 1767. **297. e. 6.**

— Autrefois aux pieds de Thémire. *Air, etc. Gravé par Mlle Labassée. Imprimé par Tournelle:* [*Paris,*] 1758. *s. sh.* 8°. *Mercure de France, March,* 1758. **297. d. 12.**

— En vain de coquettes Beautés. *Chanson.* (Les Paroles sont de M. Guichard, *etc.*) [*Paris,*] 1762. *s. sh.* 8°. *Mercure de France, Jan.,* 1762. **298. d. 1.**

— En vain un cœur bien enflammé. *Pastorale, etc. Gravé par Me Charpentié. Imprimé par Tournelle:* [*Paris,*] 1760. *s. sh.* 8°. *Mercure de France, August,* 1760. **297. d. 25.**

— Un matin sur son chalumeau. *Air, etc. Gravé par Mlle Labassée. Imprimé par Tournelle: Paris,* [1757.] *s. sh.* 8°. *Mercure de France, Nov.,* 1757. **297. d. 10.**

— Oeconomie du Plaisir. Ronde de Table. (Les Paroles de M. P***.) *Gravé par Me Charpentié. Imprimé par Tournelle:* [*Paris,*] 1762. *s. sh.* 8°. *Mercure de France, June,* 1762. **298. d. 3.**

— On peut encor dans la prairie. *Chanson. Gravé par Mlle Labassée:* [*Paris,* 1757.] *s. sh.* 8°. *Choix des Anciens Mercures, Tom. VIII., p.* 121. **297. h. 31.**

— Le Pour et le Contre, Romance, *etc.* (Les paroles sont de M. le Chevalier de Juilly Thomassin, *etc.*) *Gravé par Me Charpentié. Imprimé par Tournelle:* [*Paris,*] 1760. *s. sh.* 8°. *Mercure de France, Dec.,* 1760. **297. d. 26.**

— Que je vous aime! *Air, etc. Gravé par Mlle Labassée. Imprimé par Tournelle:* [*Paris,*] 1758. *s. sh.* 8°. *Mercure de France, April,* 1758. **297. d. 12.**

— Sans frayeur dans ce bois. *Air, etc. Gravé par Mlle Labassée:* [*Paris,* 1757.] *s. sh.* 8°. *Choix des Anciens Mercures, Tom. VI., p.* 144. **297. h. 30.**

— Nouveaux Solfèges ou Leçons de Musique dans le Genre moderne ... Gravés par Gerardin. *Chez Mr Bouin: Paris,* [1787.] fol. **G. 494.**

— Les Souvenirs du Vieux Temps. Romance [begins: "Giroflée au printems"]. Paroles de Mr. Salgat. *Paris,* [1820?] fol. **G. 557. (5.)**

— Vos yeux du tendre Amour. *Air, etc.* (Les Paroles sont de M. de Murville.) [*Paris,*] 1778. 8°. *Mercure de France, Oct.,* 1778. **297. f. 26.**

LÉGAT DE FURCY (Antoine)

— Vous chantés lorsque tout sommeille. *Petit Air, etc.* [*Paris*, 1785?] 8°.   **B. 362. b. (9.)**

LEGATI (Benedetto)

— [Sonata per Cembalo e Organo.] Adagio ... Arranged for the Piano by I. Philipp, *etc. G. Schirmer: New York*, 1935. 4°. [*Three Old Italian Airs. No.* 1.]   **g. 1127. uu. (27.)**

LE GATOR (A.) *pseud.*

— The Crocodile ... Song [begins: "Who hasn't heard"] written by F. W. Green. *London*, [1874.] fol. *No.* 4489, 4490 *of the "Musical Bouquet".*   **H. 2345.**

LEGAY (Marcel)

— Brune et Blonde. Chanson [begins: "Sur la terre"]. Paroles de P. Champagne. *Paris*, [1881.] fol.   **H. 1786. e. (33.)**

— Fauvette et Pinson. Idylle [begins: "Un jour au fond des bois"]. *Paris*, [1881.] fol.   **H. 1786. e. (28.)**

— La Fiancée. Romance [begins: "J'ai reçu ce matin"]. *Paris*, [1881.] fol.   **H. 1786. e. (32.)**

— Finis coronat opus. Histoire horrible. [Song, begins: "Écoutez bien la légende"]. Paroles de P. Champagne. *Paris*, [1881.] fol.   **H. 1786. e. (30.)**

— N'vous gênez pas. Chansonnette [begins: "Je sais une phrase française"]. Paroles de P. Champagne. *Paris*, [1881.] fol.   **H. 1786. e. (29.)**

— Que la femme est donc belle ... Chanson [begins: "Lorsque dans l'épais nuage"]. Paroles de P. Champagne. *Paris*, [1881.] fol.   **H. 1786. e. (31.)**

— *See* Chansonniers. Les Chansonniers de Montmartre. [Music by M. Legay.] [1906–09.] fol.   **H. 2275.**

LEGE (Wilhelm)

— Abendruhe. Romanze. Op. 103. [P. F.] *Berlin*, [1884.] fol.   **h. 3099. (6.)**

— Aeols-Glocken. Caprice-Nocturne für Clavier. Op. 105. *Berlin*, [1884.] fol.   **h. 3099. (8.)**

— Alpenveilchen. Salon-Caprice für Pianoforte. *Leipzig*, [1875.] fol.   **h. 1487. p. (25.)**

— Alpine Rose. Mélodie pour piano. *R. Cocks & Co.: London*, [1885.] fol.   **h. 1484. s. (33.)**

— Aus Wald und Flur. Sechs melodische Charakterstücke ... für angehende Pianofortespieler. *Leipzig*, [1877.] fol.   **h. 1493. o. (1.)**

— Blau-Veilchen ... Lyrisches Tonstück für Pianoforte. Op. 108. *Leipzig*, [1885.] fol.   **h. 3099. (11.)**

— Blau Veilchen. Lyrisches Tonstück. Op. 108 [for zither]. *See* Gutmann (F.) Compositionen für Zither ... No. 44. [1886.] *obl.* 4°.   **b. 244.**

— Blumengruss. Salonstück für Piano. Op. 100. *Berlin*, [1884.] fol.   **h. 3099. (3.)**

— Bravour-Polka für Pianoforte. Op. 6. Neue veränderte Ausgabe. *C. A. Challier & Co.: Berlin*, [1888.] fol.   **h. 3099. (14.)**

— Cœur-Bube. Concert-Polka für Clavier. *Berlin*, [1878.] fol.   **h. 1493. o. (6.)**

— Cœur Dame, polka brillante pour Piano. *Leipzig*, [1875.] fol.   **h. 1487. p. (20.)**

LEGE (Wilhelm)

— Elfenspiele. Salonstück für Pianoforte. *Leipzig*, [1876.] fol.   **h. 1487. p. (28.)**

— Entsagung. Mélodie für Pianoforte. *Offenbach a. M.*, [1875.] fol.   **h. 1487. p. (19.)**

— Epheuranken. Mélodie für Piano. *Leipzig*, [1875.] fol.   **h. 1487. p. (22.)**

— Fantasie über Kucken's Lied "Das Sternlein" für Pianoforte. *Leipzig*, [1876.] fol.   **h. 1487. p. (32.)**

— Frühlings-Klänge ... für Pianoforte. Op. 106. *Leipzig*, [1885.] fol.   **h. 3099. (9.)**

— Für Dich. Mazurka-Mélodie für Pianoforte. *Leipzig*, [1875.] fol.   **h. 1487. p. (21.)**

— Gedenkblatt. Salonstück für Piano. Op. 102. *Berlin*, [1884.] fol.   **h. 3099. (5.)**

— Glöcklein's Morgengruss. Idylle für Piano. *Leipzig*, [1875.] fol.   **h. 1487. p. (26.)**

— Herzensklänge. Nocturne pour piano. *R. Cocks & Co.: London*, [1885.] fol.   **h. 1484. s. (32.)**

— Im Morgenduft ... Op. 109. [P. F.] *Leipzig*, [1885.] fol.   **h. 3099. (12.)**

— In's Herz geschlossen. Lyrisches Tonstück für Pianoforte. *Leipzig*, [1875.] fol.   **h. 1487. p. (23.)**

— Klänge der Sehnsucht. Melodie für Clavier. *Berlin*, [1878.] fol.   **h. 1493. o. (3.)**

— Liebesgeständnis. Salonstück für Piano. Op. 99. *Berlin*, [1884.] fol.   **h. 3099. (2.)**

— Locken im Winde. Bild in Tönen für Piano. *Leipzig*, [1876.] fol.   **h. 1487. p. (30.)**

— Lose Blätter. Potpourri. Op. 98. [P. F.] *Berlin*, [1884.] fol.   **h. 3099. (1.)**

— Maithau. Clavierstück. Op. 110. *Leipzig*, [1885.] fol.   **h. 3099. (13.)**

— Mein Heim die Schweiz. Melodie für Pianoforte. Op. 101. *Berlin*, [1884.] fol.   **h. 3099. (4.)**

— Zwei melodische Uebungsstücke ... für Piano. *Leipzig*, [1876.] fol.   **h. 1487. p. (29.)**

— Perlen und Rubinen. Elegante Salon-Mazurka für das Pianoforte. *Offenbach a. M.*, [1879.] fol.   **h. 1493. o. (8.)**

— La Reine du Jour, fantaisie-mazourka pour Piano. *Berlin*, [1878.] fol.   **h. 1493. o. (2.)**

— Rhein-Nixen. Salontanz für Clavier. *Berlin*, [1878.] fol.   **h. 1493. o. (5.)**

— Schlummernde Rose. Leichtes Tonstück für Pianoforte. *Leipzig*, [1875.] fol.   **h. 1487. p. (24.)**

— Schmachtende Blume. Lyrisches Tonstück für Pianoforte. *Leipzig*, [1876.] fol.   **h. 1487. p. (31.)**

— Sehnen und Hoffen. Tonstück für das Pianoforte. *Offenbach a. M.*, [1879.] fol.   **h. 1493. o. (9.)**

— Sternblumen ... Salon-Walzer für Pianoforte. Op. 107. *Leipzig*, [1885.] fol.   **h. 3099. (10.)**

— Steyrische Alpenklänge für Clavier. *Hannover*, [1880.] fol.   **h. 3272. j. (19.)**

— Stilles Sehnen. Meditation für Clavier. *Bielefeld*, [1878.] fol.   **h. 1493. o. (7.)**

— Tanz der Grazien. Fantasie-Mazurka für das Pianoforte. *Offenbach a. M.*, [1879.] fol.   **h. 1493. o. (10.)**

LEGE (Wilhelm)

— Tanz der Waldnixen für Piano. Op. 104. *Berlin*, [1884.] fol.
h. 3099. (7.)

— Thauperlen, fantaisie für Pianoforte. *London*, [1876.] fol.
h. 1482. z. (21.)

— Wanderlust. Clavierstück. Op. 111. *C. A. Challier & Co.: Berlin*, [1888.] fol.
h. 3099. (15.)

— Wasserfahrt am Abend. Charakterstück für Piano. *Leipzig*, [1876.] fol.
h. 1487. p. (27.)

— Zauberglöckchen, Tonstück für Clavier. *Berlin*, [1878.] fol.
h. 1493. o. (4.)

LEGEAY (Georges)

— Noëls anciens. Avec accompagnement de Piano par le P. D. Legeay. 2 sér. *V. Palmé: Paris*, [1875, 76.] fol.
H. 3162.

— Noels anciens avec accompagnement de Piano par ... G. Legeay. 2 sér. *Solesmes*, [1880?] 4°.
H. 3162. a.

— *See* MÉLODIES. Mélodies de Chant Gregorien, *etc.* (4ᵉ Livraison ... avec accompagnement ... par ... Dom Legeay, *etc.*) [1892.] 4°.
G. 867.

LEGÈLE (C.)

— Les Abeilles. Danse caractéristique for the pianoforte. *Bowerman & Co.: London*, [1894.] fol.
g. 605. f. (14.)

LEGEND

— The Legend. Lyric Tragedy. *See* BREIL (J. C.)

— Legend. Song. *See* CHAIKOVSKY (P. I.) [16 Chansons pour la Jeunesse. Op. 54. No. 5. Légende.]

— Legend. [Song.] *See* KHACHATURYAN (A. I.) [3 Arias.]

— Legend. Spiritual Folk-Song. *See* KOSHETZ (A.)

— A Legend. [Song.] *See* SCHINDLER (K.) Fünf Lieder ... Op. 9. No. 1.

— The Legend Act of the Piper. [Musical play.] *See* FREER (E. E.)

— The Legend Beautiful. [Recitation with music.] *See* HAWLEY (S.) Recitation-Music Series. No. 11.

— The Legend Beautiful. Interpretative Music. *See* HENNEMAN (A.)

— The Legend beautiful. [Cantata.] *See* LYON (J.)

— The Legend of Blue Beard. Song. *See* OFFENBACH (J.) [Barbe Bleue.]

— A Legend of Bregenz. Ballad. *See* BENDALL (W. E.)

— A Legend of Bregenz. Cantata. *See* HATHAWAY (J. W. G.)

— A Legend of Cashmere. Song. *See* ARCHER (F.)

— The Legend of Champagne. [Song.] *See* GREY (Henry)

— The Legend of Clopton. Operetta. *See* CASELEY (J. H.)

— The Legend of Elöisa. Cantata. *See* MORGAN (R. O.)

— The Legend of good Saint Christopher. Carol. *See* SAWYER (F. J.)

— A Legend of Granada. Cantata. *See* HADLEY (H. K.)

— Legend of Jocassee. Song. *See* STRICKLAND (L. T.)

— The Legend of Jonas Bronck. [Song.] *See* CASTELNUOVO-TEDESCO (M.)

LEGEND

— A Legend of Kashmir. [Song.] *See* KOVEN (H. L. R. de) Three Pictures from the Orient ... Op. 358. No. 2.

— The Legend of Kleinzack. *See* OFFENBACH (J.) [Les Contes d'Hoffmann.—Il était une fois.]

— The Legend of Lampetia. Cantata. *See* FOWLES (E.)

— The Legend of Life. Song. *See* ROECKEL (J. L.)

— The Legend of Lough Rea. [Part-song.] *See* LARCHET (J. F.)

— The Legend of Love. Ballad. *See* LEE (A.)

— A Legend of Mann. [Cantata.] *See* TOOTELL (G.)

— A Legend of Mullaghmast. [Part-song.] *See* JACKMAN (P.)

— A Legend of Mullaghmast. [Part-song.] *See* LE CRAS (T. L.)

— The Legend of Narcissus. Cantata. *See* MELY, afterwards VAN DEN HEUVEL (M.)

— The Legend of Nerbudda. Cantata. *See* BATH (H. C.)

— The Legend of Oriella. Cantata. *See* HOFFMANN (J.)

— The Legend of Robin Hood. [Musical play.] *See* ODAM (George)

— The Legend of St. Cecilia. Cantata. *See* BENEDICT (*Sir* J.)

— The Legend of St. Christopher. Oratorio. *See* PARKER (H. W.)

— The Legend of St. David. Oratorio. *See* JENKINS (D.) *of Aberystwyth.*

— The Legend of St. Dorothea. Cantata. *See* DOLBY, afterwards SAINTON (C. H.)

— The Legend of St. Yvonne. Operetta. *See* COOPER (W. S.)

— The Legend of Sleepy Hollow. Cantata. *See* BURTON (F. R.)

— The Legend of Spectresheim. Ballad. *See* FITZWILLIAM (E. F.) A Set of Songs. No. 10.

— A Legend of the Avon. Solo and chorus. *See* DOWLAND (J.) [The First Booke of Songes.—Now, O now I needs must part.]

— The Legend of the Bells. Song. *See* LACONINI (L.)

— Legend of the Bells. [Trio.] *See* PLANQUETTE (R.) [Les Cloches de Corneville.—Chanson des Cloches.]

— A Legend of the Brocken. Song. *See* MACEVOY (A. T.)

— The Legend of the Castle. Four-part song. *See* HOELTZE (W.)

— The Legend of the Castle. [Song.] *See* IGNOTUS, *pseud.* Melodies of England. No. 4.

— The Legend of the Christmas Rose. Carol. *See* BISHOP (J. S.)

— Legend of the Crossbill. Song. *See* HOPPER (A.)

— The Legend of the Crossbill. Part song. *See* LAWRENCE (C.)

— The Legend of the Crossbill. [Cantata.] *See* PARSONS (H.)

— The Legend of the Crossbill. [Song.] *See* WEST (W.)

— The Legend of the Dandelion. Cantata. *See* CLOKEY (J. W.)

— The Legend of the East Window. [Recitation with music.] *See* HAWLEY (S.) Recitation-Music Series. No. 19.

— The Legend of the Edelweiss. Song. *See* SOMERVILLE (R.) [The Mountaineers.]

— The Legend of the Fan. Song. *See* TAYLOR (Billee)

— The Legend of the first Cam-u-el. Chorus. *See* KERNOCHAN (M.)

LEGEND

— The Legend of the Forget me Not. [Song.] *See* GILL (W. H.)

— The Legend of the Forget-me-not. [Song.] *See* WATSON (G. L.)

— The Legend of the Lily. Song. *See* CALDICOTT (A. J.)

— The Legend of the Maguire. [Song.] *See* MACK (Andrew)

— The Legend of the Nile. Song. *See* ALLEN (G. B.)

— Legend of the North. *See* GODFREY (P.)

— The Legend of the Piper. [Musical play.] *See* FREER (E. E.) [The Legend Act of the Piper.]

— A Legend of the Rhine. [Part-song.] *See* BRUCH (M. C. F.) Fünf Lieder ... Op. 38. No. 4.

— A Legend of the Rhine. [Part-song.] *See* SMART (H.)

— The Legend of the Rock-Buoy Bell. Ballad. *See* GRAY (A.)

— The Legend of the Rose. Song. *See* LEVY (W. C.)

— The Legend of the Rose. [Cantata.] *See* OPERTI (Giuseppe)

— The Legend of the Snowdrop. Cantata. *See* CAMPBELL (H. A. J.)

— The Legend of the Violin. [Song.] *See* BRAHMS (J.) [Ungarische Tänze.]

— The Legend of the wondrous Book. [Part-song.] *See* LEVENSON (B.)

— The Legend of the Wood. Operetta. *See* GAUL (A. R.)

— The Legend of Tours. Song. *See* BARRI (O.)

— A Legend of Wicklow. [Song.] *See* QUINLAN (A. C.)

— The Legend olden. Duet. *See* CARYLL (I.) *pseud.* [The Duchess of Dantzic.]

LEGENDA

— Legenda o sv. Zitě. [Cantata.] *See* OSTRČIL (O.)

— Legenda z dýmu bramborové nati. [Cantata.] *See* MARTINŮ (B.)

— Legenda z Erinu. Zpěvohra. *See* OSTRČIL (O.)

LEGENDARNUY

— Легендарный рядовой. Баллада. *See* BELUY (V. A.)

LEGENDE

— Légende. [Song.] *See* BLOCH (E.) Historiettes au crépuscule. [No. 1.]

— La Légende de Béthléem. Duo. *See* BORDÈSE (L.)

— La Légende de l'Ondine. Drama lyrique. *See* ROSENLECKER (G.)

— Légende de la Mère Angot. [Song.] *See* LECOCQ (A. C.) [La Fille de Madame Angot.]

— La Légende de Saint Amour. [Song.] *See* HOLMÈS (A. M. A.)

— La Légende de Saint-Christophe. [Oratorio.] *See* INDY (P. M. T. V. d')

— Légende de Saint Nicolas. Folk Song. *See* FERRARI (G.)

— La Légende de St. Nicolas. [Duet.] *See* GOUZIEN (A.)

— La Légende de S¹ Nicolas. [Song.] *See* MASSENET (J. É. F.)

— Légende de Ste. Azénor. [Song.] *See* LEFEBVRE (Charles Edouard)

LEGENDE

— La Légende de Sainte Cécile. Drame. *See* CHAUSSON (E.)

— La Légende des Mois. Recueil de mélodies. *See* ROUGNON (P.)

— La Légende des Roses. [Song.] *See* WECKERLIN (J. B. T.)

— La Légende des Vers luisants. [Song.] *See* ERLANGER (C.)

— La Légende du baiser. [Song.] *See* MASSENET (J. É. F.) Trois poèmes chastes ... III.

— La Légende du grand Saint Nicolas. [Song.] *See* INGHELBRECHT (D. E.)

— La Légende du Pâtre. [Song.] *See* CROZE (L. de)

— La Légende du Point d'Argentan. Pièce. *See* FOURDRAIN (F.)

— La Légende du Rouet. [Song.] *See* AU. Au moment de la veillée. [1899.] fol.   H. 2399. (17.)

— Legende o drugu Titu. [Cantata.] *See* PAPANDOPULO (B.)

— A Legende of Old St. Caradoc's Welle. Ballad. *See* GLOVER (C. W.)

— Legende vom Apfelbaum. [Incidental music.] *See* SUK (Josef) [Pod jabloní.]

— Legende vom Ritter St. Georg. [Song.] *See* REITER (J.) Balladen ... N° 3.

— Die Legende vom Storch. [Song.] *See* STERN (C. J.)

— Legende vom Weisen und Zöllner. [Cantata.] *See* SCHILLING (H. L.)

— Die Legende von der heiligen Elisabeth. Oratorium. *See* LISZT (F.)

LÉGENDES

— Les Légendes de l'Art. Musiciens. Ouvrage illustré, *etc.* [With musical examples.] *A. Hatier: Paris*, [1892.] 8°.
                      7896. ee. 38.

— Légendes populaires d'Allemagne. L'Anneau brisé. Transcription pour Piano. [*Paris*,] 1902. 8°. *Supplement to "L'Illustration," No.* 3090.   **P. P. 4283. m. (3.)**

LEGENDRE (JULES)

— American Air varié. [Orchestral parts.] *London*, [1873.] 8°. *Part of the "Alliance Musicale".*   **f. 400. c. (17.)**

— The American quadrille. [P. F.] *London*, [1878.] 8°. *No.* 499 *of the "Alliance Musicale. Album Bijou".*   **f. 406.**

— Anna, Cornet polka. [Orchestral parts.] *London*, [1877.] 8°.
                      f. 410. (17.)

— Anna. Cornet polka. *London*, [1877.] fol.   **h. 2731. d. (34.)**

— Duo Polka avec solo pour 1 ou 2 Cornets. [Orchestral parts.] *London*, [1875.] 8°. *Part of the "Alliance Musicale".*   **f. 400. c. (18.)**

— Fantaisie-polka pour Cornet solo. [Orchestral parts.] *Paris*, [1875.] 8°. *Part of the "Alliance Musicale".*   **f. 400. c. (19.)**

— Julietta polka. [P. F.] *London*, [1875.] 8°. *No.* 100 *of the "Alliance Musicale. Album Bijou".*   **f. 406.**

— Original Air varié ... arranged by Bousquet. [Orchestral parts.] *London*, [1878.] 8°. *Part of the "Alliance Musicale".*   **f. 400. q. (2.)**

— Original Air varié ... arranged by N. Bousquet. *London*, [1878.] 8°. *No.* 507 *of the "Alliance Musicale. Album Bijou".*   **f. 406.**

LEGENDRE (JULES)

— Souvenir de Chasseloup, polka de concert pour Cornet ... et Piano. *Paris,* [1868.] fol. **h. 1462. r. (34.)**

— Souvenir de Poitou, air varié. ... [Octet band parts.] *London,* [1877.] 8°. **f. 411. b. (13.)**

— Souvenir de Poitou, air varié. *See* CONCERT. Concert Pieces for Cornet, *etc.* No. 18. [1877.] fol. **h. 2203.**

— Tabac-Lune, grande polka de concert avec variations pour le Cornet à pistons. [Orchestral parts.] *Paris,* [1875.] 8°. *Part of the "Alliance Musicale".* **f. 400. c. (20.)**

— Traité complet de l'Articulation, ou le secret des coups de langue ... pour Cornet à Pistons, Bugle et Saxhorn, *etc. Paris,* [1877.] 8°. **f. 176.**

— La Viennoise. Polka. 1st Cornet [part]. *London,* [1874.] 8°. *Part of the "Alliance Musicale". Imperfect; wanting the other parts.* **f. 402. f. (15.)**

LEGER (FRANÇOIS PIERRE AUGUSTE)

— Ziste et Zeste ... Folie en un Acte, *etc.* [With music to the concluding vaudeville, by F. P. A. Leger.] [1796.] 8°. *See* ZISTE. **11738. h. 11. (6.)**

— [Ziste et Zeste.] Plein de la plus vive ardeur. *Vaudeville* ... Paroles et Musique du C^en Leger. *Chez la C^n Lebeau:* [*Paris,* 1796.] 8°. **B. 362. (111.)**

LEGERDEMAIN

— Legerdemain. [Song.] *See* DIBDIN (C.) [Tom Wilkins.]

LÉGÈRETÉ

— La Légèreté. Romance. *See* SAUVAGE (A.)

LEGG (CATHERINE)

— The Fold. Song, words and music by C. Legg. *West & Co.: London,* 1914. fol. **H. 1793. s. (44.)**

LEGG (CYRUS)

— The Lily of the Lake waltzes. [P. F.] *London,* [1878.] fol. **h. 1494. q. (11.)**

— The Water Lily schottische for the Pianoforte. *London,* [1877.] fol. **h. 1482. z. (22.)**

LEGGE (ALFRED)

— Whither. Song, words by Longfellow. *Weekes & Co.: London,* [1898.] fol. **H. 1798. u. (39.)**

LEGGE (GILBERT INNES)

— The Hour of Love. Serenade. [Song.] Words by E. Oxenford. *Penn Music Co.: N[ew] Y[ork],* (1912.) fol. **H. 1792. r. (51.)**

LEGGE (J. G.)

— *See* NICHOLSON (S. H.) British Songs for British Boys ... With a preface by J. G. Legge. 1903. 8°. **F. 207.**

LEGGE (ROBIN HUMPHREY)

— The Angels' Carol. A Carol for Christmas Day. [Words by] A. E. Alston. *Novello, Ewer and Co.: London & New York,* [1895.] 8°. *No. 243 of "Novello's Christmas Carols".* **D. 434.**

LEGGE (ROBIN HUMPHREY)

— Ballad of Earl Haldan's Daughter. Four-Part Song ... [Words] by C. Kingsley. 1894. *See* PERIODICAL PUBLICATIONS.— *London.* The Musical Times, *etc.* No. 619. 1844, *etc.* 8°. **P. P. 1945. aa.**

— The Birth ever new. A Carol for Christmas Eve. [Words by] A. E. Alston. *Novello, Ewer and Co.: London & New York,* [1895.] 8°. *No. 237 of "Novello's Christmas Carols".* **D. 434.**

— Twelve Carols. Written by A. E. Alston. [Eight for Christmas, two for Epiphany, one for Candlemas and one for the Annunciation.] pp. 24. *London Music Publishing Co.: London; Leipzig* printed, [1891.] 8°. **F. 1124. t. (6.)**

— Children's Chorus. A Carol for Christmas Day. [Words by] A. E. Alston. *Novello, Ewer and Co.: London & New York,* [1895.] 8°. *No. 244 of "Novello's Christmas Carols".* **D. 434.**

— Christmas Eve. A Carol for Christmas Eve. [Words by] A. E. Alston. *Novello, Ewer and Co.: London & New York,* [1895.] 8°. *No. 239 of "Novello's Christmas Carols".* **D. 434.**

— The Christmas Vision. A Carol for Christmas Day. [Words by] A. E. Alston. [*Novello, Ewer and Co: London & New York,* 1895.] 8°. *No. 240 of "Novello's Christmas Carols".* **D. 434.**

— Dawns the Day, the natal Day. Carol-Anthem, the words ... by A. E. Alston. *See* NOVELLO AND CO. Novello's Collection of Anthems, *etc.* No. 449. [1876, *etc.*] 8°. **E. 618. a.**

— The Five Kings. A Carol for the Epiphany. [Words by] A. E. Alston. *Novello, Ewer and Co.: London & New York,* [1895.] 8°. *No. 246 of "Novello's Christmas Carols".* **D. 434.**

— The Holy Quest. A Carol for the Epiphany. [Words by] A. E. Alston. *Novello, Ewer and Co.: London & New York* [1895.] 8°. *No. 245 of "Novello's Christmas Carols".* **D. 434.**

— Hunting Song. Four-part Song. No. 4 of Five Poems by C. Kingsley. 1894. *See* NOVELLO AND CO. Novello's Part-Song Book. Second Series, *etc.* No. 719. [1869, *etc.*] 8°. **F. 280. b.**

— A Lament. Four-part Song. No. 1 of Five Poems by C. Kingsley. 1894. *See* NOVELLO AND CO. Novello's Part-Song Book. Second Series, *etc.* No. 716. [1896, *etc.*] 8°. **F. 280. b.**

— Mary's Cradle-Song. A Carol for Christmas Day. [Words by] A. E. Alston. *Novello, Ewer and Co.: London & New York,* [1895.] 8°. *No. 242 of "Novello's Christmas Carols".* **D. 434.**

— Nazareth Town in Slumber lay. A Carol for the Annunciation. [Words by] A. E. Alston. *Novello, Ewer and Co.: London & New York,* [1895.] 8°. *No. 248 of "Novello's Christmas Carols".* **D. 434.**

— Twelve new Christmas Carols for unison singing, written by A. E. Alston. [Two no. Staff and tonic sol-fa notation.] *Novello, Ewer and Co.: London & New York,* 1894. 8°. **D. 619. k. (14.)**

— The Old News. A Carol for Christmas Eve. [Words by] A. E. Alston. *Novello, Ewer and Co.: London & New York,* [1895.] 8°. *No. 238 of "Novello's Christmas Carols".* **D. 434.**

— Praise we now the Holy Light. A Carol for Candlemas. [Words by] A. E. Alston. *Novello, Ewer and Co.: London & New York,* [1895.] 8°. *No. 247 of "Novello's Christmas Carols".* **D. 434.**

LEGGE (ROBIN HUMPHREY)

— The Shepherds' Carol. A Carol for Christmas Day. [Words by] A. E. Alston. *Novello, Ewer and Co.: London & New York*, [1895.] 8°.
No. 241 *of "Novello's Christmas Carols".*   **D. 434.**

— The Starlings. Four-Part Song. No. 3 of Five Poems by C. Kingsley. 1894. *See* NOVELLO AND CO. Novello's Part-Song Book. Second Series, *etc.* No. 718. [1869, *etc.*] 8°.   **F. 280. b.**

— Drei Stücke für Violine mit Begleitung des Klaviers. Op. 4. *Steyl & Thomas: Frankfurt a/Main*, [1890?] fol.
    g. 505. m. (11.)

— The Watchman. Four-Part Song. No. 2 of Five Poems by C. Kingsley. 1894. *See* NOVELLO AND CO. Novello's Part-Song Book. Second Series, *etc.* No. 717. [1869, *etc.*] 8°.   **F. 280. b.**

— *See* HOFMANN (R.) Practical Instrumentation ... Translated by R. H. Legge. 1893. fol.   **g. 741.**

LEGGENDA

— La Leggenda di Sakùntala. [Opera.] *See* ALFANO (F.)

— La Leggenda di Tours. Song. *See* BARRI (O.)

LEGGERO

— Leggero invisibile. Bolero. *See* ARDITI (L.)

LEGGETT (ALFRED)

— The Kittens. Gavotte ... for the Pianoforte. *H. Beresford: London and Birmingham*, [1895.] fol.   **h. 1489. s. (30.)**

— Linda Gavotte.—Prize dance.—Invented by F. Moore. Op. 48. [P. F.] *Reid Bros.: London*, 1919. fol.   **h. 3284. nn. (39.)**

— *See* CONLEY (Tom) Oh! Beautiful Marriage ... [Song.] —Arranged by A. Leggett. [1896.] fol.   **H. 3980. l. (7.)**

— *See* GODWIN (W.) Christmas Bells ... arranged by A. Leggett, *etc.* [1895.] fol.   **H. 1798. n. (3.)**

— *See* OSBORNE (C.) Lost for ever. [Song.] (Arranged by A. Leggett.) [1890.] fol.   **H. 3710. (8.)**

— *See* OSBORNE (C.) The Warder's Story, *etc.* (Arranged by A. Leggett.) [1890.] fol.   **H. 3710. (16.)**

— *See* OSBORNE (C.) The Wreck of the Life-boat, *etc.* (Arranged by A. Leggett.) [1889.] fol.   **H. 1260. h. (40.)**

— *See* ROGERS (E. W.) Since Bill's been crossed in Love. Coster song, *etc.* ⟨Arranged by A. Leggett.⟩ [1897.] fol.
    H. 3981. p. (38.)

— *See* SAINT CLAIR (F. V.) "Only a few more Miles from Home," *etc.* [Song.] ⟨Arranged by A. Leggett.⟩ [1897.] fol.
    H. 3981. s. (14.)

— *See* THORN (Geoffrey) *pseud.* The Bounders' Football Club, *etc.* ⟨Song. Arranged by A. Leggett.⟩ [1893.] fol.
    H. 3981. ii. (23.)

LEGGETT (CHARLES)

— *See* HAWKES AND SON. Hawkes & Son's No. 1 Cornet Solo Album, *etc.* (No. 2. Edited by C. Leggett.) 1913–37. 4°.
    g. 1120. d.

LEGGETT (L. GERTRUDE)

— All aboard for the bright Land of Glory. [Sacred song and chorus, words by] W. I. Leggett. *W. I. Leggett Co.: Chicago*, 1906. *a card.*   **I. 600. c. (118.)**

— My dainty Maria. [Song.] Words by W. I. Leggett. pp. 4. *W. I. Leggett Co.: Chicago*, [1906.] fol.   **H. 3985. q. (21.)**

LEGGETT (L. GERTRUDE)

— The Picket is off for you. ⟨A little story and song.⟩ Words by W. I. Leggett. pp. 3. *W. I. Leggett Co.: Chicago*, [1907.] fol.
    H. 3985. q. (22.)

— The Red Light in the Cab ... [Song.] Words by W. I. Leggett. pp. 5. *W. I. Leggett Co.: Chicago*, [1903.] fol.
    H. 3985. q. (23.)

— So soon we are forgotten. ⟨A little story and song.⟩ Words by W. I. Leggett. pp. 3. *W. I. Leggett Co.: Chicago*, [1908.] fol.
    H. 3985. q. (24.)

— Sweet little Baby Girl. ⟨A little story and song.⟩ Words by W. I. Leggett. pp. 3. *W. I. Leggett Co.: Chicago*, [1909.] fol.
    H. 3985. q. (25.)

LEGGI

— Leggi, deh! leggi. Aria. *See* HAENDEL (G. F.) [Almira.—Leset, ihr funkelnden Augen.]

LEGGIADRA

— Leggiadra. Donzella. Duetto. *See* HÉROLD (L. J. F.)

LEGGIADRE

— Leggiadre Nimphe a Tre Voci. Alla Napolitana. De Diuersi Eccellentissimi Autori. Nouamente Con diligentia Stampate. Canto. (Tenore.) 2 pt. *Apresso Angelo Gardano, & Fratelli: Venetia*, 1606. 4°.
The composers named in this collection are: Luigi Francese del Liuto, O. Vecchi, Sabino and B. Donato.   **D. 191.**

— Leggiadre ninfe. [Madrigal.] *See* MARENZIO (L.) [Il quinto libro de madrigali a sei voci.]

LEGGIADRETTO

— Leggiadretto Clorino. [Madrigal.] *See* VECCHI (H.)

LEGGIADRO

— Leggiadro e costante. Valzer. *See* VASCHETTI (C.)

LEGH (MAUD)

— The Frederica, polka mazurka. [P. F.] *London*, [1857.] fol.
    h. 977. f. (29.)

LEGINSKA (ETHEL) *pseud.* [i. e. ETHEL LIGGINS.]

— Cradle Song, for the piano. *J. Church Co.: Cincinnati, etc.*, 1922. 4°.   **g. 1127. g. (20.)**

— Dance of a Puppet. For the piano. *J. Church Co.: Cincinnati, etc.*, 1924. 4°.   **g. 1127. w. (1.)**

— Six Nursery Rhymes for Piano Solo with Soprano, ad lib., *etc.* 6 no. *J. Church Co.: Cincinnati, etc.*, 1925. 4°.
    g. 1127. dd. (9.)

— Four Songs. [No. 1.] Bird voices of spring. (Words by C. S. Whittern.) [No. 2.] The gallows tree. [No. 3.] The frozen heart. (O. J. Bierbaum, English version by F. H. Martens.) [No. 4.] At dawn. (Words by A. Symons.) 4 no. *G. Schirmer: New York, Boston*, 1919. 4°.   **G. 390. w. (12.)**

LEGION

— The Legion of Honour. Song. *See* SYKES (H. P.)

LEGIONNAIRE

— The Legionnaire. Chorus. *See* GROVER (J. M.)

LEGKEDVELTEBB

— Legkedveltebb csárdás-tánczok gyüjteménye. Collection des danses hongrois [sic] favorites. Sammlung der beliebtesten ungarischen Volkstänze. pp. 35. *Rózsavölgyi és társa: Budapest; Leipzig* [printed, c. 1900.] 4°. **g. 230. s. (4.)**

LEGLEY (VICTOR)

— Quintette à vent ... Op. 58. [Score.] pp. 28. *Centre belge de documentation musicale: Bruxelles,* [1963.] 4°.
h. 2785. cc. (2.)

— Sonate pour orgue ... Op. 35. pp. 24. *Centre belge de documentation musicale: Bruxelles,* [1958.] fol.
h. 2732. aa. (1.)

— Symphonie n° 3. [Score.] pp. 126. *Centre belge de documentation musicale: Bruxelles,* [1958.] 8°. **e. 669. ii. (1.)**

— 4ᵉ symphonie pour orchestre ... Op. 61. pp. 140. *Ce Be De M: Bruxelles,* [1966.] 8°. **d. 240. m. (2.)**

LEGNANI (LUIGI RINALDO)

— [6 capriccetti, che servono di compimento dell' op. 250.] Sei capricci. Op. 250. Per chitarra. pp. 12. *Bèrben: Ancona, Milano,* [1979.] fol. **h. 255. i. (1.)**

— [6 capriccetti, che servono di compimento dell' op. 250. No. 3.] Capriccio. Spanish guitar solo. *Clifford Essex Music Co.: London,* [1953.] *s. sh.* 4°. **g. 660. f. (27.)**

— [6 capriccetti, che servono di compimento dell' op. 250. No. 5.] Caprice in F major. Spanish guitar solo. Edited by Peter Sensier. *Clifford Essex Music Co.: London,* [1957.] *s. sh.* 4°. **h. 259. q. (3.)**

— 36 capricci per tutti i tuoni maggiori e minori per la chitarra ... Op. 20. pp. 36. *Presso Artaria et comp.: Vienna,* [1822.] fol. **h. 259. ff. (7.)**

— [36 Capricci. Op. 20.] 36 Capricen für Gitarre ... Neu-Ausgabe von ... H. Ritter. 2 Hft. *B. Schott's Söhne: Mainz-Leipzig,* 1926. 4°.
Gitarre Archiv, No. 35, 36. **g. 660. c. (20.)**

— 36 capricci op. 20. Per chitarra. Revisione di Mario Gangi. Collaborazione di Carlo Carfagna. pp. 63. *Bèrben: Ancona,* [1980.] fol. **h. 255. i. (5.)**

— [36 capricci. Op. 20. No. 9.] Capriccio No. 2. Spanish guitar solo. *Clifford Essex Music Co.: London,* [1953.] 4°.
g. 660. f. (29.)

— Sei capricci. Op. 250. *See* supra: [6 capriccetti, che servono di compimento dell' op. 250.]

— Grand caprice pour la guitare ... Euv. [sic.] 34. pp. 9. *Pacini: Paris,* [c. 1830.] fol. **h. 259. jj. (12.)**

— Fantaisie facile et brillante pour la guitare ... (Œuv: 19. pp. 7. *Chez Richault: Paris,* [c. 1825.] fol. **g. 1650. m. (18.)**

— Introduzione e variazioni per la chitarra sopra la cavatina favorita (Sorte secondami) nell'opera: Zelmira, di Rossini ... Opera 21, *etc.* pp. 11. *Presso Cappi e Diabelli: Vienne,* [1822.] 4°. **g. 271. qq. (3.)**

— Introduction, thême avec variations & finale ... pour la guitare ... Œuvre 40. pp. 11. *Au magasin de musique de Pacini: Paris,* [c. 1830.] fol. **g. 1650. m. (19.)**

— Introduzione e tema con variazioni sopra un motivo della Norma [by V. Bellini], cantabile e finale per chitarra ... Opera 201. pp. 10. *Presso Artaria e comp.: Vienna,* [1839.] fol. **h. 259. ee. (4.)**

— Introduction, Thême et Variations pour Guitare ... Opus 224. Nouvelle édition par ... V. Avila. *B. Schott's Söhne: Mainz und Leipzig,* [1929.] 4°.
Gitarre-Archiv, No. 74. **g. 660. d. (14.)**

LEGNANI (LUIGI RINALDO)

— Introduction et Thême pour Guitare ... Opus 237. Nouvelle édition par ... V. Avila. *B. Schott's Söhne: Mainz und Leipzig,* [1929.] 4°.
Gitarre-Archiv, No. 75. **g. 660. d. (13.)**

— Gran ricercario o studio per chitarra sola ... Op. 3. pp. 8. *Giovanni Ricordi: Milano,* [1819?] *obl.* fol. **d. 240. l. (3.)**

— Scherzo ossia quattro variazioni a sola chitarra da eseguirsi con un solo dito della mano sinistra ... Op. 10. pp. 3. *Presso Artaria & Comp.: Vienna,* [1825.] fol. **g. 660. g. (2.)**

— Spanish Gipsy Dance. (La Cachucha.) Spanish guitar solo. *Clifford Essex Music Co.: London,* [1953.] *s. sh.* 4°.
g. 660. f. (28.)

— Terremoto con variazioni per chitarra solo ... Opᵃ Iᵃ pp. 7. *Presso Gio. Ricordi: Milano,* [1820?] *obl.* fol. **d. 240. l. (2.)**

— Thême avec variations brillantes et faciles pour la guitare ... Œuvre. 29. pp. 5. *A. Meissonnier: Paris,* [c. 1830.] fol.
h. 259. jj. (13.)

— Gran variazioni per la chitarra sul duetto ("Nell' cuor più non mi sento") nell' opera La Molinara [by G. Paisiello] ... Op: [ᴹˢ 16.] pp. 13. *Presso Artaria et comp.: Vienna,* [1824.] fol. **h. 259. jj. (14.)**

— Variazioni per la chitarra sopra la marcia favorita nell'opera: La Donna del lago, di Rossini ... Opera 24. pp. 7. *Presso Cappi e Diabelli: Vienna,* [1823.] 4°. **g. 271. qq. (2.)**

— Variazioni per la chitarra sola sopra un tema originale ... Autore del tema ... Vincenzo Schuster ... Opera 25. pp. 9. *Presso Cappi e Diabelli: Vienna,* [1823.] 4°. **g. 271. qq. (4.)**

— Variations agréables pour la guitare sur la romance favorite de Cendrillon (Non più mesta accento [sic] al foco). [By G. A. Rossini.] ... Opera: 30. pp. 5. *A. Meissonnier: Paris,* [c. 1825.] fol. **h. 259. jj. (15.)**

— *See* PHILOMÈLE. Philomèle. Wessel & Cᵒˢ series of ... Songs with accompaniments for the Guitar arranged by Derwort ... Legnani, *etc.* [1845–51.] fol. **H. 2285.**

— *See* ROSSINI (G. A.) [Guillaume Tell.—Overture.] Andante & allegro ... ridotta per chitarra sola da L. Legnani. Opera 202. [1840.] fol. **h. 259. ee. (5.)**

LEGNANI (LUIS)

— *See* LEGNANI (Luigi Rinaldo)

LEGNE (COSLO)

— Sonata. [C major.] *In:* LESSONS. Six easy Lessons for the Harpsichord. pp. 13, 14. [1765?] *obl.* fol. **e. 5. k. (5.)**

LEGOUIX (ISIDORE EDOUARD)

— [La Clef d'Argent.] Ronde. *See* RÉCRÉATIONS. Récréations Musicales. Chœurs ... extraits d'Opéras-Comiques ... par ... I. E. Legouix, *etc.* [1884.] 4°. **C. 457.**

— The Crimson Scarf. *See* infra: [La Tartane.]

— Le Lion de St. Marc. Opéra-bouffe en un acte. Paroles de MM. Nuitter et Beaumont. Partition Piano et Chant. *Paris,* [1866.] 8°. **F. 444.**

— Le Mariage d'une Étoile. Opérette en un acte. Paroles de MM. E. Grangé and V. Bernard. Partition Piano & chant. *Paris,* [1876.] 8°. **F. 444. c.**

— Une nouvelle Cendrillon. Opérette bouffe en un acte. Paroles de E. Adenis. Partition piano et chant. *Paris,* [1885.] 8°.
The libretto (with separate titlepage and pagination) is inserted at the end. **F. 158. a. (5.)**

LEGOUIX (Isidore Edouard)

— [Une nouvelle Cendrillon.] Le Bal. *See* Récréations. Récréations Musicales. Chœurs ... extraits d'Opéras-Comiques ... par ... I. E. Legouix, *etc.* [1888.] 4°.
C. 457.

— L'Ours et l'Amateur des Jardins, bouffonnerie musicale en un acte. Paroles de MM. Busnach & Marquet ... Partition Piano & Chant. *Paris*, [1869.] 8°.
F. 444. b.

— [Quinolette.] La Fête. *See* Récréations. Récréations musicales. Chœurs ... extraits d'Opéras-Comiques ... par ... I. E. Legouix, *etc.* [1888.] 4°.
C. 457.

— [La Tartane.] The Crimson Scarf. Comic opera in one act, written by H. B. Farnie. *London*, [1872.] 4°.
No. 2 of "Metzler & Co's Opera Bouffe series".
F. 155. (2.)

— [La Tartane.] The Crimson Scarf. Comic opera in one act, written by H. B. Farnie. *See* Farnie (H. B.) Cramer's Opera-Comique Cabinet ... No. 4. [1874, *etc.*] 4°.
F. 159.

— Le Vengeur. Opéra-bouffe en un acte. Paroles de MM. Nuitter & Beaumont ... Partition Piano et Chant. *Paris*, [1869.] 8°.
F. 444. a.

— *See* Laurent de Rillé (F. A.) Le petit Poucet ... Partition réduite pour le Piano par I. Legouix. [1868.] 8°.
F. 38.

— *See* Laurent de Rillé (F. A.) Le Petit Poucet ... Réduite pour le Piano par J. Legouix. [1868.] 8°.
R. M. 25. f. 7. (2.)

LE GOURIADEC (Lohic)

— Monsieur le Roi. Lettre du front, paroles et musique de L. Le Gouriadec. Chant seul. *P. Gury: Montréal*, [1916.] 8°.
F. 636. pp. (6.)

LEGOUX (L. R.)

— Lovely Sally. A Favorite Ballad for the Piano Forte. The Words and Music by L. R. Legoux. *Printed for the Author: London*, [1787.] fol.
H. 1653. (35.)

LE GRAND (Ernest)

— Adorée. Valse lente. [P. F.] *Schott & Co.: London*, [1905.] fol.
h. 3286. dd. (57.)

— Brunette. Mélodie [begins: "Voici qu'Avril est de retour"], paroles de A. Theuriet. *Paris*, [1885.] fol. **H. 2836. h. (40.)**

— Elégie [begins: "Hélas! si j'avais su"]. Poésie de H. Moreau. *Paris*, [1886.] fol. **H. 2836. h. (38.)**

— La Fleur et le Papillon. Mélodie [begins: "La pauvre fleur disait au papillon céleste"], poésie de V. Hugo. *Paris*, [1884.] fol. **H. 2836. h. (37.)**

— Légende, extraite du drame de Jean-Marie [begins: "Le brick n'eut pas plutôt sombré"], poésie de A. Theuriet. *Paris*, [1886.] fol. **H. 2836. h. (39.)**

LEGRAND (Frederick)

— The Dear old Home far away. [Song.] Words by Capt. F. W. Marshall, *etc. Phillips & Page: London*, 1899. fol.
H. 1799. h. (24.)

— Mother, my own! [Song.] Words by Capt. W. F. Marshall, *etc. Phillips & Page: London*, 1899. fol. **H. 1799. h. (25.)**

— When my Love comes back. Song. Words by Capt. Marshall. *Phillips & Page: London*, 1898. fol. **H. 1799. h. (26.)**

LE GRAND (Jean Pierre)

— Sonata. [B flat major.] *In:* Venier (Jean B.) xx sonate per cembalo composte da vari autori, *etc.* pp. 2, 3. [1768?] fol.
i. 38. yy. (2.)

LEGRAND (Michel)

— [The Hunter.] Theme from the Paramount picture The Hunter. ⟨Piano solo.⟩ *Hansen House: Miami Beach*, [1980.] 4°.
f. 65. uu. (3.)

— Picasso Suite Sketch ... Arranged [for military band] by Robert Russell Bennett. ⟨Full score.⟩ pp. 24. *Warner Bros. Publications: New York*, [1973.] 4°. **g. 860. ss. (1.)**

— Picasso Suite Sketch ... Arranged by Robert Russell Bennett. ⟨Condensed score [and military band parts].⟩ 67 pt. *Warner Bros. Publications: New York*, [1973.] 4°.
With several copies of various parts. **h. 3210. j. (597.)**

— [The Three Musketeers.] Themes from the Three Musketeers ... Arranged for concert band by Bill Holcombe. ⟨Condensed score [and parts].⟩ 57 pt. *Chappell Music Co.: New York*, [1974.] 4°.
With several copies of various parts. **h. 3210. j. (715.)**

LE GRAND (Nicolas Ferdinand)

— A. Alewyns Harderszangen. Met Zangkunst verrykt door N. F. Le Grand. Opera Seconda. Tot gemak der Speelers op de G. sleutel gesteld. De tweede Druk. *Gedrukt by de Wed: Hermanus van Hulkenroy: Haarlem*, 1716. 4°. **B. 331.**

— Tweede deel der mengel-zangen, van Kornelis Sweerts; bestaande in cantus en bassus continuus, mede om op de viool, fluit, en andere instrumenten te konnen speelen. Op muzyk gestelt door F. Le Grand, *etc.* [Parts.] *By Kornelis Sweerts: Amsterdam*, 1695. 4°.
With an additional titlepage, engraved. Imperfect; wanting the bassus continuus part. The "Erste deel der mengelzangen" is entered under Sweerts (*Cornelis*). **B. 586. (2.)**

LE GRAND (Paul)

— La Novice. Morçeau. [P. F.] *Francis, Day & Hunter: London*, 1916. fol. **h. 3284. nn. (40.)**

— Papillons de Nuit. Valse intermezzo pour piano. *Francis, Day & Hunter: London*, 1915. fol. **h. 3284. nn. (41.)**

— Springtime in my Garden. Six ... pieces for the piano ... 1. Sweet lavender ... 2. By the old sundial ... 3. Dragon flies ... 4. Rosemary ... 5. 'Neath the trees ... 6. The spider's web. *Francis, Day & Hunter: London*, 1919. 4°. **g. 1129. r. (15.)**

LE GRANGE (Dollie)

— Dollie waltz for the Pianoforte. *London*, [1872.] fol.
No. 4996 of the "Musical Bouquet". **H. 2345.**

LEGRAS ( )

— *See* Patrat (A.) La Nuit ... Accompagnement de lyre ou guitare, par Le Gras professeur. [c. 1815.] 8°.
E. 1717. p. (55.)

— *See* Patrat (A.) Le Premier regard ... Accompagnement de lyre ou guitare par Legras professeur. [c. 1815.] 8°.
E. 1717. p. (56.)

LEGRENZI (Giovanni)

— Acclamationi divote a voce sola. ⟨Libro primo opera x.⟩ [A facsimile of the edition published by Giacomo Monti, Bologna, 1670.] pp. 99. *Arnoldo Forni editore: [Bologna,]* 1980. obl. 8°.
Bibliotheca musica bononiensis. sez. 4. no. 207. **D. 68. c.**

— Cantate, e Canzonette a Voce Sola ... Opera Duodecima, *etc. Per Giacomo Monti: Bologna*, 1676. obl. 4°. **B. 315.**

LEGRENZI (GIOVANNI)

— Cantatas and Canzonets for solo Voice. Part I: Music for alto and bass voices. ⟨Part II: Music for soprano (or tenor) voice.⟩ Edited by Albert Seay. 2 vol. *A — R Editions: Madison,* [1972.] 4°.
[Recent Researches in the Music of the Baroque Era. vol. 14, 15.] **G. 1490.**

— Canzone [begins: "Farci pazzo"] ... verso il 1670. *See* GEVAERT (F. A.) Les Gloires de l'Italie, *etc.* No. 16. [1868.] fol. **H. 566. g.**

— [La Cetra. Op. 10. Bk. 4. No. 6, 4, 3.] Tre sonate a 4 ... per archi e basso continuo. Revisione e realizzazione del basso continuo di Raffaele Cumar. [Score.] pp. 35. *G. Ricordi & c.: Milano,* [1965.] 8°.
Part of "Antica musica strumentale italiana". **f. 390. n. (5.)**

— [La Cetra. Op. 10.—Sonata prima à quatro violini.] Sonate für vier Violinen mit Basso continuo ... Herausgegeben von Karl Gustav Fellerer. [Score and parts.] 6 pt. *Bärenreiter-Verlag: Kassel, Basel,* [1951.] 4°.
Hortus musicus. 83. **f. 390. dd. (5.)**

— [La Cetra. Op. 10.—Sonata quarta à 2.] Sonate für Violine und Violoncello mit Basso continuo ... Herausgegeben von Karl Gustav Fellerer. [Score and parts.] 3 pt.
Bärenreiter-Velag: Kassel, Basel, [1951.] 4°.
Hortus musicus. 84. **f. 390. dd. (6.)**

— Che fiero costume. *See* infra: [Eteocle.]

— Compiete con le Lettanie & Antifone della B. V. à 5 voci ... Opera VII. Canto. (Alto.) (Tenore.) (Basso.) (Quinto.) (Basso Continuo.) 6 pt. *Appresso Francesco Magni detto Gardano: Venetia,* 1662. 4°.
Imperfect; wanting all the titlepages except those of the basso and quinto. **D. 68. b.**

— Concerto Bernardi. *See* infra: [Sonate dà chiesa. Op. 4. No. 1.]

— [Eteocle.—Che fiero costume.] Arietta ... 1675. *See* GEVAERT (F. A.) Les Gloires de l'Italie, *etc.* No. 56. [1868.] fol. **H. 566. g.**

— [Eteocle.] Che fiero costume. Arietta. *See* BANCK (C.) Arien, *etc.* No. 4. [1880.] fol. **H. 1786. (5.)**

— [Eteocle.] Che fiero costume. How proudly Love reigneth ... English version by M. Sutro. Edited by L. Lebell. [With accompaniment for strings and P. F.] *Stainer & Bell: London,* 1926. 4°.
[Arias and Songs from the 17th and 18th Centuries. No. 6.] **G. 1190.**

— Il Giustino. Melodrama in tre atti su libretto di Nicolò Beregani. Riproduzione integrale (dai mss. di Venezia, Roma e Napoli). Realizzazione del basso continuo e revisione di Luciano Bettarini. Partitura, *etc.* [With facsimiles.] pp. xxxiv. 557. *Casa editrice Nazionalmusic: Milano,* [1980.] fol.
[Collezione settecentesca Bettarini. no. 12.] **H. 350.**

— Sacri e Festivi Concenti Messa e Salmi à due Chori con stromenti à beneplacito ... Opera Nona. Canto (Alto) (Tenore) (Basso) Primo Ch. (Canto (Alto) (Tenore) (Basso) Sec. Ch.) [Basso Continuo.] (Violino Primo.) (Violino 2.) (Tenore (Alto) Viola.) (Basso Viola da brazzo.) 14 pt. *Appresso Francesco Magni Gardano: Venetia,* 1667. 4°.
Only the voice parts and the alto viola have titlepages. **D. 68.**

— Sentimenti Devoti. Espressi con la Musica di Due e Tre Voci ... Libro Secondo. Opera Sesta. Prima (Seconda) Parte. (Basso Continuo.) 3 pt. *Presso i Heredi di P. Phalesio: Anversa,* 1665. 4°. **D. 68. a.**

— Sonata dà chiesa. Op. 4—Op. 8. Édition par Albert Seay. [Score and parts.] 4 pt. *Heugel & c^{ie}: Paris,* [1968.] 4°.
[Le Pupitre. 4.] **G. 51.**

LEGRENZI (GIOVANNI)

— Two Sonatas in five Parts. Five recorders. ⟨1. La Fugazza. 2. La Marinona. Edited and arranged by Carl Dolmetsch.⟩ [Score and parts.] 6 pt. *Universal Edition: London,* [1975.] 4°.
[Dolmetsch Recorder Series. no. 98.] **g. 125.**

— [Sonate da chiesa. Op. 4. No. 1.] Concerto Bernardi ... Transcribed for strings by Wesley Sontag, *etc.* [Score.] pp. 10. *Skidmore Music Co.: New York,* [1957.] 4°. **g. 1620. (5.)**

— [Sonate da chiesa. Op. 4. No. 1.] Concerto Bernardi ... Transcribed for strings by Wesley Sontag, *etc.* [Score.] pp. 10. *Skidmore Music Co.: New York,* [1957.] 8°. **b. 400. k. (2.)**

— [Sonate. Lib. 3. Op. 8.] Sonata 'La Buscha' ... For 2 trumpets (cornetti), bassoon, and strings. ⟨Piano reduction by R. P. Block.⟩ A. Trumpet and piano reduction. B. Score and parts. 2 no. 15 pt. *Musica rara: London,* [1972.] 4°. **g. 1780. rr. (3.)**

— Sonate pour deux violons et basse. La Cornara. ⟨Réalisation de Claude Crussard.⟩ [Score and parts.] *In:* PERGOLESI (G. B.) [Twelve sonatas. No. 7.] G. B. Pergolèse. Sonate à trois pour deux violons et basse, *etc.* 1966. 4°. *[Flores musicae.* 16.] **G. 519. y.**

— Sonata a 3 per due viole, violone e basso continuo, *etc.* ⟨Brit. Mus. Ms. Add. 11588. Herausgegeben von Alfred Planyavsky. Continuo-Aussetzung von Peter Planyavsky.⟩ [Score and parts.] 4 pt. *Verlag Doblinger: Wien, München,* [1970.] 4°.
Diletto musicale. no. 407. **g. 934. v. (1.)**

— Sonate für vier Violinen mit Basso continuo. *See* supra: [La Cetra. Op. 10.—Sonata prima a quatro violini.]

— Sonate für Violine und Violoncello mit Basso continuo. *See* supra: [La Cetra. Op. 10.—Sonata quarta à 2.]

— Totila ... Introduction by Howard Mayer Brown. ⟨Libretto by Matteo Noris. Score, reproduced from Venice, Biblioteca nazionale Marciana, MS It. IV., 460.⟩ ff. 98. *Garland Publishing: New York, London,* 1978. obl. 4°.
[Italian Opera 1640–1770. 9.] **F. 1899.**

— [Totila.] Berceuse tragique, *etc. See* LÉVY (E.) Deux Airs italiens, *etc.* [No. 2.] 1923. 8°. *[La Revue Musicale.* 4e *année. No.* 9. *Supplément musical.]* **P. P. 1948. tda.**

— *See* BACH (J. S.) [Fugue. B. G. Jahrg. 38. No. 14.] Thema Legrenzianum elaboratum cum subjecto pedaliter. [1831.] fol. **h. 3007. s. (2.)**

LEGROS (   )

— L'Amour et la gloire. [Song.] Avec accompagnement par Mr Legros. *Chez Decombe: Paris,* [c. 1810.] 8°.
A slip bearing the imprint "Chez Louis" has been pasted over the original imprint. **E. 1717. o. (51.)**

— Oui, oui. Romance ... Paroles, musique, accomt. de flûte, lyre ou guitare, par Mr. Le Gros. *Chez Corbaux: Paris,* [1825.] 8°.
A slip bearing the imprint "Chez Frère fils" has been pasted over the original imprint. **E. 1717. c. (11.)**

LEGROS (JOSEPH)

— D'une voix timide et sincère. *Ariette Nouvelle, etc.* [*Paris,* 1780?] 8°. **B. 362. c. (21.)**

— L'Olympe est-il sur la terre. *Rondeau.* (Les paroles de M. Mantelle, *etc.*) [*Paris,*] 1767. *s. sh.* 8°.
Mercure de France, July, 1767. **297. e. 9.**

— 1er recueil d'airs & duo ... Gravé par Beaublé. [Vocal score, and parts for violin, viola and bass.] 4 pt. *Chez l'auteur: [Paris,* c. 1790.] fol. **H. 2004. a.**

LEGROS DE LANEUVILLE (   )

— Le Voeu. [Song, begins: "Après vingt cinq ans".] *Paris*,
[1814.] fol.   **G. 807. c. (36.)**

LEGUAY (J. B.)

— La Belliqueuse. Ouverture solennelle pour harmonie militaire.
[Score.] *Paris*, [1884.] 8°.   **e. 666. g. (17.)**

LEGUAY (Jean Pierre)

— Au maître de la paix. Trois pièces pour grand orgue. pp. 24.
*Éditions musicales de la Schola cantorum et de la Procure
générale de musique: Paris*, [c. 1970.] 4°.
Orgue et liturgie. no. 73.   **g. 863. (3.)**

LE GUILLOU (C. M.)

— La Lyre de Jésus. Cantiques nouveaux sur la vie, les
souffrances, les grandeurs, les mystères, l'amour, les bienfaits
de N. S. … mis nouvellement en musique. Texte. (Musique.)
2 vol. *Sagnier et Bray: Paris*, 1848. 12°.   **3436. f. 36.**

— La Lyre pieuse. Cantiques nouveaux … à la gloire de Dieu,
sur les vérités de la religion, sur les principaux sujets de la
morale chrétienne … mis nouvellement en musique. Texte.
(Musique.) 2 vol. *Sagnier et Bray: Paris*, 1848. 12°.
                                                3436. f. 35.

LÉGURE (C. Roget)

— Marjory's Fortune. A Ballad, the words by M. Frewen.
W. Morley & Co.: London, [1892.] fol.   **H. 1650. p. (1.)**

LEGUY (Sylvette)

— Méthode de psalterion à archet. Suivie de pièces extraites du
folklore français. A l'usage des scolaires et des amateurs de
musique populaire. Method for Bow Psaltery, *etc.* Fr.,
Eng. & Ger. pp. 54. *Chappell: Paris*, [1979.] 4°.
                                                f. 759. yy. (1.)

— *See* Machaut (Guillaume de) [*Collections.*] Oeuvres
complètes. Édition commémorative établie par S. Leguy, *etc.*
[1977, *etc.*] 4°.   **G. 21. c.**

LEHANE (Maureen)

— *See* Purcell (Henry) [*Collected Works.—b.*] Songs. Edited by
P. Wishart and M. Lehane, *etc.* [1976.] 8°.   **E. 137. g. (1.)**